CREDITS

Working Group
Tony Abbott, Gina Baldo, Trevor Coleman
Wally Menne, David Johnson, Sally Johnson
Geoff Nichols, Lawrence Peacock, Sheila Peacock
Rob Scott-Shaw, Dennis Slotow
Rosemary Williams

Scientific Editor
Rosemary Williams

Photography Co-ordination
Lawrence and Sheila Peacock

Key to Families
Trevor Edwards

Drawings
Angela Beaumont

Mapping
Trevor Arnold
Gina Baldo, Cheryl van Groeningen

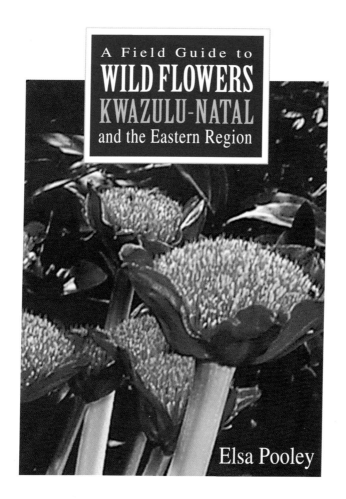

A Field Guide to
WILD FLOWERS
KWAZULU-NATAL
and the Eastern Region

Elsa Pooley

Natal
Flora

Publications
Trust

CONTENTS

> ## WARNING
>
> The publisher and author do not assume responsibility for any sickness, death or other harmful effects resulting from eating or using any plant in this book.

Published by
Natal Flora Publications Trust
c/o Natal Herbarium
Botanic Gardens Road, Durban 4001

Distributed by
ABC Bookshop
PO Box 100 001, Scottsville, 3209
e-mail: abc_book@tcs.co.za

First edition published 1998
Copyright (text), Natal Flora Publications Trust
Copyright (photographs), the photographers

Binding of collectors' and sponsors' editions by Peter Carstens
Cover design sponsored by Paton Tupper Associates (KZN)
Pre-press, printing and binding by Colorgraphic, Durban

ISBN 0-620-21502-X (collectors edition)
ISBN 0-620-21501-1 (hardcover edition)
ISBN 0-620-21500-3 (softcover/paperback edition)

Cover photograph: *Scadoxus puniceus* (Geoff Nichols)

FOREWORD

uture generations might well refer to the 1990s as the 'biodiversity decade' – a period of unprecedented interest in and concern for the richness of life on Earth. The catastrophic loss of species throughout the globe, most especially in the moist tropics, has long been recognised, but it was not until the signing of the Convention on Biological Diversity in Rio de Janeiro in 1992 that meaningful action was initiated at an international scale. Over 170 nations have now ratified the Convention, committing their governments to effective programmes of conservation and sustainable use.

The eastern provinces of South Africa, from the shores of the Indian Ocean to the peaks of the Drakensberg, from the Kei to the Limpopo, encompass an astounding diversity of habitats, fauna and flora. This natural wealth has been valued and utilised for centuries, most significantly in the long history of traditional medicine and magical practice of the Zulu people. The European settlers that came to the region in the mid nineteenth century soon recognised the natural beauty of the country. Early travellers and botanical collectors were amazed by the richness of the grasslands, savannas and forests of the often hot, drought-prone hills and valleys. The grasslands, in particular, produced a delightful show of colour after early spring veld fires, a sight which has become increasingly difficult to witness as agricultural, industrial and urban development has overtaken our countryside.

Although this book also includes the flowers of Lesotho, Swaziland, southern Mozambique and the eastern parts of the Free State, Gauteng and Mpumalanga, there are three important 'hot spots' of botanical diversity in the region – the Drakensberg, Maputaland and Pondoland centres – which are now internationally recognised. The flora of these areas is being surveyed by bio-prospectors for use in pharmaceutical development and by horticulturists for the massive global trade in cut-flower and bedding plants.

This book is not only a celebration of the beauty and diversity of our flora. It is also testimony to the commitment of people throughout the region who contributed knowledge, photographs, energy and both private and corporate support and shared the vision of the late Michael Noyce for a project that will be a tool of considerable influence in conserving a unique resource.

Brian J Huntley
Chief Executive: National Botanical Institute
Harold Pearson Professor of Botany, University of Cape Town

DEDICATION

In memory of

Michael Noyce

founding Chairman of the Trust, who conceived

both the Tree and Wild Flower books,

and

David Hatton

past Chairman and driving force for many years.

THE NATAL FLORA PUBLICATIONS TRUST

The Trust was established in April 1992 with the aim of raising and administering funds to publish a book on the trees of KwaZulu-Natal and the Transkei, to publish further books on related subjects and to keep these books in print. This volume, a companion to the tree book, will prove, I am sure, to be the definitive reference to the magnificent flora of this region.

The trustees are deeply appreciative of the support received from so many companies, organisations and individuals whose financial and personal contributions have made this book a reality. It is hoped that this book will stimulate interest in the flowers of the region and that many people will be inspired to explore and enjoy this rich natural heritage and thereby contribute to its conservation.

A L Crutchley
Chairman

PRINCIPAL SPONSORS

The Trustees of Natal Flora Publications Trust gratefully acknowledge the generous support of the Principal Sponsors of this book

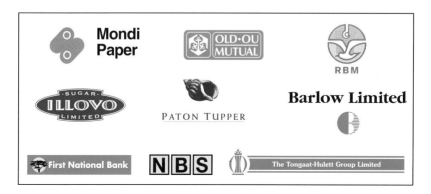

MAJOR SPONSORS

AECI Operations Services (Pty) Ltd • Deloitte & Touche • The Fulton Trust
National Botanical Institute : In recognition of the invaluable contribution made to Botany
in KwaZulu-Natal by the late Mr Michael Noyce
H. F. Oppenheimer • Mark and Christine Read • South African Sugar Association
Yellowwood Property Fund Managers Ltd

INSTITUTIONAL SPONSORS

African Oxygen Limited
Mrs Coby Bride
Mrs ND Charrington
   née Mignon Herring
David and Janet Cruse
Durban Botanic Gardens Trust
Durban Metro Library Services and
   Raven Hart Bequest Fund
Ian and Jean Garland

Grindrod Unicorn Group Ltd
Island View Holdings Limited
Masonite (Africa) Limited
McCarthy Retail Limited
Nasionale Pers Beperk
Natal Parks Board
Umgeni Water
WESSA, Natal Region -
   Plant a National Tree Project

SPONSORS

Mr & Mrs L Backhouse
Jill Berning
Botanical Society of SA - Durban & Coastal Branch
Botanical Society of SA - Midlands Branch
Harry Brunskill Educational & Charitable Trust
BTR Dunlop Limited
Mr & Mrs Radclyffe Cadman
Pam Cooke
Pietro Corgatelli
Evelyn Cresswell- in memory of Christopher Cresswell
Charles & Jean Crookes
Jack Crutchley
Mr. & Mrs. D.K. Duane
Durban & Coast Horticultural Society
Dr Pio Eggstein
Fowler Farming KwaZulu-Natal
Peter Garland
Mr & Mrs Michael Garlick
Mike & Carole Groves
Guy & Melanie Harris
John Hooper Properties (Pty) Ltd
Bruce Hopwood
Ruth Hough
Mick & Paula Hyatt
Illovo Sugar Limited - in memory of Michael Noyce

Keith Edward Kirsten
Mr & Mrs W.I. Ladlau
Mr & Mrs R.E. Levitt
Mr & Mrs E.G. Long-Innes
Bruce & Carol Lovemore
Robert & Sally Lovemore
Rod Mackenzie
Richard & Penelope Mansell-Jones
A.M. Moolla Charity Trust
H.B. Nicholson
Diana Noyce
Pick n' Pay KwaZulu-Natal
Violet Poynton
Sappi Saiccor, Umkomaas
Dudley & Jackie Saville
Mary Slack
June Stannard
E.A. Stewart
Charles & Jana Stirton
L.J. Thomas
TIMBERWATCH
Top Crop Nursery
Stephan & Ilse Wentzel
Wildlife & Environment Society - Umvoti Branch
Roy & Val Wise

COLLECTORS

P.D. Adams
Gordon Anderson
Steve Bales
Diana L. Barrell
Mr & Mrs L.G. Baumann
The Brenthurst Library
Esther Campbell
Hamish Campbell
Arnold & Anne Colenbrander

Durban Branch Wildlife and
   Environment Society of SA
Malcolm Foster
Eugene & Lalie Fourie
E.S.C. Garner
Rupert, Nadia, Brett, Grant &
   Dylan Horley
Yoshito Iwasa
Geoff Jewell
Jean Marie & Astri Leroy

Hilton & Louise Lissack
Allen & Carol Miller
Missouri Botanical Garden Library
Ian Outram
G.A. Pigg
Richard J. Price
W.J. Scadden
E. Taeuber
W.C. Vandeverre
Willem van Rÿswÿck

6

SUBSCRIBERS

A B C Bookshop
Tony & Maggie Abbott
Adams & Co
M. Alberts
Mike & Monica Amm
G.K.H. Anderson
Dr Ingram F. Anderson
Des & Elizabeth Andersson
Jo Arkell

Mike Balcomb
Gina & Sergio Baldo
Keith Mitchell Bales
David Balfour
Marijke & Ken Ball
Bill & Leila Barnes
Malcolm & Peta Anne Basford
F.J. Bashall
Randall J. Bason
Beacon Sweets and Chocolates
Yvonne Becker
Carole M. Beckett
A.J. Bell
Mr & Mrs A.W. Bell
Josiane & Jean-Pierre Bello
H.N. Bentley
John S. Bentley
Patricia Berjak
Jane Bertram
Jean-Luc Bestel
Prof Gerhard & Isolde Beukes
Henry A. Bird
Kevin & Carol Bleksley
Engela Bloch
Agnes Bodenstein
Fay Boik
Richard Boon
Glenda & Richard Booth
Gert T.H. Bosch
Steve Bosch
Charles & Julia Botha
Charles Boucher
Marcel W. Bouwer
Julie Braby
Dieter & Susan Brandt
Peter Brett
Pamela R. Brink
Eugene Brock
J.P. Bruyns-Haylett
Anton Bryant
Pat & Mike Buchel
E.W. Buhr
Margaret Burger
Fay & Roy Burrett
Hazel Burrett & Steven Roskelly
T.E. Burton

Piers J.M. Burton-Moore
Betty Busby
Marie Byrne

Glen Campbell
Robert Guy Carr
Vincent & Jane Carruthers
Rhona J. Carte
W.M. Case
D.B. Cathcart
Caulton – Pelican Safaris
Mark & Jean Caulton
Charles Cawood
Mignon M. Charrington
Colin Christian
L.R. Church
N.L. Church
Lynley Clarke
Mary Clarke
Tony Clarkson
Pam Cole
Trevor Coleman
Roger & Wendy Colley
In loving memory of W.H. Collinson
Howard & Patricia Cook
Doug & Nola Cooke
N.R. Court
C.L. Cousins
Jill & Graham Cox
Stanley & Dorothy Craven
Jack & Rosalie Crutchley
Russel Currie
Jocelyn Cuthbert

Vernon T. Daly
Chris Dalzell
Mike & Penny Damp
Ivor & Margaret Daniel
Patricia & Robert d'Avice
Richard, Mary & Tom Davies
Piet de Jager
Stoffel de Jager
C.J. & M.J. Dekker
Brigitte de Kock
Linda de Luca
Olivia Denny-Nucci
Patricia & Peter Dinkelmann
Carol Ditz
Linda Dobson
Neil Donkin & Marylynn – in loving
    memory of David Hatton
Dr Philip E. Downs
Pat & Beryl Draper
Siegfried & Dawn Drewes
Frieda Duckitt
Fanus & Dalene du Toit

Pieter & Louise Duys
Rob & Helen Dyer

B.G.S. Earl
Rob & Trudi Earle
Roxana, Sean & Justin Earle
Anna Ebuli
Gary Ronayne Edwards
Brenda & Scott Engles
F. Evans
Elaine Eyre

Frank & Joan Farquharson
Val S. Farquharson
Ivor D. Ferreira
Selma A. Ferreira
Mr & Mrs M.P. Finch
Dr J.B.R. Findlay
Di Fitzsimons
Floral Art Club, Durban
Floral Art Demonstrators Association,
    KwaZulu-Natal
Kirby W. Fong
Richard C. Foster
Johan & Henny Fourie
Keith G. Fuller
Quintin A. Fuller
Malcolm Funston

Annemarie Gebhardt
Neil Gerber
Jason L. Gifford
Ted & Rem Gilfillan
Lily & Lionel Gill
I.F.G. Gillatt
Valda Goble
Peter & Tessa Goemans
Peter Goldschmidt
Jeremy Goodall
Mick & Libby Goodall
Jerry Gosnell
Jill Gowans
Dr J.E. Granger
Alec & Catherine Grant
Lindsay Gray
Robin & Sharon Greaves
Lal & Pauline Greene
Peter & Fiona Greenfield
D. & M. Grice
Clive & Norma Griffin
Murray Grindrod
Gro-on Nursery
L. & B. Grové
Iain & Emma Guthrie

Christopher A. Hammond

N.G. Hampson
Franz & Arleen Hannweg
Karin Hannweg
Shirley Hanrahan
Errol & Peggy Harrison
George & Joan Harvey
Peter Haselau
Colin A.S. Hayne
Gavin & Ann Hayhoe
Tessa Hedge
Valerie Hegarty
Doreen Hemp
David John Henry
Joyce Annie Henry
Paul Maurice Henry
D.G. Herbert
K.A. Herbert
Antoinette Hersov
Angela Hesom-Williams
Adele Hesp
F.R. Hewat
Reuben Heydenrych
Di Higginson
Highway Garden Club
Dave & Goldie Hill
Leslie Hill
Jo-Anne Hilliar
Mr & Mrs R.B. Hindle
Rob Hirsch
Mark Hitchins
Ruth Hodgson
Willem Hofland
Margaret Hoile
J.R.L. Hoog
M.J. Hoole
Bruce Hopwood
Yasuo Hori
Sally & Jeremy Horne
Jim & Ann Horton
Ann R. Hotchkiss
Tim & Paula Howes
Doreen Hoyle
Lynette Hoyle
Barbara & Dave Huckett
John & Mary Hughes
J.J. Hugo
Ben & Renèe Human
Jan & Mariana Human
Ian B. Huntley
Anne Hutchings

David Ibarra
Island View Holdings
Tim Ivins

Dennis A. Jackson
N.H.G. Jacobsen
Andrew James

Barry & Danielle James
Chris James
Dick & Hazel Japp
Anne & John Jerman
Shirley Jex
John Joannou
Pam & Lynn Johnson
Roland O. Jones
Alain Jubault
Jaqueline Julyan

Anthony Kee
Gordon Kerr
H.C. Kewley
Michael W. King
Colin & Lesley Kitchener
Shirley & Willy Klingenberg
Dr R.L. Kluge
Karl W. Kohrs
Denise Jane Kraunsoe
KwaZulu-Natal Panel of
    Floral Art Judges

Yvonne Leemann
Helen Leibel
Anton & Robin Leisegang
Mrs S.L. Leisegang
Emma & Reinhard le Roux
Michael & Coral le Sueur
Jean Lindsay
Graham Lister
M.A. Lister
Gill & Rupert Lorimer
A. Barrie Low
Roy A. Lubke

Christo Maakal
Ron Macdonald
Macdonald's Garden Centre
Brian Mackenzie
O.J. Mackenzie
Mike & Lyn Mair
Myles & Jenny Mander
Alexander E. March
Mark & Deanne
Einar Marklund
Derick McKenzie
Cameron & Rhoda McMaster
Raymond & Rosemary McMurray
Trevor & Val McWade
Lucy Melouney
Wally Menne
Lauren Margaret Michel
Roxanne Milne
Peggy Tyson Milstead
Missouri Botanical Garden Library
N.J. Mitchley
Buddy & Jenny Mockford

Mits & Jacky Morford
Keith Morgan
Mrs B. Morrison
Nigel Wayne Mudge
Dulcie Mulholland
R.M. Murray

Natal Herbarium, NBI
National Botanical Institute, Pretoria
Mike & Heidi Neethling
Bruce & Cilla Nel
Andrew & Evelyn Nesbitt
Geoff, Lynne & Douglas Nichols
H.B. Nicholson
Anne Nicolson
Dr H.F. Niebuhr
Des Nielsen
Mrs A. Nikschtat
K.M. Nixon

Chris Oberholster
Old Mutual Head Office – in memory
    of the late Mr Michael Noyce
Willem & Ingrid Oosthuizen
Pat Outhwaite

Meg Coates Palgrave
Robert Pallett
N.W. Pammenter
R. Pampel
Errol & Rosemary Pearman
Jonathan & Daphne Pearse
Karl H. Pegel
Jonothan Pennefather
Pennington Environmental Group
Dr Jim Phelps
Julie Phillips
Ann Pistor
Mr G.T. Platt
Ailsa Plummer
Dorothy Ponsie
Terry & Debbie Pooley
Barry & Lyn Porter
Ingrid & Roger Porter
Carel Potgieter
J.D. Pratt
Jenny & John Price
G.L. Prosser
Dr D.J. Pudifin

Adrian & Michelle Rall
David Rattray
R.F. Raymond
Suzette M. Raymond
Dallas Reed
J. & M. Reed
Julian Reed
Michael R. Reed

Mike & Rose Reed
In memory of Phyllis Reim
Anne Rennie
Sally Reunert
Colin E. Richards
Keith & Leanna Richardson
Waveney & Allen Richardson
Morelle & Bob Rickards
Judith Roberts
Neal Roberts
Bruce & Kim Robertson
H.G. Robertson
Nigel & Hilary Robson
Cedric Roché
Fred & Anne Rodwell
S. Romijn
E.S. Roodt
Edgar Vivian Rosenberg
Ron & René Rossler
Pippa Rowland
Dr P. Rush

M.J.V. Samuels
Grace Sandalls
Rod & Rachel Saunders
Francesca E. Scharf
Ernst Schmidt
Rudolf Schneebeli
Trevor Schoerie
Carol Ann Schroenn
V.J. Schütte
Donald Seaton
C. Seele
Dr R. Sevin
Charlie & Sheona Shackleton
Cassim Shaikh
Shayamoya Lodge
Russell & Basil Sheasby
Freddie, Miriam, Cinderella, Jason
    & Leanne Shingange
Marilyn Shire
Joel Mbhazima Sibiya
Hymie Sibul
H. & D.W. Skawran
Mark Skinner
Dennis, Ansie, Jennifer & Ryan Slotow
Jenny & Charles Smith
In memory of Suzanne Smith
Barry Spicer
Lesley Stainbank
Malcolm Stainbank
June Stannard
Mike Stapleton
Ines & Basil Stathoulis
Michael Stevenson
Gideon F. Steyn
Dorothea Stielau
Sandy Stretton

Margaret E.J. Stride
Johannes & Leonore Strobos
Brian Strode
Henriette Stroh
Jeremy Stubbs
Adam Stutzer
Sutherland Seedlings
Andrew C. Sutherland
Trevor & Vorn Sweeney
Richard J. Symmonds

E. Taeuber
June Taeuber
Dr Sumitra Talukdar
Irvine G. Taylor
Daryl Koutnik & Rana Tayyar
Colin & Ann Tedder
Mary-Lynne & Peter Tennant
Duro Dalmae Thole
Hugh Thompson
M.C. Thompson
Pete & Lu Thompson
Sharneen Thompson
Craig J. Thomson
Diana Ruth Thomson
Keith Thomson
Nicholas R. Thurston
Peter & Sue Timm
C.L. Tinley
Jack & Pat Tissiman
Mervyn Todd
Nick & Janine Tredger
Dave & Jo Trickett
Christine M. Tully
Bill & Di Turner
Mr & Mrs J.J. Turner
Mr & Mrs Q.K. Turner

Umhlali & District Garden
    & Flower Club

Ismail Ebrahim Vahed
Alan van Coller
Peggy van Coller
Dick & Liz van der Jagt
Maria van der Mark
Eduard van Dijk
Barry van Ginkel
Anne & Errol van Greunen
Albert van Jaarsveld
    & Ronnie van Rooyen
H. van Kerken
André & Cynthia van Niekerk
M. & M.A. van Rijswijck
J.C. & Ina van Rooyen
Paul van Uytrecht & Nikki Brighton
Steaphan & Elan Venter
E.W. Vermunt

Carl Vernon
Graham & Milly Vickers
Miriam G. Vigar
Coral Vinsen
Hartwig A. von Dürckheim
Martin von Fintel
Richard & Maureen von Rahden
Dr & Mrs P. Vorster
Trelss McGregor & Wayne Vos

Sharlee, Paul, Helen & Susan Wade
Kerry Wafer
Joan Walker
C.J. (Roddy) Ward
Mrs Wendy Warner
H.C. Watson
Ms W.G. Welman
Diana & Tony Weston
Laura & Gilbert Whiteley
Andrew Whitley
Norman & Hantie Weitz
Wildlife Nursery
B.J. & S.M. Wilkes
M.C. Wilkes
Michael & Carol Willetts
Dr A.A.B. Williams
Brenda Williams
Huw & Carol Williams
Jumbo & Trevlyn Williams
Rosemary Williams
Helen Williamson
Alan Wilson
Denise A. Wilson
Graham T. Wilson
Graham Winch
B.C. Winkler
Richard Winn
Pieter Winter
P.L. Wiseman
Joan Barbara Withers
Dr G.S. Withinshaw
B. Nigel Wolstenholme
Rob & Janet Wood
Robin & Rose Woodhead
E. Anne Wyatt-Goodall

In memory of Bruce & Helen Young
Jennifer Young

George & Liz Zaloumis
A.N. Zulman

9

ACKNOWLEDGEMENTS

The effort required to bring this field guide to the bookshelves has been immense. It has drawn a large community of people into its orbit. As author I take full responsibility for all errors and omissions. However, I wish to pay tribute to the generous spirit that has prevailed amongst the many people who made the book possible.

Natal Flora Publications Trust
I thank the Trustees and Trust secretary Marylynn Grant for their unfailing support throughout the project. Their efforts in approaching sponsors and securing funding has been remarkable. I offer my most grateful thanks to the Chairman Jack Crutchley who has overseen the difficult final stages of the project with resolve and enthusiasm.

Working Group
Tony Abbott, Gina Baldo, Trevor Coleman, David Johnson, Sally Johnson, Wally Menne, Lawrence Peacock, Sheila Peacock, Geoff Nicols, Rob Scott-Shaw, Dennis Slotow, Rosemary Williams - these colleagues have helped plan the book and contributed time and extensive knowledge to its contents. Their support has been wonderful and greatly appreciated. Braam van Wyk, *Schweickerdt Herbarium*, University of Pretoria, has been friend, colleague and adviser since the earliest stages. He has been generous with his time and expertise. So too has Otto Leistner, past editor of NBI publications.

Photographers
All photographs were donated. The remarkable colour illustrations represent an enormous amount of time and effort in the field. Whilst credit is given next to the relevant photograph, I must record special thanks to a small group who worked closely with me over the last few years. In particular, Martin von Fintel, Geoff Nichols and Lal Greene, who made their very large collections available to the Trust. Also Tony Abbott, Trevor Coleman, Tom de Waal, Wally Menne, Jo Onderstall, Darrel Plowes, Lorraine van Hooff, Braam van Wyk and Roddy Ward.

Lawrence and Sheila Peacock have devoted much of the last four years to assessing, cataloguing and storing over 30 000 colour slides. Their professional volunteer work ensured the confidence of the photographers. I appreciated our collaboration on design and layout of the colour pages.

Editing
I am indebted to Rosemary Williams, scientific editor and colleague since the earliest days of the project, for her critical advice and wholehearted support. Also to Di Smith, technical editor, for her enthusiastic and informed input. To my sister, Creina Alcock, who, with her skillful general editing and research assistance, shared the load in the final stages.

Mapping
This very important and successful part of the book has been based on computer programmes provided by Trevor Arnold of the NBI (see box). It was supervised by Gina Baldo who undertook the same enormous task for 'Trees of Natal, Zululand & Transkei'. Words do not adequately describe the trials, tribulations and satisfaction that have been part of the work. Gina has been ably assisted on the computers by Cheryl van Groeningen, Jason Stone and Michael Gardiner. Data information from ± 150 000 specimens was recorded by: Catherine Ford, Anne Haselgrove, Bronwen Jenkins, Isabel Johnson, Tafline Knowles, John McCosh, Meena Nathoo, Shamila Nunkumar, Catherine Prentice, Christina Potgieter, Shernice Soobramoney, Nirvashnie Sukdeo and Wendy Taylor. In the final moments of the work, Andrea Boem provided crucial assistance. Helena Margeot, Geomap, went out of her way to provide the excellent colour frontispiece map of the region and back cover locality map.

NATIONAL BOTANICAL INSTITUTE (NBI)

Our thanks to Prof Brian Huntley, Chief Director of the NBI for making available facilities at Natal Herbarium and, through NBI staff in Durban, Pretoria and Kirstenbosch, assistance in many aspects of the book.

Mapping: Trevor Arnold has been enthusiastic in his support for our quest to provide maps. His pilot version of Specimen Database (SPMNDB) for the herbarium search and MAPPIT to draft the maps, linked to PRECIS (National Herbarium **Pre**toria Computerized Information System) have enabled us to produce the precise and informative maps in the guide. Carole de Wet and Hannelie Snyman have provided essential backup.

Natal Herbarium, Durban: Rosemary Williams, Curator, and the whole staff, particularly Yashica Singh, Alfred Ngwenya and Helen Noble have been helpful in many different aspects of the project. They have provided facilities for the data capturers on the mapping programme, identified photographers' specimens and dealt with botanical queries, providing logistical support and a wonderful working environment .

The following NBI staff members provided prompt and generous assistance, including text queries and identification of colour slides:
Kirstenbosch: Dave Davidson, Grahame Duncan, Hubert Kurzweil, John Manning, Ted Oliver, Ernst van Jaarsveld, John Rourke, Di Stafford.

National Herbarium, Pretoria: Clare Archer, Robert Archer, Christine Bredenkamp, Priscilla Burgoyne, Emsie du Plessis, Gerrit Germishuizen, Hugh Glen, Rene Glen, Paul Herman, Pitta Joffe, Marie Jordaan, Marinda Koekemoer, Estelle Potgieter, Elizabeth Retief, Gideon Smith, Shirley Smithies, Mienkie Welman.

Specialist advice:
The botanical community have been generous in sharing their knowledge. I am indebted to:
Kath Gordon Gray for drafting most of the Cyperaceae text, with help from Jane Browning and Roddy Ward.
Ashley Nicholas for generously providing very extensive research notes on Asclepiadaceae and Periplocaceae on which the text was based, much of it from his doctoral thesis. He also identified this section of the slide collection.
Olive Hilliard and Bill Burtt for invaluable advice. Olive Hilliard generously made her checklist of KZN plants available to me. It was used as a guide to selecting the species to be included in the book.
Trevor Edwards for designing and illustrating the key to the families and for identifying colour slides.
My thanks to the Head of Botany Department, Hannes van Staden, University of Natal, for making facilities available for mapping and plant illustration research, and to Ed Granger, Trevor Edwards (curator *Bews Herbarium*) and Jane Browning, for their assistance.

Thanks for specialist advice and identification of slides to the following: Snowy Baijnath, *Ward Herbarium*, University of Durban-Westville, Kevin and Mandy Balkwill, University of Witwatersrand, Angela Beaumont, University of Natal, Elise Cloete, *UNITRA Herbarium*, Peter Linder and Tony Hall, University of Cape Town, Peter Goldblatt, Missouri Botanic Gardens, Gavin McDonald, Earth Sciences, Mangosothu Technikon, Tracy McLennan, University of Witwatersrand, Rob Scott-Shaw, *Killick Herbarium*, KZN Conservation Services; Charles Stirton, National Botanic Gardens, Wales, Fanie Venter. Pete Phillipson, Rhodes University, Tony Dold and Estelle Brink, *Schoenland Herbarium*, Grahamstown, for providing insight into the southern part of the region and help with Xhosa names and plant uses.

Common names:
I am very grateful to Alfred Ngwenya for checking the list of Zulu names. Adrian Koopman, Department of Zulu, University of Natal, gave invaluable assistance in the final stages. Roddy Ward also shared his work on Zulu names of plants. C J Skead's list of Xhosa plant names and uses was incorporated (courtesy of Schoenland Herbarium). Gideon Dlamini, Department of Agriculture, Swaziland, supplied a list of Swazi names. English and Afrikaans names were checked by Gina Baldo, Trevor Coleman, Geoff Nichols, Wally Menne, Rosemary Williams, assisted by Ian Garland, Ashley Nicholas and Roddy Ward.

Computers:
Mike Mills, Compumend, has sorted out our computer problems at any time of day, night or weekend. He remained calm and patient in the light of our ignorance of both equipment and software, unaffected by our panic when failures occurred at critical moments. Dave Armstrong, X-Tech, and NewMac Technologies were most helpful when the vintage machine used for final typesetting threatened to expire.

Design and Printing:
To Sue Rae Fox of Paton Tupper, and Lauren Smart, our thanks for the design of the cover, introductory pages and promotional material for the book. The company's creative contribution to the project is much appreciated. Richard Noyce laid the foundation for this work and advised on the sponsors' brochure.

My thanks to all the staff at Colorgraphic, particularly in pre-press: Willy Pather and Collin Lauten. To Gundi Haywood, whose exacting and professional eye has overseen the typesetting and proofing, my appreciation for her infinite patience and the insight that her love of wild flowers has brought to the job.

General:
Our appreciation to the KZN Conservation Services (Natal Parks Board/KwaZulu Nature Conservation) who provided facilities for the initial Wild Flower Guide planning workshop in 1994, and assistance from collecting permits to help with research enquiries; and to Durban Parks and Gardens for assistance and publicity. My thanks to Angela Beaumont who provided excellent drawings to tight deadlines with good humour and efficiency; Ann Haselgrove filled the position of part-time research assistant, ready to chase down queries at a moment's notice and Sally Johnson researched the derivation of scientific names. For assistance in many ways, my appreciation to: Ruari Alcock, Margaret Appleton, Auriol Batten, Pat Berjak, Ann Brand, Orty Bourquin, Sizwe Cawe, Coby Bride, Keith Cooper, Di Dold, Colleen Downs, Roxanna Earle, East London Museum, Kate Emge, Ian and Jean Garland, Helene Groom, Elizabeth Hatton, Dick Hollway, Bill Hunt, Anne Hutchings, Anthea Johnston, Noelline Kroon, Roy Lubke, Wayne Matthews, Eve McKay, Megan Mills, Rodney Moffett, Hugh Nicholson, Jo Onderstall, Dave Rattray, Sue Swan, Francois Smith, Joan and Godfrey Symons, Elsa van Wyk and Di Wills.

Working group families:
Special thanks for their patience and enthusiastic support to: Sergio Baldo; Lester and David van Groeningen, Bradley and Barry Ahern, Eric and Valerie Hansen; Lorraine Coleman; Lynne and Douglas Nichols; Brian, Peter and Michael Smith; Verdan and Robus Menne.

To my family - Tony and Thomas, Justin, Simon and Susan, thank you. Words hardly express my appreciaton for the part my husband Tony has played in the realisation of this book. His natural history knowledge and experience as an author has impacted on the text and his strong support enabled me to keep up the work when it seemed insurmountable. He and Thomas have been immensely understanding of the demands required to realise my dream of a wild flower field guide, accessible to all, which would reflect the remarkable diversity of this region.

11

Panorama of the N KZN Drakensberg, from the Golden Gate National Park, eastern Free State - The highest mountain range in southern Africa (over 3 300 m), it is one of Africa's 'hot spots' - a place of high plant diversity and endemism. The montane belt, with grassland, *Protea* woodland, scrub and forest extends from the valley floors to just above the Clarens sandstone cliffs, the edge of the Little Berg. The subalpine belt extends from the edge of the Little Berg to just below the summit and includes subalpine fynbos where the sheer basalt cliffs may drop 500 m or more. On the summit plateau the vegetation is adapted to survive conditions where snow may lie on the ground for up to 2 months. This Drakensberg Alpine Tundra contains unique heath and bog communities. *Lorraine van Hooff*

Pam Cooke

Cameron McMaster

Hesperantha grandiflora   *Hesperantha grandiflora*

Martin von Fintel

Polygala hispida

INTRODUCTION

The region

This book provides a guide to the wild flowers of the eastern region of South Africa - with over 10 000 species of plants, one of the richest floral regions in Africa. However it has probably received more international than local attention. Few people are aware that three of the world's centres of plant diversity (CPD's) or 'hots spots', lie within this region. Although the richness of the Cape flora has long been acknowledged, it was not until 1994 that Maputaland, Pondoland and the Drakensberg Alpine regions were singled out in a world atlas of CPD's - areas of global botanical importance with high diversity and large numbers of endemic or threatened species with social, economic, cultural or scientific importance.

Plants do not recognise political boundaries. Rather, they are affected by temperature, rainfall, altitude, geological formations and land use practices. Because of the wide distribution of many of the plants, the main study area of the Field Guide, KwaZulu-Natal (KZN) and

Sandersonia aurantiaca Christmas Bells — *Martin von Fintel*
Streptocarpus porphyrostachys — *Martin Kunhardt*

Montane Forest - occuring up to 1900 m above sea level.
Neil Crouch

Transkei (Eastern Cape), was extended to include the area from the Buffalo River in the south to Delagoa Bay, Mozambique in the north, and inland to the eastern Free State, Gauteng, Mpumalanga, Lesotho and Swaziland.

This Field Guide includes over 2000 species of flowering plants, some of them familiar and common, some weeds, some of them rare, many of them little known. Much of the information on the plants was buried in the scientific literature, many species with no update since they were first described in *Flora Capensis* between 1859 and 1912. Compiling the distribution maps for each plant was a major task and a 'first' for a wild flower field guide. The distribution of plants is not haphazard. Each species has its own requirements, some very exclusive, confining them to a small area, where they might be quite common. Others are adaptable and become widespread. A blank spot on the map does not necesarily mean that it's not there - it could just indicate that no collectors have passed that way.

Scope of guide

Every effort has been made to include as many of the flowering plant families and genera occurring in the region as possible. The illustrations feature the extraordinary range of growth forms such as the *Vanilla* orchid vine found at the tropical coast in the east, the carpets of *Rhodohypoxis* lilies on summit of the Drakensberg in the west, *Leucospermum* Pincushion shrubs in the cooler south and the brilliant succulent Impala lilies, *Adenium*, in the subtropical north.

Southern KZN Drakensberg - Sani Pass. The Southern Berg is colder than the northern Berg. The 'overwhelming impression ... is of grass-covered slopes' (Hilliard & Burtt). Forest patches and tree clumps are confined to gullies and sheltered places. Streams cut deeply into the Cave sandstone forming deep, often cliffed valleys, separated by steep grassy ridges forming parallel spurs running south cast. *Philip de Moor*

Gerbera aurantiaca
Hilton Daisy   *Cynthia Giddy*

KZN Midlands - Rolling hills and well tended farmlands. This Highland Sourveld is a species rich grassland. It ranges from about 1350 to 2150 m above sea level. At lower altitudes, down to 900 m, the Mistbelt Ngongoni Veld is also well suited to farming and under threat from tree and sugar plantations. It still has some beautiful forest patches surviving in places.   *Pam Cooke*

The Field Guide describes flowering plants including sedges and aquatics, and a few cycads. In a region with more than 11 000 species (including subspecies and varieties) it is inevitable that some will be left out. Certain plants are not included because a suitable photograph could not be found. The book does NOT include grasses or the trees and larger woody plants which have been described in a companion volume, 'A Complete Field Guide to the Trees of Natal, Zululand and Transkei' (1993).

Traditional uses
The medicinal and magical uses of plants have been included with much of this information drawn from the literature. Plants such as impepho, *Helichrysum* species, are in daily use in African homes throughout the country. The demand for plants for traditional uses is growing, not declining, and the volume of the trade is having considerable impact on wild populations.

Ethnobotany, the study of interactions of people and plants, including the influence of plants on human culture, is a distinct branch of natural science involving many disciplines. There has been an explosion of interest and academic research into many aspects of the subject, from documenting past and existing uses to analysing the chemical and curative properties of plants. Some of this research is taking South African plants into mainstream medicine.

Gardening notes
South African plants have been prized in gardens around the world since the first species were introduced to Europe in the 1600s. *Gladiolus*, *Geranium*, Chincheree, *Protea*, Barberton Daisy and *Agapanthus* are international household names - and big business. South Africa is a major source for development of the massive global trade in cut-flower and bedding plants. Many of the Drakensberg species are already in the flourishing trade in 'alpines' in Europe and the USA. A popular yellow form of *Phygelias aequalis*, discovered in KZN and introduced to the UK as 'Yellow Trumpets', is sold in florist shops in London and won a medal at the Chelsea Flower show. Christmas Bells *Sandersonia aurantiaca*, an endangered species in South Africa, has been developed for export by horticulturalists in New Zealand. Wild Ginger *Siphonochilus aethiopicus*, extinct in the wild in KZN, is now freely available through tissue culture developed at Kirstenbosch Botanic Gardens, Cape Town. Hybrids of the Barberton daisy *Gerbera jamesonii*, closely related to KZN's Hilton daisy, are now the fastest growing cut-flower product in Europe.

Conserving indigenous plant assets
This Field Guide is a celebration of the remarkable flora of the region. Whilst marvelling at the amazing plant life, the very real threats to survival of viable populations of many species and entire

14

Pachycarpus grandiflorus

Gladiolus oppositiflorus
Transkei Gladiolus

Dimorphotheca jucunda Trailing Mauve Daisy *Martin von Fintel*

habitats must not be overlooked. Expanding agricultural monocultures, conversion of grasslands to timber plantations and rapid urbanisation threaten the biodiversity of the region. Indigenous plant resources have enormous economic benefits to the country which are not yet fully recognised. Balanced development including mandatory environmental impact assessments is urgently required, with proper care and attention given to all areas.

Scientific names

Scientific names, unlike common names, are internationally applicable and are only applied after strict rules have been followed by the plant taxonomist. The plant enthusiast who becomes familar with the scientific names is often frustrated by fairly frequent name changes. This is the penalty of having an exciting and still-to-be-explored flora. SA has over 23 000 plants, the richest temperate flora of any area of comparable size in the world. With more than 16 500 endemics, it is the largest flora in Africa.

Disa saxicola *Martin von Fintel*

Moraea inclinata Nodding Wild Iris *Martin von Fintel*

Pondoland - a view of the Mtentu River showing the spectacular gorge, forest and rolling grassland typical of the region. This unique area is characterised by surface outcrops of Natal Group sandstone. Rugged plateaux (100-500 m above sea level) are dissected by narrow river gorges. Coastal dunes are mostly absent. *Tom de Waal*

15

Cyrtanthus galpinii   Geoff Nichols

Huernia zebrina   Darrel Plowes

Euphorbia grandicornis   Strophanthus luteolus

Tanzania lags far behind in second place with 10 000 species, 1122 endemics. New species are still being discovered, and, as more information becomes available on plants and the relationships between species and their distribution, scientific name changes will be necessary.

The scientific name is usually derived from Greek or Latin and consists of a **genus** name (always spelt with a capital letter) e.g. *Erythrina*, reflecting a group of similar species and a **specific name** e.g. *zeyheri*, which identifies different species. This two-part name is in turn part of a larger **family** unit, e.g. Fabaceae, which groups genera with characters in common. Every name is based upon a **type specimen**, the plant upon which the original gdescription of the species was based.

Common names

A major effort has been made to include as many common names in as many local languages as possible. Sometimes, where there are no English names, these have been created, especially where the scientific names are difficult to pronounce. Any additional common names would be greatly appreciated, and can be sent to the Trust address. One of the problems with common names is that they are often very localised, while the plant may be widespread. The names can confuse rather than inform, the same name often being applied to quite different species or groups.

Msihlengeni waterfall - bushveld in north western KZN, 980 m above sea level.   Martin von Fintel

Euphorbia pulvinata   Martin von Fintel

Ammocharis coranica   Trevor Coleman

16

However, all local names are of value and should be recorded, particularly in the case of Zulu, Xhosa, South Sotho, Swazi and Thonga, which are largely spoken, not written languages. Plant names, like dialects, vary from district to district. Attempting to provided a single common name is therefore difficult. African common names pose problems for the English reader. The Zulu common names for example are made up of a prefix (e.g. um-) and stem (e.g. -bhendula) and they have been indexed as they are spoken (umbhendula). Names can be found under the following prefixes: um-, m-, isi-, a-, ama-, na, with c, q, x pronounced as clicks. To avoid confusion, and because of the difficulty of locating the stem, capital letters have not been used.

HOW TO USE THE BOOK
Colour coding
Colour coding provides a quick and easy guide to identifying plants. You will find flowers and/or fruits in one of seven colour sections. This is an artifical system. Flower colour varies considerably. The colours seen in the wild may differ from the photographic reproduction. *It is important to check in all related colour sections.* The colour coding strips indicate the range of colours to be found in each section.

Maps
The distribution maps were compiled using information derived from herbarium records in the National Botanical Institute PRECIS data base, the Natal Herbarium (NBI, Durban), Bews Herbarium (Natal University, Pietermaritzburg) and UNITRA Herbarium (University of Transkei). There are places where the text distribution descriptions might not match the map. This reveals the incomplete state of knowledge and will hopefully encourage further observation and clarification. Distribution beyond KZN and the eastern region is indicated in the text. No maps have been provided for alien species (indicated with a ★).

Flowering times
To find some wild flowers you may need to catch the brief flowering season. Unlike the larger woody plants and trees, many herbaceous or bulbous flowering plants die back completely in winter or after flowering. Brilliant displays of Fire Lilies *Cyrtanthus* species are all but invisible to the casual eye after a few weeks in bloom. Even succulents such as the giant *Crassula acinaciformis* die right back after flowering.

Maputaland - Nhlonhlela Pan, Mkuzi Game Reserve - an example of the many floodplain lakes and pans that are spread along the rivers of this flat country. It is a subtropical region of great wetlands, riverine forest, palmveld, grassland, bushveld and sand forest. Bounded on the west by the Lebombo Mountains (up to 800 m above sea level) which rise abruptly from the coastal plain, and on the east by some of the highest forested sand dunes in the world, edging white sandy beaches and clear blue seas, it forms one of Africa's 'hot spots', a region of exceptional diversity of species.   *David Johnson*

A view of steeply rolling hills, a mixture of grassland and bush, in the southern KZN coastal hinterland, about 600 m above sea level. *Rosemary Williams*

'Like the spirits, the plant does not die. It lives forever. It has a fellowship with the spirits' (Berglund). Dried bundles of impepho, *Helichrysum* species, can be found for sale at taxi ranks and on street corners throughout the country - perhaps the most widely used of all wild plants. The sweetly scented stems are burnt as incense to draw the ancestors close, and to give clarity to diviners.

Helichrysum aureonitens Golden Everlasting, impepho *Lal Greene* (above right)

Helichrysum odoratissimum impepho *Tony Abbott* (right)

Flowering times are taken from herbarium records. However, they must be considered approximate. There is great variation in flowering time between coastal and mountain plants of the same species and between plants in the extreme south or extreme north of the region. Factors such as fire, drought and unseasonal rainfall also produce unusual flowering records. The region has summer rainfall with a flush of flowers in spring (August to October) and autumn (March to May). The average annual rainfall ranges from about 600 mm in the more arid regions, to more than 2000 mm on the Drakensberg peaks and in localised sub-tropical parts. In coastal and the southernmost areas some winter rainfall can be expected.

Species descriptions
Family and genus descriptions are run in full in at least one of the colour sections. Often they draw attention to characters useful for identification.
Scientific names are given in *italics*, synonyms in square brackets.
Measurements are always length x breadth unless otherwise stated. When only one measurement is given, it is always length or height.
Unusual or exceptional records, whether size, colour or form, are given in brackets.
Red Data Book categories are included immediately after the distribution sentence.
Flowering times are given in brackets after the flower description.
Ecological and gardening notes are given where known.
Under the heading 'Similar species:' the type face conveys certain information e.g.
Similar species:

Erythrina zeyheri	the plant has a description and photograph in the book.
Erythrina zeyheri	the plant has a description but no photograph in the book.
Erythrina zeyheri (see p. 10)	the plant is described and illustrated elsewhere in the book.

Technical terms are kept to a minimum.
An illustrated glossary (p. 590) explains those that were unavoidable.

KEY TO THE WILD FLOWER FAMILIES OF KWAZULU-NATAL

This key has been designed to facilitate family identification of KwaZulu-Natal wild flowers by the layperson. Every attempt has been made to produce a user friendly key by concentrating on easily observable characters and using colloquial terminology. Unfortunately this is impossible in some instances.

Where possible, underground organs have been avoided to prevent destruction of specimens. The key will not work well outside the region due to the reliance on generic rather than familial characters. Marginal icons have been included to assist in interpretation and the quick guide allows one to short-cut the key.

Quick guide:
- Gymnosperms, leaves rosulate & pinnate ... 1
- Monocots 3
- Dicot parasites 52
- Dicot climbers 58
- Aquatic dicots 83
- Dicots with tiny flowers 92

1. Plants bearing cones & leaves pinnate **2**
   If leaves pinnate never cone-bearing **3**
2. Leaflet midveins prominent
   . . . . **Stangeriaceae**   p.500
   Leaflet midveins obscure
   . . . . **Zamiaceae**   p.500
3. Petals three or six; leaves usually with a set number of longitudinal veins running more or less parallel **4**
   Petals in 4's or 5's; leaves with net veins **45**
4. Most leaves borne in a tuft, stems not visible between leaves **20**
   Leaves well spaced, stems clearly visible between leaves **5**
5. Stems thorny **6**
   Stems without thorns **7**
6. Leaf stalk with tendrils

   . . . . **Smilacaceae** p.514, 572
   Tendrils absent . . . . . **Asparagaceae** p.100, 514
7. Leaves with tendril tips **8**
   Leaves without tendril tips **9**
8. Stems perennial, tough forest vines

   . . . . **Flagellariaceae**   p.26
   Stems annual, fragile herbs
   . . . . **Colchicaceae**   p.26, 86
   p.222, 342
9. Plants aquatic **19**
   Plants terrestrial **11**
   Plants epiphytic **10**
10. Roots fibrous, brown
   . . . . **Piperaceae** p.132, 524
   Roots fleshy, white . . . **Orchidaceae**   p.48, 114
   p.240, 360, 456, 516, 572

11. Leaves insignificant, stems consisting of branching inflorescences
   . . . . **Hyacinthaceae**   p.508
   Leaves prominent **12**
12. Leaves with stalks **13**
   Leaves without stalks **14**
13. Plants climbers
   . . . . **Dioscoreaceae** p.108, 514
   Plants erect (stems rigid)
   . . . . **Piperaceae** p.132, 524
14. Leaves succulent . . . **Asphodelaceae**   p.26, 86
   p.90, 224, 226, 342, 448, 508
   Leaves not succulent **15**
15. Stems solid **16**
   Stems false composed of narrow leaf bases rolled together **18**
16. Mature stems wiry **17**
   Mature stems soft . . **Commelinaceae**   p.222
   p.340, 448
17. 'Leaves' subtended by a small 'bract'

   . . . . **Asparagaceae** p.100, 514
   Leaves not subtended by a bract
   . . . . **Luzuriagaceae**   p.230
18. Leaves in 2 ranks on a stem

   . . . . **Zingiberaceae**   p.360
   Leaves rarely with a stem, radiating

   . . . . **Amaryllidaceae** p.36, 104
   p.232, 346
19. Ovary above the petals
   . . . . **Potamagetonaceae**   p.502
   Ovary below the petals
   . . . . **Hydrocharitaceae**   p.84

76. Plants with milky latex . . . **Apocynaceae**   p.166
  p.298, 416

  Plants lacking milky latex **77**

77. Flowers white flushed with pink, star-shaped
  . . . . **Oleaceae**   p.162, 296

  Flowers not star-shaped **78**

78. Fruit composed of 2 carpels (slice a fruit
  transversely) **79**

  Fruits separating into three carpels
  (paddle-like units)

  . . . . **Hippocrataceae**   p.536

  Fruit composed of many separate carpels

  . . . . **Ranunculaceae**   p.138
  p.250, 382

79. Fruit a short explosive capsule; seeds
  slightly compressed, attached by stiff
  stalks to the placenta

  . . . . **Acanthaceae**   p.76, 198
  p.306, 434, 488

  Fruit and seeds not as above **80**

80. Fruit a large, elongate capsule; seeds flattened,
  with a delicate silver wing

  . . . . **Bignoniaceae**   p.76, 434

  Fruit a short capsule . . **Scrophulariaceae**   p.72
  p. 190, 304, 428, 480, 588

81. Flowers flared funnels with
  conspicuous star-shaped folds

  . . . . **Convolvulaceae**   p.176,
  p.302, 418, 468

  Flowers not as above **82**

82. Leaves simple **83**

  Leaves compound

  . . . . **Fabaceae** (Leguminosae)   p.56, 150
  p.256, 388, 460, 530

83. Stems thorny . . . . **Capparaceae**   p.142
  p.252, 384, 528

  Stems not thorny . . . **Malpighiaceae**   p.276

84. Plants aquatic **85**

  Plants terrestrial **93**

85. Leaf blade floating, leaf stalks very long **86**

  Leaf blade submerged or emergent,

  Leaf stalks average **89**

86. Leaf blade round **88**

  Leaf blade elongate or triangular **87**

87. Floating leaf blade triangular,
  Leaf stalk inflated

  . . . . **Trapaceae**   p.540

  Floating leaf blade elongate, leaf stalk slender

  . . . . **Scrophulariaceae**   p.192

88. Flowers with 5, fringed petals

  . . . . **Menyanthaceae**   p.298

  Flowers with many, unfringed petals

  . . . . **Nymphaeaceae**   p.138, 460

89. Ovary below petals . . **Onagraceae** p.160, 294, 410

  Ovary above petals **90**

90. Ovary units (carpels) separate

  . . . . **Crassulaceae**   p.54
  p.142, 254, 384, 530

  Ovary units united **91**

91. Submerged stems thread-like with tiny
  bladders, flowers like tiny snapdragons

  . . . . **Lentibulariaceae**   p.198
  p.306, 486

  Stems without tiny bladders **92**

92. Plants never forming short, dense mats

  . . . . **Polygonaceae**   p.134,
  p.250, 374, 526

  Plants rosulate, forming short, dense mats

  . . . . **Scrophulariaceae**   p.192

93. Flowers minute < 3 mm in diameter **94**

  Flowers > 3 mm in diameter **105**

94. Leaves basal (radical) **95**

  Leaves on stems (cauline) **97**

95. Leaves narrow, needle-like

  . . . . . . **Aizoaceae** (*Psammotropha*)   p.528

  Leaves with a distinct stalk and blade **96**

96. Leaf main veins striate (joined
  apically and basally)

  . . . . **Plantaginaceae**   p.588

  Leaf venation palmate (diverging)

  . . . . **Gunneraceae**   p.578

97. Flowers unisexual **98**

  Flowers bisexual **102**

98. Leaves opposite **99**

  Leaves alternate **100**

99. Woody dwarf, gnarled shrubs from exposed
  rock outcrops . . . . **Myrothamnaceae**   p.576

  Soft herbs, usually in forest vegetation

  . . . . **Urticaceae**   p.524

  Small succulents, usually on trees or

  rocks in forests . . . . **Piperaceae** p.132, 524

100. Leaves with stipules **101**

  Leaves without stipules . . **Myricaceae**   p.524

101. Fruit with 1 locule, plants often with stinging
  hairs usually in moist shaded habitats

  . . . . **Urticaceae**   p.524

  Fruit with 3 carpels, plants in grassland or
  forest, often with milky latex

  . . . . **Euphorbiaceae**   p.62
  p.154, 276, 530

23

24

159. Leaves with three main veins
. . . . **Melastomataceae** p.410, 466
Leaves with one main vein **160**

160. Plants succulent; petals many
. . . . **Mesembryanthemaceae** p.134, 378
Plants not succulent; petals < 10 . . . . **161**

161. Stamens many (brush flowers); calyx never
tubular . . . . **Myrtaceae** p.68, 158
Stamens less than 12; calyx tubular
. . . . **Onagraceae** p.160
p.294, 410

162. Leaves with pin-prick gland dots
. . . . **Hypericaceae** (Clusiaceae) p.290
Leaves not gland dotted **163**

163. Small interpetiolar gland present
. . . . **Linaceae** p.276
Interpetiolar gland absent **164**

164. Ovary embedded in a fleshy disk
. . . . **Celastraceae** p.64
p.154, 536
Ovary not embedded in a fleshy disk **165**

165. Style simple; petals crinkled
. . . . **Lythraceae** p.410
Style branched; petals smooth
. . . . **Caryophyllaceae** p.136, 382

166. Leaves with glistening fluid droplets atop long
hairs . . . . **Droseraceae** p.384
Leaves not as above **167**

167. Leaves connected to the stalk asymmetrically,
flowers unisexual
. . . . **Begoniaceae** p.68
p.156, 408
Plants not as above **168**

168. Petals 4 . . . . **169**
Petals not 4 . . . . **170**

169. Petals extending beyond the calyx
. . . . **Brassicaceae** (Cruciferae) p.140
p.252, 460
Petals equal to the calyx
. . . . **Dichapetalaceae** p.530

170. Sepals 2 . . . . **Portulacaceae** p.250, 382
Sepals > 2 . . . . **171**

171. Leaves round **172**
Leaves not round **175**

172. Styles 2 . . . **Apiaceae** (Umbelliferae) p.160
p.294, 540
Styles more than 2 . . . . **173**

173. Styles and stamens > 20
. . . . **Ranunculaceae** p.138
p.250, 382
Styles and stamens < 20 . . . .**174**

174. Stamens fused, forming a tube around
the style . . . . **Malvaceae** p.66
p.156, 282, 406
Stamens fused only basally
. . . . **Geraniaceae** p.62, 152,
p.398, 466

175. Leaves vestigial . . . . **Cactaceae** p.68
p.158, 290, 466, 540
Leaves not vestigial **176**

176. Stamens united into a fringed tube surrounding
the style . . . . **Meliaceae** p.154
Stamens not united; leaves with pin-point
transparent glands (pellucid gland dots)
. . . . **Rutaceae** p.402

177. Style single **178**
Styles more than 1 . . . . **182**

178. Ovary below petals . . . **Santalaceae** p.134, 250
Ovary above petals **179**

179. Ovary unilocular **180**
Ovary with more than one locule
. . . . **Rhamnaceae** p.154, 536

180. Leaves opposite, often unequal
. . . . **Nyctaginaceae** p.378
Leaves alternate, usually similar **181**

181. Perianth tubular, bark stripping
. . . . **Thymelaeaceae** p.68
p.158, 292
Perianth not tubular, bark not stripping
. . . . **Phytolaccaceae** p.52, 528

182. Leaf base expanded into a papery sheath
. . . . **Polygonaceae** p.134
p.250, 374, 526
Leaf bases not expanded
. . . . **Phytolaccaceae** p.52, 528

MONOCOTYLEDONS Single seed leaf, parallel veins; flower parts in threes or multiples of three.

FLAGELLARIACEAE - Erect or climbing perennials. Leaves tendril tipped. Fruit a berry. Old World trop, 2 genera, ± 6 species, 1 genus in SA. *Flagellaria* (*flagellum* - a whip; *aria* - like, refers to long flexible stems) - Climbers; leaves with tubular basal sheath, slit to base; flowers in terminal inflorescences. Asia, Afr, Fiji, 3 species, 1 in SA.

Flagellaria guineensis Climbing Bamboo; Kanotgras (A); ugonothi (Z) (*guineensis* - of Guinea)

Robust, herbaceous climber, up to canopy. In forest, coast to midlands. E Cape to Moz. Stems bamboolike. **Leaves:** 100-220 mm, tapering to **tendril tip**, sheathing stem. **Flowers:** In terminal branched inflorescences, ± 100 x 90 mm; creamy white (Oct-Jan). **Fruit:** Red berry (Jan-Apr). **General:** Fruit eaten by birds. Stems used for tying thatch and weaving baskets. Good garden subject as a juvenile. Grown from seed.

COLCHICACEAE Formerly part of Liliaceae. Herbs with buried, starchy corms, sometimes with runners. Stems erect or twining. Leaves sheathing at base. Flowers with 6 tepals of similar size and shape, free or basally joined, 6 stamens, free, ovary superior. Fruit a capsule. Afr, Medit, W Asia, Austr. ± 15 genera, ± 165 species, 12 genera in SA, most common in summer rainfall regions.

Gloriosa (*gloriosus* - handsome) - A few closely related species found in Afr and Asia, 1 in SA.

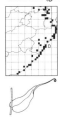

Gloriosa superba Flame Lily; Vlamlelie (A); ashikolohwani (Th); ihlamvu, ihlamvu lasolwandle, isikhwali sasolwandle, isimiselo (Z)

Trailing or scrambling, up to 2 m. On coastal dunes, forest margins, in thicket, E Cape to E Trop Afr. Tuber white, deeply buried. **Leaves:** Shiny, tapering to tendril tips. **Flowers:** Tepals ± 70 x 20 mm, yellow, red and yellow, red or deep pink (Nov-Mar). **Fruit:** Green capsules, seeds red. **General: Poisonous.** Tubers eaten by porcupines. Used in traditional medicine to treat intestinal worms, skin problems, sprains, bruises, impotence and infertility. Grown commercially for chemical compounds. Good container or garden plant, grown from seed. Cut-flowers last well. (See p. 222)

Littonia (named in honour of Dr Samuel Litton, prof of botany, Royal Dublin Society) - Afr and Arabia, 7 species, 2 in SA.

Littonia modesta Littonia; Geelklokkies (A); ihlamvu lehlathi, uhlamvu lwen-tombazana (Z)

Slender, erect or climbing, up to 2 m. On forest margins, damp areas in grassland, coast to 1450 m. Small tuber. **Leaves:** Narrow, ± 130 mm, often in whorls of 3-4, tips form tendrils in shade. **Flowers:** ± 30 mm, yellow-orange (Nov-Jan). **Fruit:** Capsule ± 50 mm, drying brown, seeds round, red. **General:** Used medicinally, especially for infertile women and if a female child is desired. Easily grown from seed.

Sandersonia (named after John Sanderson died 1881, Natal plant collector) - 1 species, endemic to SA.

Sandersonia aurantiaca Christmas Bells; Geelklokkie (A); ihlamvu lasenhla, umagobongwana, ushayabhici (Z) (*aurantiaca* - between yellow and red, ie orange)

Erect, up to 750 mm. In damp grassland, on forest margins, up to 1950 m. Tuber branched. **Leaves:** ± 90 x 20 mm, 3 main parallel veins, tips form tendrils in shade. **Flowers:** ± 26 mm, bright orange (Nov-Jan). **Fruit:** Capsule ± 25 mm, seeds round, rough. **General:** Endangered by picking and loss of suitable damp grassland habitat. Traditionally used as an aphrodisiac and charm for protection from evil. Developed for horticulture in New Zealand, now available worldwide. Long lasting cut-flower.

ASPHODELACEAE - Formerly part of Liliaceae. Mostly herbs, also woody forms such as the tree Aloes. Leaves often thick, succulent, in rosette, basal or just below inflorescence, margins often toothed and spiny. Inflorescence unbranched or branched, tepals free or fused into a tube, ovary superior. Fruit a capsule. Europe, Asia, Afr, centred in S Afr, particularly *Kniphofia* and *Aloe*, 17 genera, ± 750 species, 10 genera in SA.

Bulbine (*bulbine* - bulbous plant) - Perennial herbs with fleshy leaves (for description see p. 224).

Bulbine asphodeloides Spreading Bulbine (see p. 224)

Kniphofia (named after J H Kniphof, 1704-1763, prof of medicine at Erfurt University) - **Red-hot Pokers** Leaves soft, basal; inflorescence usually a simple dense spike. Mostly Afr, ± 70 species, 47 in eastern SA.

Kniphofia angustifolia [= *K. rufa*] Grass-leaved Poker; icacane (Z) (*angustifolia* - narrow leaves)

Up to 650 mm, **solitary or in small groups**. In moist areas in mountain grassland, up to 2450 m. **Leaves:** Grasslike, 400-700 x **2-3 mm**, dull bluish green, soft, erect, then arching, slightly keeled below. **Flowers: In loosely arranged inflorescence,** 100-300 x 60 mm, stem slender; buds cream, dull yellow to orange-red, flowers **19-32 mm**, hanging, creamy white, yellow or red (Nov-Apr). **Similar species:** *K. laxiflora* (see p. 28), *K. ichopensis* (see p. 508).

Flagellaria guineensis

Flagellaria guineensis

Bulbine asphodeloides

Gloriosa superba

Littonia modesta

Sandersonia aurantiaca

Kniphofia angustifolia

27

Kniphofia albomontana (*albus* - white; *montanum* - mountain, refers to Thabamhlophe, the Zulu name for the type locality)

Up to 1,2 m, 3-4 stems at base. In seepages in mountain grassland. Stems ± 250 x 40-60 mm, covered in matted roots and **leaf fibres. Leaves:** In rosette, 600-1000 x 22-36 mm, **stiff, V-shaped,** recurved, margin and upper keel toothed. **Flowers:** In dense, oval inflorescence, 110-220 x 50-70 mm; buds brownish purple, purple-orange, erect to spreading, flowers pale yellow-green or tinged orange, 30-35 x 3 mm, **stamens protrude 2-5 mm,** bracts ± 22 x 6 mmm, stalks short (Jan-Mar). **Fruit: Large,** ± 13 x 10 mm, erect. **General:** This species formerly considered to be a V-shaped leaf form of *K. northiae* (see p. 30).

Kniphofia caulescens Lesotho Red-hot Poker; Basoeto Vuurpyl; leloele-la-loti, lelutla (SS); icacane, umathunga (Z) (*caulis* - stem, refers to the distinct stem, uncommon in the genus)

Robust, 0,6-1 m, in groups or large colonies. In marshes, on damp mountainsides, amongst rocks, at higher altitudes 1800-3000 m. Rhizome thick, with **simple or branched stem,** ± 300 mm. **Leaves:** In dense rosette, 450-700 x 25-50 mm, **blue grey-green,** erect or bending in upper half, **margins finely toothed. Flowers:** In **very dense, bi-coloured inflorescence,** ± 300 x 60 mm; buds pink to red; **flowers ± 24 mm,** pale greenish to creamy yellow, **stamens protruding** (Jan-Mar). **General:** Often grown around rural homesteads as a charm against lightning .

Kniphofia coddiana [= *K. elegans*] **Codd's Poker** (named after L E W Codd born 1908, agriculturalist and botanist, specialist on *Kniphofia*)

Up to 650 mm, solitary or small groups. In grassland associated with Natal Group Sandstone. **Leaves: Erect, narrow,** 300-600 x 8-15 mm, dull blue-green. **Flowers:** In dense **roundish** inflorescence, ± 70 x 60 mm; **buds red,** spreading, **flowers** ± 32 mm, **yellow** to orange-yellow, hanging (Aug-Oct).

Kniphofia evansii Evans' Poker, Cathedral Peak Poker (named after Maurice Evans, 1854-1920, businessman, politician and plant collector)

Up to 650 mm, solitary or in small groups. On streambanks in KZN Drakensberg 1800-2100 m. **Leaves:** Grasslike, spreading, 600-760 x 3 mm. **Flowers:** In dense inflorescence, ± 100 x 40 mm; buds hanging, flowers 12-16 mm, yellow-orange to scarlet, spreading to hanging, buds the same colour (Dec-Feb).

Kniphofia fluviatilis River Poker (*fluviatilis* - growing in running water)

Up to 700 mm, in groups. **On mountain streambanks,** usually partly in water, up to 2800 m. **Leaves:** Erect, firm, 350-700 x 8-**25 mm,** dull **blue-green. Flowers:** In dense inflorescence, ± 90 x 80 mm, stem stout; buds hanging, dark to orange-red, flowers **42-50 mm,** hanging, yellowish to luminous apricot (Oct-Feb). **Similar species:** *K. porphyrantha* (see p. 226).

Kniphofia gracilis Graceful Poker (*gracilis* - slender, graceful)

Up to 1 m, solitary or in small groups. In grassland, 100-1400 m. **Leaves:** Curving from middle, 400-1200 x 4-14 mm. **Flowers:** In loosely arranged inflorescence, short or elongate, ± 350 x 38 mm, tapering to tip; buds erect to hanging, white tinged pink to yellow tinged orange, flowers ± 20 mm, spreading, whitish, creamy yellow or yellow, bracts oblong to oval (Dec-Apr). **General:** Considerable variation in length and density of the inflorescence. (See p. 92)

Kniphofia laxiflora Slender Poker; icacane, inxonya, umathunga (Z) (*laxiflora* - loose flowers)

Up to 1 m, **solitary or in small groups.** In moist grassland, coast to mountains, up to 2450 m. **Leaves:** Grasslike, 500-120 x 6-10 mm. **Flowers: In loosely arranged inflorescence;** flowers 24-35 mm, yellow, orange, salmon pink to red-orange, **not** white or cream, **bracts blunt or rounded** (Nov-May). **General:** Very variable shape and colour in a single colony. Rhizome used in traditional medicine to treat chest ailments. **Similar species:** *K. angustifolia* (see p. 26), *K. ichopensis* (see p. 508).

Kniphofia albomontana

Martin von Fintel

Kniphofia caulescens

Darrel Plowes

Kniphofia caulescens

Auriol Batten

Kniphofia coddiana

Tony Abbott

Kniphofia coddiana

Tony Abbott

Kniphofia evansii

Roy Boardman

Kniphofia gracilis

Martin von Fintel

Kniphofia laxiflora

Trevor Coleman

Kniphofia fluviatilis

Trevor Coleman

29

Kniphofia linearifolia **Common Marsh Poker; Vuurpyl (A); icacane, umathunga (Z)**
(linearifolia - narrow leaves)

Robust, up to 1,5 m, in groups. Widespread in marshy areas, streambanks, mountain grassland, up to 1980 m, E Cape to Zim. **Leaves:** 600-1400 x 12-28 mm, **yellow green to dull green,** strongly keeled, margins finely toothed or smooth. **Flowers:** In dense inflorescence, ± 160 x 65 mm, neatly arranged, oval, tapering to tip; **buds pinkish red to green, flowers 25-35 mm,** greenish yellow to yellow, **stamens hardly protrude, bracts oblong to blunt or rounded,** ± **10 x 4 mm** (Dec-May). **Similar species:** *K. uvaria* Leaves hard, fibrous, narrower; inflorescence roundish. *K. bruceae* Stamens protrude, bracts with long pointed tips. *K. tysonii* Up to 2 m, in grassland; leaves erect then folding at middle, ± 1500 x 40 mm; buds orange to dull dark red, flowers smaller, 20-28 mm, yellow to greenish, stamens protruding.

Kniphofia northiae **Broad-leaved Poker, Marianne North's Poker; leloele (SS); icacane, umathunga (Z)** (named after Marianne North, intrepid Victorian traveller and botanical artist who first illustrated this plant and supplied a live specimen to Kew Gardens in the late 1800s)

Up to 1,7 m, solitary. In mountain grassland, on streambanks, basalt cliffs, seepage lines. **Leaves:** In rosette, 500-1500 x 35-120 mm, leathery, recurved, **without keel,** margins toothed. **Flowers:** In dense inflorescence, 100-220 x 50-60 mm, stem stout; buds and flowers spreading, stamens **protruding,** buds pinkish red, flowers whitish or orange-red to yellow (Oct-Feb). **General:** Colour varies from E Cape to KZN.

Kniphofia ritualis **leloele, lelutla (SS)**

Up to 800 mm, solitary or in small groups. On grassy, wet mountain slopes, shallow soil on rock, 1800-3000 m. **Leaves:** In 3-4 ranks, erect then bending, 400-900 x 12-24 mm, spreading, soft, deeply keeled, margins toothed. **Flowers:** Inflorescence 90-140 x 40-50 mm; buds hanging, orange or salmon to red, flowers hanging, 25-30 mm, greenish yellow (Jan-Mar). **General:** Leaves used for plaiting ropes. Used in traditional medicine to treat pain, also in initiation rites for girls.

Kniphofia rooperi **Winter Poker; Lentevuurpyl (A); icacane, umathunga ompofu (Z)** (named after Capt Edward Rooper, stationed in East London between 1848-1850, painter of flowers and landscapes, who sent this plant to England.)

Robust, up to 1,4 m, in groups. In marshy coastal areas. **Leaves:** In 4 ranks, spreading, **500-1100 x 15-35 mm,** dull green, deeply keeled, margins and keel **usually toothed. Flowers:** In dense **round** inflorescence, **80-110 x 50-80 mm,** stem stout; buds enclosed in overlapping bracts when young, bright red, orange-yellow or greenish, flowers ± 42 mm, orange-red to yellow-green, **bracts brownish (winter,** Apr-Sep). **Fruit: Small, roundish. General:** Plants more robust in wetter areas. Dry rootstock used as good luck charm by children. Used in traditional medicine to treat chest complaints. Excellent garden subject. **Similar species:** *K. littoralis* Leaves dark green; bracts white, tips pointed; fruit large, ± 15 x10 mm, oval.

Kniphofia thodei **Thode's Poker** (named after Justus Thode, 1859-1932, plant collector who collected particularly in the Drakensberg)

Up to 500 mm, solitary. In moist mountain grassland, up to 2750 m. **Leaves:** Narrow, erect then bent, 250-500 x 2-5 mm, **pale blue-green, soft,** margins slightly toothed. **Flowers: In dense inflorescence,** ± 60 x 50 mm; buds hanging, dull red to red-brown, tipped white, flowers 28-35 mm, white or tinged reddish brown (Nov-Mar).

Kniphofia triangularis [= *K. macowanii*] **Mandarin Poker; leloele-le-lenye-nyane, motosi, qaloe (SS)** *(triangularis - 3 sided, refers to fruit)*

Up to 600 mm, singly or in small groups. In mountain grassland, streambanks, moist areas amongst sandstone rock, up to 2500 m. **Leaves:** Soft, curved, 280-600 x 1,5-8 mm, keeled beneath, margins smooth or toothed. **Flowers:** Inflorescence 50-80 x 40-50 mm; buds hanging, flowers 24-35 mm, mostly reddish (Jan-Apr). **General:** Subsp. *triangularis,* leaves narrow, 3-6 mm wide, **grasslike, margins smooth to finely serrated.** Subsp. *obtusifolia,* Mpum; **leaves soft, 4-10 mm broad, margins entire. Similar species:** *K. galpinii* Leaves narrow, grasslike, 8-25 mm wide; inflorescence with sterile bracts at tip, tepal lobes not spreading.

Kniphofia linearifolia

Kniphofia northiae

Kniphofia ritualis

Kniphofia rooperi

Kniphofia thodei

Kniphofia uvaria

Kniphofia triangularis

Kniphofia triangularis

Kniphofia triangularis

31

Aloe - succulent plants, stemless, single stemmed or with massive trunks up to 20 m; leaves in rosettes; inflorescences candlelike, often branched. Afr, Arabia, Medit, Madag, India and China, ± 350 species, ± 125 in SA.

Aloe aristata Guinea-fowl Aloe; Tarentaalaalwyn (A); sereleli (SS); umathithibala (Z)
(aristata - awned, refers to tips of leaves)

Up to 700 mm, in ± 12 rosettes. In moist areas, on rocks, up to 2450 m in KZN Drakensberg, on dry, sandy flats in E Cape, Free State. **Leaves:** Narrow, incurved, 80-100 mm, green with white spots ± forming small soft spines, margins with soft white teeth, **tip a long bristle. Flowers:** In branched inflorescences, heads ± 180 mm; flowers ± 40 mm, dull orange-red (Nov-Dec). **General:** Common house plant. Used traditionally to induce pregnancy and as a protective charm against lightning.

Aloe boylei Broad-leaved Grass Aloe; lisheshelu (Sw); incothobe, isiphukuthwane, isiphuthumane (Z) (named after F. Boyle, botanist)

Robust, up to 900 mm. On moist grassy slopes, up to 2400 m, E Cape to N Prov. **Branched stems ± 200 mm. Leaves:** Deciduous, **erect, flat, broad for most of the length,** ± 600 x 60-90 mm, spotted near base, margins with white teeth, **abruptly narrowing** to pointed tip. **Flowers:** In dense **flattish** inflorescences, 100-120 mm wide, 1-3(15) stems; flowers **large,** ± 40 mm, **tubular,** salmon-pink, tips greenish, anthers not exserted (Nov-Feb). **General:** Leaves cooked.

Aloe chabaudii Chabaud's Aloe; inhlaba (Sw, Z); inkalane (Z) (named after John Chabaud; the type specimen flowered in his garden)

Up to 1 m, in dense groups. Bushveld, rocky outcrops, in low-lying areas, KZN to Tanz. **Leaves:** In rosette, ± 500 x 100 mm, grey-green, turning pinkish red in exposed dry conditions. **Flowers:** In much branched inflorescences, heads broadly rounded (or spreading), ± 160-100 mm; flowers 35-40 mm, brick red to pinkish (Jun-Jul). **General:** Leaves used for snuff; also browsed by game. Very good garden subject.

Aloe cooperi Cooper's Aloe; lisheshelu (Sw); inqimindolo, isiphukuthwane, isiphuthumane (Z) (named after Thomas Cooper, 1815-1913, English plant collecter who visited SA)

Up to 1,2 m. In open grassland, coast to 1500 m. **Leaves: In fan** or rosette in large plants, 600-800 x 50-60 mm, **V-shaped, keeled,** spotted beneath, margins with narrow, white, toothed edge. **Flowers:** Inflorescences ± 200 mm, 1-3 stems; flowers ± 40 mm, red with green tips **(Sep-Mar). General:** Flowers, leaves cooked and eaten. Used in traditional medicine for easy birth. Smoke from burning leaves protects cattle from eating unsuitable food. Lovely garden plant. Subsp. *pulchra,* in drier areas; leaf margins smooth, hard, white tubercles with hairlike tip at base; (blooms **Apr-May).**

Aloe dewetii De Wet's Aloe; inhlaba (Sw) (named after Vryheid headmaster, J F de Wet)

Large, up to 2,5 m, singly. In grassland. **Leaves: In large rosette ± 1 m diam,** broad at base, **shiny above,** with dull white spots scattered or in loose bands, **margins horny with large, spreading, brown teeth. Flowers:** In branched inflorescences, heads ± 400 x 70 mm, **stem robust;** flowers widely spaced, ± 42 mm, bright pink to dull scarlet (Feb-Mar). **General:** Leaves used to make snuff. Good garden plant.

Aloe ecklonis Ecklon's Aloe; Ecklonse-aalwyn (A); maroba lihale (SS); isiphukuthwane, isiphuthumane (Z) (named after Christian Ecklon, 1795-1868, apothecary, plant collector)

Up to 500 mm, often in clumps. In grassland, coast to 2125 m. **Leaves:** Deciduous, **spreading, broad,** ± 400 x 100 mm, margins with white teeth. **Flowers:** In dense inflorescences, ± 50 x 120 mm, 1-3(30) stems; flowers **short, roundish, ± 24 mm,** swollen in the middle, yellow, orange to red, **anthers exserted** (Nov-Jan). **General:** Inflorescence eaten as a vegetable. Used in traditional medicine to treat tuberculosis, as a protective charm and in initiation rites for girls.

Aloe gerstneri Gerstner's Aloe; isihlabana (Z) (named after Rev J Gerstner, amateur botanist, who first collected the plant in 1931)

Up to 1,3 m, solitary. On rocky slopes. Critically endangered. Stem short or absent. **Leaves:** In rosette, up to 600 x 120 mm, dull grey-green, **smooth,** margins with **brown teeth on white base;** young leaves spiny on both surfaces. **Flowers:** In branched inflorescences, spikes ± 360 x 70 mm; buds deep red, flowers ± 30 mm, reddish orange (Feb-Mar). **General:** Grows well in gardens.

Aloe aristata

Aloe boylei

Aloe chabaudii

Cameron McMaster

Tom de Waal

Lorraine van Hooff

Aloe cooperi

Lawrence Peacock

Aloe ecklonis

Martin von Fintel

Aloe ecklonis

Cameron McMaster

Aloe cooperi

Trevor Coleman

Aloe dewetii

Neil Crouch

Aloe gerstneri

Rosemary Williams

33

Aloe greatheadii var. *davyana* Grasaalwyn (A)

Robust, up to 1,5 m, solitary or in small colonies. In rocky grassland. Var. *greatheadii* found from N Prov to Zim, Congo, Moz. **Leaves:** In spreading rosette, shiny green, oblong white spots in bands, dull whitish green beneath, margins with dark brown teeth. **Flowers:** 1-2 inflorescences, heads compact, 150-200 x 70-80 mm; flowers 30-35 mm, dusty pink to reddish (Jun-Jul). **General:** Used in traditional medicine to treat burns, wounds. Useful soil binder, good garden plant in sun or semi-shade.

Aloe kniphofioides Grass Aloe; Grasaalwyn (A); inhlatjana (Sw) (*kniphofioides* - resembling *kniphofia*)

Up to 600 mm, solitary. Scattered in damp grassland, rocky areas on hills and mountainsides up to 1500 m. **Bulblike swelling underground. Leaves:** Erect, 200-300 x 6-10 mm, thin (only slightly succulent), margins entire or with tiny teeth. **Flowers:** Inflorescence ± 150 mm; flowers 35-50 mm, pink to scarlet with green tips (Aug-Dec). **General:** Grows well in rich, well drained soil, with plenty of water in spring.

Aloe maculata [= *A. saponaria*] Common Soap Aloe; Bontaalwyn (A); lekhala (SS); lihlala (Sw); ingcelwane (X); amahlala, icena (Z) (*maculata* - spotted or blotched)

Up to 1 m, in colonies. Widespread, coast to 2000 m. Variable. **Leaves:** Recurved towards dry, twisted tip, 250-300 x 80-120 mm, dull white spots in irregular bands, margins with hard, brown teeth. **Flowers:** 1-2 branched inflorescences, heads **flat topped, ± 120 x 160 mm**; young buds erect, **flowers ± 45 mm**, bright yellow, orange to red, **colour uniform** (May-Oct). **General:** Leaves cooked, eaten. Used in traditional medicine to treat colds, wounds, ringworm, dysentery in poultry, as a protective charm against lightning and in hide tanning preparations. Popular garden plants.

Aloe mudenensis Muden Aloe; Kleinaalwyn (A); icena (Z) (named after the village of Muden, KZN, the type locality)

Up to 1 m. In hot, dry areas. Stemless or with stem ± 800 mm. **Leaves:** 250-300 x 80-90 mm, upper surface blue-green, irregularly scattered white oblong spots, margins with brown horny teeth. **Flowers:** 1-2 branched inflorescences, heads ± 120 x 90 mm, **tip rounded**; buds erect, flowers ± 35 mm, yellowish to pinkish orange, red (Jul-Aug). **General:** Leaves reddish in hot, dry situations. Attractive garden plant.

Aloe parvibracteata inhlaba (Sw); icena, inkalane (Z) (*parvibracteata* - short bracts)

Up to 1,5 m, in **large colonies**. In thicket, grassland, N KZN to S Moz. **Leaves:** Spreading, recurved, 300-400 x 60-80 mm, **bright to purplish green**, scattered pale spots above, usually in broken bands, margins with hard, red-brown, teeth, tips drying off. **Flowers:** 2-3 branched inflorescences, heads 150-200 x 70 mm, stems **slender**; flowers 30-33 mm, pink to red (Apr-Sep). **General:** Flower buds eaten by monkeys; leaves, flowers browsed by rhino, antelope. Popular garden plant.

Aloe pratensis Meadow Aloe; lekhala qhalane (SS) (*pratensis* - growing in meadows, an inappropriate description by the person who described the plant - it actually grows amongst rocks.)

Up to 600 mm. On cliffs, rocky hillsides, up to 1900 m. **Leaves:** In rosettes ± 250 mm diam, 150 x 50 mm, grey-green, upper surface smooth, lower surface with scattered brown spines **on white bases**, margins with red-brown teeth. **Flowers:** Inflorescences ± 200 x 100 mm, 1-4 **stems covered in large, white, striped, papery bracts**; flowers ± 40 mm, red to orange (Jun-Nov). **General:** Does not do well in cultivation.

Aloe suprafoliata Book Aloe; Boekaalwyn (A); inhlaba (Sw); icena, umhlabandlazi (Z)
(*suprafoliata* - above the leaves, refers to young leaves which seem to grow on top of each other in rows)

Up to 1 m, solitary. On rocky slopes, misty mountain tops. Stemless or with short stem. **Leaves: In a flat fan in young plants, maturing into a rosette**; 300-400 x 70 mm, **bluish to silvery grey-green**, turning reddish towards dry twisted tip, margins with sharp red-brown teeth. **Flowers:** 2-3(6) **unbranched inflorescences**; ± 250 x 100 mm, buds densely packed, almost covered by **large, round, silvery bracts**, red with blue tips, flowers ± 50 mm, deep pink to scarlet (May-Jul). **General:** Leaves are used for snuff. Attractive garden plant, needs water in summer and no hot afternoon sun.

Aloe greatheadii var. *davyana*

Martin von Fintel

Aloe maculata

Olaf Wirminghaus

Aloe maculata

Tom de Waal

Aloe mudenensis

Trevor Coleman

Aloe kniphofioides

Tom de Waal

Aloe parvibracteata

Martin von Fintel

Aloe pratensis

Cynthia Giddy

Aloe suprafoliata

Martin von Fintel

35

AMARYLLIDACEAE - Bulbous herbs. Flowers in umbels; ovary inferior. Fruit a berry (*Clivia, Scadoxus, Haemanthus*) or a capsule; seeds with or without black pigment. Popular horticultural subjects which attract the Amaryllis Caterpillar pest. Trop and warm regions, ± 65 genera, ± 750 species, 19 genera in SA.

Scadoxus (*doxus* - glory or splendour) - Rhizomatous or bulbous herbs; leaves thin, with stalks and distinct midrib, forming false main stem; flowers in dense inflorescence. Mainly Afr, 3 species in SA.

Scadoxus membranaceus [= *Haemanthus puniceus* var. *membranaceus*] **Dwarf Paintbrush; Seeroogblom (A); idumbi (Z)** (*membranaceus* - texture of membrane or parchment)

Evergreen, up to 500 mm. In shade of low-lying coastal forest, sea-facing dunes. Bulb small, ± 30 mm diam. **Leaves:** 2-7 directly from bulb, **no false stem**, stalk ± 200 mm, blade ± 230 x 70 mm, margins wavy, **midrib prominent beneath. Flowers:** In small inflorescence, ± 50 mm wide, stem ± 250 mm; flowers and fruits **enclosed within bracts** (Dec-Apr). **Fruit:** Red, ± 10 mm diam, bracts remain intact, erect.

Scadoxus multiflorus subsp. *katharinae* [= *Haemanthus katharinae*] **Katharine Wheel, Blood Flower; Bloedblom (A); idunjana, ubukhoswane (Z)** (named after Katharine Saunders, 1824-1901, plant collector and botanical artist)

Deciduous, robust plants, up to 1,2 m. In coastal and swamp forest. **Leaves:** Blade ± 350 x 150 mm, false stem ± 600 mm, produced before flowers. **Flowers:** Inflorescence ± 200 mm diam, stem ± 650 mm; flower tube ± 22 mm, **deep pinkish red**, stalks ± 45 mm (Jan-Mar). **General:** Fruit eaten by birds. Used to make love charms. Excellent garden and container plant, suitable even in deep shade.

Scadoxus multiflorus subsp. *multiflorus* [= *Haemanthus multiflorus*, *H. sacculus*] **Fire-ball Lily; isiphompo, isiphungo (Z)** (*multiflorus* - many flowers)

Deciduous, up to 1 m. In light shade, in bushveld, grassland, coast to 2700 m, KZN to Trop Afr. **Leaves:** ± 450 x 410 mm, shiny, margins wavy, produced after or with flowers, false stem and 2 reduced leaves speckled red-brown at base. **Flowers:** Inflorescence round, ± 150(260) mm diam, stem speckled towards base; flower tube ± 15 mm, tepal lobes ± 30 mm, pink, stamens red (Oct-Dec). **Fruit:** Berry red. **General:** Browsed by antelopes, eaten by bushpigs. Reputed to be poisonous. Good garden plant.

Scadoxus puniceus [= *Haemanthus magnificus*, *H. natalensis*] **Blood Lily, Snake Lily; Rooi-kwas, Seerooglelie, Skeerkwas (A); idumbe-lika-nhloyile, idumbelentaba, isiphompo, umgola (Z)** (*puniceus* - scarlet, carmine or purple)

Robust, up to 1 m. In shade and full sun, coast to 2100 m, S Cape to Trop Afr. Bulb ± 100 mm diam. **Leaves:** ± 300 x 120 mm, margins wavy, after or with flowers, false stem ± 300 mm, scale leaves at base speckled reddish brown. **Flowers:** Inflorescence, ± 150 mm diam, **within** bracts, stem ± 900 x 40 mm, speckled reddish brown near base, separate from leaves; flower tube ± 10 mm, tepal lobes ± 23 x 15 mm, orange-red, **bracts** ± 100 x 50 mm, **shiny reddish brown, erect at first** (Jul-Feb). **Fruit:** Berry red, ± 10 mm diam. **General:** Bulb poisonous. Pollen reputed to be poisonous. Sunbirds, weaver birds feed on nectar; ripe berries eaten by birds, monkeys. Used in traditional medicine for poultices, to treat coughs, headaches, stomach ailments, poisoning. Excellent garden and container plant.

Clivia (named after Lady Charlotte Clive, Duchess of Northumberland, died 1866) - No true bulbs; leaves in 2 ranks. In cultivation in Europe since 1828, now popular garden and container plant worldwide. Endemic to SA, 4 species.

Clivia gardenii **Major Garden's Clivia, Natal Drooping Clivia; Boslelie (A); umayime, umgulufu (Z)** (named after Major Robert Garden, soldier, naturalist, stationed in KZN from 1848 to 1853)

Evergreen, up to 600 mm. In deep shade, forest. **Leaves:** In loose fan, overlapping at base, ± 600 x 40 mm, **tapering to pointed tip, margins faintly rough. Flowers: 14-20, in inflorescence**; flowers hanging, **tubular, ± 50 (70) x 10 mm**, orange-yellow, lobes tipped greenish, stalks ± 20 mm (40 mm in fruit) (Jun-Sep). **Fruit:** Round, red, 20 mm diam. **General:** Used in traditional medicine. Garden plant for shady areas. **Similar species:** *C. nobilis* **Eastern Cape Clivia; Boslelie (A)** Up to 800 mm; E Cape; leaf **margin rough, narrowing abruptly to rounded or indented tip**; flowers in **large flattish inflorescence**, ± 100 mm diam, **40-60 flowers**, flowers ± **40 mm, mouth 15 mm diam**, stalks ± 30 mm (60 mm in fruit) (Apr-Aug); introduced into cultivation in England in 1854. *C. caulescens* Mpum; plant stem ± 500 mm or more; inflorescence with ± 20 flowers, ± 30 x 10 mm.

Trevor Coleman

Geoff Nichols

Scadoxus membranaceus

Geoff Nichols

Scadoxus multiflorus subsp. *katharinae*

Geoff Nichols

Lal Greene

Scadoxus puniceus

Martin von Fintel

Scadoxus multiflorus subsp. *multiflorus*

Auriol Batten

Tony Abbott

Clivia gardenii

Clivia nobilis

37

Clivia miniata Clivia, Bush Lily, St John's Lily; Boslelie (A); ubuhlungu-bemamba, ubuhlungu-beyimba, umayime (Z) *(miniata - colour of red lead)*

Evergreen, up to 500 mm, in clumps, in large colonies. In partial shade of forest, coastal bush, coast to midlands. **Leaves:** ± 500 x 65 mm, hairless, dark green, tapering to pointed tip, bases overlapping. **Flowers:** ± 30 in inflorescence, stem ± 450 mm; flowers ± 70 mm diam, red to orange, **trumpet-shaped, tepal lobes spreading** (Aug-Oct), lovely scent. **Fruit:** Fleshy red berry ± 20 mm diam, remains on plant until next flowering season. **General:** Used in traditional medicine to treat fever and snakebite, ease childbirth and as a protective charm. Popular garden and container plant worldwide. Long lasting cut-flower. *C. miniata* **var.** *citrina*, rare in the wild; flowers creamy yellow; fruit yellowish orange. Now available in selected nurseries.

Brunsvigia (honours the House of Brunswick) - Large bulbs; leaves widely spreading or prostrate; inflorescence large, round, flowers on long stalks, stamens curving down and up at ends, stalks elongate as fruit ripens; fruiting head breaks off as a whole and rolls in the wind, distributing seed. Mainly S Afr, ± 16 species.

Brunsvigia undulata Ruby Brunsvigia *(undulata - refers to wavy margins)*

Up to 800 mm. In grassland. Bulb ± 120 x 80 mm. **Leaves: Erect,** ± 15, in a fan, ± 500 x 40-100 mm, shiny blue-grey-green, **margins wavy to tightly wavy, produced with flowers. Flowers:** 35-80 in inflorescence, stem stout, 300-450 mm, bracts leathery, ± 95 x 50 mm; flowers 45-60 mm, **deep red,** tepal lobes recurved, ± 5-9 mm wide, **stalks erect,** ± 300 mm (Jan-Feb).

Cyrtanthus (*kyrtos* - curved; *anthos* - flower, refers to the frequently curved flower tube) - Bulb buried; leaves few, narrow; 1 to few flowers in inflorescence, flower tube narrow or trumpetlike, tepal lobes shorter than tube, free. Afr, mainly in S Afr, ± 50 species.

Cyrtanthus brachyscyphus [= *C. parviflorus*] Dobo Lily, Orange Ifafa Lily; Kleinrooi-pypie (A); unompingi (Z) *(brachyscyphus - short cups)*

Deciduous, up to 300 mm, solitary or in clumps. In moist grassland, on rocky stream-banks, mostly coastal. Bulb oval, ± 25 mm diam, neck short. **Leaves:** ± 300 x 8 mm, with flowers. **Flowers:** 6-10 in inflorescence, stems hollow; flowers ± 26 mm, **tube narrow, swollen in centre,** curved at base, lobes **short, straight,** bright orange-red to pale red, stalks ± 45 mm (Aug-Nov-Apr). **General:** Brilliant colour makes this a popular garden specimen despite being one of the smallest *Cyrtanthus* species.

Cyrtanthus brachysiphon

Perennial herb, up to 160 mm. On moist rock ledges, near waterfalls. **Leaves: Broad,** ± 350 x 13-18 mm, **tips ± blunt. Flowers:** 5-6 in inflorescence; flowers ± 26 mm, red, **tube short,** ± 10 mm, paler, lobes ± spreading, 16-18 mm, stalks 10-45 mm (Dec).

Cyrtanthus contractus Fire Lily; Brandlelie, Vuurlelie (A); impingizana (Z)
(contractus - narrowed)

Perennial herb, 200-400 mm. Scattered in grassland, E Cape to N Prov. Bulb 40-60 mm diam, oval, neck ± 30 mm. **Leaves:** 300-500 x 8-12 mm, flat, narrowed to tip and base, produced after flowers. **Flowers:** 2-10, hanging, in inflorescence, stem hollow, mauve, **bracts ± 50 mm, withering early**; flowers 65-80 mm, scarlet, **tube contracted** above, **lobes spreading,** ± 15 x 7 mm, stalks 20-40 mm (Aug-Oct, after fires). **General:** Used as a protective charm. Hollow stems used as whistles by children. Does not do well in cultivation.

Cyrtanthus epiphyticus Tree Lily, Tree Cyrtanthus; Boomlelie (A) *(epiphyticus -*
growing on another plant, not parasitically)

Epiphytic on trees, also on boulders, in rock crevices, in moist conditions. Bulb 90-110 mm, with long neck. **Leaves:** Flat, tapering to base and tip, 300-500 x 10-20 mm, appearing with flowers. **Flowers:** 6-15 in inflorescence, bracts ± 35 mm, stem shorter than leaves; flower tube narrow, curved, lobes ± 8 mm broad, red, roundish, blunt tipped, recurved, stalks 15-25 mm, red (Nov-Feb). **General:** Potential as a hanging basket plant.

Clivia miniata

Clivia miniata var. *citrina*

Cyrtanthus brachyscyphus

Cyrtanthus contractus

Cyrtanthus epiphyticus

Brunsvigia undulata

Cyrtanthus brachysiphon

39

Cyrtanthus falcatus Fire Lily *(falcatus - sickle-shaped)*

Hanging out of cracks in cliff faces, usually below 1800 m. Bulb 50-80 mm diam, neck ± 120 mm. **Leaves:** ± 250 x 30 mm, leathery, sickle-shaped, appear with flowers. **Flowers:** 6-10 in inflorescence, **stem ± 300 mm, curves upwards from hanging bulb then tip bends sharply downwards**; flowers ± 60 mm, red, throat ± 10 mm wide, lobes ± 20 x 12 mm (Sep-Nov). **General:** Suitable for hanging baskets.

Cyrtanthus galpinii [= *C. balenii*] Galpin's Cyrtanthus, Fire Lily; Galpin-cyrtanthus, Vuurlelie (A); umpimpilizi (Sw) (named after Ernest Galpin, 1858-1941, banker and amateur botanist)

Up to 200 mm, solitary, or in colonies. Among rocks, in grassland. Bulb oval, ± 30 mm diam. **Leaves:** ± 200 x 3 mm, after flowers. **Flowers:** 1-3, stem purple; flowers trumpet-shaped, 50-80 x 50 mm, lobes ± 20 mm, blunt tipped, red to orange, scattered with gold dust, stalks short (Apr-Aug), sweetly scented. **General:** Edible.

Cyrtanthus obliquus Giant Cyrtanthus; Knysnalelie (A); umathunga (Z) *(obliquus - slanting)*

Robust, evergreen, up to 600 mm. In dry rocky grassland or thicket. Bulb ± 100 mm diam, neck above ground. **Leaves:** In a fan, 200-600 x 30-60 mm, blunt tipped, **twisted**, margins edged yellow-red. **Flowers:** 6-12 in inflorescence, stem hollow; flowers hanging, ± 70 x 25 mm, with waxy bloom, yellowish green and red, lobes ± 25 x 15 mm, tipped green (Aug-Feb). **General:** Used in traditional medicine to treat coughs, headaches. Hardy garden plant, cultivated in Europe for over 150 years.

Cyrtanthus obrienii Red Ifafa Lily; Rooi-ifafalelie (A)

Up to 450 mm. On rocky hillsides at higher altitudes. **Leaves:** ± 300 x 8 mm, shiny bright green, speckled red at base. **Flowers:** ± 8 in inflorescence, stem round; flowers ± 40 mm, bright scarlet, lobes ± 5 mm (Jul-Sep). **General:** Good cut-flower, attractive when massed in garden. There is some doubt over identity. Specimens from the wild are required to confirm identification.

Cyrtanthus sanguineus Large Red Cyrtanthus, Inanda Lily, Kei Lily; Keilelie (A); isilawu esimhlophe (X) *(sanguineus - blood red)*

Up to 300 mm, in clumps. On rock faces, near water, coast to 600 m, E Cape to Trop Afr. Bulb oval, ± 100 x 80 mm, neck long, mostly above ground. **Leaves:** ± 400 x 20 mm, green with waxy bloom, reddish at base, appearing with flowers. **Flowers:** 1-2, **± 100 mm**, bracts ± 80 mm, drying out before flowers open, stem hollow; flowers red, lobes ± 50 x 17 mm, curling back, remain open for days (Feb-Mar, Jan-Apr), faintly scented. **General:** Used in traditional medicine during pregnancy to ensure easy labour. Popular, beautiful garden plant, in cultivation since 1846.

Cyrtanthus stenanthus Long-tubed Cyrtanthus; Ifafalelie (A); lepontoana, moroloanane-oa-litsoene (SS); umpimpilizi (Sw); impingizana encane ebomvu (Z) *(stenanthus - narrow anthers)*

Up to 400 mm, in clumps. In damp grassland, up to 2800 m. Bulb ± 20 mm diam, neck short. **Leaves:** ± 300 x 2-5 mm, present or absent at flowering. **Flowers:** 3-7 in inflorescence, erect to nodding; flowers, turned to one side, 25-45 mm, red, orange or yellow, **very slender, slightly contracted at throat**, lobes oval, spreading, ± 3 mm, stalks short (Oct-Mar), sweetly scented. **General:** Bulb is eaten. Used as protective charm against lightning. Var. *stenanthus*, flowers ± 30 mm, red, greenish red. Var. *major*, flowers ± 45 mm, yellow. (See p. 232)

Cyrtanthus tuckii Green-tipped Fire Lily; Brandlelie (A); umpimpilizi (Sw); isiwesa (Z) (named after William Tuck, 1824-1912, horticulturalist and collector, who introduced the navel orange to SA)

Up to 450 mm, scattered. In grassland, wet areas. Bulb oval, ± 37 mm diam. **Leaves:** 300-450 (usually shorter than flowering stem) x 9 mm, appearing after flowers. **Flowers:** ± 15 in inflorescence, **bracts ± 90 mm, green, erect at flowering**, stem mauve-red; flowers ± 60 mm, **tube curved**, widening to throat, ± 9 mm diam, **lobes** reddish orange, ± 9 mm, **straight, not spreading** (Aug-Nov-Mar, best after fires). **General:** Does not do well in cultivation. Bulb eaten. Used as protective charm against evil, lightning. Var. *tuckii*, flower **yellow at base**. Var. *transvaalensis*, flowers **plain red**. Var. *viridilobus*, **flower lobes green**.

Cyrtanthus galpinii

Geoff Nichols

Cyrtanthus obliquus

Trevor Coleman

Cyrtanthus obrienii

Darrel Plowes

Cyrtanthus sanguineus

Geoff Nichols

Cyrtanthus stenanthus

Tony Abbott

Cyrtanthus tuckii

Lawrence Peacock

Cyrtanthus falcatus

Martin von Fintel

41

IRIDACEAE - Iris Family Corms or rhizomes. Leaves sword-shaped, in 2 ranks. Flowers regular or irregular, 3 stamens, ovary inferior. Cosmop, ± 82 genera, ± 1700 species. Over half the species occur in SA in 38 genera. *Schizostylis* (split style) - Flower with well developed tube. Single species genus, E Cape to Zim.

Schizostylis coccinea [now *Hesperantha coccinea*] Scarlet River Lily, Crimson Flag; Rooirivierlelie (A); khahlana (SS) *(coccinea* - scarlet)

Perennial herb, up to 900 mm, in clumps. On streambanks, 900-1675 m. **Leaves:** Narrow, ± 400 x 10 mm, midrib distinct. **Flowers:** 6-14 in inflorescence, stem sturdy; flowers ± 65 mm diam, scarlet (pink), tube ± 30 mm (Feb-Apr). **General:** Popular garden plant in UK and Europe, frost resistant. Good cut-flower. (See p. 352)

Dierama (*dierama* - a funnel) - **Hairbells, Wand-flowers; Grasklokkies** (for description see p 354).

Dierama latifolium *(latifolium* - broad leaves)

In large clumps, up to 2,5 m. In open grassland, 600-2100 m. **Leaves:** 500-1500 x **5-15mm**. **Flowers:** Inflorescences with 6-11 branches, each with 5-16 flowers, **stem long**, drooping; flowers ± 33 mm, pink (deep red), **bracts white**, 18-27 x 7-10 mm (Oct-Jun). **Similar species:** *D. atrum* small clumps; E Cape; leaves narrow, 3-6 mm; flowers deep maroon. *D. dubium* Solitary; 1200-1500 m, KZN; leaves slender; flowers small, ± 18 mm, dark purple-red. *D. reynoldsii* Solitary; E Cape to C KZN; leaves narrow; flowers large, 20-30 mm, deep red. *D. tyrium* Tall, 1,2-2 m, in small clumps; 1200-2100 m, N KZN, Mpum; flowers large, magenta-red, bracts mostly red-brown. (See p. 356)

Tritonia (triton - a weathercock, refers to the variable direction of the stamens of the different species) - Flowers regular, tube short, style branches undivided. Afr, 40 species, 27 in SA, mostly concentrated in coastal areas of S Cape.

Tritonia disticha [= *T. rubrolucens*] Red Tritonia; isidwe esibomvu (Z) *(disticha* - in 2 rows)

Perennial herb, up to 800 mm. In grassland, coast to 2300 m, SE Cape to Mpum. **Corm annual**, ± 30 mm diam. **Leaves:** 350-500 x 8-12 mm, strong midvein and marginal veins. **Flowers:** 4-12 in 1-3 inflorescences; flowers ± 30 mm, bright red or pink, small yellow blotch on 3 lower lobes (Nov-Mar). **Fruit:** Capsule, ± 10 mm. **General:** Used traditionally to treat stomach complaints in babies. Two subspecies.

Crocosmia (*krokos* - saffron; *osme* - a smell, dried flowers have a strong smell of saffron when placed in warm water) - Flower lobes spreading, stamens equal; plants die back in winter. S Afr, 9 species, 7 in SA.

Crocosmia aurea Falling Stars, Montbretia; umlunge, udwendweni (Z,Sw) *(aurea* -yellow)

Up to 1,2 m, in colonies. In forest, coast to 2000 m. Corm with long stolons. **Leaves:** In a fan, soft, 20-30 mm wide, midrib distinct, forming 'stem' at base. **Flowers:** Nodding, in branched inflorescence; flowers ± 40 mm diam, luminous orange and red, tepal lobes spreading (Jan-Apr). **Fruit:** Leathery orange capsule, shiny purplish black round seeds. **General:** Seeds eaten by birds; corms eaten by bushpigs. Used in traditional medicine to treat dysentery. Excellent shade plant, can become invasive.

Crocosmia masonorum Golden Swans Crocosmia; Goueswane (A) (named after Marianne Mason, 1845-1932, artist and social worker who came to SA in 1910, collected seeds and bulbs)

Up to 750 mm. On forest margins. **Leaves:** Broad, stiff, ± 750 x 50 mm, finely ribbed, veins prominent, tapering to tip and base. **Flowers:** 1-sided inflorescence, tip curving over; flowers ± 40 mm wide, orange-red (Dec-Jan). **General:** A beautiful garden plant and cut-flower, dies back in winter.

Crocosmia paniculata [= *Curtonus paniculatus*] Falling Stars, Pleated Leaves, Zigzag Crocosmia; Vallendesterretjies, Waaierlelie (A); khahla-ea-bokone, moloke (SS); udwendweni, umlunge (Z) *(paniculata* - panicles or tufts of flowers)

1-2,4 m, in large clumps. In moist grassland, up to 1500 m. **Leaves:** Pleated, ± 750 x 60 mm. **Flowers:** In dense inflorescences, **branches zigzag**; flowers tubular, curved, ± 70 mm, yellow-orange, lobes scarlet-brown, ± 15 x 7 mm (Dec-Feb). **General:** Used traditionally to treat dysentery, infertility. Attractive garden plant.

Crocosmia pottsii Slender Crocosmia; umlunge, udwendweni (Z) (named after George Potts, 1877-1948, born England, died Bloemfontein, botanist)

Up to 1 m. In stony grassland, streambanks, forest. **Leaves:** Narrow, rigid, blue-green. **Flowers:** In curved inflorescence, ± 5 flowers open at a time; flowers narrow, red, tube curved, ± 45 mm, tepal lobes short, blooms for 3-4 weeks (Dec-Feb). **General:** Used traditionally to treat dysentery, infertility. Excellent garden plant.

42

Cynthia Giddy

Schizostylis coccinea

Martin von Fintel

Crocosmia paniculata

Hilliard & Burtt

Dierama latifolium

Lorraine van Hooff

Crocosmia masonorum

Tom de Waal

Lawrence Peacock

Tritonia disticha

Trevor Coleman

Tony Abbott

Crocosmia aurea

Lal Greene

Crocosmia pottsii

Gladiolus (*gladiolus* - small sword, refers to leaf shape) - Bracts green; style branches short, undivided or shortly divided in 2; seeds winged; deciduous. Hybrids created since the early 1800s have produced the cut-flowers and garden plants popular worldwide. Known as *itembu* (X), 'fruits of the earth', the corms are dug up and eaten. A large genus of ± 259 species found mostly in S Afr, also Trop Afr, S Europe and Middle East, over 126 species in SA.

Gladiolus aurantiacus sidvana (Sw); isihlanzi (Z) (*aurantiacus* - colour orange)

Up to 900 mm. In grassland on moist stony ground. Corm, **irregular**, flattish, ± 40 mm diam, **at an angle in soil**. **Leaves:** Basal, in a fan, 450-750 x 1-2 mm, firm, overlapping, strongly ribbed, **appearing weeks after flowering**, only maturing in March; stem leaves ± 70 mm. **Flowers:** Closely or widely spaced in inflorescence, mostly turned to one side, bracts ± 40 mm, clasping sturdy stem; flowers ± 100 mm, golden yellow or orange and yellow, finely streaked red (Sep-Dec). **Fruit:** Capsule ± 25 mm. **General:** Used in traditional medicine to treat fevers.

Gladiolus cruentus Blood-red Gladiolus; Rooigladiolus, Rooiswaardlelie (A)
(*cruentus* - blood red, dull red)

Plants hanging, in profusion. Restricted to seasonally wet rock faces, up to 900 m, on Natal Group Sandstone in the Valley of a Thousand Hills. **Leaves: Soft, with thickened margins. Flowers:** Similar to *G. saundersii*, **not drooping, shallowly cupped, tepals not reflexed. General:** These spectacular plants have been grown in the UK and Europe since the 1800s. This species has been confused and lumped with *G. saundersii* since they were first described. **Similar species: G. flanaganii** Restricted to cliffs, ± 3000 m, KZN Drakensberg.

Gladiolus dalenii [= G. dracocephalus, G. natalensis, G. psittacinus] African Gladiolus, Natal Lily; Papegaaigladiolus, Wildeswaardlelie (A); khahla-e-kholo (SS); sidvwana (Sw); isidwi esibomvu, uhlakahle, udwendweni (Z) (named in 1828, after Cornelius Dalen, Director, Rotterdam Bot Gardens)

Up to 2 m. Widespread, in grassland, woodland, coast to 2500 m, E Cape to Trop Afr, W Arabia. Corm 20-50 mm diam, surrounded by cormlets. **Leaves:** Erect, ± 20 mm wide, grey-green, in a fan. **Flowers:** 2-7(25) in inflorescence, bracts ± 30 mm, clasping, green to red-brown; flowers ± 80 x 50 mm, variously coloured, orange-red with clear yellow lower tepals, pale green to yellowish orange, finely speckled brown to red (Oct-Jan, **Feb-Jun,** different colour forms flower at different times). **Fruit:** Capsule ± 30 x 10 mm. **General:** Corms eaten by bushpigs, used as tops for childrens' games. Leaves plaited into ropes. Used in traditional medicine to treat diarrhoea, chest ailments caused by sorcery, sterility in women, as good luck charms and in the medicine horns of nyangas. A spectacular sight in the wild, sometimes in large colonies. Cultivars developed in Europe in the early 1900s are grown worldwide and have become very successful cut-flowers. (See p. 516, 572)

Gladiolus densiflorus (*densiflorus* - densely covered with flowers)

Up to 1,3 m, solitary or in small clumps. In grassland, up to 1300 m. Corm ± 30 mm diam, tunics of wiry brown fibres, with cormlets. **Leaves:** Basal, 6-8, in spreading fan, 250-500 x 10-35 mm, **soft**, blue-green, midvein raised, yellow, **many fine, closely spaced veins**, tips pointed, leaves 3-4, bractlike, sheathing. **Flowers:** 15-30, in dense spikelike inflorescence, on one side, overlapping, buds, capsules, 2 ranked; **flowers funnel-shaped**, small, 30-40 mm, **densely spotted** with dark red, maroon, mauve or pink raised dots on whitish or greyish background, tube yellow-green inside, lower tepal lobes with yellowish midline near tips (Feb-Apr). **Fruit:** Round capsule, 10 mm diam, woody. **General:** Flower colour can seem pure red or mauve when spotting is very dense. (see p. 456) **Similar species:** *G. crassifolius* (see p. 356, 456).

Gladiolus saundersii Saunders' Gladiolus, Lesotho Lily; khahla ea maloti (SS)
(named after Wilson Saunders who first grew and illustrated the plant in 1870)

Up to 900 mm, in colonies. On rocky hillsides, mountains, 1700-3000 m. Corm roundish, ± 40 mm diam. **Leaves: Sturdy, erect, in a fan**, 250-600 x 6-26 mm, margins thickened, veins prominent. **Flowers:** Inflorescence with stout, straight, stem, bracts ± 45 mm; flowers large, ± 60 mm diam, **downward facing, strongly hooded**, bright red with broad white mark and speckling on 3 lower tepals (Jan-Mar). **Fruit:** Round capsule ± 20 mm diam. **General:** Flowers eaten as salad or cooked as pot herb. Used in traditional medicine to treat diarrhoea.

Gladiolus aurantiacus

Martin von Fintel

Gladiolus cruentus

Martin von Fintel

Gladiolus flanaganii

Martin von Fintel

Gladiolus saundersii

Godfrey Symons

Gladiolus densiflorus

Martin von Fintel

Gladiolus dalenii

Lal Greene

Gladiolus dalenii

Darrel Plowes

45

Watsonia (*Watsonia* - named after English scientist Sir William Watson, 1715-1787) Flattened corm with persistent fibrous tunics; leaves firm, basal and sheathing stem leaves; inflorescence a spike, flower tube curved, widening to funnel-shaped, lobes spreading, ± equal, 6 stigmas, bracts rigid, usually brown. Mostly SA, ± 52 species, 1 in Madag.

Watsonia bachmannii (named after Frans Bachmann, a German medical doctor and naturalist who was one of the first people to collect in S KZN and Transkei)

250-400 mm. In open marsh, restricted to Pondoland coast. **Leaves:** 1 basal, 1 sheathing, half as long as stem. **Flowers:** 2-7, orange, stem ± 500 mm (Jul-Oct). **General:** Pondoland endemic.

Watsonia gladioloides (gladioloides - like *Gladiolus*)

Up to 0,5(1) m, in clumps. In rocky grassland, mountains, not below 1000 m. **Leaves:** 2, basal, 3-15 mm wide, reaching base of inflorescence, midrib and **margins heavily thickened**; 2 shorter, sheathing stem leaves. **Flowers:** ± 25, in closely packed inflorescences, stem unbranched, sheathed with bract leaves; flowers ± 70 mm, tepal lobes narrow, ± 20 mm, dark red, **bracts dry, brown, ± 32 mm**, clasping (Sep-Jan).

Watsonia latifolia sidvwa (Sw) (latifolia - broad leaves)

Up to 1,5 m. In open rocky grassland, granite outcrops at higher altitudes. **Leaves: 50-90 mm wide, sword-shaped**, margins slightly thickened. **Flowers:** ± 25, inflorescences ± 700 mm, bracts ± 30 mm, green at flowering, stem rarely branched; flowers **dark maroon-red**, tube ± 45 mm, horizontal in upper part, nearly round, tepal lobes ± 30 x 8 mm, stamens protrude ± 10 mm from tube (Dec-Feb). **General:** Corm edible. Used in traditional medicine.

Watsonia pillansii [= *W. socium*] **Pillan's Watsonia; Knolpypie, Lakpypie, Suurknol (A)** (named after Cape Town botanist Neville Pillans)

Up to 1,2 m, in clumps, large colonies. In grassland, rocky areas, coast to 2400 m, S Cape to KZN Drakensberg. **Leaves:** 3-4, basal, 12-18 mm wide, slightly twisted, light green, margins translucent yellow, tips sharp, usually dry. **Flowers:** ± 35 in inflorescences, bracts ± 33 mm, green to reddish, tips dry; flowers ± 80 mm, bright orange to orange-red, upper half of tube nearly cylindrical (Sep-Apr). **General:** Popular garden plant. Grown as a cut-flower in Durban from 1930s to 1960s.

Freesia (named in the 1800s, after Dr F H T Freese, a physician at Kiel) - The small genus *Anomatheca* has been sunk under *Freesia*, a genus which is famous worldwide as a garden plant and cut-flower. SA, ± 16 species.

Freesia grandiflora [= *Anomatheca grandiflora, Lapeirousia grandiflora*] (grandiflora - large flowers)

Up to 450 mm, in small colonies. In thicket, rocky woodland, N KZN to Tanz. **Leaves:** In a fan, soft, bright green, flat, deciduous. **Flowers:** Large, ± 40 mm diam, scarlet, **wide at throat**, tepal lobes longer than tube, dark red blotch at base of 3 tepals (Dec-Apr). **Fruit:** Bright orange seeds. **General:** Corms eaten by bushpig. Good garden subject, autumn-winter flowering, grows well from seed.

Freesia laxa [= *Anomatheca laxa, Lapeirousia laxa*] **Small Red Iris, Woodland Painted Petals; Bospaletblaar, Rooipypie (A)** (laxa - loose, not dense)

Dainty, up to 300 mm. In shade of forest, woodland, thicket, E Cape to Moz. **Leaves:** Thin, in a fan. **Flowers:** Small, ± 25 mm diam, pale blue, lilac, red, with deep magenta blotches, **tepal lobes held at right angles to, and shorter than the tube** (throughout the year). **General:** Hardy garden plant, survives winters in England and USA.

STRELITZIACEAE - Crane Flower Family Leaves often large, in a fan. Trop America, SA, Madag, 4 genera, ± 60 species, 1 genus in SA. *Strelitzia* (named in honour of Queen Charlotte, wife of George III, from the house of Mecklenburg-Strelitz) - Leaves bananalike, opposite; flowers from within boat-shaped spathes; seeds dry, with aril. Eastern S Afr, 5 species.

Strelitzia reginae **Bird-of-paradise-flower, Crane Flower; Kraanvoëlblom (A)** (reginae - queen)

Up to 1,5 m. In rocky grassland, near coast. **Leaves:** Blade up to 500 x 100 mm, margins red edged. **Flowers:** ± 6 in spathe, ± 200 mm, covered in waxy bloom; flowers brilliant orange, bright blue, arrowlike nectary (throughout the year). **Fruit:** 3 valved capsule, black seeds with woolly orange aril. **General:** Thick nectar attracts sunbirds. Birds eat the seeds. Well known cut-flower worldwide. Popular, hardy garden plant.

Darrel Plowes

Watsonia gladioloides

Geoff Nichols

Watsonia latifolia

Darrel Plowes

Watsonia pillansii

Trevor Coleman

Freesia grandiflora

Lawrence Peacock

Freesia laxa

Tom de Waal

Watsonia pillansii

Trevor Coleman

Strelitzia reginae

Tony Abbott

Watsonia bachmannii

47

CANNACEAE - *Canna* Tall, erect perennial herbs. Rhizomes thick branching; main stem simple. Leaves large, stalk sheathing. Flowers irregular. Popular ornamentals. Trop, subtrop, ± 60 species, 2 naturalised in SA.

★ *Canna indica* Wild Canna

Perennial herb, up to 1,5 m. In disturbed damp areas. From Trop America, naturalised weed in SA. Rhizome stout; leaves ± 450 x 200 mm. Inflorescence branching, flowers red, lip oranged spotted red, ± 75 mm (Nov-Jul). Visited by sunbirds.

ORCHIDACEAE - Orchid Family (for description see p. 240).

Disa (possibly from *dis* - rich or opulent, alluding to the beauty and magnificence of the first species described in this genus, *D. uniflora*) - Underground tubers; several leaves; median sepal hooded, prolonged into a spur or pouch, direction in which spur points is useful in identification. Afr and Madag, ± 130 species, ± 94 in SA.

Disa chrysostachya Red or Yellow Torch Orchid; uklamkleshe, umnduze wotshani obomvu, umnduze wotshani ompofu (Z) *(chrysostachya - golden spots)*

0,25-1 m. In damp grassland, marshy areas, coast to 2000 m. **Leaves:** Basal, 3-5, mostly up stem. **Flowers: In slender, tapering, spikelike inflorescence,** ± 550 mm; flowers densely packed, yellow to red suffused with orange or deep pink, ± 12 mm wide, **spurs ± 11 mm, inflated, hanging straight down** (Dec-Jan). **General:** Like glowing candles, often seen on roadsides in KZN midlands.

Disa polygonoides Honey Disa; ihlamvu elibomvu, uklamkleshe, umnduze wotshani obomvu (Z) *(polygonoides - resembles Polygonum, Knot-grass)*

150-800 mm. In marshy areas, coast to 1600 m, E Cape to S Moz. **Leaves:** ± 150 x 15 mm, clasping, erect. **Flowers:** In dense spikelike inflorescence, ± 170 x 20 mm; flowers red, orange, **spurs slender, ± 4,5 mm, facing down** (Oct-May). **General:** Infusion of tubers used in traditional medicine to restore loss of voice after illness.

DICOTYLEDONS Two seed leaves, net veins; flower parts in fours, fives or multiples of these.

LORANTHACEAE - Mistletoe Family Partially parasitic shrubs, rootless, attached to host by suckers. Stems brittle, woody. Leaves opposite. Flower tube brightly coloured, large, calyx small or absent. Fruit a large, brightly coloured berry with 2-6 seeds. Fruit eating birds squeeze the large sticky seeds from the fruit skin. They stick to branches once regurgitated or defecated by the birds and germinate quickly. Attracts butterflies, particularly the blues (Lycaenidae). 'Wood roses' are the remains of the host branch, after its death, at the point of the parasite's attachment. Trop and S Temp, ± 67 genera, ± 900 species, 11 genera in SA.

Tapinanthus [= *Loranthus*] *(tapeinos* - humble; *anthos* - flower, refers to size of flowers) - Flowers with 'V'-shaped split, base swollen or tube cylindrical, lobes erect or reflexed, explosive flower opening and release of pollen; pollinated by birds. Largest Afr genus, ± 200 species, 20 in SA.

Tapinanthus gracilis *(gracilis - slender)*

Parasitic shrub, less than 1 m. Found on a large number of species. Stems grey-brown. **Leaves:** 15-30 x 5-15 mm, mostly on short branchlets 10-30 mm, in 2-4 pairs, stalkless or short stalks ± 4 mm. **Flowers:** 2-6 in inflorescence, stems 6-8 mm; flower tube cylindrical, 35-40 x 1-2 mm (Nov-Feb). **Fruit:** Oval, 8-10 x 5 mm, red. **General:** Birds feed on nectar and fruits. (See p. 132)

Tapinanthus kraussianus [=*Loranthus kraussianus*] Krauss's Mistletoe, Lighted Matches; Voëlent (A) (named after Christian Krauss, 1812-90, German scientist, traveller and collector in SA in 1839-40)

Parasitic shrub, up to 2 m. On trees, shrubs in thicket and woodland. **Leaves:** 50-70 x 15-25 mm, stalks ± 10 mm. **Flowers:** In massed clusters, 6-8 in each, stems short; flowers 30-45 mm, orange reddish towards tip, greenish orange at base, tube split 10-15 mm below **erect lobes,** style deep red (Oct-Apr). **Fruit:** Oval berry 10-12 mm, pink. **General:** Birds feed on nectar and fruits. Subsp. *kraussianus,* leaves oval to rounded, deep green. Subsp. *transvaalensis,* leaves lance-shaped, light grey-green, thickly leathery. (See p. 248)

Tapinanthus rubromarginatus [= *Loranthus rubromarginatus*] Red Mistletoe; Rooivoëlent, Vuurhoutjies (A) *(rubromarginatus - red edge)*

Deciduous, robust, up to 1 m or more. Parasitic on species of *Acacia, Dichrostachys, Dombeya, Faurea, Populus, Protea, Prunus.* Stems 10-20 mm diam, with scattered raised white dots. **Leaves:** In clusters, often on swollen nodes, 20-50 x 10-15 mm, **thin to slightly leathery, margins red. Flowers:** 2-4, in dense inflorescences, on swollen nodes of older stems; flowers 40-50 mm, tube split 14-16 mm, dark red to purplish with whitish spots, lobes purplish black, folded back (Sep-Nov). **Fruit:** Round, ± 10 mm, reddish. **General:** Birds feed on nectar and fruit.

★ *Canna indica*

Tony Abbott

Tapinanthus kraussianus

Geoff Nichols

Tapinanthus kraussianus

Geoff Nichols

Disa chrysostachya

Lal Greene

Tapinanthus rubromarginatus

Olaf Wirminghaus

Disa polygonoides

Darrel Plowes

Tapinanthus gracilis

Lawrence Peacock

49

Tieghemia (named after Phillipe van Tiegham, prof of botany in Paris) - Small parasitic shrubs; stems with dense raised dots, nodes swollen; flower base conspicuously swollen, tube marked with bands of colour. 2-3 species in SA.

Tieghemia quinquenervia [= *Loranthus quinquenervius*] Elm Mistletoe; iphakama (Z)

(*quinquenervius* - 5 veins from base of leaf)

Dense clumps, up to 1 m diam. Parasitic on *Chaetacme, Cassine* and *Celtis* trees. **Leaves:** Alternate, 40-50 x 15-25 mm, stalks 3-5 mm. **Flowers: Produced with leafy shoots**, 35-40 mm, dark red with **white bands**, tube split 10-12 mm (Mar-Dec). **Fruit:** Oval, 8-10 mm, red. **General:** Flowers, fruit visited by birds. Attracts butterflies. Used in traditional medicine. **Similar species:**
T. bolusii [= *Loranthus bolusii*] On bushveld trees; flowers red and **pale green, clustered on swollen nodes of older branches** and on leafy shoots, **calyx tube shorter, broader**.

Erianthemum (*erion* - wool; *anthemon* - flower) - Partially epiphytic shrubs (for description see p. 374).

Eriathemum dregei [= *Loranthus dregei*] Hairy Mistletoe; Voëlent (A); inovu (Sw); idumba (X); inevu emhlophe, inomfi, udumba, i(ama)phakama (Z) (see p. 374)

Plicosepalus (*plicatus* - folded) - Buds, flowers, strongly curved. More arid regions of Afr, ± 10 species, 5 in SA.

Plicosepalus kalachariensis [= *Loranthus kalachariensis*]

Up to 1 m. Parasitic on *Acacia* species, KZN to Bots, Nam. **Leaves:** Size very variable, 25-60(85) x 7-20 mm, hairless. **Flowers:** 2-6, in clusters, often on older branches; flowers ± 45 mm, pink to reddish orange, darker at base, lobes separating to base (Apr-Aug). **Fruit:** ± 10 mm, red. **General:** Attracts birds to nectar and fruits.

VISCACEAE - Mistletoe family Perennial parasites. Leaves sometimes reduced to scales, nodes often swollen. Tiny separate male and female flowers, often on separate plants. Pollinated by insects. Fruit a fleshy sticky berry with 1-2 seeds, distributed by birds. Mostly trop and warm regions, 7 genera, ± 385 species, 1 genus in SA.
Viscum (*viscum* - bird lime) - Shrubby, parasite, densely branched; leaves opposite, well developed or reduced to small scales. Widely distributed in Afr, Asian trop, in temp zones of Europe, Asia, ± 100 species, 17 in SA.

Viscum rotundifolium Round-leaved Mistletoe, Red-berried Mistletoe; Rooibessie, Voëlent (A) (*rotundifolium* - round leaves)

Leafy shrub, in small rounded clumps, less than 500 x 500 mm. Most widespread mistletoe parasite in S Afr. Stems pale grey-green, much branched, young branches 6 ribbed, round. **Leaves:** Very variable, 8-12 x 4-8 mm. **Flowers:** In small clusters in axils (Apr-Sep). **Fruit:** In profusion, oval, 4-5 mm, **smooth**, orange-red, stalk 3-4 mm long when ripe, persistent style. **General:** Fruit eaten by birds. Attracts butterflies. Used in traditional medicine to remove warts. (See p. 526)

CHENOPODIACEAE - Goosefoot Family Annual or perennial herbs or shrubs. Often weeds of cultivation. Includes Beetroot, Spinach and Swiss chard. Cosmop, 103 genera ± 1300 species, 15 genera in SA.
Salicornia (*sal* - salt; *cornu* - horn, refers to saline habitat and horn-shaped stems) - Fleshy herbs; leaves reduced. In salt marshes worldwide (except Austr), ± 46 species, widespread in coastal areas, 4 in SA.

Salicornia meyeriana Saltmarsh Plant

Succulent shrublet up to 450 mm. Pioneer in mainly coastal salt marshes. Main branches erect, ± 10 mm diam at base, often twisted, secondary branches spreading. **Leaves:** Segments cylindrical, 5-15 x 2-3 mm, blue-green to bluish red, often shiny. **Flowers:** In terminal spikes 5-30(120) mm, tapering when flowering, cylindrical when fruiting (Aug-May). **General:** Browsed. Edible but a bit salty. (See p. 526)

AMARANTHACEAE - Amaranthus Family Mostly herbs. Flowers hidden by persistent bracts, often stiff, translucent, sharply pointed or hooked, forming inflorescence. Trop, ± 71 genera with ± 750 species, 24 genera in SA.
Hermbstaedtia (named after S F Hermbstaedt 1785-1833, prof of chemistry and pharmacy at Berlin) - Herbs or undershrubs; flowers white or red. Afr genus, ± 14 species, 11 in SA.

Hermbstaedtia odorata Wild Cockscomb; Rooi-aarbossie (A); ubuphuphu, umlwandle, uvelabahleke (Z) (*odorata* - sweet smelling)

Slender-stemmed shrublet, up to 600 mm. In grassland, woodland. Tuberous rootstock. **Leaves:** Alternate, ± 50 x 10 mm, tapering at both ends, **gradually reducing up the stem**, stalks short. **Flowers:** In dense, inflorescences, 50-300 mm, stem unbranched, leafless, **hairy;** flowers white tinged red to purple (Jan-Jun). **General:** Leaves eaten as spinach. Used in traditional medicine as a cleansing stomach wash, and as a love charm (mixed with the flesh of kingfishers). **Similar species:**
H. caffra Inflorescence hairless; leaves abruptly reducing in size above.

50

Tieghemia bolusii

Olaf Wirminghaus

Tieghemia quinquenervia

Geoff Nichols

Erianthemum dregei

Geoff Nichols

Plicosepalus kalachariensis

David Johnson

Viscum rotundifolium

Tony Abbott

Plicosepalus kalachariensis

Geoff Nichols

Salicornia meyeriana

Caroline Fox

Hermbstaedtia odorata

Martin von Fintel

51

PHYTOLACCACEAE - Pokeweed Family Herbs, undershrubs, more rarely trees. Mostly in American trop, subtrop, ± 18 genera, ± 65 species, 3 genera in SA.
Rivina (named after August Rivinus, 1652-1723, German physiologist, prof of botany at Leipzig) - 1(3) variable species, Trop, subtrop America, introduced to Afr, Asia tropics.

★ *Rivina humilis* Rivina *(humilis - small)*

Shrublet, 0,3-1 m. In disturbed forest, woodland. Leaves 20-100 x 10-45 mm, stalks 8-50 mm, finely hairy. Flowers small, inflorescences ± 130 mm, sepals green, white or pinkish, with bracteoles (Sep-Apr). Fruit ± 3 mm diam, red, eaten by birds.

Phytolacca (phyton - a plant; *lakha* - Persian for red dye, refers to red juice of fruit) - Herbs, shrubs (trees); male and female flowers sometimes on separate plants; fruit flattened, round, fleshy. Trop, warm regions, ± 35 species, 5 in SA.

Phytolacca octandra Inkberry, Pokeweed; Bobbejaandruif, Inkbessie (A); amahashe, ayatsala (X); umnanja (X,Z); umnyandla (Z) *(octandra - 8 stamens)*

Robust, slightly succulent herb 1-2 m. A weed (possibly introduced), in disturbed areas, coast to 1800 m, E Cape to Trop Afr. Root swollen, tuberous. Stem reddish pink. **Leaves:** 35-135 x 10-50 mm, margins red. **Flowers:** In terminal inflorescences, ± 130 mm; flowers small, greenish white (Sep-Jul). **Fruit:** Fleshy, 7-8 mm, red turning purplish black. **General:** Flowers visited by beetles and flies. Fruit eaten by birds and baboons. Ripe fruit used in the past as ink. Used in traditional medicine to treat snakebite, chest complaints, septic wounds and lung sickness in cattle.(See p. 528)

MENISPERMACEAE - Moonseed family Woody climbers or scramblers. Male and female flowers, small, dull, on separate plants. Fruit slightly fleshy. Trop and warm regions, ± 72 genera, ± 450 species, 7 genera in SA.
Stephania (named after Christian Stephan, 1757-1814, prof botany and chemistry in Moscow, director of Forestry Institute at Petersburg) - Scandent shrubs or herbs; leaves peltate. Afr, Asia, Austr, ± 30 species, 1 in SA.

Stephania abyssinica umbombo, umthambana, umthombo (Z) *(abyssinica - from Abyssinia, now Ethiopia)*

Perennial climber. In woodland, thicket, E Cape to Trop Afr. **Leaves:** Well spaced on stem, ± 100 mm diam, stalks ± 70 mm. **Flowers:** Small, greenish, in slender inflorescences (Oct-Jun). **Fruit:** ± 8 mm diam, dull yellow, small blunt prickles in 3 lines. **General:** Used in traditional medicine to treat boils and as a charm to find lost articles or discover secrets. Two subspecies which vary in degree of hairiness.

Cissampelos (kissos - ivy; *ampelos* - vine, refers to rambling habit, fruit like a bunch of grapes) - Slender climbers; small leaflike bracts with each flower, enlarging as fruit develops. Afr, trop Asia, America, ± 20 species, 4 in SA.

Cissampelos mucronata Heart-leaved Vine; Davidjies(wortel) (A); umbombo (Z) *(mucronata* - pointed tip)

Velvety climber, woody at base. In thicket, near water, KZN to Trop Afr. **Leaves:** 40-120 x 40-130 mm, heart-shaped with hairlike tip, 5-7 veins from base, stalks 20-45 mm. **Flowers:** Male: In compact, dangling inflorescences, 50-150 mm. Female: Inflorescences elongated, 50-160 mm, with leaflike bracts (Sep-May). **Fruit:** Fleshy, 5-8 mm, orange-red. **General:** Used in Afr and India to treat a wide variety of ailments, and reputed to be used for easing childbirth in KZN.

Tinospora (teino - to stretch; *spora* seed, elongated seed) - Herbaceous twiners or woody lianas. 3 species in SA.

Tinospora caffra Orange Grape Creeper; isidumuke (Z)

Briefly deciduous woody climber. In forest, dry woodland, coast to 2000 m, KZN to Trop Afr. **Leaves:** 25-80 x 15-70 mm, oval to roundish, heart-shaped at base, narrowing abruptly to narrow or hairlike tip; stalks 25-100 mm. **Flowers:** Male: In long inflorescences 70-300 mm. Female: Inflorescences 70-150 mm (Oct-Feb). **Fruit:** Fruit fleshy, 8-12 x 4-7 mm, orange. **General:** Used as a fish poison.

PAPAVERACEAE - Poppy Family Herbs, with milky or yellow latex. Fruit a capsule, opening by pores or slits. *Papaver somniferum* used to produce opium. Popular ornamentals. Mostly N Hemisp, ± 23 genera, ± 230 species, 4 genera in SA. *Papaver* (Latin name for the poppy) - Herbs. Mostly N Hemisp, ± 100 species, 1 in SA.

Papaver aculeatum Orange Poppy; Doringpapawer, Koringpapawer, Wilde-papawer (A); sehlohlo (SS) *(aculeatum* - with thorns)

Prickly herb 0,1-1,5 m. In disturbed areas, 600-3000 m, widespread in SA. **Covered in stiff yellow spines, hairs. Leaves:** In basal rosette, 120-130 mm, deeply lobed, margins toothed. **Flowers:** In terminal inflorescence; flowers ± 50 mm diam, orange to red (Oct-Apr). **Fruit:** Ribbed, oval, 10-20 mm. **General:** A weed on wheat farms. Young plants used as a pot herb by the Sotho. Very pretty, can be grown from seed.

Geoff Nichols

Tony Abbott

★ *Rivina humilis*

Stephania abyssinica

Geoff Nichols

Martin von Fintel

Geoff Nichols

Phytolacca octandra

Stephania abyssinica

Cissampelos mucronata

Trevor Coleman

Darrel Plowes

Tom de Waal

Tinospora caffra

Papaver aculeatum

Papaver aculeatum

53

CRASSULACEAE - Crassula Family Herbs or soft shrubs, usually succulent. Leaves usually opposite, often joined round stem, or in basal rosette. ± Cosmop, especially S Afr, C America, ± 33 genera, ± 1100 species, 6 genera in SA.
Cotyledon (kotyledon - cup-shaped hollow, refers to the leaves of some species) - Large succulent herbs or shrubs; leaves opposite; flowers erect or hanging, 5 petals, joined to form tube, lobes spreading or curling back, 1 stamen per petal, 5 sepals; fruit a many seeded small pod. Attracts butterflies. W, S Europe, E Asia, Mexico and Afr. ± 150 species, ± 21 species in SA.

Cotyledon barbeyi [= C. wickensii] Plakkie (A)

Erect, many stemmed, succulent shrub, up to 2(3) m. In bushveld, occasional on rocky outcrops, N KZN, eastern parts of Afr to Ethiopia. Sturdy stems covered in white bloom. **Leaves:** Shape variable, 60-120 x 20-45 mm, thick, shiny green to greyish brown. **Flowers:** In flattened inflorescence, ± 200 mm diam, downy, stem 200-600 mm; flowers erect, spreading or hanging, tube 20-25 mm, **bulging between calyx lobes,** red-orange, lobes curling back, 10 mm, calyx lobes 8-10 mm, pointed (Mar-Sep). **General:** Very attractive, suitable for frost-free gardens.

Cotyledon orbiculata Pig's Ears; Plakkies (A); serilele (SS); ipewula (X,Z)
(orbiculata - disc-shaped)

Evergreen, succulent shrublet, reclining to suberect, up to 1 m. On rocky outcrops, in grassland, bushveld, E Cape to N Prov. Stem slightly woody at base, 12-25 mm diam. **Leaves:** 50-110 x 35-60 mm, closely packed at base, green to grey-green, margins usually red in upper half, sharp tipped; young leaves with waxy bloom. **Flowers:** In compact inflorescence, stem 0,35-1 m, purplish grey; flowers 20-25 mm, orange, pinkish red, **bulging slightly in middle of tube,** lobes 10-13 mm, usually curled back (throughout year). **General:** Used traditionally to treat corns, plantar warts, toothache, earache, also as a poultice on boils (hence the Afrik name 'Plakkie'). Five varieties, the differences mostly in leaf and flower shape. A popular garden plant.

Kalanchoe (Chinese name for the species) - Succulent herbs or small shrubs; leaves opposite; 4 petals joined at base to round or angled tube, 8 stamens (2 per petal). Attracts butterflies. Asia, Afr, Madag, Arabia, Brazil, ± 200 species, 14 in SA.

Kalanchoe lanceolata Narrow-leaved Kalanchoe (lanceolata - lance-shaped)

Robust, erect, single stemmed herb, up to 1,2 m. In bushveld, Swaz to Trop Afr. Stem 4 angled, from perennial base. **Leaves:** 60-150 x 25-60 mm, yellowish green to green, folded, curved under, blunt tipped, hairless or with glandular hairs, margin irregularly lobed, clasping at base. **Flowers:** In elongated inflorescence, branches in opposite pairs; flower tube with long neck, 9-11 mm, yellowish green, lobes 3-5 mm, pointed, orange, calyx lobes 3-5 mm (Apr-Jul).

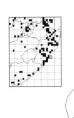

Kalanchoe rotundifolia Common Kalanchoe; Nentabos, Plakkie (A); mfayisele yasehlatini (X) idambisa, uchane, umadinsane (Z) (rotundifolia - round leaves)

Perennial, sparsely branched, erect or straggling succulent herb, 0,3-1,2 m, often in colonies. In bushveld, thicket, in shade or semi-shade, widespread, NE Cape to Bots, Nam, Tanz. **Leaves:** Size and shape very variable, 30-50(75) x 8-25(50) mm, margin entire, scalloped or lobed, blue-green, usually with bloom, tips rounded, stalks 0-25 mm, not clasping. **Flowers:** In sparse, branched inflorescence; flower tube 6-10 mm, lobes twisting, 2-4 mm, red to orange, calyx lobes ± 1,5 mm (Mar-Dec). **General:** Poisonous to stock. Used in traditional medicine as an emetic. **Similar species:** *K. neglecta* N KZN, leaves thick, folded upwards.

Crassula (crassus - thick, refers to fleshy leaves) - Delicate annuals or perennial herbs, shrubs, soft-wooded to succulent, growth form very variable (for description see p 142).

Crassula alba [= C. rubicunda] feko, khato (SS); isidwe, isikhelekhehlane (Z) (alba - white, inappropriate because most petals are red)

Perennial or biennial, unbranched, up to 500 mm. In grassland, up to 2500 m, E Cape to Ethiopia. Very variable in growth form, hairiness and flower colour. **Leaves:** Basal rosette, 60-150(170) x 5-15 mm, sometimes with reddish purple markings or purple beneath, slightly fleshy, sharp tipped. **Flowers:** In flat topped inflorescence, ± 150 mm diam, stem covered with leaflike bracts; flower tube deep red, pink,white or yellow, lobes 3-6 mm, pointed, calyx lobes 1-4 mm, fleshy, green (blooms throughout year). **General:** Used as a charm to make one invisible. The robust red flowering specimens are rewarding garden plants, blooming for many weeks, dying back after flowering, either reshooting from the old base or seeding prolifically. (See p. 386)

Cotyledon barbeyi

Cotyledon barbeyi

Cotyledon orbiculata

Cotyledon orbiculata

Kalanchoe lanceolata

Kalanchoe neglecta

Kalanchoe rotundifolia

Crassula alba

Crassula alba

Martin von Fintel

Martin von Fintel

Martin von Fintel

Martin von Fintel

Darrel Plowes

Wayne Mathews

Van Wyk & Malan

Godfrey Symons

Martin von Fintel

Crassula streyi **Pondoland Crassula, Maroon-leaved Fairy Crassula** (named after R G Strey, 1907-88, German farmer, botanist, Natal Herbarium 1962-1975)
Perennial, succulent, reclining herb, up to 350 mm. On moist, shady rock outcrops in forest, near coast. **Leaves:** 40-65 x 25-40 mm, dark green with white spots along veins on upper surface, **purplish red below, margins with row of pits,** curved under when young, narrowing abruptly to a short point, broad sheath at base. **Flowers:** In terminal, sparse inflorescence, branches at right angles; flowers 6-9 mm diam, yellowish green with red vein (Mar-Jun). **General:** A very attractive foliage plant. **Similar species:** *C. multicava* (see p. 386).

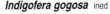

FABACEAE (Leguminosae) - Pea or Legume Family Second largest plant family (for description see p. 388).

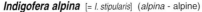

Indigofera (indigofera - bearing indigo, a blue dye that is obtained from several species of the genus) - Annual or perennial herbs, dwarf shrubs; leaves pinnately 1-9 foliolate; flowers in inflorescences, often pink or red; pods cylindrical. Economic potential for forage crops, green manure, soil stabilizers, chemical compounds for the pharmaceutical industry, traditional medicines, poisons, insecticides, dyes, seed gums and horticultural ornamentals. Attracts butterflies, including *Syntarucus brevidentatus, S. telecanus, Lepidochrysops lacrimosa, Freyeria trachilus, Zizina antanossa, Cyclyrius pirithous* Common Blue. Cosmop, in warm regions, ± 750 species, ± 500 in Afr, ± 200 in SA.

Indigofera gogosa ined
Low sturdy shrublet, up to 300 mm. In grassland, ± 400 m, Pondoland endemic. Branches spreading. Flowers in small dense inflorescences.

Indigofera alpina [= *I. stipularis*] (alpina - alpine)
Grey hairy slender herb. In damp rocky grassland. Stems reclining, roughly hairy. **Leaves:** Leaflets ± 25 x 10 mm, pale green, stalks ± 20 mm, stipules leaflike, broad, pointed. **Flowers:** In slender inflorescences, stems 75-250 mm; flowers pink to red. **Fruit:** Pods hanging. **General:** Petals produce an indigo blue.

Indigofera eriocarpa **isikhubabende (Z)** (eriocarpa - woolly fruits)
Erect, robust, much branched shrublet, 0,3-1,5 m. In grassland. **Plant covered with spreading short, whitish hairs. Leaves:** Crowded, spreading, ± 75 mm, up to 6 pairs leaflets, ending in a single leaflet, ± 12 mm, variable shape and size, stalks ± 75 mm. **Flowers:** In compact, erect inflorescences, **stems ± 150 mm;** flowers pink to reddish purple (Jan-Mar). **Fruit:** Pod 10 x 2 mm. **General:** Visited by large black ants. Used in traditional medicine to treat dysentery. **Similar species:** *I. cuneifolia* Strong, woody shrublet, on streambanks, open hillsides; leaflets wedge-shaped, 12-25 mm, grey-green, tips pointed, stipules conspicuous; inflorescences on short stems, flowers pink or red, bracts broad, longer than buds, blue-green to purplish (Jul-Feb).

Indigastrum fastigiatum [= *Indigofera fastigiata, I. rostrata*] **Slender Indigo; leta-laphofu, phehleloane (SS); uluhlomantethe (oluncane) (Z)** (fastigiata - parallel, erect, clustered branches)
Narrow, erect herb, up to 700 mm. In grassland. Few branches, **sparsely leafy. Leaves: 3-foliolate;** leaflets narrow, ± 25 x 5 mm, tapering to base, tip with tiny point. **Flowers:** Inflorescences crowded in bud, stem ± 250 mm; flowers small, ± 6 mm, red (Jan-Feb). **Fruit:** Pod ± 30 mm. **General:** Used in traditional medicine to treat headaches and as a good luck charm.

Indigofera foliosa [= *I. vestita*] (foliosa - leafy)
Erect, robust shrublet, 600-900 mm. In grassland, coast to 3000 m. **Stems straight, densely leafy. Leaves:** Overlapping, 2-3 pairs leaflets, **very narrow, margins rolled under,** mostly hairless. **Flowers:** 3-6, in short inflorescences, ± 20 mm; flowers, small, petals tawny hairy behind. **Fruit:** Pods ± 12 mm, black.

Indigofera hedyantha **Black-bud Indigo; Aambeibossie (A); 'musa-pelo-oa-mafika (SS); ilidolo-lendoda, uluhlomantethe (oluncane) (Z)** (hedyantha - sweet flowers)
Perennial herbaceous shrublet up to 300 x 600 mm. In grassland, coast to 2100 m, E Cape to Kenya. Tap root. Branches covered in short hairs. **Leaves: 3-5 pairs leaflets,** ± 15 x 3 mm, rachis 15 mm. **Flowers:** Inflorescence **stem longer than leaves,** ± 40 mm; flowers ± 12 mm, **red with darker spot in centre of standard, buds crowded, covered in golden brown hairs, calyx densely covered in fine black hairs** (Sep-Feb). **Fruit:** Pod ± 40 x 2 mm, cylindrical. **General:** Used in traditional medicine to treat fevers and as a good luck charm. Suitable garden plant.

Crassula streyii   *Indigofera alpina*   *Indigofera hedyantha*

Indigofera eriocarpa   *Indigofera hedyantha*

Indigofera gogosa ined

Indigastrum fastigiatum   *Indigofera foliosa*

57

Indigofera hilaris Red Indigo Bush; chubhujeje (Sw); igqokisi, isikhubabende, uluhlomantethe (oluncane) (Z) *(hilaris - cheerful, gay)*

Perennial shrublet, up to 600 mm. In open grassland, E Cape to Malawi. Woody rootstock. Annual stems, covered with silky hairs. **Leaves:** Crowded, ± 5 leaflets, ± 8 x 2 mm, grey-green, tip a fine point. **Flowers:** In short dense inflorescences, in profusion; flowers ± 10 mm, pink, red, **stalks short** (Jul-Jan). **Fruit:** Pod ± 20 mm. **General:** Blooms in response to fire, becomes taller and more straggly in the absence of fire. (See p. 390) **Similar species:** *I. rubroglandulosa* E Cape to KZN; plant with red glandular hairs; leaflets wider, 12-17 x 5-9 mm; calyx lobes longer.

Indigofera pondoensis ined

Soft, many stemmed shrublet, ± 500 mm, in colonies. Scattered in grassland, Pondoland endemic.

Indigofera sanguinea chubhujeje (Sw) *(sanguinea - blood red)*

Semi-erect, spreading, perennial shrublet, up to 800 mm. In grassland. Woody rootstock. Branches covered with soft spreading hairs. **Leaves:** ± 70 mm, ± 7 pairs leaflets, ± 10 x 7 mm, blunt tipped, soft spreading hairs beneath and on margins, stalk short, no stipules. **Flowers:** In crowded inflorescences, stems stiff, ± 70 mm; flowers ± 14 mm, red, pink (Sep-Apr). **Fruit:** Pod ± 40 x 2 mm, hairy.

Indigofera tristis Velvety Indigo; mothimo-kholo, 'musa-pelo (SS) *(tristis - sad, dull coloured)*

Erect, slender shrub, 0,4-2,5 m. In grassland. **Leaves:** Widely spaced, 3-5 pairs leaflets, 10-20 mm, deep green above, paler beneath, velvety. **Flowers:** In inflorescences, ± 70 mm; flowers pink, mauve, red, **covered in silky dark brown hairs behind and on buds**, calyx white hairy (Oct-Feb). **Fruit:** ± 35 x 2 mm. (See p. 390.)

Indigofera woodii Wood's Indigo *(named after John Medley Wood, 1827-1915, botanist, curator of Natal Bot Garden and Natal Herbarium, who published widely on KZN flora)*

Perennial herb, up to 150 mm, forming loose mats. In rocky grassland, on boulder beds, up to 2000 m. Much branched. **Leaves:** 5-20 mm, 3-4 pairs leaflets. **Flowers:** Inflorescences 25-55 mm, stems slender; flowers ± 5 mm (Dec-Feb). **Fruit:** ± 20 mm. **General:** Variable.

Tephrosia *(tephros - ashen, refers to grey-green or silvery leaves of many species)* - Herbs, shrublets, shrubs; leaves pinnate, with close parallel veins; flowers in heads; pods flattened. Some species are used as a fish poison and as insecticides. Trop, subtrop, ± 400 species, mostly Afr, ± 40 in SA.

Tephrosia elongata Orange Tephrosia; isiwisa (Z) *(elongata - elongated)*

Erect to trailing perennial herb, 0,2-1 m. In grassland, KZN to Tanz. Woody rootstock. Stems and leaves with downy short spreading hairs. **Leaves:** 3-5 leaflets, ± 80(150) x 15 mm, thick, hairy beneath, stipules up to 8 mm, stalks short. **Flowers:** In sparse terminal inflorescences, ± 300 mm; **flowers red, yellow, ± 15 mm, brown hairy behind** (Aug-Apr). **Fruit:** Pod ± 60 x 4 mm. **General:** Used in traditional medicine as an emetic to cleanse the stomach.

Similar species: *T. marginella* isidala (Z) Slender, up to 300 mm; in mountain grassland; stems slender; leaves 1 foliolate, 15-100 x 12 mm, margins thickened, yellow, stalks 6-30 mm; flowers ± 10 mm, orange (Dec-Feb); fruit, ± 45 x 3 mm.

Sutherlandia (named after James Sutherland, 1639-1719, first Superintendent of Edinburgh Bot Gardens) - Soft- wooded shrubs; leaves pinnate; flowers large, red; pods inflated. Cultivated in Europe since 1683. Endemic, 5 species in SA.

Sutherlandia montana Mountain Balloon Pea; Bergkankerbos, Gansies (A); unwele (Z) *(montana - growing in mountains)*

Soft shrub, up to 1,2 m, sprawling or erect. On boulder beds, 1500-3000 m. **Leaves:** Leaflets 4-10 mm, grey-green. **Flowers:** Small inflorescences in leaf axils; flowers drooping, ± 35 mm, red marked white (Jul-Jan). **Fruit:** 50-60 mm, inflated, papery, **conspicuously stalked beyond calyx lobes. Similar species:** *S. frutescens* Balloon Pea; Kankerbossie (A); umnwele (X,Z) In dry areas and near water; leaflets 10-20 x 3-6 mm; fruit not stalked beyond calyx lobes. Browsed by stock. Used in traditional medicine as a tonic, to treat eye ailments, pain, influenza, reputed to delay spread of cancer. Quick growing, short lived garden plant, survives snow and frost. (For photograph see p. 530)

Indigofera hilaris   Rosemary Williams

Indigofera sanguinea   Martin von Fintel

Tephrosia elongata   Van Wyk & Malan

Indigofera pondoensis ined   Tony Abbott

Tephrosia marginella   Tony Abbott

Indigofera tristis   Tony Abbott

Indigofera woodii   Martin Kunhardt

Sutherlandia montana   Martin von Fintel

59

Desmodium (*desmos* - bond or chain, refers to jointed pod which resembles the links of a chain) - Herbs or shrubs; usually 3 foliolate; pods flat, separating into 1 seeded segments. Warm regions, ± 300 species, 12 in SA.

Desmodium repandum Orange Desmodium (*repandum* - slightly undulating margins)

Scrambling shrub, up to 1,4 m. In forest, coast to 3000 m, Trop, subtrop Afr, SE Asia. **Leaves:** Near base, stalks ± 80 mm; 3(5) leaflets, ± 100 x 7 mm, margins slightly wavy, stipules 10-25 x 2-6 mm. **Flowers:** In branched, terminal inflorescences, ± 500 mm; flowers ± 14 mm, orange-red (Dec-Jun), scented. **Fruit:** Pod bluish, sticky.

Alysicarpus (*alysis* - chain; *karpos* - fruit, pod constricted between seeds) - Herbaceous or woody; leaves 1 foliolate; flowers in pairs; pods constricted between seeds. Valuable fodder plants. Trop Afr, Asia, ± 25 species, 5 in SA.

Alysicarpus rugosus Pioneer Fodder Plant; inkonazana, untshiphintshiphi (Z)
(*rugosus* - wrinkled)

Perennial, spreading herb, up to 600(900) mm. SA to Tanz. Rootstock woody. **Leaves:** ± 40 x 10 mm, stalks and stipules ± 7 mm. **Flowers:** In dense inflorescences ± 200 mm; flowers ± 8 mm, dark pink (Aug-May). **Fruit:** Pods erect, 4-5 segments. **General:** Used in traditional medicine to treat chest complaints.

Abrus (*abros* - soft, refers to leaves) - Twining herbs; leaves pinnate, terminal leaflet replaced by a bristle; pods with shiny red and black seeds. Roots used as a liquorice substitute; seeds as rosary beads. Trop, 6 species, 2 in SA.

Abrus precatorius Luckybean Creeper; Paternostertjie (A); umphitsi (Sw); umuthi wenhlanhla (X,Z); umkhokha (Z) (*precatorius* - used in worship, refers to use of seeds in rosaries)

Vigorous deciduous creeper. In woodland, E Cape to Trop Afr, Asia. **Leaves:** ± 100 mm; leaflets, ± 15 x 5 mm. **Flowers:** In terminal inflorescences; flowers lilac (Sep-Apr). **Fruit:** Pods 25-30 mm, in clusters about 100 mm diam, conspicuous for months. **General:** Seeds used to decorate ceramic pots, in musical instruments. Toxic if **chewed**. Used in traditional medicine to treat chest complaints and as love charms. (See p. 464)

Erythrina (*erythros* - red; *inus* - possession) - **Coral Trees** Shrubs, trees; usually armed with prickles; leaves 3 foliolate, pair of glands at base of leaflets; flowers large, showy, usually red. Trop, subtrop, ± 170 species, 6 in SA.

Erythrina zeyheri Ploughbreaker; Ploegbreker (A); khungoana, motumo (SS); umnsinsana (Z) (named after Carl Zeyher, 1799-1858, German naturalist who collected in SA)

Dwarf, deciduous shrublet, up to 600 mm. In grassland. **Large, underground stem. Leaves:** Very large; terminal leaflet ± 260 x 210 mm, stalks 80-200 mm, covered in rough hairs, prickles. **Flowers:** Large inflorescences; flowers red, ± 45 mm (Oct-Jan). **Fruit:** Pods ± 200 x 20 mm. **General:** Used as a good luck charm for barren women. Seeds used for necklaces. Interesting garden plant, withstands extreme cold.

Mucuna (name of a Brazilian plant) - Herbs or climbing shrubs; leaves 3 foliolate, leaflets often oblique; flowers large, inflorescences in leaf axils. In warm countries, ± 145 species, 3 in SA.

Mucuna coriacea Hellfire Bean; Brandboon (A); umkhoka (Sw) (*corium* - skin)

Vigorous scrambler, up to 4 m. In grassland, thicket, (KZN) Swaz to C Afr. Rootstock woody. Stems annual. **Leaves:** 3 foliolate, stalk ± 40 mm; terminal leaflet ±70 x 40 mm, blue-green. **Flowers:** Flowers ± 40 mm, wine red, calyx ± 15 mm (Jan-May). **Fruit:** Pods 60-80 x 12 mm, densely golden velvety, **hairs highly irritant. General:** Hairs continue to irritate, even after falling off the pods. (See p. 576)

Eriosema (*erion* - wool; *sema* - sign, refers to woolly standard petal) - Herbs or shrubs; usually 3-foliolate, terminal leaflet stalked, with resinous dots; petals pouched. Attracts butterflies. Warm regions, Afr ± 150 species, ± 36 in SA.

Eriosema distinctum Scarlet Eriosema; ubangalala olukhulu (Z) (*distinctum* - separate)

Robust herb, 100-250 mm. In grassland, up to 2000 m. Rootstock woody. Stems trailing. **Leaves:** Large, stalks short, ± 20 mm; terminal leaflets ± 95 x 50 mm, stalklets ± 10 mm, stipules large, ± 20 x 5 mm. **Flowers:** In short inflorescences, stems ± 180 mm; flowers ± 14 mm, red (Aug-Mar). **General:** Unpalatable to cattle, flowering in heavily grazed pastures. Used in traditional medicine to treat urinary complaints.

Eriosema rossii (named after Dr James Ross, botanist who worked on S Afr legumes)

Erect herb, up to 350 mm. In grassland. **Leaves:** Terminal leaflet 45-65 x 25-30 mm, densely covered in silky hairs, **pale green with yellow glands below**, stipules erect, clasping stem. **Flowers:** 30-60, **hidden by leaves at first**, bracts persistent, as long as flowers; flowers ± 12 mm, pale orange, red behind with darker veins, with yellow glands, calyx golden hairy (Oct-Dec). **Fruits:** 15 x 10 mm, with long reddish hairs. **Similar species:** *E. preptum* (see p. 274).

Desmodium repandum

Desmodium repandum

Alysicarpus rugosus

Abrus precatorius

Mucuna coriacea

Erythrina zeyheri

Eriosema distinctum

Eriosema rossii

61

Eriosema salignum Narrow-leaved Eriosema, Brown Bonnets; lesapo (SS); ubangalala, uluphondongozi, uqonsi (Z) *(salignum , like a willow)*

Slender, erect herb, 0,5-1 m. In grassland. Rootstock woody. Stems unbranched, covered in silvery hairs. **Leaves:** Few, stalks very short, leaflets narrow, ± 100 x 10 mm, dark green above, velvety white beneath. **Flowers:** In dense terminal inflorescences, stems ± 60 mm; flowers ± 13 mm, yellow to orange, red-brown behind (Aug-Jun). **Fruit:** Pods flat, covered in long golden hairs. **General:** Used in traditional medicine to treat impotence, as an expectorant, diuretic and to stimulate bulls in spring. Commonly hybridises with *E. cordatum.* (See p. 274)

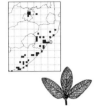

Eriosema squarrosum Apricot Eriosema *(squarrosum - rough)*

Erect to sprawling herb, 150-400 mm. In grassland. Stems branched from woody base, covered with short, rusty to whitish hairs. **Leaves:** Stalks short, ± 12 mm; **leaflets wide,** oval at base, sword-shaped upwards, 25-55 x 15-20 mm, terminal leaflet larger, dark green above, **whitish beneath, finely downy,** stipules 7-10 mm, downy. **Flowers:** 10-20, **reflexed, overlapping,** in short dense inflorescences, 50-100 mm, longer than leaves, **bracts shorter than flowers, dropping;** flowers small, 7-9 mm, pinkish orange, calyx white downy (Sep-Mar). **Fruit:** Pod 11-15 x 8-10 mm, covered in long stiff yellow hairs.

GERANIACEAE - Geranium Family Herbs or soft-wooded shrubs (for description see p. 398). *Pelargonium* (for description see p. 400).

P schlechteri Two-tiered Pelargonium (see p. 400)

Pelargonium tongaense Tonga Pelargonium *(tongaense - refers to Tongaland/Maputaland, NE KZN where it was discovered)*

Deciduous, low growing herb, up to 300 mm. **In shade on sand.** Slightly succulent stems and leaves. **Leaves:** 40-60 mm diam, lobed, tips of lobes sharp to rounded, softly hairy, stalks 30-120 mm. **Flowers:** 3-8, in inflorescences; petals scarlet, tips rounded (summer). **General:** Excellent garden plant, suitable for shade or sun, grown from seed or cutting. Free flowering.

EUPHORBIACEAE - Rubber or Euphorbia Family Herbs, shrubs, trees, twiners, succulent or not, often with milky sap. Leaves simple, divided or absent. Flowers unisexual, male and female within a cuplike structure (cyathium) or in a regular inflorescence, petals absent or reduced to a rim or three lobes. Fruit usually a 3 chambered capsule. Economically important species produce Rubber (*Hevea*), Tung Oil (*Aleurites*), Castor Oil (*Ricinus*), Cassava and Tapioca (*Manihot*) and are grown as ornamentals such as Poinsettia, Crown of Thorns (*Euphorbia*) and Croton (*Codiaeum*). Cosmop, ± 313 genera, ± 8100 species, 49 genera in SA.

Acalypha (*akalephe* - a nettle, refers to the leaves which resemble a nettle) - Annual or perennial herbs, shrubs or trees; leaves alternate; male and female flowers usually on separate plants, male flowers in catkinlike inflorescences, female flowers with stigmas greatly elongated, conspicuous. In warmer regions, ± 450 species, ± 24 in SA.

Acalypha glandulifolia Red Catkins; umsongo (Sw); ungibonisele, usunundu omncane (Z) *(glandulifolia* - leaves bearing small glands)

Perennial herb, up to 200 mm. In grassland. Stems branched from base, almost hairless. **Leaves:** ± 30 x 10 mm, veins prominent beneath, margin with short, sharp teeth, **each tooth tipped with stalked (hairlike) gland,** stalkless. **Flowers:** Male and female on different plants. Male inflorescences ± 40 mm, stems slender, ± 40 mm, female flowers hidden in leaves, stigma long, red (Sep-Dec). **General:** Root eaten raw. Used in traditional medicine to treat diarrhoea and other complaints.

Acalypha peduncularis Brooms and Brushes; ikhothe, usunundu (Z)

(peduncularis - with stalk, supporting a cluster)

Perennial herb, up to 450 mm. In grassland, conspicuous on newly burnt veld. Stems stout, prostrate to erect, hairy. **Leaves:** Oval, ± 60 mm, hard, densely to slightly hairy, margins toothed. **Flowers:** Male and female on separate plants. Male inflorescence a slender spike, stems long, flowers red and white. Female flowers tiny, stigmas long, red (June-Sep-Feb). **General:** Used in traditional medicine to treat coughs and chest complaints, and as tonics. **Similar species:** *A. caperonioides* 150 -700 mm; leaves shiny, thinly hairy to shaggy, stalkless (Sep-Jan). *A. angustata* Leaves lance-shaped.

Eriosema salignum

Eriosema squarrosum

Acalypha peduncularis ♀ & ♂

Pelargonium tongaense

Pelargonium schlechteri

Acalypha glandulifolia ♂

Acalypha glandulifolia ♀

Acalypha punctata Sticky Brooms and Brushes; umsongo (Sw); usun, unundu (Z)
(*punctata* - marked with dots)

Perennial herb up to 500 mm. In grassland, coast to mountains. Rootstock woody. Stems stout, sparsely hairy. **Leaves:** ± 70 x 30 mm, tapering to narrow point, margins sharply toothed, **surface with tiny gland dots**, stalks short, ± 3 mm. **Flowers:** Male and female on separate plants. Male inflorescences ± 50 mm, stems ± 60 mm. Female flowers partly within leaves, stigmas long, red, **bracts gland dotted** (Sep-Mar). **General:** Used in traditional medicine to treat diarrhoea and chest complaints.

Acalypha schinzii Bearded-leaved Brooms and Brushes; umsongo (Sw) (named
after Hans Schinz, 1858-1941, Swiss botanist who collected in SA 1884-87)

Slender perennial herb, up to 500 mm. In grassland. Stems slender, erect, hardly branched, **with long hairs**. **Leaves: Narrow**, ± 30 x 5 mm, **margins entire**. **Flowers:** Male and female on separate plants. Male inflorescences ± 50 mm, stems ± 50 mm. Female flowers with long red stigmas (Aug-Dec-Mar). **General:** Used in traditional medicine to treat diarrhoea.

Acalypha villicaulis [= A. petiolaris] Heart-leaved Brooms and Brushes; umpendulo, umsongo, uvelabahleke (Z) (*villicaulis* - shaggy stem)

Erect, slender stemmed herb or shrublet, 0,6-1,5 m. In grassland, thicket, on sandy soils. **Covered in long hairs. Leaves:** ± 40 x 25 mm, **heart-shaped**, shiny grey-green beneath, margins finely toothed, **stalks ± 30 mm. Flowers: Male and female flowers on same plant.** Male inflorescence ± 15 mm, stems ± 10 mm. Female flowers terminal on main stems and side branches, stigmas long, red (Sep-Mar). **General:** Used in traditional medicine to treat diarrhoea.

Euphorbia (named after Euphorbus, 1st Century physician to King of Mauritania) - Herbs, shrubs, trees, usually with milky sap, sometimes succulent; flowers within cyathia, rimmed with glands. Cosmop, ± 2000 species, ± 200 in SA.

★ Euphorbia cyathophora [kyathos - cup; phoros - bearing] Wild Poinsettia Weed

Shrubby annual herb, up to 1 m. Pantrop weed, in disturbed areas. Leaves ± 100 x 50 mm. Basal floral bracts leaflike, bright red blotch at base, upper bracts red. **Similar species:** *E. heterophylla* [= E. geniculata] Floral bracts mostly pale green with cream or purplish blotch.

CELASTRACEAE - Spike-thorn Family (for description see p. 536). **Gymnosporia** (*gymno* - naked; *sporia* - seed) Trees, shrubs, sometimes scrambling (for description see p. 154).

Gymnosporia heterophylla [= Maytenus heterophylla, Gymnosporia angularis] Angular-stemmed
Spike-thorn; Vierkantstingel-pendoring (A) (see p. 154)

Salacia (sea goddess, wife of Neptune) - Trees, shrubs or climbers. Trop, subtrop, ± 150 species, 5 in SA.

Salacia kraussii ibhonsi, umbhonsi, ihelehele, umgunguluzane, umnozane (Z)
(named after Christian Krauss, 1812-90, German scientist, traveller and collector in SA 1839-40)

Branched shrublet, up to 1 m, **in colonies**. In grassland, open woodland. Young stems purplish red, maturing grey. **Leaves:** Alternate, 37-90 x 10-55 mm, shiny olive green above, dull, pale beneath, margins entire or shallowly toothed towards tip, stalks short, stout. **Flowers:** 2-16 in clusters in leaf axils; flowers greenish yellow, ± 8 mm diam. **Fruit:** Red-orange, 35-50 mm diam (Dec-Mar). **General:** Browsed. Visited by large black ants. Fruits delicious, eaten by people and animals. (See p. 536)

MELIANTHACEAE - Melianthus Family Trees or shrubs. Leaves simple or compound. Inflorescence with regular or irregular flowers. Fruit dry. A number of species grown as ornamentals. Afr, 2 genera, ± 8 species, 2 genera in SA. **Melianthus** (*meli* - honey; *anthos* - flower, refers to abundant nectar) - **Honey Flowers** Shrubs or subshrubs, often strong smelling; flowers greenish or reddish; fruit a capsule. S Afr, 6 species.

Melianthus dregeanus Red Honey Flower

Shrub, up to 2 m. On forest margins, 900-1800 m. **Leaves:** ± 180 mm; 5-15 leaflets 30-80 x 9-30 mm, densely hairy, margins toothed, stipules 7-35 x 1-3 mm. **Flowers:** In terminal, drooping inflorescences, 40-130 mm; petals reddish, 15 mm, bracts 35 mm, sepals 20-35 mm, green with dark red spot at base, stalks ± 35 mm (Nov-Jan). **Fruit:** Woody, downy, 4 rounded lobes, 5-20 mm. **General:** *Subsp. insignis,* found inland, at higher altitudes; much larger in all parts. *Subsp. dregeanus,* occurs in E Cape; all parts smaller. E Cape; all parts smaller.

Acalypha villicaulis ♂

Martin von Fintel

Acalypha villicaulis ♀

Martin von Fintel

Acalypha punctata

Pam Cooke

Acalypha punctata ♂ & ♀

Tony Abbott

Acalypha punctata ♀

Tony Abbott

Acalypha schinzii ♂

Trevor Coleman

★ *Euphorbia cyathophora*

Geoff Nichols

Gymnosporia heterophylla

Tony Abbott

Salacia kraussii

Geoff Nichols

Melianthus dregeanus

Geoff Nichols

65

VITACEAE - Vine or Grape Family Climbers with tendrils or shrubs, sometimes succulent (for description see p. 280).
Cyphostemma (*kyphos* - bent; *stemma* - wreath) Prostrate or climbing herbs (soft shrubs). About 150 species, ± 34 in SA.

Cyphostemma cirrhosum Droog-my-keel, Wildedruif (A) (*cirrhosum* - curled tendrils)

Robust, climber. In woodland, on forest margins, Cape to Malawi. Stems hairy, with tendrils. **Leaves: 3-5 leaflets,** ± 130 x 75 mm, margins toothed, stalklets ± 30 mm, stalks ± 50 mm. **Flowers:** Inflorescences branched; flowers small, yellow (Oct-Dec). **Fruit:** Round, ± 10 mm diam, downy. **General:** Ripe fruit astringent, edible. Root reported to be poisonous. (See p. 280) **Similar species:** *C. flaviflorum* Climber; in coastal bush, dune forest; leaves, thick, succulent, 1-3 leaflets, margins bluntly toothed.

Cyphostemma woodii Hairy Grape Bush; Bobbejaandruif, Jakkalsdruif (A)
(named after John Medley Wood 1827-1915, botanist, curator of Natal Bot Gardens)

Soft shrub, up to 1 m. In open woodland, on dry rocky hillsides, KZN to Moz. Large tuberous root. Covered with long hairs, tendrils present or absent. **Leaves:** 3-5 stalkless leaflets, ± 100 x 40 mm, stalk ± 70 mm, margins toothed, sparse, short white hairs, stipules ± 20 mm. **Flowers:** In branched inflorescence, stem ± 120 mm; flowers small, yellow (Oct-Mar). **Fruit:** ± 15 x 7, red, hairy. **General:** Fruit edible. Attractive feature plant. **Similar species:** *C. barbosae* Covered in long sticky hairs.

MALVACEAE - Hibiscus Family Trees, shrubs or herbs (for description see p. 282).
Modiola (*modiolus* - a small measure) - Herbs; leaves palmately divided; fruit segments splitting along inner side.

★ *Modiola caroliniana*

Annual herb, stems prostrate, up to 500 mm. Introduced from Trop America. Lower leaves 15-30 mm, rounded to heart-shaped at base, upper leaves deeply 3-5 lobed. Flowers ± 15 mm diam. Fruit segments 2 horned at top. A useful forage plant.

Hibiscus (Greek name for marsh mallow) - Trees, shrubs or herbs (for description see p. 284).

Hibiscus barbosae Small Red Wild Hibiscus (named after G Barbosa who made the first
collection of this plant in Mozambique)

Perennial herb, up to 1,5 m. In grassland, disturbed areas, KZN to Moz. Woody rootstock. Annual stems, covered in bristly hairs. **Leaves:** At base of stems, 3-5 lobed, ± 60 x 40 mm diam, margins blunt toothed, stalks slender, 30-45 mm. **Flowers:** Clustered towards tip of stems, ± 35 mm diam, red, open till evening, epicalyx of 5-7 bracts, calyx densely hairy, lobes ± 10 x 3 mm (Nov-Feb).

STERCULIACEAE - Cocoa or Sterculia Family Herbs, shrubs, trees. Star-shaped hairs. Petals usually twisted in bud. Fruit splitting into carpels. Economically important for cocoa from the seeds of the S American tree *Theobroma cacao*; and the ornamentals, Bottle and Chinese Parasol Trees. Trop, ± 67 genera, ± 1500 species, 7 genera in SA.
Hermannia (named after Paul Herman, 1640-1695, prof of botany in Leyden, collector at the Cape) - Herbs, shrubs; stipules often leaflike; calyx papery. Attracts butterflies. Afr, Arabia, Austr, S America, ± 240 species, ± 150 in SA.

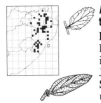

Hermannia depressa Creeping Red Hermannia; Rooiopslag (A); moleko, sele-tjana (SS); itshesizwe, umphuphuthelo (Z)

Prostrate herb. In grassland, on edge of marshes, Cape to Zim. Sparsely hairy, slightly glandular. **Leaves:** ± 40 x 25 mm, margins **bluntly toothed. Flowers:** In slender, inflorescences just above leaves; petals ± 8 x 4 mm, yellow tinged pink or red (Oct-Jan). **General:** Used traditionally to treat diarrhoea, coughs, and as a protective charm. **Similar species:** *H. cristata* Crested Hermannia **Up to 300 mm;** in rocky grassland, up to 1900 m, E Cape to N Prov; leaves 20-65 x 3-20 mm; flowers ± 20 mm, red-orange, calyx segments about 15 mm; fruit deeply 5 angled, with **long crests.** (See p. 538) *H. woodii* Prostrate herb, in grassland, 1300-2000 m; flowers on long stalks, dull pink, red, cream or yellow.

TURNERACEAE - Herbs, shrubs. Leaves alternate, often with 2 nectar glands at base. Flowers twisted in bud. Fruit a 3 valved capsule. Trop, warm regions, Americas , Afr, ± 10 genera, ± 100 species, 4 genera in SA.
Tricliceras (*tricliceras* - three chambered) - Herbs, often from deeply buried woody rootstock. Afr, 11 species, 7 in SA.

Tricliceras mossambicense [= *Wormskioldia mossambicense*] Lion's Eye

Slender herb, up to 400 mm. In grassland, KZN to Moz. **Leaves:** 80-150 x 2-8 mm, margins entire or with shallow teeth, stalkless. **Flowers:** 2-7; ± 25 mm diam, orange above, dull yellow beneath, close at night, re-open next day (Aug-Mar). **Fruit:** Capsule ± 70 mm. **General:** Attracts butterflies. **Similar species:** *T. longipedunculatum* Stems, young leaves with long reddish brown bristles; 6-12 flowers.

Cyphostemma cirrhosum

Cyphostemma woodii

★ *Modiola caroliniana*

Hibiscus barbosae

Hermannia cristata

Hermannia depressa

Hermannia woodii

Tricliceras mossambicense

67

PASSIFLORACEAE - Granadilla Family Climbers with tendrils (shrubs or herbs) (for description see p. 538).
Adenia (*aden* - gland, refers to glands on leaf stalk, flower) - Climbers; leaves simple or compound; male and female flowers separately, fruit wall leathery. Often poisonous. Trop Afr, Madag, SE Asia, N Austr, ± 93 species, ± 10 in SA.

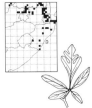

Adenia digitata Finger-leaved Adenia; Bobbejaangif (A); isifulwane, umbulelo, umaphatha (Z) (*digitata* - fingers)
Climber or scrambler, up to 2 m. Widespread, coast to 1850 m, KZN to Tanz. **Leaves:** 40-180 x 30-170 mm, stalk ± 90 mm; 3-5 lobes, entire to deeply lobed, grey-green beneath, main veins, margins reddish, stalklets ± 20 mm. **Flowers:** 1-5 on slender stalk, ending in tendril; flowers ± 15 mm, cream (Sep-Nov). **Fruit:** ± 55 x 35 mm, yellow to red (Sep-Mar). **General:** Fruit, root poisonous to man, leaves used as spinach in some areas. (See p. 290) **Similar species:** *A hastata* Leaves heart-shaped; fruit dark green marked yellow, edible but often indistinguishable from poisonous species.

BEGONIACEAE - Begonia Family Herbs or shrublets, often succulent. *Begonia* (for descriptions (See p. 390)).

Begonia sutherlandii Wild Orange Begonia; Sutherlandbegonia (A); uqama-mawene (Z) (named after P C Sutherland, 1822-1900, surveyor-general of Natal, keen plant collector)
Soft, succulent herb, up to 500 mm, in colonies. In forest, up to 1900 m, E Cape to Zim. **Small tuber.** Annual stems, green tinged red. **Leaves: Base very oblique,** ± 120-250 x 40-150 mm, margins irregularly lobed, sharply toothed, stalks 30-150 mm. **Flowers:** ± 35 mm diam, orange-red, **male tepals 4,** female 5 (Aug-May). **Fruit:** ± 20 x 30 mm across wings. **General:** Used in traditional medicine to treat heartburn and as a protective charm. Popular container and garden plant.

CACTACEAE - Cactus/Prickly Pear Family Spiny, succulent herbs or shrubs. *Opuntia* - **Prickly Pear/Jointed Cactus** Perennial succulent shrubs (for descriptions see p. 290).

★ *Opuntia ficus-indica* Sweet Prickly Pear; Turksvy (A); umthelekisi (Z) (see p. 290)

THYMELAEACEAE - Fibre-bark /Gonna Family Shrubs, small trees, often with fibrous bark (for description see p. 292).
Synaptolepis (*synaptos* - joined together, *lepis* - a scale, refers to the disc composed of scales) - Erect or climbing shrubs; flowers solitary or in clusters. Afr, ± 7 species, 2 in SA.

Synaptolepis kirkii uvuma omhlophe (Z)
Much branched, scrambling shrub, up to 2 m. In woodland, dry forest, N KZN to Moz. Stems slender, tough, twining, with raised red-brown dots. **Leaves:** Small, ± 30 mm, shiny dark green above, paler beneath. **Flowers:** In small clusters, creamy yellow (Oct-Mar), scented. **Fruit:** 25 x 20 mm, orange when ripe. **General:** Tasty fruit, eaten by birds, children. Used in traditional medicine as an emetic. (See p. 158)

MYRTACEAE - Eucalyptus/Myrtle Family Trees or shrubs. Leaves usually opposite, glandular, aromatic. Fruit fleshy. Economically important for edible fruits (Guava), spices (Cloves, Allspice), timber (*Eucalyptus*) and ornamentals. Trop, warm temp, ± 123 genera, ± 4620 species, 9 genera in SA, 4 introduced.
Eugenia (named after Gen F Eugene, Prince of Savoy, 1663-1736, patron of botany, horticulture) - Trees, shrubs, shrublets. Trop, subtrop, especially America, ± 900 species, ± 14 in SA.

Eugenia albanensis Dwarf Grassland Eugenia; Vlakappel (A); umnanjwa, unobebe (Z) (from Albany, E Cape)
Dwarf shrub, up to 300 mm, in large communities. **In coastal grassland.** Stems purplish. **Leaves:** 10-15 mm diam, shiny dark green. **Flowers:** 1-3 in clusters, white (Sep-Jan). **Fruit: Large, ± 25 mm diam, red. General:** Delicious fruit eaten by people and animals. Used in traditional medicine to treat diarrhoea. **Similar species:** *E. capensis* inontsane, inhlelehlele (Z) Shrub up to 1(2) m; bark grey-brown, flaky; flowers scented. Differs from the larger coastal plant. (For photograph see p.158)

ERICACEAE - Erica/Heath Family Large or small shrubs. *Erica* (for descriptions see p. 410).

Erica cerinthoides Red Hairy Heath; Rooihaartjie (A); morita-nkoe, semo-monyane (SS) (*cerinthoides* - resembling honeywort, *Cerinthe*)
Erect shrublet, 300-500(900) mm. On rock outcrops, SW Cape to Mpum. Woody base. **Leaves:** Clusters of 4-6, 5-16 mm, glandular. **Flowers:** In terminal inflorescences; **flowers large, 25-35 mm,** dark pinkish red (white tipped red), sepals densely glandular hairy (bloom throughout year). **General:** Popular garden plant, grown in Europe since the 1700s. Stunted by fire. *Var. barbertona,* flowers shorter, broader, ± 15 mm. **Similar species:** *E. oatesii* (see p.70).

Adenia digitata   Jo Onderstall

Begonia sutherlandii   Lorraine van Hooff

Begonia sutherlandii   Lal Greene

★ *Opuntia ficus-indica*   Lal Greene

Synaptolepis kirkii   Geoff Nichols

Eugenia albanensis   Tony Abbott

Erica cerinthoides   Martin von Fintel

Erica cerinthoides   Lal Greene

Erica cerinthoides var. *barbertona*   Tony Abbott

69

Erica oatesii (named after Frank Oates, 1840-1875, naturalist and traveller who came to SA in 1873)

Robust, erect shrub, up to 1,2 m. On streambanks, grassy slopes, up to 2000 m. Branches spreading, hairy. **Leaves:** 3-4 in clusters, 6-9 mm, spreading, recurved or suberect, sharp edged, tipped with long, gland tipped hair. **Flowers:** In few flowered, terminal inflorescences; flowers 10-13 x 7 mm, pink to scarlet, lobes short, **hairless** (Mar-Jun). **Similar species:** *E. cerinthoides* var. *barbertona* (see p. 68).

PRIMULACEAE - Primrose Family Herbs with simple leaves. Flowers regular. Well known ornamentals such as Primula, Primrose, Cyclamen. Subcosmop, mostly N temp, ± 22 genera, ± 825 species, 3 genera in SA.

Anagallis (*anagelao* - Greek for Pimpernel plant) - Herbs. W Europe, Afr, Madag, ± 30 species, 4 in SA (2 weeds).

★ ***Anagallis arvensis*** **Bird's Eye, Pimpernel; Blouselblommetjie (A)**

Annual herb, up to 250 mm. Widespread weed in damp areas. Stems winged. Leaves 5-20 x 5-15 mm. Flowers blue, pink or red. Poisonous to birds, animals.

GENTIANACEAE - Gentian Family Herbs, sometimes aquatic (for description see p. 414). *Chironia* (for description see p. 414).

Chironia baccifera **Christmas Berry, Piles Bush, Toothache-berry; Aambeiebos, Bitterbos, Perdebossie, Tandpynbossie (A)** (see p. 414)

PERIPLOCACEAE - Periploca Family Perennial herbs, shrubs, lianas, with milky latex (for description see p. 542).

Mondia (from umondi, the Zulu name) - Perennial climbers; large stem tuber; leaves opposite, stalks with large frill-like stipule at base. Afr endemic, 2 species, 1 in SA.

Mondia whitei [= *Chlorocodon whitei*] **White's Ginger; umondi (Z)** (named after A S White, who farmed in KZN in about 1860)

Robust climber. In forests, riverine woodland, KZN to Nigeria. Threatened. **Leaves:** Large, 100-300 x 50-150 mm, stalks 30-55 mm, **stipules with reflexed frilly teeth.** **Flowers:** In branched inflorescences; flower lobes ± 14 mm, purple-red inside, margins green; **corona of 5 free lobes, erect hornlike purple appendage arising from middle** (Nov-Feb). **Fruit:** 75-100 x 44 mm, **almost woody. General:** Roots aromatic, bitter at first, then like ginger or liquorice, smelling of vanilla (makes a type of ginger beer). Widely used to stimulate appetite, treat indigestion.

LAMIACEAE (LABIATAE) **- Sage/Mint Family** Herbs or shrublets (for description see p. 470).

Tinnea (commemorates a scientific expedition on the Nile in 1861 by three Dutch women, Henrietta Tinne, her daughter and sister, during which seeds of *T. aethiopica* were collected) - Herbs or shrubs; Afr, ± 19 species, 4 in SA.

Tinnea galpinii **Black Lip-flower, Galpin's Tinnea** (named after Ernest Galpin, 1858-1941, banker, amateur botanist)

Herb up to 600 mm. In rocky grassland. Woody rootstock. **Hardly branched,** erect, stems **softly woody below, velvety above. Leaves:** 15-25 x 6-10 mm, thinly hairy, gland dotted. **Flowers: In pairs, in terminal inflorescences, 80-200 mm;** flowers hairy, 12-18 mm, maroon to chocolate-brown, calyx ± 7 mm, purple tinged (Jan-Mar), violet scented. **Fruit:** Calyx becomes enlarged, inflated. **General:** Cultivated by seed, cuttings. **Similar species:** *T. barbata* Mpum, Swaz; less hairy; leaves larger, softer; flowers scattered, larger, mauve to blue.

Leonotis (*leon* - lion; *ous*, *otis* - ear, refers to hair fringed upper lip) - **Wild Dagga** Coarse herbs, shrubs; flowers in dense, many flowered compact clusters around square stems, bracts, calyx teeth spine tipped. Common name refers to the leaves which are reported to be narcotic when smoked. Afr, ± 12 species, 1 pantrop weed, ± 10 in SA.

Leonotis leonurus **Leonotis, Wild Dagga; Wildedagga, Duiwelstabak (A); imvovo, utywala-bengcungcu (X); umfincafincane (X,Z); umcwili, imunyane, utshwala-bezinyoni (Z)** (*leonorus* - lion coloured)

Robust shrub, up to 2(3) m. In tall grassland, coast to 2000 m. Stems velvety, woody at base. **Leaves: Narrow,** 50-100 x 10-20 mm, margins toothed in upper half, rough above, velvety beneath. **Flowers: 3-11 compact clusters,** 25-40 mm diam; flowers ± 50 mm, bright orange (creamy white), velvety (Feb-Sep). **General:** Nectar attracts birds, bees, butterflies. Used in traditional medicine to treat feverish headaches, coughs, asthma, dysentery, haemorrhoids, as a remedy for snakebite and a charm to keep snakes away. Popular, frost resistant garden plant, first grown in Europe in the 1600s.

Similar species: *L. dubia* [= *L. ocmifolia* var. *ocymifolia*] **Forest Leonotis; Rooidagga (A); umfincafincane (X)** Slender, much branched shrub; in forest, coast to 1980 m; leaves thin, stalks long, slender, 30-90 mm; flowers in small, loose clusters, amongst leaves (Feb-Jul). Used as a tonic and to treat nervous conditions.

Erica oatesii

Sheila Peacock

Mondia whitei

David Johnson

★ *Anagallis arvensis*

Wally Menne

Chironia baccifera

Braam van Wyk

Tinnea galpinii

Trevor Coleman

Leonotis leonurus

Tom de Waal

Leonotis leonurus

Ken Farnsworth

Leonotis dubia

Martin von Fintel

71

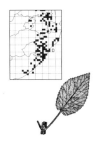

Leonotis intermedia [= L. dysophylla] **Broad-leaved Leonotis; Klipdagga (A); joala-ba-li-nonyana, moseneke (SS); fincane, isihlungu sedobo, umuncwane (X); imunyane, utshwala-bezinyoni obuncane (Z)** (intermedia - intermediate between L. leonorus and L. nepetifolia)
Robust, perennial shrub, 1-2 m. In grassland, scrub, on rocky hillsides, coast to mountains, Cape to Tanz. Stems **branching from brittle woody base**, green stems velvety. **Leaves:** 30-90 x 10-50 mm, velvety, silvery to yellowish beneath, margins toothed, stalks short, 10-50 mm. **Flowers:** 5-8 compact clusters, ± 65 mm diam; flowers 32-44 mm, dull orange (Jan-Jun). **General:** Flowers full of nectar, sucked by children, birds, visited by bees, wasps. Used in traditional medicine to treat colds also sick fowls and cattle with gall sickness. Hardy garden plant. **Similar species:** L. nepetifolia Annual, pantrop weed; flowers smaller, with 3 rings of hairs inside.

Hoslundia (named after O Hoslund-Smith, naturalist from Guinea) - Fruit fleshy, berrylike. Afr genus, 1 species.

Hoslundia opposita **Orange Bird Berry; amahibane, isaphulageja, ubukhukhud-wane, uyaweyawe (Z)** (opposita - set in pairs)
Spreading herb or soft shrub up to 1,2 m. In open woodland, KZN to Ethiopia. **Leaves:** 35-65 x 18-25 mm, hairy, margin with rounded shallow teeth, stalk 3-8 mm. **Flowers:** In loose, slender, branched inflorescences; flowers 6-7 mm, white, calyx ± 4 mm, tube cylindric, 5 narrow teeth (Oct-Feb). **Fruit:** Berrylike, ± 5 mm diam, orange-red. **General:** Browsed by game. Fruit tasty, eaten by birds, people. Leaves strongly, unpleasantly scented, reputed to repel bees. Hardy garden plant.

SOLANACEAE - Tomato/Potato/Tobacco Family Herbs,shrubs, climbers; often spiny (for description see p. 478).

Withania - Shrubs; leaves entire; flowers in clusters. N Afr, Medit, S America. 1 species in SA.

Withania somnifera **Poisonous Gooseberry; Bitterappelliefie, Geneesbossie, Vernietsiektebossie (A); ubuvimba, umaqhunsula (Z)** (somnifera - sleep producing)
Soft woody shrub, up to 1,5 m. In thicket, woodland, on disturbed areas. **Leaves:** ± 80 x 40 mm, stalk ± 10 mm. **Flowers:** Small, greenish, in small clusters, calyx ± 4 mm, hairy (Aug-Jun). **Fruit:** Calyx enlarging to 12 mm diam, bladder-like, enclosing fleshy fruit ± 7 mm diam. **General:** Used in traditional medicine to treat fevers, intestinal infestations, asthma, to heal sores and stimulate milk production in cows and treat gallsickness in cattle.

Solanum (ancient Latin name for these plants) - Shrubs, herbs, small trees or climbers, spiny or not (for description see p. 478).

★ *Solanum seaforthianum* **Slender Potato Creeper; ijalamu (Z)** (see p. 478)

SCROPHULARIACEAE - Snapdragon Family Herbs, shrubs (trees or climbers), some parasitic. Leaves opposite. Flowers often 2 lipped, sometimes with pouches or spurs. Famous for the drug plants Foxgloves (*Digitalis*) and ornamentals such as Snapdragons, Veronicas, Penstemons. Cosmop, ± 269 genera, ± 5100 species, 79 genera in SA.
Dermatobotrys (derma - skin, botrys - bunch of grapes) - Epiphytic shrub; leaves fleshy; flowers usually in 3s, clustered at nodes. Endemic, 1 species genus.

Dermatobotrys saundersii

Epiphytic shrublet, up to 1 m. On forest trees. Rare. Roots ± 1 m, ± 50 mm thick, furrowed, rootlets fibrous. Stems thick, 4 angled. **Leaves:** 50-150 x 25-90 mm, semi-succulent, margins shallowly toothed, veins reddish, stalks ± 50 mm. **Flowers:** About 40 mm, red, stiff white hairs within tube (Jun-Dec). **Fruit:** Oval, smooth berry, 20-30 x 10-15 mm, green to dull brown when ripe, numerous seeds in sweet figlike pulp. **General:** Fruit delicious. Sap has a pungent smell. An interesting container plant.

Phygelius (phugo - to shun; (h)elios - the sun; shade loving) - Shrubs; leaves opposite; flowers tubular, dull red or pink, in branched inflorescences; fruit a capsule. Endemic, 2 species.

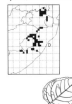

Phygelius aequalis **River Bell, Wild Fuchsia; Foksia, Rivierklokkie (A); mafifi-matso, metsi-matso (SS)** (aequalis - similar in size, equal)
Herbaceous shrub, up to 1 m. On rocky streambanks, 1200-2200 m. Woody at base, stems 4 angled. **Leaves:** 75-100 x 40 mm, margins toothed, stalk ± 20 mm. **Flowers:** In tall, branched inflorescence, flowers fleshy, ± 40 mm, red to dusky pink, petal lobes, yellow and red inside, stamens protruding, calyx ± 6 mm, lobes pointed (Oct-Jul). **General:** Used in traditional medicine and as a charm against hail damage to crops. Hardy, lovely garden plant, needing damp soil. A yellow 'sport' known as Yellow Trumpets, has become popular in gardens in the UK. **Similar species:** P. capensis Only at high altitude; flower tube curved, mouth oblique.

Martin von Fintel

Leonotis intermedia

Martin von Fintel

Hoslundia opposita

C J Ward

★ *Solanum seaforthianum*

Tony Pooley

Leonotis intermedia

Wally Menne

Dermatobotrys saundersii

Wally Menne

Dermatobotrys saundersii

C J Ward

Withania somnifera

Tom de Waal

Phygelius aequalis

Trevor Coleman

Phygelius aequalis

73

Manulea (*manus* - a hand refers to 5 spreading flower lobes) - Annual or perennial herbs; rarely shrubby; leaves mostly clustered at base; flowers in clusters in long inflorescences; fruit a capsule. Afr, mostly S Afr, ± 70 species.

Manulea parviflora Pepper and Salt; isola (Z) (*parviflora* - small flowers)

Erect, perennial herb, up to 1 m. In grassland, rocky or swampy places, SA to Angola, Zim, Moz. Finely hairy throughout. Tuberous root. **Leaves:** Clustered at base, 30-120 x 4-22 mm, margins toothed or entire, finely glandular hairy. **Flowers: In many dense, irregular clusters, in much branched terminal inflorescences; flowers small,** 6 mm, yellow to orange, red (Aug-Jun). **General:** Used in traditional medicine as enemas for children with intestinal disorders. Hardy garden plant, in full sun.

Jamesbrittenia (named after James Britten, 1846-1924, British botanist) - Stamens hidden or invisible. Differs from *Sutera* which has stamens protruding. Mostly Afr, SA to Angola, Zam.

Jamesbrittenia aurantiaca [= *Sutera aurantiaca*] Cape Saffron; Geelblommetjie, Saffraanbossie (A); phiri-ea-hlaha-e-nyenyane (SS)

Small, bushy, aromatic herb, 60-300 mm. Often in damp or marshy places, 1370-1900 m. Woody, much branched at base, branchlets slender, wiry, prostrate or erect. Glandular hairy, leafy throughout. **Leaves:** 5-30 x 5-16 mm, **finely dissected,** in tufts, covered in short hairs beneath, **glistening glands above,** shortly stalked. **Flowers:** Solitary, in axils, ± 12 mm, red or orange, stalks ± 7-25 mm (Oct-Mar).

Jamesbrittenia breviflora [= *Sutera breviflora*] Short-flowered Sutera; Kortblom-sutera (A)

(*breviflora* - short flowers)

Straggling, tufted herb, up to 300 mm. In grassland, rocky places, 1050-3000 m. **Stems sticky hairy. Leaves:** Aromatic, opposite, alternate to clustered upwards, 10-35 x 8-35 mm, oval, margins entire or shallowly toothed, tapering to short stalk. **Flowers:** Solitary in axils, forming long leafy inflorescences; flowers 2 lipped, ± 12 x 20 mm wide, red to rose pink, centre yellow, tube very short (Nov-Apr). **General:** Hybridises with *J. pristisepala* (see p. 480).

Glumicalyx - Perennial herbs or shrublets; leaves opposite or alternate; flower tube cylindric or more or less bell-shaped, 2 lobed, cream to orange, in nodding inflorescences, ± elongated and erect in fruit; fruit a capsule. 6 species.

Glumicalyx goseloides [= *Zaluzianskya goseloides*] Gooseneck Drumstick Flower

(*goseloides* - looks like *Gosela*)

Perennial herb, up to 450 mm. On boulder beds, damp rocky grass slopes, 1600 -2800 m. Several stems, usually simple, closely leafy, finely hairy. **Leaves:** Opposite below, alternate above, 20-65 x 4-15 mm, thick, decreasing upwards, margins entire to toothed, ± stalkless. **Flowers: Nodding inflorescences,** 30 -60 mm, **lengthening and becoming erect in fruit;** flower tube 20-29 mm, creamy, lobes orange, roundish (Oct-Feb).

Striga (*striga* - witch or furrow) - Parasitic herbs; leaves opposite or alternate, sometimes reduced; flowers solitary in axils of bracts. Afr, Asia, Austr, ± 40 species, ± 7 in SA.

Striga elegans Large Witchweed; Grootrooiblom, Kopseerblommetjie (A); lethi-bela, mohohlong, seona (SS); sono (Sw); umnaka (X); isona (Z) (*elegans* - graceful)

Slender, erect, up to 300 mm. In grassland, SA to Trop Afr. Stems simple or slight-ly branched, **plant roughly hairy. Leaves:** ± 20 x 3 mm. **Flowers:** In terminal inflorescence; **flowers large, 15-20 mm,** red, orange-yellow below (pink), **upper lip ± the same as lower,** tube erect, ± 13 mm, calyx ± 10 mm, lobes long, narrow (Dec-Mar). **General:** Parasitic on grasses. Used in traditional medicine and as a protective charm against evil and lightning. **Similar species:**
S. asiatica Witchweed Flowers smaller, ± 12 mm, upper lip much shorter than lower; a problem plant, parasitic on roots of maize, sorghum and sugar cane.

Harveya (named after Dr William Harvey, 1811-1866, author of early vols of Flora Capensis, prof of botany in Dublin, Ireland) - Parasitic herbs; leaves reduced to scales; flowers showy, in dense spikes, 2 lipped, style curved downwards, stigma flattened, anthers 2 celled, only one containing pollen. Afr, Mascarene Is, ± 40 species, ± 25 in SA.

Harveya scarlatina moshoa-feela (SS)

Dwarf parasitic herb, up to 150 mm. In scrub on rocky streambanks, in rock crevices, 1800-2200 m. **Leaves:** Scalelike, stalkless, ± 20 x 2 mm, flat against stem. **Flowers:** In dense inflorescence, ± 75 mm; flowers ± 30 mm diam, petal lobes small, orange-red, yellow in throat, tube narrowly funnel-shaped, ± 50 x 10 mm (Dec-Jan). **Similar species:** *H. pumila* Flowers white or pinkish with yellow throat.

Manulea parviflora

Lorraine van Hooff

Manulea parviflora

Martin von Fintel

Jamesbrittenia aurantiaca

Darrel Plowes

Jamesbrittenia breviflora

Tom de Waal

Jamesbrittenia breviflora

Martin von Fintel

Glumicalyx goseloides

Martin von Fintel

Striga asiatica

Rosemary Williams

Striga elegans

Darrel Plowes

Harveya scarlatina

Hilliard & Burtt

75

BIGNONIACEAE - Bignonia Family Trees, shrubs or woody climbers. Leaves compound. Flowers usually showy, irregular, two lipped, ovary superior. Fruit dry, splitting, seeds often with papery wing. Economically important for timber, West Indian Boxwood (*Tabebuia*) and many ornamentals such as the Jacaranda, Tulip Tree, Sausage Tree, Cape Honeysuckle. Mainly trop, especially S America, ± 109 genera, ± 750 species, 8 genera in S A.
Tecoma (Aztec name for a plant Tecomaxochitl) - Scandent shrubs. Afr, ± 4 species, 1 in SA.

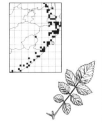

Tecoma capensis [= *Tecomaria capensis*] **Cape Honeysuckle; Kaapse Kanferfoelie, Trompetters (A); bopu, malangula (Sw); icakatha, umsilingi (X); incwincwi, uchacha, udodo, ugcangca, imunyane (Z)**
Scrambling shrub, up to 4 m. In thicket, on forest margins, S Cape to Trop Afr. **Leaves:** 2-4 pairs leaflets; terminal leaflet ± 25x15 mm, margins blunt toothed. **Flowers:** In terminal inflorescences; upper petal lobe ± 25 x 35 mm, orange-red, pale orange (throughout year). **Fruit:** ± 100 x 12 mm. **General:** Browsed by game and stock. Visited by sunbirds, butterflies, honey-bees. Used in traditional medicine to treat fevers, pain, sleeplessness, chest ailments, dysentery and to encourage flow of milk in feeding mothers. Popular garden and hedging plant, deciduous in cold areas.

PEDALIACEAE - Sesame Family Annual or perennial herbs. Flowers irregular, 2 lipped, tube obliquely funnel-shaped or cylindrical, calyx deeply lobed. Fruit usually beaked, barbed or winged, seeds often winged. Economically important for Sesame seed oil, from *Sesamum indicum*. Trop, ± 17 genera, ± 85 species, 10 in SA.
Dicerocaryum (*di* - two; *keras* - horn; *karyon* - nut, refers to the hard fruit with two spines) - Perennial trailing herbs; flowers held erect above leaves; fruit with two erect spines forming a 'trample burr'. Afr, 3 species, 2 in SA.

Dicerocaryum senecioides **Devil Thorn, Stud Thorn; Elandsdoring (A)**
Perennial, prostrate herb, up to 1 m. In grassland, disturbed areas, KZN to Moz, Malawi. **Leaves:** Opposite, ± 30 mm diam, deeply, irregularly lobed, powdery white beneath. **Flowers:** ± 35 x 25 mm, tube ± 60 mm, calyx ± 10 mm, deeply lobed (Feb-May). **Fruit:** Oval, ± 27 x 19 mm, **upper central part raised**, with 2 sharp spines. **General:** Plant produces slime when immersed in water, used as a soap substitute.

GESNERIACEAE - African Violet Family Mostly herbs. *Streptocarpus* (for description see p. 482).

Streptocarpus dunnii (named after E J Dunn, a geologist of the late 1800s)
Perennial herb (plant dies after flowering), up to 150 mm. Among rocks. **Covered in red granules**, except upper leaf surface. **Leaves:** 1-several, 150-300 x 40-200 mm, thick, covered in grey hairs, main veins white beneath, margins scalloped. **Flowers:** ± 50 mm, red, hairy outside, pinkish inside, floor white striped red (Nov-Feb). **Fruit:** Capsule 25-30 x 4 mm. **General:** Beautiful flowers reputed to be pollinated by birds.

ACANTHACEAE - Acanthus Family Herbs, shrubs, climbers. Leaves opposite. Inflorescence often with large leafy bracts, flowers irregular or 2 lipped. Fruit an explosive capsule, ± club-shaped, seeds often with water absorbent hairs. Some popular ornamentals. Largely trop, ± 229 genera, ± 3450 species, 43 genera in SA.
Thunbergia (named after Carl Thunberg, 1743-1828) - Herbs, sometimes climbing (for description see p. 306).

Thunbergia alata **Black-eyed Susan; Swartoognooi (A)** (*alata* - wings)
Creeper, up to 4 m. On forest margins, E Cape to E Afr. **Leaves:** 20-65 x 20-55 mm, lobed at base, margins entire or toothed, veins prominent beneath, stalks 20-50 mm. **Flowers:** ± 30 mm wide, tube ± 20 mm, orange (yellow), deep blackish purple in tube, bracts 13-19 x 10-16 mm (blooms throughout year). **General:** Visited by bees. Popular garden plant worldwide; a number of cultivated forms available.

Barleria (named after Rev James Barrelier MD of Paris) - Herbs or shrubs, sometimes scrambling (for description see p. 488).

Barleria crossandriformis **Orange Crossandra** (*crossandriformis* - like *Crossandra*)
Shrub, up to 1 m. In thicket, KZN to N Prov. Stems mostly spineless. **Leaves:** ± 100 x 40 mm. **Flowers:** In terminal inflorescences, ± 70 x 35 mm; flowers orange, ± 30 mm wide, tube ± 15 mm, **calyx lobes leafy, overlapping**, glandular (Feb-Jun). **General:** Hardy garden plant. **Similar species:** *B. prionitis* [= *B. coriacea*] **Thorny Orange Barleria** In bushveld, KZN to Trop Afr; leaves: ± 50 x 20 mm, narrowing to sharp point; a few straight spines in axils; flowers solitary, ± 20 mm wide, tube ± 20 mm, calyx divided to base, lobes tapering to long spiny points. Hardy garden plant.

Barleria repens **Small Bush Violet** (*repens* - creeping and rooting)
Low-growing herb, 200-600 mm (scrambling up to 2 m). In dune forest, KZN to Trop Afr. Woody at base. **Leaves:** ± 35 x 20 mm, **shiny dark green**, shortly hairy, stalk short. **Flowers:** ± 35 mm wide, red, tube ± 30 mm, calyx ± 15 mm wide, oval, cream with reddish veins (summer, throughout year). **General:** Popular garden plant, in full sun, as a groundcover and also flowering in shade.

Tecoma capensis

Tecoma capensis

Dicerocaryum senecioides

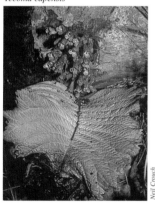

Streptocarpus dunnii

Thunbergia alata

Barleria crossandriformis

Barleria prionitis

Barleria repens

Crossandra (*krossos* - fringe; *andros* - male, refers to fringed anthers) - Low-growing herbs, shrublets; flowers 1 lipped, in terminal inflorescences, bracts overlapping, margins spiny, calyx cut to base. Afr, ± 50 species, ± 4 in SA.

Crossandra fruticulosa Shade Crossandra (*fruticulosa* - small bush)

Robust, **perennial shrublet**, up to 500 mm. In thicket, woodland, KZN to Moz. Woody at base, **stems branching**, densely velvety throughout. **Leaves: Well spaced, oval**, ± 80 x 30 mm, narrowing to **slender, stalklike base**, dark green above, paler beneath. **Flowers:** In terminal inflorescences ± 60 x 20 mm; flowers ± 20 x 30 mm, **dull orange**, lobes broad, rounded, tube slender, ± 20 mm, **bracts with long spines** (throughout year). **General:** Browsed by game. Rewarding, hardy garden plant.

Crossandra greenstockii Bushveld Crossandra; Rooiblom (A) (named after Canon
William Greenstock, died 1912, clergyman, teacher, collector who collected this plant in Mpumalanga)

Low-growing herb, up to 300 mm. In grassland, woodland, KZN to Malawi. Woody rootstock. **Stems annual, unbranched. Leaves: In basal cluster**, 50-140 x 20 -60 mm, **blunt tipped**, narrowing to stalklike base, hairy. **Flowers:** In terminal elongate inflorescence, ± 50 x 25 mm, **stem long, ± 300 mm**; flowers ± 12 x 20 mm, 5 lobed, bright orange-red, **bracts broad**, 25-18 mm, overlapping, **glandular hairy, margins with few, short teeth** (Oct-Jun). **General:** Hardy garden plant, in full sun. **Similar species:** *C. zuluensis* Zulu Crossandra **Leaves oval**, 30-80 x 18-35 mm, margins slightly wavy, tips rounded or indented, **stalkless; flowers in short, elongate inflorescence**, 18-55 mm, stem softly hairy; **flowers large**, ± 30 mm wide, 6 lobed, dark orange with yellow throat, tube ± 20 mm, cream, bracts 18-24 x 8-14 mm, finely hairy, **margins with long spines** (Sep-Mar).

Ruspolia (named after Prince Eugenio Ruspoli, 1866-93, an Italian explorer of Somaliland who was killed by an elephant) - Shrubs; leaves opposite; flowers in terminal inflorescence. Afr ± 4 species, 3 in SA.

Ruspolia hypocrateriformis Red Ruspolia

Scrambling shrub, 1-1,5 m. On dry, wooded hillsides, N KZN to W Afr. Branches 1-3 m, conspicuously 4 angled, pithy, with elongate raised dots. **Leaves:** 9-120 x 60 -80 mm, margins entire. **Flowers:** Terminal inflorescences, ± 90 mm, stems finely hairy; flowers ± 23 mm wide, orange-scarlet, pink to flesh coloured beneath, tube ± 25 x 1 mm, bracts narrow, 6-10 x 1 mm, calyx deeply 5 lobed (summer). **Fruit:** Capsule 40-45 mm. **General:** Attractive shrub for frost-free gardens.

RUBIACEAE - Gardenia/Coffee Family Herbs, shrubs or trees (for description see p. 556). **Mitriostigma** (see p. 204)

Mitriostigma axillare Small False Loquat; Basterlukwart (see p. 204)

CUCURBITACEAE - Cucumber/Pumpkin/Gourd Family Herbs. Stems prostrate, trailing or climbing with spirally coiled tendrils. Leaves simple or lobed. Male and female flowers on same or separate plants, 5 lobed, ovary inferior, stigma 2-3 lobed, fleshy. Fruits usually fleshy, seeds flattened. Important food plants, pumpkins, squashes, cucumbers, watermelons and ornamental gourds and luffas. Trop, ± 119 genera, ± 775 species, 18 genera in SA.
Mukia - Scandent herbs; leaves simple, tendrils simple; flowers very small; fruit small, roundish. Trop, 4 species, 1 in Afr.

Mukia maderaspatana [= *Melothria maderaspatana*]

Creeper, prostrate or scrambling, up to 4 m. On floodplains, in woodland, wooded grasslands, 300-1250 m, KZN to Egypt, India, China, Austr. Plant bristly hairy. **Leaves:** 10-110 x 10-110 mm, bristly hairy especially on veins beneath, 3-5 lobed, stalks 5-115 mm. **Flowers:** Small, yellow, ± 5 mm diam; a few in clusters, on long stem (Dec-Mar). **Fruit:** ± 10 mm diam, red.

Zehneria (named after J Zehner, botanical artist) - Scrambling herbs. Paleotrop, ± 30 species, 3 in SA.

Zehneria scabra itanga, simbene, ukalimela (X) (see p. 206)

Kedrostis (Greek for the plant *Bryonia dioica*) - Scrambling or prostrate herbs, with tendrils; male and female flowers usually on same plant, male flowers clusters on long stems, female flowers stalkless, solitary or in clusters. Mostly Afr, ± 20 species, ± 8 in SA.

Kedrostis foetidissima umafuthasimba (Z) (*foetidissima* - very unpleasant smell)

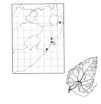

Herbaceous climber, up to 1(1,5) m. In woodland, Cape to Ethiopia, 75-1300 m. Tuberous rootstock. Stems annual, slender, softly hairy; tendrils unbranched, thinly downy. **Leaves:** ± 50 x 30 mm, thin, 3-5 lobed or not, margins toothed or not, stalks ± 10 mm. **Flowers:** Few. Male ± 5 mm, in small clusters. Female solitary, cream or pale yellow (Apr). **Fruit:** Small, ± 13 x 7 mm, red, finely hairy. **General:** Unpleasant smell when broken. Edible. Used in traditional medicine.

Crossandra zuluensis

Crossandra fruticulosa

Ruspolia hypocrateriformis

Mitriostigma axillare

Mukia maderaspatana

Crossandra greenstockii

Zehneria scabra

Kedrostis foetidissima

79

Momordica (*mordeo* - bite, refers to jagged seed) - Herbaceous climbers; leaves entire, or lobed, with tendrils; male and female flowers separate, usually on same plant; fruit fleshy. Trop, subtrop, mostly Afr, ± 40, ± 9 species in SA.

Momordica balsamina African Cucumber, Balsam Apple, Bursting Beauty; Aloentjie, Laloentjie (A); intshungwana yehlathi, umkaka (Z) (see p. 206)

Momordica cardiospermoides [= *M. clematidea*]

Vigorous climber, up to 10 m. In woodland, KZN to Tanz. Tuberous rootstock. Stems annual, ribbed. **Leaves:** Compound; leaflets opposite, ± 60 mm, dark green, rough, above, paler beneath, deeply lobed, margins toothed, stalks 10-50 mm. **Flowers:** Male: yellow-orange, ± 30 mm, stem ± 150 mm. Female: smaller, stalk ± 50 mm (Oct-Jan). **Fruit:** ± 90 x 50 mm, rounded at base, ribbed with rounded protuberances, red. **General:** Foul smelling when bruised. Fruit eaten by birds.

Momordica foetida Gifappel (A); intshungu (Z) (*foetida* - foul smelling)

Vigorous creeper, up to 7 m. In woodland, riverine forest, KZN to Trop Afr. Tuberous rootstock. **Leaves:** Alternate, 13-190 x 13-18 mm, stalks 13-170 mm. **Flowers:** ± 35 mm, creamy yellow-orange, solitary (female) or in small clusters (male), stem 20-120 mm (Oct-Feb). **Fruit:** 35-80 x 25-50 mm, oval, softly spiny, seeds covered in red pulp. **General:** Foul smelling when bruised. Leaves cooked as spinach, aril of seeds eaten by people, birds. Used in traditional medicine to treat stomach complaints, boils, high blood pressure, diabetes and as insect repellents.

Cucumis (Latin for cucumber) - Herbaceous climbers or creepers, annual or perennial (for description see p. 308).

Cucumis metuliferus Jelly Melon, Horned Cucumber; Rooi-agurkie, Rooikom-kommer, Wildekomkommer (A); uhufafa (Z) (*metuliferus* - forming projections)

Annual creeper, stems up to 5 m. In woodland, grassland, SA to Trop Afr. Stems slender, hairy, tendrils slender, simple. **Leaves:** 35-120 x 35-135 mm, heart-shaped, roughly hairy, margins shallowly lobed, toothed, stalks 20-110 mm. **Flowers:** Male: in small clusters, ± 15 mm wide, yellow. Female: solitary (Dec-Mar). **Fruit:** 65-130 x 35-65 mm, rounded at ends, **stout, fleshy spines**, **dark mottled green ripening red**, stalk ± 70 mm, flesh 'jellylike'. **General:** Fruit eaten by birds and people, eaten raw or cooked, possibly poisonous when bitter. Leaves cooked as spinach.

Trochomeria (*trochos* - a wheel; *meris* - a part) - Scrambling or prostrate herbs; rootstock thick; leaves often with bract at base of stalk; tendrils simple or none; fruit oval, fleshy, few seeded. Trop & S Afr, ± 8 species, 4 in SA.

Trochomeria hookeri (named after Sir Joseph Hooker, 1817-1911, English botanist and traveller, medical doctor, Director of Kew Gardens 1865-85, visited the Cape twice)

Prostrate or scrambling creeper, stems up to 2 m. In wooded grassland, E Cape to Moz. Tuberous rootstock. Stems annual, hairs short, stiff. **Leaves:** 25-90 mm, shallowly to deeply lobed, shortly hairy, margins toothed, stalks ± 40 mm, **leafy bracts at base, ± 25 mm diam**. **Flowers:** Male and female on separate plants. Male: solitary or clustered on **short stem**. Female: solitary, lobes ± 25 x 3 mm, green, reflexed (Sep-Jan). **Fruit:** ± 30 mm diam, roundish, red. (See p. 558)

Coccinia (*coccinus* - scarlet; *kokkos* - berry, refers to red fruit) - Herbaceous creepers; usually with tuberous rootstock; tendrils simple or forked; male and female flowers on separate plants. Mainly Afr, ± 30 species, ± 7 in SA.

Coccinia hirtella (hirtella - rather hairy)

Climbing or trailing herb, stems up to 3 m. Among rocks, scrub, up to 2300 m. Woody rootstock. Stems annual, grooved, **densely to thinly white hairy**. **Leaves**: 40-100 x 30-90 mm, soft, **deeply lobed**, midlobe longer, thinly hairy, margins lobed and irregularly toothed. **Flowers**: Solitary, orange-yellow. Male: ± 23 mm, stems ± 150 mm. Female: stems ± 40 mm (Oct-Mar), faintly scented. **Fruit**: Long, tapering at tip, ± 80 x 40 mm, grey-green to red. **General**: Leaves cooked. (See p. 308)

Coccinia palmata Wild Cucumber; Bospampoentjie, Wildepampoentjie (A); uthangazane omncane, uthangazane lwehlathi (Z) (*palmata* - lobed like a hand)

Climber with stems up to 8 m. In shady places, E Cape to S Moz. Stems corky with age, **tendrils forked**. **Leaves**: 40-120 mm, sparsely hairy, with small black dots, ± 5 lobed, margins toothed, lobed. **Flowers**: Male: on long stem. Female: solitary, ± 30 mm, cream or yellow, stem short (Dec-Jun). **Fruit**: 50-80 x 20-35 mm, red. **General**: Leaves cooked as spinach. Used in traditional medicine. (See p. 308)

Momordica balsamina

Momordica cardiospermoides

Momordica foetida

Geoff Nichols

Geoff Nichols

Martin von Fintel

Momordica balsamina

Trochomeria hookeri

C J Ward

Martin von Fintel

Cucumis metuliferus

Coccinia hirtella

Coccinia palmata

Lorraine van Hooff

Martin von Fintel

Geoff Nichols

81

ASTERACEAE (COMPOSITAE, alternative name, refers to composite flowerheads) - **Daisy Family** (for description see p. 208). *Helichrysum* - Herbs, shrubs, sometimes dwarf and cushion forming (for description see p. 212).

Helichrysum appendiculatum   Sheeps' Ears Everlasting; Skaapoorbossie (A); senkotoana (SS); ibode, indlebeyemvu (Z)   (*appendiculatum* - elongated or having an appendage)

Perennial herb, up to 600 mm. In grassland, coast to 2100 m, SW Cape to Mpum. **Rootstock thick**, woody. Stems grey woolly. **Leaves:** In rosette, ± 80 x 20 mm, woolly on both surfaces, tapering to tip, base broad, clasping. **Flowerheads:** In compact clusters, in branched inflorescence; 7-15 mm, bracts creamy white, pink to red tips pointed (Sep-Mar). **General:** Woolliness variable. White underside of leaves stripped for fringes and body ornaments in the past. (See p. 310)

Helichrysum griseum   (*griseum* - somewhat grey)

Robust perennial herb, up to 700 mm. In grassland, coast to 1200 m. Rootstock stout, woody, crown brown silky woolly. Stems woolly felted. **Leaves:** Few, ± 200 x 80 mm, erect, narrowing slightly to base, thinly cobwebby at first, later harshly hairy above, greyish white felted beneath, faintly 5-9 veined. **Flowerheads:** In congested to loose inflorescence; ± 6 x 5 mm, **bracts pointed**, tips glossy bright pinkish red or buff (Aug-Oct).

Zinnia (named after Johann Zinn, 1727-59, prof of botany at Göttingen) - Annual or perennial herbs; flowering stem swollen below flowerheads. S USA to S America, ± 20 species, 1 introduced weed in SA.

★ *Zinnia peruviana*   Redstar Zinnia; Wildejakobregop (A)

Annual herb, up to 500 mm. Widespread weed, in dry river valleys, up to 2000 m, (from Peru). Leaves opposite, ± 60 x 15 mm, rough hairy. Flowerheads ± 60 mm diam, red, stalk thickening below flowerheads (Jan-Mar).

Tithonia (from Tithonis, another name for Aurora, goddess of dawn) - Coarse, ± annual herbs; leaves entire or lobed; flowers showy, on long stalk, thickened near tip. Mexico, C America, W Indies, ± 10 species, 2 widespread weeds in SA.

★ *Tithonia rotundifolia*   Red Sunflower; Rooisonneblom (A)

Bushy annual, 1,5-3 m. Disturbed areas, 600-1400 m, invasive weed, (C America). Leaves ± 150 x 100 mm, 3 lobed, rough hairy, stalks winged. Flowerheads ± 90 mm diam, ray florets orange-red, yellow beneath, stalks long, velvety (Feb-Jul).

Crassocephalum (*crassocephalum* - thick head) - Erect or straggling herbs. Afr, Madag, ± 40 species, ± 4 in SA.

Crassocephalum crepidioides

Erect, branching, annual herb, up to 1,2 m. Widespread in warmer parts of Afr, Madag. Stems ribbed, thinly hairy throughout. **Leaves:** ± 250 x 150 mm, upper leaves entire or with a pair of lobes, lower leaves deeply lobed, margins coarsely, sharply toothed, stalks ± 40 mm, winged, **eared and clasping at base**. **Flowerheads:** In loosely branched terminal inflorescence, **nodding at first**; ± 15 mm, purplish red (Sep-May). **General:** Aggressive weed in Trop E Asia, **not a weed in SA.**

Kleinia (named after Dr J T Klein, 1685-1759, German zoologist)

Kleinia fulgens   [= *Senecio fulgens*]   Coral Senecio; Koraalsenecio (A)   (*fulgens* - shining)

Succulent, perennial herb, up to 600 mm. In bushveld, on rocky cliffs, KZN to Moz, Zim. Rootstock creeping, tuberous. Stem branching from near leafy base. **Leaves:** ± 150 x 50 mm, margins entire to coarsely, irregularly toothed or lobed, grey-green, purple edged, stalkless. **Flowerheads:** Solitary, ± 25 mm diam, orange, scarlet, stems bare, simple or forking (Jan-Aug). **General:** Browsed by game. Attractive, hardy garden plant, colour variable. **Similar species:** *K galpinii* N KZN to Zim; leaves narrow, margins entire; flowerhead bracts leafy.

Gerbera (named after Traugott Gerber died 1743, German naturalist) - Perennial herbs; often with woolly crown; leaves in rosette. Barberton Daisy *G. jamesonii*, a well known ornamental with many cultivars. About 30 species, mostly SA.

Gerbera aurantiaca   Hilton Daisy   (*aurantiaca* - orange-yellow)

Perennial herb, up to 300 mm, in colonies. In rocky grassland, 800-1800 m. Rare. **Roots thick, thonglike**, stock woody, crown white silky. **Leaves:** Erect, ± 250 x 60 mm, leathery, cobwebby when young, margins entire or faintly toothed, **short, winged, stalklike base**. **Flowerheads:** Solitary, ± 60 mm diam, ray florets red, coppery beneath, disc florets pinkish red, anthers black (Aug-Oct). **Fruit:** Pappus violet-purple. **General: Hybridises** with *G. kraussii,* flowers larger, pink, yellow and every shade of red and orange. (See p. 446)

82

Helichrysum appendiculatum

Helichrysum griseum

★ *Zinnia peruviana*

★ *Tithonia rotundifolia*

Crassocephalum crepidiodes

Kleinia fulgens

Gerbera aurantiaca

Gerbera aurantiaca

Gerbera aurantiaca

83

MONOCOTOLYEDONS - Single seed leaf, parallel veins; flower parts in threes or multiples of three.

APONOGETONACEAE - Waterblommetjie Family   Aquatic herbs. Family with 1 genus. Old World, 43 species, 7 in SA.

Aponogeton junceus Aponogeton; Wateruintjie (A); lijo-tsa-liho-hoana (SS) *(apon - water; geiton - neighbour, junceus - rushlike)*

Aquatic herb. In ponds, marshes, summer rainfall areas of S Afr. Tubers ± 30 mm diam. **Leaves:** Erect, narrow to spoon-shaped, 40-250 mm; **or** floating, oblong, ± 170 x 45 mm. **Flowers:** Inflorescence 20-40(90) mm; flowers white to pink (summer). **Fruit:** Seeds float. **General:** Leaves, flowers and tubers eaten by people and stock.

ALISMATACEAE - Water-plantain Family   Perennial aquatic or marsh herbs. Cosmop, 14 genera, ± 100 species, 5 genera in SA. *Alisma* *(alisma* - Linnaean name for a water plant) Cosmop, 1 species in SA.

Alisma plantago-aquatica Water Plantain; Padda-lepel (A) *(plantago - plantlike, aquatic)*

Perennial aquatic herb, up to 1 m. On margins of streams and ponds, cosmop, possibly introduced in SA. **Leaves:** Erect, blade ± 100 x 60 mm; stalks ± 400 mm. **Flowers:** In branched inflorescences, stems ± 500 mm; flowers small, ± 4 mm diam, white (summer). **Fruit:** Seeds float. **General:** Eaten by water birds.

HYDROCHARITACEAE - Water-weed family   Freshwater or marine herbs. Cosmop, 15 genera, ± 80 species, 5 genera in SA. *Ottelia* (Ottel, a Malabar name) **-** Aquatic rooted annuals. In warmer regions, ± 40 species, 4 in SA.

Ottelia exserta Ottelia *(exserta - protruding)*

Floating aquatic. Permanent and seasonal pools, KZN to Malawi. **Leaves:** Floating, ± 125 x 55 mm, young leaves submerged. **Flowers:** In separate male and female inflorescences; flowers 30-40 mm, spathe ± 55 x 25 mm; ± 60 male flowers, 1-3 open at a time; female flowers solitary (Jan-Jul). **Fruit:** Narrowly oval, beaked, 40-50 mm. **General:** Suitable for garden ponds in frost-free areas.

CYPERACEAE - Sedge Family (see p. 502). *Ascolepis* *(askos* - bladder*; lepis* - scale) - Cosmop, ± 15 species, 2 in SA.

Ascolepis capensis umuzi (Sw)

Tufted perennial herb, 200-900 mm. Marshes, coast to 2250 m, E Cape to Ethiopia. **Leaves:** Basal, tufted, grasslike, grey-green. **Flowers:** Spikelets in **compact, shiny white head,** ± 15 mm diam, bracts ± 50 mm (throughout the year). **General:** Used for beer strainers and mats. Suitable for damp areas of the garden. **Similar species:** *Kyllinga alba* and *Mariscus dubius,* both found in dry (not marshy) habitats.

Cyperus (from Latin and Greek for sedge) - Herbs, sometimes with corms, tubers. Cosmop, ± 650 species, ± 70 in SA.

Cyperus obtusiflorus White-flowered Sedge; khukhu (SS) *(obtusiflorus - flowers blunt at end)*

Perennial, up to 900 mm, tufted. In grassland, widespread, up to 1370 m. Rhizome compact, woody. **Leaves:** Basal, tufted, tough, smooth, ± 500 mm, blue-green. **Flowers:** Inflorescence ± 30 mm diam, white, bracts ± 95 mm (throughout year). **Similar species:** The bright yellow form (usually at higher altitudes) is sometimes called *C. sphaerocephalus* and is described under that name (see p. 222).

Kyllinga (named after P Kylling, a Danish botanist) - Cosmop, ± 45 species, ± 14 in SA.

Kyllinga alba White Button Sedge; Witbiesie (A); monokotsoai-oa-litsoene, qheme, robo (SS); umuzi (Sw); umxhopho (Z) *(alba - whitish)*

Perennial, 300-450 mm. On sandy or rocky areas. **Leaves:** Basal, grasslike. **Flowers:** In **white head,** ± 15 mm diam, bracts ± 120 mm (summer). **General:** Used to make beer strainers. **Similar species:** *K. alata* Moister areas; flowerheads golden green.

ARACEAE - Arum Lily Family   Popular ornamentals. *Zantedeschia* (for descriptions see p. 340).

Zantedeschia aethiopica White Arum Lily; Varklelie, Witvarkoor (A); mhala-litoe, moth-ebe (SS); umfana-kamacejane (Sw); intebe (X,Z); ihlukwe (Z) *(aethiopica - from S Afr)*

Evergreen or deciduous, 0,6-1(2,5) m, in large colonies. Marshy areas, coast to 2250 m, W Cape to N Prov. Tuber large. **Leaves:** 150-200 x 100-150(800) mm, stalks ± 600 mm. **Flowers:** Spathe ± 150 x 100 mm, **funnel-shaped (wide mouthed),** white, upper part withers, lower part turns green (throughout year), faintly scented. **Fruit:** Flowering stem **erect at fruiting;** soft, ± 12 mm diam, **orange,** tip green when ripe. **General:** The plant is boiled and eaten in rural areas. Tubers eaten by pigs, porcupines, fruit by birds. Leaves used traditionally to treat headaches and as a poultice. Popular garden plant and cut-flower, tolerates snow.

84

Aponogeton junceus

Lal Greene

Ottelia exserta

Alex Wood

Ascolepis capensis

Van Wyk & Malan

Alisma plantago-aquatica

Van Wyk & Malan

Cyperus obtusiflorus

Van Wyk & Malan

Kyllinga alba

Van Wyk & Malan

Rick Taylor

Zantedeschia aethiopica

Nolly Zaloumis

Zantedeschia aethiopica

Lorraine van Hooff

85

Zantedeschia albomaculata Arrow-leaved Arum, Spotted-leaved Arum; Klein-varkoor, Witvlekvarkoor (A); mohalalitoe, mothebe (SS); umfana-kamacejane (Sw); **intebe (Z)** (*albomaculata* - white-spotted)

Deciduous, up to 750 mm. In marshy ground, on rocky or grassy mountainsides, up to 2400 m, survives dry conditions. **Leaves:** ± 400 x 250 mm, **arrow-shaped, with or without white spots.** Flowers: Spathe **cylindrical (mouth narrow)**, ± 170 mm, white, pale yellow to pinkish, with or without **deep purple blotch at base inside, spathe turns green with age** (Oct-Apr). **Fruit:** ± 20 mm diam, **green, flowering stem bends towards ground. General:** Produces a yellow-green dye. Used in traditional medicine as a poultice, to treat frequent miscarriage and used for cattle ailments. Subsp. *albomaculata*, leaves densely spotted (or not); spathes **recurved, tips tapering.** Subsp. *macrocarpa*, leaves sparsely spotted (or not); spathes **blunt tipped. Similar species: *Zantedeschia valida*** [= *Z. albomaculata* subsp. *valida*] KZN; leaves heart-shaped, usually unspotted; spathe white, wide mouthed, spreading, blunt tipped.

ERIOCAULACEAE - Pipewort Family Mostly S America, 9 genera, ± 1100 species, 2 genera in SA. *Eriocaulon* (*erion* - wool; *caulos* - stem, refers to woolly hairs on rhizome) - Tufted herbs. Warm regions, ± 250 species, ± 12 in SA.

Eriocaulon dregei Water Pom-pom; nyokoana-ea-likhoho, sekolana (SS) (named after Johann Drège, a German botanist who visited the Cape in the 1800s)

Perennial herb, 100-500 mm, forming colonies. In marshy areas, coast to 3000 m, E Cape to N Prov. Rhizome covered with soft white hairs. **Leaves:** In basal rosette, bright green, flat, ± 250 x 8 mm, tapering to pointed tip. **Flowers:** In compact, hard, **round inflorescences**, ± 10 mm diam; flowers white (Aug-Apr). **General:** Attractive plant for damp areas in the garden. Size varies according to altitude and climate.

COLCHICACEAE Formerly part of Liliaceae (for description see p. 26). *Androcymbium* (*andros* - male; *kymbion* - cup) - Flowers small, inflorescence hidden within large, colourful, petal-like bracts. Mostly SA, ± 30 species.

Androcymbium natalense [=*A. decipiens, A. longipes*] Pyjama Flower; Bobbejaanskoen, Patrysblom (A)

Common in coastal grassland. No stem, or stem poorly developed. **Leaves:** 2-3, dark green, **erect**, ± 200 mm. **Flowers:** Bracts white, striped pinkish green, appear before leaves have fully developed (Jun-Sep). **General:** Best seen after fires.

Androcymbium striatum [= *A. melanthioides* var. *striatum*] Pyjama Flower; Patrysblom (A); khara, khukhoana e nyenyane, metsane (SS)

Up to 300 mm. In rocky grassland at higher altitudes, seldom below 1800 m, KZN to Ethiopia. **Leaves:** ± 300 mm, slender, keeled, **forming a stem 150-220 mm. Flowers:** Bracts **white striped green**, ± 75 mm (Dec-Mar, Jul-Sep). **General:** Easily overlooked in grassland, best seen in recently burnt areas. Used in traditional medicine to treat earache. **Similar species:** *A. melanthioides* Stemless; leaves flat on ground; flower bracts showy, white striped pink.

Wurmbea (named after F von Wurm, a Dutch merchant in Java) - Afr, Austr, ± 25 species, 19 in SA.

Wurmbea elatior Pepper-and-salt Flower; Sout-en-peper-blommetjie (A); khahlana -ea-loti (SS) (elatior - tall)

Perennial, up to 400 mm. In marshes, on streambanks, 1200-3000 m. Corm deeply buried. **Leaves:** ± 450 x 7 mm, sheathing stem, tips slender. **Flowers:** ± 20, inflorescence ± 150 mm; flowers white with shiny deep red to **purplish black marks in middle of tepals** (Jan-May), musky smell, variously described as horse dung, naphthalene, vanilla, tonquin beans and a sewage farm! **General:** One of only two species found outside the Cape.

ASPHODELACEAE - Formerly part of Liliaceae. Mostly herbs, leaves in basal rosette, usually sheathing at base. Tepals free or fused into a tube. Fruit a capsule. Europe, Asia, Afr, 17 genera, ± 750 species, 6 genera in SA. *Trachyandra* (*trachys* - rough; *andros* - male) - Leaves grasslike, in clumps; rhizomes yellow inside; flowers always solitary in axil of single bracts. Afr, ± 50 species, 49 in SA.

Trachyandra affinis (*affinis* - neighbouring)

Slender or robust herb, up to 1 m, singly or in groups. In grassland. **Leaves:** Erect, fleshy, ± 400 x 16 mm, grey-green, **fringed at base. Flowers:** In slender inflorescences, stems erect, branched; flowers white, ± 20 mm diam, open in early morning (Jun-Sep), sweetly scented. **Fruit:** Capsule ± 5 mm diam.

Zantedeschia albomaculata

Zantedeschia albomaculata

Olaf Wirminghaus

Ken Farnsworth

Eriocaulon dregei

Tony Abbott

Eriocaulon dregei

Tony Abbott

Trachyandra affinis

Martin von Fintel

Zantedeschia valida

Yashica Singh

Androcymbium natalense

Wally Menne

Androcymbium striatum

Jo Onderstall

Wurmbea elatior

Auriol Batten

87

Trachyandra asperata **Wilde Knoflok (A); Ieloelenyana-la-lilomo, motoropo (SS); unjwazi (Z)** (*asperata* - rough with points or hairs)
Perennial herb, up to 1 m. In grassland. Rootstock compact, sometimes with a short woody stem with fibres from old leaf bases. **Leaves:** In basal rosette, grasslike, wiry, keeled, 150-400 x 1-5(20) mm, fleshy, grey olive-green, faintly hairy at base. **Flowers:** In slender inflorescences, stems branched; flowers 15-20 mm diam, white, open till dark (Sep-Mar). **Fruit:** Capsule ± 5 mm diam, sparsely or densely hairy. **General:** Very variable over its range. Acrid smell when touched.
Similar species: ***Trachyandra gerrardii*** More robust, roughly hairy; flowers strongly scented, open in evenings; capsules large, ± 10 mm diam, **burrlike**. Used in traditional medicine to heal newborn infants' navels.

Trachyandra saltii (named after Henry Salt ,1780-1827, British traveller)
Common herb, up to 500 mm. In grassland, widespread from S Afr to Trop Afr. **Leaves:** Grasslike, 1-2 mm wide. **Flowers:** Several inflorescences, stems, 60-400 mm, **unbranched**, lax and spreading; flowers ± 20 mm diam, open about 15h00, close at dusk (Aug-Mar). **Fruit:** Capsule ± 5 mm diam, hairless. **General:** Very variable in size.

ANTHERICACEAE - Rhizomatous herbs. Leaves mostly in basal rosette. Flowering stem erect, mostly leafless, inflorescence simple or branched, ovary superior. Fruit a capsule, seeds black. Widespread over most parts of the world. The large genus *Chlorophytum* is mainly trop. Although most Afr species of the genus *Anthericum* have been placed in *Chlorophytum*, for the purposes of field identification they have been retained in this book. In SA it is easy to recognise '*Anthericum*' from *Chlorophytum* in the field. Subcosmop, ± 29 genera, ± 500 species, 3 genera in SA.

Anthericum (*antherikon* - asphodel) - Herbaceous perennials, aerial shoot deciduous; rhizomes usually creeping, woody, knobbly, with fibrous remains of old leaves, roots ± long, thin; leaves 2-ranked or in basal rosette, sometimes folded; inflorescence central; flowers usually solitary, tepals translucent white with midrib, often open mornings only; fruit round, seeds small, black, rough.

Anthericum angulicaule [= *Chlorophytum angulicaule*] **Giant Anthericum** (*angulicaule* - angled stems)
Robust perennial, up to 1,5 m. On grassy mountainsides, S KZN to Moz. **Leaves: In 2 ranks**, ± 750 x 25 mm, leathery, ribbed, grey-green. **Flowers:** Inflorescence with **flattened, zigzag, branched stem**, sometimes winged; flowers white with green-brown keel, ± 20 mm diam, 3-4 in cluster, bracts small, dark, 2-3 flowers open at once (Jun-Jan).

Anthericum cooperi [=*Chlorophytum cooperi*] **Cooper's Anthericum** (named after Thomas Cooper, 1815-1913, plant collector)
Slender, erect, perennial, up to 400 mm. In grassland, widespread, E Cape to Moz. **Leaves: In 2 ranks, in a fan**, 50-300 x 3-10 mm, flat or folded, curved. **Flowers:** 1-3 in axil of bracts, clustered near tip of **unbranched, winged stem**, ± 25 mm diam; tepals white with dark keel, flowers close at noon (Oct-Mar). **General:** Good garden plant.

Anthericum haygarthii (named after Walter Haygarth, 1862-1950, plant collector who worked with John Medley Wood)
Up to 800 mm, rigid, erect. On rocky hillsides, swamps. **Leaves: In rosette or 2 ranked**, ± 800 x 14 mm, **flat**, ribbed. **Flowers:** Many-flowered inflorescence, stem unbranched, **sticky above** (Nov-Feb).
Similar species: ***Anthericum transvaalense*** Leaves in rosette, often spirally twisted, shorter, narrower, ± 6 mm, with long white hairs.

Anthericum saundersiae [=*Chlorophytum saundersiae*] **Weeping Anthericum** (named after Katharine Saunders, 1824-1901, botanical artist and collector)
Up to 700 mm, in groups. On coastal forest floor and in grassland. **Leaves:** Erect, ± 500 x 10 mm, soft, flattish. **Flowers:** In crowded inflorescence, **branched or unbranched**, flat, winged; flowers ± 20 mm diam (Jul-Feb). **General:** Popular garden plant, blooms continuously in sun or shade.

Van Wyk & Malan

Trachyandra asperata

Lal Greene

Trachyandra asperata

Lal Greene

Trachyandra gerrardii

Tony Abbott

Anthericum angulicaule

Lal Greene

Trachyandra saltii

Geoff Nichols

Anthericum saundersiae

Tony Abbott

Anthericum cooperi

Van Wyk & Malan

Anthericum transvaalense

Martin von Fintel

Anthericum haygarthii

89

Chlorophytum (*chloros* - green; *phyton* - plant) - Usually more robust than *Anthericum*; roots usually swollen; leaves in basal rosette, broader; flowers usually in larger clusters, open all day; fruit deeply 3 lobed, seeds flat.

Chlorophytum comosum Green Hen and Chickens; Hen-met-kuikens (A); ujejane (X); iphamba, umhlambezo (Z) (*comosum* - tufted with hair)

Up to 800 mm, in large colonies. In forest, moist shady areas, up to 1700 m, Cape to Moz. **Leaves:** In rosette, ± 300 x 20 mm, **tapering at both ends. Flowers:** In slender inflorescence, stem erect, **simple** or with 1-2 branches; flowers ± 20 mm diam (throughout year). **General:** Used traditionally to ensure a healthy birth. **Tuft of leaves on the tip of the reclining flowering stem roots on reaching the ground.** The cultivated form with white striped leaves is grown worldwide.

Chlorophytum krookianum Giant Chlorophytum (named after P Krook ± 1895, a plant collector)

Deciduous, robust, up to 2 m. In damp areas in grassland, in swamps, on forest margins, coast to 1800 m. Perennial rootstock. **Leaves: Broad,** ± 1360 x 90 mm, soft, flat or folded. **Flowers:** In erect, **much branched inflorescences,** stems stout, ± 15 mm diam; flowers white, ± 30 mm diam, tepals with green vein and tip, bracts small, falling early (Dec-Apr). **Fruit:** Capsule oblong. **General:** Largest species of this genus in SA. Excellent garden plant.
Similar species: *C. bowkeri* Robust, up to 1 m, in large groups; in damp, shady, rocky areas, E Cape to Zim; leaves 300-800 x 20-60 mm, tips curved back; inflorescence densely packed, **stem unbranched;** flowers pure white, ± 20 mm diam, **large bracts** ± 20 mm, hiding stem, flowers close in evening.

Chlorophytum modestum Small Chlorophytum; umathunga wehlathi omncane (Z)
(*modestum* - unobtrusive)

Small, up to 300 mm. In shade of forest, thicket, E Cape to Moz. **Leaves:** Narrow, 150-230 mm, thin, soft, flat. **Flowers: In few-flowered inflorescences, stems unbranched, from outside leaf rosette;** flowers shiny white, ± 20 mm diam (Oct-May). **General:** Used as a protective charm. Good pot plant.

ERIOSPERMACEAE - Formerly part of Liliaceae. Perennial herbs with edible tubers. Seeds covered in long white hairs. Afr, 1 genus, ***Eriospermum*** (*erion* - wool; *sperma* - seed, refers to woolly seeds) ± 100 species, ± 50 in SA.

Eriospermum cooperi [= *E. natalense, E. sprengerianum*] White Fluffy-seed; Kapokblom-metjie (A); khongoana-tsa-ngoana, khukhu-e-kholo, lekoto-la-litsoene, tsebe-ea-khomo (SS) (named after Thomas Cooper, 1815-1913, plant collector)

Up to 600 mm. In rocky grassland, open scrub, coast to 2250 m, E Cape to Zim. Tuber ± 100 x 40 mm. **Leaf:** Solitary, erect, sheath ± 100 x 40 mm, red at base, blade ± 150 x 85 mm, roughish, **after flowers,** or from different growing point. **Flowers:** In slender inflorescence, ± 200 x 15-30 mm, **stem with sheathing bract, tipped with small blade at base;** flowers white to pale green, sometimes with red speckles or outer tepals reddish brown or green, stalks 8-30 mm, copious nectar from base of filaments (Aug-Jan). **General:** Does well in the garden, in full sun.

Eriospermum ornithogaloides khongoana-tsa-ngoana, khongoana-tsingoana (SS); incameshela (Z) (*ornithogaloides* - resembles the genus *Ornithogalum*)

Up to 200 mm. On damp, rocky slopes, up to 2400 m. Tuber ± 35 x 12 mm. **Leaf:** Solitary, **prostrate,** sheath ± 15 mm, red, **blade heart-shaped,** ± 35 x 28 mm, **margins red, fringed with hairs. Flowers:** Inflorescence 30-40 mm, bracts purple; flowers ± 10 mm diam, tepals white, **midvein blue-green,** outer tepals spreading, inner erect (Oct-Dec). **General:** Used to treat earache, barrenness in women.

ASPHODELACEAE - Formerly part of Liliaceae. Mostly herbs, also woody forms such as the tree aloes. Leaves often thick, succulent, in rosette, basal or just below inflorescence, margins often toothed and spiny. Inflorescence unbranched or branched, tepals free or fused into a tube, ovary superior. Fruit a capsule, seeds black. Europe, Asia, Afr, centred in S Afr, particularly *Kniphofia* and *Aloe*; 17 genera, ± 750 species, 10 genera in SA.
Kniphofia - Red-hot Pokers Leaves soft, basal; inflorescence a simple spike. Mostly Afr, ± 70 species, 47 in SA.

Kniphofia albescens (*albescens* - becoming white)

Up to 750 mm, in clumps. In mountain grassland, marshy places, 1500-2000 m. **Leaves:** 600-1000 x **8-15 mm,** keeled, spreading, curved, tough, fibrous, margins and keel smooth or rough. **Flowers:** In **dense inflorescence,** 60-100 x 27-35 mm, tapering to tip and base; buds greenish white or pinkish, erect, flowers cream or white, 11-15 x 2-3 mm, spreading at first, then hanging, lobes rounded, slightly spreading, stamens protruding, bracts pointed, 7-9 x 2 mm, longer than buds (Jan-May).

Chlorophytum bowkeri

Martin von Fintel

Chlorophytum comosum

Lal Greene

Chlorophytum krookianum

Lal Greene

Chlorophytum modestum

Geoff Nichols

C. comosum

Lorraine van Hooff

Kniphofia albescens

Martin von Fintel

Eriospermum cooperi

Lal Greene

Eriospermum ornithogaloides

Lorraine van Hooff

91

Kniphofia breviflora Poker (*breviflora* - short flowers)

Slender, up to 800 mm, solitary. In damp grassland, on foothills, mountain slopes, up to 2450 m. **Leaves: Narrow, grasslike,** 400-700 x **2-6 mm,** erect then bending over, keeled, **margins smooth. Flowers:** Inflorescence dense at tip, 50-80 x 20-24 mm; buds erect, spreading, yellow-green, tinged red, **flowers 7-11 mm,** erect to spreading, later hanging, **whitish yellow,** sometimes dull brownish red (Oct-Mar).

Kniphofia buchananii Small White Poker; ihlinzanyoka elincane (Z) (named after Rev John Buchanan, 1821-1903, Presbyterian clergyman, botanical collector in KZN and Free State)

Up to 1 m, solitary. In grassland, on rocky slopes, 200-1600 m. **Leaves: Narrow,** grasslike, erect, recurving, 400-600 x **2-4 mm,** keeled, **margins smooth. Flowers:** Inflorescence with rounded tip, ± 90 x 14 mm; buds erect, greenish cream or tinged red, **flowers 4-5 mm, white,** erect to spreading, bracts with narrow, pointed tip, **straw coloured** (Oct-Apr). **General:** Used traditionally as a snake deterrent.

Kniphofia gracilis Graceful Poker (*gracilis* - slender, graceful)

Up to 1 m, solitary or in small groups. In grassland, coast to midlands, 100-1400 m. **Leaves:** Curving from middle, 400-1200 x 4-14 mm. **Flowers: In loosely arranged inflorescence,** short or elongate, ± 350 x 38 mm, tapering to tip; buds erect to hanging, white tinged pink to yellow tinged orange, flowers ± **20 mm,** spreading, whitish, creamy yellow or yellow, **bracts oblong to oval** (Dec-Apr). **General:** Considerable variation in length and density of the inflorescence. (See p. 28)

ALLIACEAE - Onion Family Perennial herbs with a rhizome in SA species. Leaves basal, sometimes sheathing the flowering stem. Inflorescence with membraneous bracts at base, ovary superior. Some species have an onion or garlic smell (*Tulbaghia*). Fruit a capsule, seeds black. Subcosmop, ± 30 genera, ± 850 species, 4 genera in SA.

Tulbaghia (named after Ryk Tulbagh, Governor of the Cape, 1751-71, who sent specimens to Linnaeus) - Herbaceous perennials; flowers with a corona or fleshy ring at mouth of tube. Afr, mostly SA, ± 20 species.

Tulbaghia leucantha Highland Wild Garlic; sefothafotha (SS) (*leucantha* - bearing white flowers)

Up to 300 mm. In damp grassland, rocky areas in mountains, E Cape to Zim, up to 2500 m. **Leaves:** 50-150 x 3-6 mm. **Flowers:** 4-8 in inflorescence; flowers ± 5 x 3 mm, light green, tepal lobes rolled in, **not** conspicuously recurved, whitish green, fleshy ring orange or crimson, bracts ± 20 x 3,6 mm (Sep-Mar). **General:** Used as a culinary herb (garlic smell disappears after cooking), also to strengthen tobacco and as a protective charm.

Nothoscordum (*nothos* - bastard; *skordon* - garlic) - Onionlike, odourless. America, 20 species, 1 naturalised in SA.

★ Nothoscordum gracile Onion Weed (*gracile* - slender)

Up to 400 mm. Weed in gardens, KZN coast, midlands. Flowers white. A problem plant in gardens and the nursery trade. Sometimes confused with garlic chives!

LILIACEAE - Lily Family 10 genera, ± 350 species, 1 genus naturalised in SA. *Lilium* (Greek and Latin name for lily, common to almost all European languages) N temp, ± 100 species, 1 naturalised in SA.

★ Lilium formosanum Trumpet Lily (formosa - old name for Taiwan, country of origin)

Up to 1,5 m, fairly widespread on roadsides, KZN to Mpum. A garden escape, from Taiwan. Leaves ± 100 x 10 mm, with 2-4 veins prominent beneath. 3-10 flowers in terminal inflorescence, ± 180 mm, white (Feb-Mar), fragrantly scented.

HYACINTHACEAE - Formerly part of Liliaceae. Mostly perennial herbs. Bulbs sometimes with a number of free scales. Inflorescences elongated; stamens 6, filaments often broad, flat, ovary superior. Fruit a capsule, seeds black. Subcosmop, ± 41 genera, ± 770 species, 27 genera in SA.

Albuca (*albus* - white or *albicans* - becoming white) - Bulbous herbs; flowers with 3 inner tepals erect and touching, outer tepals spreading. Afr, Arabia, ± 100 species, 56 in SA.

Albuca fastigiata Large Spreading White Albuca; umaphipha-intelezi (Z) (*fastigiata* - parallel, erect branches)

Up to 900 mm, hanging from rock crevices, or erect. In damp, rocky ground, up to 2400 m. Bulb ± 70 mm diam. **Leaves:** ± 1000 x 20(30) mm, **narrow throughout,** with silvery band down the middle. **Flowers:** In few-flowered, flattish inflorescences; **flowers held erect,** tepal lobes ± 20 mm, white sometimes tipped yellow, with broad green stripe, lower stalks ± 100 mm (Jan-Feb), unpleasant scent. **General:** Used as a protective charm. Easily grown in gardens.

Rob Scott-Shaw

Kniphofia breviflora

Martin von Fintel

Kniphofia buchananii

Martin von Fintel

Kniphofia gracilis

Lal Greene

Albuca fastigiata

Van Wyk & Malan

★ *Nothoscordum gracile*

Martin von Fintel

Tulbaghia leucantha

Lorraine van Hooff

★ *Lilium formosanum*

93

Albuca nelsonii Candlelabrum Lily; umaphipha-intelezi, umababaza (Z) (named after William Nelson, 1852-1922, nurseryman and collector)

Robust, up to 1 m, in clumps. In grassland, on rocky slopes. Bulb buried. **Leaves:** ± 1000 x 50 mm, **broader at base**, tapering to pointed tip, bright green. **Flowers:** Inflorescence 300-400 mm, flowers widely spaced, stem stout, **stiffly erect**; flowers erect, 35 mm diam, tepal lobes ± 35 mm, white with greenish or reddish brown central stripe, stalks 50-75 mm (Sep-Dec). **General:** Used as a protective charm. Good garden plant. **Similar species:**
A. batteniana Wild Coast Albuca Sea-facing cliffs, E Cape; bulb above ground; leaves 400-600 x 30-40 mm; inflorescence ± 800 mm, **held horizontally**.

Albuca setosa Small White Albuca; Slymstok, Slymuintjie (A); mototse (SS); gib'iziphoso (Sw); ingcino (Z) (setosa - bristly)

Deciduous, up to 400 mm. On rocky ground up to 2400 m, widespread in summer rainfall areas. Bulb large, **outer scales end in black bristles**. **Leaves:** Few, ± 300 mm, ± 20 mm broad at base, dark green, produced **after** flowers. **Flowers:** Few in inflorescence; flowers ± 25 mm, erect, white with broad green to brownish central stripe, inner tepals sometimes tipped yellow (Aug-Jan), sometimes scented. **General:** Used in ritual cleansing and as a protective charm against lightning, also to end quarrels between enemies. Does well in the garden. **Similar species:** *A. pachychlamys* Smaller, leaves narrow, 3 mm or less wide; flowers few, 10-15 mm; sometimes considered a dwarf form of *A. setosa.*

Urginea (from Beni urgen, a tribe living in Algeria where the type specimen was found) - Bulbous herbs, usually flowering before leaves; bracts coloured, with tails, often falling early. Poisonous to livestock. Afr, Medit, India, ± 100 species, ± 24 in SA.

Urginea altissima [= *U. epigea*] Tall White Squill; Jeukbol (A); lukhovu (Sw); isiklenama, umahlokolosi, umgulube (Z) (altissima - high)

Deciduous, up to 1 m, in large colonies. In hot, dry bushveld, thicket, E Cape to N Prov. Bulb large, **above the ground**, ± 150 mm diam, with tough, greyish, **overlapping, fleshy scales**. **Leaves:** 150-300 x 20-30 mm, tough, erect, greygreen, with bloom, produced after flowers. **Flowers:** In dense inflorescence, ± 600 mm, stem robust; flowers white with central green stripe, opening early, closing by 13h00 (except on heavily overcast days), stalks 25-75 mm, horizontal (Sep-Oct). **General:** Leaves and bulbs browsed by duiker and nyala. Used as soap. Used in traditional medicine to treat colds, backache and also for magical purposes. Interesting garden plant for hot, dry places.

Urginea capitata Bergslangkop, Jeukui (A); moretele (SS) (capitata - composite flowerhead)

Up to 300 mm, in groups. In grassland, coast to 2400 m, E Cape to N Prov. Bulb fleshy. **Leaves:** ± 150 x 6 mm, produced after flowers. **Flowers:** In compact inflorescence, stem stout (Jun-Oct). **General:** Toxic to sheep and cattle. Traditionally used as a powerful good luck charm, or to cause harm to enemies.

Urginea macrocentra Poison Snake-head; Natalse Slangkop (A); injoba (X,Z); isiklenama, ujobo (Z) (macrocentra - large spurs)

Up to 1,5 m, in colonies. In marshy ground, near streams. Bulb large, round, 40-60 mm diam. **Leaf:** Solitary, ± 600 mm, cylindrical, appearing separately from, and usually after, the flowering stem. **Flowers:** In dense inflorescence (resembling a snake), ± 150 x 30 mm, stem robust, ± 20 mm diam; flowers white, lower bracts with tails ± 40 mm, falling early (Oct-Dec). **General:** Poisonous to stock. Used in traditional medicine to treat roundworm and tapeworm.

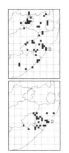

Urginea tenella Dainty Urginea; khoho-ea-lefika (SS) (tenella - dainty)

Small, slender, 50-150 mm, in colonies. In shallow soil on sheet rock or cliffs, 1800-2600 m. **Bulb round**, ± 15 mm diam. **Leaves:** Threadlike, **appearing after flowers**. **Flowers:** In small, elongate inflorescence, stem slender; flowers ± 8 mm diam, pinkish white, **stalks 12-20 mm, erect to horizontal** (Oct-Dec). **Similar species:** *U. calcarata* [= *U. modesta*] 100-300 mm, scattered, on grassy slopes; flower stalks shorter, ± 10 mm. *U. rubella* Bulb oval; flowers scented. *U. multisetosa* 300-500 mm; in rocky grassland, up to 1600 m, KZN to N Prov; bulb topped with tuft of bristles; leafless at flowering.

Albuca nelsonii

Trevor Coleman

Albuca batteniana

Auriol Batten

Urginea altissima

Tony Abbott

Albuca setosa

Rosemary Williams

Urginea capitata

Lal Greene

Urginea tenella

Anne Rennie

Urginea macrocentra

Lal Greene

95

Galtonia (named after British scientist Sir Francis Galton, 1822-1911, who travelled widely in SA) - Bulbous herb with drooping bell-shaped flowers. Genus endemic to SA, 4 species.

Galtonia candicans   Common Berg Lily; Berglelie (A)   (candicans - pure white)

Up to 1,5 m. In damp or marshy ground on mountain slopes, on forest margins, 1350-2150 m. Bulb ± 35 mm diam. **Leaves:** 400-1500 x 20-77 mm, erect, green, with slight bloom, margins folding inwards, tips blunt. **Flowers:** 18-55, inflorescence 350-650 mm, stem robust; flower tube ± 20 mm, tepal lobes ± 26 x 12 mm, **hardly spreading, pure white** or tube pale green outside with central pale green band on outer tepal lobes (Jan-Mar). **Fruit:** Capsules erect when mature. **General:** Cultivated in England since 1862. Excellent garden plant, frost resistant.

Galtonia princeps   Berg Lily; Berglelie (A)   (princeps - first, chief)

Up to 1,5 m. In marshy areas near streams, amongst rocks, coast to 1250 m. Bulb ± 50 mm diam. **Leaves:** 450-900 x 27-50 mm, erect, green. **Flowers:** 12-30, inflorescence 200-450 mm; flower **tube ± 23 x 10 mm, pale green,** tepal lobes ± 17 x 9 mm, **pale creamy green with central pale green band, spreading widely in upper section, recurved at tips** (Nov-Feb). **Fruit:** Round, base abruptly narrowed.

Galtonia regalis   Royal Berg Lily   (regalis - royal, refers to Royal Natal National Park, where the type specimen was collected)

Up to 800 mm. On wet cliffs up to 2000 m. Bulb ± 70 x 60 mm. **Leaves:** 150-550 x 30-70 mm, lax, green. **Flowers:** 8-30, inflorescence 100-300 mm; flower tube ± 14 x 8 mm, greenish or greenish cream, tepal lobes spreading, ± 25 x 9 mm, pale creamy yellow, bracts ± 55 x 12 mm (Jan-Feb). **Fruit:** Conical with pointed tip. **Similar species:** *G. viridiflora* **Green Berg Lily** In drier areas above escarpment, Free State, Les; leaves with bloom, erect; flowers pale green. (For photograph see p. 510)

Drimia (*drymis* - acrid or pungent, all parts of some species are poisonous and irritants) - Bulb with very loose scales, usually above ground; flowers with short tube, tepal lobes rolled back. SA, ± 13 species.

Drimia elata   [= D. alta, D. robusta] Satin Squill; Brandui, Jeukbol (A); gib'iziphoso (Sw); undongana-zibomvana, isiklenama, umqumba (Z)   (elata - tall)

Up to 1,2 m, often in clumps or colonies. Widespread, in grassland, coast to mountains, up to 2100 m, S Cape to Bots. Bulb 40-100 mm diam, with overlapping red scales, tipped with remains of old leaves. **Leaves:** ± 440 (1000) x 25-55 mm, after flowers. **Flowers:** 30-100, inflorescence slender, erect; flowers 12-24 mm, purplish brown, greenish or whitish, stalks erect to spreading, 5-10(20) mm, bracts inconspicuous, with distinct spur near base (Sep-Jan), faintly scented. **Fruit:** Roundish, deeply lobed. **General:** Poisonous to stock. Used in traditional medicine for pain relief, feverish colds and as a protective charm. Attractive garden plant.

Drimia sphaerocephala   Round-head Drimia; Snotuintjie (A); hlare-sa-noko (SS)
(sphaer - a ball or sphere; cephal - a head)

Up to 500 mm. In marshy areas. Bulb 20-30 mm, oval, pale yellowish. **Leaves:** 115-170 x 6-8 mm, margins with long fine hairs, after flowers. **Flowers: In dense round inflorescence** ± 80 mm diam; flowers ±10 mm, tube very short, tepal lobes folded back, white, pink, mauve, greenish grey, stamens straight, stalks ± 15 mm (Oct-Nov). **General:** Used in traditional medicine to treat external tumours.

Scilla (*squilla* - the sea squill) - Bulbous herbs, flowering with or without unspotted leaves; flowers blue or white. Afr, Europe, Asia, ± 40 species, 6 in SA.

Scilla nervosa   [= S. rigidifolia] White Scilla; Sandlelie (A); magaqana (X); seboka (SS); imbita-yebantwana, ndvwendvweni (Sw); ingcino, ingcolo, umgcinywana, imbizankulu ingema (Z)   (nervosa - veined, nerved)

Up to 400 mm, forming rounded clumps. In grassland, coast to 2000 m, E Cape to Tanz. Bulb ± 100 mm diam, covered in fibrous sheaths, buried beneath ground. **Leaves:** Stiff, erect, sometimes twisted, ± 300 x 30 mm, conspicuous veins on both surfaces, margins thickened, produced with flowers. **Flowers:** In compact inflorescence at first, extending ± 200 mm, stem at an angle; flowers small, white or creamy yellow with emerald green spot at base of tepals, flower stalks lengthening ± 50 mm (Sep-Feb). **General:** Used in traditional medicine to treat rheumatic fever and dysentery. Dried out inflorescences very attractive. Easily grown from seed, hardy garden plant.

Galtonia candicans

Lal Greene

Galtonia candicans

Lal Greene

Galtonia princeps

Martin von Fintel

Galtonia regalis

Rodney Moffett

Drimia elata

Lal Greene

Martin von Fintel

Drimia sphaerocephala

Lal Greene

Scilla nervosa

Tony Abbott

Scilla nervosa

Wayne Matthews

Eucomis (*eucomis* - beautiful hair or topknot) - Bulbous herbs with large broad leaves; inflorescence dense, topped with leafy bracts, resembling pineapple, hence the common name. S Trop Afr, ± 10 species.

Eucomis bicolor Forest Pineapple Flower; Bontpynappelblom, Bospynappel-lelie (A); kxampumpu-ya-thaba (SS); umbola (Z) (*bicolor* - two coloured)

Up to 1 m, in clumps. On grassy streambanks, boulders, in forest, at higher altitudes, up to 2800 m. **Leaves:** ± 600 x 100 mm, often purple spotted at base, margins wavy, purplish red. **Flowers:** Inflorescence ± 300 x 75 mm, terminal bracts large, floppy, margins purple, stem hardly tapering to base; flowers densely packed, drooping, tepals white, green or mauve, edged with purple or purple in centre, stamens purple, stalks ± 20 mm (Jan-Mar), unpleasant smell. **General:** Used in traditional medicine to treat colic. Interesting garden plant.

Eucomis comosa [= *E. punctata*] Slender Pineapple Flower; Krulkoppie, Pynappel-lelie (A); ubuhlungu-becanti (X,Z) (*comosa* - hairy tufts, shaggy)

Up to 1,2 m. In swamps, on grassy hillsides, inland. **Leaves:** 200-900 x 30-150 mm, **firm**, bright green, **purple streaked beneath**. **Flowers:** Inflorescence ± 400 x 75 mm, terminal bracts relatively small, stem stout, cylindrical; flowers cream, ovary purple, tepals ± 15 mm, stalks ± 30 mm (Dec-Mar), sweetly scented. **General:** Used in traditional medicine to treat rheumatism. Good garden plant. Var. *comosa*, 200-600 mm, in dry and damp areas. Var. *striata*, up to 1,2 m, in swamps.

Eucomis humilis Dwarf Pineapple Flower; Beskeie Berglelie (A) (*humilis* - low)

Up to 400 mm. In grassland below cliffs, on rocky streambeds, wet rock faces, up to 2400 m. Large bulb, ± 150 mm. **Leaves:** ± 400 x 70 mm, keeled, narrow at base, margins wavy, tinged purple, spotted purple beneath. **Flowers:** Inflorescence 80-220 mm, tuft small, terminal bracts edged purple, sometimes spotted purple, stem cylindrical, strongly tapered at base; **flowers densely packed**, ± 10 mm, greenish white tinged and/or edged purple, stamens purple, stalks **short** (Nov-Feb), unpleasant scent. (See p. 512) **Similar species:** *E. montana* Up to 300 mm, in groups; leaves erect, oval, margins not wavy; flowers green; stamens and ovary brown.

Ornithogalum (*ornis* - a bird; *gala* - milk, Greek name for bulbous plant with white flowers) - Bulbous herb, with few leaves; stamens flattened or thickened towards base. Some species poisonous to livestock. Chincherinchee *O. thyrsoides* is a well known cut-flower, exported from SA to Europe. Afr, Europe, Asia, America, ± 200 species, ± 58 in SA.

Ornithogalum juncifolium [= *O. leptophyllum*] Grass-leaved Chincherinchee; lijo-tsa-noko (SS); indlolothi encane (Z) (*juncifolium* - leaves like rushes)

Up to 400 mm. In damp, grassy areas, on cliffs, up to 2300 m. Widespread, SE Cape to Mpum. Bulb buried, 10-40 mm diam, with long neck. **Leaves:** 100-300 x 2-3 mm, ribbed, bases sheathing, **persisting as dark brown fibres at base**, with flowers. **Flowers:** Inflorescence 20-80 mm; flowers 10-20 mm diam, white with central green stripe (Sep-Feb). **General:** Used in traditional medicine as protection against storms and evil. **Similar species:** *O. paludosum* Up to 600 mm; in moist montane grassland, up to 3200 m; early leaves 80-200 x 10-20 mm, later leaves longer, narrower, no black fibres at base; flowers small, white, tepals 6-12 mm.

Ornithogalum saundersiae Giant White Chincherinchee; Transvaalse Tjienkerien-tjee (A)

Up to 1,5 m, in colonies. Very localised, on rocky outcrops. Bulb ± 60 mm diam. **Leaves:** In erect rosette, leaves ± 750 x 70 mm, soft, shiny, dark green. **Flowers:** **In flat topped inflorescence**, stem sturdy, erect, lengthening with age; flowers ± 25 mm diam, white, ovary dark greenish black, stalks erect to spreading, ± 40 mm (Dec-Apr). **General:** Bulb very poisonous to stock. Excellent garden plant, grown from seed, must not be over watered, blooms for at least a month.

Ornithogalum tenuifolium subsp. *tenuifolium* [= *O. virens*] Common Chincherinchee; Bosui (A); moretele-o-monyenyane (SS) (*tenuifolium* - slender leaves)

Up to 1 m. In grassland, thicket, widespread, S Afr to Trop Afr. **Variable.** Bulb 20-30 mm diam, without neck. **Leaves:** ± 900 x 8-20 mm, tapering to long slender tip, **forming sheath at base**. **Flowers:** In tapering inflorescence, stem erect; tepals ± 8 mm, white with central green stripe (spring-summer), sweetly scented in some areas. **General:** Sap causes extreme skin irritation. Used as a charm to cause good or evil. Subsp. *aridum*, drier areas; bulb forming neck; leaves many, narrow.

Eucomis bicolor — Martin von Fintel

Eucomis comosa — Godfrey Symons

Eucomis humilis — Lal Greene

Ornithogalum saundersiae — Jo Onderstall

Ornithogalum paludosum — Tony Abbott

Ornithogalum tenuifolium — Lal Greene

Ornithogalum saundersiae — Jo Onderstall

Ornithogalum juncifolium — Geoff Nichols

Ornithogalum tenuifolium — Lal Greene

99

DRACAENACEAE - Dragon Tree Family Shrubs, trees or perennial herbs. Trop, especially Afr, 5 genera, ± 200 species, 2 genera in SA. *Sansevieria* (named after Raimondo de Sangro, Prince of San Severo, 1710-1771, Italian scholar) - Rhizomatous herbs; leaves basal, thick, fibrous. Afr and Asia, ± 40 species, 4 in SA.

Sansevieria hyacinthoides [= *S. guineensis*, *S. thyrsiflora*] **Mother-in-law's-tongue; Skoonmase-tong, Aambeiwortel (A); ashitokotoko (Th); isikholokotho (X,Z); isikhwendle, isitokotoko (Z)** (*hyacinthoides* - resembling a hyacinth)

Up to 600 mm, in large colonies. In thicket, woodland, E Cape to Trop Afr. Rhizome sturdy, fibrous, bright orange. **Leaves:** 5-12 in loose cluster, ± 600 x 80 mm, **flat**, dark green with paler markings, margins red. **Flowers:** In dense inflorescence, ± 450 mm; flowers ± 30 mm, greenish white to pale mauve, ± 6 **in clusters**, open at night (Sep-May), faintly scented. **Fruit:** Berry, ± 8 mm diam, orange. **General:** Browsed by rhinos, antelopes; rhizome eaten by mole rats. Weaver birds strip the leaves for fibre to build nests. Fibre from leaves made into binding twine. Used traditionally to treat earache, toothache, intestinal worms, haemorrhoids and as a protective charm. Common garden and container plant.

Similar species: *S. metallica* **Giant Sansevieria** Robust, up to 1,6 m; in sand forest, N KZN to Trop Afr; 2-3 leaves, ± 1 m, pale green with white markings, stalk ± 150 mm, deeply channelled; flowers caramel-toffee scented.

S. concinna **Dune Forest Sansevieria** Slender, spreading; in coastal dune forest, N KZN to Moz; leaves ± 700 x 50 mm, stalk slender, channelled, ± 220 x 5-8 mm; flowers ± 45 mm, solitary or in pairs.

Sansevieria pearsonii [=*S. desertii*] **Spiky Mother-in-law's-tongue; Bobbejaan-se-dood (A)**
(named after Henry Pearson, 1872-1916, botanist, founder of the National Bot Gardens, Kirstenbosch)

Up to 1 m, in large colonies. In dry thicket, KZN to Trop Afr. **Leaves:** In a fan, 500 -800 x 50 mm, **cylindrical**, hard, **tip spikelike**; in a rosette in young plants. **Flowers:** In dense inflorescence ± 600 mm; flowers ± 35 mm, creamy pink to bluish mauve, ± 6 in clusters, open in evenings (irregular flowering), scented. **Fruit:** Round, orange. **General:** Contact with the leaf tip causes painful bump on human skin. Occasionally browsed by rhinos and antelopes. Well known garden and container plant.

ASPARAGACEAE - Asparagus Family Subshrubs or climbers. Leaves reduced to scales. The leaflike cladodes are modified stems. Flowers small, white, scented, ovary superior. Cosmop except S America, 6 genera, ± 150 species, 1 genus in SA. *Asparagus* (*aspharagos* - after the name given to the edible asparagus) - In SA this genus was formerly split into *Protasparagus* and *Myrsiphyllum*. These are now reduced to subgenera. The berrylike fruits are eaten by birds. Popular container and garden plants and decorative foliage for florists. About 120 species, ± 80 in SA.

Asparagus aethiopicus [= *Protasparagus aethiopicus*]

Robust climber, up to 3 m. Widespread in dry areas, coastal bush, N Cape to KZN. Rhizome compact, roots forming tubers ± 20 mm. Stems smooth, pale, woody, much branched, branches ± 120 mm, surrounded at base by flush of small bracts; spines 10-20 mm, recurved, hard. **'Leaves':** 4-6 in clusters, **long**, 10-40 x 1 mm, **triangular, blue-green. Flowers:** In massed clusters, simple or branched; flowers white, on short stalks, pollen orange-red (Dec-Mar). **Fruit:** Red berry.

Asparagus africanus [= *Protasparagus africanus*] **Bush Asparagus; Haakdoring (A); lelalatau-le-leholo, leunyeli, (SS); ubulawu ubumhlope, umthunzi (X); isigobo (Z)**

Slender shrub or twiner. In light shade, SW Cape to Moz. Stems ± 3 m, branches spreading, woody with age; **spines small, sharp, reddish brown, below 'leaf' clusters. 'Leaves':** ± 10 mm, threadlike, tip a sharp point, ± 12 in a cluster. **Flowers:** ± 6 in clusters, in profusion; flowers ± 8 mm diam, whitish (Apr-Nov), lovely scent. **Fruit:** ± 5 mm diam, orange. **General:** New shoots cooked by early settlers. Used in traditional medicine to treat kidney and stomach complaints, chest infections, nausea, colic and as a protective charm. Used in traditional initiation.

Asparagus falcatus [= *Protasparagus falcatus*] **Large Forest Asparagus, Yellowwood Asparagus; Doringtou (A); imbelekazana (Z)** (*falcatus* - sickle-shaped)

Robust climber. On forest margins, in thicket, E Cape to Trop Afr, India. Stems woody, **pale grey**; spines short, hooked. **'Leaves': Large**, ± 60 x 7 mm, shiny dark green, flat, with **prominent vein. Flowers:** In elongate inflorescences, in profusion, ± 60 mm; flowers ± 6 mm diam, white (Sep-Dec), sweetly scented. **Fruit:** Red, ± 6 mm diam. **General:** Fruits eaten by birds, monkeys. Leaves browsed by antelopes. Sometimes mistaken for young plants of the Common Yellowwood *Podocarpus falcatus*. Cultivated in Europe for the florist trade.

Geoff Nichols

Ernst van Jaarsveld

Sansevieria hyacinthoides

Martin von Fintel

Sansevieria concinna

Wayne Matthews

Rosemary Williams

Asparagus aethiopicus

Sansevieria metallica

Lal Greene

Asparagus africanus

Lawrence Peacock

Geoff Nichols

Asparagus falcatus

Lawrence Peacock

Sansevieria pearsonii

Asparagus densiflorus [= *Protasparagus densiflorus*] **Emerald Fern; isiqobola, umgca-gcazane, uvelabahleke (Z)** (*densiflorus* - densely covered with flowers)
Erect to scrambling shrublet. In woodland. Rhizome with tubers on side roots. Branches short, close together; spines short or absent. '**Leaves**': Solitary or few in a cluster, 5-15 x 1-2 mm, **with midrib**, evergreen. **Flowers:** In **simple elongate** inflorescences, 20-50 mm; flowers ± 8 mm diam, white tinged pink, glossy (Nov-Apr), scented. **Fruit:** ± 10 mm diam, red. **General:** Used in traditional medicine. Popular garden plant with many horticultural varieties. **Cultivar 'Sprengeri'**, found in the wild, introduced into horticulture by Medley Wood in early 1900s. **Cultivar 'Meyersii' Cat's Tail Fern; Jakkalsstert (A)** Erect, compact; found in the wild in open woodland; 'leaves' smaller; flowers in small clusters. **Similar species:** *A. natalensis* 1-4 'leaves' per cluster, no midrib; flowers white, in long, branched or unbranched inflorescences ± 80 mm, stems stout, frilly base.

Asparagus intricatus [= *Protasparagus intricatus*]
Compact, dense, erect, perennial shrub, up to 600 mm. In open woodland, on dry rocky hills. **Branchlets short, stout, zigzagging** with short internodes. '**Leaves**': Alternate, solitary, ± 10 mm, cylindrical, spiny. **Flowers:** In clusters as long as leaves, at tips of stems; flowers small, white. **Fruit:** Berry 5 mm diam.
Similar species: *A. divaricatus* Erect or scrambling, branchlets long, thin; 'leaves' slender, 30-40 mm; flower clusters much shorter than 'leaves'. *A. subulatus* Upper branchlets with 'leaves' in clusters of 3-8; flowers within 'leaves'.

Asparagus laricinus [= *Protasparagus laricinus*] **Cluster-leaved Asparagus; Bergkatbos, Katdoring (A); ibutha (Z)** (*laricinus* - larchlike)
Erect, dense, multi-stemmed shrub, up to 2,5 m. In thicket, disturbed areas, in summer rainfall region, S Afr. Young stems and branches zigzag, ribbed, whitish; spines short, hard, on stems, branches and below 'leaf' clusters. '**Leaves**': ± 60, in clusters, ± 35 mm, very fine, cylindrical. **Flowers:** 1-8, on outside of 'leaf' clusters; flowers white, pollen red or orange (summer), sweetly scented. **Fruit:** Berry ± 5 mm diam, red. **General:** Rich in pollen and nectar. Used in love charms.

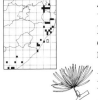

Asparagus macowanii [= *Protasparagus macowanii*] **Zulu Asparagus** (named after Peter MacOwan, 1830-1909, botanist, teacher, lecturer)
Deciduous, erect, **single stemmed**, shrub up to 2 m. Near rivers, in rocky places, dry forest, S Cape to Moz. Stems smooth, white; spines short, hooked or straight; **new main stem produced each spring**, dying down after a couple of years. '**Leaves**': ± 50 in clusters, ± 15 mm, dark green, 2-3 oval papery bracts at base. **Flowers:** In clusters, in profusion, usually before leaves; flowers ± 6 mm diam, white (Aug-Nov). **Fruit:** ± 12 mm diam. **General:** Very attractive shrub, introduced into horticulture, long lasting in flower arrangements.

Asparagus microraphis [= *Protasparagus microraphis*] **lala-tau, leu-nyeli, mankoe (SS)** (*microraphis* - small needles)
Evergreen, dome-shaped shrub up to 1 m. Montane, at foot of cliffs and on steep rocky slopes, up to 2400 m. Branches spreading, stems erect to tangled, **ribbed**, pale grey; spines thin, sharp, ± 4 mm. '**Leaves**': **Small**, in dense clusters, 2-4 mm, cylindrical. **Flowers:** Solitary, **hanging**, in masses; flowers ± 8 mm diam, cream or pinkish with central green stripe (Oct-Dec), fragrant. **Fruit:** Berry ± 7 mm diam, orange. **General:** Used in traditional initiation of girls and as a treatment for venereal diseases.

Asparagus minutiflorus [= *Protasparagus minutiflorus*] (*minutiflorus* - small flowers)
Erect shrublet with 'fox-tail habit', up to 500 mm. In bushveld, on stony hillsides, KZN to Moz. Stems covered with short, upward pointing branches and branchlets, bark grey, **all parts with rough edges;** spines ± 8 mm, curved upwards. '**Leaves**': ± 10 in starlike clusters, ± 10 mm, **grey-green**, threadlike, **3 angled**. **Flowers: Solitary**, at or near stem, along branches and branchlets, in profusion; flowers ± 4 mm diam (Aug-Nov), scented. **Fruit:** Berry ± 7 mm diam, red.
Similar species: *A. biflorus* Twin flowers, on the stem.

Asparagus densiflorus cultivar *sprengeri*

Pitta Joffe NBI

Asparagus densiflorus

Lorraine van Hooff

Asparagus laricinus

Rosemary Williams

Asparagus densiflorus cultivar *meyersii*

Wally Menne

Asparagus intricatus

Geoff Nichols

Asparagus laricinus

Wally Menne

Asparagus macowanii

Trevor Coleman

Asparagus microraphis

Rosemary Williams

Asparagus minutiflorus

Rosemary Williams

103

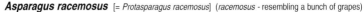

Asparagus racemosus [= *Protasparagus racemosus*] (*racemosus* - resembling a bunch of grapes)

Tall climbers or tangled shrubs. In thicket in frost-free savanna, E Cape to Trop Afr and India. Stems shiny, yellow, branches soft, feathery when in 'leaf', bare when in flower; spines 5-10 mm at base of plant, spreading to hooked. '**Leaves**': 4-8 per cluster, **fine**, 10-16 mm, **droopy**, dark green. **Flowers:** Inflorescences ± 30 mm, simple, **usually clustered**; flowers ± 6 mm diam, white with central red stripe, **anthers red** (summer). **Fruit:** Berry **rounded at base.**

Asparagus ramosissimus [= *Myrsiphyllum ramosissimum*] khopa, sesilatsane (SS); ibutha (Z)
(*ramosissimus* - much branched)

Weak herbaceous scrambler, up to 2 m. In scrub, on forest margins, in montane areas, S Cape to Mpum. Stem green, angled, branches spreading. '**Leaves**': In threes, ± 12 x 1 mm, flat above, keeled below. **Flowers:** Solitary, ± 8 mm diam, hanging, tepals spreading, white, stalk ± 10 mm (Nov-Mar). **Fruit:** Berry red, ± 10 mm diam. **General:** Roots sometimes eaten. Used traditionally to treat colic and as a protective charm against snakes.

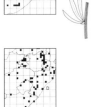

Asparagus setaceus [= *Protasparagus setaceus*] ibutha (Z) (*setaceus* - bristly)

Evergreen perennial, erect or scrambling, up to 2 m. In thicket, S Cape to Trop Afr. Rhizome compact, woody, young roots with swellings. Stems woody, with few, basal, short, hard spines, branches spreading, branchlets short. '**Leaves**': In **round clusters**, curved, ± 12 mm, **soft, shiny**. **Flowers:** Solitary, ± 6 mm diam, white, on tips of branchlets (Feb-May). **Fruit: Berry black**, ± 5 mm diam. **General:** Used in love charms. **Similar species:** *A. plumosus* Asparagus fern; iphinganhloya (Z) Branches, branchlets spreading in one plane; 'leaves' ± 5 mm, in compressed clusters; berry red; popular container plant.

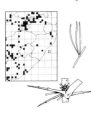

Asparagus suaveolens [= *Protasparagus suaveolens*] Bushveld Asparagus; Katdoring (A); mvane (X) (*suaveolens* - fragrant)

Erect, occasionally scrambling, up to 1 m. In bushveld, thicket, widespread in S Afr. Annual stem slightly zigzagging; spines **straight,** clustered on branches, branchlets spineless. '**Leaves**': 1-6 in clusters, ± 19 mm. **Flowers:** 1-3 in clusters; flowers ± 6 mm diam, **white with central red stripe**, stalks ± 10 mm (spring/summer), sweetly scented. **Fruit:** Black berry ± 5 mm diam. **General:** Roots used in traditional medicine. Xhosa children paint their faces with juice from the berries.

Asparagus virgatus [= *Protasparagus virgatus*] Broom Asparagus; ibutha, ihabiya, iphinganhloya, unwele (Z) (*virgatus* - composed of willowy twigs)

Erect, stiff shrublet 0,5-1 m. In low-lying scrub, forest understorey, up to 1675 m, E Cape to Zim. **Stem slender, green,** branches slim, curved upwards, **spineless.** '**Leaves**': Threadlike, ± 15(25) mm, maturing after flowers. **Flowers: Solitary,** hanging along branches, ± 10 mm diam, tepals recurved, greenish white (summer). **Fruit:** Berry red, ± 5 mm diam. **General:** Browsed by game, monkeys. Groundcover for shady areas. Used in traditional medicine to treat syphilis and intestinal worms. Also used for protective charms.

AMARYLLIDACEAE – Bulbous herbs, rarely rhizomatous. Ovary inferior. Fruit a berry or a capsule, seeds with or without black pigment. Popular horticultural subjects, attract the Amaryllis Caterpillar pest. Cosmop in trop and warm regions, ± 65 genera, ± 725 species, 19 genera in SA.
Haemanthus (*haima* - blood; *anthos* - flower) – Bulbous herb with few, fleshy leaves, in two ranks; no stem; flowers small, in dense inflorescence. S Afr endemic, ± 21 species in SA.

Haemanthus albiflos White Paint Brush; Witpoeierkwas (A); licishamlilo (Sw); uzeneke (Z) (*albiflos* - white flowers)

Evergreen, up to 400 mm, solitary or in clumps. In shade of forest, thicket, S Cape to KZN. Bulb ± 80 mm wide, often on surface, green when exposed to light. **Leaves:** Erect to flat, 90-400 x 25-115 mm, two **new leaves** each year, **sometimes white spotted**, hairless to slightly hairy, tips blunt or pointed. **Flowers:** Inflorescence 25-70 mm wide, stem ± 350 x 14 mm; flowers ± 23 mm, **bracts erect, slightly apart**, white with green veins (**May-Sep**, Jan-Oct). **Fruit:** Berry oval, ± 10 mm diam. **General:** Leaf size, shape and number variable. Used in traditional medicine to treat chronic coughs and as protective charms against lightning. Good garden shade plant.

Asparagus racemosus

C J Ward

Asparagus ramosissimus

Olaf Wirminghaus

Asparagus setaceus

Van Wyk & Malan

Asparagus suaveolens

Wally Menne

Asparagus virgatus

Tony Abbott

Asparagus virgatus

Geoff Nichols

Asparagus virgatus

Geoff Nichols

Haemanthus albiflos

Geoff Nichols

Haemanthus albiflos

Geoff Nichols

105

Haemanthus deformis [= *H. baurii, H. mackenii*] Dwarf Haemanthus; uzeneke (Z) (*deformis* - misshapen, deformed)

Evergreen, up to 60 mm, solitary or in clumps. In shade of thicket and on moist rocky banks, 300-1000 m. Bulb ±100 mm wide. **Leaves:** 80-260 x 70-250 mm, **thick, flat,** hairy or not, margins hairy, persisting for over a year; **new leaves appearing after flowers. Flowers:** Inflorescence 45-70 mm diam, **stem less than 60 mm**; flowers ± 30 mm, **6-7 bracts, erect, overlapping,** white, margins hairy (May-Oct). **Fruit:** Oval berry, ± 15 mm diam. **General:** Used in traditional medicine. Described as 'singular and indeed grotesquely ugly' by Joseph Hooker in 1871. This plant continues to fascinate people. Perhaps better described as 'a water lily floating on the ground'! The Zulu *ukuzeneke* means 'to spread yourself'.

Haemanthus montanus Mountain Haemanthus (see p. 346; for fruit see p. 232)

Nerine (Nerine was a sea nymph, daughter of sea god Nereus and Doris) - Bulbous herbs; leaves few; flowers without tube or very short tube, lobes narrow, spreading; fruit not fleshy. Many horticultural hybrids. S Afr, ± 22 species.

Nerine pancratioides White Nerine (*pancratioides* - resembling *Pancratium*, the Spider Lily)

Up to 600 mm. On moist ground, 1380-1800 m. **Leaves:** Up to 300 mm, bright green, narrow, round at base, flattened towards tip. **Flowers:** 10-20, in crowded inflorescences, stem robust, round; tepals ± 25 mm, white (Mar-Apr). **General:** Eaten by stock.

Apodolirion (*apod* - without a foot; *lirion* - white lily) - Bulbous herbs with neck of old leaf bases. SA endemic, ± 6 species.

Apodolirion buchananii Natal Crocus; icukudwane, indwa (Z) (named after Rev John Buchanan, 1821-1903, Presbyterian clergyman in Natal who collected plant specimens)

Up to 60(200) mm. Scattered in grassland, blooms after fires in spring, widespread. Bulb ± 15 mm diam, with long, fibrous neck, **enclosing ovary. Leaves:** 1-2, grasslike, after flowers. **Flowers:** Solitary, white to pink, stemlike tube ± 60 mm; funnel 25-35 mm; tepal lobes ± 12 mm wide (Aug-Sep), sweetly scented. **General:** Used in traditional medicine to treat stomach complaints.

Crinum (*krinon* - lily) - Robust, deciduous bulbous plant; leaves soft, spirally arranged; spreading inflorescence with very large flowers, tube long, trumpet-shaped, with spreading or reflexed tepal lobes; seeds few, large, without hard coat, irregular. All are rewarding garden plants. Mainly Afr, ± 130 species, ± 21 in SA.

Crinum paludosum Bushveld Vlei Lily (*paludosum* - growing in marshy places)

Up to 550 mm, in large colonies. In seasonal pans, marshy areas, N KZN to N Prov, Nam. Bulb ± 200 mm diam, narrowing to long neck. **Leaves:** Soft, pale green, **gracefully arching,** margin wavy. **Flowers:** 5-11, in inflorescence; flower tube ± 120 mm, tepal lobes ± 100 x 30 mm, suberect to spreading, **white** to pale pink with darker pink keel, open fully only at midday, **stigma red,** stem erect (Dec-Jan), slightly scented. **Fruit:** Not beaked, up to 35 mm diam. **General:** Usually blooms whilst submerged in ± 300 mm water. Leaves browsed by stock. (See p. 350)

HYPOXIDACEAE - Star Flower Family (for family and genus description see p. 232). ***Hypoxis*** (*hypo* - beneath; *oxys* - sharp pointed, refers to capsule)

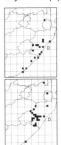

Hypoxis membranacea Small White Hypoxis (*membranacea* - texture of parchment)

Deciduous, up to 140 mm. Common in swampy areas, grassland, mistbelt forest, coast to mountains. Corm 4-5 mm diam. **Leaves:** 5-140 x 8-20 mm, veins not prominent, covered with scattered white hairs, dark green glands. **Flowers:** 1-3, ± 15 mm diam, **white,** 1-2 slender stems (Oct-Jan).

Hypoxis parvula (*parvula* - very small)

Robust, small, up to 150 mm, in large colonies. In moist grassland, up to 2500 m. Corm 30-60 mm diam, oblong. **Leaves:** 25-70 x 5-15 mm, hairy. **Flowers: Solitary,** 10-20 mm diam, **white or yellow** (Sep-Mar). **General:** Var. *parvula,* widespread on mountain slopes at **high altitude, 1800-2500 m, flowers yellow.** Var. *albiflora,* in short grass amongst rock sheets at **lower altitudes, 1200-2000 m; flowers white.** May hybridise with *Rhodohypoxis* species. **Similar species:** *H. limicola* In large colonies, in very damp areas, Mpum; plants thinner, weaker, lower leaves flat on ground.

Martin von Fintel

Trevor Coleman

Rob Scott-Shaw

Haemanthus deformis   *Haemanthus deformis*   *Haemanthus montanus*

Lal Greene

Wally Menne

Nerine pancratioides   *Hypoxis membranacea*

Johan Bodenstein

Wally Menne

Lal Greene

Crinum paludosum   *Hypoxis parvula*   *Apodolirion buchananii*

107

VELLOZIACEAE - Black-stick Lily/Bobbejaanstert Family Fibrous perennials. Stems protected by non-inflammable leaf bases, dwarf or up to 4 m. Leaves in tufts. Afr, Madag and Brazil, 8 genera, ± 280 species, 2 genera in SA.
Xerophyta (*xeros* - dry; *phytos* - plant) - Ovary rough, hairy. Afr, Madag, Brazil, ± 50 species, ± 9 in SA.

Xerophyta retinervis [= *Vellozia retinervis*] Black-stick Lily; Besembos, Bobbejaanstert (A); sifunti (Sw); isigqumana, isiphemba (Z) (see p. 352)

Talbotia (named after Patrick Talbot, 1919-1979, mycologist from Natal) - Ovary smooth, hairless. 1 species in SA.

Talbotia elegans [= *Vellozia elegans*, *V. talbotii*] (*elegans* - graceful)
Tufted herb, up to 300 mm, mat-forming. On damp, shady rock faces and boulders, up to 1675 m. Stem creeping, branching, fibrous. **Leaves:** 80-200 mm, sheathing at base, sharply keeled, margins rough towards pointed tip. **Flowers:** Solitary, ± 20-35 mm wide, white to pale violet, green with age; stems slender, ± 140 mm (Dec-Mar). **General:** Good container plant.

DIOSCOREACEAE (named after Pedanios Dioscorides, 1st century AD Greek herbalist) - **Yam Family** Climbers with tuberous or thick woody rootstock. Leaf blade flat, narrowed into a stalk, simple or compound. Male, female flowers on separate plants. In tropic and warm regions, 8 genera, ± 850 species, 1 genus, 19 species in SA.

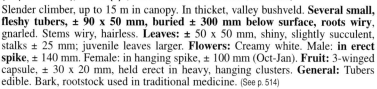

Dioscorea cotinifolia Wild Yam; Olifantsvoet (A); umtane (X); unyawo-lwendlovu (Elephant's Foot), intana (Z) (*cotinifolia* - leaves like *Rhus cotinus*, the Sumach)
Slender climber, up to 15 m in canopy. In thicket, valley bushveld. **Several small, fleshy tubers, ± 90 x 50 mm, buried ± 300 mm below surface, roots wiry,** gnarled. Stems wiry, hairless. **Leaves:** ± 50 x 50 mm, shiny, slightly succulent, stalks ± 25 mm; juvenile leaves larger. **Flowers:** Creamy white. Male: **in erect spike,** ± 140 mm. Female: in hanging spike, ± 100 mm (Oct-Jan). **Fruit:** 3-winged capsule, ± 30 x 20 mm, held erect in heavy, hanging clusters. **General:** Tubers edible. Bark, rootstock used in traditional medicine. (See p. 514)

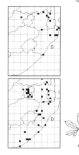

Dioscorea quartiniana unyawo-lwendlovu (Sw) (named after Richard Quartin-Dillon, botanist)
Slender climber. In thicket, woodland. Tubers clustered. Stems wiry, downy. **Leaves: Five leaflets, ± 50 x 20 mm,** arched back, tapering to threadlike tip, with distinct midrib, partly folded upwards. **Flowers:** In hanging spikes of ivory white flowers (Dec-Feb), scented. **Fruit:** Short, squat.

Dioscorea retusa (*retusa* - blunt)
Slender twiner, stems downy. On forest margins, woodland, on rocky outcrops. Underground stems join 2 or more groups of tubers. **Leaves:** Alternate, palmate, leaflets ± 50 x 30 mm, narrowing to short stalks, tips with long hairlike point, stalks ± 30 mm. **Flowers:** Male: inflorescence on slender hairy stem. Female: large, oval to pointed bracts, shorter than flowers, greenish white (Dec-Jan).

IRIDACEAE - Iris Family Corms or rhizomes. Leaves sword-shaped, in 2 ranks. Flowers regular or irregular, stamens 3, ovary inferior. Temp regions, ± 80 genera, ± 1700 species, ± 38 genera in SA.
Moraea (Linnaeus altered the spelling to *Moraea* to associate the name with his father-in-law, J Moraeus, a physician in Sweden) - End of style branches petal-like. Afr, Madag, Austr, ± 119 species, ± 100 in SA, mostly SW Cape.

Moraea albicuspa (*albicuspa* - tipped with white sharp points. Discovered by Harry Bolus at Engcobo and Maclear in late 1800s but unnamed until 1973 when Peter Goldblatt revised eastern S Afr species of the genus)
Erect, up to 600 mm. On damp grassy slopes, among rocks or in clumps of grass or sedge, 1800-2525 m. Corm ± 20 mm diam with fibrous brown tunic, fibrous brown cataphylls on neck at base. **Leaves:** Longer than flowering stem, 2-4 sheathing bract leaves, 40-60 mm. **Flowers: Large, white to cream** (pale yellow) with yellow nectar guides, **outer tepals ± 35 mm, inner tepals reduced, slender, narrow, needlelike,** 7-8 mm, limb horizontally spreading, claw long, suberect; spathes brown tipped, ± 70 mm (Jan-Mar).

Moraea brevistyla (*brevistyla* - short style)
Up to 350(600) mm. In grassland, often near streams and damp areas. Corm ± 15 mm diam, with fibrous dark brown tunic. **Leaf:** Solitary, 600 x 4 mm. **Flowers: Small,** outer tepals ± 20 mm, **spreading horizontally,** white to pale lilac-blue, grey to purple beneath, inner tepals, claws and nectar guides yellow with brown spots, **inner tepals upright, side lobes erect,** ± 10 mm, **central lobe longer, curving outwards;** stem branched, all flowers on one side (Nov-Mar).

Xerophyta retinervis   Geoff Nichols

Talbotia elegans   Trevor Coleman

Dioscorea retusa   Tony Abbott

Dioscorea cotinifolia ♀   Jo Onderstall

Dioscorea cotinifolia ♂   Martin von Fintel

Dioscorea quartiniana   Jo Onderstall

Moraea albicuspa   Hilliard & Burtt

Moraea brevistyla   Tony Abbott / Lal Greene

109

Moraea elliotii Blue Tulp; Bloutulp (see p. 452)

Moraea modesta (modesta - modest size)
Small, up to 200 mm. In mountain grassland, 1525-3000 m. Corm ± 10 mm diam. **Leaf:** Solitary, round, **dry at time of flowering. Flowers:** Outer tepals ± 27mm, white to pale blue-mauve, veined with purple, inner tepals tiny, ± 6 mm, inner tepals and style crests dark purple, nectar guides yellow; stem slender, erect (Sep-Dec). **Similar species:** *M. dracomontana* Found above 2200 m, in KZN Drakensberg; flowers larger, tepals deep blue-purple, a living leaf attached to the flowering stem.

Dietes (*Dietes* - two relatives, drawing attention to the position of this genus between *Moraea* and *Iris*) - Short creeping rhizome (*Moraea* has a corm); leaves flattened; flower similar to that of *Moraea*. SE and C Afr, 5 species in SA.

Dietes butcheriana Forest Iris
Robust, up to 1,2 m. In deep shade, mistbelt forest. KZN/Transkei endemic. **Leaves:** In a fan, **broad,** sword-shaped, ± 1000 x **30-50 mm, dark green,** leathery, erect, **abruptly narrowed below into folded sheath. Flowers: Large, ± 70 mm, white, flat, spreading,** oblong claw ± 12 x 5 mm, densely velvety hairy, spotted orange on yellow; **stem sturdy,** shorter than leaves, short side branches (Sep-Dec). **Fruit: Large, roundish, smooth,** shiny capsule ± 35 x 20 mm, rounded at tip, fruiting stem bends to lie on ground, **fruit disintegrating (not splitting).**

Dietes grandiflora Large Wild Iris; Groot Wilde-iris (A) (grandiflora - flowers large)

Up to 1,5 m, in clumps. On forest margins, in thicket, near streams. **Leaves:** In a fan, ± 1000 x 15 mm, dark green. **Flowers:** Large, ± 100 mm diam, white with yellow nectar guides and beard on outer tepals, style branches violet, open for three days; stem erect, irregularly branched (spring-summer). **Fruit:** Large capsule ± 45 mm, furrowed, held erect, splits wide open to release seeds. **General:** Popular garden plant, blooms in sun or shade. Blooms in advance of, and in response to rain. **Similar species:** *D. iridioides* indawo yehlathi, isiqiki-sikatokiloshe, isishupe somfula (Z) Up to 600 mm, coast to 1950 m; flowers up to 60 mm diam, closed by midday except on overcast days; fruit capsule oval, beaked, ± 30 x 14 mm, disintegrates to release seeds; young plants develop on the flowering stem.

Dierama (*dierama* - a funnel) - **Hairbells, Wand-flowers; Grasklokkies (A)** Fibrous-coated corms; leaves grasslike; flowering stem tall, slender, usually branched, arching, flowers with dry papery bracts, hanging on slender stalks. Lovely plants for the garden. Afr, ± 38 species in SA.

Dierama argyreum (argyreum - silvery)
Slender herb, 0,5-1 m, solitary or in small clumps. In grassland, 200-1900 m. **Leaves:** 500-750 x 3-6 mm. **Flowers:** Drooping inflorescence with 3-7 branches, each spike with 4-9 flowers, ± 30 mm, **white to ivory,** tinged pink or mauve, bracts ± 24 x 10 mm, **silvery white;** stem ± 1,35 m (Sep-Feb). **General:** Flowers are larger at higher altitudes.

Dierama luteoalbidum White Hairbell (luteoalbidum - yellowish white)
Solitary or in small clumps, 0,65-1 m. In open grassland, 915-1700 m. **Leaves:** 350 -600 x 3-4 mm. **Flowers:** Inflorescence with 1-3 branches, each with ± 5 flowers, 30 -50 mm, **white to palest creamy yellow,** parallel sided, bracts 24-32 x 12-16 mm, white to lightly flecked; stems ± 1,1 m long, drooping (Oct-Dec). **General:** This beautiful, unusual species is severely threatened by afforestation and overgrazing.

Gladiolus (*gladiolus* - small sword, referring to leaf shape) - Bracts green; style branches short, undivided or shortly divided in 2; seeds winged; deciduous. Hybrids created since the early 1800s have produced the cut-flowers and garden plants popular worldwide. A large genus of ± 259 species found mostly in S Afr, also Trop Afr, S Europe and Middle East, over 126 species in SA.

Gladiolus appendiculatus (appendix - that which hangs; latus - side)
350-500(800) mm. In grassland, on mountain slopes, up to 2100 m. Corm round, small, ± 20 mm diam, with light brown fibres forming a short neck. **Leaves:** 140 -330 x 10-20 mm, softly leathery, ± sword-shaped, tapering to sharp or blunt tip, narrowing below, slightly downy at base, margins white. **Flowers:** 5-11(20), in inflorescence 300-400(700) mm; flowers overlapping, borne on one side, small, 20-30 mm, white marked pale mauve or pink, tube thin, ± 15 mm, anthers tailed, bracts erect, 20-30 mm (Feb-Mar). **General:** Var. *longifolius*, more robust, ± 800 mm; leaves narrow; inflorescence with ± 20 flowers (Apr-May).

Tom de Waal

Moraea elliotii

Martin von Fintel

Moraea modesta

Trevor Coleman

Dietes butcheriana

Trevor Coleman

Lorraine van Hooff

Dietes grandiflora

Martin von Fintel

Dierama argyreum

Martin von Fintel

Dierama luteoalbidum

Martin von Fintel

Gladiolus appendiculatus

Martin von Fintel

Dierama argyreum

111

Gladiolus inandensis

Up to 600 mm, in large groups. In coastal grassland. Corm round, ± 25 mm diam. **Leaves:** In a fan, erect, evergreen under favourable conditions. **Flowers:** 6-8 in loose inflorescence; flowers funnel-shaped, white to cream, tips and midribs pink to reddish purple; stem slender. **General:** Corms eaten by gamebirds and small mammals.

Gladiolus papilio Butterfly Gladiolus; sidvwana (Sw); ibutha, igulusha (Z) (papilio - butterflylike)

Up to 1 m, in colonies. In marshes, damp grassland, coast to 2400 m, E Cape to N Prov. Corm roundish, ± 30 mm diam. **Leaves:** In basal fan, ± 500 x 20 mm, firm, midrib, margins slightly prominent. **Flowers: Drooping**, on slender, erect stem, tip bending over, bracts ± 20 mm, purplish green; flowers ± 50 mm, tube strongly curved, dull pale to dark purplish mauve, with or without yellow flare, or pale creamy yellow with dark blotch at base of lower tepals (Aug-Feb). **Fruit:** Capsules ± 25 mm, ridged. **General:** Used as a lucky charm. Grown in UK since 1866.

Gladiolus permeabilis Small Afrikander; Kleinaandblom, Patrysuintjie (A); khahla-e-nyenyane (SS); sidvwana (Sw) (permeabilis - able to pass through, refers to gap between upper and lower tepals so that one can see through the flower in profile)

Up to 600(900) mm, solitary or in small clumps. On grassy slopes, sandy flats, rocky ridges, coast to 3000 m, SA to Bots, Zim. Corm roundish, ± 30 mm diam, with soft brown fibres. **Leaves:** Erect, 3-5 in a fan, ± 500 x 2 mm, midrib, margins prominent, 2 tubular sheaths at base, ± 80 mm. **Flowers:** 4-8 in inflorescence, stem erect, simple or branched; flowers small, **tepal lobes with long slender tips**, dull creamish white tinged mauve, green, brown or yellow, keel pink or purplish, lower tepal lobes with irregular yellow band, bracts ± 20 x 5 mm, grey-green to purplish (Sep-Apr, depending on rains), sometimes strongly scented. **Fruit:** Capsule ± 20 mm. **General:** Corms sweet and tasty, roasted and eaten in some areas.

Gladiolus sericeovillosus Large Speckled Gladiolus; Bloupypie (A); sidvwana (Sw); isidwa, isidwa esincane, umlunge, udwendweni (Z) (sericeovillosus - grey haired, refers to the dense silvery hairs)

0,35-1,5 m, solitary or in small colonies. In grassland, coast to 1750 m, E Cape to Zim. Corm round, ± 30 mm diam, old flattened corms persist, densely covered in thick fibres. **Leaves:** Forming a stem at base, fanning out, 6(35) mm wide, firm, margins prominent, short hairs or hairless. **Flowers:** 20-40, in 2 ranks, overlapping, in crowded inflorescence, stem woolly, with curly white hairs; flowers ± 45 x 20 mm, pale green or cream, ± speckled pink or mauve, dark edged yellow-green blotches on lower 2 tepal lobes, bracts woolly, ± 30 mm (**Jan-May**). **Fruit:** Capsule oval, ± 20 mm. **General:** Pollinated by bees. Used as a fertility charm for good harvest and in traditional medicine to treat dysentery, sprains, swollen joints, menstrual pain, sterility in women and to expel afterbirth. (See p. 358)

Gladiolus vernus (vernus - native)

Up to 800 mm. In rocky grassland, up to 3000 m. Corms flattened, 20-40 mm, covered with coarse matted fibres, forming side corms. **Leaves:** 4 in a fan, ± 800 x 2 mm, upper stem leaves sheathing, finely ribbed. **Flowers:** ± 20, in erect inflorescence ± 250 mm; flowers small, ± 30 mm, overlapping, 2 lobed, pale pink, lower lobes with yellow blotch edged red, tube narrow, ± 10 mm (spring).

Gladiolus wilsonii

Tufted, 300-500 mm, sometimes in colonies. In grassland. Corms roundish, 10-30 mm, producing many, stalkless cormlets. **Leaves:** In a fan, erect, 200-500 mm. **Flowers:** In erect inflorescence; flowers 30-50 mm, pale creamy white, tips and midribs ± dark reddish purple or mauve, lobes broad, upper lobe more hooded, 3 lower lobes sometimes with fine reddish lines at base (Sep-Nov). **General:** E Cape plants bloom with leaves, KZN plants are found at higher altitudes where frost and veld fires occur and usually bloom without leaves. (Seé p. 456)

Gladiolus woodii (see p. 240, 572)

Gladiolus inandensis

Wally Menne

Martin von Fintel

Gladiolus papilio

Martin von Fintel

Gladiolus sericeovillosus

Godfrey Symons

Gladiolus permeabilis

Lal Greene

Gladiolus papilio

Rosemary Williams

Gladiolus vernus

Martin von Fintel

Gladiolus wilsonii

Martin von Fintel

Gladiolus woodii

113

Watsonia (named after English scientist Sir William Watson, 1715-1787) - Flattened corm with persistent fibrous tunics; leaves firm; inflorescence a spike, flower tube curved, widening to funnel shape, lobes spreading, ± equal, 6 stigmas, bracts rigid, usually brown. Mostly SA, ± 52 species, 1 in Madag.

Watsonia densiflora Natal Watsonia; sidvwa (Sw); kxahla (SS, X); incembuzane, intshumo, isidwa, umlunge (Z) (*densiflora* - densely flowered, refers to crowded spike)

Up to 1,2 m, in clumps. In open grassland, coast to 1400 m. **Leaves:** Half as long as inflorescences, ± 15 mm wide, grey-green, midvein, margins thickened, yellow. **Flowers:** ± 42, in **densely flowered inflorescences, bracts** ± 25 mm, **dry, brown with dark margins, pale veins,** ± 3 stems, **inclining at base**; flower tube ± 30 mm, lower part enclosed in bracts, tepal lobes ± 24 x 9 mm, pink with dark pink streak in middle of each tepal, white and deep red colour forms occur (Nov-Jun). **General:** Corm edible. Used in traditional medicine to treat diarrhoea and as a charm to ensure good harvests. Easy to germinate seed, difficult to maintain, requires plenty of water and rich soil in garden. (See p. 358) **Similar species:** *W. pulchra* NE KZN to Mpum escarpment; leaves broader, 15-30 mm, midrib not thickened, margins strongly thickened; bracts dark brown. *W. lepida* (see p. 360).

ORCHIDACEAE - Orchid family (for description see p. 240)

Huttonaea (named after Caroline Hutton, who collected with her husband who was an officer during the frontier war and later a Cape civil servant) - Small terrestrial herbs; petals and lip fringed, petals erect, clawed at base, no spur. Genus endemic to SA, 5 species, more or less confined to the Drakensberg mountain range.

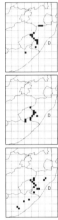

Huttonaea fimbriata (*fimbriata* - fringed margin)

Slender, erect, in colonies. On cool forest floor, 1400-1900 m. **Leaves:** 2, blades ± 80 x 50 mm, **lower leaf with stalk** ± **60 mm. Flowers:** Inflorescence with 6-20 small white flowers, ± **10 mm wide** (Jan-Mar). **General:** Leaves and flowers produced well into summer.

Huttonaea grandiflora (*grandiflora* - flowers larger than normal)

Slender, up to 250 mm. In damp grassland on steep slopes, in rock crevices, 1800-2500 m. **Leaves:** 2, oval, less than 50 mm diam, stalkless. **Flowers:** 1-4, **large,** ± **30 mm**, white, inner margins of petals speckled purple, **fringes long,** ± **8 mm, claws joined**, lip ± 20 mm wide, with short claw (Feb-Mar). **Similar species:** *H. oreophila* Flowers smaller, less than 18 mm.

Huttonaea pulchra (*pulchra* - beautiful)

Slender, up to 350 mm. On forest floor, on damp rocks, 1400-1800 m. **Leaves:** Spreading, sheathing stem, blade ± 90(150) x 70 mm. **Flowers:** Inflorescence with 6-9 large flowers, ± 15 mm, **pale creamy green, petal claws free** (Jan-Apr). **General:** Leaves and flowers produced well into summer.

Habenaria (*habena* - strap or thong; *aria* - possessing, refers to the long spur) - Terrestrial herbs; flowers mostly green and white; median sepal joined with whole or upper lobes of petals forming a hood, lip lobed, spur long. Widely distributed in trop and subtrop regions, ± 600 species, 35 in SA.

Habenaria dives Death Orchid; lekoesha, 'mametsana (SS); inhluthi yotshani (Z) (*dives* - rich)

Up to 700 mm. Widespread in well drained grassland, 100-2450 m. **Leaves:** Clasping at base, ± 150 x 20 mm, stiff, with prominent veins. **Flowers:** In dense inflorescence, ± 300 mm, bracts erect, ± 15 mm; flowers small, white with green veined sepals, lip 3 lobed, **spur 8-15 mm**, stalks short, very slender (Dec-Mar). **General:** Ground and dried tubers used as an evil charm.

Habenaria epipactidea [= *H. foliosa*] 'mametsana (SS); umabelebuca omkhulu, uklamkleshe, unokleshe (Z) (*epipactidea* - similar to *Epipactus*, a genus of orchid)

Robust, up to 500 mm. In damp grassland, coast to 1950 m, E Cape to Trop Afr. **Leaves:** ± 100 x 20 mm, **clasping stem**, overlapping, ribbed, **grading into bracts. Flowers:** In dense inflorescence, ± 120 mm, bracts erect, ± 40 x 10 mm; flowers creamy green with white lip, midlobe of lip ± 15 mm, side lobes tiny, hairlike, spur ± 30 mm, slender with thickened tip, stalks ± 10 mm (Nov-Feb). **General:** Used as a protective charm against lightning.

Watsonia densiflora

Huttonaea fimbriata

Huttonaea pulchra

Huttonaea grandiflora

Huttonaea grandiflora

Huttonaea pulchra

Habenaria dives

Habenaria epipactidea

Huttonaea oreophila

115

Habenaria falcicornis uklamkleshe (Z) (*falcicornis* - sickle-shaped horn)

Slender to robust, up to 700 mm. In grassland, marshy places. **Leaves:** ± 180 x 20 mm, greyish green, **sheathing pale lemon yellow stem**. **Flowers:** In loose inflorescence; flowers green and white, **petals 2 lobed**, lip 3 lobed, ± 15 mm, **spur 20-40 mm** (Nov-Mar). **General:** Subsp. *caffra*, in grassland; front petal lobe narrower, as long as the back petal lobe. Subsp. *falcicornis*, in marshy areas; front petal lobe oval, half as long as back petal lobe.

Habenaria kraenzliniana

Slender, up to 300 mm. On stony, grassy hillsides, 1000-1400 m. **Leaves:** Basal, ± 40 mm diam. **Flowers:** In loose, crowded inflorescence; flowers yellowish green, front petal lobes ± 30 mm, lip 3 lobed, midlobe narrow, ± 5 mm, side lobes long, slender, 30-33 mm, spur ± 40 mm (Feb-Apr).

Bonatea (named after Guiseppe Bonato, 1753-1836, prof of botany at Padua) - Terrestrial; roots tuberous, fleshy. Distinguished from *Habenaria* by the large, 3 lobed rostellum and the elongated toothlike structure in the mouth of the spur and all lower parts of the flower - side sepals, lower petal lobes, lip base, stigmatic arms - which are partially united near their base. Afr, ± 20 species, 10 in SA.

Bonatea cassidea (*cassidus* - a helmet)

Slender, up to 460 mm. In thicket, 60-1200 m, E Cape to Zim. **Leaves:** ± 170 x 12 mm. **Flowers:** In loose inflorescence with 3-21 flowers, white and green, upper petal lobes narrow, 8-11 mm, lower petal lobes pointed, not sickle-shaped, 11-18 x 3-6 mm, lip 3 lobed from undivided base, side lobes pointed, not sickle-shaped, 8-12 mm, midlobe narrow, 7-11 mm, spur 11-14 mm (Aug-Oct).

Bonatea lamprophylla (*lamprus* - shining or radiant; *phylla* - leaves)

Handsome, robust, up to 1,2 m. In dune forest. Elongated tubers. **Leaves:** 10-14, ± 130 x 75 mm, shiny dark green, margins tightly wavy. **Flowers:** In loose inflorescence with 6-13 flowers, green and white, hood 35-40 mm, **lower petal lobes stiff, forward pointing**, narrow, 45-50 mm, whitish, curved upwards, lip 3 lobed, **side lobes long, 130-160 mm**, very narrow, tapering, pale green, midlobe ± 50 mm, sharply bent above the middle, spur 110-120 mm, swollen and flattish in the lower part (Sep-Oct). **General:** A magnificent plant, first described in 1976.

Bonatea porrecta (*porrecta* - lanky)

Robust, up to 650 mm. In grassland, thicket, semi-shade of coastal forest, 150-600 m. **Leaves:** ± 110 mm, **withered at flowering**. **Flowers:** Inflorescence ± 150 mm; flowers large, green and white, hood ± 10 mm, lip with 3-4 lobes ± 30 mm, spur ± 30 mm, often swollen towards tip, bracts ± 25 mm (Jun-Aug). **General:** A wonderful winter surprise.

Bonatea saundersiae (named after Katharine Saunders, 1824-1901, collector and botanical artist)

Slender, up to 400 mm. In dry thicket. **Leaves:** ± 140 x 18 mm, margins wavy, mostly dying off before flowering. **Flowers:** In loose inflorescence with ± 10 flowers, green and white, sepals ± 15 mm, upper petal lobes long, narrow, **pointed**, ± 14 mm, lower petal lobes oblong, ± 19 x 4 mm, strongly sickle-shaped, lip 3 lobed from undivided base, **side lobes pointed, strongly hooked at tip**, ± 15-20 x 3 mm, white, midlobe narrow, green, bent about the middle, spur ± 18 mm (May).

Bonatea saundersioides

Slender, up to 350 mm. In shade of woodland. **Leaves:** ± 140 x 25 mm, wavy edged or not, often withered at time of flowering. **Flowers:** In loose inflorescence, ± 150 mm; flowers white and green, lip 3 lobed, **side lobes long, narrow, 25-30 mm**, spur ± 23 mm (May-Jul). **General:** Browsed by antelope.

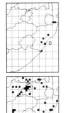

Bonatea speciosa Green Wood Orchid; Moederkappie, Oktoberlelie (A)

(*speciosa* - beautiful)

Robust, up to 1 m. In thicket, on forest margins, coast to 1200 m, SW Cape to Zim. **Leaves:** ± 130 x 40 mm, sheathing stem, **flat, with one central vein**. **Flowers:** In dense inflorescence; flowers green and white, hood ± 24 mm, **upper petal lobes ± 25 mm**, lower petal lobes ± 36 mm, lip 3 lobed, outer lobes 13-30 mm, **midlobe bent in the middle**, spur 25-47 mm, swollen towards tip (Jun-Feb). **General:** Flower shape variable (two varieties described).

116

Bonatea lamprophylla

C J Ward

Habenaria falcicornis

Martin von Fintel

Habenaria kraenzliniana

Godfrey Symons

Bonatea porrecta

Martin von Fintel

Bonatea cassidea

Tony Abbott

Bonatea saundersioides

Tom de Waal

Bonatea speciosa

C J Ward

Bonatea speciosa

Martin von Fintel

Bonatea saundersiae

Rosemary Williams

117

Satyrium (*Satyros* - refers to the 2 horned satyr, half man half goat - the two spurs are said to resemble a satyr's horns) - Terrestrial herbs with underground tubers; ovary not twisted; lip forms a hood, 2 conspicuous spurs or 2 pouches; used in traditional medicine, mixed with other medicines, to help with illnesses that are difficult to cure. Mostly Afr, a few in Mascarene Is, India and S China, ± 140 species, 33 in SA.

Satyrium cristatum   lekholela-la-bana-ba-seng, 'ma-metsana (SS) (*cristatum* - tassel-like tips, crested)

Slender, 140 to 550 mm. In moist or marshy grassland, up to 2000 m, E Cape to N Prov. **Leaves:** Basal, 2-3, overlapping, erect to spreading, 20-160 x 50 mm; stem leaves few, sheathing. **Flowers:** ± 85, in compact inflorescence, ± 300 mm, bracts pointed, turned downwards; flowers **greenish to creamy white, streaked red**, spurs ± 12 mm (Oct-May). **General:** Var. *cristatum,* sepals and petals **fused for half their length** with the lip, forming a shallow sac beneath the column, spurs 3-7 mm. Var. *longilabiatum,* less common, sepals and petals **fused for up to a third of their length** with the lip, not forming a shallow sac beneath the column, spurs ± 12 mm.

Satyrium hallackii (named after Russell Hallack, 1824-1903, businessman and amateur botanist)

Robust, 0,19-1 m, solitary or in large colonies. In marshy ground, in water, 600-2000 m, E Cape to Trop Afr. **Leaves:** 4-6, 70-200 mm, sheathing stem, tips pointed. **Flowers:** ± 70, densely or well spaced, inflorescence ± 180 mm; flowers **white, pink to deep pink**, ± 15 mm wide, spurs ± 30 mm (Nov-Mar), faintly scented. **General:** Subsp. *ocellatum* [= *S. ocellatum*], E Cape to Trop Afr. Subsp. *hallackii,* SW and SE Cape endemic. (See p. 362)

Satyrium longicauda Blushing Bride Satyrium, Long-tailed Trewwa; Langstert-trewwa (A); lekoesha (SS) (*longicauda* - long tailed)

Slender, 170-800 mm, in small groups or large colonies. In grassland, rocky areas, marshes, 600-3000 m, (coastal in Transkei), S Cape to Trop Afr. **Leaves:** Basal, 1-2, ± 200 mm, prostrate or partly erect, **on separate shoot from flowering stem or absent**; stem leaves sheathing;. **Flowers:** ± 60, inflorescence ± 200 mm, bracts deflexed, flowers ± 20 mm, white, pink, veins and tips often darker pink, **flap above lip entrance hairy**, spurs slender, ± 46 mm (Sep-Apr), sweetly scented. **General:** Var. *longicauda,* up to 2100 m; flowers large. Var. *jacottetianum,* up to 3000 m; flowers smaller, pink to red, spurs ± 26 mm. Used as protective and love charms. **Similar species: *S. longicauda* x *S. neglectum* subsp. *woodii*** [= *S. rhodantha*] **ilabatheka elibomvu (Z)** Very localised, deep pink to red. A hybrid or possibly a valid species. (For photograph see p. 362)

Satyrium sphaerocarpum   uklamkleshe, unoklamu, unokleshe (Z) (*sphaerocarpum* - round fruit)

Robust, up to 500 mm. In moist grassland, coast to 2000 m, E Cape to Moz. **Leaves:** 1-2, prostrate to partly erect, 30-170 mm, stem leaves sheathing. **Flowers:** Large, ± 27, in inflorescence ± 180 mm; flowers **white to cream, speckled, streaked with dark reddish brown to purple**, spurs ± 15 mm, **basal third of sepals fused with petals and lip** (Oct-Apr), faintly scented.

Satyrium trinerve [= *S. atherstonei*] (*trinerve* - 3 veined from base of leaf)

Slender, up to 870 mm. In marshy ground, coast to 2000 m, E Cape to Trop Afr. **Leaves:** 2-5, narrow, 60-250 mm, slightly pleated with veins protruding beneath; stem leaves sheathing. **Flowers:** In crowded inflorescence, **bracts distinctive, horizontally spreading**, green with broad white margins, 70-180 mm; flowers white and yellow, sepals 4-5 mm, spurs 1-5 mm (Oct-Feb).

Schizochilus (*schizein* - splinter or split; *cheilos* - a lip) - Terrestrial herb with few, narrow leaves near base of stem; inflorescence dense, usually drooping over at tip. Afr genus, ± 20 species, 8 in SA.

Schizochilus flexuosus (*flexuosus* - winding, bending)

Slender, up to 250 mm. In montane grassland or on damp sheet rock, damp cliffs, 1500-2500 m, **Drakensberg foothills. Leaves:** 6-20, slender, basal. **Flowers:** 5-30, in compact inflorescence; **flowers white with yellow lip**, sepals 5-9 mm (Jan-Feb), scented. **General:** Small beetle found in nectary lobe. **Similar species:** *S. angustifolius* Only found above 2200 m; spur shorter than 2 mm.

Lal Greene

Satyrium cristatum

Martin von Fintel

Satyrium cristatum

Lal Greene

Satyrium hallackii

Trevor Coleman

Satyrium longicauda

Martin von Fintel

Satyrium longicauda

Nolly Zaloumis

Satyrium sphaerocarpum

Martin von Fintel

Satyrium trinerve

Lal Greene

Satyrium trinerve

Lal Greene

Schizochilus flexuosus

119

Brownleea (named after Rev John Brownlee, early Scottish missionary who collected the type species of the genus, *B coerulea*, in E Cape) - Terrestrial (rarely epiphytic or lithophytic) herbs, with few leaves; median/odd sepal joins with two lateral petals to form trumpet-shaped hood which tapers gradually into curved spur, lip very small. Afr, ± 15 species, 5 in SA.

Brownleea parviflora (*parviflora* - small flowers)

Up to 600 mm. In grassland, often in rocky places, near coast to 2500 m, E Cape to Kenya and Cameroon. **Leaves:** (2)3(5), narrow. **Flowers:** ± 60, in **dense, cylindrical inflorescence**; flowers white, **petals oblong to square**, dorsal sepal less than 6 mm (Feb-Apr).

Disa (possibly from *dis* - double, refering to two large wings in the style) - Underground tubers; several leaves; median sepal hooded, prolonged into a spur or pouch, direction in which spur points is useful in identification in the field. Afr and Madag, ± 130 species, ± 94 in SA.

Disa cephalotes (*cephalotes* - a head)

Erect, up to 500 mm. **Leaves:** Narrow, lower leaves ± 200 mm. **Flowers:** In terminal cluster; flowers white to pink with **darker spots on tips of sepals**, sepals 5-8 mm, spur slender, horizontal, 3-6 mm, lip blunt (Jan-Mar). **General:** Subsp. *cephalotes*, slender, 200-500 mm, in dry to damp grassland, 1500-2500 m; leaves hard, narrow; flowers white. Subsp. *frigida*, robust, less than 250 mm; on summit of Drakensberg, 3000 m; leaves ± soft; flowers deep pink or rose.

Disa crassicornis [= *D. jacottetiae*] (see p. 366)

Disa montana (*montana* - belonging to mountains)

Slender, up to 600 mm. On dry, rocky, grassy slopes, 1000-2400 m. **Leaves:** Long, narrow, erect, largest near base of stem. **Flowers:** In loose inflorescence; flowers pale, spotted maroon, sepals 10-18 mm, hood with slender spur, horizontal, 8-15 mm, pointed (Nov-Dec).

Disa oreophila (*oreophila* - mountain loving)

Up to 350(800) mm, erect or hanging. On damp grassy slopes, rock ledges and cliffs, 1200-2700 m. **Leaves: Narrow**, ± 200 x 3 mm, leafy. **Flowers:** White flushed pink, with reddish purple spots, **spur 5-10(25) mm, almost horizontal** (Nov-Feb). **General:** Subsp. *oreophila*, 1200-2100 m, curved or hanging; flowers small, spur 5-10 mm. Subsp. *erecta*, 2100-2700 m, erect; flowers larger, spur 10-25 mm.

Disa saxicola (*saxum* - a stone; *colo* - inhabit)

Usually trailing, up to 400 mm. In moss on rock ledges, in rock crevices, often in half shade, KZN to Tanz. **Leaves:** On stem, long, ± 17 mm wide. **Flowers:** In loose inflorescence; flowers white with purple markings on hood, **sepals 4-8 mm**, hood with round, gently curved spur, 4-10 mm (Nov-Feb).

Disa thodei (named after Hans Justus Thode, 1859-1932, naturalist and itinerant tutor, who collected widely all over SA, particularly in KZN Drakensberg)

Slender, up to 300 mm. Along streams, in damp alpine grassland, 1800-3000 m. **Flowers:** 3-8, in loose inflorescence; flowers white to mauve, mottled pink, sepals short, 10-17 mm, **spur slender, horizontal** or gradually curving down, 20-40 mm (Dec-Jan), strongly scented. **Similar species:** *D. crassicornis* (see p. 366).

Disa tripetaloides (*tripetaloides* - 3 petalled)

Slender, up to 600 mm. Widespread, on streambanks and damp mountain slopes, coast to 1000 m, SW Cape to KZN. **Leaves: Clustered at base**, long, narrow, becoming smaller and sheathing stem. **Flowers:** ± 20, widely spaced, in inflorescence, stem reddish; flowers ± 30 mm diam, white tinged pink, more or less dotted with pinkish red dots, **spur short, ± 3 mm, greenish** (May-Oct). **General:** Cultivated in the UK.

Martin von Fintel

Brownleea parviflora

Cameron McMaster

Disa crassicornis

Maureen Boardman

Disa oreophila

Martin von Fintel

Disa cephalotes

Maureen Boardman

Disa montana

Ray Boardman

Disa thodei

Martin von Fintel

Disa saxicola

Martin von Fintel

Disa saxicola

Tessa Hedge

Disa tripetaloides

121

Disa tysonii (named after William Tyson, 1851-1932, teacher and collector)
Robust, up to 600 mm. In damp, mountain grassland, 1800-3000 m. **Leaves:** Overlapping, pointed. **Flowers:** In dense, cylindrical inflorescence; flowers creamy yellow with green veins, lip yellow, sepals 6-9 mm, hood with cylindrical to ± club-shaped spur, 4-6 mm, horizontal (Dec-Jan).

Disperis (*dis* - double; *pera* - pouch, refers to spurs on side sepals) - **'Granny Bonnet' Orchids** Slender perennial herbs; few-leaved; with undergound tubers; petals joined to median sepal to form helmet-shaped hood; side sepals with noticeable spur or pouch. Afr, India, New Guinea and Mascarene Is, ± 75 species, ± 26 in SA.

Disperis cardiophora (*cardiophora* - bearing hearts)
Slender, up to 250 mm. Common but easily overlooked, in moist grassland, 400-2700 m. **Leaf:** Solitary, 10-30 mm, clasping base of stem. **Flowers: Small, all facing same direction, white and green with purple at tips, petals only slightly extending from hood, outer surface exposed,** sepals ± 7 mm, spreading, **bracts heart-shaped** (Dec-Mar), sweetly pungent scent. (See p. 520) **Similar species:** *D. renibractea* (see p. 370, 520).

Disperis disaeformis (*disaeformis* - like a *Disa*)
Slender, 70-180 mm. In grass and scrub in dryish areas, 100-500 m, S Cape to KZN. **Leaves:** 2, clasping, ± 30 mm, dark green with silvery veins. **Flowers:** 1-4, whitish, tinged purple, **hood elongated, tipped backwards,** 3-5 mm, side sepals ± 6 mm, bracts leaflike (Jul-Nov).

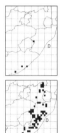

Disperis fanniniae **Granny Bonnet; Moederkappie (A)** (named after Marianne (Fannin) Roberts, 1845-1938, housewife and artist who pressed and painted plants collected by her brother G F Fannin. Mother of noted ornithologist and zoologist Austin Roberts)
Slender to stout, 150-450 mm. In damp shade on forest floor, on mossy rocks, in pine plantations, 800-2000 m. **Leaves:** 3-4, clasping, 20-80 x 10-30 mm, dark green above, purple beneath, tapering. **Flowers:** 1-8, large, white flushed pink or green, petals dotted with green or purple, **hood very deep,** broad, rounded, ± 20 mm, **side sepals ± 14 mm,** finely pointed, spreading downwards, bracts leaflike (Dec-Apr).

Disperis lindleyana (named after John Lindley)
150-400 mm. In shade of forest and pine plantation, 600-1800 m. **Leaf: Solitary, half way up stem, shiny,** 30-60 x 20-40 mm with broad basal lobes. **Flowers:** 1-5, white or cream, sometimes pinkish, often spotted deep pink, lateral sepals ± 9 mm, spreading, from within leaflike bracts (Nov-Feb).

Disperis wealii (named after James Weale, born 1838, graduated in law, amateur naturalist, interested in pollination by insects, particularly in orchids, corresponding with Charles Darwin on this subject)
Slender, 50-250 mm. Common in moist grassland and scrub, along streams, 1200 -2500 m. **Leaves:** 2-4, clasping, 12-20 mm. **Flowers:** 1-6, size variable, **white with green markings,** hood rounded, 10-12 mm diam, side sepals 9-12 mm, spreading, with long pointed tips (Jan-Apr). **Similar species:** *D. cooperi* (see p. 368).

Pterygodium (*pterygoeides* - winglike, refers to side petals) - Terrestrial herbs; flowers with median sepal and petal joined to form a very shallow hood, lip with short or tall appendage, no spur. Mainly in SW Cape, ± 17 species.

Pterygodium cooperi (named after Thomas Cooper, 1815-1913, plant collector and grower who came to SA in 1859)
Slender, up to 290 mm. On forest margins, in grassland, 1500-2800 m. **Leaves:** 2-4, basal leaf large, ± 130 mm. **Flowers:** Crowded, pale green to purplish green, hood ± to 8 mm, white, flushed pink with age, dark speckling within, lip white, ± 5 mm, appendage white, erect, ± 4 mm (Jan-Mar), sharply scented.

Disa tysonii — Trevor Coleman

Disperis cardiophora — Martin von Fintel

Disperis fanniniae — Tessa Hedge

Disperis lindleyana — Martin von Fintel

Disperis lindleyana — Martin von Fintel

Disperis disaeformis — Dez Weeks

Disperis wealii — Auriol Batten

Pterygodium cooperi — Lal Greene

Pterygodium cooperi — Darrel Plowes

123

Pterygodium hastatum (hasta - spear-shaped)

Slender, up to 350 mm. In damp grassland, among rocks, occasional on cliffs or in scrub, 1200-2400 m. **Leaves:** 2, basal leaf larger, ± 210 mm. **Flowers:** Crowded, pale green to whitish yellow, hood 9-13 mm, sometimes spotted purple inside, margins of petals **tightly wavy**, lip 4-5mm, appendage erect, 6-8 mm, **tip 3 toothed** (Jan-Apr), sometimes heavily scented.

Pterygodium leucanthum (leucanthum - white flowers)

Slender, up to 400 mm. In montane grassland, 1300-2400 m. **Leaves:** ± 170 mm. **Flowers:** In fairly loose inflorescence; flowers creamy green, hood ± 8 mm, petals ± 7 mm, lip short, ± 1,5 mm, with two rounded lobes, appendage ± 6 mm (Jan-Mar).

Vanilla (*vanilla* - a sheath or *vainilla* - small pod) - Climbers with shiny leaf at each node along glossy green stems or leaves reduced to scales; flower lip encircles the column. *V. planifolia*, from Mexico, is the main commercial source of vanilla pods and essence, cultivated in Madag, Comoro Is and now in KZN. Trop, subtrop, ± 100 species, 1 in SA.

Vanilla roscheri

Strong liana, scrambling over thicket, coastal forest. Stems succulent, round, with two shallow channels on either side, roots arise at the nodes, either clasping vegetation or absorbing nutrients where they touch the soil. **Leaves:** Imperfectly developed, scalelike, papery brown, ± 30 mm. **Flowers:** In terminal or axillary inflorescences, stems ± 200 mm, flowers arranged spirally, creamy white.

Didymoplexis (*didymus* - double or twin; *plexus* - plaited) - Leafless herbs with fleshy, horizontal tubers; stems erect with few sheaths; flowers clustered at top of stems, stalks elongate as erect capsule matures. 1 species in SA.

Didymoplexis verrucosa (verrucosa - warty, refers to sepals and lip)

Small, saprophytic herb (living off dead organic matter), up to 75 mm. In leaf litter on dune forest floor. Tubers colourless. **Leaves:** None. **Flowers:** White, tinged pinkish brown, sepals warty outside, united with petals at base, lip uppermost, 3 lobed at tip with a band of yellow warty growths, open for only a couple of hours (August), vanilla scented. **Fruit: Stalk lengthens rapidly after pollination,** 100-200 mm at maturity. **General:** Discovered in 1975 by visiting botanist Prof C van Steenis with Ian Garland at his farm 'Twinstreams', Mtunzini, Zululand.

Platylepis (*platys* - broad; *lepis* - scale) - Terrestrial herbs. Afr, Mascarene Is, Madag, ± 10 species, 1 in SA.

Platylepis glandulosa (glandulosa - having glands)

Up to 300 mm, stem creeping at base, becoming erect, leafy. Common in seepage zones in swamp forest, in dense shade, coastal, KZN to Trop Afr. **Leaves:** 40-100 x 20-40 mm, sheathing at base, veins conspicuous, stalks 20-60 mm. **Flowers:** In short, erect, crowded inflorescences; **flowers conspicuously glandular (hairy),** greenish white to pinkish brown, sepals ± 9 x 2 mm (Sep-Mar). **General:** Easily mistaken for a *Commelina* or *Aneilema* species, with which it grows. **Similar species:** *Cheirostylis gymnochiloides* (see p. 370).

Corymborkis (*korymbos* - a cluster) - Terrestrial herbs; fibrous rootstock; stems reedlike, leaves folded like a fan; flowers with very narrow segments, lip wider than other parts towards tip. Trop, ± 17 species, 1 in SA.

Corymborkis corymbis [= Corymbis corymbosa]

Up to 1 m. In deep shade of dense forest in widely scattered localities, E Cape to KZN, widespread in Trop Afr, Madag, Reunion Is. **Leaves:** 110-340 x 30-100 mm, margins wavy. **Flowers:** ± 16, short inflorescences, mostly terminal, erect or drooping; flowers cream to greenish white, fading orange, segments 45-90 mm, sepals and petals very narrow, lip narrow, widening 5-13 mm below tip (Nov-Feb).

Polystachya (*poly* - many; *stachys* - ear of corn) - Usually epiphytic (for description see p. 242).

Polystachya ottoniana   amabelejongosi, iphamba lehlathi (Z) (named after Friedrich Otton, Garden Director of Schoneberg, Germany, in the 1800s)

Up to 80 mm. On rocks, tree trunks, in light shade of cool, moist forest, near coast to 1800 m. **Pseudobulbs vertically flattened, tapering to one end,** ± 25 x 15 mm, **forming long strings. Leaves:** 2-4, ± 80 x 10 mm, blunt, notched. **Flowers: 1-6,** in slender, erect inflorescences, shorter than leaves; flowers white to pinkish or yellow, 10-14 mm wide, **lip 3 lobed, curled, with yellow mid stripe,** pink streak in triangular side sepals (Aug-Dec), delicately scented. **General:** Used in traditional medicine to treat diarrhoea and soothe teething babies. Seeds used as snuff.

Pterygodium hastatum

Martin von Fintel

Pterygodium leucanthum

Darrel Plowes

Platylepis glandulosa

CJ Ward

Vanilla roscheri

CJ Ward

Vanilla roscheri

CJ Ward

Didymoplexis verrucosa

CJ Ward

Corymborkis corymbis

Geoff Nichols

Polystachya ottoniana

Martin von Fintel

125

Eulophia (*eu* - well; *lophos* - crest, refers to the crested lip) - Terrestrial herbs; rhizomes thickened into fibrous tubers, some with pseudobulbs; leaf-bearing shoot separate from flowering stem, sepals more or less equal, lip ridged on upper surface. Old World trop, subtrop, most common in Afr, over 200 species, ± 42 species in SA.

Eulophia aculeata lekholela, 'mametsana (SS) (*aculeata* - thorns, prickly, pointed)

Slender to stout, 60-650 mm. In grassland, 1500-2600 m, SW Cape to Mpum. **Leaves:** Stiff, ± 600 x 17 mm, partly to fully grown at flowering. **Flowers:** 3-30, in **dense, crowded inflorescence**; petals and sepals ± 18 mm, same colour, ivory to greenish white, pink or purple, **spur absent** (Sep-Apr), faintly scented. **General:** Subsp. *aculeata*, flowers small, median sepal 5-9 mm, sepals, petals and lip ivory to white or greenish white (Nov-Jan). Subsp. *huttonii*, E Cape to Mpum; flowers with median sepal 9-18 mm, sepals, petals, lip greenish white to pink to dark reddish purple, lip crests usually yellowish green to white (Sep-Apr). (See p. 370)

Eulophia clavicornis lekholela, maholohanya, 'mametsana (SS); elihlaza, imfeya-masele (Z) (*clava* - club; *cornis* - horn)

Slender, 0,10-1 m. Widespread in grassland, coast to 1700 m, S Cape to N Prov. **Leaves:** 50-730 mm, partly to fully developed at flowering. **Flowers:** Widely spaced, sepals green to purplish brown, ± 19 mm, petals and lip white to purple or yellow, **spur cylindrical, 14-89 mm, crests tall to end of lip** (Jul-Feb). **General:** Flower colour, size and leaf development very variable. Grazed by stock. Infusion from tubers used in traditional medicine as protection from evil and to treat infertility. Subsp. *clavicornis*, flowers white, pale pink to pale blue, lip as long as median sepal, 9-18 mm (Aug-Sep). Subsp. *inaequalis*, flower lip often shorter than median sepal (Sep-Oct). Subsp. *nutans*, leaves fully developed at flowering, 100-730 mm; flowers white to pale or deep purple or yellow (Dec-Feb). (See p. 372)

Eulophia ovalis lekholela, lekoesha, 'mametsana (SS); ihamba lesigodi, phamba (Z) (see p. 244)

Eulophia parvilabris (*parvus* - small; *labrum* - lip)

Stout, up to 850 mm. In grassland, marshy areas, on moist steep slopes, scattered distribution from E Cape to Mpum. **Leaves:** Fully developed at flowering, ± 600 x 55 mm, pleated, sheathing at base, tapering to long point. **Flowers:** In loosely spreading inflorescence; flowers large, held 'upside down' with lip and spur uppermost, sepals ± 35 mm, green, petals cream, **lip with purple blotch**, spur ± 5 mm (Dec-Feb). **Similar species:** *E. macowanii* Flowers held 'upside down'; lip white.

Oeceoclades (*oikos* - house; *cladus* - branch, shoot) - Terrestrial herbs; aerial pseudobulbs, each with a single, folded, leathery leaf; inflorescence with 1-2 branches, lip 4 lobed, 2 central lobes often curved at tip. 3 species in SA.

Oeceoclades lonchophylla (*lonchophylla* - spearlike leaves)

Up to 300 mm. In dark, shady forests, KZN coast to Moz, Comores Is. Pseudobulbs oval, closely packed. **Leaves:** ± 100 x 40 mm, **dark green, erect**, blade thin, margins wavy, **stalks ± 150 mm**. **Flowers:** ± 50, in simple or branched inflorescence; flowers pale green to cream with purple markings, lip sidelobes striped purple, spur narrow (Nov-Apr). **General:** Easily grown in sandy leaf litter. (See p. 246)

Angraecum (from the Malay *angurek* for this type of orchid) - Epiphyte; without pseudobulbs; lip concave, without obvious side lobes, extending into spur at base. Widespread in Afr and Madag, ± 200 species, 6 in SA.

Angraecum conchiferum Small Spider Angraecum (*conchiferum* - shellbearing, refers to lip)

Slender, up to 300 mm, in large, pendulous, tangled clumps. In cool, moist, inland forest, S Cape to E areas of Afr. **Roots warty.** Stems ± 3mm diam, covered with minute blackish protruberances. **Leaves:** 30-60 x 5-7 mm, tips unequally bilobed. **Flowers:** In 1-2 inflorescences, ± 30 mm, with 1-2 flowers each; flowers cream to pale yellowish green, ± 60 mm wide, **lip white, round**, ± 18 mm wide, spur ± 50 mm (Sep-Jan), scented at night. **General:** Easily cultivated.

Angraecum cultriforme (*cultriforme* - in shape of knife blade)

Small, up to 150 mm, in tangled mass of stems. In deep shade, **at low altitudes**, KZN, E areas of Afr. Stems held together with twisted roots. **Leaves:** ± 18, in 2 rows, ± 60 x 7 mm, strap or sickle-shaped, with raised dark spots over the surface, tips with 2 sharply pointed, unequal lobes. **Flowers:** In ± 4 inflorescences, 30-40 mm; flowers **pale beige to salmon pink**, ± 16 mm wide, **lip boat-shaped, sharply pointed**, spur ± 25 mm, tip swollen (Oct-Apr). **General:** Easily cultivated.

Martin von Fintel

Durrel Plowes

Eulophia ovalis

Eulophia aculeata

Lal Greene

Eulophia aculeata

Hilde & Oskar Kurze

Eulophia parvilabris

Geoff Nichols

Lal Greene

Hilde & Oskar Kurze

Eulophia clavicornis   *Eulophia parvilabris*   *Angraecum conchiferum*

C J Ward

C J Ward

Geoff Nichols

Oeceoclades lonchophylla   *Oeceoclades lonchophylla*   *Angraecum cultriforme*

127

Angraecum pusillum *(pusillus - very small)*
Miniature plants, up to 100 mm. Epiphyte in deep shade of forest and scrub, widespread from S Cape to Mpum. Stems ± 20 mm, with brown sheaths. **Leaves:** 5-7, shiny, grasslike, ± 100 x 6 mm. **Flowers:** In several inflorescences, from stem below leaves; ± 14 flowers, small, ± 4 mm diam, white (Sep-Mar). **General:** Difficult to cultivate inland.

Tridactyle *(tri* - three; *dactyl* - finger) - Epiphyte; without pseudobulbs. Flowers differ from *Angraecum* in the lip which is flat, thin, divided into 3 lobes, side lobes toothed or fringed at tip, spur long, slender. Afr, ± 36 species, 4 in SA.

Tridactyle bicaudata [= *Angraecum bicaudatum*] **iphamba (Z)** *(bicaudata* - two tailed, refers to lip)
Up to 250 mm, in large clumps. Dry forest, on trees and rocky outcrops, S Cape to Trop Afr. Roots grey, rough, stems, erect to pendulous. **Leaves:** 60-120 x 10-15 mm. **Flowers: 12-16, in 2 rows,** ± 6 stems; flowers, 12-16 mm diam, lip 3 lobed, **side lobes fringed,** spur 10-18 mm (Oct-Apr), vanilla scented. **General:** Used as a protective charm. Subsp. *rupestris* Stelzen Orchid, on rocks, in full sun; **erect;** leaves stiff, fleshy, curved, 35-60 mm. Subsp. *bicaudata,* in shade; **hanging from branches,** leaves thin, 60-160 mm. (See p. 246)
Similar species: *T. gentilii* N KZN to Trop Afr; flowers larger, pale green or yellowish, side lobes of lip longer than midlobe, fringed at tips, spur 40-80 mm.

Tridactyle tricuspis [= *Angraecum tricuspe*] *(tricuspis* - with three sharp points)
In tangled clumps, 100-200 mm. On forest trees in cooler forest, up to 1800 m, E Cape to Trop Afr. Stems ± 8 mm diam. **Leaves:** ± 160 x 12 mm, thin, narrow, deeply folded at base, flattened towards unequal, bilobed tips. **Flowers: 15-30 per stem,** 2-4 arching inflorescences, ± 80 mm; flowers whitish, ± 13 mm diam, sepals, petals pointed, lip 3 lobed, **lobes pointed,** spur ± 15 mm (Apr-May).

Diaphananthe *(dia, phainein* - to show through; *anthos* - flower) - Epiphyte with woody stems; leaves very unequally bilobed at tips; flowers semi-transparent (diaphanous), sepals and petals similar, spreading, lip broader than long, spur variable. Trop Afr, ± 42 species, 4 in SA.

Diaphananthe caffra [= *Mystacidium caffrum*] *(caffra* - from Kaffraria, Transkei)
Dwarf, almost stemless. In cool inland forests, up to 1800 m. Roots 2-3 mm diam, greyish green with elongated white dots. **Leaves:** 2-3, ± 60 x 6-8 mm. **Flowers:** Inflorescences ± 30 mm; flowers white, ± 12 mm diam, petals, sepals and lip **rounded,** short, with **bright green anther cap,** spur ± 17 mm, tip swollen (Sep-Jan).

Diaphananthe millarii [= *Mystacidium millari*] **iphamba (Z)** (named after Harold Millar who discovered the species in the early 1900s)
Up to 100 mm. Epiphyte, beneath branches of small trees and shrubs. Rare. Roots 4-5 mm diam, grey-green, with elongated white dots. Stems ± 25 mm. **Leaves:** 3-10, 70-120 x 15-17 mm, leathery, **stiff, veins conspicuous, velvety. Flowers:** 7-13, in 1-2 hanging inflorescences, ± 27 mm; flowers ±12 mm wide, **sepals rounded, anther caps green, spur with broad mouth,** slender tip (Dec-Jan). **General:** Used as a protective charm. Easily cultivated. Found on plants of the family Rubiaceae.

Bolusiella (named after Harry Bolus, 1834-1911) - Very small epiphytes. One species in SA.

Bolusiella maudiae [= *Angraecum maudiae*]
Small, succulent epiphyte, in upper branches of trees. In warmer forests, KZN endemic. Rare. Roots thin, short. Stems very short. **Leaves:** 3-10, fleshy, succulent, overlapping at base to form fan-shape, 20-30 x 5-8 mm, dark green. **Flowers:** 20-30 mm diam, partly hidden by bracts, lip 3 lobed at base with short rounded spur (Feb).

Microcoelia *(micro* - tiny; *coelos* - hollow) - Leafless epiphytes.with the smallest flowers of the orchid family in SA. Afr, Madag, ± 30 species, 2 in SA.

Microcoelia exilis Pin-head Orchid; iphamba (Z) *(exilis* - thin, weak)
Leafless, forming a mass, up to 400 mm diam, **of fine, branching, grey roots, tipped orange,** ± 2 mm diam. Common in hot, dry forest, thicket at lower altitudes, KZN to Kenya, Madag and Comores Is. Stems 20-100 x 3 mm. **Leaves: None. Flowers:** In numerous slender inflorescences, 60-120 mm; 20-80 tiny white flowers, less than 2 mm diam (more or less throughout the year). **General:** Used as a love charm. Easily cultivated. **Similar species:** *Mystacidium gracile* (see p. 130).

128

Angraecum pusillum

Tony Abbott

Tridactyle bicaudata

Trevor Coleman

Diaphananthe millarii

Tessa Hedge

Tridactyle gentilii

Geoff Nichols

Tridactyle tricuspis

Lal Greene

Diaphananthe millarii

Tessa Hedge

Diaphananthe caffra

Martin von Fintel

Tridactyle tricuspis

Lal Greene

Bolusiella maudiae

Hilde & Oskar Kurze

Microcoelia exilis

CJ Ward

129

Aerangis (*aer* - air; *angio* - vessel, refers to bloodvessel-like long spur) - Epiphyte; column protruding, with conspicuous rostellum protruding below the anther cap, spur very long. Afr, Mascarene Is, ± 70 species, 3 in SA.

Aerangis mystacidii *(mystax* - moustache, refers to shape of side sepals)*

Epiphyte, up to 80 mm. Low down in forest, in deep shade, often near streams, coast to 600 m, E Cape to Tanz. Roots silvery green, new tips orange-green. Stem 40 mm. **Leaves:** In a fan, 80-130 x 20-40 mm, dark green, **flat,** leathery, oblong or wider at bilobed tip. **Flowers:** In 2-6 inflorescences, ± 280 mm; 4-14(24) flowers, ± 20 x 25 mm, white tinged pink, **spur 60-80 mm** (Feb-Jun), lovely scent at night. **General:** Used in traditional medicine, probably for love or protective charms.

Rangaeris (imperfect anagram of *Aerangis*, a related genus) - Epiphyte or lithophyte with stiff, deeply keeled leaves; flowers white turning orange with age, lip broad, triangular, spur long. 6 species in Afr, 1 in SA.

Rangaeris muscicola *(muscicola* - growing on or near mosses)*

Epiphyte, up to 130 mm, in clusters. On rock faces, boulders, **often amongst mosses,** E Cape to Trop Afr. Roots 4-6 mm diam, grey. Stem woody, ± 25 x 10 mm. **Leaves:** 70-120 x 10-13 mm, erect, **deeply keeled,** curving, tips unequally bilobed. **Flowers:** Inflorescences, 70-100 mm; 5-15 flowers, ± 25 mm diam, white, aging cream to orange, **lip triangular,** tip pointed, spur 50-90 mm (Dec-Mar), sweetly scented at night. **General:** Easily cultivated, needs high humidity when flowering.

Cyrtorchis (*cyrtorchis* - curved orchid, all segments are strongly curved) - Robust epiphyte; stems woody; floral bracts turn black; sepals, petals and lip strongly recurved at tips, spur broader near mouth. Afr, ± 15 species, 2 in SA.

Cyrtorchis arcuata   imfeyenkawu, iphamba, umbambela (Z) *(arcuata* - bent like a bow)*

Robust epiphyte, up to 600 mm, in large clusters. On trees, rocks, in dry scrub, moist forests, coast to 1000 m, throughout Afr. Roots whitish, tips greenish orange. Stems ± 400 x 10 mm. **Leaves:** Strap-shaped, 110-160 x **25-30** mm, wide, stiff, leathery. **Flowers:** In 2-6 hanging inflorescences, 80-100 mm; flowers large, ± 50 mm diam, cream, aging orange, **spur 40-60 mm** (Sep-May), sweetly scented at night. **General:** Used in traditional medicine as a love potion. Easily cultivated.

Cyrtorchis praetermissa *(praetermissa* - overlooked, neglected)*

Fairly robust epiphyte, erect, up to 300 mm, in large clusters. In light to deep shade, in forests, coast to 600 m, KZN to Trop Afr. Roots ± 4 mm diam, grey with reddish brown tips. Stems 80-140 x 7-9 mm. **Leaves: Narrow,** ± 100 x **10 mm,** dark green. **Flowers:** In 1-2 inflorescences, ± 80 mm; 5-15 smaller flowers, 10-20 mm diam, white aging deep orange, **all parts narrow,** strongly reflexed, **spur 20-30 mm** (Nov-Feb), scented at night. **General:** Easily cultivated. Subsp. *zuluensis,* KZN to S Moz; root tips brown, leaves flat, spur curved. Subsp. *praetermissa,* Mpum to Trop Afr; root tips green; leaves deeply keeled; spur straight.

Mystacidium (*mystax* - moustache; *idium* - diminutive, refers to rostellum lobes) - Small epiphytes; sepals and petals curved back, pointed at tip, spur mouth wide, tapering to long, narrow point. S and E Afr, ± 12 species, 7 in SA.

Mystacidium capense   iphamba (Z) *(capense* - of the Cape)*

Dwarf, erect epiphyte, up to 80 mm, in masses. On trees (on rocks), in **hot dry** thornveld, dry river valleys. Roots, 4-6 mm diam, pale grey with elongated white dots. **Leaves:** Stiff, flat, **long, 30-130** x 10-15 mm, unequally bilobed. **Flowers:** In 2-4 hanging inflorescences, 60-100 mm; 6-14 white flowers, ± 23 mm diam, widely spaced, **spur 40-60 mm,** pale green (Sep-Jan), strongly scented at night. **General:** Used as a protective and love charm. **Summer flowering.**

Mystacidium gracile *(gracilis* - slender , refers to the slender roots and flowers)*

Epiphyte with mass of **thin, unbranched, bluish green roots**. On trees and shrubs, in cool inland forests, up to 1900 m, E Cape to Zim. **Leaves: Usually leafless,** occasionally 1-2 leaves ± 20 x 3 mm. **Flowers:** In 1-3 inflorescences, 40-50 mm; 4-12 delicate flowers, 9-14 mm wide, pale yellowish green, spur straight, white, 20-25 mm (Aug-Nov). **Similar species:** *Microcoelia exilis* (see p. 128).

Mystacidium venosum *(venosum* - having veins)*

Small, stemless epiphyte, in large numbers. In trees, in hot, humid coastal areas and cool inland forests. **Mass of roots 4-5 mm diam, grey-green** with white streaks, tips green. **Leaves:** 30-50 x 8-11 mm, often absent or stunted, veins distinctive. **Flowers:** In 1-2 hanging inflorescences, 30-50 mm; 4-7 white flowers, 15-20 mm diam, spur 30-50 mm **(Apr-Jul),** scented at night. **General: Winter flowering.**

Aerangis mystacidii

Rangaeris muscicola

Cyrtorchis arcuata

Rangaeris muscicola   *Cyrtorchis praetermissa*

Mystacidium capense

Mystacidium gracile   *Mystacidium gracile*   *Mystacidium venosum*

DICOTYLEDONS - Two seed leaves, net veins; flower parts in fours, fives or multiples of these.

PIPERACEAE - **Pepper Family** Herbs or shrubs. Leaves slightly succulent. Inflorescence a dense spike, flowers tiny, without petals. Cosmop in warm areas, ± 3000 species, 8 genera, 2 in SA. *Piper (pippali* or *pippul* - Sanskrit or Benghales for pepper) - Erect or scrambling shrubs; branches jointed at the nodes. Black, white and betel pepper are obtained from *P. nigrum*, and *P. betle*. Warmer regions of N and S Hemisp, ± 2000 species, 1 in SA.

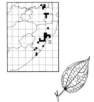

Piper capense   Wild Pepper; Bospeper, Stertpeper, Sterkpeper (A); ihlolane, uluphokwane (Z)

Soft straggling shrub, up to 4 m. In moist shade, in forests, SE Cape to Zim, Moz. Bark light brown, corky. **Leaves:** Alternate, 70-150 x 50-110 mm, thin, quilted, base shallowly lobed, **5-7 conspicuous veins**, stalks 20-40 mm, stipules leaflike, falling early. **Flowers:** In dense spikes, 20-80 x 5 mm, stems ± 20 mm; flowers small, white (Aug-Apr). **Fruit:** Berry 2 mm diam, in dense clusters, green turning black. **General:** Eaten by monkeys. Used in the past to flavour soups and stews. Used in traditional medicine. Garden or container plant for shady places.

PROTEACEAE - **Protea Family** Woody. Leaves leathery. Flowers in dense inflorescences, ± surrounded by showy bracts, sepals 4, petal-like, petals absent or reduced to scales, ovary with long style. Mostly Austr and SA, ± 75 genera, ± 1600 species, ± 14 genera in SA. *Protea* (named after the Greek god Proteus) - **Sugarbush** Shrubs or small trees; flowers massed in heads surrounded by coloured bracts. Afr, ± 115 species, ± 83 in SA, mostly in SW Cape.

Protea dracomontana   Drakensberg Dwarf Sugarbush/Protea; Drakensbergse Dwergsuikerbos (A)   (*dracomontana* - from the Drakensberg) (see p. 374)

Protea welwitschii   Dwarf Savanna Sugarbush/Protea; Troshofiesuikerbos (A)

(named after Friedrich Welwitsch, 1806-1872, Austrian medical graduate who collected this plant in Angola)

Multi-stemmed shrub or small tree, 0,5-1,5(4) m. In rocky grassland, 300-2000 m, KZN to Uganda, Tanz. Very variable. Stems erect, simple or branched, 5-8 mm diam, covered in dense white or russet hairs when young. **Leaves:** 50-120 x 15-60 mm, covered with dense white or brown hairs when young, hairless except at base when mature. **Flowers: In tight clusters of 3-4 inflorescences**, 30-60 mm diam, stalks ± 10 mm, **bracts open out into flat, saucer shape**, with white-brown silky hairs (Dec-May), **strongly honey scented**. **General:** Visited by beetles.

LORANTHACEAE - **Mistletoe Family** Partially parasitic, attached to host by suckers. Shrubby, stems woody. Leaves opposite. Flower tube large. Fruit a large berry. Birds squeeze the large sticky seeds from the fruit skin. Once regurgitated or defecated by the birds, these stick to the branches and germinate quickly. 'Wood roses' are the remains of the host branch after its death. Flowers attract butterflies. Trop, Temp, ± 67 genera, ± 900 species, 11 genera in SA. *Tapinanthus (tapeinos* - humble; *anthos* - flower) - Flowers with V-shaped split, tube cylindrical or with swollen base, lobes erect or reflexed; explosive flower-opening and release of pollen; pollinated by birds. Afr, ± 200 species, 20 in SA.

Tapinanthus gracilis   (*gracilis* - slender) (see p.48)

Tapinanthus natalitius   [=*Loranthus natalitius*] Natal Mistletoe; Voëlent (A); umhlalanyoni (Z)

Up to 1(2,5) m, hairless or downy. Parasitic on *Acacia* and *Combretum* species. **Leaves:** Mostly on short side branchlets, deciduous, 20-70 x 10-20 mm, stalks short. **Flowers:** 2-5, on short side branchlets, 20-50 mm, hairless, finely hairy or white woolly; flowers large 45-65 mm, base conspicuously swollen, tube split 20-30 mm, lobes erect, yellow-green or red, smooth to hairy (Oct-Apr), faintly scented. **Fruit:** Round, 12-15 x 10 mm, red to black. **General:** Birds feed on nectar and fruits. Two subspecies differ in distribution, leaf size, hairy or hairless. Used as bird lime.

Helixanthera (helix - spiral; *anthera* - anther) - Petal lobes fold back, filaments erect. Trop Asia, Afr, ± 50 species, 3 in SA.

Helixanthera subcylindrica [= *Loranthus subcylindricus*]   (*sub* - almost; *cylindrica* - cylinder)

Open, loosely branched shrub. Parasitic on *Ochna* species. **Leaves:** 30-40 x 10-15 mm, **margins flat**. **Flowers:** 10-20 in terminal inflorescence, 20-30 mm; flowers ± 10 x 1 mm, whitish (Dec-Feb). **Fruit:** Berry **pink, 8-9 mm**.

Helixanthera woodii [=*Loranthus woodii*] Wood's Dainty Mistletoe   (named after John Medley Wood 1827-1915, botanist, founding curator of Natal Herbarium)

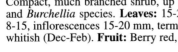

Compact, much branched shrub, up to 0,5(2) m. In forest, parasitic on *Coddia* and *Burchellia* species. **Leaves:** 15-25 x 10-15 mm, **margins wavy**. **Flowers:** 8-15, inflorescences 15-20 mm, terminal or in axils; flowers small, 5 x 0,5 mm, whitish (Dec-Feb). **Fruit:** Berry red, 5-6 mm.

Piper capense

Tony Abbott

Protea dracomontana

Tony Abbott

Protea welwitschii

Trevor Coleman

Protea welwitschii

Tom de Waal

Tapinanthus natalitius

Martin von Fintel

Tapinanthus gracilis

Martin von Fintel

Tapinanthus natalitius

Olaf Wirminghaus

Helixanthera subcylindrica

Olaf Wirminghaus

Helixanthera woodii

Trevor Coleman

133

SANTALACEAE - Sandalwood Family Usually parasitic on roots of other plants (for description see p. 250). *Thesium* (*thesium* - from the Latin for Toad Flax) **-** Herbs or shrubs; stems green; leaves scalelike or well developed. Attracts butterflies. Europe, Asia, Afr, S America ± 250 species, ± 160 in SA. Genus not well understood in SA.

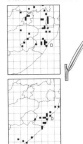

Thesium costatum (*costatus* - having lines or riblike ridges)

Erect, tufted herb, up to 150(300) mm. On rocky ground, in valleys. Stems slender. **Leaves:** ± 10 mm, blunt tipped, lower leaves spreading, upper much smaller, close to stem. **Flowers:** Solitary, ± 2 mm diam, lobes blunt, incurved, stalks very short or on short branches in upper axils (Sep-Jan).

Thesium natalense   Natal Thesium

Low-growing herb. In grassland. Rhizome short, knotty. Stems few, branched in upper half, nearly leafless, grooved. **Leaves:** Few, narrow, 2-3,5 mm, closely pressed to stem, hairless. **Flowers:** In slender spikes, suberect; flowers ± 5 mm diam, petal lobes flat with dense, woolly beard and hairy margins, bracts shorter than flowers, keeled, with scurfy, papery margins.

POLYGONACEAE - Rhubarb family Herbs, shrubs, climbers. Base of leaf stalk often forming a sheath. Flowers within dry bracts. ± Cosmop, ± 46 genera, ± 1100 species, 4 genera in SA. *Persicaria* (*persicum* - peach; *aria* - like) **-** Perennial (annual) herbs or shrubs; flowers in terminal inflorescences; fruit angled or flattened, enclosed in persistent flower parts. Cosmop, ± 300 species, ± 18 in SA, some introduced.

★ Persicaria hydropiper [= *Polygonum hydropiper*]

Slender annual herb, up to 1 m. In damp places, a widespread weed, from Europe. Leaves broad, 60-120 x 14-27 mm, gland dotted beneath. Inflorescence ± 120 mm, bracts red-brown, flowers greenish white, brownish gland dotted (Dec-Apr). Previously confused with *P. salicifolium* Leaves narrow; flowers pink, not gland dotted.

Oxygonum (*oxys* - sharp; *gonia* - an angle) Herbs; leaf stalk with papery sheath at nodes. Afr, ± 30 species, 6 in SA.

Oxygonum dregeanum   Starstalk; umdambane, umkhandu, untabane (Z) (named after
Johann Drège, 1794-1881, German horticulturalist, botanical collector, traveller, visited the Cape in 1826)

Robust, erect perennial herb, 200-500 (800) mm. In grassland, widespread in SA. Rootstock woody. Stems much branched, usually ridged, slightly succulent. **sheaths papery, lobed, tipped with long red bristle. Leaves:** 13-70 x 5-12 mm, **slightly succulent,** margins entire, lobed or with blunt teeth near base. **Flowers:** In terminal spikes 150-250 mm; flowers 10-15 mm diam, white, tinged pink, in small clusters (Aug-Apr). **Fruit:** Small, oval, ribbed. **General:** Very variable, 4 subspecies. Used in traditional medicine.

AMARANTHACEAE - Amaranthus Family Mostly herbs (for description see p. 50). *Kyphocarpa* [= *Cyphocarpa*] (*khypho* - bent; *karpos* - fruit) **-** Herbs or shrubs. Afr genus, 5 species, 3 in SA.

Kyphocarpa angustifolia   umahlabahlabane (Z) (*angustifolia* - narrow leaves)

Annual herb up to 700 mm. In dry grassland, woodland, thicket, disturbed areas, 350-1460 m, widespread in SA. **Leaves:** Opposite, ± 60 x 5 mm, **sharp tipped,** tufts of leaves in axils. **Flowers:** Dense terminal inflorescences, ± 200 mm; flowers white to pinkish, bracts spine tipped, woolly between flowers (Feb-Jun). **Fruit:** Spiky, woolly.

Gomphrena (*gomphos* - club, refers to flower heads) - Erect or prostrate herbs. S America, ± 90 species, 1 weed in SA.

★ Gomphrena celosioides   Batchelor's Button; Kruip-knopamarant, Mierbossie (A); intandangulube, unyawo-lwengulube (Z) (*celosioides* - like *Celosia*)

Prostrate perennial weed, up to 200 mm. Widespread in disturbed areas. Stems angled, plant with long silky hairs. Flowers in terminal inflorescences, white, papery, woolly.

MESEMBRYANTHEMACEAE - Vygie Family Succulent herbs or shrublets. Flowers brightly coloured, petals many, free, stamens numerous. Fruit a capsule. *Mesembryanthemum* comes from the Greek for midday or noon flowering and refers to the flowers which usually open only in full sunlight. Mainly S Afr, ± 126 genera, a few thousand species. *Delosperma* (*delos* -visible; *sperma* - seed) **-** Succulent shrublets or herbs; leaves opposite. Popular garden plants. About 140 species in Afr, mostly SA.

Delosperma carterae

Loosely branched, slender shrublet up to 200 mm. Branches prostrate to spreading, 1-2 mm thick, hairless, internodes 25-40 mm, covered in prominent, tiny bumps. **Leaves:** Erect, joined, ± 30 mm, 3-4,5 mm thick, upper surface concave, lower surface rounded, tip pointed. **Flowers:** ± 15 mm diam, in repeatedly forking inflorescences, stalks 10-35 mm. (See p. 380)

134

Thesium costatum   Wally Menne

Thesium natalense   Tony Abbott

Oxygonum dregeanum   Tony Abbott

Thesium natalense   Tony Abbott

Oxygonum dregeanum   Tony Abbott

Delosperma carterae   Tony Abbott

★ *Persicaria hydropiper*   Martin von Fintel

Kyphocarpa angustifolia   Martin von Fintel

★ *Gomphrena celosioides*   Van Wyk & Malan

135

Delosperma hirtum (hirtus - rough)

Low growing herb, 50-80 mm. Branches spreading, ± 3,5 mm diam, flowering branchlets erect, densely leafy, internodes invisible. **Leaves:** Broadest at base, ± 50 x 7 mm, concave to flat above, keeled, covered with tiny bumps ending in short bristle, margins fringed with almost rigid bristles. **Flowers:** Solitary, ± 33 mm diam, white or magenta with white towards base, petals in 3 whorls, stalks 5-30 mm (summer). **Fruit:** Open capsule ± 16 mm diam. **General:** Open in full sun. (See p. 380).

Delosperma lineare (linearis - a line or lines)

Erect, dainty, shrublet, up to 180 mm. In rocky grassland, coast to high altitudes. Stems spreading, often prostrate, branching, older stems white, rough, internodes 20-40 mm. **Leaves:** Spreading, 20-48 x 3-4 mm, yellow-green, semi-cylindrical, obscurely keeled beneath, upper surface concave. **Flowers:** In loosely branched inflorescences; flowers ± 20 mm diam, stalks 20-50 mm.

Delosperma subpetiolatum Trailing Vygie (sub - almost, somewhat; petiolatus - stalked)

Compact shrublet, hairless. Branches elongated, creeping, reddish, more than 170 mm, 1,5 mm diam, internodes 15-25 mm. **Leaves:** Suberect, 15-20 x 5-6 mm, thick, narrowed to base, upper surface concave, keeled beneath, dull blue-green, tinged reddish. **Flowers:** Solitary, ± 18 mm diam, stalks ± 10 mm.

Delosperma tradescantioides (tradescantioides - resembles habit of Tradescantia)

Trailing, perennial, succulent herb. In hot, dry areas, thicket, rocky grassland. Stems long, branching, long internodes, rooting at nodes. **Leaves:** Flat, 25-60 x 12-25 mm, light grey-green, tapering to tips, with very fine protruberances, joined into sheath at base. **Flowers:** Solitary, 15-25 mm diam, creamy white, rarely pink, almost stalkless (throughout year).

BASELLACEAE - Basella Family Climbing perennial herbs, often fleshy. No petals, 5 sepals, often coloured. Fruit enveloped by persistent calyx. *Anredera* - Trop America, 1 species naturalised in SA.

★ Anredera cordifolia Madeira Vine, White Shroud (cord - heart; folia - leaves)

Perennial semi-succulent climber or creeper, 3-6 m. A weed in disturbed places, from S America. Leaves glossy green, slightly succulent. Flowers in spikes ± 300 mm (Feb-May), fragrant scent. Reproduces from aerial tubers. Tubers edible. Cultivated as an ornamental, becoming a problem in coastal and inland areas. **Similar species:** *A. baselloides* Differences in the style.

ILLECEBRACEAE - Algerian Tea Family Herbs, shrublets. Leaves opposite or spirally arranged, often joined at base, often with papery stipules. Flowers insignificant. 5 genera in SA. *Pollichia* (named after Dr J A Pollich, author of a history of plants in the Palatinate, practised medicine in Kaiserslatnern in 1780s) - Shrublet; flowers surrounded by translucent, succulent white bracts, closely overlapping to give appearance of a berry. Afr, Arabia, 1 species.

Pollichia campestris Waxberry, Barley Sugar Bush; Teesuikerbossie (A); amangabangaba, behlungulu, utywala (X); ukudla kwamabhayi, umhlungulu (Z)
(campestris - growing in the fields)

Soft shrublet, up to 800 mm. Woodland, Cape to Ethiopia. Branches woolly when young. **Leaves:** Whorled, 5-30 x 5-9 mm, grey-green, finely hairy, tips pointed. **Flowers:** In dense clusters, surrounded by waxy white bracts, closed at mouth (throughout year). **Fruit:** Bracts become swollen, turning yellow-brown enclosing seed capsule. **General:** Sweet fruit eaten by people and birds, plant browsed by stock and game. Used traditionally to treat chest complaints and rheumatism.

CARYOPHYLLACEAE - Carnation Family Annual or perennial herbs. Leaves in opposite pairs, joined at base, nodes ± swollen. Flowers with 5 petals, tips often notched or lobed. A number of species have become naturalised weeds in SA. The family includes a large number of horticultural ornamentals including the Carnation, Gypsophila, Silene. Mostly in N temp regions, ± 87 genera, ± 2300 species, 18 genera (11 of them naturalised aliens) in SA. *Cerastium* (keras - horn, refers to the horned capsules) - Annual or perennial herbs; leaves opposite; flowers in terminal loose inflorescences. Cosmop, ± 60 species, 6 in SA.

Cerastium arabidis Snow Flower (arabidis - from Arabia)

Perennial herb up to 300 mm. In damp grassy areas, boulder beds, 1500-3000 m. Stem covered in short glandular hairs. **Leaves:** ± 25 x 7 mm, margins with long hairs, both surfaces mostly hairless. **Flowers:** Delicate, ± 20 mm diam, white, petals deeply 2-lobed, sepals 5, ± 8 mm, glandular (Sep-Jan). **Similar species:** *C. capense* Petals inconspicuous.

Delosperma lineare   Tony Abbott

Delosperma hirtum   Godfrey Symons

Delosperma lineare   Tony Abbott

Cerastium arabidis   Lal Greene

Delosperma subpetiolatum   Wally Menne

Cerastium arabidis   Martin von Fintel

★ *Anredera cordifolia*   Geoff Nichols

Delosperma tradescantioides   Geoff Nichols

Pollichia campestris   Geoff Nichols

137

Silene (*sialon* - saliva, refers to some species having sticky stems) - Annual or perennial herbs or shrubs; leaves opposite; flowers with inflated tubular calyx. Mostly in N Hemisp, ± 500 species, 15 in SA.

Silene undulata [=*S. capensis*] Gunpowder Plant, Large-flowered Campian; Wilde-tabak (A); lithotoana, molokoloko (SS) (*undulata* - wavy margin, refers to leaves)

Robust, perennial herb up to 1,2 m. In grassland, on rocky slopes, up to 2800 m, SW Cape to Zim. **Stem ribbed**, shortly hairy, sticky or not. **Leaves:** In basal rosette, ± 150 x 40 mm; stem leaves ± 80 x 20 mm, **margins wavy** or not. **Flowers:** In loose, branching inflorescence; flowers 20-40 mm diam, white to pale pink, petals two lobed, calyx ± 35 mm, dark ribbed, open in late afternoon (Oct-Apr), scented. **Fruit:** Capsule 12-18 x 9 mm, woody, opening by recurved valves at tip. **General:** Used in traditional medicine to treat many ailments including fever. **Similar species:** *S. bellidioides* ugwayelaso, ugwayintombe, umjuje (Z) Stems sticky hairy; flowers, ± 30 mm diam, **petals stalked**, calyx ± 20 mm; used as a love potion.

Dianthus (*dios* - divine; *anthos* - flower, refers to the scent of some species) - Tufted herbs (for description see p. 382).

Dianthus basuticus Lesotho Dianthus, Lesotho Carnation; Lesothose Grootblom-wilde-angelier (A); hlokoa-la-tsela (SS) (*basuticus* - from Basutuland, now Lesotho)

Herb up to 250 mm, in small mats. In grassland, rocky areas, 1400-3000 m. Rootstock woody. **Leaves:** Narrow, grasslike, 15-120 mm. **Flowers:** 20-30 mm diam, white or pink, petals toothed or long fringed, stalks 100-250 mm (Oct-Apr), scented. **General:** Used as a love charm and to increase fertility of bulls. (See p. 382)

NYMPHAEACEAE - Waterlily Family Perennial aquatic herbs. Leaf and flower stalks elongate to match water depth, blade usually floating. Cosmop, ± 6 genera, ± 75 species, 1 genus in SA. *Nymphaea* (*nymphe* - goddess of springs, water nymph) - Aquatic herbs; rhizome often tuberous; leaves large; flowers with 4 sepals, many petals; fruit fleshy, ripening under water, seeds small, often with pulpy, sac-like aril. Sometimes known as the Blue or White Lotus, not to be confused with the Lotus Lily of the East, *Nelumbium* which has leaves and flowers raised out of the water on long emergent stalks. Cosmop, ± 45 species, 2 in SA.

Nymphaea lotus White Waterlily; Witwaterlelie (A); amahlolwane (Z)

Robust aquatic herb. In rivers, lakes, pools, KZN, to Trop Afr, Madag, Comores Is. **Leaves:** 170-400 x 160-320 mm, margins lobed with blunt or sharp teeth, upper surface smooth, shiny bright green, lower surface purple with prominent forking green veins, stalk attached inside margin. **Flowers:** 100-180 mm diam, creamy white, opening at night, till mid-morning (Apr-Jul). **Fruit:** 40-60 mm diam. **General:** Sometimes forming floating rafts of vegetation at the edge of lakes.

RANUNCULACEAE - Buttercup Family Herbs or woody climbers. Leaves compound or palmate, bases forming a sheath. Petals ± equal to sepals, or absent, sepals petal-like. Includes ornamentals Anemone, Delphinium, Ranunculus. N Hemisp, ± 62 genera, 2450 species, 7 genera in SA. *Anemone* (*nahamea* - corrupted name for Greek god Adonis, who was killed hunting wild boar on Mt Olympus, his blood causing red *A. coronaria* plants to spring up) - Perennial herbs; leaves in basal rosette; flowers with cluster of leaves at base of stalk, no petals, sepals petal-like. Mostly N Hemisp, ± 150 species, 4 in Afr, 3 in SA.

Anemone caffra Anemone; Anemoon, Syblom (A); iyeza elimnyama (X); intingwe, umanzamnyama (Z)

Perennial herb up to 450 mm. In grassland, on rocky slopes, 1200-1800 m, E Cape, scattered localities in KZN. Woody rootstock. **Leaves:** Basal, 5-7 lobed, covered in erect short hairs, margins toothed, stalks sheathing the flowering stem. **Flowers:** Solitary, ± 80 mm diam, petal-like sepals, white tinged pink or deep pink, hairy beneath, 2-3 bracts below flower, stalk covered with woolly hairs above bracts (Oct-Jan, after fires). **General:** Used traditionally to treat biliousness, colds, headaches, toothache, and for love charms, sorcery and magical purposes. (See p. 382)

Anemone fanninii Giant Wild Anemone; Groot Anemoon (A); umanzamnyama (Z)

(named after Marianne Roberts, 1845-1938, artist who pressed and painted plants collected by her brother G F Fannin. Mother of noted ornithologist Dr Austin Roberts)

Perennial herb, up to 1,2 m. In moist depressions, near streams, 1400-2000 m. Woody rootstock. **Leaves: Large,** 5-7 lobed, 250-350(600) mm diam, thick, velvety above, long hairs beneath, margins with red tipped teeth, stalks ± 700 mm. **Flowers:** 2-3, stems 350-800 mm, 4-6 leaflike bracts, 50-100 mm; flowers 90-140 mm diam, creamy white tinged pink, hairy beneath, stalks 130-420 mm (Aug-Dec), scented. **General: Leaves only partly developed at flowering**. Used in traditional medicine. Lovely in flower and when leaves are fully developed. Not easily cultivated.

Silene bellidioides

Silene undulata

Dianthus basuticus

Van Wyk & Malan

Lal Greene

Martin von Fintel

Anemone caffra

Dianthus basuticus

Rosemary Williams

Trevor Coleman

Anemone caffra

Rosemary Williams

Nymphaea lotus

Wally Menne

Anemone fanninii

Anemone fanninii

Geoff Nichols

Pam Cooke

139

Knowltonia (named after Thomas Knowlton, 1691-1781, English horticulturalist, director of the once famous botanical garden at Eltham) - Perennial, stemless herbs; leaves basal, compound, stem leaves absent or reduced to bracts; flowers in irregular inflorescences; fruits small, berries in dense clusters. Endemic to SA, 14 species.

Knowltonia bracteata Blistering Leaves; Brandblaar (A); umvuthuza (X,Z) (*bracteata* - with bracts)

Erect, 350-900 mm. In forest understorey, edge of seeps and vleis in grassland. **Stem, leaf stalks ± densely hairy. Leaves:** 150-225 mm diam, thick, nearly hairless, leaflets ± 25-50(90) x 16-50 mm, **margins sharply toothed, teeth hair tipped**, stalks long, hairy. **Flowers:** In much branched inflorescence; **flowers small** 8-18 mm diam, greenish white, **bracts leaflike** (Oct-Mar). **Fruit:** Clusters of small dark fleshy berries. **General:** Used in traditional medicine and sorcery. Bruised leaves cause blistering. Easily grown from seed. **Similar species:** *K. transvaalensis*. Leaves few, leaflets ± 60 x 20 mm, hairless, stalks ± 250 mm; inflorescence leafless, flowers ± 30 mm diam, stalks long.

Clematis (*klema* - a (vine) branch or twig, used as a cutting or graft) - Mostly woody climbers or scrambling shrubs; leaves opposite, compound, stalk and stem capable of twining; petal-like sepals sometimes present; fruits small, dry, in a cluster, styles often persistent, feathery. Mostly temp, ± 250 species, 4 in SA.

Clematis brachiata Traveller's Joy; Klimop, Lemoenbloeisels (A); morarana-oa-mafehlo (SS); litinyo-lemamba (Sw); ityolo (X); ihlonzo leziduli, inhlabanhlanzi, umdlandlathi (Z) (*brachiata* - branches spreading, at right angles)

Vigorous perennial climber. In woodland, scrub, coast to 2200 m, widespread in SA, Trop Afr. Young stems softly hairy, ribbed. **Leaves:** 3-7 leaflets, ± 70 x 40 mm, tapering to narrow tips, sparsely hairy beneath, widely spaced, leaf stalks clasping. **Flowers:** In much branched inflorescences, longer than leaves; flowers 20-30 mm diam, petal-like sepals hairy outside (Feb-Jun), fragrantly scented. **Fruit:** Round heads of mature fruits with long styles ± 40 mm, covered in persistent silvery white hairs. **General:** Churning sticks made from stems. Used traditionally to treat abdominal disorders, intestinal worms, headcolds, syphilis, as a snakebite remedy and a good luck charm. Lovely garden plant, easily grown from seed or cuttings.

MENISPERMACEAE - Moonseed Family Woody climbers or scramblers. Male and female flowers on different plants. Leaves alternate, margins entire. Flowers small. Fruit slightly fleshy. Trop, 72 genera, ± 450 species, 7 genera in SA. **Albertisia** (*isia* - connection, with Prince Albert of Belgium) - Shrubs, more or less scrambling, or lianas; leaves simple; male flowers in clusters of 1-4; female usually solitary; fruit oval to roundish. 1 species in SA.

Albertisia delagoensis [=*Epinetrum delagoense*] cudodo, cumbato (Th); umgandaganda (Z)
(*delagoensis* - from Delagoa Bay, Mozambique)

Scrambling shrub, in dense communities. In thicket, woodland, dry forest, N KZN to Moz. Stems velvety grey hairy. **Leaves:** 40-90 x 20-50 mm, shiny dark green above, grey beneath, tips needlelike, stalks 10-15 mm. **Flowers:** Male, in small clusters in leaf axils; female, solitary (Feb-May). **Fruit:** Oval, 22 x 15 mm, velvety, orange. **General:** Fruits eaten raw or soaked in water and mashed. (See p. 252)

LAURACEAE - Laurel or Avocado Family Woody plants, herbaceous parasites *Cassytha* (for descriptions see p. 528).

Cassytha pondoensis   (for description see under ★ *Cassytha filiformis*, p. 528).

PAPAVERACEAE - Poppy Family Herbs with milky or yellow latex (for description, see p. 52).

★ Argemone ochroleuca White Mexican Poppy; Mexikaanse Papawer (A) (see under ★ A. mexicana, p. 252)

BRASSICACEAE (CRUCIFERAE) **- Cabbage Family** Annual or biennial herbs. Many species of economic importance such as Cabbage, Cauliflower, Broccoli and ornamentals such as Nasturtium, Candytuft, Wallflower. Cosmop, ± 365 genera, ± 3250 species, ± 34 genera in SA. **Heliophila** (*helios* - sun; *philein* - to love) - Annual or perennial herbs or shrubs, rarely climbing; leaves entire or divided; flowers with 4 petals, white, blue, purple or pink; fruit with style short or long, slender or stout. Attracts butterflies, including Meadow or Cabbage Whites *Pontia helice*. Endemic to SA, ± 90 species, mostly in winter rainfall areas.

Heliophila elongata White Cross Flower (*elongata* - elongate, stretched out)

Perennial shrublet up to 600 mm. In grassland, Cape to N KZN. Woody base. Stems often annual. **Leaves:** Usually crowded near base, 10-110 x 1-7 mm, entire or with a few sharp teeth or lobes. **Flowers:** In sparse, terminal inflorescences; flowers ± 20 mm diam, translucent white, cream to yellow, sepals and stalks tinged pale purple (throughout year). **Fruit:** 50-80 x 2-3 mm, hanging.

Knowltonia transvaalensis

Knowltonia bracteata

Clematis brachiata

Albertisia delagoensis

Knowltonia bracteata

Clematis brachiata

Clematis brachiata

★ *Argemone ochroleuca*

Heliophila elongata

Cassytha pondoensis

141

Heliophila scandens Wild Bridal Wreath, Dune Creeping Heliophila; Bruidskransie (A)
(*scandens* - climbing)

Straggling perennial climber, up to 3 m high. In coastal thicket, woodland. **Leaves:** Fleshy, 40-80 x 7-30 mm, needle tipped. **Flowers:** In terminal inflorescences; flowers 15-25 mm diam (Jun-Nov), scented. **Fruit:** 25-40 x 8-13 mm. **General:** Visited by honey-bees, wasps, flies, beetles. Lovely creeper for shady places.

CAPPARACEAE - Caper Family Woody or herbaceous, some climbing. Leaves alternate, simple or 3-5 foliolate. Ovary usually on long stalk (gynophore). Fruit a long narrow capsule or a berry. Economically important for capers to season food (dried flower buds of *Capparis spinosa*). Warmer regions, ± 39 genera, ± 650 species, 8 genera in SA.
Cleome (*Cleoma* - a plant name used in the Middle Ages) - Mostly annual herbs, sometimes shrubby; leaves simple or 3-9 foliate; flowers in terminal inflorescences, 4 sepals, 4 petals. In warm regions, ± 150 species, 25 in SA.

Cleome bororensis

Annual herb, up to 1,3 m. In woodland, sandy soils, N KZN to Moz. Stems finely hairy. **Leaves:** 3 leaflets, 15-5 x 6-25 mm, ± stalkless, tips pointed, broad at base, sparsely hairy, scattered glands beneath, stalks ± 40 mm. **Flowers:** In terminal inflorescence, elongating; flowers ± 12 mm, creamy yellow, glandular hairy. **Fruit:** Capsule ± 80 x 5 mm on elongated gynophore ± 15 mm, flattened, finely hairy.

Cleome gynandra Single-leaved Cleome, Spider-wisp; Oorpynpeultjie, Snotterbelletjie, Vingerblaartee (A); umzonde (Z) (*gynandra* - both sexes)

Erect, annual herb, up to 600 mm. In grassland, a weed in disturbed areas, widespread throughout trop regions of the world. Stems much branched, glandular hairy. **Leaves:** 3-5 leaflets, margins shallowly toothed. **Flowers:** In crowded, terminal inflorescence; flowers white to pink, 10-26 mm (summer). **Fruit:** Capsule long, narrow, 30-150 mm, held erect. **General:** A popular spinach in rural areas, leaves and flower buds cooked well to remove bitter taste.

Maerua (from *Meru*, an Arabian name for a mountain) - Shrubs, trees or scramblers; spineless; leaves simple or with 3 leaflets; calyx tubular at base, with 3-4 lobes; petals small or absent, stamens numerous; fruit round, oval or like a string of beads. Asia, India, Afr, ± 100 species, 12 in SA.

Maerua edulis [= *Courbonia glauca*] Blue-leaved Bush-cherry; inswaniswani (Z)

Blue-grey-green shrub, 1-2 m. In thicket, on roadsides, N KZN to Trop Afr. **Leaves:** Simple, leathery, ± 15-55 x 7-55 mm, 3-5 veined from near base, tip short, hard, pointed, stalk 3-6 mm. **Flowers:** Solitary, in leaf axils towards ends of branches, sepals 3, ± 20 x 15 mm, yellowish to whitish green, stamens massed, ± 20 mm, slender, curly (Sep-Mar). **Fruit:** Roundish, ± 20 mm diam, ripening yellow-orange, fleshy inside, stalk long, curved, ± 20 mm. **General:** Further north, the fruit is said to be edible; a piece of freshly cut root is used to clear muddy water.

Maerua juncea subsp. *crustata* Rough-skinned Bush-cherry (*juncea* - rushlike; *crustata* - encrusted, refers to fruit)

Straggling shrub or climber, up to 5 m. In dry, low altitude, open woodland, N KZN to Tanz, Congo. Woody main stems. **Leaves:** 1-3 leaflets, 20-75 x 5-20 mm, tapering to both ends, tips with short point, stalks 3-45 mm. **Flowers:** 2-8 in terminal clusters, sepals ± 15 x 8 mm, petals white, 5-8 x 3-6 mm, stamens stiff, ± 25 mm, gynophore ± 24 mm (Aug-Jan), faintly scented. **Fruit:** 30-45 x 25 mm, **rough lemonlike skin**, orange when ripe, heavy, hanging on stalk ± 15 mm. **General:** Subsp. *juncea*, found in Namibia; fruit with a smooth skin. (See p. 528)

CRASSULACEAE - Crassula Family Herbs or soft shrubs, usually succulent. Leaves, often joined round stem, or in basal rosette. Popular ornamentals. More or less cosmop, ± 33 genera, ± 1100 species, 6 genera in SA.
Crassula (*crassus* - thick, refers to fleshy leaves) - Delicate annual or perennial herbs or soft wooded to succulent shrubs, also aquatics; flowers small, (4)5(12) petals, stamens and sepals. Attracts butterflies,including Tailed Blackeye *Leptomyrina hirundo* and Cape Blackeye *Gonatomyrina lara*. Mostly SA, ± 300 species, ± 255 in SA.

Crassula acinaciformis Giant Crassula; Reuseplakkie (A); igekle (Z) (*acinaciformis* - sword-shaped)

Robust succulent herb, up to 2 m. In rocky grassland, open woodland. **Leaves:** In basal rosette, 150-300(400) x 30-60(100) mm, broad at base, narrowing to sharp point, margins with fine teeth. **Flowers:** In flat, branched inflorescence, ± 450 mm diam; flowers massed, tiny, creamy white (Jan-Jun), honey scented. **General:** Rosette of leaves grows for 1-2 years before the flowering stem develops, taking 3-4 years to mature, dying after flowering. Size varies according to local conditions.

Geoff Nichols

Heliophila scandens

Martin von Fintel

Cleome bororensis

Van Wyk & Malan

Cleome gynandra

Martin von Fintel

Maerua edulis

Martin von Fintel

Maerua edulis

Geoff Nichols

Maerua juncea

Jo Onderstall

Crassula acinaciformis

143

Crassula capitella (*capitella* - small head)

Perennial herb, up to 400 mm. In grassland, on dry rocky slopes, widespread in S Afr. Base ± tuberous. **Leaves:** 10-50 x 8-15 mm, fleshy, green to brown, tinged red or with red spots, hairless to hairy, margins with short hairs, tips pointed. **Flowers:** In elongated, narrow inflorescence with leaflike bracts up stem; flowers tubular, white, cream or tinged pink (Dec-Apr). **General:** 5 subspecies described, 3 found in this region.

Crassula compacta (*compacta* - compact)

Dwarf succulent, up to 200 mm, in colonies. On exposed rock, in moist grassland, in mountains. **Leaves:** 1-2 rosettes, 15-35 x 10-25 mm, green to reddish brown, red beneath, margins hairy. **Flowers:** In spikelike inflorescence, stem covered in bracts; flowers creamy white (Nov-Mar).

Crassula dependens (*dependens* - hanging down)

Perennial herb, up to 200 mm. On rocky outcrops, widespread from Karoo to Mpum with one population in Nam. Much branched, stems thin, wiry, hairy. **Leaves:** 5-15 x 1-2 mm, green to brownish red, sharp tipped. **Flowers:** In almost flat-topped inflorescence; flowers small, white to cream (Jan-Mar). **General:** Used as a protective charm against lightning.

Crassula expansa Fragile Crassula (*expansa* - spread)

Perennial herb, up to 200 mm. On rocky or sandy slopes, Cape to Moz. **Leaves:** 6-20 x 1-4 mm, almost stalkless, almost round with flat upper surface. **Flowers:** In terminal inflorescences or solitary in axils, clustered towards ends of branches; flowers cup-shaped, white tinged red, lobes ± 4 mm, recurved, calyx fleshy, green to brown (throughout year, after rain). **General:** Very variable. Subsp. *fragilis* [= *C. woodii*], cushionlike; leaves broader, ± 10 mm; flowers solitary (Nov-Apr).

Crassula lanceolata [= *C. schimperi*] **moriri-oa-letlapa (SS)** (*lanceolata* - swordlike)

Small erect succulent herb, 50-150 mm. In shade of rocks or trees (subsp. *lanceolata*), in grassland (subsp. *transvaalensis*), SW Cape to Mpum, Angola to Zim, Moz. Branching from base. **Leaves:** Small, 5-12 x 1,5-2 mm, triangular, fleshy, soft to leathery, green to grey to brown. **Flowers:** Clustered in axils, creamy green (Dec-Jul). **General:** Subsp. *lanceolata,* **often mat-forming**, rooting at nodes; leaves ± 6 mm, all of equal length. Subsp. *transvaalensis,* **erect**, annual stems from fleshy, carrotlike roots, branches not rooting at nodes; lower leaves longer, tips colourless.

Crassula natans Watergras (A); mohata-metsi-o-monye-nyane, morarana (SS)

(*natans* - swimming, with floating leaves)

Reclining or floating aquatic with long unbranched stems. In mud of pools, along streams, up to 3000 m, SW Cape to Mpum. Rooted at nodes. Stem tips just emerge from water. **Leaves:** 3-12 x 1-4 mm, flattened, slightly fleshy. **Flowers:** 1-2, terminal within leaflike bracts, cup-shaped, white, 3-4 mm diam, stalks 3-15 mm (Oct-Jan, in summer rainfall areas). **General:** Used as a lucky charm. **Similar species:** *C. inaninis* Up to 3 flowers in each leaf axil; leaves broader towards base.

Crassula nudicaulis (*nudus* - naked; *caulis* - stem)

Succulent perennial, up to 400 mm. In rock crevices, SW Cape to KZN. Stems slightly woody, more or less branched. **Leaves:** 50-80 x 6-15 mm, green to yellowish brown, spreading, flat above, rounded beneath, narrowing to pointed tip, hairless to finely hairy. **Flowers:** In elongate inflorescence; flowers cream, anthers yellow (Sep-Dec). **General:** Var. *nudicaulis* is found in this region.

Crassula capitella

Van Wyk & Malan

Crassula dependens

Tony Abbott

Crassula expansa

Wally Menne

Crassula compacta

Martin von Fintel

Crassula natans

Hilliard & Burtt

Crassula lanceolata

Van Wyk & Malan

Crassula nudicaulis

Tony Abbott

145

Crassula obovata Stonecrop *(obovata - egg-shaped, attached at small end)*
Straggling perennial with erect or reclining branches, up to 300 mm. On rocky outcrops in grassland or forest. Stems purplish red. **Leaves:** In rosettes when young; stem leaves in pairs, 10-30 x 5-10 mm, green tinged red, tips pointed or blunt, hairless or covered in hairs. **Flowers:** In elongated to flat-topped inflorescences, stems covered in leaflike bracts; flowers white or cream, lobes 5-8 mm, pointed (Dec-Jun). **General:** A very variable species. Two subspecies, differing in types of hairs on leaves and size of flower.

Crassula orbicularis [= *C. rosularis*] **Stone Crassula; Klipblom (A); umadinsane (Z)** *(orbicularis - circular)*
Perennial, succulent herb, up to 400 mm, solitary or in clusters. On rocky outcrops, in shade, S Cape to KZN. **Leaves:** In rosettes, 15-80 x 5-20 mm, flat, slightly fleshy, narrowing to pointed tip, margins with fine, dense, stiff, spreading hairs. **Flowers:** In elongated inflorescence, stem 50-200 mm, greenish red; flowers small, white to yellow, tinged pinkish brown (Jan-Nov). **General:** Runners are sometimes produced.

Crassula pellucida subsp. *brachypetala* *(pellucida - transparent; brachypetala - short petals)*
Perennial, succulent herb, stems reclining, up to 600 mm. In grassland, in KZN plants have fleshy underground rhizome; in moist areas on forest margins, on rock outcrops plants produce all stems above the ground, E Cape to Trop Afr. Very variable, hairy or hairless. **Leaves:** 10-25 x 5-12 mm, sharp tipped, green or with brown stripes, margins clear or red, irregularly fringed, leaf bases fused to a hairy sheath, stalked or not. **Flowers:** In terminal inflorescences; flowers white tinged pink, white to purple anthers (Dec-Apr). **General:** A number of other subspecies are confined to the Cape.

Crassula perfoliata var. *heterotricha* **Pointed-leaved Crassula, Ngoye Crassula, Red Treasure; Rooiplakkie, Heuningbossie (A)** *(perfoliata - stem passing through the leaf; heterotricha - with hairs of more than one kind)*
Perennial, erect, succulent herb, up to 400 mm. On rocky outcrops in grassland, E Cape to Trop Afr. **Leaves:** 40-120 x 12-35 mm, grey-green, with purplish red spots, grooved, especially at base, blunt to sharp tipped, covered with tiny rounded bumps. **Flowers:** In flat-topped, round inflorescence; flowers 6-12 mm diam, white with pink stamens (May-Oct). **General:** Three other varieties occur from SW Cape to E Cape. Var. *minor* also reaches this region (Transkei), flowers red or pink (Nov-Feb),sweetly scented; introduced into cultivation in Europe in the late 1700s, a favourite container plant.

Crassula sarcocaulis **serelilenyane (SS); umadinsane (Z)** *(sarkos - flesh; caulis - stem)*
Perennial, erect succulent shrublet with spreading branches, up to 600 mm. On damp, partially shaded rocky outcrops, up to 2745 m. Hairlike little bumps on young branches, peeling bark on older ones. **Leaves:** 10-30 x 1-8 mm, dark green, sharp tipped, flattened (subsp. *sarcocaulis*), needlelike (subsp. *rupicola*). **Flowers:** In dense, round inflorescences, ± 20 mm diam; flowers 6-10 mm diam, cup-shaped, creamy white (Oct-Mar), scent unpleasant. **General:** Used in traditional medicine as an emetic.

Crassula sarmentosa *(sarmentosa - long slender runners)*
Scrambling or hanging perennial succulent herb, up to 1 m. On rocky outcrops. Stems sparsely branched, from tubers. **Leaves:** 20-40 x 10-25 mm, green to yellowish green with red margins, entire or toothed, narrowing abruptly to short stalks ± 3 mm. **Flowers:** In round to flat-topped inflorescences; flowers spreading at right angles, creamy white (tinged red), anthers pink (Jun-Aug). **General:** Cultivated as a garden plant.

Martin von Fintel

Crassula obovata

Tony Abbott

Crassula orbicularis

Lorraine van Hooff

Crassula pellucida

Jo Onderstall

Crassula perfoliata

Martin von Fintel

Crassula sarmentosa

Tony Abbott

Crassula pellucida

Tony Abbott

Crassula sarcocaulis

147

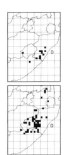

Crassula sediflora (*sedum* - to sit; *flora* - flower)
Perennial herb, up to 400 mm. On rock faces. Stems wiry, reclining. **Leaves:** 6-15 x 1-3 mm, in spirally arranged pairs, smooth or with tiny bumps, leathery. **Flowers:** In rounded inflorescence with loosely arranged flowers, stem with leaflike bracts; flowers cream, anthers yellow (Feb-May).

Crassula setulosa **Furry Crassula; serelilienyana (SS)** (*setulosa* - resembling fine bristles)
Perennial herb, up to 250 mm, forming clumps when young. On rocky areas, above 500 m. **Leaves:** In rosettes when young, 6-20 x 2-10 mm, green tinged red, blade flattened, tips pointed, rough hairs (or hairless), **margins with short, hard hairs**. Old leaves remain on stem. **Flowers:** In round, flat-topped inflorescences, stems with leaflike bracts; flowers 5-7 mm diam, white tinged pink (Jan-Jul). **General:** Widespread in the summer rainfall region. 5 varieties described, with differences in leaf and flower shape and size.

Crassula swaziensis [= *C. argyrophylla*]
Erect perennial herb, up to 250 mm. On exposed rocky outcrops in grassland and bushveld, N KZN to Zim. **Leaves:** In rosettes, 20-60 x 15-40 mm, green to grey-green, rounded, covered with hairs especially on margins, or hairless. **Flowers:** In dense, flat-topped inflorescence, stem 40-100 mm, densely velvety bracts midway and below inflorescence; flowers 6-10 mm diam, white to cream tinged pink in bud (Jan-Apr).

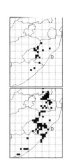

Crassula umbraticola (*umbraticola* - liking shade)
Perennial succulent herb, up to 110 mm. In moist rocky places. Stems erect, unbranched. **Leaves:** 20-35 x 15-25 mm, yellowish green, round, blunt tipped, short stalks on lower leaves. **Flowers:** In loosely branched terminal inflorescence; flowers creamy white, anthers yellow (Jan-Apr).

Crassula vaginata **White Stonecrop, Yellow Crassula; umakhulefingqana, umdumbukane (Z)** (*vaginata* - sheathed)
Unbranched perennial herb up to 500 mm, solitary. Widespread in moist grassland, E Cape to Trop Afr. Tuberous rootstock. **Leaves:** Single rosette; 5-250 x 3-20 mm, sharp tipped, flat, hairy or hairless, margins fringed with transparent teeth, **base of leaves fused**, old leaves remaining on stem, **Flowers:** In flat-topped, much branched inflorescence, ± 100 mm diam; flowers ± 8 mm diam, **yellow**, white (Sep-May), scented. **General:** Ground roots used in sour milk as famine food by the Zulu. Used in traditional medicine to treat earache, bruises and as a love charm. Easily grown from seed. Subsp. *minuta*, very small; Swaziland; leaves opposite, narrow, shortly fused; 2-5 inflorescences. (See p. 254) **Similar species:** *C. alba* (see p. 54, 386).

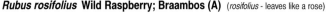

ROSACEAE - Rose family Trees, shrubs or herbs, often prickly. Leaves simple or compound, with pair of stipules at base of leaf stalk. Flowers 5 petalled, numerous stamens. Fruits variable, many edible. Of great economic value for a number of deciduous fruits such as the Apple, Pear, Cherry, Plum, Peach, Blackberry, Raspberry, Strawberry and many ornamental trees and shrubs such as the Cotoneaster, Japanese Cherry and the Rose. Mostly in N Hemisp in colder areas, ± 95 genera, ± 2835 species, 18 genera in SA.

Rubus (*ruber* - red, also the old Latin name for the plant) - Prickly, mostly scrambling shrubs; leaves simple or 3-5 foliolate; fruits edible. Mostly in N Hemisp, ± 3000 species, ± 20 in SA, many of them introduced invasive plants.

Rubus rosifolius **Wild Raspberry; Braambos (A)** (*rosifolius* - leaves like a rose)
Slender, suberect shrub. On forest margins, in forest undergrowth. Stems and leaf stalks with soft hairs and few, small, recurved prickles. **Leaves:** 5 leaflets, side leaflets ± 50 x 25 mm, thin, soft, tapering to tip, margins sharply double toothed, leaflet pairs well spaced. **Flowers:** Solitary, in axils or terminal, petals white, shorter than long pointed hairy sepals. **Fruit:** Rather dry, red.

Crassula sediflora

Martin von Fintel

Crassula swaziensis

Van Wyk & Malan

Crassula vaginata

Tony Abbott

Crassula setulosa

Lal Greene

Crassula setulosa

Lal Greene

Crassula umbraticola

Martin von Fintel

Rubus rosifolius

Martin von Fintel

149

Cliffortia (named after George Clifford, 1685-1760, owner of a famous garden in Amsterdam, patron of Linnaeus) - Shrubs; leaves small, usually with 3 leaflets, stalk runs into stipule. Mostly SW Cape, 142 species in SA.

Cliffortia paucistaminea (*paucus* - few; *staminea* - stamens)

Sprawling shrub up to 1,2 m. On cliffs, rocky watercourses, near coast to mountains. Old stems brownish grey. **Leaves:** Closely clustered, 3 leaflets, narrow, 5-10 x 0,8 mm, sword or ± sickle-shaped, tips pointed, margin with hairs, **midrib swollen, prominent,** tufts of hairs in axils of the leaves, stalk ± absent. **Flowers:** Male: short stalks; female: stalkless, small, creamy white, receptacle greenish brown (Sep-Nov). **Similar species:** *C. serpyllifolia* Galls often present; leaves oblong, flat, margins slightly rolled under, few hairs, midrib protruding on both sides.

FABACEAE (LEGUMINOSAE) - Pea or Legume Family The second largest plant family (for description see p. 388).
Elephantorrhiza (*rhiza* - root, elephant root) - Unarmed dwarf shrubs, small trees; enlarged rootstock; leaves bipinnate; flowers in a compact spike, clustered; pods straight or curved, often large. Afr, S of equator, 9 species, 8 in SA.

Elephantorrhiza elephantina Elephant's Root; Baswortel, Olifantswortel (A); intolwane (Sw, X, Z); ugweje, umdabu (Z) (*elephantina* - thick skinned)

Shrublet, 200-900 mm, often in large colonies. In grassland, open scrub, Cape to Zim, Nam, Bots. **Rhizome large, long, woody.** Annual stems, unbranched. **Leaves:** 35-135 mm, stalks 13-36 mm, 2-17 pinna pairs; leaflets, ± 5-10 x 0,5-2 mm, base asymmetric, tips hairlike. **Flowers:** In spikes 35-80 mm, creamy white, **at base of stem** (Aug-Mar), scented. **Fruit:** Woody pod, flattened, red-brown, 90-150 x 30-55 mm. **General:** Browsed by game, stock. Roasted beans used as a coffee substitute. Rootstock used in the past to tan and colour hides. Used traditionally to treat fever, dysentery, chest complaints, ulcers, syphilis, heart conditions and to stop bleeding.

Lotononis (a combination of two genus names, *Lotus* and *Ononis*) - Herbs or shrublets; leaves 3(5) foliolate; flowers 1-3, clustered on long stems or massed in inflorescences, usually yellow (white, blue or violet). Mostly Afr, ± 150 species in SA.

Lotononis viminea [= *Buchenroedera viminea*] White Lotononis (*viminea* - twig)

Erect shrublet, up to 1,5 m. In open grassland. Stems mostly simple from perennial rootstock, **covered in silvery white hairs,** leafy in upper two thirds. **Leaves:** Alternate, closely overlapping; leaflets ± 7-25 mm, no stipules, stalks short. **Flowers:** In 2s, in terminal, slender, leafy inflorescences, ± 700 mm; flowers white, with mauve veins, small, shorter than leaves, calyx silky silvery (Jan-Mar).

Aspalathus (*aspalathos* - a scented bush) - Shrubs or shrublets, sometimes spiny (for description see p. 260).

Aspalathus chortophila Tea Bush; impishimpishi (Z) (see p. 260)

Lotus (*lotos* - legendary fruit eaten to produce dreamy forgetfulness) - Herbs or undershrubs; leaves 3 foliolate and 1-2 leaflets near base of stalk, resembling stipules. Old World, mostly in Medit region, ± 100 species, 5 in SA, some introduced.

Lotus discolor Coral Plant; isiphunga, umhlambaluku, umhloboluku (Z) (*discolor* - having different colours)

Erect, perennial herb, up to 700 mm. In moist grassland, E Cape to Trop Afr. Stems sparsely hairy. **Leaves:** Stalks short, ± 5 mm; 2 side pairs leaflets, 1 terminal, ± 20 x 8 mm. **Flowers:** Small inflorescence, stem ± 150 mm; flowers cream tinged pink or pale yellow, ± 12 mm, calyx ± 7 mm; stalks short (throughout year). **Fruit:** Pod ± 25 mm.

Indigofera (bearing indigo, a blue dye) - Annual or perennial herbs, dwarf shrubs, shrubs (for description see p. 56).

Indigofera zeyheri [= *I. acutisepala*] (named after Carl Zeyher, 1799-1858, a German naturalist)

Slender, sparsely branched, perennial herb, up to 1 m. In grassland, in moist depressions, on rocky ridges, E Cape to N Prov. **Leaves:** 5-7 leaflets, ± opposite, grey-green. **Flowers:** Inflorescences on long, slender stems, 40-80 mm; flowers pinkish white, buds with darkish hairs (Sep-Jan).

Desmodium (*desmos* - bond or chain, refers to jointed pod) - Herbs or shrubs (for description see p. 394).

Desmodium salicifolium Willowy Desmodium (*salicifolium* - leaves like a willow)

Woody, perennial herb or shrub, erect, up to 2,6 m or creeping with erect flowering stems. In damp areas, coast to 1000 m, KZN to Trop Afr. Stems reddish to pale brown, round to angular, soft spreading hairs. **Leaves:** Terminal leaflet 60-175 x 20-65 mm, side leaflets smaller, hairy on midrib, beneath on veins, stipules 5-15 x 2-5 mm. **Flowers:** In terminal inflorescences; flowers small, yellow to pinkish green or cream with blue or mauve keel (Aug-May). **Similar species:** *Pseudarthria hookeri* (see p. 396).

Cliffortia paucistaminea　　　Tony Abbott

Cliffortia paucistaminea　　　Tony Abbott

Elephantorrhiza elephantina　　　Martin von Fintel

Lotononis viminea　　　Tony Abbott

Lotononis viminea　　　Tony Abbott

Aspalathus chortophila　　　Geoff Nichols

Lotus discolor　　　Martin von Fintel

Indigofera zeyheri　　　Van Wyk & Malan

Desmodium salicifolium　　　Geoff Nichols

Neonotonia (refers to *Notonia*, a genus in the family Asteraceae) - Three or more flowers per node of inflorescence; petals hairless, inside calyx teeth downy. The genus *Glycine* has been transferred to this new genus.

Neonotonia wightii [= *Glycine wightii*] **Robust Pioneer Creeper**

Robust hairy creeper, stems up to 10 m. In shade of forest, thicket. **Leaves:** 3 foliolate; terminal leaflets ± 40 x 25 mm, rough, tapering to tip, asymmetrical at base, stalked. **Flowers:** In erect inflorescences, ± 150 mm; flowers small, ± 5 mm, white with blue markings, calyx shaggy (Sep-May). **Fruit:** Pod flat, ± 25 x 5 mm, hairy. **General:** Browsed by bushbuck.

Sphenostylis (*sphenostylis* - wedge-shaped, refers to the shape of the style) - Herbs or shrublets with perennial rootstock. Afr, 2 species in SA.

Sphenostylis angustifolia **Wild Sweetpea Bush; Wilde-ertjie (A); insololo, ithethe (Z)**
(see p. 396)

Macrotyloma (*makros* - long; *tylos* - swelling) - Annual or perennial climbing herbs; leaves 1-3 foliolate; flowers axillary, calyx 4-5 lobed, standard petal with 2 appendages, keel not twisted; pods straight or curved. Afr, Asia, now spreading through the trop, ± 24 species, 6 in SA.

Macrotyloma axillare **Lime-yellow Pea; umhlanzo wenhliziyo (Z)** (*axillare* - growing in an axil)

Abundant creeping or trailing herb. In grassland, woodland, E Cape to Ethiopia, Arabia, Madag. Rootstock woody. Stems slender, forming masses covering grasses. **Leaves:** Leaflets 10-75 x 7-42 mm, hairy, **stipels hairlike**, stalks 10-55 mm. **Flowers:** 2-4, ± 15 mm, **pale greenish yellow** or creamy white with pale lilac blotch at base, **very narrow wings** (Aug-Jun). **Fruit:** Pod 30-80 x 6-8 mm, beaked. **General:** Attracts bumble-bees. Browsed by nyala. Used in traditional medicine to treat cows after calving. Good creeper in garden, over fences. (See p. 274)

GERANIACEAE - Geranium Family. *Geranium* Annual or perennial herbs or shrubs (for description see p. 398).

Geranium wakkerstroomianum **White Geranium** (from the Wakkerstroom area)

Straggling herb, stems up to 1 m, often forming loose clumps. In damp sheltered places round rocks, on forest margins, in marshes, 1040-2500 m, E Cape to N Prov. Tap root thick and woody. Stems with spreading white hairs. **Leaves:** ± 90 mm diam, thinly hairy above, sparsely to densely hairy beneath, lower leaf stalks ± 300 mm; stipules deeply dissected. **Flowers:** Petals ± 17 x 5 mm, **narrow, deeply notched**, white veined pink or red (pink), sepals ± 8 x 3 mm, stalks 20-65 mm, with long spreading hairs (Oct-May). **Similar species:** *G. schlechteri* (see p. 400).

Monsonia (*monsonia* - named after Lady Anne Monson, 1714-76, known for her botanical knowledge) - Herbs or undershrubs; often with simple stem from woody rootstock or deep tap root; leaves toothed or divided; flowers regular, petals 5, separate, tip broad, blunt or slightly notched, stamens in 5 groups with 3 stamens in each, 1 longer than others, ovary 5 lobed; fruit beaked. Afr, W Asia, E India, ± 40 species, ± 21 in SA.

Monsonia attenuata (*attenuata* - narrowing to a point)

Slender or tufted, densely leafy herb, 100-300 mm. In grassland, on rocky mountainsides. Rootstock tuberous. Covered in long straight, glandular, **whitish hairs. Leaves: Alternate, long, narrow,** ± 70 x 6 mm, folded upwards, margins sharply, finely toothed, stalks slender, ± 30 mm, reddish, often with **bend at base of blade, stipules long, needlelike. Flowers:** Petals greyish white to creamy yellow, ± 30 mm, margins wavy, tip square, toothed, strongly **net veined beneath**, sepals narrow, ± 15 mm, tips with long slender point, stalks ± 70 mm (Sep-Mar).

Monsonia grandifolia **Large-leaved Monsonia** (*grandifolia* - leaves larger than usual)

Robust, erect, tufted herb, 100-600 mm. In montane grassland, up to 1900 m. Stems soft and woody, often ribbed. **Plant hairy** and glandular. **Leaves:** Large, oval, margins finely scalloped, stalks long. **Flowers: 1-2**, petals 20-30 mm, white to cream, veins grey, **sepals sometimes joined at base, covered in stalked glands** (Sep-Apr). **General:** Grazed by stock. **Similar species:**

M. natalensis unakile (Z) Prostrate, many stemmed, 100-250 mm; in hot, dry grassland, 400-700 m; leaves narrowly oval, sharp tipped; petals creamy white.

M. praemorsa (*praemorsa* - as though the end was bitten off) **Hairy Monsonia** In coastal grassland, up to 300 m; stems conspicuously hairy (no stalked glands); leaves very hairy on veins, margins toothed; 1-2 flowers, smaller, veins blue-grey to purplish (Jul-Nov).

Neonotonia wightii

C J Ward

Neonotonia wightii

Martin von Fintel

Sphenostylis angustifolia

Van Wyk & Malan

Macrotyloma axillare

Wally Menne

Geranium wakkerstroomianum

Lorraine van Hooff

Monsonia attenuata

Martin von Fintel

Monsonia attenuata

Van Wyk & Malan

Monsonia praemorsa

Rosemary Williams

Monsonia grandifolia

Lal Greene

Monsonia natalensis

Clinton Carbutt

153

Pelargonium (*pelargos* - stork's beak, refers to fruit) - Herbs or softly woody shrubs (for description see p. 400).

Pelargonium alchemilloides Pink Trailing Pelargonium; Wildemalva (A); bolila-ba-lit-soene (SS); inkubele (X,Z); ishwaqa, umangqengqe (Z) (*alchemilloides* - resembles *Alchemilla*)

Straggling perennial herb, 200-900 mm. **In grassland, disturbed areas**, SW Cape to Ethiopia. **Leaves:** 20-70 mm diam, silky hairy, sometimes with **purplish brown mark in centre. Flowers:** 3-7(15), petals ± 15 mm, pink or white (Sep-Mar). **General:** Leaves aromatic. Used traditionally to treat fever, diarrhoea, wounds. Grown from seed.

Pelargonium bowkeri Carrot-leaved Pelargonium, Cat's Tail Pelargonium, Frilled Pelargonium; khoara (SS) (named after Henry Bowker, 1822-1900, naturalist and Cape colonial official)

Deciduous herb, up to 350 mm. In rocky grassland, 600-2200 m. Tuber large. **Leaves:** 150-300 x 25-50 mm, **feathery**, segments ± 1 mm wide, downy to shaggy, stalks 60-130 mm; **juvenile leaves simple. Flowers:** Inflorescences with 4-12 flowers, petals ± 29 x 25 mm, yellowish green with purplish veins (Sep-Jan). **General:** Leaves eaten. Used traditionally to treat flushes, colic, diarrhoea. Interesting garden or container plant.

MELIACEAE - Mahogany Family Woody shrubs or trees. Stamens often united to a form tube around the style. Economically important for Mahogany timber. Trop, subtrop, ± 50 genera, ± 550 species, 9 genera in SA.
Turraea (named after Giorgia della Turre, 1607-1688, prof of botany at Padua University) - Trop, ± 50 species, 6 in SA.

Turraea pulchella Dwarf Honeysuckle; Kanferfoelie (A) (*pulchella* - beautiful, small)

Shrublet up to 200 mm, in colonies. In coastal grassland. Vulnerable. Rootstock strong, woody. Branchlets roughly hairy. **Leaves:** ± 30 x 17 mm. **Flowers:** Solitary (2-3); petals white, ± 9 x 3 mm, densely hairy inside (Sep-Mar), spicy fragrance. **Fruit:** 5 valved capsule. **General:** Associated with termite mounds. **Similar species:** *T. streyi* **Dainty-leaved Honeysuckle Bush** Shrublet up to 750 mm, on scrub forest margins, rare; 3-5 pairs leaflets, ± 70 mm, deeply 3-5 lobed; flowers on long stalks.

EUPHORBIACEAE - Rubber/Euphorbia Family (for description see p. 62). ***Phyllanthus*** (*phyllon* - leaf; *anthos* - flower, flowers appear on leaflike cladodes) - Shrubs or herbs. Trop, ± 700 species, ± 24 in SA.

Phyllanthus myrtaceus (*myrtaceus* - of the myrtle family)

Erect, slightly woody perennial, up to 1,2 m. Main stem woody, bark reddish, leafy. **Leaves:** Oval, ± 15 x 10 mm, blunt tipped, **dark green above, grey-green beneath**, stalks short. **Flowers:** Solitary, ± 8 mm diam, white, hanging beneath side branches (throughout year). **Fruit:** ± 3 mm diam. **General:** Fruit edible.

CELASTRACEAE - Spike-thorn Family Woody trees or shrubs (see p. 536) ***Gymnosporia*** (*gymno* - naked; *sporia* - seed) - Trees, shrubs; fruit a capsule, seed covered in fleshy aril. Trop, subtrop, ± 200 species, ± 20 in SA.

Gymnosporia heterophylla Angular-stemmed Spike-thorn; Vierkantstingel-pendoring (A) (*heterophylla* - with diverse leaves, refers to variable leaf shape)

Much branched shrub, up to 1,5 m. In rocky grassland, E Cape to Moz, Trop Afr. **Branches angular**, grey. Slender spines, ± 40 mm. **Leaves:** 10-30(70) x 6-11(50) mm, **stiff, leathery, veins obvious**, margins with tiny sharp teeth. **Flowers:** Inflorescences **much shorter than leaves**; flowers ± 6 mm diam, white (throughout year), scented. **Fruit:** Capsules 2-7 mm, pale brown tinged red, seeds red-brown, aril yellow. (See p. 64) **Similar species:** *G. markwardii* ined Maputaland Dwarf Spike-thorn Up to 800 mm, in colonies, in coastal grassland; hardly branched; capsules red, aril white.

Gymnosporia uniflora Narrow-leaved Dwarf Spike-thorn; Smalblaar-dwerg-pendoring (A) (*uniflora* - one flower)

Shrublet, up to 800 mm. In rocky grassland. Stems brown; spines slender, ± 25 mm. **Leaves: Long, narrow**, 15-50 x 3-8 mm, margins with **few teeth in top half. Flowers: In small inflorescences, stem short**; flowers small, ± 3 mm diam, white (Sep-Dec). **Fruit: Capsules reddish yellow**, 4-5 mm diam, yellow inside, aril yellow.

RHAMNACEAE - Buffalo-thorn Family Trees, shrubs, climbers, often spiny. Trop regions, ± 50 genera, ± 900 species, 9 genera in SA. ***Phylica*** - Undershrubs. Attracts butterflies. Afr, Madag, ± 190 species, ± 180 in SA, 2 in KZN.

Phylica natalensis

Much branched shrub, up to 500 mm. On rocky hillsides. Vulnerable. Branchlets wiry, slender. **Leaves:** Close set, 7-14 mm, incurved, margins rolled under, rough above, covered with downy grey hairs at first. **Flowers:** In small, dense inflorescences; flowers small, **covered outside with white down and shaggy hair**, in axils (May-Jun).

154

Pelargonium alchemilloides

Pelargonium bowkeri

Turraea pulchella

Turraea streyii

Phyllanthus myrtaceus

Gymnosporia heterophylla

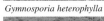

Gymnosporia uniflora

Phylica natalensis

155

TILIACEAE - Jute/Linden Family Trees, shrubs, herbs (for description see p. 282). *Sparrmannia* (named after Andrew Sparrman, 1748-1820, botanist, physician, ship's surgeon, pupil of Linnaeus) - Afr, Madag, ± 7 species, 2 in SA.

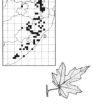

Sparrmannia ricinocarpa Sparrmannia Bush; hayihayi (Sw); isibundane (Z)
(*ricinocarpa* - seed like the castor oil plant)

Slender scrambling shrub up to 3 m. On forest margins, in forest, E Cape to Ethiopia. Stems hairy. **Leaves:** 3-7 lobed, 30-130 x 15-100 mm, lobes tapering to pointed tip, margins toothed, roughly or softly hairy, stalks ± 80 mm, stipules ± 8 mm. **Flowers:** 6-20, inflorescences opposite leaves, stems ± 80 mm; flowers ± 20 mm diam, creamy white (Jan-May). **Fruit:** Oval, dry, ± 15 x 10 mm, **covered with stiff sharp spines** ± 10 mm, splitting lengthwise. **General:** Bark produces good fibre. Leaves eaten as spinach.

MALVACEAE - Hibiscus Family Trees, shrubs or herbs (for description see p. 282). *Pavonia* (named after José Antonia Pavon, 1754-1840, Spanish botanist and traveller) - Herbs or shrubs; epicalyx of 5 or more bracts close to 5 lobed calyx, stamen tube 5 toothed at tip. Attracts butterflies. In warm countries, ± 240 species, 13 in SA.

Pavonia leptocalyx umozamoza (Z) (*lept* - slender; *calyx* - calyx)

Erect to low growing shrublet, 200-900 mm. In semi-shade, coast to 1000 m, KZN to E Afr. Hairy throughout, sometimes sticky. **Leaves:** 10-60 x 5-40 mm, **usually oval**, narrowing to pointed tip, margins toothed or entire, **dark green above, silvery white beneath**, stalks ± 60 mm. **Flowers:** Solitary, towards tips of branches, ± 35 mm diam, cup-shaped, white, **epicalyx of 9-11 bracts**, stalks ± 40 mm (Oct-Jan). **General:** Used in traditional medicine. Good potential garden plant.

Hibiscus (Greek name for marsh mallow) - Trees, shrubs or herbs; often with star-shaped hairs; flowers often large, showy, many with dark centres, epicalyx of 5-20 bracts, usually as long as calyx, 5 calyx lobes; fruit splitting along carpel walls. Attracts butterflies. Cultivated as ornamentals. Trop and subtrop, ± 300 species, ± 59 in SA.

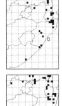

Hibiscus meyeri Dainty White Wild Hibiscus

Shrublet or perennial herb, up to 2 m. In valleys, in thicket on edge of floodplains. **All green parts bristly. Leaves:** 10-30 x 8-25 mm, **shallowly 3 lobed**, margins toothed, 3-5 veins from base, stalks ± 8 mm. **Flowers:** Solitary, **± 25 mm diam,** white, turning pink or purplish, epicalyx of 7 bracts, stalks ± 35 mm (Dec-Apr).

Hibiscus micranthus Tiny White Wild Hibiscus (*micranthus* - small thorns)

Shrub, up to 1(2) m. In woodland, in thicket on edge of floodplains, KZN to Trop Afr, Arabia, India. Roughly hairy. **Leaves:** 10-50 x 5-25 mm, margins toothed (**usually not lobed**), stalks 1-5 mm. **Flowers:** Solitary, clustered towards ends of stems, **small, ± 10 mm diam,** white turning pink to purple later in the day, **petals fold back,** epicalyx **short** with 5-7 bracts, stalks ± 20 mm (Oct-Apr). **Similar species:** *H. sabiensis* Leaves ± 50 x 30 mm, stalks longer, ± 18 mm; flower stalks short.

PASSIFLORACEAE - **Granadilla Family** Climbers with tendrils, shrubs or herbs (for description see p. 538).

★ *Passiflora subpeltata* Wild Granadilla; Granadina, Wildegrenadella (A) (see p. 538)

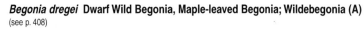

BEGONIACEAE - Begonia Family Herbs or shrublets, often succulent. Leaves often with unequal sides. Male and female flowers separate. Fruit dry or fleshy. Popular ornamentals. Trop, most widespread in N and S America, 2 genera, ± 900 species, 1 genus in SA. *Begonia* (named after Michael Begon, 1638-1710, French governer of San Domingo, patron of botany) - see family description above.

Begonia dregei Dwarf Wild Begonia, Maple-leaved Begonia; Wildebegonia (A)
(see p. 408)

Begonia geranioides Geranium-leaved Wild Begonia; Wildebegonia (A) (*geranioides* - resembling *Geranium*)

Soft, succulent, herb, up to 300 mm, often forming colonies. On damp banks, rock faces, in forest, up to 1375 m. Tuberous root. Often stemless. **Leaves:** ± 80 x 110 mm, light green, **roundish**, heart-shaped at base, margins shallowly lobed, with shallow, blunt teeth, **conspicuously hairy**, young leaves sometimes white spotted, veins pinkish, stalks ± 200 mm. **Flowers:** In leafless inflorescences; flowers 20-30 mm diam, **pure white**, male with 4 tepals, female 5 (Nov-Apr). **Fruit:** ± 20 x 20 mm across wings. **General:** Leaves die back in winter. Good container and shade plant in cooler areas.

Begonia sonderiana Sonder's Wild Begonia; Wildebegonia (A) (see p. 408)

Sparrmannia ricinocarpa

Pavonia leptocalyx

Hibiscus meyeri

Hibiscus micranthus

★ *Passiflora subpeltata*

Begonia sonderiana

Begonia dregei

Begonia geranioides

Lal Greene

Martin von Fintel

Lal Greene

Lal Greene

Tony Abbott

Jo Onderstall

Tony Abbott

Martin von Fintel

CACTACEAE - Cactus/Prickly Pear Family Spiny, succulent herbs or shrubs. Leaves rudimentary. Flowers regular, calyx tube fused with ovary (hypanthium), sepals and petals often in several rows. Fruit usually fleshy. Many species popular as container and garden plants. Widespread in Americas, naturalised and troublesome weeds elsewhere, ± 97 genera, ± 1400 species, 7 genera in SA, only one indigenous.
Rhipsalis (*rhips* - wickerwork; *alis* - pertaining to, refers to slender, interlacing branches) - Fleshy shrubs, sometimes epiphytic; stems often jointed; leaves scalelike. America, Asia, Afr, ± 50 species, 1 in SA.

Rhipsalis baccifera [=*R. cassytha*] Hanging Wild Cactus, Mistletoe Cactus; Bostou (A); ugebeleweni (Z) (*baccifera* - berries)

Straggling, pendulous, epiphytic succulent. On trees or rocks in evergreen forests, E Cape to Trop Afr, widespread in Trop America. Stems 3-6 mm diam, blue-green, woody at base, spineless. **Flowers:** Solitary or in pairs, ± 4 mm diam, greenish white, with conspicuous bulbous base (throughout year). **Fruit:** Round, fleshy, 5-10 mm diam, translucent white, pink or red, juice sticky. **General:** Fruits eaten by birds. Used in traditional medicine to treat chest complaints. (See p. 540)

Pereskia (named after N F Pieresc, 1580-1637, French patron of botany) - Trees, shrubs, scramblers; spines in pairs or clustered; fruit a soft berry, with or without spines. Mexico, W Indies, C and S America, 1 species naturalised in SA.

★ *Pereskia aculeata* Barbados Gooseberry; Barbadosstekelbessie (A); ufenisi (Z)
(*aculeata* - with thorns)

Scrambling shrub, smothering large forest trees. **Declared weed**, coastal areas of KZN. Clusters of woody spines near base, hooked spines in leaf axils. Leaves 50-70 x 30-40 mm, new leaves bronze. Flowers cream to pinkish, 25-45 mm diam (Mar-Jul), strongly scented. Succulent berry, ± 20 mm diam, green to yellow, edible. **Very difficult to eradicate** (grows easily from piece of stem or leaf). Resembles *Bougainvillea*. Grown as an ornamental, security hedging and used to protect graves. (See p. 290)

THYMELAEACEAE - Fibre-bark or Gonna Family Shrubs or small trees. *Gnidia* (for descriptions see p. 292).

Gnidia calocephala [= *Arthrosolen calocephalus*] Shrubby White Pincushion; indola, isidikili esimhlophe (Z) (*calocephala* - beautiful head)

Slender shrub, up to 1,2 m. In damp grassland, on forest margins. Stems woody, tough, sparsely branched in upper third, bark red-brown. **Leaves:** Clustered around stem, overlapping, hairy. **Flowers:** In terminal inflorescences, ± 30 mm diam; flowers white, hairy (throughout year). **General:** Used in traditional medicine to treat open wounds. Easily grown from seed.

Gnidia woodii Wood's Pinhead (named after John Medley Wood, 1827-1915, botanist, curator Natal Bot Gardens, Natal Herbarium, who published on flora of Natal)

Erect shrublet, up to 600 mm. In grassland. Branches slender, leaf scars small. **Leaves:** Small, closely overlapping, ± 25 x 3 mm, pointed, hairless. **Flowers:** A few towards tips of branches, calyx tube ± 18 mm, hairy outside, sepals oval, ± 5 x 2 mm, pointed, petals 8, narrow, thick, 2 mm x 0,5 mm.

Struthiola (*struthion* - small bird, refers to seed, like the beak of a sparrow) - Ericalike shrubs or shrublets; flowers stalkless, petals surrounded by stiff hairs. Endemic to SA, ± 30 species.

Struthiola anomala Berg Struthiola (*anomalus* - irregular)

Shrublet, up to 400 mm. Mountain grassland. Woody base, many stems. **Leaves:** Opposite, erect, overlapping, **narrow**, ± 11 x 2 mm, hairless, white hairy when young. **Flowers:** In axils, ± 10 mm, creamy greenish yellow, **petals reduced to 2 very small fleshy lobes at base of each sepal, no stiff hairs** (Nov-Dec). **Similar species:** *S. pondoensis* Slender shrub 1-2 m; leaves broad, margins fringed with hairs; calyx tube slender, lobes pointed, petals 8, shorter than sepals, thick, surrounded by long hairs.

Synaptolepis (*synaptos* - joined together; *lepis* - a scale, refers to the disc composed of scales) - Erect or climbing shrubs; flowers solitary or in clusters. Afr, ± 7 species, 2 in SA.

Synaptolepis kirkii uvuma omhlophe (Z)

Scrambling shrub, up to 2 m. In woodland, dry forest, N KZN to Moz. Stems tough, twining, with raised red-brown dots. **Leaves:** Small, ± 30 mm, shiny dark green above, paler beneath. **Flowers:** In small clusters, creamy yellow, pollen orange (Oct-Mar), scented. **Fruit:** 25 x 20 mm, yellow-orange when ripe. **General:** Tasty fruit, eaten by birds and children. Used in traditional medicine. (See p. 68)

MYRTACEAE - Eucalyptus/Myrtle Family. *Eugenia* (for descriptions see p. 68).

Eugenia capensis (for description see under *E. albanensis* p. 68)

158

Rhipsalis baccifera

Geoff Nichols

★ *Pereskia aculeata*

Geoff Nichols

★ *Pereskia aculeata*

Geoff Nichols

Gnidia calocephala

Rosemary Williams

Gnidia woodii

Martin von Fintel

Eugenia capensis

Tony Abbott

Struthiola anomala

Tony Abbott

Synaptolepis kirkii

Geoff Nichols

159

ONAGRACEAE - Evening Primrose Family Perennial or annual herbs. Flowers with 4 petals, stamens 4 or 8, style 4 lobed. Cosmop, especially temp and warm Americas, ± 18 genera, ± 650 species, 4 genera in SA.
Epilobium (*epi* - upon; *lobos* - pod, flowers seem to grow on seed pod) - Perennial herbs; calyx lobes 4, tube prolonged above ovary; fruit a capsule, seeds with tuft of hairs. Cosmop, except trop, ± 450 species, 5 in SA.

Epilobium salignum   (*salignum* - like the willow)

Erect perennial herb, 0,2-1,6 m. In swamps, up to 2000 m, S Afr to Trop Afr. Stems branch towards tips, finely downy. **Leaves:** Opposite, 30-60 x 8-20 mm, margins faintly toothed, **stalks short. Flowers:** Inflorescence ± 300 mm, flowers ± 20 mm diam, nodding at first, later erect, **white turning pink after pollination**, petals shallowly notched at tip (Dec-Jul). **Fruit:** ± 70 mm, including stalk.

Oenothera (*oinos* - wine; *thera* - imbibing) - Herbs; flowers usually open in evening, close before midday; seeds without hairs. Popular ornamentals. N & S America, naturalised in Old World, ± 110 species, 15 in SA.

★ *Oenothera tetraptera* White Evening Primrose; Witaandblom, Witnagblom (A); moopeli-o-mosoeu (SS)   (*tetraptera* - 4 winged, refers to winged capsule)

Perennial herb, 150-400 mm. A weed in disturbed areas, from Texas, Mexico. Covered in long spreading white hairs. Leaves 30-100 mm, margins wavy, deeply lobed at base. Flowers ± 60 mm diam, white fading purplish, opening in late afternoon (Sep-Mar). Club-shaped capsule, ± 15 x 8 mm, prominently winged.

APIACEAE (UMBELLIFERAE) - **Carrot Family** Mostly herbs, a few small trees (for description see p. 294).
Alepidea (*a* - without; *lepis* - a scale) - Perennial herbs; leaf margins toothed, bristle tipped; 'flowers' made up of many small flowers in each head, surrounded by conspicuous petal-like bracts in ± 2 rows. Afr, ± 25 species, mostly S Afr.

Alepidea amatymbica Giant Alepidea, Larger Tinsel Flowers; Kalmoes, Slangwortel (A); lesoko (SS); inkatsankatsa (Sw); iqwili (X); ikhathazo (Sw,X,Z)   (*amatymbica* - after the amaThembu people)

Robust, erect herbs, up to 2 m. In grassland, near streams, up to 2100 m, Cape to Zim. Rootstock large. Stems strongly grooved, **leafy throughout. Leaves:** Basal, ± 300 x 100 mm, **not in rosette**, margins prominently toothed, each tooth ending in a bristle, stalks ± 250 mm, stem-clasping; stem leaves stalkless. **Flowerheads:** Inflorescence widely branched; flowerheads ± 20 mm diam, white, 5 large, **unequal bracts** (Jan-Apr). **General:** Used in traditional medicine to treat colds, coughs (the root is sucked for relief), rheumatism, wounds, and to wash divining bones.

Alepidea natalensis   [= *A. baurii*]

Herb, 200-600 mm. In mountain grassland. Stems bare in upper parts. **Leaves: In basal rosette**, margins entire or toothed, with bristles, narrowing to stalk 10-20 mm. **Flowerheads:** ± 15 mm diam, 5 equal, triangular bracts 5-6 mm with small, alternating teeth (Dec-Apr). **Similar species:** *A. thodei* Leaves with long marginal teeth, bent backwards; flowerheads large, ± 30 mm diam, 10-15 irregular bracts.

Conium (*koneion* - plant, and the poison derived from it 'Poison Hemlock') - Stout, erect herbs with parsniplike root; leaves carrotlike, deeply divided, dissected, leaflets well spaced, divided, ending in very fine lobes. Asia, Europe, Afr, ± 8 species, 4 in SA.

Conium chaerophylloides   (*chaerophylloides* - resembling Chervil *Chaerophyllum*)

Biennial herb, up to 2 m. In rough open grassland in damp areas. Tap root stout, white, ± 10 mm diam. Stems erect, ± 10 mm diam, green, much branched above. **Leaves:** Basal, ± 450 mm, stalks ± 150 mm, absent at time of flowering. **Flowers:** In large spreading inflorescence of flat-topped clusters, 30-50 mm diam, stems 20-60 mm with white hairs at tips, bracts white, tinged green, **bracteoles broad, united at base; petals short, greenish yellow** (Nov-Jan). **Fruit:** Strongly 5 ribbed, ± 5 x 2 mm. **General:** Can become a weed in damp places. **Similar species:** *C. fontanum* Flowers in branching inflorescence, stems 20-150 mm, with white hairs at tip, bracts white, tinged green, bracteoles narrow, free to base, petals roundish, white (Nov-Jan).

Apium (classical Latin name for parsley and celery) - Annual or perennial herbs; leaves carrotlike; lobes broad or narrow. Cosmop, ± 72 species, 2 in SA.

★ *Apium graveolens* Wild Celery; Seldery (A)   (*graveolens* - strong scented)

Erect perennial or biennial herb, up to 1 m. In moist places, a widespread weed, from Europe and W Asia. Strongly aromatic, **stems hollow**, coarsely grooved. Basal leaves 100-170 mm, shiny bright green, fleshy, leaflets 10-60 mm, lobed, margins toothed, stalk sheathing stem. Flowers white (Aug-Mar). Visited by ants and wasps.

Trevor Coleman

Epilobium salignum

Martin von Fintel

★ *Oenothera tetraptera*

Tony Abbott

Alepidea amatymbica

Trevor Coleman

Alepidea amatymbica

Lal Greene

Alepidea natalensis

Geoff Nichols

Alepidea natalensis

C J Ward

★ *Apium graveolens*

Tony Abbott

Conium chaerophylloides

161

★ Ciclospermum leptophyllum [= *Apium leptophyllum*] (*ciclospermum* - misspelt from *cyclo*, round, refers to the round seed; *leptophyllum* - slender or thin leaves)

Slender annual herb, up to 600 mm. In disturbed, low-lying places. Widespread weed from Americas. Tap root stout. Strongly aromatic. Stems usually reclining, round, solid, coarsely grooved. Leaves with fine, narrow segments. Blooms throughout year.

Stenosemis (*stenos* - narrow; *sema* - mark, refers to petals) - Fruits roundish, wings thick, fleshy, wavy. 2 species in SA.

Stenosemis angustifolia (*angustifolia* - narrow leaves)

Spreading herb, up to 0,3(1) m. On rocky hillsides. Size variable, smaller in the south. **Leaves:** Segments 25-75 mm, narrow, flat above, grooved beneath, stalks 50-75 mm, grooved. **Flowers:** In clustered inflorescences, white (Jan-May). **Fruit:** Roundish, with thick, more or less fleshy, wavy wings.

ERICACEAE - Erica/Heath Family Large or small shrubs. *Erica* (*ereiko* - to rend) - (for description see p. 410).

Erica drakensbergensis Drakensberg Heath; Drakensbergheide (A)

Shrub, up to 1(2) x 2 m. In moist places, on forest margins, rocky grassy slopes, up to 1800 m. Stems woody, twisted, much branched above, upper branches slender, wiry, with **short hairs**, bark dark grey, flaky. **Leaves:** In clusters of 3-4, 2-4 x 1 mm, stalks short. **Flowers:** Massed, in small clusters; flowers white, small, 4 x 2-4 mm, bell-shaped, **anthers brown** (Aug-Jan). **Similar species:** *E. woodii* (see p. 414).

MYRSINACEAE - Myrsine Family Woody plants. Leaves gland dotted. Fruit a berry. Trop, subtrop, ± 33 genera, ± 1225 species, 4 genera in SA. *Maesa* (*maas* - from Arabic name) - Trees or shrubs. Asia, Afr, ± 125 species, 2 in SA.

Maesa alnifolia Dwarf Maesa, Dwarf False Assegaai; cawuza (X); inhlakoshane, isidenda, udoye (Z) (*alnifolia* - leaves like the Alder)

Shrublet, up to 1,5 m. In grassland, on forest margins. Branches slender, downy. **Leaves:** 15-40 x 10-25 mm, larger on coppice shoots, **margins with rounded teeth from tip to the middle**, tips rounded, stalks 5-12 mm. **Flowers:** In small clusters in axils, creamy white. **Fruit:** Berry, 5-6 mm diam, slightly fleshy, reddish brown.

PRIMULACEAE - Primrose or Primula Family Herbs with simple leaves (for description see p. 70). *Anagallis* (*anagelao* - Greek name for Pimpernel plant, believed to remove sadness) - Erect or creeping herbs; flowers solitary, on long stalks; capsule within persistent calyx. Mainly W Europe, Afr, Madag, ± 30 species, 4 in SA including 2 weeds.

Anagallis huttonii (named after Caroline Hutton who collected in the 1800s with her husband, an officer and Cape civil servant)

Perennial creeping herb, stems up to 600 mm. In damp places, up to 2600 m. Stems rarely branched, 4 angled. **Leaves:** ± 30 mm diam, spreading, narrowing to short stalks. **Flowers:** ± 8 mm, white or pale pink, stalks longer than leaf (Nov-Apr). **Fruit:** Dry capsule, splitting open like a lid, seeds winged.

PLUMBAGINACEAE - Plumbago Family Herbs or shrubs. *Plumbago* (*plumbum* - lead) - (for descriptions see p. 466).

Plumbago zeylanica Wild White Plumbago

Scrambling shrub, up to 1,5 m. In woodland, thicket, widespread in tropics. **Leaves:** ± 50(100) x 30(60) mm, pale green above, greyish beneath, stalks stem-clasping. **Flowers:** In terminal inflorescences; flowers ± 15 mm diam, white (pale blue), tube ± 25 mm, close at night, re-open next day, calyx ± 15 mm, sticky hairy (Apr-Nov), faintly scented. **Fruit:** 5 angled capsule. **General:** Useful groundcover in shade.

OLEACEAE - Olive or Jasmine Family Trees, shrubs, climbers (for description see p. 296). *Jasminum* (Latinised form of Persian name *yasmin*) - Scrambling shrubs; leaves opposite, 1-3(5) leaflets; flowers often scented, 4-12 petals, calyx with 4-13 lobes; fruit a twin berry. Well known ornamentals. Asia, Afr, Austr, S Europe, ± 448 species, 10 in SA.

Jasminum angulare Wild Jasmine; Wildejasmyn (A); umalala (Z) (*angulare* - corners)

Scrambling shrubs, up to 7 m. In scrub, coastal bush, near rivers. Branchlets angled, bristly hairy or not. **Leaves:** 3-5 leaflets; terminal one 13-45 x 6-25 mm, side leaflets smaller, very dark green, pits in axils of lower veins beneath, stalks 3-20 mm. **Flowers: In terminal inflorescences, among leaves**; ± 30 mm diam, tube 17-35 mm, 5 petals, white (greenish beneath), calyx 7 lobed (Sep-Feb), sweetly scented. **Fruit:** Round berry, ± 7 mm diam, in pairs, bluish black. **General:** Used in traditional medicine and as a protective charm against lightning. Fresh leaves poisonous to sheep and cattle. Profuse flowering is considered an indication of a good crop. Popular garden plant. **Similar species:** *J. fluminense* N KZN to Trop Afr; flowers in branched inflorescences, held clear of leaves, 6-8 petals, greenish white, calyx very short, lobes even shorter.

★ *Ciclospermum leptophyllum*

C J Ward

Stenosemis angustifolia

Martin von Fintel

Stenosemis angustifolia

Martin von Fintel

Erica drakensbergensis

Dolf Schumann

Maesa alnifolia

Tony Abbott

Anagallis huttonii

Lal Greene

Plumbago zeylanica

Darrel Plowes

Jasminum angulare

Wally Menne

163

Jasminum breviflorum Wild Jasmine (*breviflorum* - short flowers)

Scrambling climber or shrub, up to 3 m. In thicket, open woodland, E Cape to Moz. Branchlets hairy or not. **Leaves: Simple**, ± 45 x 25 mm, shiny olive green, usually hairy on both surfaces especially on veins beneath, pits in axils. **Flowers:** 1-5, in terminal inflorescences; flowers 20-40 mm diam, tube 15-30 mm, white, ± 7 lobes; calyx 5 lobed, **very short** (Nov-Mar), strongly scented, not always pleasant. **Fruit:** Twin berry, usually only 1 develops, black. **General:** Good scrambler in dry areas.

Jasminum multipartitum Common or Starry Wild Jasmine; ihlolenkosazane, imfohlafohlane, isandla senkosikazi (Z) (*multipartitum* - divided into many compartments)

Large, scrambling shrub, up to 3 m. In woodland, thicket, E Cape to N Prov. Side twigs short, hairy. **Leaves: Simple**, 15-35 x 4-28 mm, tips pointed, mostly **hairless**, no pits in axils of veins, stalks jointed in middle, hairy. **Flowers: Solitary**, in profusion, ± 30 mm diam, white, deep pink beneath, tube ± 35 mm, ± **11 petal lobes**, buds pinkish red, 5-9 calyx lobes (Aug-Jan), sweetly scented. **Fruit:** Twin berry, ± 15 x 10 mm, shiny black. **General:** Browsed by game. Fruit eaten by birds and by people in time of famine. Used as a love charm emetic and to make a herb tea, fragrant bath and pot-pourri. A lovely, well known garden plant. **Similar species:** *J. stenolobum* Densely velvety throughout; flowers in clusters of 1-3, calyx lobes 6-13.

LOGANIACEAE - Strychnine/Wild Elder Family Woody plants. Leaves opposite or 3 whorled, connected at base by stipular line. Flowers usually in much branched inflorescences. Fruit dry or fleshy. Source of strychnine and curare poison; also cultivated for ornamentals such as *Buddleja*. Trop to temp, ± 29 genera, ± 570 species, 5 genera in SA.
Gomphostigma (*gomphos* - a club, refers to club-shaped stigma) - Branched shrublets, hairy; inflorescences simple or branched; fruit a capsule. Afr, 2 species, both in SA.

Gomphostigma virgatum River Stars; Besembossie, Otterbossie (A); koete-le-boima, moema-thata, moluku, mosika-noka (SS); isepha kanonkala, umsola (X)
(*virgatum* - willowy twigs)

Perennial shrub, 0,6-2,6 m. In rocky streambeds, up to 1980 m. Stems slender, **silvery grey**, 4 angled. **Leaves:** Opposite, 10-60 x 2-5 mm, hairless to covered in silvery hairs, stalkless with **connecting ridge**. **Flowers:** In slender, terminal inflorescences, in axils of upper leaves; flowers ± 12 mm diam, white, **anthers with purple margins**, calyx 4 lobed (Dec-Mar), scented. **Fruit:** Capsules rounded, faintly 2 lobed. **General:** Used traditionally to restore strength to a very tired person. Popular garden plant.

GENTIANACEAE - Gentian Family Herbs, sometimes aquatic. Leaves mostly opposite or basal. 4-5 petal lobes, often twisted in bud, ovary superior, calyx 4-5 lobed. Fruit usually dry, splitting lengthwise. Cultivated as ornamentals. Cosmop, mostly temp regions, ± 78 genera, ± 1225 species, 9 genera in SA.
Sebaea (named after Albert Seba, 1665-1736, Dutch naturalist and author whose museum was called 'the wonder of Europe') - Annual and perennial herbs; stems angled or winged; leaves often stalkless, eared at base; flowers twisted in bud, calyx segments keeled or winged. Afr, Madag, India, Austr, New Zealand, ± 115 species, ± 45 in SA.

Sebaea grandis Large-flowered Sebaea, Primrose Gentian; liphalana, mipa, petle (SS); umalopha omncane (Z) (*grandis* - large, refers to the flowers)

Annual herb, up to 350 mm. In grassland and marshy areas, widespread, SA to Trop Afr. Stems 4 angled, narrowly winged, simple or branched. **Leaves:** ± 40 x 15 mm, becoming smaller towards base. **Flowers:** Few, terminal, ± 30 mm diam, white to creamy yellow, petals pointed, **tube ± 23 mm**, stamens not protruding, stigma 2 lobed, calyx lobes ± 25 mm, tips pointed, **wings ± 2 mm wide near base** (Dec-May). **General:** Used as a love charm emetic. (See p. 298)

Sebaea spathulata (*spathulata* - spoon-shaped)

Perennial herbs, up to 600 mm. On damp grassy slopes, in shade of shrubs, 1950-3200 m. **Leaves:** Basal, ± 140 x 20 mm, fleshy, stem leaves smaller. **Flowers:** In compact inflorescence with few-flowered branchlets, bracts fleshy; flowers 10-15 mm diam, tube ± 10 mm, **white** (Oct-Dec), **sweetly scented**.

Chironia (named after Chiron, a centaur who studied medicine, astronomy and arts) - Herbs (for description see p. 414).

Chironia albiflora Small White Chironia (*albiflora* - white flowers)

Herb, up to 450 mm. On river banks and on weathered outcrops of Natal Group Sandstone. **Leaves:** 50-80 x 10-17 mm. **Flowers:** In loose, branched inflorescences, flowers ± 18 mm diam, tube 16-18 mm, **white**, calyx 9 mm (Oct-Feb).

Jasminum breviflorum

Jasminum breviflorum

Martin von Fintel

Geoff Nichols

Gomphostigma virgatum

Wally Menne

Jasminum multipartitum

Tom de Waal

Gomphostigma virgatum

Lal Greene

Jasminum stenolobum

Sebaea grandis

Tony Abbott

Martin von Fintel

Chironia albiflora

Tony Abbott

Sebaea spathulata

Martin von Fintel

165

APOCYNACEAE - Impala Lily Family (for description see p. 416). ***Ancylobothrys*** (*ancyl* - bent, crooked, curved; *bothrys* - a furrow or trench) - Flower tube usually hairy, lobes overlapping to the left. Afr, Madag, ± 10 species, 2 in SA.

Ancylobothrys petersiana [= *Landolphia petersiana*] Climbing Wild Apricot; umtanwala (Z)
(named after Prof Wilhelm Peters,1815-1863, a German botanist who collected extensively in Mozambique)

Climber, up to 6 m. In woodland, KZN to Trop Afr. **Leaves:** 40-110 x 15-45 mm. **Flowers:** Inflorescences 50-170 mm; flowers ± 40 mm diam, white, tube brownish (Sep-Dec), lovely scent. **Fruit:** Orange, 45-60 mm diam. **General:** Fruits tasty, edible. Grown from seed. **Similar species:** *A. capensis* [= *Landolphia capensis*] **Dwarf Wild Apricot; umdongwe (Z)** Low shrublet; leaf tips rounded; flower tube pink.

Pachypodium (*pachys* - thick; *podion* - foot) - Succulent shrubs; trunk swollen, sometimes single stemmed, up to 3 m; leaves in terminal rosette, rigid spines; flowers in terminal inflorescences. Afr, Madag, ± 13 species, 5 in SA.

Pachypodium saundersii Kudu Lily; Koedoelelie (A); ligubugubu, sikymbyambya, sisila-semphala (Sw); insema-yamatshe, isihlehle (Z) (named after Sir Charles Saunders,
1857-1935, plant collector, chief magistrate in N KZN. Son of artist and collector, Katharine Saunders,)

Succulent shrub, stem large, spreading, swollen, up to 1 m. In dry rocky areas, KZN to Zim, Moz. Bark silvery grey. Spines ± 37 mm. **Leaves:** Deciduous, ± 80 x 40 mm. **Flowers:** ± 50 mm diam, white, finely speckled maroon (Apr-Jun). **Fruit:** 2 lobed, ± 100 x 10 mm, grey. **General:** Grown from seed. Lovely garden or container plant.

Strophanthus (*strophe* - twist; *anthos* - flower) - Scrambling shrubs or lianas. Afr, Trop Asia, ± 50 species, 5 in SA.

Strophanthus petersianus Sand Forest Poison Rope; ubuhlungubendlovu (Z)
(named after Prof Wilhelm Peters, 1815-1863, German botanist who collected extensively in Mozambique)

Slender scrambling shrub. In dry woodland, KZN to Zim, Moz. Bark with raised dots. **Leaves:** 30-80(110) x 15-40 mm. **Flowers:** Tube 10-20 mm, creamy white, pinkish red outside, petal lobes **dangling**, 60-140 mm, calyx 10-15 mm, **hairless** (Sep-Nov). **Fruit:** 2 lobed, 200-300 x 30-40 mm, tapering to 10 mm at tip. **General:** Used in traditional medicine and as a charm against evil. (See p. 298)

PERIPLOCACEAE - Periploca Family (for description see p. 542). ***Cryptolepis*** (*crypto* - hidden; *lepis* - scale) - Climbers; latex red; small pocketlike flaps in sinus of flower lobes. Trop, Subtrop Afr, India, Madag, 12 species, 5 in SA.

Cryptolepis capensis Paper-leaved Vine
Slender, woody climber. On forest margins. **Leaves:** 48-90 x 12-45 mm, **pinched into long, pointed tip. Flowers:** In small branched clusters; flowers white to greenish yellow, twisted in bud, lobed halfway; lobes spreading to reflexed, twisted, narrow, **long, ± 11 mm; corolline corona hidden and fused within tube, oval at base, tip blunt, fleshy, pointed** (Nov-Feb). **Fruit:** 2 lobed, 100-220 x 5 mm, very slender.

Stomatostemma (*stoma* - mouth; *stemma* - crown) - Climbers or shrubs. KZN to Zam, Nam, 2 species.

Stomatostemma monteiroae Monteiro Vine (named after Mrs Monteiro, plant collector in Moz)
Climber. In dry, sandy forest, KZN to Tanz. **Stems smooth, orange brown. Leaves:** 25 -75 x 10-20 mm, shiny above, grey-green beneath. **Flowers:** In small clusters; flowers bell-like, ± 25 mm diam, creamy green with reddish purple speckles inside, lobes 12 x 4,5 mm, tube 4-6 mm; **corolline corona between lobes, club-shaped**, 2 mm, dark purplish brown (Dec-Jan). **Fruit:** Solitary or paired, large, broad, almost woody.

ASCLEPIADACEAE - Milkweed/Butterflyweed Family (for description see p. 416). ***Xysmalobium*** (for description see p.542).

Xysmalobium involucratum Scented Xysmalobium; Hongersnoodbossie (A); udambisa omkhulu (Z) (*involucratum* - refers to reflexed petals that resemble an involucral bract)
Erect herb, **150-360 mm.** In grassy areas, coast to 2600 m. **1-3 stems. Leaves: Long, narrow,** 35-130 x 1-9 mm. **Flowers:** Lobes **completely reflexed to expose corona and gynostegium, anther wings with distinct medial notch** (Sep-Feb), fragrant or sickly sweet scent, strong enough to induce a headache. **Fruit:** Solitary, 60-170 x 5-15 mm, tapering to sharp beak. **General:** Used as a sprinkling charm against evil.

Schizoglossum (*schizo* - cut or split; *glossa* - tongue) - Perennial herbs (for description see p. 544).

Schizoglossum elingue White or Purple Schizoglossum/Split-tongue (*e* - lacking;
lingua - tongue, refers to the simple appendage-free corona lobes)

100-280 mm. In subalpine grassland, **1950-2700 m. Leaves:** 5-45 x 7-15 mm, ± lobed at base. **Flowers:** 4-6 in 1-5 inflorescences; flowers erect, **lobes flat, 8-10** x 4 mm, corona 4-5 mm, **simple, anthers inconspicuous** (Nov-Jan). **Fruit:** Not yet known. **General:** Subsp. *elingue*, flowers white. Subsp. *purpureum*, flowers purple.

166

Ancylobothrys petersiana

Ancylobothrys capensis

Pachypodium saundersii

Cryptolepis capensis

Strophanthus petersianus

Schizoglossum elingue

Stomatostemma monteiroae

Xysmalobium involucratum

C J Ward

Braam van Wyk

Geoff Nichols

Tony Abbott

Geoff Nichols

Trevor Coleman

Johan Venter

Tom de Waal

167

Schizoglossum hilliardiae **Hilliard's Schizoglossum** (after Olive Hilliard, SA botanist, who, with Bill Burtt of Edinburgh, has collected thousands of specimens and published prodigious works on SA flora)
90-350 mm. In subalpine grassland, **1800-2670 m**. Stems sometimes branched from base. **Leaves:** 27-46 x 6-26 mm, triangular to narrow. **Flowers:** Inflorescences with 3-9 flowers, **lobes 5,5-7,5 x 3 mm, flat**, hairless outside, white striped brown, **corona ± equal to the style tip, anther appendages inconspicuous**.

Schizoglossum nitidum **Glossy Schizoglossum/Split-tongue; Stinkmelkgras (A)**
(*nitidum* - glossy)
70-300 mm. In damp grasslands, marshes or near streams, 1200-1920 m. **Leaves:** 23-85 x 4-31 mm. **Flowers: Lobes erect, arching, oblong, 6-10** x 3-4,5 mm, **margins strongly rolled under**, tips blunt, strongly inflexed, hairless, anther appendages pressed to side of style-stigma-head, **corona lobe-appendage several toothed** (Oct-Jan), sweetly scented. **Fruit:** Solitary, spindle-shaped, 54-65 mm.

Schizoglossum quadridens **Four-toothed Schizoglossum/Split-tongue** (*quadri* - four; *dens* - teeth, refers to the 4 toothed corona lobes)
Up to 150 mm. In open inland grassland. Stems sparingly branched at base. **Leaves:** 28-50 x 6-13 mm. **Flowers:** Inflorescences **in clusters of 2-3, longer than leaves**; flowers white, lobes 6 x 3 mm, corona oval with **forked tips and 2 inwardly curved teeth on inner face** (Jan).

Aspidonepsis (*aspido* - *Aspidoglossum; anepsia* - cousin) - Similar to *Aspidoglossum* but corona lobes with central recess that may or may not contain a central tonguelike appendage, pollinarium wishbone-shaped. S Afr endemic, 5 species,.

Aspidonepsis cognata [=*Asclepias cognata*] **Large Suncup** (*cognitus* - now understood, refers to the confusion in identifying it as a species separate from *Aspidonepsis flava* and *A. diploglossa*)
Slender, erect herb, 180-550 mm. In mountain grassland, in damp areas, (60)1200 -2100 m. Stems unbranched. **Leaves:** 10-68 x 0,5-6 mm, margins smooth or rolled under. **Flowers:** Flower lobes spreading, 6-10 x 2,5-6 mm, **yellow, brownish, purple outside, corona lobes large, bonnet-shaped, overtopping style tips and tonguelike recess appendage** (Nov-Dec). **Fruit:** Usually solitary, erect, spindle-shaped. (See p. 300)

Fanninia (named after George Fannin, 1832-1865, botanical collector who farmed in the Dargle area of KZN from 1847) - Small herbs; stem slender, single, unbranched; flowers large, petal lobes erect, hairy, simple, corona lobes dark purple, pollinia pendulous. E Cape, KZN, single species genus, SA endemic.

Fanninia caloglossa **Fannin's Beauty** (*calos* - beautiful; *glossa* - tongue)
100-250 mm. In annually burnt grassland, 750-1700 m. Endangered. Stems covered in white hairs. **Leaves:** 25-60 x 4-25 mm, hairy. **Flowers:** 4-6 in 1-2 terminal inflorescences, stems 19-60 mm; flower lobes 11-14,5 x 4,5-7 mm, **with long white hairs outside** especially at incurved tips, hairless inside (Nov-Jan). **Fruit:** Not yet known. **General:** Pollinated by beetles. A very pretty plant. Almost 100 years ago the well known botanist N E Brown said that this species was well worth cultivating.

Gomphocarpus (*gompho* - club; *carpus* - fruit) - Shrublike herbs ; stems hollow, milky latex; flower lobes reflexed, corona lobes sac-like; fruits usually inflated. Introduced weed in Austr, Americas. Afr, Medit, ± 18 species, ± 9 in S Afr.

Gomphocarpus physocarpus [=*Asclepias physocarpa*] **Milkweed, Balloon Cottonbush, Hairy Balls; Balbossie (A); umangwazane, umbababa, umqumbuqumbu, uphuphuma, usingalwesalukazi (Z)** (*physo* - bladdery; *carpus* - fruit, refers to inflated fruits)
Annual or perennial, 0,5-2 m. In grassland, disturbed areas, coast to ± 900 m, E Cape to Kenya. **Stems solitary below, branched well above base. Leaves:** 50-100 x 7-20 mm. **Flowers:** Lobes 7-9 x 4,5-6 mm, corona square, white (throughout year). **Fruit: Roundish, inflated**, 38-70 mm diam, covered in soft spines. **General:** A weed in places. Stems used for fibre (Zulu name refers to the fibre used for sewing *isidwaba*, leather skirts of old women). Used traditionally to treat stomach aches, headaches, warts. Hardy garden plant, attracts butterflies. (See p. 546) **Similar species:** *G. fruticosus* [= *A. fruticosus*] Stems much branched from base; fruits spindle-shaped, 50-75 x 25-30 mm.

Gomphocarpus rivularis [=*Asclepias rivularis*] **River Milkweed** (*rivularis* - growing in small rivers)
Annual or perennial, 0,5-1,8 m. In riverbeds, up to 1500 m. Many stems from base, pinkish red. **Leaves:** 3-4 whorled at nodes, 60-100 x 3-12 mm, veins pink below. **Flowers:** Lobes reflexed, ± 8 x 4 mm (Dec-Jan). **Fruit:** Solitary, erect, oval, 30-55 x 25 mm, thick, fleshy, smooth or sparsely spiny.

Schizoglossum hilliardiae

Martin von Fintel

Schizoglossum nitidum

Rosemary Williams

Schizoglossum quadridens

Tony Abbott

Aspidonepsis cognata

Lal Greene

Fanninia caloglossa

Lal Greene

Gomphocarpus rivularis

Trevor Coleman

Gomphocarpus physocarpus

Martin von Fintel

Gomphocarpus rivularis

Trevor Coleman

169

Pachycarpus (*pachy* - thick; *carpus* - fruit)- Erect, perennial herbs (for description see p. 580).

Pachycarpus campanulatus Fairy-bell Pachycarpus (see p. 548)

Pachycarpus decorus Ghost Pachycarpus (*decorus* - beautiful)

Herb, 170-460 mm. In dry grassland. Rare. **Stems unbranched. Leaves:** 50-100 x 12-35 mm, harshly hairy. **Flowers: 3-4 in inflorescences, stems long**, 10-60 mm; flowers 15-22 mm, **creamy white**, lobes 12-18 x 10-13 mm (Nov-Jan). **Fruit:** Not yet known. **Similar species:** *P. concolor* (see p. 548, 580), *P. transvaalensis* (see p. 580).

Pachycarpus scaber Large White Pachycarpus, Honey-scented Pachycarpus; ishongwe elincane elimhlope (Z) (*scabrous* - rough to touch, refers to harshly hairy leaves)

Herb 300-750 mm. In grassland, often in rocky places, 500-1900 m. **1 or more stems, occasionally branched from base. Leaves:** 50-120 x 20-70 mm, leathery, ± harshly hairy. **Flowers: 3-12(18)** flowers white, 9-14(20) mm, **lobes spreading to reflexed** (Oct-Jan), honey scented. **Fruit:** 70-100 mm, **inflated**, ridged in upper half. **General:** Infusions used to prevent dogs from eating eggs. Used as protective charm against evil.

Asclepias (Aesculapius, immortalised as god of medicine) - Perennial herbs with milky latex (for description see p.416).

Asclepias gibba Humped Turret-flower; mantsokoane (SS); umanqanda (Z)
(*gibbus* - humplike swelling, refers to the hump on the back of the corona lobe)

Herb, 14-300(450) mm. In grassland, thornveld, up to 2500 m, especially where protected from grazing, E Cape to Bots. Stems annual, much branched from base. **Leaves:** 10-105 x 1-6 mm. **Flowers: 4-10 in solitary, erect, terminal inflorescences**; flowers on same level, lobes 6,5-12 x 2,5-5 mm, silvery grey, greeny mauve, **corona lobes much taller than broad, keel with large to small humplike swellings, anther wing with distinct notch** (Jul-Feb). **Fruit:** 50-105 x 6-12 mm. **General:** Visited by ants, bees. Rootstock eaten by people. Nectar laden flowers picked by children who chew them as sweets. Used traditionally to treat snakebite.

Asclepias gordon-grayae Gordon-Gray's Wire-stem (named after Kathleen Gordon-Gray, SA botanist, plant collector and lecturer at University of Natal, who has influenced generations of botanists)

Herb 240-750 mm. In **marshy grassland**, 30-90 m. **Stem solitary, annual, unbranched**, wiry, with very long internodes. **Leaves: Spreading at right-angles to stem, long, slender**, 35-130 x 2-30 mm, margins rolled under. **Flowers:** In 1-4 semi-hanging inflorescences; flower lobes, 6-8 x 3-5 mm, **corona lobes sac-like, ± triangular-saccate, not overtopping the style apex** (Sep-Apr). **Fruit:** ± 65 x 10 mm.

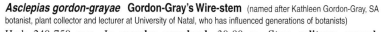

Asclepias humilis Drakensberg Meadow-star (*humilis* - low growing)

Herb 50-200 mm. In mountain grassland, 1800-2450 m. 1-2 annual stems, unbranched. **Leaves:** Crowded near base, **oblong**, 19-75 x 4,5-18 mm, veins protrude beneath, **covered in long white hairs. Flowers: In 4s**, 1(2-4) inflorescences per stem, erect; **flowers large**, all held at same level, lobe tips turned up, 8-11 x 4-5 mm, corona lobes slipper-shaped (Nov-Jan). **General:** Rootstock eaten by people.

Asclepias meliodora (*mel* - honey; *odora* - scent)

Low-growing perennial herb. In grassland, open woodland. Rootstock woody. Stems few, stout, plant covered in coarse hairs. **Leaves:** ± 120 mm, base square, tips long, tapering, stalks short. **Flowers:** In round inflorescences, stems ± 50 mm; flower lobes reflexed, corona whitish, column tinged pink (spring), scented.

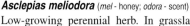

Asclepias multicaulis Doily Cartwheel; Melkbossie (A); lekhoaphela, lenkiling (SS); isikhonde, isiphofu (Z) (*multi* - many; *caulis* - stems)

Stems prostrate, 100-200(500) mm. In grassland, on riverbanks, up to 1800 m. 4-10 annual stems, **forking from near base. Leaves: Held flat on the ground**, 6-22 x 3-8 mm, veins prominent below, harshly hairy. **Flowers: 6-16 in solitary, erect inflorescence**, stems 13-60 mm; flowers all held at same level, 4 x 3 mm, **corona lobes square, compressed sideways** (Oct-Dec), sickly sweet scent. **Fruit:** Fiddle-shaped. **General:** Visited by ants. Plants eaten raw or cooked. Sotho name means 'he who draws his legs together when sitting on the ground', referring to the many, crowded, short, forking stems. **Similar species: A. flexuosa** Stems longer; leaves much thinner, not pressed against ground; flowers bigger. (For photograph see p. 416).

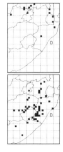

170

Pachycarpus campanulatus

Roy Wise

Pachycarpus decorus

Martin von Fintel

Pachycarpus scaber

Lal Greene

Asclepias gordon-grayae

Wally Menne

Asclepias humilis

Martin von Fintel

Asclepias multicaulis

Wally Menne

Asclepias gibba var. gibba

Martin von Fintel

Asclepias meliodora

Darrel Plowes

Asclepias gibba var. gibba

Martin Kunhardt

171

Asclepias vicaria Secret Cartwheel (*vicarius* - a substitute)
Perennial herb, up to 300 mm. In open grassland, 600-1800 m. **Leaves: Small, sword-shaped**, 25-45 x 11-25 mm. **Flowers: Small, in round inflorescences, creamy pink**, lobes ± 5 x 3 mm (Jan). **Similar species:** *A. albens*, leaves larger, up to 75 x 18 mm; flowers larger, pink, lobes ± 8 x 4 mm. (see p. 416).

Secamone (from the Arabic *squamone*, the name of *S. aegyptiaca*) - Woody climbers, twining herbs or scrambling shrubs; corona lobes 5, small, simple, fleshy. Trop, Subtrop, Afr, Madag, Asia, Austr, ± 100 species, 5 in SA.

Secamone alpini Russet Secamone; Bobbejaantou, Bostou (A) (named after Italian botanist Prospero Alpino, 1553-1617)
Slender climber. On margins of thicket, forest, E Cape to Kenya. Stems form long tendrils with **rusty reddish hairs. Leaves:** 20-90 x 5-35 mm, **rusty hairs beneath. Flowers:** Pyramidal inflorescences; **flowers very small**, lobes 1-2 x 1 mm, **white hairs above** (Nov-Apr), musty odour or sweetly scented. **Fruit:** Paired, 45-80 x 3-8 mm.

Brachystelma (*brachy* - short; *stelma* - crown) - Low growing perennial herbs (for description see p. 582)

Brachystelma circinatum Bird-cage Brachystelma; Wilde-aartappel (A) (*circinatus* - coiled inwards from tip, refers to curved tips of flower lobes)
50-300 mm. In grassland. E Cape to Bots. Stems 1-3, branching in upper part. **Leaves:** 5-15 x 1-7 mm, flat or folded upwards. **Flowers: In 2s** at nodes; **flowers cagelike**, lobes erect, narrow, 4-25 x 1-1,5 mm, tips united, tube short, 3 mm, **inner corona lobes not elongated above the style tips** (Oct). **Fruit:** 60-90 x 3-4 mm, tapering to pointed tip. **General:** Stem tubers eaten. (See p. 582)

Brachystelma franksiae Franks's Brachystelma (named after Millicent Franks (Mrs Flanders), 1886-1961, botanical artist and assistant to John Medley Wood at Natal Herbarium)
Herb 150-300 mm. In grassland, KZN endemic. 1-2 stems, **ribbed**, sparingly branched. **Leaves:** ± 50 mm, base broadly tapering, tips sharply pointed, roughly hairy. **Flowers:** 1-3, at nodes; flowers ± hanging, lobes erect, oblong, ± 8 x 3,5 mm, **margins strongly rolled under, making inner surface appear keeled**, inner corona lobes greatly overtopping the style tip (Sep-Feb). **Fruit:** Slender, ± 150 mm.

Ceropegia (*keros* - wax; *pege* - fountain, Linnaeus thought the flowers looked like a fountain of wax) - Perennial, often twining herbs; leaves present or rudimentary; flower tube long, lobes often fused at tips to form a cage, canopy or appendage-like antenna. Popular container plants. Trop, subtrop Afr, Madag, Asia, Austr, ± 170 species, 65 in S Afr.

Ceropegia ampliata Elephantine Ceropegia; Boesmanspyp (A) (*ampliatus* - enlarged)
Vine up to 2 m. In scrub, thornveld, especially dry river valleys, E Cape to Tanz, Madag. **Stems succulent**, rambling or twining, **rooting from nodes, appearing leafless. Leaves:** Rudimentary. **Flowers:** 50-70 x **13 mm**, tube straight, lobes erect, 10-20 x 5-7 mm, fused at tips, margins rolled back, with hairs (Dec-Mar), sickly sweet scent which attracts certain fly species.

Ceropegia carnosa Fleshy-leaved Ceropegia (*carnosus* - fleshy or soft but firm, refers to leaves)
Twiner, up to 2 m. In scrub or bushveld, coastal forest. **Stems thin, wiry. Leaves:** 8,5-30 x 4-25 mm, **slightly fleshy**, margins flat, stalk 5-15 mm. **Flowers: Tube bent**, lobes erect , 4-6 x 3 mm at base, tips fused to form a cage, **margins rolled under, keeled on inner surface**, with long white hairs, stalks 6-13 mm (Nov-Mar).

Ceropegia crassifolia Leathery-leaved Ceropegia (*crassus* - thick; *folia* - leaves)
Herb or vine, dwarf up to 120 mm or robust up to 1 m. In scrub, bushveld, KZN to N Prov, Nam. **Stems fleshy. Leaves:** 50-80 (100) x 5-45 mm, **leathery**, margins flat or wavy, hairless or roughly hairy. **Flowers:** 25-50 mm, tube slightly bent, lobes erect, 9-13 x 3-4,5 mm, tips **fused to form a fleshy cage over mouth, not twisted in bud, margins strongly rolled under, keeled on inner surface. General:** Habit variable, depending on habitat. Colour very variable even in same population.

Ceropegia distincta subsp. haygarthii Haygarth's Ceropegia (named after Walter Haygarth, 1862-1950, collector; nephew of John Medley Wood who introduced him to plant collecting)
Semi-succulent vine, up to 2 m. In thornveld, E Cape to S Moz, 90-1000 m. **Leaves:** 6-25 x 3-6 mm, ± fleshy, stalk 10-15 mm. **Flowers:** 34-50 mm, **tube bent at right angles**, lobes erect, **contracted into erect, wirelike tube, 10-16 mm, terminated by knoblike 5 winged structure** (Sep-Jan). **Fruit:** Spreading horizontally, 75-140 x 7-11 mm, surface wrinkled, warty. **General:** 3-4 subspecies from elsewhere in Afr.

Asclepias vicaria

Brachystelma franksiae

Martin von Fintel

Martin von Fintel

Ceropegia carnosa

Auriol Batten

Secamone alpinii

Geoff Nichols

Ceropegia ampliata

Tom de Waal

Brachystelma circinatum

Martin von Fintel

Ceropegia crassifolia

Geoff Nichols

Ceropegia distincta subsp. *haygarthii*

Martin von Fintel

173

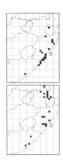

Ceropegia linearis [= *C. caffrorum*] **Slender Ceropegia** (*linearis* - long and narrow)
Vine, up to 2 m. On rocky outcrops in coastal thicket, thornveld, 30-700 m, E Cape to Moz. **Stem tubers, 20-30 mm diam**. Stems **slender**. **Leaves:** Spreading, 8-50 x 1,6-7 mm, ± fleshy. **Flowers:** ± 25 mm, **tube ± erect**, lobes **slender**, ± 8 mm, fused at tips (Oct-Apr). **Fruit:** Paired, slender. **Similar species:** *C. woodii* (see p. 584).

Ceropegia meyeri [= *C. pubescens*] **Meyer's Ceropegia** (named after E Meyer, prof at Königsberg, now Koliningrad. His herbarium of 24 000 specimens containing much type material collected by Drège in SA, was transferred to Berlin Herbarium. It was largely and tragically destroyed by bombing raids during World War II)
Vine, up to 1,5 m. On forest margins, 450-1800 m, E Cape to Zim, Malawi. **Stem tuber** 40-70 mm diam. Stems annual. **Leaves:** 19-50 x 8-30 mm, soft, **margins entire, toothed or ± lobed, wavy, hairy**. **Flowers: Skittle-shaped**, 30-60 mm, **tube straight**, lobes narrow, 9-11 x 3 mm, fused at tips, margins rolled under, velvety black with green stripes, margins with long hairs (Jan-May). **Fruit:** Paired, almost parallel, ± 100 x 3 mm, constricted between seeds. **General:** Cooked and eaten.

Ceropegia nilotica **Nile Ceropegia** (named after the Nile River)
Succulent vine, up to 1 m. In savanna thickets, on termite mounds, 100-1800 m, KZN to Trop, Subtrop Afr. **Roots fleshy, clustered**. Stem **sparsely branched**. **Leaves:** 30-80 x 18-60 mm, slightly fleshy, margins toothed. **Flowers:** 35-50 mm, lobes erect, ± 6 mm, fused at tips to form a **pyramid-shaped cage**, margins rolled back, hairy within (Nov-Mar). **General:** Roots eaten raw or roasted, reputed to taste like a firm potato.

Ceropegia racemosa subsp. *setifera* [= *C. setifera* var. *natalensis*] **Bristle-leaved Ceropegia**
(*racemosa* - cluster, refers to inflorescence; *setifer* - bristle bearing, refers to long white hairs on outer corona lobes)
Herb or vine, (0,2)2 m. In scrub or bushveld, 500-1260 m, KZN to Ethiopia. **Leaves:** 25-85 x (4)12-45 mm, **soft, tipped with long hairlike point**. **Flowers:** ± 30 mm, lobes erect, ± 7 x 1,5 mm at base, tips form cagelike structure, margins rolled under, inner keeled, with purple to white hairs (Nov-Mar). **Fruit:** Paired, spreading widely, 80-95 x 4 mm. **General:** 4 subspecies, 1 in this region.

Ceropegia rendallii [= *C. galpinii*] **Miniature Ceropegia** (named after Dr P Rendall of Barberton who first collected the plant in the early 1890s and sent a specimen to Kew)
Vine, 0,1-1(3)m. In bushveld. **Stem tuber** ± 30 mm diam. **Annual stems**. **Leaves:** 12-30 x 6-15 mm, ± fleshy, flat. **Flowers:** ± 25 mm, lobes erect, 5-7 mm, **joined above into umbrella-like canopy** ± 8 mm diam, outer margins deeply scalloped (Mar-Jun-Sep). **Fruit:** Paired, erect, slender. **General:** Growth habit variable. Stem tubers eaten raw or roasted.

Ceropegia sandersonii [= *C. monteiroae*] **Giant Ceropegia** (named after John Sanderson, 1820-1881, Scottish born journalist, trader, draughtsman, arrived in Natal in 1850. He sent plant specimens to Hooker at Kew and Harvey in Dublin and collected the type specimen of this species on the banks of the Mgeni River in 1867)
Vine, stems 2-4 m. In bushveld, scrub, KZN to Moz. **Stems fleshy, slightly warty**. **Leaves:** 17-50 x 12-25 mm, **fleshy**. **Flowers: Large**, 38-70 mm, tube opening above to funnel-shaped mouth, 12-25 mm diam, **lobes erect, broadening into 5 keeled, wavy canopy 25-50 mm diam, margins with long white to purple eyelashlike hairs** (Nov-May), scented. **Fruit:** Paired, spreading horizontally, 75-140 x 7-11 mm, surface wrinkled, bumpy. **General:** Visited by stingless bees. (See p. 554)

Ceropegia stapeliiformis [=*C. serpentina*, *C. stapeliiformis* var. *serpentina*] **Serpent Ceropegia; Slangkambro (A)** (*stapeliiformis* - refers to resemblance of some species formerly placed in genus *Stapelia*)
Succulent vine. In scrub, bushveld, dry forest, E Cape to N Prov. **Rootstock fibrous**, rooting from nodes. **Stems fleshy, trailing to twining**, 12-15 mm diam, **mottled**. **Leaves: Rudimentary, from tubercle at jointed nodes**. **Flowers:** 65-90 mm, mouth ± 18 mm diam, lobes free or twisting towards tip, (Feb-Apr). **Fruit:** Paired, widely spreading, 80-120 x 7 mm, surface warty, tips knoblike. **General:** Subsp. *stapeliiformis*, stems hardly twining; leaves with minute round stipules at base; flower lobes spreading, reflexed. Subsp. *serpentina*, stems usually twining; leaves with 2 golden yellow glands at base; flower lobes held together, twisted towards tip.

Ceropegia linearis   Ceropegia meyeri   Ceropegia nilotica

Ceropegia racemosa subsp. setifera   Ceropegia rendallii   Ceropegia stapeliiformis

Ceropegia sandersonii   Ceropegia sandersonii

175

Riocreuxia (named after French botanical artist Alfred Riocreux, 1820-1912) - Perennial herbs, usually twining; inflorescences branched, corona similar to *Ceropegia*, pollinia clear at tips. Afr, 10 species, 8 in SAfr.

Riocreuxia torulosa [= R. torulosa var. tomentosa] Candle-vine; Kandelaarblom (A); ugwapha, unquntane, ushuqu (Z) (torulosus - cylindrical with bulges or contractions at intervals, refers to the very narrow fruits which are constricted between the seeds, beadlike)

Vine, up to 5 m. In woodland, on forest margins, E Cape to N Prov. **Leaves:** 30-130 x 17-95 mm, **stalks 12-65 mm.** Flowers: 2-15 in 1-3 inflorescences at nodes, **stems 8-100 mm; flowers tubular,** 12-18 mm, lobes joined at tips to form a cage (Oct-Apr), heavily honey scented. **Fruit:** Paired, 75-180 x 3 mm, tapering to slender beak. **General:** Eaten as a pot herb, but the 'spinach' or *imifino* from these leaves is sometimes reputed to cause headaches. **Similar species:** *R. alexandrina* S KZN endemic; inflorescences with ± 5 small flowers, 10-15 mm.

Dregea (named after Jan Drège, 1794-1881, one of the first botanical collectors in SA, collecting over 200 000 specimens) - Perennial woody climbers; milky latex; leaves opposite, venation prominent below, very hairy; corona lobes simple, style tip slightly cone-shaped, exceeding the anthers, anther appendages large, erect; fruits paired, skin thick, leathery, wrinkled or with large, irregular wings. Trop, Subtrop Afr, Asia, 12 species, 2 in S Afr.

Dregea floribunda Mousy Bat-fruit (floribundus - profusely flowering)

Climber or scrambling shrub, up to 4 m. In thicket, on forest margins, in riverine vegetation, N Cape, E Cape to Moz, up to 1200 m. **Stems woody,** sparsely covered in rusty hairs on non-woody parts. **Leaves:** 17-64 x 12-38 mm, soft. **Flowers: In dense, inflorescences; flowers small,** tube 1,5-3 mm deep, lobes spreading, 2-3 x 2 mm (Jul-May), **mousy or wet dog scent. Fruit:** Paired, spreading, 63-75 x 18-25 ıııııı, **with 4 broadly irregular, toothed wings,** beautiful when dry (see p. 588).

CONVOLVULACEAE - Morning Glory Family Herbs, shrubs. Stems trailing or twining, milky sap often present. Flowers with funnel-shaped tube or petals united, with distinct mid petal zone, twisted in bud, calyx deeply 5 lobed, bracts often present. Fruit usually a dry capsule. Economically important for the Sweet Potato *Ipomoea batatas* and ornamentals. Cosmop, especially warm regions,± 56 genera, ± 1600 species, 16 genera in SA.

Falckia (named after John Peter Falck, pupil of Linnaeus) - Dwarf perennial herbs. Afr, 3 species, 2 in SA.

Falckia repens White Carpet; Oortjies (A) (repens - creeping)

Creeping perennial herb. In damp grassland. Stems firm, slender, rooting at nodes. **Leaves:** 6-25 mm diam, heart-shaped at base, stalks ± 25 mm. **Flowers:** Solitary, ± 15 mm diam, white to pinkish, stalks as long as leaves, calyx 4-7 mm, lobes enlarged in fruit (Sep-Dec). **Fruit:** Flowering stalk bends downwards, burying fruit in soil. **General:** Attractive groundcover, propagated from rooted runners.

Seddera (type specimen collected at Mt Sedder in Arabia) - Small, prostrate to suberect shrublets, not climbing; flowers in few-flowered clusters. Afr, Madag, Arabia, India, ± 15 species, 2 in SA.

Seddera capensis Seddera

Perennial herb, up to 300 mm, prostrate to suberect. In dry, rocky woodland, grassland, E Cape to Zim. Plant covered in **stiff red-brown hairs. Leaves:** 8-25 x 4-12 mm, grey-green, stalks very short. **Flowers:** Solitary, ± 10 mm diam, white, stalks short (Sep-Feb). **Similar species:** *S. suffruticosa* Spreading shrublet; silky white hairs throughout; leaves small; flowers blue or white, ± 7 mm diam.

Convolvulus (convolvere - to entwine) - Twining or erect herbs; woody rootstock or tap root; flowers with pair of bracts on upper portion of stalk. Cosmop, mainly in temp and subtrop regions, ± 100 species, ± 12 in SA.

Convolvulus farinosus Klimop (A); inabulele, uboqo (X); umkhokha wehlathi (Z)
(farinosus - covered in dusting of flour)

Perennial straggling or twining herb. In moist areas, woodland, SA to Medit, Mascarene Is. Plant covered in short grey hairs. **Leaves:** 40-90 x 30-70 mm, olive green above, grey beneath, basal lobes broadly rounded, margins bluntly toothed, stalks ± 15 mm. **Flowers:** In clusters of 1-6; flowers ± 15 mm diam, white to pale pink (Jan-Oct). **General:** Used as a purgative and emetic for stomach ache in adults.

Convolvulus natalensis Yellow Convolvulus

Perennial prostrate or twining herb. In grassland. Stems ± 1 m; plant hairy throughout. **Leaves:** 10-50 x 10-30 mm, **blunt tipped,** margins irregularly wavy or toothed, basal lobes rounded. **Flowers:** ± 40 mm diam, tube 20-35 mm, creamy white or pale yellow, stems ± 70 mm (throughout year). **Similar species:** *C. sagittatus* Bobbejaan-tou (A); uvimbukhalo (Z) In grassland, woodland, SA to Trop Afr; leaves very variable, 30-70 x 5-25 mm, margins lobed; flowers small, 8-20 mm, white to pale pink.

Riocreuxia torulosa   Lal Greene

Riocreuxia torulosa   Martin von Fintel

Dregea floribunda   Tony Abbott

Falckia repens   Tony Abbott

Falckia repens   Trevor Coleman

Seddera capensis   Van Wyk & Malan

Convolvulus farinosus   Martin von Fintel

Convolvulus natalensis   Martin von Fintel

Convolvulus sagittatus   Van Wyk & Malan

Convolvulus natalensis   Tony Abbott

177

Ipomoea (*ips* - worm; *homoios* - like, alluding to the creeping habit) **-** Mostly twiners; leaves often heart-shaped at base, sometimes lobed; flowers showy, broadly funnel-shaped. Cosmop, ± 400 species, ± 50 in SA.

★ *Ipomoea alba* Moonflower, Wooden Rose Creeper; Maanblom (A)

Perennial twiner. In low-lying areas, on forest margins, in wasteland. Garden escape, Trop America. Stems prickly, ± 5 m. Leaves 60-200 x 50-160 mm, margins entire, base heart-shaped, stalks slender 50-200 mm. Flowers large, ± 140 mm diam, tube 70-120 mm, white, opening at night, stem ± 240 mm (Oct-Jul), fragrant.

Ipomoea albivenia Climbing Kapok, Wooden Rose Creeper; Wildekatoen (A); imibuzana, ubatata wentaba, umgubasiswana, umgwiligwili (Z) (*albivenia* - white veins)

Deciduous climber, up to 10 m. In woodland, KZN to Zim, Moz. **Leaves:** 30-100 mm diam, thick, grey-green, **velvety white when young**, veins velvety beneath, stalks slender, velvety white, 10-60 mm. **Flowers:** Solitary, 60-80 mm diam, tube 60 -90 mm, white, sometimes deep pink in centre, open at night, closed by midday (Feb-Mar), scented. **Fruit:** Woody capsule ± 22 x 16 mm. **General:** Tuber eaten in times of famine. Flowers, leaves consumed by caterpillars. Used in traditional medicine to purify the blood. Lovely garden plant, grown from cuttings, with a second 'flowering' when fruits burst open to release white cottonwool-covered seeds.

Ipomoea crassipes Leafy-flowered Ipomoea; Wildewinde (A); mothokhoana, sekutle (SS); ubhoqo, uvimbukhalo (Z) (see p. 420)

Ipomoea plebeia umdzandzabuka (Sw) (*plebius* - common)

Annual twiner, up to 1 m. In open, disturbed areas, KZN to Zim, Moz. Stems hairy. **Leaves:** 20-100 x 5-65 mm, basal lobes broad, rounded, margins entire, fringed with hairs, hairless except on veins beneath, stalks slender, 5-70 mm. **Flowers:** 1-3 in small clusters, in axils, **on short, thick stem**; flowers ± 10 mm diam, tube ± 10 mm, white to pink, calyx hairy, ± 10 mm (Aug-Apr).

★ *Ipomoea purpurea* Common Morning Glory; Purperwinde (A); imbotyikatsana (X); ijalamu, ijalapha, ubhoqo (Z) (see p. 468)

Ipomoea simplex Dwarf White Ipomoea, White Narrow-leaved Ipomoea; seakhoe (SS); emagonsa (Sw); igonsi (Sw,X,Z) (*simplex* - of one piece, opposite of compound)

Erect, perennial herb, up to 100 mm. In grassland. Tuberous rootstock. Stems erect, slender, woody. **Hairless. Leaves:** Simple, 30-100 mm, entire or slightly lobed, stalks short or almost stalkless. **Flowers:** Solitary, 20-25 mm diam, tube 20-35 mm, white (Oct-Dec). **General:** Tubers edible. **Similar species:** *I. bolusiana* (see p. 420).

BORAGINACEAE - Forget-me-not or Borage Family Herbs, shrubs or trees. Flowers often in 1 sided inflorescences. Ornamentals, including herbs Borage and Comfrey. Widely distributed, ± 130 genera, ± 2300 species, 17 genera in SA. *Heliotropium* (*helios* - sun; *tropos* - turn) **-** Herbs and shrublets; inflorescence single or forked into 2 elongated spikes, coiled at tip, flowers on 1 side; ovary 4 lobed, 4 chambered. Attractive to butterflies, including the Grass Jewel *Freyeria trochylus*, Clark's Sorrel Copper *F. clarki*. Trop, temp regions, ± 150 species, ± 19 in SA.

Heliotropium steudneri String of Stars, Wild Heliotrope (named after H. Steudner, 1822-63, German who collected in Ethiopia and Eritrea in 1861-62)

Perennial herb, up to 600(900) mm. In disturbed grassland, dry thicket, SA to Ethiopia. Covered in thin, rough hairs throughout. **Leaves:** 20-60 x 4-15 mm, bright grey-green, veins indented above, margins wavy, stalkless or short stalked. **Flowers:** In single or forked inflorescences, ± 120 mm, flowers close set, small, ± 5 mm diam x 7 mm long, white, arranged on one side of arching spike (Oct-Mar).

Trichodesma (*trichos* - hair; *desmos* - bond, refers to hairs which unite the stamens) **-** Erect herbs; leaves usually opposite; flowers in terminal, much branched inflorescences, bell-shaped, calyx tube bell-shaped, enlarging around fruit. Trop and subtrop of Asia, Afr, Austr, ± 12 species, ± 6 in SA.

Trichodesma physaloides Chocolate Bells; Sjokoladeklokkies, Slangkop (A)

(*physaloides* - resembles *Physalis*, the Cape Gooseberry genus)

Shrublet, up to 500 mm. In grassland, on margins of marshes, N KZN to Sudan, Zaïre. Stems annual, **mostly hairless**, purplish brown. **Leaves:** 20-60 x 0,5-25 mm, lance-shaped, white spotted on margins and beneath, produced after flowers. **Flowers:** In branched inflorescences; flowers nodding, ± 25 mm, bluish white, **turning brown**, calyx purplish pink, ± 15 mm, lobes broad, pointed (Jul-Nov). **General:** Lovely shrublet, grown from seed. Blooms in spring, after fires.

★ *Ipomoea alba*

Geoff Nichols

Ipomoea albivenia

Geoff Nichols

Ipomoea crassipes

Tony Abbott

Ipomoea albivenia

Richard Symmonds

Heliotropium steudneri

Martin von Fintel

★ *Ipomoea purpurea*

Tony Abbott

Ipomoea plebeia

Geoff Nichols

Trichodesma physaloides

Darrel Plowes

Trichodesma physaloides

Jo Onderstall

Ipomoea simplex

Tony Abbott

179

Afrotysonia - Tall herbs; basal leaves very large; petal lobes reflexed, anthers exserted. Afr, 3 species, 2 in SA.

Afrotysonia glochidiata (gloch - a projecting point; refers to nutlets)
Erect herb, ± 1,5 m. In moist areas, 1430-2000 m. **Leaves:** Basal, 140-230 x 65-130 mm, rough, **grey-green**, stalks 260-300 mm. **Flowers: Branched, terminal inflorescences, 100-260 mm**; flowers 4-6,5 mm, white to pink with purple spots on upper lip (Dec-Mar). **Fruit:** Nutlets ± 9 x 10 mm, **covered in small bristles. Similar species:** Often misidentified as A. *tysoniana* Restricted to small area in S KZN/E Cape; leaves dark green; flowers 7-9 mm; nutlets ± 11 x15 mm, smooth, with broad marginal wing.

Lithospermum (*lithos* - stone; *sperma* - seed) - Perennial herbs. Mostly in temp areas, ± 60 species, ± 9 in SA.

Lithospermum papillosum (papillosum - warty or soft protuberances)
Tufted, perennial herb, up to 400 mm. In grassland, up to 2500 m. Rootstock woody. Stems slender, slightly branched. **Leaves:** Closely spaced, ± 25 x 8 mm, bristly hairy, stalkless. **Flowers: ± 4 mm, white to blue, hidden among densely leafy tips of shoots** (Oct-Jan). **Fruit:** Nutlets smooth, shiny white.

VERBENACEAE - Verben or Teak Family (for description see p. 422,470). *Lippia* (named after Augustin Lippi, 1678-1705, French natural historian and traveller) - Small aromatic shrubs. Mostly Trop America, ± 240 species, 6 in SA.

Lippia javanica Lemon Bush, Fever Tea; Lemoenbossie (A); mutswane, umsutane (Sw); inzinziniba (X); umsuzwane, umswazi (Z) (javanica - from Java)
Shrub, 1-2 m. In open woodland, Cape to Trop Afr. **Leaves:** ± 30 x 10 mm, margins toothed, **aromatic. Flowers:** In small inflorescences, ± 10 mm (throughout year). **General:** Infusion of leaves used as a tea. Traditionally used to treat coughs, rashes, sore muscles, for ritual cleansing after contact with a corpse and for protection against dogs, crocodiles, lightning. A fragrant cupboard freshener. Grown from seed.

Chascanum (*chascanum* - mask with wide open mouth) - Perennial herbs. Afr, ± 23 species, ± 14 in SA.

Chascanum hederaceum [= Plexipus hederaceus] White Trumpets (hederaceum - ivylike in habit)
Low growing herb, ± 300 mm. In grassland, KZN to Bots. Woody rootstock. **Roughly hairy. Leaves:** ± 30 mm diam, margins deeply toothed, reddish. **Flowers:** In slender, lengthening inflorescences; flowers ± 10 mm diam, creamy white, tube ± 20 mm, closing at night (Nov-Mar). **General:** Attractive garden plant, grown from seed.

Chascanum latifolium [= Plexipus latifolius] Broad-leaved Chascanum (latifolius - broad leaves)
Robust, **erect shrublet**, up to 500 mm. In grassland. Hairless to finely hairy. **Leaves:** ± 70 x 30 mm, **blunt tipped, margins entire. Flowers:** In slender, lengthening inflorescences; flowers ± 20 mm diam, tube slender, ± 15 mm, white to pale mauve, calyx ± 10 mm (Aug-Dec). **General:** Attractive garden plant, grown from seed.

Priva (*privus* - individual) - Erect perennials, ± harshly hairy. Afr, Asia Minor, C America, ± 16 species, ± 6 in SA.

Priva cordifolia [now P. flabelliformis] Blaasklits (A); isinama (Z)
Herb, up to 750 mm. On forest margins, disturbed areas, SA to Trop Afr. Stems 4 angled, **covered with clinging hairs. Leaves:** ± 60 x 30 mm, silvery beneath. **Flowers:** Small, white with pink stripe (Sep-Apr). **Fruit:** In enlarged calyx, **covered in hooked sticky hairs. General:** Flowers visited by butterflies; sticky fruit dispersed by animals. Used in traditional medicine to treat sores, wounds, ophthalmia.

LAMIACEAE (LABIATAE) - **Sage or Mint Family** Herbs or shrublets, aromatic (for description see p. 470). *Teucrium* (*teuknion* - named after the germander plant) - Herbs, shrubs or shrublets. Mostly N Hemisp, ± 200 species, 3 in SA.

Teucrium kraussii [= T. riparium] isihlungu (Z) (named after Christian Krauss, 1812-90, German scientist, traveller and collector in SA, 1839-40)
Erect, soft shrublet, 0,5-1,1 m. In grassland, woodland. Stems softly hairy. **Leaves:** 25-60 x 6-20 mm. **Flowers: In loose, branched inflorescences**; flowers 5-6 mm, white, downy (Dec-May). **General:** Used in traditional medicine as a tonic, to treat snakebite and to treat meat suspected of being infected with anthrax.

Acrotome (*akron* - summit; *tomos* - to slice) - Downy glandular herbs. Afr, ± 8 species, 6 in S Afr.

Acrotome hispida White Cat's Paws (hispida - with stiff bristles)
Weak, irregularly branched herb, up to 250 mm. In grassland, woodland. Woody rootstock, stems densely hairy. **Leaves:** ± 20 x 15 mm, shortly toothed at tip, almost stalkless. **Flowers:** In small clusters, in axils of upper leaves; flowers white, finely hairy, ± 10 mm, pinkish within, calyx ± 6 mm, ribbed, lobes spine tipped (Oct-Jun).

180

Afrotysonia glochidiata

Rosemary Williams

Afrotysonia glochidiata

Rosemary Williams

Lithospermum papillosum

Lal Greene

Lippia javanica

Tony Abbott

Chascanum hederaceum

Rosemary Williams

Chascanum latifolium

Rosemary Williams

Priva cordifolia

Lorraine van Hooff

Teucrium kraussii

Martin Von Fintel

Acrotome hispida

Van Wyk & Malan

Leucas (*leukos* - white) - Herbs; flowers in small clusters in axils of upper leaves, hairy, upper lip entire, erect, longer than lower 3-lobed lip, stamens protrude, calyx ribbed, up to 10 lobes. Old World trop, ± 160 species, 9 in SA.

Leucas glabrata (*glabrata* - hairless)

Spreading herb, up to 800 mm. In thicket, woodland, grassy rocky places, E Cape to Trop E Afr. Woody rootstock. **Stems brittle, 4 angled.** Thinly hairy throughout. **Leaves:** ± 40 x 20 mm, margins with few teeth. **Flowers: In small clusters**, in axils; flowers ± 20 mm, densely hairy, white, anthers red, calyx ± 10 mm, lobes ending in sharp spines (Sep-May). **General:** Leaves eaten as a vegetable. Browsed by game.

Leucas martinicensis   Tumble Weed; Tolbossie, Waaibossie (A); amandetshi (Z)

Robust annual herb, up to 1,2 m. In cultivated land, disturbed places, SA to Trop Afr, S America, a pantrop weed. Stems simple to much branched, finely hairy throughout. **Leaves:** 25-80 x 12-45 mm. **Flowers: In well spaced, crowded clusters, ± 25 mm diam**; flowers small, 6 mm, white, within bristly calyx, lobes 7-8, enlarging to 15 mm in fruit (Mar-Apr). **General:** Used as a vegetable and in traditional medicine for colds. **Similar species:** *L. lavandulifolia*   Coastal; leaves long, narrow; flowers ± 16 mm, lower lip ± 10 mm, calyx slanted, single large lobe above, 6-7 small side lobes.

Stachys (Greek for spike, originally an ear of wheat) - Annual or perennial herbs or shrubs; flowers in clusters, in terminal or axillary inflorescences, usually hairy, tube narrow, upper lip erect or arched, sometimes notched, lower lip longer, spreading, 3 lobed. Cosmop in subtrop and temp regions, ± 450 species, ± 40 in SA.

Stachys aethiopica   African Stachys, Wild Sage; Katpisbossie (A); bokhatha, bolao-ba-litaola, likhobe-tsa-bali-sana (SS)   (*aethiopica* - of Ethiopian origin)

Straggling, perennial herb, up to 600 mm. Widespread in dune bush, grassland, woodland, on forest margins, W Cape to Swaz. Variable, aromatic, hairy throughout, stems thinly branched. **Leaves:** 8-35(60) x 6-15(35) mm, **stalks short, ± 10** mm. **Flowers: In clusters of 3-6, fairly close set, lowest in axils of leaflike bracts**, in terminal inflorescences, lengthening with age; flowers ± 13 mm, white, calyx shaggy hairy, lobes pointed (Oct-May). **General:** Visited by honey-bees. Used traditionally to cure feverish delirium. Attractive groundcover in sun or shade.

Stachys cymbalaria   (*cymbalaria* - like toadflax)

Perennial, **prostrate herb**. In rocky grassland. Tap root. Stems radiate out ± 300 mm, slightly hairy to densely glandular hairy. **Leaves: Small**, 8-15 x 6-12 mm, margins with rounded teeth, sparsely hairy, stalks short or stalkless. **Flowers:** In pairs, 1-5 pairs per stem, far apart; flowers small, ± 10 mm, purple, pink or white, calyx 5-6 mm, hairy (Nov-Apr).

Stachys kuntzei   (named after Carl Kuntz, 1843-1907)

Perennial herb, 0,45-1 m. In rocky grassland, on sandstone ledges. Stems semi-succulent, stout, densely hairy throughout. **Leaves:** 35-70 x 25-50 mm, thick, margins finely toothed, stalks ± 30 mm, **upper leaves stalkless. Flowers:** In 6-flowered clusters, in simple inflorescences, branched towards base, **covered in glandular hairs**, **bracts broad, leaflike at base**, reduced towards tip; flowers ± 9 mm, white to pink, **calyx lobes spine tipped** (Jan-Mar).

Stachys natalensis   White Stachys

Straggling perennial herb, 120-500 mm. In grassland, wooded areas, E Cape to Zim. Stems few, hairy, sticky or not. **Leaves:** 10-40 x 6-24 mm, soft, dark olive green, margins with rounded teeth, stalks ± 12 mm. **Flowers:** In pairs, in terminal inflorescences; flowers ± 10 mm, white with lilac markings on lower lip, calyx densely hairy, 7-10 mm (Aug-May). **General:** Two varieties, differing in degree of hairiness.

Stachys nigricans   Swartteebossie (A); umusa (Z)   (*nigricans* - black)

Slender, erect, perennial herb, 0,4-1,2 m. In grassland, moist ground, coast to 1700 m. Stems simple or sparsely branched, covered in long spreading hairs, ridge between leaves. **Leaves:** 30-60 x 3-10 mm, margins slightly thickened, faintly toothed, stalks very short. **Flowers:** In 6-flowered, widely spaced clusters, lower bracts leaflike, inflorescence ± simple; flowers ± 10 mm, white speckles or tinged pink or mauve, calyx teeth fine pointed, densely hairy (Aug-Dec). **General:** Used in traditional medicine as a tonic and in love charm emetics. **Similar species:** *S. sessilis*   Found further inland, 600-2600 m, leaves broader.

Leucas glabrata

Leucas lavandulifolia

Leucas martinicensis

Stachys aethiopica

Stachys aethiopica

Stachys cymbalaria

Stachys kuntzei

Stachys natalensis

Stachys nigricans

183

Mentha (Latin for mint) - Aromatic herbs; flowers small, in clusters in congested spikes or round inflorescences. Several species grown for essential oils or as culinary herbs, such as Peppermint, Spearmint, Pennyroyal. Attracts butterflies, including *Cacyreus lingeus lingeus*. Cosmop, mostly N Hemisp, ± 25 species, ± 3 in SA.

Mentha longifolia Wild Spearmint; Kruisement (A); bohatsu, koena-ya-thaba (SS); inxina, inzinziniba (X); ufuthane lomhlanga (Z) (*longifolia* - long leaves)

Perennial herb, up to 1,5 m. In damp areas, Cape to Zim, then a gap to Ethiopia, Europe, E Asia. **Leaves:** Variable, 45-100 x 7-20 mm, velvety white beneath, margins entire or with short, widely spaced teeth; strongly scented. **Flowers:** In slender, terminal inflorescences, ± 100 x 12 mm; flowers small, 3-5 mm, white to mauve, stamens protruding (Dec-Feb). **General:** Used to make a herbal tea and in traditional medicine to treat chest complaints, wounds, headaches, stomach pains and during pregnancy to ease labour. Easily propagated. Two subspecies.

Hyptis (*hyptis* - laid back) - Perennial herbs; flowers densely clustered. America, ± 300 species, 3 in SA.

Hyptis pectinata (*pectinata* - comb)

Annual or short lived perennial, up to 2,3 m. On floodplains, streambanks, disturbed areas, KZN to Sudan, Trop America. Softly woody at base, downy throughout. **Leaves:** 15-45 x 10-30 mm, velvety whitish beneath, margins finely toothed, stalks 15-40 mm. **Flowers:** In dense clusters, in branched inflorescences, ± 450 mm; flowers small, 3 mm, creamy white to mauve (May-Sep). **General:** Visited by wasps.

Aeollanthus (from Aiolos, Greek god of wind; *anthos* - flower) - Flowers in loose inflorescences. Afr, ± 40 species, 6 in SA.

Aeollanthus parvifolius Pink Spur Bush (*parvifolius* - small leaves)

Perennial semi-succulent herb or shrublet, 200-500 mm. **Among rocks, on rock sheets.** Woody at base, hairy or not. **Leaves:** 12-28 x 8-25 mm, softly fleshy, margins sparingly toothed. **Flowers:** In much branched inflorescences, ± 200 mm, stems downy; flowers ± 12 mm, pink, mauve or white with mauve markings, tube deflexed, ± 9 mm, calyx very short (Nov-Apr). **General:** Easily grown from cuttings.

Plectranthus (*plektron* - a spur; *anthos*, flower, refers to base of flower tube) - Herbs or shrubs, often fleshy; flower clusters in spikelike inflorescences, bracts small. Attracts butterflies. Afr, Arabia, India, Austr, ± 300 species, ± 45 in SA, most of which are endemic to the area east of the Drakensberg plateau.

Plectranthus amboinicus Country Borage, Indian Mint, Soup Mint (*amboinicus* - after Amboina, a Moluccan Island)

Perennial succulent, many stemmed herb. In woodland, thicket, KZN to Kenya. Stems reclining, up to 1,5 m, downy. **Leaves:** 25-45 x 25-40 mm, velvety, pale brownish gland dots on both surfaces. **Flowers:** In dense, widely spaced clusters, in slender inflorescences, 100-300 mm, bracts persistent; flowers 7-9 mm, mauve to whitish (Aug-Jan). **General:** Leaves strongly aromatic. Used for flavouring food and in traditional medicine, particularly for treating cattle. In cultivation since late 1600s.

Plectranthus ciliatus Speckled Spur-flower, White Wild Sage; Gespikkelde Muishondblaar (A); lephele-phele (SS); umsuthuza (Z) (*ciliatus* - fringed with hairs)

Soft, slender herb, up to 600 mm. In forest, on forest margins, in moist areas. Stems trailing, rooting at nodes, softly hairy, maroon-purple. **Leaves:** Variable, 40-80 x 30-55 mm, **maroon-purple beneath**, veins prominent, margins toothed, stalks ± 13 mm, **Flowers:** ± 6 in clusters, in terminal inflorescences 100-280 mm; flowers ± 15 mm, white with purplish dots, humped on top, calyx bell-like (Sep-May). **General:** Formerly used to wash sheepskin garments, still sometimes used to wash clothing. Outstanding groundcover or container plant for damp, lightly shaded areas.

Plectranthus cylindraceus (*cylindraceus* - of cylindrical form)

Perennial, prostrate to scrambling herb, up to 1 m, in colonies. In woodland, thicket, on rocky slopes, E Cape to Ethiopia. **Leaves:** Clustered at base, slightly succulent, folded upwards, 25-50 x 15-40 mm, grey-green, velvety, pale yellow gland dots beneath, margins roundly toothed in upper half, stalks very short. **Flowers:** In dense, white woolly clusters, in long, sparsely branched, spikelike inflorescences, 100-350 mm; flowers small, 4-5 mm, pale mauve and white (Mar-Jul), sometimes strongly menthol-scented. **General:** A decorative plant for dry, hot, frost-free areas.

184

Mentha longifolia

Hilliard & Burtt

Hyptis pectinata

Geoff Nichols

Mentha longifolia

Wally Menne

Aeollanthus parvifolius

Tony Abbott

Aeollanthus parvifolius

Lawrence Peacock

Plectranthus cylindraceus

Martin von Fintel

Plectranthus ciliatus

Lorraine van Hooff

Plectranthus amboinicus

Wally Menne

185

Plectranthus grallatus Tuberous Spur-flower; Knolspoorsalie (A); umnyama-wempunzi (Z) (*grallatus* - stems rodlike, stilted)

Herb, 0,4-1,5 m. In forest, in rocky, shady places, 1340-2000 m. Annual stems, sparsely branched, fleshy, erect to reclining, finely hairy. **Leaves:** 50-160 x 35 -140 mm, thin to thick, smooth or rough, **red to brownish gland dots** beneath, margins irregularly toothed, **with small teeth between**, stalks 20-100 mm. **Flowers:** In branched inflorescences, 100-260 mm; flowers 9-13 mm, **white** flushed pink, a few spots on upper lip, spurred (Nov-Mar). **General:** Mosquitoes seen feeding on nectar.

Plectranthus grandidentatus Scented-leaved Spur-flower (*grandidentatus* - large teeth)

Perennial, semi-succulent, trailing herb, up to 600 mm. In dry rocky places, wood-land, E Cape to N Prov. Stems ± 2 m, velvety. Aromatic. **Leaves:** Softly succulent, 20-70 x 18-75 mm, **densely velvety**, red to brownish dots beneath, **margins with large, deep teeth**, stalks 15-45 mm. **Flowers:** In terminal inflorescences, some-times branched at base; flowers 7-13 mm, white, finely hairy (Nov-Apr). **General:** Good groundcover.

Plectranthus hadiensis [= *P. zatarhendi*] Wild Purple Salvia; iboza lehlathi, ilozane, imbozisa, inkunkwini (Z) (named after Hadiyah mountains in Yemen where it was first collected)

Perennial semi-succulent herb, 0,5-1,5 m. In rocky grassland, on forest margins, in dry woodland, E Cape to Arabia. Stems erect to trailing, **downy** or not. **Leaves:** 40-105 x 30-100 mm, bristly to velvety, gland dotted, margins toothed, stalks 10-40 mm. **Flowers:** 4-15, in tight clusters, in terminal branched inflorescences, 80-500 mm; flowers **mauve to purple** (white), 7-13 mm, finely hairy, gland dotted on lips (throughout year). **General:** Strong smelling. Used in the past as a fish poison. Used in traditional medicine as an enema, and as a sprinkling charm against evil spirits. Cultivated in Sri Lanka and India. Useful garden plant. Var. *hadiensis*, ± 0,6 m; leaves velvety; inflorescences 80-300 mm. Var. *tomentosus*, ± 1,5 m; leaves large, velvety; inflorescences 200-600 mm. Var. *woodii*, ± 0,6 m; leaves smaller, oval, sparsely bristly hairy; inflorescences 100-350 mm.

Plectranthus laxiflorus Citronella Spur-flower; Sitronellamuishondblaar (A); ubebebe, ufuthane, umadolwane, umsuthuza (Z) (*laxiflorus* - loose, limp flowers)

Slender herb or soft shrub, up to 1,5 m. On forest margins, streambanks, E Cape to Trop Afr. Much branched, stems thinly hairy. **Leaves:** 60-100 x 40-60 mm, reddish gland dots beneath, margins finely toothed, stalks 25-80 mm. **Flowers:** In simple or branched inflorescences, 100-300 mm; flowers 12-14 mm, white to pale mauve, 4-5 vertical lines on upper lip (Oct-Jun). **General:** Leaves have fresh, lemony scent. Reputed to be eaten in the Transkei. Used in traditional medicine for abdominal upsets, fevers, coughs, colds and as a mouthwash for loose, bleeding teeth.

Plectranthus madagascariensis Madagascar Spur-flower; Madagaskarmuishond-blaar (A); iboza lehlathi, ibozane, ilozane (Z)

Semi-succulent, aromatic herb, 0,4-1 m. In dry woodland, rocky grassland, on forest margins, E Cape to Moz. Stems brittle, erect to reclining. **Leaves:** 15-30(45) x 10 -25 mm, thickish, short stiff hairs above, woolly beneath, stalks 5-35 mm. **Flowers:** In slender inflorescences, 90-250 mm; flowers 5-18 mm, white to mauve, purple, calyx pouched, **upper lobe much bigger** (Feb-Nov). **General:** Used in traditional medicine to treat coughs, colds and scabies. Useful groundcover in full sun or light shade. Var. *madagascariensis*, **stems reclining, very hairy**; flowers 7-18 mm; a variegated form with white leaf margins is in cultivation. Var. *aliciae*, Pondoland, S KZN; **stems trailing or erect**; leaves thin; **flowers small**, 5-6 mm. Var. *ramosior*, **usually erect, small bush,** woolly; leaves thickish; flowers mauve, 8-12 mm.

Plectranthus rehmannii (named after Anton Rehmann ,1840-1917, Polish botanist and geographer, who visited SA between 1875-77)

Erect, branched herb or subshrub up to 1,2 m. On forest margins. Stems erect, finely hairy. **Leaves:** 80-140 x 50-80 mm, thick, sparsely hairy on veins, dark gland dots beneath, **margins finely toothed**, stalks 15-60 mm. **Flowers:** In branched inflorescences, 250-350 mm; **flowers small**, ± 7 mm, white, covered in white hairs, **upper lip very short, 2 mm**, calyx ± 9 mm, finely hairy (Jan-Apr).

Plectranthus grallatus

Plectranthus grandidentatus

Plectranthus hadiensis

Plectranthus madagascariensis

Plectranthus laxiflorus

Plectranthus rehmannii

187

Plectranthus verticillatus Gossip Plant, Money Plant; Skinderplant (A) (*verticillatus* - whorled)

Slender, straggling, semi-succulent herb, up to 750 mm. In moist and dry places, in scrub forest, woodland, on forest margins. **Leaves:** 16-40 x 12-40 mm, glossy dark green above, often purplish beneath, hairless to hairy, margins toothed, stalks 6-30 mm. **Flowers:** In slender, widely spaced inflorescences, 100-220 mm; flowers 9-25 mm, white to pale mauve with dark dots, **tube not narrowed towards throat** (Sep-Jun). **General:** Good groundcover in light shade and for hanging baskets.

Syncolostemon (*syn* - united; *kolos* - stunted; *stemon* - pillar, lower pair of filaments joined to the flower tube) - Herbs, rarely woody; leaves gland dotted, on short leafy branchlets in axils. Endemic to S Afr, 10 species.

Syncolostemon parviflorus Small-flowered White or Pink Plume; umnandi (Z) (*parviflorus* - small flowers)

Slender herb or soft shrublet, up to 1 m. In grassland, among rocks. Woody rootstock. Stems annual, sparsely branched. **Leaves:** In tufts, 12-32 x 2-12 mm, hairy, margins with few teeth near tip. **Flowers:** In 2s, in loose, widely branching inflorescences, 120-250 mm; flowers 10-12 mm, white to pinkish, calyx 5-6 mm, hairy within (Nov-May). **General:** Used in traditional medicine to treat loss of appetite.

Becium (ancient name for Sage) - Slightly woody herbs. Attracts Blues butterflies, including *Lepidochrysops asteris*, *L. ignota*, *L. ortygia*, *L. tantalus*, *L. variabilis*, *Eurychrysops dolorosa*. Mainly Afr, Arabia, India, ± 10 species, ± 4 in SA.

Becium obovatum [= *B. grandiflorum*] Cat's Whiskers; Katsnor (A); idada, iziba, ufukuzela, umathanjane (Z) (*obovatum* - egg-shaped, attached at the narrow end)

Herb, up to 300 mm. In grassland, E Cape to Bots. Woody rootstock. Annual stems. **Leaves:** 15-40 x 5-20 mm, variable, sparsely hairy to very hairy, margins entire or with few shallow teeth. **Flowers:** In well-spaced clusters, in terminal inflorescences; flowers 10-17 mm, white to pale mauve, **upper lip frilly, with violet lines, stamens protruding**, calyx wide open, enlarging to 10 mm in fruit (Sep-Feb). **General:** Used in traditional medicine for stomach complaints and as a hair restorer. (See p. 426)

SOLANACEAE - Tomato/Potato/Tobacco Family Herbs, shrubs (for description see p. 478). *Lycium* (*lykion* - name of thorny bush from Lycia, Asia Minor) - Branch tips often spiny. Warm and temp regions, ± 230 species, ± 16 in SA.

Lycium acutifolium (*acutifolium* - pointed leaves)

Shrub up to 1 m. In thicket. Much branched, **stems ending in spines**, hairless throughout. **Leaves:** Solitary or in clusters, ± 12 x 4 mm, thin. **Flowers:** Solitary, small, ± 8 mm, white, calyx cup-shaped with 5 short lobes, stalk lengthening in fruit (throughout year). **Fruit:** Oval berry, ± 7 x 3 mm, red. **General:** Browsed by game.

Solanum (Latin name for 'Nightshade') - Shrubs, herbs, small trees or climbers, spiny or not (for description see p. 478).

Solanum retroflexum Sobosobo Berry; Nastergal (A); limomonyane, lintsontso, mofukuthoane (SS); umjobo, umsobo (Sw); umsobo wesinja (X); ugqumugqumu, umsobosobo (Z) (*retroflexum* - turned back, refers to petals)

Slender, straggling herb, up to 700 mm. In disturbed areas, woodland, up to 2000 m. **Leaves:** Oval, ± 50 x 20 mm, **margins shallowly lobed**. **Flowers:** ± 16 mm diam, white, **petals and calyx lobes reflexed** (Aug-Jun). **Fruit:** Black, ± 8 mm diam. **General:** Browsed by bushbuck. Fruits eaten by people and animals **but considered poisonous when green**. A delicious preserve is made from the fruits. Leaves used as a pot herb or relish. Used in traditional medicine to treat abdominal upsets, wounds, ringworm, lumbago and many other ailments. **Similar species:**
S. nodiflorum Leaf margins entire; petals not reflexed. These species and 2 others previously mistaken for ★*S. nigrum*, cosmop weed, probably not found in this region.

Datura (from *tatorah*, Arabic name of a species of the genus) - Herbs, shrubs, trees; leaves large; flowers solitary, erect or hanging. Temp and warm regions, ± 42 species, 4 naturalised weeds in SA.

★ Datura stramonium Common Thorn Apple; Gewone Stinkblaar, Bloustinkblaar (A); lechoe (SS); lijowe (Sw); umhlavuthwa, umvumbangwe (X); ijoli, ijoye, iloyi (Z)

Annual herb, up to 1,5 m. **Declared weed**, Trop C & S America. Leaves ± 200 mm. Flowers ± 100 mm, white to purple (Aug-May). Capsule ± 50 x 30 mm, covered in slender spines ± 10 mm. Unpleasantly scented when crushed. Cultivated for atropine. Blue-green dye from leaves used to decorate hut interiors. Used for fuel and traditionally to treat asthma, headaches, wounds and as a diviner's aid. (See p. 588 for fruit)

Plectranthus verticillatus

Lorraine van Hooff

Syncolostemon parviflorus

Tony Abbott

Becium obovatum

Tom de Waal

Becium obovatum

Tony Abbott

Lycium acutifolium

Geoff Nichols

Solanum retroflexum

Tony Abbott

Solanum nodiflorum

C J Ward

★ *Datura stramonium*

Van Wyk & Malan

189

SCROPHULARIACEAE - Snapdragon Family Annual or perennial herbs, shrubs (for description see p. 72).
Nemesia (from *Nemesion* the Greek name for a similar plant) - Annual or perennial herbs (for description see p. 428).

Nemesia silvatica White Forest Nemesia (*silvatica* - from forest)
Bushy herb, up to 1 m. In rocky places **in forest, on forest margins**, 900-1950 m. **Leaves:** 20-70 x 10-35 mm, margins toothed, stalks 5-20 mm. **Flowers:** In **delicate,** branched, terminal inflorescences; flowers ± 20 mm, **mouth white** (tinged yellow), **spur long, 6-9 mm** (Oct-Apr). **Fruit:** 3-10 mm. **Similar species:** *N. melissifolia* Inflorescence more congested, flowers clustered at nodes, white to pale mauve, spur shorter, 4-5 mm, two raised hairy bosses entrance to spur.

Diclis (double folding, or 2 winged, possibly refers to flower lobes) - Annual or perennial herbs; leaves opposite; flowers in axils, tube short, spur 2 lobed; fruit a capsule. Afr, Madag, ± 10 species, ± 5 in SA.

Diclis reptans Dwarf Snapdragon, Toadflax; koenana, ponye (SS); isinama (Z)
(*reptans* - creeping and rooting)
Sprawling, mat-forming herb, up to 200 mm. In damp, shady places, open grassland, coast to 2000 m. **Roots fibrous.** Stems reddish, hairy. **Leaves:** ± 30 x 35 mm, **margins deeply, sharply toothed**, stalks long, ± 25 mm. **Flowers:** Solitary, ± 10 mm, white to pale mauve, spur slender, 2-3 mm, calyx lobes pointed, upper lobe narrow (Sep-May). **General:** Edible. Used traditionally to treat distemper in dogs. (See p. 428)

Manulea (*manus* - a hand, refers to spreading flower lobes) - Herbs, rarely shrubby; leaves mostly clustered at base; flowers in clusters in long inflorescence, tube narrow, petal lobes 5, folding back. Afr, mostly S Afr, ± 70 species.

Manulea florifera (*florifera* - bearing flowers)
Perennial herb, up to 1 m. On damp grassy slopes, 1500-2100 m. Stems simple below inflorescence, hairs balloon tipped. **Leaves:** Basal, 80-200 x 13-25 mm, tapering to both ends, margins obscurely toothed or entire; upper leaves smaller, more distant. **Flowers: In congested clusters in branched inflorescence**, ± 200 mm; flowers ± 9 mm, white (tube yellow at base) or mauve (tube purplish) (Dec-Apr).

Jamesbrittenia (named after James Britten, 1846-1924, a British botanist) - Stamens hidden (not visible to the eye). Differs from *Sutera* which has stamens protruding. Mostly S Afr.

Jamesbrittenia kraussiana [= *Sutera kraussiana*] Kerriebos (A); usikisiki lwehlathi (Z)
(named after Christian Krauss, 1812-90, German scientist, traveller and collector in SA 1839-40)
Slender perennial herb, 150-600 mm. In thicket, grassland, on forest margins, coast to 800 m. Much branched, slender, leafy, glandular hairy. **Leaves:** 15-45 x 3-20 mm, **margins coarsely toothed**, stalks short. **Flowers: In loose, leafy inflorescences**; flowers ± 8 mm, white or pale lilac, **stalks slender**, ± 25 mm, spreading, curved (throughout year). **General:** Used in traditional medicine to treat menstrual pains.

Sutera (named after Johan Suter, 1766-1827, Swiss botanist and physician) - Stamens exserted. S Afr, ± 49 species.

Sutera floribunda [=*S. arcuata*] Kerriebos (A); boluma (SS); usikisiki lwehlathi (Z)
(*floribunda* - flowering abundantly)
Much branched, aromatic, perennial herb, up to 1 m. In grassland, on forest margins, E Cape to Zim, coast to 2600 m. Stems simple at first, erect or straggling, softly hairy. **Leaves:** Opposite, 10-40 x 10-30 mm, **margins toothed**, narrowing abruptly to short stalks. **Flowers: In profusion, in large, leafy, branching inflorescences, branchlets opposite**; flowers, ± 12 mm wide, white, pollen yellow, stalks slender, ± 10 mm (Jan-May). **General:** Visited by honey-bees. Used in traditional medicine to treat chest colds and relieve menstrual pains. Grown from cuttings. (See p. 480)

Zaluzianskya (named after Adam Zalusiansky von Zaluzian, 1558-1613, physician and botanist from Prague) - Annual or perennial herbs; flowers in axils or terminal inflorescences; flower tube elongate, cylindric with 5 petal lobes, regular or 2 lipped, usually white above, red below; fruit a capsule. Afr, ± 50 species in SA.

Zaluzianskya distans (*distans* - far apart, straggly)
Short-lived perennial herb, up to 450 mm. **Under scrub and boulders**, near streams, 1765-2200 m. **Stems leafy, simple when young**, becoming **sparsely branched**, long white hairs. **Leaves:** 20-60 x 9-30 mm, margins irregularly toothed. **Flowers: In loose, spreading inflorescences;** tube 24-50 mm, lobes deeply notched, ± 10 mm, white with band of red, orange or pale yellow round mouth, pinkish red beneath, bracts leaflike, toothed, open at dusk or in dull light **(Dec-Mar). Similar species:** *Z. ovata* [= *Z. montana*] Aromatic, **twiggy, leafy shrublet**; on partly shaded cliff faces, bare slopes, 1750-3230 m; leaf margins entire to coarsely toothed or lobed; flowers in **crowded inflorescences**, occasionally with orange band around mouth (Oct-Jan).

190

Nemesia silvatica

Manulea florifera

Jamesbrittenia kraussiana

Diclis reptans

Sutera floribunda

Zaluzianskya distans

Zaluzianskya ovata

Zaluzianskya elongata (*elongata* - elongate)

Perennial herb, up to 600 mm. In mountain grassland, up to 1800 m. Tap root thick, woody, vegetative buds small. Several stems from crown, white hairy. **Leaves:** 35-70 x 2-8 mm, smaller, more widely spaced upwards, margins entire or with few small teeth. **Flowers:** In **long, narrow, elongating inflorescence**; **flower tube long, 30-44 mm**, glandular hairy, **lobes held vertically, 2 above, 3 below**, deeply notched, red outside, white inside; open at dusk or in dull light (Feb-Apr), scented.

Zaluzianskya microsiphon   Short-tubed Drumsticks; Kortbuis Zaluzianskya (A)

(*microsiphon* - small tubular flowers)

Perennial herb, up to 400 mm. In rocky grassland, 1525-2745 m. 1-3 stems, with shaggy white hairs, **thick clump of partly buried vegetative buds at base. Leaves: In basal rosette**, 35-90 x 8-20 mm, margins entire to faintly toothed, more or less hairy on margins, midrib. **Flowers:** In dense, long inflorescence, bracts 15-30 mm; **flowers erect, divided into two halves, 2 lobes above, 3 below**, tube 20-40(52) mm, lobes deeply notched (and notched again), pinkish red outside, creamy white inside, **open in full sun** (Dec-Apr). **General:** Flower size variable, tube short in some areas.

Zaluzianskya natalensis

Perennial herb, up to 350 mm. In grassland, up to 1700 m. Stem **solitary**, stout, hairy, **thick clump of partly buried vegetative buds at base. Leaves:** 60-90 x 15-25 mm, margins entire or toothed, thinly hairy. **Flowers:** In **short, dense inflorescence**, not elongating, bracts leaflike; flower tube 32-50 mm, held horizontally, lobes deeply notched, 6-8 mm, white inside, mouth with thick circlet of hairs, red beneath, **calyx 16-30 mm**, open at dusk or in dull light (Oct-Apr). **Similar species:** *Z. pachyrrhiza* In coastal grassland; thickened tap root, ± 15 mm diam, crown without clump of vegetative buds; hairless; elongating in fruit. *Z. maritima* Coastal, E Cape to S KZN; tap root woody; stems branching from base; leaves almost fleshy; flowers not hairy inside, scented. A number of species were previously misidentified as *Z. maritima*.

Mimulus (*mimo* - ape, flowers resemble monkey face) - Herbs. Mostly trop America, ± 60 species, 2 in SA, 1 introduced.

Mimulus gracilis   Wild Monkey Flowers; sehlapetsu (SS)   (*gracilis* - slender)

Perennial herb, up to 600 mm. In moist places, SA to Trop Afr, India, Austr. Stems branched from base. **Leaves:** 12-60 x 2-15 mm, clasping at base, margins entire or toothed. **Flowers:** Clustered towards ends of stems; flowers ± 10 mm, white or pink, yellow spotted in throat, stalks ± 30 mm (Oct-Feb). **General:** Used in traditional medicine to treat irregular menstruation and bathe tired, feverish patients.

Limosella (*limosus* - muddy; *sella* - a seat, refers to the habit) - Marsh or aquatic herbs, usually creeping, rooting at nodes; leaves usually in rosette; flowers among leaves. Cosmop, ± 18 species, ± 6 in SA.

Limosella grandiflora   Blouwaterblommetjie, Tongblaar (A); bolibana, tsika-metsi (SS)

(*grandiflora* - large flowers)

Small aquatic or marsh herbs, 40-200 mm, forming dense mats in ponds, marshes. Long runners, rooting, with flowers at nodes. **Leaves:** Oval, 6-40 x 4-25 mm, tips rounded, stalks 6-120 mm, robust or slender, enabling leaf blade to float on surface. **Flowers:** ± 12 mm diam, white, hairy within, **calyx lobes short**, triangular, hairless, **stalks short** (Dec-Mar). **General:** Used by diviners.

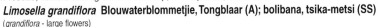

Limosella longiflora (*longiflora* - long flowers)

Tiny aquatic herb, up to 50 mm, in dense colonies. In mud and shallow water, 1800 -3000 m. **Leaves:** Needle-shaped, 25-50 mm, erect to spreading. **Flowers:** ± 7 mm diam, very pale blue to pink, **calyx strongly 5 veined**, erect, pointed, stalks slender, erect, bending in fruit (Sep-Nov).

Limosella major   bolibana, tsika-metsi (SS)

Small aquatic herb, up to 150 mm. In shallow water, marshy places, 1800-2400 m. **Runners** from nodes producing clusters of roots. **Leaves:** 12-40 x 2-15 mm, blade spoon-shaped, tapering into long stalks, margins entire or with 1-2 lobes, stalks 15-100 mm, robust, erect. **Flowers:** Solitary, ± 10 mm diam, on **erect stalks**, bending in fruit, shorter than leaves, white to blue (Sep-Mar). **General:** Used by diviners.

Zaluzianskya elongata   *Zaluzianskya microsiphon*   *Zaluzianskya microsiphon*

Zaluzianskya natalensis   *Mimulus gracilis*   *Mimulus gracilis*

Limosella longiflora   *Limosella grandiflora*

Limosella longiflora   *Limosella major*

Craterostigma (*krateros* - mouth of volcano, refers to cup-shaped stigma) - Small perennial herbs; leaves entire, in rosette at base. Afr, Madag, ± 20 species, 2 in SA.

Craterostigma nanum Mole's Spectacles (*nanum* - dwarf)

Dwarf perennial herb, up to 75 mm. In shallow soil on rocky outcrops, in moist areas, SA to Trop Afr. Rhizome thick or thin. **Leaves:** Clustered at base, ± 25 x 9 mm, thick, narrowed to base, 3 conspicuous veins, finely hairy beneath, stalks short, broad. **Flowers:** In dense inflorescences; flowers ± 14 mm, white, throat blue with two orange spots, stalks very short (Dec-Mar). **General:** A 'resurrection plant', leaves dry out in dry periods and reabsorb water to recover in 24 hours after rain. **Similar species:** *C. wilmsii* E Cape; taller, ± 300 mm.

Lindernia (named after F B von Lindern, botanist and author from Strasburg) - Previously known as *Ilysanthes*.

Lindernia conferta [= *Ilysanthes conferta*]

Aquatic herb, 100-200 mm, lower parts submerged, rooting. In shallow, rocky mountain pools, 1800-2150 m. **Leaves:** In rosettes, **floating, crowded at top of stem,** fleshy, 4-16 x 1-6 mm, shiny, minutely dotted. **Flowers:** In leaf axils, ± 8 mm diam, white blotched purple on lower lip and throat (Dec-Feb). **Similar species:** *L. parviflora* [= *L. capensis*] Annual herb, ± 300 mm; coast to mountains; stems square, trailing or erect, branched, glossy; leaves in pairs, 6-30 x 3-15 mm, 3-5 veined; flowers 10 mm, pale blue to white (Sep-Mar); previously incorrectly identified as *Ilysanthes dubia*. Grazed by cattle.

Hebenstretia (named after Johann Hebenstreit, 1720-91, prof of medicine at Leipzig, also St Petersburg) - Annual or perennial herbs or shrubs; leaves opposite or alternate, often narrow; flowers in dense slender inflorescences, tube slender, with 4 short lobes. Afr, ± 25 species, mainly W and SW Cape.

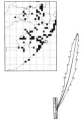

Hebenstretia comosa Katstert (A); lebohlollo, tsitoane (SS) (*comosa* - with hairy tufts)

Perennial shrublet, up to 0,6(1) m. In grassland, sandy or rocky, coast to mountains, E Cape to N Prov, Malawi. Woody rootstock. Stems many, annual, unbranched. **Leaves:** 30-60 x 1-8 mm, margins entire or toothed. **Flowers:** Densely crowded in slender, elongated inflorescences, ± 200 mm, growth indefinite; flowers ± 12 mm, white to pink or yellow with yellow or orange blotch at base of lower lip (Jul-Apr), heavily scented. **General:** Visited by a beetle species. Hardy garden plant. **Similar species:** *H. dura* Up to 600 mm; in rocky grassland, 950-2450 m, E Cape to N Prov; hairy or not; leaves crowded, 8-30 x 1-5 mm; inflorescences 30-80 (150) mm; mixed with fat to make a perfumed ointment.

Hebenstretia oatesii [=*H. polystachya*] tsitoane (SS) (named after Frank Oates, 1840-75, naturalist and traveller who came to SA in 1873)

Tall, erect herb, up to 1(2) m. In swamps, marshy grassland, KZN to N Prov. Single stemmed at base, branching in upper third, leafy. **Leaves:** ± 80 x 5 mm, margins with small teeth, clasping at base. **Flowers:** In very dense, branched inflorescences, ± 100 mm; flowers slender, ± 10 mm, white with red spot (Oct-Jun), scented. **General:** 3 subspecies described, only subsp. *oatesii* found in this region.

Selago (*sel* - sight; *jach* - salutary, refers to supposed medicinal properties) - Herbs or shrublets; leaves alternate or in clusters; flowers small, in dense, round, or broad, branching, sometimes irregular inflorescences; fruit 2 nutlets, not splitting. Attracts butterflies of the *Lepidochrysops* genus. Afr, ± 150 species, mostly SA.

Selago densiflora [= *Walafrida densiflora*] (*densiflora* - densely flowered)

Perennial, much branched herb, up to 450 mm. In grassland, woodland, W Cape to N Prov. Stems slender, sprawling, from woody rootstock. **Leaves:** In clusters, needlelike, ± 10 mm. **Flowers:** In small round clusters on side branchlets; flowers white (mauve), small (Nov-Apr).

Selago elongata (*elongata* - drawn out)

Perennial shrublet, 0,3-1 m. In scrub, rough grassland, near rivers. **Leaves: In clusters,** 10-22 x 1-2 mm, leathery, sharp tipped, margins entire. **Flowers: In elongate inflorescences**; flowers 4-5 mm, white, **stalkless** (Sep-Nov). **Similar species:** *S. trinervia* Tufted perennial herb, in grassland, on rock outcrops, coast to 2100 m; branches straggling, ± finely hairy; leaf margins entire, rarely with 1-2 pairs small teeth in upper half; flowers with short stalks, in simple, terminal, inflorescences, congested in bud, elongating with age, ± 100 mm (Nov-Feb).

Craterostigma nanum — Darrel Plowes

Lindernia conferta — Lawrence Peacock

Hebenstretia comosa — Martin von Fintel

Hebenstretia comosa — Martin von Fintel

Hebenstretia dura — Tom de Waal

Selago densiflora — Jo Arkell

Hebenstretia oatesii — Lal Greene

Hebenstretia dura — Lal Greene

Selago elongata — Tony Abbott

Hebenstretia oatesii — Olaf Wirminghaus

195

Selago monticola (*monticola* - growing on hills)
Perennial herb, 0,3-1 m. On grassy slopes, in valleys, near streams, 1300-2100 m. Woody tap root. **Stems few, erect, simple to sparingly branched below**, closely leafy, downy. **Leaves:** 7-20(35) x 1-3(10) mm, narrowed at base, margins thickened, entire, toothed on larger leaves, hairy above. **Flowers: In branching inflorescences**, branchlets tipped with flower clusters ± 10 mm diam (elongating in fruit to 30 -50 mm); flowers ± 5 mm diam, white, stalks short (blooms throughout year).

Selago tarachodes (*tarach* - trouble, disorder, refers to the confusion over the identity of this species, previously incorrectly identified as *S. woodii* or *S. hyssopifolia*)
Perennial herb, 0,2-1,2 mm. In grassland, coast to 600 m. Rootstock woody. Stems reclining to erect, downy. **Leaves:** In clusters, 7-35 x 1-7 mm, margins thickened, **hairs on margin, midrib. Flowers: In compact inflorescences**, 40-90 mm diam; flowers ± 5 mm diam, white (throughout year) faintly scented. **General:** Visited by wasps, flies, butterflies. Hardy garden plant, grown from seed or cuttings. **Similar species:** *S. hyssopifolia* In scrub, on margins of streams, forest, coast to 700 m; flowers smaller, in crowded clusters 20-40 mm diam, in large, loose inflorescences.

Cycnium (*kyknos* - swan, probably refers to slender, elongated, furry flower tube) - Perennial parasitic herbs; flowers nearly regular, large, in axils, forming terminal inflorescences. Afr, ± 40 species, ± 3 in SA.

Cycnium adonense **Ink Plant; Inkblom (A)** (*adonense* - resembles genus *Adonis* of Ranunculaceae)
Low-growing herb, 100-200 mm. In grassland, on rocky slopes, E Cape to Trop Afr. Rootstock woody. Leaves: ± 70 x 30 mm, **roughly hairy, margins sharply toothed. Flowers: Large**, ± 50 mm wide, tube ± 70 (120) mm, white, turning blue-black when bruised, calyx ± 40 mm, lobes blunt (Sep-Jan), scented. **General:** Conspicuous after fires. Used in traditional medicine as a remedy for snakebite.

Harveya (named after Dr William Harvey 1811-1866, chief author of early volumes of Flora Capensis, prof of botany in Dublin) - Parasitic herbs; leaves reduced to scales; dense spikelike inflorescences, style curved downwards with flattened stigma, anthers 2 chambered, only one containing pollen. Afr, Mascarene Is, ± 40 species, ± 25 in SA.

Harveya speciosa **Tall Ink Flower; Inkblom (A); mokunye, seona (SS); isinama (X); umshelezana omhlophe (Z)** (*speciosa* - beautiful)
Showy parasitic herb, 0,3-1 m. In grassland, thicket, damp areas, coast to 2000 m. Stems erect, orange to reddish. **Leaves:** Soft, slightly fleshy, scalelike, ± 30 mm, stem clasping, greenish yellow to reddish. **Flowers: ± 70 mm wide and long, creamy white**, yellow in throat, tube narrow, 50-100 x 3-6 mm, calyx ± 45 x 10 mm (Oct-Mar), scented. **General:** Flowers turn blue-black when bruised. Used in traditional medicine to treat bruises, dizziness, clear congested nasal passages and for mental disturbances. Parasitic on grasses and plants of Asteraceae (Compositae).

GESNERIACEAE - African Violet Family Mostly herbs. Flowers irregular, oblique, more or less 2 lipped, 5 lobed. Fruit a dry capsule. Economically important as ornamentals such as Gloxinia (*Sinningia*), African Violet (*Saintpaulia*), Cape Primrose (*Streptocarpus*) and *Achimenes*. Trop, ± 139 genera, ± 2900 species, 1 genus in SA.
Streptocarpus (*streptos*, twisted; *karpos* - fruit, capsules twist into narrow spirals) - Often epiphytic, some plants die after flowering (monocarpic); leaves solitary or in rosette, continuously growing from base, often withering at tip; flowers solitary or in inflorescence; fruit a capsule with spirally twisted valves. Afr, ± 135 species, ± 51 in SA.

Streptocarpus candidus (*candidus* - pure white)
Perennial herb, up to 300 mm. In forest, on damp banks and as an epiphyte, 1050 -1200 m. **Vertical underground stem**, ± 10 mm diam. **Leaves: In rosette**, ± 600 x 200 mm, suberect, margins scalloped, softly hairy, veins sometimes reddish beneath. **Flowers:** ± 25 in inflorescence; flowers **tubular**, ± 40 mm, **white** to palest violet, floor of tube with yellow stripe streaked violet, **two purplish chevrons** at base of lower lip, stalks ± 20 mm (Nov-Feb), honey-scented. **Fruits:** Capsule 28-65 x 2 mm. **General:** Plants on forest margins smaller, less robust than in deep forest. **Similar species:** *S. wilmsii* Leaf solitary; flowers without purplish chevrons on lip.

Streptocarpus pusillus (*pusillus* - weak, small)
Small herb, up to 120 mm. On cliff faces, banks and mossy rocks in kloof forest, 1200-2600 m. **Leaves:** 1 (2-3), ± 220 x 160 mm, margins scalloped, green on both sides. **Flowers:** ± 30 in inflorescence, many open at once; flowers ± 18 mm, white, sticky glandular outside, tube cylindric, stalks 5-10 mm (Nov-Apr). **Fruit:** Capsule 15-25 x 2 mm. **General:** Plant dies after flowering. (See p. 486)

Selago tarachodes

Tom de Waal

Selago monticola

Trevor Coleman

Ken Farnsworth

Cycnium adonense

Harveya speciosa

Godfrey Symons

Martin von Fintel

Streptocarpus candidus

Streptocarpus pusillus

Lal Greene

197

LENTIBULARIACEAE - Bladderwort Family Perennial herbs, aquatic or in swamps. Leaves alternate or in rosettes, submerged leaves modified into bladderlike pitchers with traps for catching insects. Inflorescences held above water, flowers 2 lipped, spurred or pouched at base. Fruit dry. Cosmop, ± 3 genera, ± 245 species, 2 genera in SA.

Utricularia (*utriculus* - little leather bottle, refers to insect-trapping bladders on the leaves and runners) - Perennial herbs, in water or in damp places, usually with traps; flowers 2 lobed, spurred. Cosmop, ± 40 species, ± 18 in SA.

Utricularia inflexa Bladderwort; Blaaskruid (A); tlamana-sa-metsi (SS) (*inflexa* - bent abruptly)

Free-floating aquatic herb. In lakes, pans, E Cape to Trop Afr, coast to 1700 m. Submerged stolons ± 1 m. **Leaves:** 3-10 floating leaves in rosette, 20-50 x 2-5 mm; **submerged leaves copiously divided, segments very fine**, 10-60 mm; traps, ± 2 mm diam. **Flowers:** 2-16 in inflorescences, stems 30-330 mm, supported by rosette of inflated leaf stalks; flowers ± 10 mm, white or pale mauve with red-purple veins (Dec-Jun). **Fruit:** Capsules ± 5 mm diam, within fleshy, enlarged calyx, ± 10 mm. **General:** Eaten by waterfowl. Attractive for aquaria. **Similar species:** *U. benjaminiana* Densely hairy; flowers with large inflated spur, calyx tiny.

ACANTHACEAE - Acanthus Family Herbs, shrubs or climbers (for description see p. 76). *Phaulopsis* (*phaulos* - slight, trivial; *opsis* - appearance) - Scrambling or erect herbs. Afr, Mascarene Is, India, ± 19 species, ± 3 in SA.

Phaulopsis imbricata umhlonyane (Z) (*imbricata* - covered in scales arranged like tiles of house)

Trailing herb, stems erect, 0,8-1 m. In open scrub, woodland, on forest margins, E Cape to Trop Afr. Thinly hairy. **Leaves: One of each pair larger than the other**, ± 80 x 50 mm, unequal sided at base. **Flowers:** In clusters, ± 70 x 20 mm, flowers ± 20 mm, white, bracts broad, overlapping (Mar-Aug). **Fruit:** Flattened, exploding. **General:** Unpleasantly scented. Attracts butterflies. Good garden groundcover.

Chaetacanthus (*chaite* - bristle; *akanthos* - a thorn) - Doubtfully distinct from *Dyschoriste*. Shrublets. SA, 3 species.

Chaetacanthus burchellii Fairy Stars (named after William J Burchell, 1781-1863, naturalist, traveller, artist, author)

Shrublet up to 250 mm. In grassland. Woody rootstock. Many green to reddish stems, slightly hairy throughout. **Leaves:** ± 20 x 13 mm, long hairs on margins and veins. **Flowers: In small clusters at nodes**, ± 12 x 8 mm, white with pink pollen, lobes spreading, calyx ± 10 mm, lobes deeply divided, long, narrow, mauvish with **long white hairs** (Sep-May). **Similar species:** *C. setiger* Hairy, often with stalked glands; flowers hidden amongst leaves and bracts; attracts butterflies.

Ruellia (named after Jean de la Ruelle of Soissons, physician to Francis I, author of De Natura Plantarum 1536) - Herbs; flowers solitary or in small groups in axils. Attracts butterflies. Trop America, Afr, Asia, Austr, ± 150 species, ± 13 in SA.

Ruellia sp. nov. (incorrectly known as *R. patula*)

Perennial, low-growing herb. In woodland, grassland. Rootstock woody. Stems soft, thinly hairy. **Leaves:** ± 25 x 15 mm, margins slightly wavy, **stalks ± 12 mm**. **Flowers:** ± 20 mm wide, white or mauve with darker streaks, **tube long, ± 25 mm**, finely hairy (throughout year). **General:** Attracts butterflies. Attractive groundcover.

Crabbea (named after Rev George Crabbe, 1754-1832, amateur botanist) - Perennial herbs, usually stemless; flowers 2 lipped, in dense clusters surrounded by basal bracts with marginal spines. Afr, ± 13 species, ± 7 in SA.

Crabbea hirsuta Prickle Head; manxasana (X); ihlasi, umusa (Z) (*hirsuta* - hairy)

Perennial herb, up to 400 mm. In grassland. **Stems erect to trailing, often zigzag.** Hairy. **Leaves:** ± 150 x 40 mm, narrowing to both ends. **Flowers:** In dense inflorescences, ± 60 mm diam; flowers ± 12 mm wide, tube ± 20 mm, white, outer bracts tapering to long fine point, with long white hairs, **margins with straight spines** (Feb-Mar). **General:** Used in traditional medicine. **Similar species:** *C. acaulis* Stemless; leaves flat on ground; bracts with marginal spines often curved.

Barleria (named after Jacques Barrelier, 1606-1673, monk and botanist) - Herbs or shrubs (for description see p. 488).

Barleria elegans White Bushveld Barleria; umhlalulwane (Z) (*elegans* - graceful)

Scrambling shrublet, up to 1 m. In thicket, woodland, KZN to Trop Afr. Rootstock woody. Annual stems, finely hairy throughout. **Leaves:** ± 80 x 30 mm, dark green, paler beneath, stalks ± 10 mm, **spines in axils**. **Flowers:** In few-flowered clusters in axils; flowers ± 20 mm wide, white, tube ± 20 mm, bracteoles spiny, calyx lobes erect, ± 20 mm, **margins spiny** (Mar-Apr). **Fruit:** Capsules open with explosive crack. **General:** Hardy garden plant for hot dry areas. Colonises disturbed areas.

198

Utricularia benjaminiana

Utricularia benjaminiana

Utricularia inflexa

Phaulopsis imbricata

Chaetacanthus burchellii

Ruellia sp. nov.

Crabbea hirsuta

Crabbea acaulis

Barleria elegans

199

Sclerochiton (skleros - hard; chiton - covering, refers to woody capsule) - Shrubs. Afr, ± 12 species, 6 in SA.

Sclerochiton odoratissimus (odoratissimus - very sweet odour)
Erect shrub, up to 2 m. In open forest, on forest margins, streambanks, 750-1500 m. Young stems finely hairy. **Leaves:** ± 15-45 x 7-20 mm, finely hairy on midrib and on large veins beneath, **sparsely hairy all over. Flowers:** Scattered or 2-5 in terminal clusters, ± 20 mm, **white** (pink), **deflexed,** tube short, less than 5 mm, bracteoles 5-9 mm, dark brown, not glossy (Feb), **sweetly scented. Fruit:** Capsule ± 17 mm. **Similar species:** *S. harveyanus* (see p. 490).

Asystasia - Herbs or weak shrublets. Afr, India, China, Malaya, Austr, ± 60 species, ± 7 in SA.

Asystasia gangetica Asystasia; isihobo (Z) (gangetica - Ganges River in India)
Spreading herb, up to 600 mm. In woodland, forest. **Leaves:** ± 40 x 20 mm. **Flowers:** ± 15 mm wide, white with purplish markings on lower lip (throughout year). **General:** Leaves eaten as spinach. Very attractive to butterflies. Flowers eaten by beetles, visited by large black ants. Useful groundcover in shade.

Hypoestes (hypo - beneath; estia - house, undergarment) - Evergreen herbs, shrubs (for description see p. 436).

Hypoestes forskaolii White Ribbon Bush (named after Pehr Forskaöl, 1732-63)
Straggling, perennial herb, up to 0,6(1,6) m. In thicket, woodland, rocky grassland, coast to mountains, E Cape to Kenya. Stems root at nodes. **Leaves:** 19-76(120) x 12 -35(60) mm, narrowing to stalks, ± 60 mm. **Flowers:** In slender inflorescences, **flowers arranged on one side of spike;** flowers ± 20 mm, white to pink, dark lilac nectar guides (Feb-Dec). **General:** Attracts bees and butterflies. Good garden plant.

Ruttya (named after Dr John Rutty, 1697-1775, Irish naturalist) - Shrublets. Afr, 3 species, 1 in SA.

Ruttya ovata Ruttya; unhlalwana lomfula (Z) (ovata - elliptic, broader at base)
Scrambling shrub, 1-2(4) m. On forest margins, in woodland. Stems much branched. **Leaves:** ± 120 x 40 mm. **Flowers:** In dense, terminal inflorescences, ± 75 x 30 mm; flowers ± 20 mm, white with mauve speckles, **bracts, calyx lobes long, very narrow, pale yellowish green** (Dec-May), pleasant scent. **Fruit:** Club-shaped, ± 40 x 7 mm, sharply pointed. **General:** Visited by butterflies, carpenter-bees. Popular garden plant.

Isoglossa (iso - equal; glossa - tongue) - Herbaceous or slightly woody shrubs. Afr, India; ± 15 species in SA.

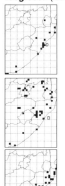

Isoglossa ciliata (ciliata - fringed)
Herb, up to 900 mm. On forest margins, streambanks. Softly hairy. **Leaves: Widely spaced,** ± 60 x 30 mm, one slightly smaller than the other. **Flowers:** In short, compact inflorescences; flowers ± 10 mm, white or pink spotted red on lower lip, bracts very hairy, calyx lobes as long as tube (Sep-Apr). **General:** Visited by honey-bees.

Isoglossa grantii (named after William Grant, 1832-62, doctor, naturalist who collected in Natal in 1854-56)
Perennial shrublet, up to 1 m. In thicket, woodland. Hairy throughout, unpleasantly scented. **Leaves:** ± 40 x 15 mm, margins slightly wavy, densely hairy. **Flowers:** In long, narrow, compact inflorescences; flowers white or mauve, lower lip with raised, pleated surface, bracts with long hairs and glands, calyx lobes narrow (May-Jun).

Isoglossa woodii Buckweed; Kiesieblaar (A); ugomane, umbomane (Z) (named after John Medley Wood, 1827-1915, botanist, first curator of Natal herbarium, who published widely on Natal flora)
Shrub up to 4 m, in colonies. In forest understorey. Much branched, sparsely hairy. **Leaves: Large,** ± 120 x 75 mm, smaller in exposed places. **Flowers:** Inflorescences ± 90 x 12 mm; flowers ± 8 mm, white (Mar-Jul). **General:** Flowering is periodic. Mass die-offs after flowering ± every 10 years. Young stems browsed by bushbuck, blue duiker. When it flowers, honey is reputed to be plentiful. Flowers visited by moths, butterflies, honey-bees, wasps and flies. Grown from seed and cuttings.

Justicia (named after James Justice, 1698-1763, Scottish horticulturalist) - Herbs or shrublets (for description see p. 438).

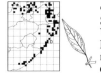

Justicia betonica Paper Plume (betonica - a variation of Vettonica, a similar plant in Spain)
Slender shrublet, 0,13-1 m. In grassland, bushveld, on forest margins, SA to India. **Very variable. Leaves:** 16-130 x 2-40 mm, hairless or with long white downy hairs. **Flowers:** In compact inflorescences, ± 100 mm; flowers ± 15 mm, cream with mauve markings, **bracts overlapping, 6-17 x 2-9 mm, papery, pale cream with dark green veins** (Apr-Dec). **General:** Good shade plant, from seed or cuttings.

Sclerochiton odoratissimus

Asystasia gangetica

Lal Greene

Johan Bodenstein

Hypoestes forskaolii

Ruttya ovata

Asystasia gangetica

Martin von Fintel

Tom de Waal

Martin von Fintel

Isoglossa ciliata

Isoglossa grantii

Isoglossa woodii

Geoff Nichols

Van Wyk & Malan

C J Ward

Isoglossa woodii

Justicia betonica

Johan Bodenstein

Van Wyk & Malan

201

Justicia campylostemon Honey Justicia; isipheka, ubomane (Z) *(campylostemon - curved stamen)*
Shrub, 0,3-3 m. In forest. Much branched, thinly hairy. **Leaves:** 20-190 x 13-84 mm, margins wavy, stalks ± 20 mm. **Flowers: Inflorescences widely branching, stems straight, slender**; flowers ± 18 mm, cream with green or reddish markings, downy, upper lip hooded (Dec-May, throughout year). **Fruit:** Capsule, cylindrical, ± 20 mm, on long stalk. **General:** Easily grown in damp shady places.

Justicia protracta Veld Justicia *(protracta - extended)*
Perennial herb or shrublet, 0,2-1 m. Widespread, in woodland, thicket, grassland. **Much branched**, stems slender, stems and leaves with long hairs or densely finely hairy. **Leaves:** 5-70 x 2-45 mm, shape variable. **Flowers:** In small clusters in axils, ± 10 mm, white, with reddish markings, downy, **bracts leaflike,** ± 13 x 8 mm (Sep-Jun). **General:** Visited by honey-bees. Good for dry sunny areas in garden.

Adhatoda (a Malabar name) - Herbaceous perennials. Old World genus, 2 species in SA, endemic to KZN.

Adhatoda andromeda Adhatoda; Valsmoeraskruid (A); umusa omncane (Z)
Perennial herbs, 60-400 mm, in colonies. In grassland. Rootstock woody. Stems annual, smooth or with short stiff hairs. **Leaves:** 7-40 x 2-15 mm. **Flowers:** In dense terminal inflorescences, ± 30 mm; flowers ± 20 mm wide, white with red markings, bracts narrow, 25-30 mm (Sep-Feb). **Fruit:** Capsule club-shaped, finely hairy. **General:** Used in traditional medicine to treat biliousness.

RUBIACEAE - Gardenia/Coffee Family Herbs, shrubs or trees (for description see p. 556). *Kohautia* (named after Francisci Kohaut, plant collector, inventor) - Annual or perennial herbs. Afr, Madag, Asia, ± 60 species, ± 20 in SA.

Kohautia amatymbica [=*Oldenlandia amatymbica*] Tremble Tops; lehlokana, mohlatsisa, morokolo-poli (SS); ikhubalo elimnyama, labantwana (X); umfana-ozacile (Thin Boy), umqanda, umhungulo (Z) (named after the AmaThembu people)
Perennial, **slender herb**, up to 600 mm. In grassland, disturbed areas, up to 2500 m, Cape to Zim, Moz. Woody rootstock. **Stem unbranched. Leaves:** ± 45 x 2 mm, widely spaced. **Flowers:** In loose terminal inflorescence; flowers ± 12 mm diam, white, cream to brownish above, green to purplish or brown beneath, tube long, ± 20 mm (Aug-Dec), sweetly scented. **General:** Conspicuous in recently burnt veld. Used in traditional medicine to improve appetite of infants, as a charm to protect babies from evil, as love charm emetics and protection against snakes, lightning.

Conostomium (*konos* - cone; *stoma* - mouth) - Perennial herbs or shrublets (for description see p. 492).

Conostomium natalense Wild Pentas; umbophe, ungcolosi (Z) (see p. 492)

Oldenlandia (named after Heinrich Oldenland, 1663-97, physician, botanist) - Herbs. About 150 species, 14 in SA.

Oldenlandia herbacea (*herbacea* - succulent stem, herblike)
Erect to spreading herb, up to 600 mm. Woodland, roadsides, rocky areas, marshy grassland, coast to 1850 m, SA to Trop Afr, Asia. Stems ribbed. **Leaves:** ± 20 x 2 mm, margins recurved. **Flowers:** Solitary, ± 5 mm, white to lilac, on slender stalks, ± 25 mm (Nov-Jun). **General:** Very variable.

Oldenlandia tenella (*tenella* - very soft, tender)
Herb up to 300 mm. In moist rock crevices, in forest, KZN to Zim. **Stems very slender**, 4 angled, **much branched**, hairless, prostrate to hanging. **Leaves:** ± 14 x 9 mm, thin, stalks ± 3 mm. **Flowers:** ± 4 mm diam, white or lilac, stalks ± 9 mm (Oct-Feb).

Pentas (*pente* - five) - Shrubby herbs; stipules much divided; styles always exserted. Afr, Madag, ± 59 species, 2 in SA.

Pentas micrantha White Wild Pentas (*micrantha* - small thorns)
Erect biennial shrublet, 450-900 mm. On forest margins, shady, wet places. Stems slightly woody, plant thinly hairy. **Leaves:** 55-100 x 15-30 mm, thin, dark green, veins conspicuous, stalks ± 35 mm. **Flowers:** In terminal inflorescences, ± 75 mm diam; flowers ± 10 mm diam, tube ± 10 mm, white, bearded in throat, calyx with 5 unequal lobes (throughout year). **Fruit:** Oval capsule, ± 5 mm, prominently ribbed. **General:** Attracts butterflies and moths. Good garden plant in shade or sun.

Justicia campylostemon

Trevor Coleman

Adhatoda andromeda

Tom de Waal

Justicia protracta

Wally Menne

Kohautia amatymbica

Martin von Fintel

Conostomium natalense

Lal Greene

Conostomium natalense

Trevor Coleman

Oldenlandia herbacea

Van Wyk & Malan

Oldenlandia tenella

Braam van Wyk

Pentas micrantha

Geoff Nichols

203

Mitriostigma (*mitron* - diminutive of *mitra* - turban; *stigma*, refers to thick stigma) - Small shrubs; stipules green, erect, persistent; flowers in small clusters in axils, tube short, cylindrical at base, petal lobes spreading or erect; fruit round to oval, seeds large, fleshy. Afr, 5 species, 1 in SA.

Mitriostigma axillare Small False Loquat; Basterlukwart (A) (*axillare* - growing in an axil)

Woody shrub or small tree, up to 3 m. In forest, E Cape to Moz. **Leaves:** 50-150 x 35-60 mm, **shiny, margins wavy. Flowers: In clusters in axils,** ± 20 mm diam, white tinged pink (Aug-Nov), **strong, lovely scent. Fruit:** Oval, ± 25 mm, **orange** (remains on plant for months). **General:** A lovely plant for shady places or containers. Slow growing at first, needs plenty of nitrogen. (See p. 78)

Pavetta (from Sinhalese name *Pawatta*) - Shrubs or trees; leaves with black dots; flowers 4 lobed, style slender, long, protruding, stigma slightly thickened. Afr, Arabia, India, China, Austr, ± 300 species, ± 20 species in SA, mostly trees.

Pavetta catophylla Christmas Bush (*catophylla* - with bracts, with leaves hanging down)

Rounded shrub, 0,6-1,5(2) m. In woodland, on sandy soils. Much branched, stems woody. **Leaves:** Oval, narrowing to short stalk, shiny dark green, crowded towards ends of branches, **leaves near flowers narrow, stalkless. Flowers: In round inflorescences with leaves at base,** ± 60 mm diam; flowers white, calyx lobes sword-shaped, enlarged on fruit (Oct-Jan), sweetly scented. **General:** Fruit edible. Leaves browsed by game. Hardy, lovely garden subject.

Pavetta gracilifolia Small Bride's Bush; Kleinbruidsbos (A) (*gracilifolia* - slender leaves)

Slender, prostrate to scrambling shrublet, up to 2 m. On rocky outcrops. **Leaves: Small,** ± 40 x 10 mm, finely downy, stalks short, ± 5 mm. **Flowers:** In round inflorescences ± 50 mm diam; flowers ± 8 mm diam, white, tube ± 8 mm, calyx short with triangular lobes, hairy, stalks hairy (blooms throughout year), scented. **Fruit:** Black. **General:** Potential garden plant, especially for colder areas.

Phylohydrax (*phylon* - leaves; *hydro* - water) - Maritime succulent herbs; stems long, creeping; leaves fleshy, stipular sheaths cup-shaped, toothed. Formerly confused with *Hydrophylax* (restricted to India). Afr, Madag, 2 species, 1 in SA.

Phylohydrax carnosa (*carnosus* - fleshy, pulpy)

Perennial, succulent herb, stems long, plant forming mats. Beach pioneer, E Cape to S Tanz. **Leaves:** 4-8 mm wide, thick, succulent, oval, blunt tipped. **Flowers:** Funnel-shaped, 3-6 mm, ± 9 mm diam, calyx short, lobes indistinct (Aug-May). **Fruit:** ± 6 x 4 mm.

VALERIANACEAE - Valerian Family Annual or perennial herbs. Flowers irregular or spurred. Fruit crowned with persistent calyx. Cosmop, ± 10 genera with ± 300 species, 2 genera in SA.

Valeriana capensis Cape Valerian; Wildebalderjan (A); Motetele (SS)

Perennial herb, up to 1,2(1,5) m. In damp ground, 270-2200 m, S Cape to Kenya. Stems erect, ribbed. **Leaves:** Mainly basal, mostly compound, ± 200 mm; terminal leaflet larger than side ones, ± 80 x 40 mm, margins irregularly, bluntly toothed. **Flowers:** In dense terminal inflorescences; flowers ± 6 mm diam, white to mauve (Oct-Apr). **General:** Unpleasant odour. Leaves used traditionally as a fumigant to drive away illness. Var. *capensis*, ± 1,5 m, unbranched; leaves compound; inflorescences branching towards top of stems, fragrant. Var. *lanceolata*, ± 750 mm, slender, often in clumps; basal leaves entire or with 1-2 lobes; inflorescences branched. Var. *nana*, found at 2200-3050 m; slightly foetid smell when dry.

DIPSACACEAE - Scabiose Family Annual or perennial herbs (for description see p. 438). *Cephalaria* (*kephale* - a head) - Herbs; flowerheads rounded, surrounded by several rows of hairy bracts. Europe, Asia, Afr, ± 78 species, ± 14 in SA.

Cephalaria oblongifolia False Scabiosa (*oblongifolia* - oblong leaves)

Erect herb, up to 1,5 m. In marshy ground. Tap root. **Stem ridged. Leaves: In basal rosette,** ± 600 x 40 mm, leathery, stalks slender, ± 300 mm. **Flowerheads:** ± 20 mm diam, white, silky outside, bracts pointed, silky (Oct-Mar). **Similar species:** *C. galpiniana* Forming mats at high altitudes, 2000-2750 m; basal leaves lobed or not, lobes small, narrow, entire or toothed.

Cephalaria pungens (*pungens* - to prick)

Perennial herb, up to 1(1,5) m. In damp grassland, on forest margins. Stems slender, erect, hairless. **Leaves:** Very variable. Basal leaves 50-250 x 10-23 mm, hairless or sparsely hairy, margins toothed, tapering to slender stalks 80-200 mm. Upper stem leaves narrow, rarely lobed at base. **Flowerheads:** 20-40 mm diam, white, stem hardly branched (Jan-Mar).

Mitriostigma axillare

David Johnson

Pavetta catophylla

Wally Menne

Pavetta gracilifolia

Jo Onderstall

Phylohydrax carnosa

Trevor Coleman

Valeriana capensis

Lal Greene

Valeriana capensis

Lal Greene

Cephalaria oblongifolia

Lal Greene

Cephalaria pungens

Geoff Nichols

Cephalaria pungens

Martin von Fintel

Cephalaria galpiniana

Lal Greene

205

Scabiosa (named after scabies) - Annual or perennial herbs (for description see p. 438).

Scabiosa columbaria **Wild Scabiosa** (see p. 438)

CUCURBITACEAE - Cucumber/Pumpkin Family Trailing or climbing herbs (for description see p. 78). *Zehneria* (named after J Zehner, botanical artist) - Scrambling herbs; rootstock thickened; fruits small, berrylike. Trop, ± 30 species, 3 in SA.

Zehneria parvifolia [=*Melothria parvifolia*]
Perennial climber, up to 2,5 m. On forest margins, in woodland, KZN to Trop Afr. Stems slender, fluted, **almost hairless**; tendrils slender. **Leaves:** 20-40 mm diam, 3-5 lobed, dark green above, paler beneath, margins toothed or not, stalks 10-25 mm. **Flowers:** Small. Male: 4-6 flowers on slender stems (Dec-May). **Fruit:** Smooth, 8-10 mm diam, **bluish purple**. **General:** Eaten by people, birds, mammals. (See p. 558)

Zehneria scabra **itanga, simbene, ukalimela (X)** (*scabra* - rough, scabrid)
Creeper, stems up to 3 m. In woodland, thicket, up to 2225 m, Cape to Ethiopia. Stems annual, branched, shortly hairy; tendrils simple. **Leaves:** Variable, 30-80 x 25-60 mm, heart-shaped, also 3-5 lobed, slightly hairy above with **rough white dots**, margins sharply toothed. **Flowers:** Small, ± 4 mm, white or yellow, male and female on separate plants. Male: 8-20 in clusters. Female: solitary (Jan-Feb). **Fruit:** Roundish or oval, ± 12 x 8 mm, yellow to red or brown, hairy. **General:** Edible. (See p. 78)

Momordica (*mordeo* - bite, possibly refers to seeds) - Herbaceous climbers (for description see p. 80).

Momordica balsamina **African Cucumber, Balsam Apple, Bursting Beauty; Aloentjie, Laloentjie (A); intshungu, intshungwana yehlathi, umkaka (Z)** (*balsamina* - like balsam)
Slender climber, stems up to 5 m. Woodland, forest margins, E Cape to Trop Afr, India. **Leaves:** ± 40 mm diam, deeply divided into 5-7 lobes, margins toothed, soft bright green. **Flowers:** ± 20 mm, white with grey veins (throughout year). **Fruit:** ± 40 x 20 mm, pointed at base, red when ripe, ridged with soft bumps, splitting when the tip is touched, seeds black. **General:** Unpleasantly scented when bruised. Ripe fruit eaten by people and birds; leaves and green fruits cooked as spinach. Used in traditional medicine to treat stomach and intestinal complaints, burns and possibly diabetes. Grown in gardens in Europe since 1800s. (See p. 80)

Trochomeria (*trochos* - a wheel; *meris* - a part) - Scrambling or prostrate herbs. Trop & S Afr, ± 8 species, 4 in SA.

Trochomeria sagittata (*sagittata* - arrow-shaped)
Slender, small creeper, stems up to 500 mm. In grassland, thicket. Small tuber. Stems annual, with few short hairs; tendrils slender. **Leaves:** 40-70 x 10-40 mm, margins entire, tapering to fine point, stalks slender, ± 20 mm. **Flowers:** Male and female on separate plants, on long slender stems. Male: in clusters. Female: solitary, smaller, petals ± 3 mm, white (Nov-Jan). **Fruit:** ± 20 x 14, with faint longitudinal ridges.

Lagenaria (*lagena* - large flask; *aria* - fruit) - Vigorous herbaceous climbers; leaves simple with 2 glands at top of stalk; flowers large, opening in evenings; fruit hard shelled, not splitting. Trop Afr, ± 6 species, 2 in SA.

Lagenaria sphaerica [= *L. mascarena*] **Wild Melon; Wildekalbas (A); iselwa-makhosi, uselwa, uthangazane olukhulu (Z)** (*sphaerica* - spherical, globelike)
Robust climber, up to canopy of riverine forest. In damp, low-lying areas, E Cape to E Afr. Woody rootstock. Stems annual. **Leaves:** 50-190 x 40-200 mm, 5 lobed, margins coarsely toothed, stalks 10-120 mm. **Flowers:** Male and female on separate plants; large, ± 90 mm diam, velvety white (Aug-Jun), fragrantly scented. **Fruit:** 75-110 mm diam, dark green with paler patches, sometimes foul smelling. **General:** Flowers visited by bees, ants and flies. Used traditionally to treat stomach ache, glandular swellings and in ceremonies after the death of a chief. (See also p. 558)

CAMPANULACEAE - Bell Flower/Canterbury Bell Family (for description see p. 492). *Wahlenbergia* (named after Dr Goran Wahlenberg, botanist, Swedish author of Flora Lapponica) - Herbs or shrublets (for description see p. 494).

Wahlenbergia grandiflora **Giant Bell Flower; umnqantula, ushayindida omhlophe (Z)** (*grandiflora* - large flowers)
Perennial herb, 250-700 mm. In colonies, in grassland. Stems robust, erect. **Leaves:** Alternate, 30-40 x 6-8 mm, hairy, **margins wavy**, stalkless. **Flowers:** At tips of slender, branched stems, ± 30 mm diam, blue, mauve to almost white, stalks 2-30 mm (Aug-Sep). **General:** Small flies attracted to flowers. Lovely garden plant, grown from seed. (See p.494)

206

Zehneria parvifolia

C J Ward

Scabiosa columbaria

Lal Greene

Scabiosa columbaria

Van Wyk & Malan

Momordica balsamina

Lorraine van Hooff

Zehneria scabra

Tony Abbott

Trochomeria sagittata

Martin von Fintel

Wahlenbergia grandiflora

Lawrence Peacock

Lagenaria sphaerica

Martin von Fintel

LOBELIACEAE - Lobelia Family Herbs, often with milky sap. Flowers often 2 lipped, inverted on the stalks. Fruit a capsule. Includes some well known ornamentals. Cosmop, ± 20 genera, ± 1000 species, 5 genera in SA.
Cyphia (*kyphos* - a twiner) - Perennial herbs, erect or twining; flowers 1-2 lipped. Afr, ± 50 species, ± 32 in SA.

Cyphia elata ibutha lentaba, igela, igonsi (Z) (*elata* - tall)

Stiffly erect herb, 100-900 mm, growth habit very variable. In rocky grassland, coast to 2745 m, E Cape to N Prov. Hairless to thinly downy. **Leaves:** Overlapping on lower part of stem, ± 100 x 60 mm, margins with small teeth, clasping stem. **Flowers:** In dense, terminal inflorescence, ± 100 x 20 mm; flowers ± 9 mm, white or yellow, mauve (Oct-Apr). **General:** Root edible. Used in traditional medicine as an emetic.

Cyphia heterophylla (*heteros* - different; *phyllum* - leaf)

Twining herb, in grassland, 1300-1700 m. **Leaves:** 20-50 x 0,5-30 mm, broad at base, tapering to tips, distinctly veined beneath, margins toothed or lobed (entire), stalks short, ± 10 mm, or absent. **Flowers:** Solitary, ± 10 mm, stalks ± 15 mm, in axils of leaves (Jan-Feb).

Cyphia longifolia intikintiki (Z) (*longifolia* - long leaves)

Slender, erect, perennial herb, up to 800 mm. In grassland, 750-2000 m. Stems simple (rarely branched). **Leaves:** Long, narrow, 25-150 x 1,5-8 mm, margins entire or more or less toothed, veins distinct beneath. **Flowers:** In well spaced clusters in inflorescence, 20-200 mm, stem 100-270 mm; flowers ± 10 mm, cream to pale mauve (Sep-Jan).

Lobelia (named after Matthias de L'Obel, 1538-1616, Flemish nobleman, botanist, physician to King James I) - Herbs or shrublets; flowers 5 lobed, regular or 2 lipped; fruit a capsule. Cosmop, mostly American, ± 300 species, ± 70 in SA.

Lobelia pteropoda (*pteropoda* - winged stalk)

Annual or perennial herb, 200-400 mm, erect or scrambling. In moist shady places near streams, up to 3000 m. Stems slender, ribbed. **Leaves:** ± 50 x 40 mm, **margins lobed** to very broadly toothed, veins protrude beneath, **stalks ± 60 mm, winged**. **Flowers:** ± 25 mm, pale blue to mauvish or white, 2 crests in mouth of tube (Dec-May). **Similar species:** *L. vanreenensis* Leaves coarsely toothed and lobed, stalks 20-50 mm; flowers white to pale blue, yellow in mouth.

GOODENIACEAE - Herbs or shrublets. Flowers irregular, stamens alternating with petal lobes, stigma surrounded by a fringed cup. Fruit fleshy. Mainly Austr, ± 12 genera, ± 400 species, 1 genus in SA. ***Scaevola*** (named after Mucius Scaevola, a Roman hero of 6th century BC) - See family description. Austr, Asia, Pacific Is, Afr, ± 80 species, 2 in SA.

Scaevola plumieri [=*S. thunbergii*] Scaevola; Seeplakkie (A); umqhaphu (X)

Evergreen, succulent shrublet, 0,3-0,9(1,5) m, in large colonies. On coastal sand dunes, cosmop. Roots slender, fibrous, from woody, underground stems. **Leaves:** 50-90 x 20-50 mm, fleshy, tips rounded, tapering to base. **Flowers:** In clusters in axils; flowers ± 25 mm, white, yellowish inside (May-Sep). **Fruit:** 10-15 mm diam, fleshy, bluish purple. **General:** Flowers visited by bees, fruit eaten by birds. Leaf sap used to treat blue-bottle stings. Bark used traditionally as a temporary replacement for a charm. **Similar species:** *S. sericea* Spreading shrub, ± 1,5 m; leaves smaller, ± 50 x 25 mm, stalkless, margins toothed in upper part; flowers smaller.

ASTERACEAE (COMPOSITAE, this alternative name refers to the composite nature of the flowerheads) - **Daisy Family** The largest family of flowering plants, mostly herbs, sometimes shrubs, rarely trees. Leaves usually simple (compound), very variable. Flowers crowded into a dense head (capitulum) made up of few to many small florets clustered on a base (receptacle), surrounded by one or more rows of sepal-like bracts. Florets either tubular or strap-shaped and resembling petals (ray florets). Fruit usually small, dry (rarely fleshy), usually surmounted by a tuft of hairs or scales (the much reduced calyx; pappus). Economically important for Lettuce, Globe Artichoke, Sunflowers, Chicory, the contact insecticide Pyrethrum, and for a large number of ornamentals such as Aster, Chrysanthemum, Dahlia, Gerbera, Everlasting, Cineraria, Marigolds.
Vernonia (named after William Vernon, died 1711, English botanist who collected in Maryland, USA) - Herbs, shrubs, climbers or trees; leaves alternate; flowerheads solitary or in more or less branched inflorescences on long stems, bracts in 4-10 rows. Afr, America, Asia, Madag, ± 1000 species, ± 50 in SA, absent from winter rainfall area.

Vernonia anisochaetoides [now *Distephanus anisochaetoides*] ikhambi-lesimungumungwane (Z)
(*anisochaetoides* - like unequal bristles)

Scrambling shrub, up to 5 m. On forest margins. **Leaves:** 70 x 80 mm wide, margins entire or coarsely, irregularly toothed, finely hairy or not, narrowing to stalks. **Flowerheads: Inflorescences widely, stiffly branched**; ± 5 mm diam, whitish grey (Jun-Oct). **Fruit:** Pappus of rough bristles. **General:** Used in traditional medicine. **Similar species:** *Anisochaete mikanioides* Pappus of scales. (See p. 216)

Cyphia elata
Martin von Fintel

Cyphia longifolia
Lal Greene

Scaevola plumieri
Rick Taylor

Cyphia heterophylla
Tony Abbott

Scaevola plumieri
Caroline Fox

Lobelia pteropoda
Lorraine van Hooff

Scaevola sericea
Tony Abbott

Lobelia pteropoda
Lorraine van Hooff

Vernonia anisochaetoides
C J Ward

Vernonia galpinii Bloukwasbossie, Perskwasbossie **(A)** (for description see p. 498).

Chromolaena (*chromo* - coloured; *chlaina* - blanket) - Cosmop, ± 129 species, 1 introduced in SA.

★ **Chromolaena odorata** [= *Eupatorium odoratum*] **Triffid Weed, Paraffin Weed; Paraffienbos (A); usandanezwe (Z)** (*odoratus* - sweet smelling)
Scrambling shrub, up to 4(8) m. In disturbed places, E Cape to N Prov. **Vigorous invader**, from C and S America. Leaves opposite, ± 100 x 60 mm, margins coarsely toothed to entire, rough, 3 veined from base. Flat topped inflorescences, flowerheads ± 10 x 3 mm, white to mauve (Jun-Jul), sweetly scented. Attracts butterflies. Plant smells strongly of paraffin when bruised. **A serious threat to natural vegetation.**

Mikania (named after Joseph Mikan, 1743-1814, prof of botany at Prague) - Shrubs or twining herbs; leaves opposite; flowerheads in branched inflorescences. America, ± 200 species, 3 in Afr, Madag, Asia.

Mikania natalensis Mikania; ihlozi (elimhlophe), ikhambi-lesiduli, umdlonzo (Z)
Vigorous perennial climber. On forest margins, up to 1200 m, E Cape to Trop Afr. Downy throughout. **Leaves:** ± 80(100) x 40(70) mm, margins widely toothed, 5 veined from base, **velvety grey beneath. Flowerheads:** In loosely branched inflorescences; 8-10 mm, cream, anthers purplish (Apr-Sep), heavily scented. **General:** Used traditionally to treat urinary complaints, headache, backache, head colds and horse sicknesss. Visited by butterflies, bees, wasps and flies. Grown from cuttings.

Aster (*astron* - a star, refers to flower shape) - Perennial herbs or soft shrublets (for description see p. 440).

Aster pleiocephalus (*pleiocephalus* - many heads)
Erect herb, up to 700 mm. On forest margins, rocky outcrops, 900-1900 m. Woody rootstock. Stems annual, rough hairy. **Leaves:** ± 100 x 10 mm, **margins toothed or not, rough hairy on both surfaces**, stalkless. **Flowers:** In open, branched inflorescences; ± 20 mm wide, **ray florets white**, disc florets yellow (Sep-Jan).

Felicia (named after Herr Felix, died 1846, a German official at Regensburg) - Shrubby herbs; fruits hairy, no glands. Afr. ± 80 species, mainly SA.

Felicia erigeroides Wild Michaelmas Daisy; isithelelo, ixhaphozi (Z) (*erigo* - to raise)
Slender, erect shrublet, up to 600 mm. On forest margins, up to 1000 m. **Stems stiff, closely leafy, downy. Leaves:** Often in tufts, ± 40 x 8 mm, margins fringed with hairs. **Flowerheads:** In terminal inflorescences; ± 20 mm wide, ray florets white, pink or mauve, disc florets yellow (Mar-Jul). **General:** Used in traditional medicine to treat intestinal parasites and abdominal pain. Rewarding garden plant.

Felicia muricata White Felicia; Blouheuning Karooblommetjie, Kapokblomme-tjie (A); koelehane, mohantsoane, moroka-hloho, mosala-tsela (SS) (*muricata* -pointed)
Bushy herb, up to 500 mm. In grassland, overgrazed areas, 60-1900 m, SW Cape to Kenya. Woody at base, **twigs thinly roughly hairy. Leaves:** ± 15 x 1 mm. **Flowerheads:** ± 15 mm wide, solitary, on long stems, ray florets white, pink, blue, mauve, disc florets yellow (Aug-May). **General:** Browsed by sheep and goats. Used in traditional medicine to relieve headaches and as a douche for cows ill after calving.

Microglossa (*mikros* - small; *glossa* - tongue) - Often scrambling shrubs; Afr, Madag, ± 60 species, ± 2 in SA.

Microglossa mespilifolia Trailing Daisy; ikhambi-lentwala, ikhambi-lesiduli, indlondlo (Z) (*mespilifolia* - leaves like Medlar *Mespilus*)
Vigorous, scrambling shrub. In open scrub, woodland, on forest margins, coast to 600 m, SW Cape to KZN. Stems slender, woody. **Leaves:** ± 40 x 30 mm, thinly hairy, margins with few broad teeth. **Flowerheads: In dense, flattish, terminal inflores-cences;** ± 5 mm diam, **ray florets short, white**, disc florets yellowish (throughout year). **General:** Used in traditional medicine to treat fever and as tonics for stock animals. **Similar species:** *Vernonia angulifolia* (see p 440).

Denekia (named after a Dutch botanist friend of Thunberg) - Perennial herb. S Afr, 1 species.

Denekia capensis toane-mohlaka (SS)
Perennial herb, up to 700 mm. In damp places, shallow water, coast to 2000 m, KZN to Zim, Zam. Stems simple, glandular. **Leaves:** 10-200 x 2-25(50) mm, **velvety white beneath. Flowerheads:** In terminal inflorescences; ± 3 mm wide, **white, bluish, pinkish**, bracts reddish (throughout year). **General:** Hats sometimes woven from the plant. Tall, robust in very wet places; shorter, wiry in dry places.

Lawrence Peacock

Geoff Nichols

Lal Greene

★ *Chromolaena odorata*   *Mikania natalensis*   *Denekia capensis*

Lal Greene

Tom de Waal

Martin von Fintel

Vernonia galpinii   *Aster pleiocephalus*   *Felicia erigeroides*

Rosemary Williams

Tony Abbott

Felicia muricata   *Microglossa mespilifolia*

211

Helichrysopsis (*helichrysopsis* - like *Helichrysum*) - Perennial herb; disc florets only. KZN, S Moz coastal plain.

Helichrysopsis septentrionale [= *Gnaphalium septentrionale*] (*septentrionale* - from the north)
Perennial, **prostrate, ashy grey herb**. In sandy grassland. Stems much branched, leafy. **Leaves:** ± 15 x 1 mm, silky grey above, **margins strongly rolled under, white cottony beneath**. **Flowerheads:** In terminal inflorescences; ± 5 x 3 mm, greenish yellow in centre, bracts palest brown tipped whitish, outer ones longer than florets (Dec-Apr). **Fruit:** Pappus bristle tips feathery, fused to form a smooth ring at base.

Tenrhynea (named after William ten Rhyne 1647-1700, Dutch physician with East India Co, who collected plants in the Cape on his way to Java) - Shrubby, similar to *Helichrysum*. 1 species genus, endemic to SA.

Tenrhynea phylicifolia (*phylicifolia* - leaves like *Phylica*)
Shrubby perennial, up to 1,5 m. In grassland, near forest margins, coast to 1220 m. **Leaves:** ± 30 x 10 mm, often much smaller, flat, grey-green above, **velvety white beneath, base narrowly winged onto stem**. **Flowers:** In terminal clusters, in branched inflorescences; ± 5 x 2 mm, bracts white to pink (Feb-Jul). **General:** Resembles *Helichrysum* which does not have winged, stem-clasping leaves.

Helichrysum (*helios* - sun; *chrysos* - gold) - Herbs, shrubs, sometimes dwarf and cushion forming; usually hairy or woolly; flowerheads solitary or in compact or spreading inflorescences. Mainly Afr, ± 500 species, ± 250 in SA.

Helichrysum adenocarpum Pink or Red Everlasting; **Pienk of Rooisewejaartjie (A); senko-toana, toane-balingoana (SS); uhlambahloshane obomvu (Z)** (see p. 442)

Helichrysum argentissimum (*argentissimum* - very silvery)
Mat-forming, grey woolly, perennial herb, up to 150 (400) mm, mats up to 1 m diam. On stony grassy slopes or sandstone cliffs, 900-2400 m. Branched, woody, underground stems. **Leaves:** In crowded basal rosettes, 30-50(120) x 3-6 mm, silvery grey, silky woolly. **Flowerheads: Solitary**, ± 20 x 40 mm, bracts overlapping, much longer than florets, glossy white with red or pink blotch at base inside (Sep-Jan).

Helichrysum argyrolepis (*argyrolepis* -silver scales)
Soft woody shrublet, ± 300 mm. In grassland, among rocky outcrops. **Loosely branched**, stems grey-white felted. **Leaves:** 6-25 x 1-2 mm, tips pointed, reflexed, thickly greyish white woolly above, felted beneath. **Flowers:** Solitary, 13-15 x 25 mm, bracts loosely overlapping, much longer than florets, glossy white inside, palest to dark chestnut outside (Nov-Apr). **General:** In large, tangled clumps.

Helichrysum argyrosphaerum Wild Everlasting; **Poprosie (A)** (*argyros* - silvery; *sphaera* - globe, refers to flowerheads)
Prostrate herb, stems radiate up to 300 mm. In hot, dry, sandy places, easily becomes a weed, KZN to Zam, Moz, Malawi. **Leaves:** ± 25 x 7 mm, narrowing to flat, stalklike base, thinly grey woolly. **Flowerheads: Solitary**, at tips of branchlets, 7-10 mm diam, bracts shining silvery becoming pink inwards, tips blunt, disc florets yellow tipped pink (Jun-Dec). **General:** Browsed by wild and domestic animals but reportedly poisonous if stock eat too much. Pungently scented when picked.

Helichrysum chionosphaerum Dwarf Everlasting; **Sewejaartjie (A); molepelle, senko-toana (SS)** (*chio* -white, snow; *sphaer* - ball, refers to seeds like snowflakes)
Mat-forming perennial herb or subshrub, 0,15 x 1 m. In rocky grassland, on cliffs, rock sheets, up to 2250 m, NE Cape to Zim. Stems well branched, prostrate, young parts leafy. **Leaves:** In rosettes on short branchlets, 10-100 x 1-3 mm, greyish white on upper surface, **silky woolly or white felted beneath**, confined to margins when mature, 3 parallel veins. **Flowerheads:** Solitary or in small terminal inflorescences; 7-12 x 12-25 mm, bracts glossy white, disc florets yellow (Jul-Jan).

Helichrysum confertifolium (*confertifolium* - closely set with leaves)
Mat-forming perennial herb, 50-400 mm. In rocky grassland, on rock sheets, 600-2000 m, E Cape to N Prov. **Leaves: Rosettes crowded, arising from prostrate, rooting branches**, 10-40 x 2-3 mm, **silvery white felted**. **Flowerheads:** Solitary (2-3), 12-15 x 25 mm, bracts glossy white to reddish brown outside (Nov-Jul). **General:** Plants on Natal Group Sandstone in KZN produce taller flowering stems.

Helichrysum ecklonis [= *H. lamprocephalum, H. scapiforme*] **umuthi wechanti (X)** (see p. 442)

Helichrysopsis septentrionale

Tenrhynea phylicifolia

Wayne Matthews

Tony Abbott

Helichrysum adenocarpum

Wayne Matthews

Helichrysum argentissimum

Martin von Fintel

Helichrysum argyrolepis

Rosemary Williams

Helichrysum argyrosphaerum

Darrel Plowes

Helichrysum chionosphaerum

Martin von Fintel

Helichrysum confertifolium

Lal Greene

Helichrysum ecklonis

Rosemary Williams

Helichrysum mundtii   **phefo-ea-liliba (SS)** (named after Johannes Mundt, 1791-1831, Prussian pharmacist, botanist, land surveyer)
Robust perennial herb, up to 1,5 m, forming dense stands. In marshy places, Cape to Angola, Tanz. Stems leafy, simple, woody at base, thinly white felted in upper parts. **Leaves:** Basal, ± 600 x 60 mm, finely net veined, **surface wrinkled, hairless above, white felted beneath**, base tapering into **long narrowly winged stalk**, expanding and clasping stem; stem leaves narrow, running onto stem. **Flowerheads: In large, much branched inflorescences**; 4 x 3,5 mm, bracts **creamy white** (Feb-Apr). **General:** Used in traditional medicine to treat chest complaints.

Helichrysum panduratum (*panduratum* - fiddle-shaped, refers to leaves)
Loosely branched, soft woody subshrub. In large, tangled clumps in mixed grassland near forest margins, E Cape to Kenya. Stems thinly grey-woolly. **Leaves:** ± 70 x 35 mm, **fiddle-shaped, thinly grey-woolly above, dense beneath**, margins very wavy, eared, half clasping at base. **Flowerheads:** In loose terminal inflorescences; 5-6 x 12 mm, bracts woolly, white, equal to yellow disc florets (Dec-Jan), honey scented. **General:** Used to make a herbal tea. Easily grown, attractive groundcover.

Helichrysum populifolium   **Poplar Helichrysum** (*populifolium* - leaves like the poplar)
Softly woody shrub, up to 2 x 2 m. On large rocky outcrops, cliffs above gorges, up to 800 m, confined to Natal Group Sandstone. Branches white felted. **Leaves: Large**, ± 130 x 110 mm, **cobwebby grey above, white felted beneath, stalks ± 70 mm, white felted. Flowerheads: In small clusters**, in **large, terminal branched inflorescences**; 3 x 2 mm, outer bracts pale brown, woolly, inner white (Feb-May), honey scented. **General:** Attractive foliage plant for the garden. Grown from seed.

Helichrysum rugulosum   **marotole, motoantoanyane, pulumo-tseou (SS); impepho (Sw)** (*rugulosum* - wrinkled)
Perennial herb, 100-300 mm. In poor stony or sandy grassland, invades overgrazed areas and roadsides. **Leaves: Narrow**, 15-25 x 2-5 mm, wrinkled, thinly cobwebby above, white felted beneath, margins rolled under. **Flowerheads:** In compact, branched inflorescences; 5 x 4 mm, bract tips curly, toothed, creamy or purplish or pink, equal to yellow disc florets (Nov-Mar). **General:** Used in traditional medicine to fumigate huts when children are ill, and an ingredient in protective charms.

Helichrysum spiralepis (*spiralepis* - coiled scales)
A tufted perennial herb, up to 300 mm. In grassland, Cape to Zim. Stems annual, numerous, grey woolly, leafy. **Leaves:** In basal rosette, ± 70 x 15 mm. **Flowerheads: Congested in small terminal clusters surrounded by leafy bracts, in compact or spreading inflorescences**; 5 x 3 mm, outer bracts shorter, woolly, inner longer, whitish cream, pink or red-purple (Sep-Mar). **General:** Very variable over its range.

Helichrysum sutherlandii   **molepelle, ntlo-ea-mokhoabane, senkotoana, senkot-wana (SS)** (named after James Sutherland, 1639-1719, first superintendent of the Edinburgh Bot Garden)
Well branched shrublet, up to 400 mm. **In clumps hanging from cliffs and rock outcrops**, 800-2700 m. Branchlets closely leafy, **flowering stem leaves more distant. Leaves:** ± 25 x 12 mm, thinly grey woolly to hairless above, white felted, 3 nerved beneath, abruptly narrowed to flat, clasping base, ± 12 mm. **Flowerheads:** In much branched inflorescences 20-120 mm, **held well away from plant**; 4-5 x 5-7 mm, outer bracts pale brownish, webbed together with wool, inner milky white **(Feb-Jul). General:** Used in traditional medicine.
Similar species: *H. confertum* Dwarf shrub, cushions up to 1 m diam; on cliff faces, 1800-3000 m; flowering stems closely leafy, inflorescences close to plant (Jul-Sep).

Helichrysum teretifolium (*teret* - smooth, rounded off, elegant; *folium* - leaves)
Much branched, compact or straggling shrublet, up to 450 mm, often in dense stands. In shrub communities, on dunes. **Branchlets thinly white felted, closely leafy. Leaves: Narrow**, 3-15 x 1-1,5 mm, **rigid**, spreading, hairless above, white woolly beneath, margins rolled under, base running onto stem. **Flowerheads:** In compact terminal inflorescences; 5 x 5 mm, bract tips blunt, curled, creamy white, outer bracts sometimes rosy (Jul-Nov). **General:** Attractive garden plant, from seed.

Helichrysum mundtii   *Helichrysum panduratum*   *Helichrysum rugulosum*

Helichrysum populifolium   *Helichrysum spiralepis*

Helichrysum sutherlandii   *Helichrysum confertum*

Helichrysum teretifolium   *Helichrysum teretifolium*

215

Stoebe (*stoibe* - a stuffing, a shrubby plant used for packing wine jars and making brooms) - Shrubs; leaves alternate, often ericoid, twisted, sometimes clustered. Afr, ± 34 species, mostly in SW Cape, 1 in summer rainfall area.

Stoebe vulgaris Bankrupt Bush, Zigzag Bush; Bankrotbos (A); sehalahala (SS)
(*vulgaris* - common)

Spreading, much branched shrub, up to 2 m. On forest margins, disturbed areas, coast to 2200 m, E Cape to Zim. Branches densely leafy, young parts woolly. **Leaves:** Ericoid, ± 4 x 0,5 mm, **grey-green**, often twisted, hairless or cobwebby beneath, white woolly above. **Flowerheads: Tiny,** clustered in spreading inflorescences on short side shoots (throughout year). **General:** Weedy at times. **Small, white woolly galls,** frequently mistaken for flowers.

Athrixia (*thrix* - hair, plant extremely hairy) - Erect perennial herbs or shrubs Afr. Madag, + 25 species, 13 in SA.

Athrixia angustissima phefshoane-e-nyenyane (SS)

Perennial herb, up to 350 mm. In grassland, on forest margins. **Stems straggling, wiry. Leaves:** Terminal rosettes, ± 200 x 100 mm; stem leaves ± 50 x 1-3 mm, smooth above, white felted below. **Flowerheads:** ± 25 mm diam, solitary, **ray florets white,** disc florets yellow, bracts cobwebby, pointed, tips recurved (Dec-Feb). **General:** Leaves used for a tea. Used in traditional medicine to bathe aching feet.

Printzia (named after H C Printz of Christiana, Mpumalanga) - Shrubs. Endemic, 6 species.

Printzia laxa [= *P. auriculata*] Giant Daisy Bush (*laxus* - wide, loose)

Perennial herb, up to 2 m. In scrub, on forest margins, 600-2300 m. Stems annual, **much branched. Leaves:** ± 70 x 45 mm, rough above, white hairy beneath, **margins coarsely, irregularly toothed,** stalks with **conspicuous roundish ears,** ± 25 mm. **Flowerheads:** On leafy side branchlets, in **large pyramidal inflorescences;** ± 30 mm diam, ray florets white, pink or mauve, disc florets white tinged mauve (Apr-Oct). **General:** Very variable. Good garden plant, grown from seed. **Similar species:** *P. pyrifolia* Stems simple below; leaves roundish, margins closely, regularly toothed; flowerheads in long, narrow inflorescences.

Anisochaeta (*aniso* - unequal; *chaeta* - bristle, refers to varying size of pappus scales) - Climber. Endemic, 1 species.

Anisochaeta mikanioides (*mikanioides* - like *Mikania*)

Scrambling, climbing shrub. On forest margins. Branches zigzag, wide apart. **Leaves:** ± 80 x 60 mm, **coarsely, deeply lobed, 3 veined from base. Flowerheads:** In stiff, widely branched inflorescences; whitish, bracts gland-dotted (Apr-May). **Fruit: Pappus of scales. Similar species:** *Vernonia anisochaetoides* Pappus with bristles (see p. 208).

Callilepis (*kallos* - beauty; *lepis* - scale) - Perennial herbs. Endemic, ± 4 species.

Callilepis laureola Ox-eye Daisy; Wildemargriet (A); mila (Sw); amafuthomhlaba, ihlamvu, impila (Z) (*laureola* - smaller Laurel)

Perennial herb, up to 600 mm. In grassland, coast to 1800 m, E Cape to Moz. Large woody tuber. **Leaves:** Very variable, ± 65 x 20 mm, **3** veined, margins entire or toothed. **Flowerheads:** Solitary (2-4), **large, ± 60 mm diam, ray florets white, disc florets purplish black** (Aug-Nov, after fires). **General:** Tubers poisonous. Used in traditional medicine to treat tapeworm, snakebite, infertility, ensure easy childbirth, kill maggots in cattle and as a protective charm. Lovely garden plant. **Similar species:** *C. leptophylla* Bergbitterbossie (A) Rare; leaves very narrow.

Eclipta (*ekleipo* - deficient) - Annual or perennial herbs. Pantrop, 1 in SA.

★ *Eclipta prostrata* Eclipta; ikhambi lakwangcolosi, ingcolozi, iphamphuce, umphamaphuce, ungcolozi (Z)

Annual herb, erect or prostrate. Cosmop weed, in damp places. Leaves ± 120 x 25 mm, margins toothed. Flowerheads in upper leaf axils (Jan-Mar). Used traditionally as love charms, for sorcery and in Afr, India, to treat skin infections and hepatitis.

Montanoa (named after Lius Montana, a Mexican politician in the 1800s) - Trop America, ± 50 species, 1 naturalised in SA.

★ *Montanoa hibiscifolia* Tree Daisy, Montanoa (*hibiscifolia* - leaves like *Hibiscus*)

Perennial shrub, up to 6 m. In disturbed areas, introduced from C America. Leaves large, ± 250 x 250 mm, dark green above, paler beneath. Flowerheads in terminal branched inflorescences; ± 40 mm diam, ray florets white, disc florets yellow, (May-Oct). Fruits ± 35 mm, papery, reddish brown. **A problem invader plant.**

216

Stoebe vulgaris

Tony Abbott

Stoebe vulgaris (galls)

Van Wyk & Malan

Martin von Fintel

Printzia pyrifolia

Athrixia angustissima

Martin von Fintel

Callilepis laureola

Wally Menne

★ Eclipta prostrata

Tony Abbott

Callilepis leptophylla

Jo Onderstall

Printzia laxa

Lal Greene

Anisochaeta mikanioides

Tony Abbott

★ Montanoa hibiscifolia

Geoff Nichols

217

Spilanthes (*spilos* - spot or blemish) - Annual branching herbs. Trop America, Afr, Malaysia, N Austr, ± 60 species, 2 in SA.

★ *Spilanthes mauritiana*   isisilili, isisinini (Z)
Annual herb, up to 300 mm. In wet places, coast to 1300 m, E Cape to Trop Afr. Leaves ± 40 x 30 mm. Flowerheads ± 12 mm diam. Used traditionally for toothache, sore gums and sore throats, chewed leaves numb the mouth. Attracts bees, insects.

Bidens (*bidens* - 2 toothed) - **Black-jacks or Cosmos**   Herbs. Cosmop, mostly America, ± 250 species, ± 7 in SA.

★ *Bidens pilosa* Common Black-jack; Gewone Knapsekêrel (A); umhlabangubo (X,Z); amalenjane, isikhathula, ucucuza, ugamfe, umesisi, uqadolo (Z) (*pilosa* - hairy)
Widespread weed, up to 1,5 m. Leaves ± 100 mm, 3-5 leaflets. Flowerheads ± 10 mm diam. Seeds barbed. Leaves cooked as a vegetable, browsed by game, stock, birds. Used traditionally to treat rheumatism, pain, diarrhoea and ear ailments. **Similar species: ★ *B. bipinnata* Spanish-Blackjack** Leaflets lance-shaped; yellow ray **florets**. (For photograph see p. 318) **★ *B. biternata*** 5-9 leaflets, narrowly oval, basal pair ± deeply divided into 2 asymmetrical lobes; yellow ray florets. (For photograph see p.318)

★ *Achillea millefolium* Common Yarrow, Milfoil; Duisendblaar-achillea (A) (named after Achilleus, hero of Homer's Iliad; *mille* - thousand; *folium* - leaf)
Perennial herb, up to 1 m. In disturbed places, introduced from Europe as an ornamental. Leaves ± 150 mm, segments very narrow. Ray florets few, white (Nov-May).

Adenanthellum - Previously incorrectly named *Adenanthemum*. SA endemic, 1 species.

Adenanthellum osmitoides [= *Adenanthemum osmitoides, Chrysanthemum osmitoides*]
Perennial herb, up to 500 mm, in colonies. In grassland, above 1300 m. Stems annual, simple. **Leaves:** Alternate, ± 45 x 20 mm, rigid, sparsely hairy or hairless, narrowing to pointed tips, margins sharply toothed. **Flowerheads:** ± 30 mm diam, stems ± 150 mm, ray florets white, disc florets deep yellow (Oct-Feb).

Cotula (*kotule* - a cup) - Annual or perennial herbs. Mainly S Hemisp, ± 90 species, ± 40 in SA, 1 a widespread weed.

Cotula nigellifolia [= *Matricaria nigellifolia*] **Staggers Weed; Rivierals, Stootsiektebossie, Waterkerwel (A); ukudliwa ngumlambo, umhlonyane omncane, umsolo (X); ikhambi elimpofana, udlabose , umhlonyane (Z)** (*nigellifolia* - resembles *Nigella* leaves)
Indigenous weed, in damp places. **Leaves:** ± 60 x 60 mm. **Flowerheads:** ± 15 mm diam, (Sep-Apr). **General:** Used traditionally to treat colds, skin rashes and anthrax poisoning in people. Fatal to cattle, causing 'bovine staggers', stock losses occur mostly in KZN midlands.

Senecio (*senex* - old man, refers to whitish grey hairy pappus) - Herbs, shrubs, rarely trees (for description see p. 320).

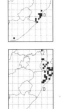

Senecio chrysocoma   umthithimbili wentaba (Z) (*chrysocoma* - golden hair)
Slender biennial herb, 1-2 m. In disturbed grassland, common pioneer, Cape to KZN, coast to 900 m. **Leaves: Long, narrow,** ± 150 x 3 mm. **Flowerheads:** In terminal, flattened inflorescences; ± 10 mm diam, **creamy white or creamy yellow** (Sep-Oct). **General:** Flowers visited by bees, wasps, moths, thrips, flies and small beetles.

Senecio viminalis   Leafless Climbing Senecio; umhlambamasi, uqobaqoba (Z)
(*viminalis* - long flexible shoots like the Osier Willow)
Succulent, scrambling climber. In dry thicket, bushveld, KZN to Moz. Stems ± 10 mm diam, mostly bare. Milky sap. **Leaves:** ± 20 x 20 mm, succulent, shiny dark green, falling early. **Flowerheads:** In compact terminal inflorescences; white (Dec-Jan), scent strong, sweet. **General:** Browsed by game. Useful in dry gardens.

Dimorphotheca - Herbs, shrubs or subshrubs (for description see p. 446).

Dimorphotheca caulescens [= *Osteospermum caulescens*] (*caulesc* - stem)
Tufted, perennial herb, up to 300 mm. In moist, rocky grassland, 1645-2500 m. Stiffly hairy. **Leaves:** Basal ± 150 x 20 mm, margins entire or with few, hard teeth, narrowed to stalklike base. **Flowerheads:** Solitary, ± 40 mm diam, ray florets creamy white above, bluish mauve beneath, disc florets whitish (Sep-Mar). **Similar species:** **D. fruticosa** [= *Osteospermum fruticosum*] **Creeping Marguerite; Rankmargriet (A)** Sprawling, slightly succulent herb; on coastal sand dunes, grassland, Cape to KZN; leaves ± 100 x 25 mm; flowerheads ± 40 mm diam, ray florets white above, bluish mauve beneath, disc florets mauve (throughout year); visited by thrips and a small black bee. Sand stabiliser and groundcover, from cuttings.

218

★ *Spilanthes mauritiana*

Adenanthellum osmitoides

★ *Bidens pilosa*

★ *Achillea millefolium*

Cotula nigellifolia

Dimorphotheca caulescens

Senecio chrysocoma

Senecio viminalis

Dimorphotheca fruticosa

219

Hirpicium (*hirpex* - a harrow) - Annual or perennial herbs. SA, ± 12 species.

Hirpicium armerioides Mountain Gerbera; Skynloodkruid (A) (resembles *Armeria*)

Mat-forming perennial herb, up to 250 mm. On poor, stony ground, 760-3100 m. **Leaves:** In basal rosette, ± 100 x 4 mm, sometimes lobed, bristly above, often with long white hairs, white felted beneath. **Flowers:** 25-50 mm diam, ray florets white above, yellow to purplish black beneath, disc florets yellow (Sep-Apr).

Berkheya (after Dutch botanist Jan le Francq van Berkhey, 1724-1812) - Perennial herbs, shrubs (for description see p .334).

Berkheya bipinnatifida (*bipinnatifida* - twice-cut, in pinnate manner)

Perennial herb, 1-3 m. On forest margins. **Leaves: Deeply lobed**, ± 300 x 180 mm, rough above, white felted beneath, teeth and lobes spine tipped. **Flowerheads:** Terminal inflorescences; 10-20 mm diam, disc florets white to mauve, bracts with 2-4 stout spines in lower parts (Dec-Jun). **General:** A weed on roadsides.

Berkheya rehmannii [=*B. zeyheri* subsp. *rehmannii*]

Perennial herb, up to 400 mm, in clumps. In rocky grassland, N KZN to N Prov. **Leaves:** ± 80 x **4-8(15) mm wide**, with long marginal bristles on lower half. **Flowerheads:** Large, ± 80 mm diam, ray florets creamy white, **disc florets yellow tipped black** (Nov-Dec).

Dicoma (*di* - two; *kome* - tuft of hairs) - Woody perennials; flowerhead bracts sharp, pointed. Afr, ± 32 species, ± 25 in SA.

Dicoma anomala Maagbitterwortel (A); hloenya, mohlasetse (SS); inyongana (Sw, X); isihlabamakhondlwane, umuna (Z) (*anomala* - irregular)

Reclining, perennial herb, stems 50-600 mm. In stony or wooded grassland, 365 -2075 m, Afr S of Sahara. **Leaves: Narrow,** ± 90 x 2-10 mm, grey felted beneath. **Flowerheads:** 15-50 mm diam, pink, white (Jan-May). **General:** Used to treat coughs, dysentery, toothache, sterility, gallsickness in stock and wounds on horses.

Dicoma speciosa Knoppiesdoringbossie (A); ihlabamakhondlwane (Z)

Stout, perennial herb, up to 850 mm, in small colonies. In grassland, up to 700 m. **Leaves:** ± 150 x 15(30) mm, leathery, **sharp tipped, base broad, clasping**. **Flowerheads: In terminal branched inflorescences**; 20-40 mm diam, purplish, bracts ± 30 x 5 mm, **sharp tipped, shiny silvery**, sometimes purplish (Dec-May). **General:** Used traditionally to treat coughs. **Similar species:** *D. zeyheri* (see p. 446).

Gerbera (after Traugott Gerber, died 1743, German naturalist) - Herbs, leaves woolly below (for description see p. 82).

Gerbera ambigua [= *G. discolor*] Pink and White Gerbera; Botterblom, Griekwateebossie (A); moarubetso, ripa-lithaate, seboka (SS); ucabazane, uhlamvuhloshane, ulimi-lwenkomo (Z) (*ambigua* - doubtful, uncertain)

Perennial herb, up to 350 mm. In grassland, woodland, up to 1900 m. **Roots thick, thonglike. Leaves: Variable**, 50-80(150) x 25-35(90) mm, thinly hairy above, white felted to thinly hairy beneath, stalks 20-30(150) mm. **Flowerheads:** 30-50 mm diam, ray florets white above, pink beneath, or yellow, coppery beneath, **pappus white** (throughout year). **General:** Used traditionally to treat tapeworm, coughs. Hardy garden plant. **Similar species:** *G. kraussii* Leaves densely hairy above, white felted with strongly raised veins beneath; flowerheads smaller, pappus purple. *G. natalensis* Covered in long white silky hairs; roots tuberous; flowerheads appear before leaves.

Gerbera piloselloides Small Yellow Gerbera; Swartteebossie (A); moarubetso, mothuntsetso, tsebe-ea-pela (SS); mabophe (Sw); ubulawu, umqwashu (X); indlebeyempithi, uhlango olimpofu, umoya-wezwe (Z) (*piloselloides* - with shaggy hairs)

Perennial herb, up to 300(450) mm. In grassland, woodland, coast to 1900 m, Cape to Ethiopia. **Leaves:** ± 90 x 60 mm. **Flowerheads:** 15-25 mm diam, **ray florets short**, white, pink, yellow, **stems swollen beneath flowerheads**, golden hairs (Jul-Feb). **General:** Used to treat tapeworm, earache, headache, coughs and as tonics.

Lactuca (Latin word for lettuce) - Annual or perennial herbs. Temp Eurasia, Afr, ± 100 species, ± 6 in SA.

Lactuca inermis [= *L. capensis*] Wild Lettuce; kho-loboto, lekologoto (SS); iklabeklabe (Z)

Perennial herb up to 1 m, in colonies. Pioneer in disturbed areas, Afr S of Sahara. Milky sap. **Leaves:** ± 50-150 x 3-10 mm, margins entire, irregularly toothed or lobed. **Flowerheads:** In loosely branched inflorescence; ± 15 mm diam, white, yellow or bluish (throughout year). **General:** Young leaves cooked as pot herb.

Hirpicium armerioides

Berkheya bipinnatifida

Berkheya rehmannii

Dicoma anomala

Gerbera ambigua

Dicoma speciosa

Gerbera piloselloides

Lactuca inermis

221

MONOCOTYLEDONS Single seed leaf, parallel veins; flower parts in threes or multiples of three.

CYPERACEAE - Sedge Family Grasslike herbs usually found near water or damp areas. Stems triangular or cylindric, solid, mostly without joints (grass stems jointed, often hollow). Leaves present, in 3 ranks or reduced to tubular sheaths. Flowers small, clustered in spikelets on upright or spreading branches or in heads forming collectively an inflorescence. Cosmop, ± 98 genera, ± 4350 species, 40 genera in SA. (See also p. 502)

Cyperus (*cyperus* - sedge) - Cosmop, ± 650 species, ± 70 in SA.

Cyperus sphaerocephalus [= *C. flavissimus, C. obtusiflorus* var. *sphaerocephalus, C. obtusiflorus* var. *flavissimus*] **Yellow Sedge; Geelbiesie (A); leya-butle, monokotsoai-oa-litsoene (SS)** (*sphaerocephalus* - round head)

Perennial, up to 450 mm. In rocky grassland, 670-2100 m, E Cape to Trop Afr. **Leaves:** Basal, stiff, 40-450 mm. **Flowers:** Inflorescence unbranched, bright golden yellow, ± 30 mm diam, bracts ± 50 mm (spring). **General:** Flowerheads plaited into necklets by girls in Lesotho. **Similar species:** *C. obtusiflorus* (see p. 84).

XYRIDACEAE (*xyron* - plant with sharp leaves) - **Yellow-eyed Grass Family** Perennial marsh herbs. Rhizome thick, erect. Leaves grasslike, forming sheath at the base. Flowers small, inflorescence with overlapping papery bracts, on stiff erect stem. Fruit a berry. Trop, 5 genera, ± 260 species, 1 genus in SA. *Xyris* Leaves basal; flowers with 3 spreading, very delicate tepals. Trop, ± 240 species, 7 in NE SA.

Xyris capensis **Common Xyris; hloho-tsa-makaka, kaka-hlothoana (SS); umuzi (Sw); udoyi oluncane (Z)**

Perennial herb, 60-300 mm, in clumps. In marshy areas, coast to 2400 m, SW Cape to Trop Afr, Madag, S America, India, China, Malaysia. **Rhizome weak. Leaves:** Grasslike, erect, 50-150 x 4 mm, tapering to hard points, **arranged in a fan. Flowers:** In roundish inflorescence, ±10 mm diam, bracts shiny brown, stem **round, wiry, golden brown at base**, usually twice as long as leaves; 3-5 flowers open at a time, yellow (spring-summer). **General:** Used for making beer strainers.

Xyris gerrardii (named after Wiliam Gerrard who collected widely in SA in the early 1800s)

Up to 550 mm, in clumps. In standing water, moist grassland, KZN to Zim. Rhizome hard, compact, covered in dark, hard, shiny, sheathing leaf bases ± 50 mm, roots thin. **Leaves:** Grasslike, ± 50 x 1 mm, soft, thin. **Flowers:** 5-8, in inflorescence ± 7 mm diam, bracts dark shiny brown with **rough margins**, stems thin (Dec-Feb).

COMMELINACEAE - Commelina Family Herbs. Nodes swollen, stems slightly succulent. Leaves with closed basal sheath. Flowers often within spathes and valves. Trop, ± 39 genera, ± 640 species, 7 genera in SA.

Commelina (named by Linnaeus after the three Commelin brothers. Johann and Caspar were well known botanists but the third brother died before achieving anything in the botanical world. The 2 large and 1 insignificant tepals in *Commelina* flowers refer to this.) - Flowers appear from within boat-shaped bract; 3 petals (2 large, 1 small), 3 equal sized sepals. Trop, ± 230 species, 16 in SA.

Commelina africana **Yellow Commelina; Geeleendagsblom (A); khopo, khotsoana, tabola-lefalo (SS); lidzangamane (Sw); lekzotswana (X); idangabane (Z)**

Perennial herb, up to 500 mm, prostrate, spreading. Widespread, SA, Trop Afr, Madag. **Leaves:** Flat or folded, ± 120 mm, smooth or hairy. **Flowers:** Yellow, tepals ± 15 mm, usually close before midday, spathe ± 25 mm (Aug-Jun). **General:** Size of leaves, flowers very variable. Used for pig food. Used in traditional medicine to treat a wide variety of ailments including fits, pain, heart complaints, venereal disease and bladder ailments. Useful to speed up decomposition of compost and as a foliar feed. **Similar species:** *C. subulata* Annual; usually confined to seasonally wet areas inland.

Aneilema (*aneilema* - without sheaths) - Inflorescence loosely branched, terminal; 3 petals (2 large, 1 small), 3 equal sized sepals. Cosmop, in warm and temp regions, ±80 species, 11 in SA.

Aneilema aequinoctiale **Clinging Aneilema; lidzangamane (Sw); idangabane elikhulu (Z)** (*aequinoctiale* - refers to the equinox, when day and night are of equal length)

Perennial up to 600 mm, erect or trailing. On forest margins, in moist or humid areas, E Cape to Trop Afr. **Leaves:** 35-130 x 15-40 mm, pale shiny green beneath, sheath 'sticky' with hooked hairs. **Flowers:** In terminal inflorescences; flowers ±15 mm diam, yellow, close at midday (Sep-Jun). **General:** Leaves used as spinach, roots boiled or roasted. Used for pig food. Attractive garden groundcover in shade.

COLCHICACEAE - Formerly part of Liliaceae. Herbs with buried, starch corms (for description see p. 26). *Gloriosa* (*gloriosus* - handsome) - A few closely related species, Afr and Asia, 1 in SA.

Gloriosa superba **Flame Lily; Vlamlelie (A); ashikolohwani (Th); ihlamvu, ihlamvu labafana, ihlamvu lasolwandle, isimiselo (Z)** (see p. 26)

Cyperus sphaerocephalus　　　Jo Arkell

Cyperus sphaerocephalus　　　Trevor Coleman

Aneilema aequinoctiale　　　Trevor Coleman

Commelina africana　　　Lal Greene

Commelina africana　　　Pam Cooke

Aneilema aequinoctiale　　　Lorraine van Hooff

Xyris capensis　　　Lal Greene

Xyris gerrardii　　　Lal Greene

Gloriosa superba　　　Geoff Nichols

223

ASPHODELACEAE - Formerly part of Liliaceae. Mostly herbs, also woody forms such as the tree aloes. Leaves often thick, succulent, in rosette, basal or just below inflorescence, margins often toothed and spiny. Inflorescence unbranched or branched, tepals free or fused into a tube, ovary superior. Fruit a capsule, seeds black. Europe, Asia, Afr, centred in S Afr particularly *Kniphofia* and *Aloe*, 17 genera, ± 750 species, 10 genera in SA.

Bulbine (*bulbine* - bulbous plant) - Perennial herbs; flowers with hairy stamens. Superficially resembles *Bulbinella* flowers which have non-hairy stamens, occur only in the Cape. Afr, Austr, ± 55 species, ± 41 in SA.

Bulbine abyssinica Bushy Bulbine; Geelkatstert, Wildekopieva (A); moetsa-mollo (SS); intelezi (X); ibhucu (Z) (*abyssinica* - Abyssinia, now Ethiopia)

Robust perennial, up to 800 mm, in clumps. Very variable. In rocky grassland, coast to 2400 m, E Cape to Ethiopia. Rootstock simple or branched. **Leaves:** Erect, in basal rosette, 100-350 mm, fleshy, rounded beneath, flat above, tapering to tip, grey-green or dark green, **lower margins winged white, base tinged pink. Flowers:** In 1(2) **large, densely crowded inflorescences**, 160-250 x 70 mm, stems ± 650 mm, extending and reclining as flowers open; flowers ± 14 mm diam, yellow, stalks 15-30 mm, **held straight after flowers or fruits fall** (Aug-Mar). **Fruit:** Round capsule held upright. **General:** Used in traditional medicine to treat bilharzia, dysentery and cracked lips. Hardy, attractive garden plant.

Bulbine asphodeloides Spreading Bulbine; Balsamkopieva, (A); khomo-ya-ntsuka, moetsa-mollo, pekane (SS); intelezi, itswelemyoka (X); ibhucu, ithethe elimpofu (Z)

Up to 500 mm, in large tufts. In grassland, S Cape to N Prov. Stems branching at base. **Leaves:** ± 300 mm, roundish. **Flowers:** In loose inflorescences, **yellow (coppery orange), stalks curl back after flowers or fruits fall. General:** Leaves used to treat cracked lips, skin complaints, burns, to stop bleeding and also as an antidote to poison and to treat sick livestock. Hardy garden plant. (See p. 26) **Similar species:** *B. frutescens* SW and E Cape; popular garden plant. *B. inflata* Robust, up to 1 m; on rocky hillsides, KZN to Mpum; tepals yellow with orange spot, flowers sweet smelling; capsule large, round, inflated, ± 20 mm diam.

Bulbine capitata (=*B. stenophylla*) Narrow-leaved Bulbine (*captitata* - knoblike head)

Up to 450 mm, mat-forming. In grassland, widespread in S Afr. **Leaves:** Slender, 150-450 x 1-2 mm, transparent, clasping sheath at base. **Flowers:** In **flat topped inflorescences** (Aug-Nov), sweetly scented. **Fruit: Capsule woody.**

Bulbine natalensis Broad-leaved Bulbine; Geelkopieva (A); incelwane (X); ibhucu (X,Z)

Perennial, up to 600 mm, in large colonies. Widespread, in hot, dry areas. Tuberous root. **Leaves:** In rosette, ± 300 x 75 mm, thick, fleshy, **bright green to yellow green**, tapering to pointed tip. **Flowers:** Inflorescences ± 320 mm, stems long; flowers ± 14 mm diam, stalks ± 10 mm, bracts 3 mm (throughout the year). **General:** Used in traditional medicine to treat skin ailments, vomiting, diarrhoea, urinary complaints, rheumatism and as a charm. Excellent garden plant, thriving in full sun and shade. A smaller form is found in S KZN (Umtamvuna) and Pondoland. **Similar species:** *B. latifolia* E Cape; leaves narrower, deep green; inflorescence crowded, dense.

Bulbine narcissifolia Strap-leaved Bulbine; Wildekopieva (A); khomo-ea-balisa, serelelile (SS) (*narcissifolia* - leaves like *Narcissus*)

Perennial, 300 mm, singly or in colonies. On poor soils, in grassland. Dense tuft of root fibres. **Leaves: In a fan,** ± 300 x 12-20 mm, **flat, hard,** grey-green, sometimes twisted. **Flowers:** In short, dense inflorescences, 25-35 mm diam, stems ± 350 mm (Nov-Apr). **General:** Used in traditional medicine to induce pregnancy in barren women and barren cows. Proliferation of this plant indicates overgrazing in some areas.

Bulbine abyssinica

Lawrence Peacock

Lorraine van Hooff

Bulbine asphodeloides

Martin von Fintel

Bulbine capitata

Bulbine capitata

Van Wyk & Malan

Geoff Nichols

Trevor Coleman

Bulbine natalensis

Bulbine natalensis

Martin von Fintel

Bulbine narcissifolia

Bulbine sp. (Umtamvuna)

Tony Abbott

225

ERIOSPERMACEAE - formerly part of Liliaceae. Perennial herbs with edible tubers. Ovary superior. Capsule 3-6 lobed, seeds covered in long white hairs. Afr 1 genus, ± 100 species, ± 50 in SA, mostly in SW Cape. *Eriospermum* (*erion* - wool; *sperma* - seed, refers to woolly seeds) - Flowers superficially resemble *Bulbine* genus but stamens not feathery.

Eriospermum abyssinicum [= *E. luteorubrum*] **umathinta (Z)**

300-400 mm. In grassland, woodland, KZN to Ethiopia. Small tuber, **flattened, round**, tipped with bristles from old leaves, flesh white. **Leaves:** Solitary, **slender**, erect, blade ± 140 x 17 mm, leathery, **parallel veins prominent**, narrowing to slender sheath (stalk), ± 130 x 2 mm, purple at base, after flowers. **Flowers:** ± 50, in **loose inflorescence**, 90-320 x 100 mm; flowers ± 14 mm diam, yellow with green vein tinged reddish, **stalks 10-20 above, ± 180 mm below** (Sep-Dec). **General:** Very variable over the vast range. Used in traditional medicine.

Eriospermum mackenii **Yellow Fluffy-seed; Geel Kapokblommetjie, Perdepootjie (A);**
insulansula (Z) (named after Mark McKen, 1823-1872, first curator of the botanical gardens, Durban)

Up to 400 mm. In damp grassland, E Cape to E Afr. Tuber round, flesh deep pinkish red. **Leaves:** 2-5, **with flowers**, blade ± 90 x 40 mm, fleshy to leathery, dark glossy green above, pale glossy beneath, deep red at base, old sheaths form fibrous neck ± 65 x 25 mm. **Flowers:** ± 50, inflorescence ± 200 x 30 mm; flowers ± 20 mm diam, yellow, stalks ± 25 mm, blooms in response to rain, opening ± midday, closing after dark (Oct-Feb). **General:** Used as a charm to ward off lightning. Good in full sun in garden. Subsp. *mackenii*, E Cape to E Afr; hairless, leaves broadly oval. Subsp. *galpinii*, N KZN to Bots, Nam; smaller; short hairs on leaf sheath, base of blade.

ASPHODELACEAE - Formerly part of Liliaceae. Mostly herbs, also woody forms such as the tree Aloes. Europe, Asia Afr, centred in S Afr, particularly *Kniphofia, Aloe*; 17 genera, ± 750 species, 10 genera in SA. (See p. 224)
Kniphofia (named after J H Kniphof, 1704-1763, prof of medicine at Erfurt University) - **Red-hot Pokers** Leaves soft, basal; inflorescence terminal, usually a simple dense spike. Mostly Afr, ± 70 species, 47 in E areas of SA.

Kniphofia drepanophylla **Poker** (*drepanophylla* - sicklelike leaves)

Up to 500 mm, in small groups. Marshes, Pondoland, S KZN. **Leaves:** Floppy, 150-300(600) x **15-30 mm**, **curved**, pale **yellow-green**, folded along midrib, **margins and keel finely toothed**. **Flowers: Short inflorescence**, ± 70 x 60 mm; buds spreading, greenish yellow, tinged red, flowers ± 40 mm, lemon-yellow (Aug-Jan).

Kniphofia fibrosa **Poker** (*fibrosa* - fibre)

Solitary, up to 600 mm. In grassland. **Leaves:** 6-10, grasslike, erect then bending over in middle, 350-600 x 3-4 mm, keeled, forming fibres at base, margin finely toothed, smooth near base. **Flowers:** Inflorescence 25-70 x 25-30 mm; buds spreading, flowers ± 15 x 3 mm, hanging, pale yellow(Feb-Mar).

Kniphofia multiflora **Giant Poker; Reusevuurpyl (A); tokoloshi (Sw)** (*multiflora* - many flowers)

Up to 2 m, in colonies. In marshy areas, 1300-2000 m, N KZN to N Prov. **Leaves:** 800-1800 x 20-40 mm, margins and keel toothed. **Flowers: In tall, narrow inflorescence**, 300-800 x 25-40 mm; **buds and flowers point upwards**, flowers 7-12 mm (Feb-Apr). **General:** Used in traditional medicine to treat female ailments. **Two colour forms**. Van Reenen/Wakkerstroom, buds greenish white, flowers cream. Carolina/Barberton northwards, buds orange-yellow, tinged red, flowers yellow.

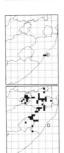

Kniphofia pauciflora **Dainty Poker** (*pauciflora* - few flowers)

Up to 500 mm, in small clusters. Originally found in marshy grassland. **Extinct in the wild.** **Leaves:** 200-350 x 2-8 mm, soft, erect, pale green, keeled beneath, smooth. **Flowers:** In loose, few-flowered inflorescence, 30-100 x 30-35 mm; flowers yellow (Sep-Nov). **General:** A popular garden plant at the coast.

Kniphofia porphyrantha **Dwarf Red-hot Poker; Hoëveld Vuurpyl (A); licaca-latokoloshi (Sw); icacane, umathunga (Z)** (*porphyrantha* - purple flowers)

Up to 600 mm. In damp grassland, marshy areas, 1500-2300 m. **Leaves:** Erect to arching, 300-450 x 6-14 mm, soft, **yellow-green**, often with waxy bloom, **margins smooth**. **Flowers:** In dense, **bi-coloured inflorescence**, ± 80 x 50 mm, sterile bracts at tip; buds spreading, orange-red tipped yellow, flowers 30-42 mm, lemon yellow (Oct-Feb). **General:** Used in traditional medicine to treat female ailments. **Similar species:** *K. galpinii* Leaves narrower, grasslike; inflorescence mostly red, autumn flowering. *K. thodei* (see p. 30), *K. fluviatilis* (see p. 28).

Eriospermum abyssinicum

Eriospermum mackenii

Lawrence Peacock

Rob Scott-Shaw

Geoff Nichols

Eriospermum mackenii

Kniphofia multiflora

Kniphofia fibrosa

Martin von Fintel

Sheila Peacock

Kniphofia drepanophylla

Kniphofia pauciflora

Kniphofia porphyrantha

Cynthia Giddy

Lawrence Peacock

Martin von Fintel

Aloe (appears to be derived from an old Greek name for the plant, allied to the Hebrew word 'allal' meaning bitter, although it may also have its origins in an Arabic word 'alloch'. Medicinal aloes were known to the Greeks from the island of Socotra as early as 4 BC, while the plant was cultivated in pots in the days of Rome and Naples)- Succulents with leaves in rosettes, stemless, singlestemmed or with massive trunks ± 20 m; inflorescences candlelike, often branched. Afr, Arabia, Medit, Madag, Socotra, India, China, ± 350 species, ± 125 in SA.

Aloe dominella (derivation unclear, perhaps refers to the plant being locally dominant in small areas)

Up to 400 mm, in branched clusters. On rocky slopes. **10-20(50) stems, ± 150 mm long**. **Leaves: Grasslike**, erectly spreading, ± 350 x 10 mm, dull green, white spots beneath, near base, margins narrowly edged with small firm white teeth. **Flowers:** In compact inflorescences, ± 40 x 80 mm; flowers ± 18 mm, yellow, **outer tepals free to base** (Jun-Oct), sweetly scented. **General:** Flowering usually after fires followed by rain. Does not always flower in cultivation.

Aloe kraussii Broad-leaved Yellow Grass Aloe; lekxalana, hloho-tsa-makaka (SS); isiphukuthwane, isiphuthumane (Z) (named after Christian Krauss, 1812-1890, German scientist, traveller and collector)

Up to 600 mm, solitary or in small groups. In grassland, on sandy soils and rocky ground, coast to midlands. **Leaves: In a fan** (or rosette in very old plants), 300-400(600) x **35(50) mm**, light green, margins with very narrow white edge. **Flowers:** In compact inflorescences, densely packed with 30-40 flowers, 1-3 stems; buds held upwards, **flowers short, 16-18 mm**, tubular, lemon yellow, green tips (Nov-Feb). **General:** Young inflorescences eaten as a vegetable. Attractive in the garden. **Similar species:** *A. ecklonis* (see p. 32).

Aloe linearifolia Dwarf Yellow Grass Aloe; inkuphuyana (Z) (*linearifolia* - long, narrow leaves)

Up to **250 mm**, solitary or in small groups. On damp grassy or stony slopes. **Leaves:** In a fan, **leaves narrow**, ± 250 x 8 mm, often with spiral twist, densely spotted beneath, near base, margins entire or with tiny teeth towards base. **Flowers:** 16-24, in tight inflorescences; buds held erect, flowers **small, ± 12 mm**, greenish yellow to orange (Jan-Apr). **General:** Used in traditional medicine. **Similar species:** *A. ecklonis* (see p. 32).

Aloe modesta (*modesta* - modest, unassuming)

Small, up to 300 mm. In rocky mountain grassland. Rare. Underground, bulblike basal swelling, roots fleshy, tapering. **Leaves: Erect to spreading**, long, slender, swollen at **base**, margins with tiny white teeth, more or less absent towards tip, elongate whitish spots beneath, near base. **Flowers: In dense inflorescences**; flowers greenish yellow, tubular, ± 13 mm, curved upwards (Jan-Feb), **fragrant**. **General:** The only scented Aloe in Afr.

Aloe reynoldsii Yellow Spineless Aloe (named after Gilbert Reynolds, 1895-1967, optometrist, authority on the genus *Aloe*)

Up to 600 mm, forming groups of 3-12 plants. On cliffs. Stemless or short stem. **Leaves:** ± 350 x 110 mm, pale green with white bloom, **H-shaped dull white spots, margins wavy**, with pinkish border, sometimes with minute teeth. **Flowers:** Widely spaced, inflorescences ± 60 mm, **stem slender**, branched; flowers ± 28 mm, yellow tinged orange (Sep-Oct). **General:** Attractive garden plant.

Aloe spicata [= *A. sessiliflora*] Lebombo Aloe; Lebombo-aalwyn (A); inhlaba (Sw, Z) (*spicata* - spikelike, refers to flowerhead)

Up to 2 m, solitary or multi-stemmed. Size very variable. On rocky outcrops in hot dry areas in bushveld, KZN to N Prov, Moz. Stem simple or branched. **Leaves: Spreading, recurved**, ± 600 x 90 mm, green to red, margins with red edge, reddish teeth. **Flowers:** Dense inflorescences, 300-400 x 40-50 mm, with 1-5 deep reddish brown stems; **flowers stalkless**, ± 15 mm, greenish yellow, stamens protruding, sap brown (Jul-Aug). **General:** Leaves used for snuff. Used in traditional medicine as an enema for babies. Leaf sap is rubbed on breasts to hasten weaning. Leaves green in cooler, moist conditions, almost entirely red in hot, dry localities. Very attractive garden plant.

Godfrey Symons

Martin von Fintel

Aloe dominella

Aloe modesta

Tony Abbott

Aloe linearifolia

Nolly Zaloumis

Aloe kraussii

Trevor Coleman

Aloe spicata

Aloe reynoldsii

Geoff Nichols

229

Aloe tenuior Fence Aloe; Heiningaalwyn (A); ikhalene, intelezi (X); inhlaba empofu (X,Z) (*tenuior* - very thin, refers to slender branches)

Up to 3 m. In thicket, on forest margins, coast to midlands. Rootstock woody. Stems branching, semi-woody. **Leaves:** Thin, 100-150 x 10-15 mm, sheathing at base, margins with tiny, white teeth. **Flowers:** Inflorescences 100-160 x 40 mm; flowers ± 15 mm, lemon yellow to orange-red (summer flowering, May). **General:** Used in traditional medicine to treat tapeworm and as protective charms. Popular garden plant.

Aloe vanbalenii Van Balen's Aloe; lihlala (Sw); icenalamatshe, icenalendlovu, inhlahlwane (Z) (named after J C van Balen, director of parks, Johannesburg, who first collected the species)

Up to 1 m, forming large dense groups. On rocky outcrops and hillsides. Stemless or short creeping stem. **Leaves: Strongly recurved, tips touching ground, deeply channelled,** 700-1000 x 120-150 mm, green to coppery red, margins with hard, sharp, reddish brown teeth. **Flowers:** Inflorescences 250-300 x 80-100 mm, 2-3 branches; flowers ± 35 mm, buff yellow to yellow-orange, sometimes bi-coloured or dull red (May-Jul). **General:** Cooked leaves eaten as a vegetable. Good garden plant.

Aloe vryheidensis Vryheid Aloe; Bruinaalwyn (A) (named after Vryheid, a town in N KZN)

Up to 2 m, solitary. On rocky mountain tops, N KZN. Stemless or short trunk with old leaves. **Leaves: In compact rosette, erect** to spreading, ± 650 x 130 mm, **± 25 mm thick,** blue-green, with bloom, reddish in dry periods, margins with sharp straight red-brown teeth. **Flowers: In dense, erect inflorescences,** 300-400 x 70 mm, 2-5 dark brown stems, at an **oblique angle;** flowers stalkless, ± 20 mm, pinkish red, **dark brown nectar, stamens bright yellow, protruding** (Jul). **General:** Flowers open first on north side (sun-facing). Bees attracted to pollen, birds to the copious nectar and to insects.

HYACINTHACEAE - Formerly part of Liliaceae. Mostly perennial herbs. Bulbs sometimes with a number of free scales. Inflorescences elongated, stamens 6, filaments often broad, flat, ovary superior. Fruit a capsule, seeds black. Subcosmop, ± 41 genera, ± 770 species, 27 genera in SA. *Albuca* (*albus* - white; or *albicans* - becoming white) - Bulbous herbs; flowers with 3 inner tepals erect and touching, outer tepals spreading. Afr, Arabia, ± 100 species, 56 in SA.

Albuca shawii Small Yellow Albuca; Lanternblom (A) (named after John Shaw, 1837-1890, teacher, geologist, bryologist and amateur botanist)

150-400 mm. On cliffs, in rocky grassland, mostly in mountains, up to 2400 m. **Leaves:** Few, long, very narrow, **covered with short sticky hairs. Flowers:** Few, ± 15 mm, **nodding,** yellow (Sep-Feb), scented. **General:** Liquorice smell when crushed. **Similar species:** *A. rupestris* NE Cape, S KZN; flowers larger, ± 24 mm, held erect, yellow (Nov-Dec), pleasant scent. *A.xanthocodon* E Cape; leaves more robust, smooth; flowers ± 20 mm, nodding, greenish yellow.

LUZURIAGACEAE - Slender forest climbers. Stems much branched, woody. Rhizomes with swollen roots. Fruit a berry. South America, New Zealand, SA, ± 4 genera, ± 9 species; 1 genus, 1 species in S A. *Behnia* (named after Danish botanist Behn) - Leaves with prominent parallel veins with cross connections. S Afr endemic.

Behnia reticulata Forest Smilax; Witbessieklimop (A); isigoba, izaza elimhlophe (Z) (*reticulata* - netted)

Evergreen, scrambler or climber. In forest, E Cape to Zim. **Stems thin, wiry. Leaves:** Alternate, ± 100 x 50 mm, thin, shiny, dark green, oval with pointed tips, **distinct midrib,** stalkless, size variable. **Flowers:** In small branched inflorescences; flowers ± 10 mm diam, tube short with short spreading lobes, creamy or greenish white, on very thin stalks (throughout year), sweetly scented. **Fruit:** Berry, ± 20 mm diam, light yellow to greenish white. **General:** Used in love potions. Attractive shade plant for gardens and flower arranging (skeleton leaves).

HAEMODORACEAE - Perennial herbs with rhizome, tuber or corm; red sap. 3 stamens opposite the inner tepals. S Afr, Trop America, Austr, ± 16 genera, ± 75 species, 4 genera in SA. *Barberetta* (named after Mrs Mary Barber (neè Bowker), 1818-99, who, with her brother, was the first to collect this plant in Natal) - Single species genus, SA.

Barberetta aurea (*aurea* - golden colour)

Herbs, up to 300 mm, in colonies. In kloof forests, on wet rocky forest floor, up to 1600 m. Stoloniferous corm. **Leaves:** ± 350 x 6-20 mm ribbed. **Flowers:** Inflorescences ± 300 mm; flowers ± 15 mm diam, yellow, 3 upper tepals with orange spot at base, stalks 8-15 mm (Nov-Mar).

Aloe vryheidensis

Martin von Fintel

Aloe tenuior

Lorraine van Hooff

Aloe vanbalenii

Geoff Nichols

Albuca shawii

Van Wyk & Malan

Albuca rupestris

Tony Abbott

Behnia reticulata

Martin von Fintel

Barberetta aurea

Tony Abbott

Barberetta aurea

Martin von Fintel

231

AMARYLLIDACEAE (for description see p. 36). **Haemanthus** (*haima*- blood; *anthos* - flower) - Bulbous herbs (for description see p. 104).

Haemanthus montanus Mountain Haemanthus (see p. 106, 346)

Cyrtanthus (*kyrtos* - curved; *anthos* - flower) - Buried bulbs (for description see p. 38).

Cyrtanthus breviflorus Yellow Fire Lily, Wild Crocus; Geelvuurlelie, Wildekrokus (A); umpimpilizi (Sw); injobo, uvelabahleke (Z) (*breviflorus* - short flowers)

Perennial herb, 75-300 mm. In moist or dry grassland, coast to 3000 m, E Cape to Kenya. Bulb 20-40 mm diam. **Leaves:** Strap-shaped, 60-250 x 1-14 mm. **Flowers:** 1-10(20), tube 5-10 mm, lobes 20-25 mm (throughout year), scented. **General:** Bulb edible. Used traditionally to treat intestinal worms and as protective and love charms. Good garden plant. **Variable growth forms.** Inland marshy areas: leaves robust, broad, with flowers, 20(30) in inflorescence, stem long. Coastal to midland grassland: leaves slender, after flowers, 1-3 in inflorescence, stem very short.

Cyrtanthus flanaganii Yellow Dobo Lily; Geeldobolelie (A) (named after Henry Flanagan 1861-1919, citrus farmer, plant collector, gardener who bequeathed his collections to the nation)

Up to 200 mm. In marshes, on wet cliffs, up to 3300 m, withstands frost, snow. Bulb ± 30 mm diam, neck ± 110 mm. **Leaves:** ± 200 x 20 mm, tips blunt, with flowers. **Flowers:** 4-7, in inflorescence, stem flattish, bracts ± 50 x 11 mm, white with red veins; flowers yellow, tube 40-55 mm, lobes ± 15 x 9 mm (Aug-Jan), scented.

Cyrtanthus mackenii Ifafa Lily; Ifafalelie (A); impingizana encane empofu (Z) (named after Mark McKen, 1823-1872, horticulturalist and collector, first curator, Durban Bot Gardens)

Up to 400 mm, in clumps. On streambanks. Bulb ± 40 mm diam. **Leaves:** ± 300 x 10 mm, with flowers. **Flowers:** 4-10, stem grey-green, hollow, bracts green spotted red-brown; flowers ± 50 mm, lobes ± 7 x 6 mm, white to creamy yellow (Jul-Feb), scented. **General:** Used as a protective charm. A garden plant, cultivars with pink to orange flowers. Var. *mackenii*, flowers white. Var. *cooperi*, flowers yellow or cream.

Cyrtanthus nutans (*nutans* - nodding)

Up to 200 mm, in colonies. In grassland, localised in N KZN and Swaz. Bulb ± 50 mm diam, neck 30-50 mm. **Leaves:** 150- 200 x 3-7 mm, after flowers. **Flowers:** ± 4, nodding, stem slender, hollow, bracts ± 60 mm; flowers 35-50 mm, pale yellow, divided more than one third the length, expanding to mouth, ± 12 mm wide, lobes 20-25 mm, **tapering to pointed tips**, stalks 15-45 mm (Aug-Oct).

Cyrtanthus stenanthus Long-tubed Cyrtanthus; Ifafalelie (A); lepontoana, moroloanane-oa-litsoene (SS); umpimpilizi (Sw); impingizana encane (Z) (see p. 40)

HYPOXIDACEAE - Star-flower Family Tuberous rhizome or corm. Leaves fibrous, often with long hairs Ovary inferior. Capsule splits in half, seeds small, black. S Hemisp, 8 genera, ± 220 species, 6 genera in SA.
Empodium (*em* - within; *pous* - foot, refers to underground ovary) - Flowers solitary, anthers long. SA, ± 10 species.

Empodium monophyllum [= *Forbesia monophylla*] Golden Star (*monas* - single; *phyllon* - leaf)

Herb, up to 100 mm. In grassland. Rhizome elongate, old leaf remains brown, not bristly. **Leaf:** 1(2), erect, 50-60 x 2-3 mm, subrigid, slender, narrow, tip pointed, after flowers. **Flowers:** 1-4 stems per plant, 80-90 mm; flowers solitary, ± 20 mm diam, yellow inside, green outside, (Sep-Nov).

Hypoxis (*hyp* - beneath; *oxys* - sharp pointed) - Rhizome vertical, tuberous, often fibrous. Research into the properties of Hypoxis indicates positive results in treating certain tumours. Mostly Afr, + 88 species, 43 in SA.

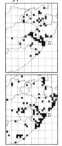

Hypoxis acuminata moli-motsanyane, thotolinyenyane (SS) (acuminata - long pointed)

Up to 300 mm, in large communities. In damp grassland, coast to 1980 m. Tuberous rootstock, 15-25 mm, topped with erect bristles. **Leaves:** In spiral tuft, stemlike at base, 150-300 x 2-5 mm, V-shaped, ribbed, long hairs dense above, sparse beneath. **Flowers:** 2-6, 20-35 mm diam (Aug-May).

Hypoxis angustifolia molinyana (SS) (angustifolia - narrow leaves)

Up to 100 mm, scattered. In grassland, Trop Afr, Mauritius, Seychelles. Carrotlike tuber, 6-25 mm diam. **Leaves:** 70-600 x 2-17 mm, parchmentlike, 3 ranked, 2-4 prominent ribs, fine white hairs on margins, keeled. **Flowers:** + 7 flowers, + 20 mm diam, stem slender (Jul-May). **General:** Var. *angustifolia*, leaves long narrow, 2-6(10) mm wide, semi-erect. Var. *buchanii*, leaves broad, 6-15 mm, floppy, papery.

Cyrtanthus breviflorus Geoff Nichols

Cyrtanthus breviflorus Lal Greene

Cyrtanthus nutans Martin von Fintel

Cyrtanthus flanaganii Martin von Fintel

Cyrtanthus mackenii Geoff Nichols

Haemanthus montanus Geoff Nichols

Cyrtanthus stenanthus Martin von Fintel

Empodium monophyllum Tony Abbott

Hypoxis angustifolia Tony Abbott

Hypoxis acuminata Lal Greene

233

Hypoxis argentea Small Yellow Star-flower; leihlo-khoma le leholo, lesikitlane (SS); ixalanxa (X); inongwe (X,Z); isinana (Z) (*argentea* - silvery)
Up to 400 mm. In grassland, on rocky outcrops. Tuber 5-20 mm diam. **Leaves:** Narrow, **V-shaped**, 50-500 x 1-7 mm, 2 prominent ribs, **covered in long, fine, yellowish hairs. Flowers:** 2-4, in pairs, ± 20 mm diam, stem slender, much shorter than leaves (Aug-Apr). **General:** Rootstock eaten, also used to treat cracked cows' teats, wounds on horses. Var. *argentea,* not in KZN; leaves firm, densely silky hairy on keel, margins and **lower surface.** Var. *sericea,* widespread; leaves long, not firm, hairs **mainly on margins, keel.**
Similar species: *H. filiformis* Grass Star-flower; moli-letsane (SS); izinongwe (Z) In moist areas, coast to 2500 m; leaves threadlike, 60-300 x 1-3 mm, erect, rigid, U-shaped, covered in fine white hairs; 1-3 flowers, often with 4 lobes (Jul-Apr).

Hypoxis colchicifolia [= *H. latifolia, H. oligotricha*] **Broad-leaved Hypoxis; igudu, ilabatheka, ingcobo, inkomfe (Z)** (*colchicifolia* - leaves like *Colchicum*)
Up to 600 mm, solitary. On sandy or poor soils, in grassland. Tuber large, round, 40-70 mm diam. **Leaves: In 3 ranks,** 110-600 x 25-110 mm, erect, firm, strongly ribbed, grey-green, **hairless** (or with sparse hairs on margins). **Flowers:** 6-20, in inflorescence, ± 140 mm, stem slender (Aug-Feb). **General:** Used in traditional medicine to treat impotence, barrenness, bad dreams, hysterical fits and as a love charm. Much in demand for medicinal purposes and as a garden plant. **Similar species:** *H. galpinii* Leaves much narrower, margins and midrib very hairy.

Hypoxis hemerocallidea [= *H. rooperi*] **Star-flower; Sterblom, Gifbol (A); lotsane, moli-kharatsa (SS); inkomfe (Z)** (*hemerocallidea* - resembling *Hemerocallis,* the Day Lily)
Up to 400 mm. In grassland, woodland, widespread. Large tuber, 25-70 mm diam, covered with bristly hairs. **Leaves: In 3 ranks,** 600-950 x 10-50 mm, erect, soft, **sickle-shaped**, keeled, ribs prominent, tapering to tips, with dense white hairs on **lower surface**, margins and keel. **Flowers:** 6-16 per stem, ± 50 mm diam, open at first light, close at midday, many slender, erect stems, almost as long as leaves (Aug-Apr). **General:** Leaves used to make lasting rope, bulb used to blacken floors. Used in traditional medicine to treat headaches, dizziness, mental disorders and, in western medicine, to treat cancers, inflammation and HIV. Incorrectly known as African Potato. Attractive hardy garden plant. **Similar species:** *H. iridifolia* [*H. nitida, H. obtusa*] **moli-boea (SS); inkomfe (Z)** Up to 600 mm; S Afr to Trop Afr; leaves ± in 3 ranks, 70-600 x 3-20 mm, shiny, blade hairless, folded, erect to arching, twisted with age, prominently ribbed, margins with dense white hairs.

Hypoxis multiceps Winter Star-flower; moli-kharatsa, moli-motsane; morethetho (SS); inkomfe (Z) (*multiceps* - bearing many heads)
Up to 300 mm. In grassland, up to 2000 m. Tuber 15-40 mm diam, bristle topped. **Leaves:** In 3 ranks, ± 300 x 55 mm, **arching**, flat, hairs dense, rough, yellowish, **after flowers. Flowers:** 1-4, 20-40 mm diam, opening in more or less **opposite pairs**, stem thick, short, flat, hairy (Jun-Nov). **General:** Leaves continue to grow when flowering is over. Used as a protective charm against lightning. **Similar species:** *H. costata* kharatsa (SS) Up to 150 mm; leaves ± 180 x 40 mm, rigid, conspicuously ribbed, densely hairy or hairless, thickened submarginal veins; flowers on hairy stems as long as leaves (Oct-Jan).

Hypoxis rigidula Silver-leaved Star-flower; moli-teane(SS); inkomfe (Z) (*rigidula* - stiff)
Up to 900 mm, in small to large groups. In grassland, on rocky slopes, marsh margins, widespread. Tuber oblong, 20-60 x 20-45 mm. **Leaves:** Erect, ± 900 (1400) x 3-15 mm, strongly ribbed, covered in white hairs, forming a 'stem' at base, ± 200 mm. **Flowers:** Alternate to clustered, ± 40 mm diam, 1-5 stems (Aug-Mar). **General:** Leaves used to make strong, lasting rope. Leaf bases eaten by baboons. Used in traditional medicine. Attractive garden plant. Subsp. *rigidula,* widespread; hairs in channels between ribs of leaves. Subsp. *pilosissima,* more common inland; densely woolly on both surfaces.

Hypoxis argentea

Hypoxis filiformis

Hypoxis multiceps

Hypoxis colchicifolia

Hypoxis costata

Hypoxis iridifolia

Hypoxis hemerocallidea

Hypoxis rigidula

IRIDACEAE - Iris Family Corms or rhizomes. Leaves sword-shaped, in 2 ranks. Flowers regular or irregular, stamens 3, ovary inferior. Cosmop, ± 82 genera, ± 1700 species. Over half the species occur in SA, in 38 genera.
Moraea (Linnaeus altered the spelling to *Moraea* to associate the name with his father-in-law, J Moraeus, a physician in Sweden) - End of style branches petal-like. Afr, Madag, Austr, ± 90 species, ± 101 species in SA, mostly SW Cape.

Moraea graminicola (*graminicola* - favouring grassland)
Up to 600 mm, solitary. In open grassland. Corm ± 15 mm diam, **cataphylls pale, papery, unbroken or frayed above.** Leaf: Solitary, ± 25 mm wide, erect, sturdy, usually longer than flowering stem at time of flowering. **Flowers: Large**, pale yellow-grey with mauve veins, crests sometimes blotched mauve at base, outer tepals ± 75 mm, claw suberect, limb oval, ± 45 x 30 mm, inner tepals ± 50 x 15 mm, erect (Aug-Nov). **General:** Poisonous to stock. Subsp *graminicola*, KZN, up to 450 mm; stem unbranched; style crests sometimes flushed pale mauve, not blotched at base (Aug-Nov). Subsp *notata*, Transkei, up to 600 mm; stem occasionally branched; style crests darkly blotched at base (Sep-Jan).

Moraea hiemalis (*hiemalis* - of the winter, referring to midwinter flowering)
Up to 450 mm, solitary. In open grassland, 1000-2000 m. Corm ± 15 mm diam, with dark brown tunics. **Leaf:** Solitary, margins tightly inrolled, round, longer than flowering stem, usually dying back at time of flowering. **Flowers:** Yellow with dark veins and deep yellow nectar guides, outer tepals ± 50 mm, limb ± 35 x 24 mm, inner tepals erect, ± 40 x 15 mm, broad style branches with conspicuous crests (Jul-Sep). **General: Winter flowering.**

Moraea huttonii **Large Golden Vlei Iris** (named in honour of Henry Hutton, amateur botanist who collected in E Cape in the mid 1800s)
Tall, up to 1 m, **in large clumps. In or close to mountain streams, rivers.** Corm ± 20 mm diam, papery pale tunics covered by **dark brown cataphylls** ± 200 mm, covering lower part of stem and leaves. **Leaves:** Usually longer than flowering stem, ± 25 mm wide, straplike, margins incurved. **Flowers:** Yellow with deeper yellow nectar guides, **dark brown to purple blotch on each style crest**, outer tepals ± 55 mm, limb ± 35 x 25 mm, spreading, inner tepal erect, narrow, ± 45 mm, stem erect, rarely branched (Jul-Dec), sweetly scented; Lovely garden plant. **Similar species:** *M. alticola* Found above 2200 m; robust; cataphylls pale, fibrous.

Moraea spathulata **Large Yellow Moraea; Grootgeeltulp (A); teele-e-kholo (SS); indlolotsi (Sw); ihlamvu elincane, ihlamvu lentaba, indlolothi, ingqunda (Z)**
(*spathulata* - spatulalike, refers to shape of inner tepals, broadest near tips)
Large, up to 900 mm, solitary or in small clumps. In open grassland, often amongst rocks, coast (in the south) to 2600 m (further north), SE Cape to Zim. Corm ± 20 mm diam. **Leaf:** Solitary, flat above, twisted, **± 2 m x 15 mm. Flowers:** Yellow with deep yellow nectar guides on outer tepals, ± 50 mm, limb ± 35 mm, spreading to reflexed, inner tepals erect, ± 40 mm (May-Nov in south, Aug-Apr in north). **Fruit: Round**, ± 55 mm. **General:** Leaves used to make rope. Used in traditional medicine to treat infertility and as a protective charm. Poisonous to stock. Hardy garden plant, flowers last 3 days.

Moraea trifida (*trifida* - refers to 3 lobed inner tepals)
Solitary, up to 550 mm. In moist grassland, on streambanks, seepages at higher altitudes, up to 2400 m. Corm ± 20 mm diam, covered in pale fibres. **Leaf:** Solitary, ± 600 x 4 mm, stiff, hard, **inserted some way above ground**, often short at time of flowering, **usually shorter than flowering stem. Flowers:** ± 20 mm, **creamy yellow** with brownish green markings, outer tepals reflexed, inner tepals ± 15 mm, erect, **trilobed**, stem erect (Oct-Mar).

Moraea unibracteata (*unibracteata* - single bract, refers to solitary sheathing bract on flowering stem)
200-350 mm, solitary. In mountain grassland. Corm 8-12 mm diam, cataphylls brown. **Leaf:** Solitary, stiffly erect, **usually longer than flowering stem**, 2-10 mm wide, channelled, **clasping in lower half. Flowers:** Stem erect, **bract leaf sheathing, overlapping spathes**; flowers pale yellow veined green, with deep yellow nectar guides on outer tepals, outer tepals 30-45 mm, claw suberect, ± 15 mm, shorter than limb, inner tepals 27-40 mm, erect (Oct-Nov).

236

Moraea alticola   *Martin von Fintel*   Moraea graminicola   *Lal Greene*   Moraea hiemalis   *Lal Greene*

Moraea huttonii   *Martin von Fintel*   Moraea spathulata   *Martin von Fintel*   Moraea trifida   *Lal Greene*

Moraea huttonii   *Lal Greene*   Moraea spathulata   *Cameron McMaster*   Moraea unibracteata   *Lal Greene*

237

Dietes (*Dietes* - two relatives, drawing attention to the position of this genus between *Moraea* and *Iris*) - Perennial evergreen with short, creeping rhizome like *Iris* (*Moraea* has a corm); flower similar to *Moraea*, with free perianth segments (united at base in *Iris*). Restricted to SE and C Afr except for 1 species on an island E of Austr; 5 species in SA.

Dietes bicolor Peacock Flower, Yellow Wild Iris; Poublom, Uiltjie (A) (*bicolor* - 2 colours)

Up to 1,2 m, in clumps. Near streams, in marshy areas. **Leaves:** In a fan, 500-1000 x 6-12 mm, tough, pointed, pale green, curving outwards, **double central vein. Flowers:** Flat, ± 60 mm diam, pale lemon yellow, **tepals rounded**, outer tepals with dark brown patch, forming brown and orange-spotted claw, stem round, erect, as long as leaves, much branched above; flowers close after a day (Aug-Feb). **Fruit: Club-shaped capsule** ± 25 mm, **splitting partially** to release seeds. **General:** Popular garden plant, in sun and shade. Cultivated in Europe since the early 1800s.

Dietes flavida (*flavida* - pale yellow)

Up to 700 mm, in clumps. In thicket, rocky areas. **Leaves:** In a fan, glaucous grey-green, ± 500 x 20-35 mm, base sheathing. **Flowers:** Pale yellow with orange-brown markings, outer tepals oval ± 40 mm, inner ± 38 mm, open in late afternoon, earlier on overcast day, stems not rigid, as long as leaves, with short side branches (Sep-Jan). **Fruit: Hanging, oval capsule** ± 35(75) x 12 mm, partially splitting or disintegrating to release seeds. **General:** Decorative, hardy garden plant for shady and sunny positions.

Homeria (probably from *omereo* - to meet together, refers to filaments united around the style) - Corm with coarse dark fibres; flowering stem usually branched, tepals spreading from base. Mainly in SW Cape, ± 32 species in SA.

Homeria pallida Yellow Tulip; Geeltulp (A); indlolothi, ingqunde (Z) (*pallida* - somewhat pale)

Small, slender, erect, often in large colonies. In grassland, damp marshy areas, up to 1525 m, widespread, Cape to Nam, Mpum. **Leaf:** Solitary, trailing, much longer than stem, ± 2000 x 20 mm (usually smaller), bluish green, ribbed. **Flowers:** Stem erect; tepals ± 30 x 10 mm, yellow with greenish brown speckles at base (Sep-Dec-Apr), sweetly scented. **General:** Very poisonous to cattle. Indicates overgrazing.

Tritonia (*triton* - a weathercock, refers to the variable direction of stamens of different species) - Flowers regular, tube short, style branches undivided. Afr, ± 40 species, 27 in SA, mostly in coastal areas of S Cape.

Tritonia lineata Pencilled Tritonia, Yellow Tritonia; Bergkatjietee (A); khahla-e-nye-nyane (SS); isidwi esimpofu (Z) (*lineata* - marked with lines)

Perennial herb, up to 600 mm. Widespread in grassland, coast to 2400 m, SE Cape to Mpum. Corm oval, ± 20 mm diam with fine tunic fibres. **Leaves:** Erect to spreading, 150-300 x 7-10 mm, prominent midvein and marginal veins. **Flowers:** 7-12 in inflorescence, stem simple or branched; flowers funnel-shaped, ± 35 x 25 mm, cream to pale yellow (pale apricot) with dark veins, **tube short**, bracts papery, brown (Aug-Feb, **spring**). **Fruit:** Elongated capsule ± 8 mm. **General:** Varies in size and flower colour. Used traditionally to treat stomach complaints in babies and heal infection in the navel of a newborn child. Suitable for gardens.

Gladiolus (*gladiolus* - small sword, refers to leaf shape) - Deciduous; bracts green; style branches short, undivided or shortly divided in 2; seeds winged. Hybrids created since the early 1800s have produced the cut-flowers and garden plants popular worldwide. Mostly in S Afr, also Trop Afr, S Europe, Mid East, ± 259 species, over 126 in SA.

Gladiolus longicollis Honey Flower; Aandblom (A); khahla-e-nyenyane, khukhu-rupa (SS); sidvwana (Sw); umbejo (Z) (*longicollis* - long stalked)

Up to 0,8(1) m, solitary. Widespread in grassland, coast to 3300 m. Corm with wiry fibrous tunics. **Leaf:** Sheathing stem, usually solitary, ± 750 x 5 mm, tips sharp. **Flowers:** 1-4, one open at a time, at night, stem slender; flowers ± 40 mm, cream, yellow, with reddish brown to purple speckles and dark lines, tube narrow, ± **120 mm**, tepal lobes variable in shape, bracts ± 50 mm (Jul-Jan), strong, sweet scent in evening. **Fruit:** Capsule ± 25 mm. **General:** Especially noticeable after a burn, scattered but frequent. Corms eaten by gamebirds and small mammals. Pollinated by sphinx moths.

Gladiolus ochroleucus Triangular Gladiolus; Pypie (A) (*ochroleucus* - very pale yellow ochre)

0,75(1) m, solitary. In grassland, coast to 2000 m. Corm round, ± 40 mm diam, covered with matted pale fibres. **Leaves:** In a fan, not forming a stem, often evergreen, ± 300 x 15 mm with yellow margins, raised ribs. **Flowers:** Variable, 35-70 mm, whitish cream, yellowish or pinkish with darker veins and throat, bracts 30-70 mm, erect (Dec-Apr). **Fruit:** Capsule ± 12 mm.

Trevor Coleman

Dietes bicolor

Trevor Coleman

Dietes bicolor

Wally Menne

Dietes flavida

Martin von Fintel

Homeria pallida

Wally Menne

Dietes flavida

Wally Menne

Gladiolus longicollis

Tom de Waal

Tritonia lineata

Trevor Coleman

Gladiolus ochroleucus

Lal Greene

Gladiolus longicollis

239

Gladiolus pubigerus (*pubigerus* - downy)
200-400 mm. On grassy mountain slopes, 1500-2500 m. Corms roundish, 10-15 mm diam. **Leaf:** Solitary, **sheathing stem,** 0-20 mm free at tip, with long hairs. **Flowers:** + 7, stem with 1 **sheathing bractlike leaf well below flowers**; flowers + 30 mm, greenish yellow (KZN), mauve or orange (Oct-Nov). **Similar species:** *G. parvulus* (see p. 358).

Gladiolus woodii   sidvwana (Sw) (see p. 112, 572)

Watsonia (named after English scientist Sir William Watson, 1715-1787) **-** Flattened corms with persistent fibrous tunics; leaves firm, basal and sheathing stem; inflorescence a spike, more or less equal, bracts rigid, usually brown. Mostly SA, ± 52 species, 1 in Madag.

Watsonia watsonioides [= *W. flavida*] sidvwana (Sw) (*watsonioides* - resembling a *Watsonia*, applied when the plant was first described as a *Tritonia* with *Watsonia*-like features)

0,5-1 m. In rocky grassland, 1000-1800 m. Corm 2-3 mm diam, tunics light brown, finely fibrous, forming a neck. **Leaves:** 2, ± basal, as long as flowering stem, narrow, 4-6 mm wide, **margins heavily thickened. Flowers:** 25-50 flowers, **in congested spike, stem simple or 1-2 branches,** covered with overlapping bracts, dry and brown above; flowers **small, pale yellow, cream** (maroon), tube 15-18 mm, mostly within bracts, upper part flared, horizontal to drooping; tepal lobes 10-18 x 5-7 mm (Dec-Mar). **Fruit:** Capsule round, 5-8 mm. **General:** Corm eaten. Used in traditional medicine.

ORCHIDACEAE - Orchid Family Highly specialised flowers, in 2 whorls, outer 3 sepals and inner 3 petals often all the same colour. One of the sepals can be differently shaped and is called the median, dorsal or odd sepal. One of the petals is usually lobed and crested and called the lip. Either the median sepal or the lip may have a sac or spur. Single stamen and stigma and style are united to form a structure called the column. Pollen grains are collected into waxy or grainy pollinia which are attached to a sticky gland. Cosmop, ± 788 genera, ± 18500 species, ± 54 genera in SA.

Holothrix (*holos* - entire; *thrix* - hair, meaning hairy all over) **-** Terrestrial herbs; 2 leaves flat on ground; flowering stem leafless, bractless, flowers white to yellowish green. Afr, ± 55 species, 22 in SA.

Holothrix scopularia [= *H. multisecta*] (*scopulinus* - bearing small brushes; or *scopulosus* - rocky)

Slender to robust, up to 330 mm. In rocky grassland, 1200-2800 m. **Leaves:** ± 52 mm broad, with scattered long thin hairs near margins above. **Flowers:** In dense inflorescence, stem with long thin hairs; flowers small, white to dull yellow or pink, lip ± 9 mm, deeply divided into ± 11 lobes (Oct-Jan). (See p. 362)

Schizochilus (*schizein* - splinter or split; *cheilos* - a lip) **-** Terrestrial herb; leaves few, narrow, near base of stem; inflorescence dense, usually drooping over at tip. Afr genus, ± 20 species, 8 in SA.

Schizochilus bulbinella
Slender, up to 200 mm. In shallow soil over rock, 1500-2500 m. **Leaves:** 10-30, **lower leaves clustered at base. Flowers:** In dense inflorescence; flowers small, yellow, sepals 2,5-3,5 mm, petals ± 2 mm (Jan-Feb).

Schizochilus zeyheri (named after Carl Ludwig Zeyher, 1799-1858, botanical collector who came to the Cape in 1822)

Slender, 150-600 mm. In wet grassland, coast to 2000 m, widespread. **Leaves:** 3-8, mostly sheathing stem. **Flowers:** ± 30, in inflorescence; flowers large, **bright yellow,** sepals ± 11 mm, lip deeply 3 lobed, central lobe 2 mm, lateral lobes 1 mm, **spur 2-6 mm** (Nov-Mar).

Disa (possibly from *dis* - rich or opulent, alluding to the beauty and magnificence of the first species described in this genus, *D. uniflora*) **-** Underground tubers; several leaves; median sepal hooded, prolonged into a spur or pouch, direction in which spur points is useful in identification. Afr and Madag, ± 130 species, ± 94 in SA.

Disa woodii (named after John Medley Wood, 1827-1915, botanist, founder of Natal Herbarium, who published works on the Natal Flora)

Stout, up to 700 mm. In damp grassland, E Cape to Zim. **Leaves:** Rosette of basal leaves, extending up stem, sheathing, fleshy, purplish at base, tips drying reddish brown. **Flowers:** In densely crowded inflorescence, ± 160 mm; flowers small, bright yellow with orange tinge, spur slender, ± 1,5 mm, lip narrow, horizontal to hanging (May-Sep-Dec). **General:** Look like glowing candles in damp marshy areas. Also found on disturbed damp soils and road cuttings.

Van Wyk & Malan

Gladiolus woodii

Martin von Fintel

Watsonia watsonioides

Martin von Fintel

Watsonia watsonioides

Martin von Fintel

Gladiolus pubigerus

Tony Abbott

Schizochilus bulbinella

Martin von Fintel

Holothrix scopularia

Lal Greene

Schizochilus zeyheri

Durrel Plowes

Disa woodii

241

Liparis (*liparos* - shiny, oily, refers to leaves) - Usually terrestrial, with or without pseudobulbs. Throughout warm and temperate regions, most common in Trop Asia, ± 250 species, 4 in SA.

Liparis bowkeri (named after Mary (Bowker) Barber, 1818-1899, an ardent student of nature, writer, painter, who came to SA in 1820 with her family)

Up to 150 mm, terrestrial or epiphytic. Widespread in forests, in leaf litter on rocks and trees, up to 1800 m, E Cape to Kenya. **Pseudobulbs soft, green,** 20-70 mm, **in closely packed surface groups. Leaves:** 2-4, ± 70 x 60 mm, pale green, soft, with side veins. **Flowers:** 4-12, stem slender; flowers translucent yellowish green fading brown, side sepals flat, ± 12 mm, **petals very narrow,** lip 6-8 mm broad (Dec-Mar). **General:** Used as a good luck or love charm. **Similar species:** *L. remota* Extended rhizome between pseudobulbs.

Polystachya (*poly* - many; *stachys* - ear of corn, meaning an ear of corn or spike) - Usually epiphytic; base of stem swollen to form a pseudobulb; ovary not twisted, lip uppermost. Trop, mostly Afr, ± 200 species, 12 in SA.

Polystachya concreta [= *P. tessellata*] **amabelejongosi (Z)** (*concreta* - growing together)

Up to 450 mm, erect. Size, colour variable. Widespread in warm forests, woodland, E Cape to Trop Afr. Pseudobulbs ± 20 x 12 mm. **Leaves:** 2-5, thin, **long, broad,** ± 200 x 40 mm. **Flowers:** Stem **long,** slender, flattened, with 5-7 branches; **12-20 flowers per branch,** flowers fleshy, **small, ± 5 mm,** glossy yellowish green to dull pink (Dec-Feb). **General:** Used as protective charms. Easily grown, flowers freely.

Polystachya pubescens **Hairy-lipped Polystachya; amabelejongosi (Z)** (*pubescens* - downy, slightly hairy)

Up to 160 mm. On rocks and trees, rocky outcrops in sun, in light shade of forests, from coast to warmer drier areas. **Pseudobulbs clustered,** 20-60 x 1-15 mm. **Leaves:** 2-3, ± 100 x 17 mm, not fully developed until after flowering. **Flowers:** 8-20 in inflorescence; **flowers golden yellow,** opening fully, ± 23 mm, side sepals ± 12 mm wide, **streaked with dark red lines,** lip veined with red, covered in **white silky hairs** on lobes (Sep-Jan), strongly scented. **General:** Used as a protective and love charm. Popular container plant in Japan.

Polystachya sandersonii **amabelejongosi (Z)** (named after John Sanderson, 1820-1881, plant collector and honorary secretary to the Horticultural Society of Natal)

Up to 150 mm. On trees, in coastal and lower altitude forests. **Pseudobulbs short,** ± 30 x 15 mm. **Leaves:** 2-3, ± 100 x 15mm (often smaller). **Flowers:** 6-12, ± 13 mm wide, yellowish green and brownish orange, side sepals narrowly triangular, **outer surface smooth or velvety,** lip 3 lobed, creamy white, **heavily spotted maroon in basal half** (Oct-Jan). **General:** Used as a protective and love charm.

Ansellia (named after John Ansell, assistant botanist on Niger Expedition in 1841) - Epiphyte with thick, bamboolike stems; old pseudobulbs form large clumps surrounded by short, fine, upright roots; flowers large. Afr, 1 species in SA.

Ansellia africana [= *A. gigantea* var. *gigantea, A. gigantea* var. *nilotica*] **Leopard Orchid, Tiger Orchid; Luiperdorgidee (A); imfeyenkawu (Z)**

Robust, up to 1,8 m, in clumps up to 1(3) m diam. In hot, humid, dry forest, scrub, KZN to Trop Afr. Pseudobulbs 250-1000 x 30 mm, canelike, papery white sheaths in lower parts. **Leaves:** Alternate, 200-400 x 25-40 mm, tough, stiff, with parallel veins. **Flowers:** In branching inflorescence ± 500 mm, stem ± 500 mm; flowers, 30-50 mm diam, yellow or yellow marked with reddish brown, lip brighter yellow (Jun-Nov), lovely light scent, pungent at night. **General:** Eaten by monkeys. Blooms for weeks. Used in traditional medicine as a love charm and antidote to bad dreams. Planted at homesteads to ward off lightning. A popular, hardy garden subject.

Eulophia (*eu* - well; *lophos* - crest, refers to crested lip) - Terrestrial herbs; rhizomes thickened into fibrous tubers, some with pseudobulbs; leaf-bearing shoot separate from flowering stem; sepals ± equal, lip with ridges on upper surface, spur short or about half length of flower. Old World trop, subtrop, ± 200 species, ± 42 species in SA.

Eulophia angolensis **Vlei Orchid; Vlei-orgidee (A)**

Robust, up to 2 m, in small clumps or large colonies. In marshy grassland, from coast to inland areas, E Cape (N Transkei) to Trop Afr. **Leaves:** ± 900 x 50 mm, pleated, stiff, erect. **Flowers:** Inflorescence ± 300 mm; 4-10 flowers, bright lemon yellow, sometimes tinged purplish brown or olive, **sepals large, blunt tipped,** ± 26 mm, spur poorly developed (Oct-Apr), sweetly scented. **General:** Used as a love charm. Easily grown, dormant in winter.

242

Liparis bowkeri

Polystachya pubescens

Polystachya pubescens

Eulophia angolensis

Polystachya concreta

Polystachya sandersonii

Eulophia angolensis

Ansellia africana

243

Eulophia calanthoides (*calanthos* - bearing beautiful flowers, resembling *Calanthe*)
Slender, 300-750 mm. In thicket, on forest margins, up to 3000 m. **Leaves:** ± 700 x 60 mm. **Flowers:** Inflorescence with ± 25 large flowers; sepals spreading, ± 33 mm, green, petals and lip very pale yellow, crest of lip bright yellow, spur ± 5 mm (Dec-Feb).

Eulophia clitellifera (*clitellifera* - small pack saddle, refers to the central lobe of the lip)
Slender, up to 350 mm. In arid succulent scrub, coastal grassland, bushveld, E Cape to S Sudan and Madag. **Leaves:** Absent or ± 40 mm at flowering, maturing ± 240 x 13 mm, thick, stiff. **Flowers:** Inflorescence with 5-25 small flowers, petals and sepals spreading, 4-9 mm, white to pale yellow with reddish purple lines, crest on lip bright yellow, spur ± 4 mm (Jul-Nov). **General:** Used as protective charm.

Eulophia ensata   iphamba lentaba (Z) (*ensata* - sword-shaped)
Slender, ± 1 m. In grassland and plantations, coastal areas, E Cape to N Prov. **Leaves:** Partly to fully grown at flowering, ± 900 x 15 mm, stiff, erect, **pleated,** tapering to long point. **Flowers:** 6-30, in dense inflorescence; flowers, **pure yellow,** ± 20 mm, lip ± 25 x 12 mm, blunt, 3 lobed, spur very slender, ± 7 mm (Sep-Feb). **General:** Infusion from tubers used as a love charm and to treat infant ailments.

Eulophia leontoglossa   Lion's Tongue or Lion's Tooth Orchid; Leeutong (A); iphamba (Z) (*leontoglossa* - tongue like a lion)
Slender to stout, **60-400 mm.** In stony grassland, marshy soils. **Leaves:** Partly to fully grown at flowering, ± 450 x 9 mm, stiff, erect. **Flowers:** 7-35 in dense, nodding inflorescence, stem shorter than leaves; flowers ± 16 mm, white to lemon yellow to pink tinged green, petals and lip white, pale yellow or pink, lip with yellow to brown crests, spur slender, 3-5 mm, bracts overlapping, projecting above flowers (Aug-Feb), sweetly scented. **General:** Used as a protective charm against lightning.

Eulophia longisepala (*longisepala* - long sepals)
Slender, 200-600 mm. In coastal sands, bushveld, N E KZN to Tanz. **Leaves:** Absent or partly developed at flowering, ± 200 x 6 mm. **Flowers:** ± 10, **sepals long, narrow, spreading, 17-46 mm,** petals half as long, green to yellow-green tinged purple, side lobes of lip pale green, midlobe white, spur almost cylindrical, 2-4 mm (Dec).

Eulophia odontoglossa (*odontogloss* - toothed tongue, refers to the teethlike projections on lip)
Tall, slender, 0,5-1,2 m. In coastal thornveld, sour grassland, well drained to marshy areas, KZN to Trop Afr. **Leaves:** Partly to fully grown at flowering, stiff, erect, ± 100 x 10 mm. **Flowers:** 10-30 in inflorescence, ± 150 mm, **stem covered in overlapping dry,** straw coloured **sheaths**; flowers small, golden yellow, spreading, all segments ± 16 mm, lip orange-yellow with **dense masses of reddish brown hairs on midlobe, spur very short** (Sep-Mar). **General:** Widespread in Afr where the colour varies from white, yellow, greenish with brown or purple to brownish purplish.

Eulophia ovalis   lekholela, lekoesha, 'mametsana (SS); ihamba lesigodi, iphamba (Z)
(*ovalis* - broadly elliptic, oval)
Robust, up to 650 mm. In dry to seasonally marshy grassland, up to 2000 m, E Cape to Zim. **Leaves:** Fully developed at flowering, ± 600 x 30 mm. **Flowers:** ± 18 in loosely spreading inflorescence, dry sheaths; flowers flattened, **lip with fleshy, peglike outgrowths,** spur 1-5 mm (Oct-Apr). **General:** Infusion from tubers used by young men when courting and to treat infertility. Subsp. *ovalis,* flowers **smaller, petals white** tinged yellow or purple. Subsp. *bainesii,* **flowers larger,** sepals 18-36 mm, **petals pale yellow,** brownish purple at base, with a few dark speckles inside, veins lemon yellow, **spur flattened,** short, ± 3 mm (Dec-Jan). (See p. 126)

Eulophia parviflora [=*E. olivieriana*] **imfeyamasele (Z)** (*parviflora* - with small flowers)
Stout, up to 600 mm, solitary or in dense clumps. In grassland, coastal thornveld, rocky slopes, up to 2000 m, leathery. **Leaves:** Partly developed at flowering, maturing 250 x 16 mm, leathery. **Flowers:** 5-30, sepals and petals blunt, 7-20 mm, sepals brownish green outside, orange-brown inside, petals pale yellow with brownish red veins outside, side lobes of lip purplish brown, midlobe yellow with broad fleshy ridges, spur 2-5 mm (Aug-Dec), pleasant scent. **General:** Used in traditional medicine.

Eulophia ensata Lorraine van Hooff

Eulophia calanthoides Lal Greene

Eulophia calanthoides Tony Abbott

Eulophia clitellifera Geoff Nichols

Eulophia ensata Tessa Hedge

Eulophia leontoglossa Lal Greene

Eulophia longisepala Wayne Matthews

Eulophia odontoglossa Martin von Fintel

Eulophia ovalis Geoff Nichols

Eulophia parviflora Hendrelien Peters

245

Eulophia speciosa umabelejongosi ompofu, umlunge omhlophe (Z) (speciosa -beautiul)

Stout, up to 1,2 m, in groups. In grassland, coastal bush, woodland, S Cape to Trop Afr (where it has been known under different names). **Leaves:** Mature at flowering, ± 600 x 20 mm, stiff, smooth, thick. **Flowers:** Inflorescence with 10-30 flowers, sepals small, pale green, petals large, ± 20 x 15 mm, spreading, bright yellow, spur blunt (Aug-Jan). **General:** Blooms over a long period (± 2 months). Used in traditional medicine as an emetic for people and animals and an infusion of roots and stems as a protective charm against storms. Rewarding garden plant, in full sun.

Eulophia streptopetala Twisted-petal Eulophia; amabelejongosi (Z) (streptopetala - twisted petals)

Robust, up to 2,3 m. In thicket or on forest margins, E Cape to E Trop Afr. Short pseudobulb partially exposed above ground. **Leaves:** Not fully developed at flowering, ± 750 x 70 mm, pleated, thin. **Flowers:** 30-50, in simple or branching inflorescence, stem sturdy and erect or very long and reclining; sepals green, mottled purplish brown, ± 20 mm, petals yellow, **roundish**, ± 20 mm, side lobes of lip streaked red-brown, spur stout, 1-2 mm (Sep-Feb). **General:** Used as a protective or love charm. Easily grown in semi-shade. Blooms for 2-3 months.

Eulophia welwitschii [=E. zeyheri] umlunge (Z) (named after Friedrich Welwitsch, 1806-1872, botanist in Namibia)

Slender, up to 900 mm. In grassland or marshy areas, E Cape to Trop Afr. **Leaves:** ± 700 x 23 mm, stiff, erect, pleated. **Flowers:** 4-25 in dense inflorescence; **flowers large, sepals and petals not spreading,** pale creamy lemon to bright yellow, 25(46) x 12 mm, lip with reddish purple on side lobes, spur slender, 3-7 mm (Nov-Feb). **General:** Infusion of tubers used by young men when courting.

Oeceoclades (oikos - house; cladus - branch, shoot) - Terrestrial herbs; aerial pseudobulbs, each with a single, folded, leathery leaf; inflorescence from base of pseudobulb, lip 4 lobed. 3 species in SA.

Oeceoclades lonchophylla [= Eulophia dissimilis] (lonchophylla - spearlike leaves)

Up to 300 mm. In dark, shady forests, KZN coast to Moz, Comores Is. Pseudobulbs oval, closely packed. **Leaves:** ± 100 x 40 mm, **dark green, erect,** blade thin, margin wavy, **stalk ± 150 mm**. **Flowers:** ± 50, in simple or branched inflorescence; flowers pale green to cream with purple markings, lip side lobes striped purple, spur narrow (Nov-Apr). **General:** Easily grown in sandy leaf litter. (See p. 126)

Cirrhopetalum - Epiphyte with stout, creeping rhizome; pseudobulbs oval, widely spaced; solitary leathery leaf; median sepal and petals have tufts of hairs at tips, lip delicately hinged, carrion scented. Afr, Asia.

Cirrhopetalum umbellatum [also known as Bulbophyllum longiflorum]

Creeping epiphyte, 100-200 mm. In riverine forest, N KZN to Trop Afr, Comore Is, Java, New Guinea. Rhizome stout, creeping. Pseudobulbs oval, 25-40 mm, 5-6 angled, with fibrous remains of rhizome sheath. **Leaf:** Solitary, 120-200 x 20-40 mm, fleshy, dull green. **Flowers:** 5-8 in terminal inflorescence, stem slender, wiry; flowers pinkish yellow, dotted dull red with dark red appendages, median sepal oval, tip bristlelike, 10-12 mm, side sepals 25-40 mm, petals narrow, margins hairy, fringed, tip with a slender bristle, lip mobile (Oct-Jan), carrion scented. **General:** Flowers all open at once, pollinated by flies.

Acampe (acampe - rigid, refers to thick fleshy nature of the plants) - Epiphyte; leaves large, strongly keeled, very leathery; seed pods relatively massive, ± 35 mm. Mostly in E Asia, 1 species in eastern areas of Afr.

Acampe praemorsa [=A. pachyglossa] (praemorsa - as if the ends were bitten off)

Robust epiphyte, up to 300 mm. In hot, humid areas along streams, rivers, NE KZN to Trop Afr. **Strong stems,** ± 300 x 17 mm. **Leaves:** 8-12, ± 200 x 25 mm, V-shaped, in two rows, thick, fleshy, clasping at base. **Flowers:** ± 25 in dense inflorescence, stem branched, 80-150 mm, shorter than leaves; flowers ± 20 mm wide, thick, waxy, yellow barred red-brown, lip white with reddish spots (Nov-Mar), fragrant. **Fruit:** Large, ± 40 x 6 mm, cigar-shaped pod. **General:** Easily cultivated, slow growing.

Tridactyle (tri - three; dactyl - finger) - Epiphyte; no pseudobulbs; flower differs from Angraecum in the lip which is flat, thin, divided into 3 lobes, side lobes toothed or fringed at tip, spur long, slender. Afr, ± 36 species, 4 in SA.

Tridactyle bicaudata [=Angraecum bicaudatum] iphamba (Z) (see p. 128)

Eulophia speciosa

Eulophia speciosa

Sheila Peacock

Eulophia welwitschii

Martin von Fintel

Geoff Nichols

Eulophia streptopetala

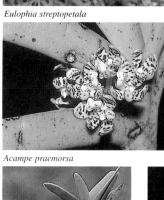

Eulophia streptopetala

Lawrence Peacock

Lal Greene

Eulophia welwitschii

Lal Greene

Cirropetalum umbellatum

Geoff Nichols

Acampe praemorsa

Tessa Hedge

Tridactyle bicaudata

Martin von Fintel

Oeceoclades lonchophylla

Geoff Nichols

247

DICOTYLEDONS Two seed leaves, net veins; flower parts in fours, fives or multiples of these.

PROTEACEAE - Protea family Woody shrubs or trees. Leaves leathery. Flowers in dense heads, sometimes surrounded by showy bracts, sepals 4, petal-like, petals absent or reduced to scales, stamens fused to sepals, ovary with long style. Ripe fruit with hairs or hairless. Mostly SA and Austr, ± 75 genera, ± 1600 species, ± 16 genera, in SA, including exotics *Hakea* and *Macadamia.*

Leucospermum (*leukos* - white; *sperma* - seed) **- Pincushions** Leaves sometimes with glandular teeth at tip; floral bracts small, styles long, protruding. Mostly SA, ± 46 species.

Leucospermum gerrardii (named after William Gerrard, naturalist and traveller; collected in KZN in 1860) Dwarf shrub, up to 400 mm, in colonies. In grassland, on rocky outcrops, up to 2000 m. Woody underground rootstock. Stems erect, hairy. **Leaves:** 50-90 x 8-20 mm, tapering to base, tips with 1-5 horny teeth. **Flowers:** In roundish heads, ± 70 mm diam, stem 10-20 mm; flowers densely woolly, 30-35 mm, pinkish yellow, styles long, ± 50 mm, yellow to orange-red (Sep-Nov). **General:** Leaves of the lowland form are broader, 15-20 mm, than escarpment form, 8-16 mm.

Leucospermum innovans **Pondoland Pincushion** (*innovans* - sprouting) Erect, multi-stemmed shrub, up to 1 m. Coastal grassland, Pondoland, S KZN endemic. Stems slender. **Leaves:** 70-100 x 30-50 mm, ± 10 glandular teeth. **Flowers:** In round heads, 80-90 mm diam; flower tube swollen at base, narrow at tip, yellow turning reddish orange, stalks 15 mm (Jul-Dec). **General:** A rare species.

Leucadendron (*leukos* - white; *dendron* - tree, refers to the 'silver tree' *L. argenteum* on which the genus was based) **- Conebush** Male and female flowers on separate bushes. Female plants produce flowerheads in woody cones. Male plants do not form cones and are usually more branched. Genus endemic to SA, ± 83 species, mostly SW Cape.

Leucadendron spissifolium subsp. *natalense* **Natal Spear-leaved Conebush** (*spissifolium* - sticky leaves) Shrub up to 750 mm. Isolated patches of scattered plants, in grassland in damp sandstone sands, 30-500 m. Many stems from persistent rootstock. **Leaves:** 46 x 8 mm, tips finely pointed, red, twisted below. **Flowers: Flowerhead leaves conspicuous,** larger than stem leaves, **tips pointed, bractlike; cone bracts hairy across middle.** Male heads round, ± 18 mm diam, bracts brown, margins hairy, recurved. Female heads oval, 16-20 x 13-15 mm (throughout year), lemon scented. **Fruit:** Cones 36 x 26 mm diam, red, bracts rounded with slight notch. **General: Subsp.** *oribinum* **Oribi Spear-leaved Conebush** On steep grassy slopes above cliffs, rare, 100-450 m, S KZN; leaves 31 x 3 mm in male plants, ± 45 x 4 mm in female, tips with pale fine points, sickle-shaped, twisted; **male flowerheads without leaves** (Oct-Nov).

LORANTHACEAE - Mistletoe Family Partially parasitic, rootless, attached to host by suckers. Stems brittle, woody. Leaves opposite. Flower tube brightly coloured, large, calyx small or absent. Fruit a large, brightly coloured berry. Fruit eating birds squeeze the large sticky seeds from the fruit skin. Once regurgitated or defecated, the seeds stick to branches and germinate quickly. Flowers attract butterflies, particularly the blues (Lycaenidae). 'Wood roses' are the remains of the host branch, after its death, at the point of the parasite's attachment. Trop and S temp, ± 67 genera, ± 900 species, 11 genera in SA..

Tapinanthus (*= Loranthus*) (*tapeinos* - humble; *anthos* - flower, refers to size of flowers) - Flowers with 'V'-shaped split, tube with swollen base or cylindrical, lobes erect or reflexed. Flowers open explosively to release pollen. Pollinated by birds. Largest Afr genus, ± 200 species, 20 in SA.

Tapinanthus kraussianus [= *Loranthus kraussianus*] **Matches, Mistletoe; Voëlent (A)** (named after Christian Krauss, 1812-90, German scientist, traveller and collector in SA in 1839-40) Parasitic shrub, up to 2 m. On trees, shrubs in thicket and woodland. Stems less than 5 mm thick. **Leaves:** More or less opposite, 50-70 x 15-25 mm, stalks ± 10 mm. **Flowers:** In massed clusters, 6-8 in each; flowers 30-45 mm, reddish orange towards tip, greenish orange at base, tube split 10-15 mm below **erect lobes,** style deep red (Oct-Apr). **Fruit:** Oval berry 10-12 mm, pinkish red. **General:** Birds feed on nectar and fruits. Subsp. *kraussianus*, leaves oval to rounded, deep green. Subsp. *transvaalensis*, leaves lance-shaped, light grey-green, thickly leathery. (See p. 48)

Leucospermum gerrardii

Rosemary Williams

Leucospermum gerrardii

Rosemary Williams

Leucospermum innovans

Geoff Nichols

Leucadendron spissifolium subsp. *natalense*

Tony Abbott

Leucadendron spissifolium subsp. *oribinum*

Tony Abbott

Leucadendron spissifolium subsp. *natalense*

Tony Abbott

Leucadendron spissifolium subsp. *oribinum*

David Johnson

Tapinanthus kraussianus

Martin von Fintel

249

SANTALACEAE - Sandalwood Family Woody or herbaceous plants, usually parasitic on roots of other plants. Flowers small, petals absent. Fruit a nut. Trop, subtrop, ± 34 genera, ± 540 species, 6 genera in SA.
Osyridicarpos (*karpos* - fruit like *Osyris*) - Undershrubs; branchlets long, slender. Afr genus, 5 species, 1 in SA.

Osyridicarpos schimperianus [= *O. natalensis*] **umalala, umayime (Z)**

Slender, branched, scrambling shrub, up to 2,5 m. In forest, up to 1800 m. Stems conspicuously ribbed, horny. **Leaves:** Scattered, spreading, ± 25 x 10 mm, tapering to short stalks, tips sharply pointed. **Flowers:** 1-3 in slender inflorescences; flowers ± 5 mm diam, creamy white (throughout year). **Fruit:** Oval to roundish, small, smooth, fleshy, translucent greenish white. **General:** Used as a protective charm.

Thesium (from the Latin for 'Toad Flax') - Herbs or shrubs, parasitic on roots of other plants; leaves scalelike or well developed; fruit dry. Europe, Asia, Afr, S America, ± 250 species, ± 160 in SA. Genus not well understood in SA.

Thesium pallidum [= *T. floribundum*] **Yellow Thesium; umahesaka-obomvu (Z)** (*pallidus* - pale)

Rounded clumps, up to 500 mm. In grassland, rocky areas, coast to 2450 m. Slender woody rootstock. Stems erect, angular. **Leaves:** Narrow, ± 30 mm, rubbery. **Flowers:** In small inflorescences; flowers small, creamy white (Sep-Mar). **Fruit:** Oval, shniy, prominently ribbed. **General:** Whole plant has a yellowish appearance at certain times of the year. Widely used in traditional medicine.

POLYGONACEAE - Rhubarb Family (for description see p. 374). *Persicaria* [= *Polygonum*] - (for description see p. 376).

Persicaria senegalensis [= *Polygonum senegalensis* forma *albotomentosum*] **Silver Snake Root**

Robust perennial, up to 3 m. In moist areas, widespread. Stems thick, rooting at basal nodes, hairless to velvety white, sheaths ± 35 mm, with fringe of short hairs. **Leaves:** Large, ± 270 x 65-100 mm, hairless or **covered in silvery hairs, yellow gland dotted beneath**, midrib, side veins conspicuous, stalks 10-50 mm. **Flowers:** In branched inflorescences; flowers white, green, pink, **stalks covered with golden orange glands** (Dec-Jun). **General:** Forma *albotomentosa*, covered in silvery hairs, leaves grey. Forma *senegalensis*, mostly hairless, leaves green. (See p. 376)

AMARANTHACEAE - Amaranthus Family (for description see p. 50). *Cyathula* (*kyathos* - cup, refers to stamens which may be reduced to a cup at base) - Herbs; flowers surrounded by spiny bracts, tips sharply hooked, woolly hairs amongst flowers. About 24 species, 6 in SA.

Cyathula cylindrica **bohome-bo-boholo (SS)** (*cylindrica* - cylindrical)

Robust, much branched. Among rocks, on forest margins. Stem and leaves covered with fine flat hairs, dense when young. **Leaves:** Blade ± 50(80) mm diam, sometimes narrowed to tip, stalks 10-20 mm. **Flowers:** Inflorescences with many flowers, white to cream, bracts hooked at tips (late summer). **General:** Roots used as soap.

PORTULACACEAE - Purslane Family Herbs with succulent leaves. Fruit a capsule which opens by means of valves or a lid. Includes popular ornamentals. Cosmop, ± 32 genera, ± 380 species, 7 genera in SA.
Talinum (from a native Senegalese name) - Flowers open in afternoon, close at night. Cosmop, 5 species in SA.

Talinum caffrum **Porcupine Root; Ystervarkwortel (A); khutsana (SS); mphun-yuka (Sw); inkucula, umpunyu (Z)**

Erect or reclining perennial herb, up to 400 mm. Woodland, grassland, widespread in SA. Tuberous root. **Leaves:** 20-40 (80) x 3-10 mm, margins curving under, stalks short. **Flowers:** 1-3, 10-20 mm diam, yellow, stalks ± 20 mm (summer). **Fruit:** Capsule, ± 10 x 7 mm, stalk curving downwards, broadening to base. **General:** Bushbuck, porcupines eat tuberous root. Used traditionally to treat stomach ache, chest and abdominal complaints, as a charm against lightning. Leaves used as a soap.

RANUNCULACEAE - Buttercup Family Herbs or woody climbers. Leaves compound, often palmate, bases forming a sheath. Sepals usually petal-like, petals present or absent. Includes a large number of ornamentals including Anemones, Delphiniums and Ranunculus. Mostly N Hemisp, ± 62 genera, ± 2450 species, 7 genera in SA.
Ranunculus (diminutive of *rana* - a frog, because the plant is found in damp marshy areas) - Annual or perennial herbs; leaves simple or compound; flowers solitary or in branched inflorescences. Cosmop, ± 400 species, 7 in SA.

Ranunculus baurii **Large-leaved Ranunculus; qojoana (SS)** (named after Rev Leopold Baur, born 1825 Germany, died 1889 in Queenstown, pharmacist, missionary, botanist)

Up to 1,2 m, in pure stands or solitary. In moist grassland, wet ground near streams, on forest margins, 1400-2000 m. Very variable. **Leaves:** 80-200 mm diam, blade roundish, **white veined**, margins red, with blunt teeth, stalks ± 300 mm, **attached to centre of blade**. **Flowers:** Solitary in small plants, branched inflorescence in large plants; flowers ± 30 mm diam, shiny yellow (Sep-Jan).

Osyridicarpos schimperianus

Tony Abbott

Thesium pallidum

Tony Abbott

Persicaria senegalensis

Geoff Nichols

Talinum caffrum

Lorraine van Hooff

Ranunculus baurii

Lal Greene

Cyathula cylindrica

Martin von Fintel

Ranunculus baurii

Lal Greene

251

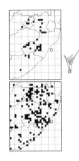

Ranunculus meyeri Bog Buttercup; bolila-ba-linkuba-metsi, hlapi-ea-metsi-e-nyen-yane (SS)
Small herb with trailing stems. In damp grassland, midlands to 3000 m. Creeping by runners, often rooted in water. **Leaves:** Few, roundish, heart-shaped, fleshy, stalks ± 75 mm. **Flowers:** On stalks ± 75 mm, yellow (Sep-Mar).

Ranunculus multifidus Common Buttercup; Botterblom (A); hlapi (SS); ishasha-kazane , isijojokazana (Z); uxhaphozi (Sw,Z) (*multifidus* - divided into segments)
Perennial herb, up to 1 m, in tufts. In damp ground near streams, marshes, coast to 2900 m, SA to Trop Afr, Madag, Arabia. Very variable. Hairy all over. **Leaves:** In basal rosette, bright green, blades with 2-3 pairs leaflets, divided again, margins with deep, sharp teeth. **Flowers:** In branched inflorescences; flowers ± 20 mm diam, stems hollow (Sep-May). **General:** Used in traditional medicine to treat coughs, headaches, urinary complaints, throat ulcers, wounds and pain. Good plant for swampy areas or water features.

MENISPERMACEAE - Moonseed Family Woody climbers or scramblers. Male and female flowers on different plants. Fruits slightly fleshy. Trop and warm regions, ± 72 genera, ± 450 species, 7 genera in SA.
Cissampelos (*kissos* - a climber; *ampelos* - a vine) **-** Slender climbers; male inflorescence much branched, female not branched, small leaflike bracts with each flower. Afr, Trop Asia, America, ± 20 species, 4 in SA.

Cissampelos torulosa Kidney-leaf; Davidjies(wortel) (A); ukhalimele-omkhulu, umthombo (Z) (*torulosa* - small swellings)
Slender twiner. In woodland, thicket, forest, E Cape to Trop Afr. **Leaves:** 20-50 x 20 -70 mm, broadly heart- or kidney-shaped, silvery beneath, slightly hairy, 3-5 veins from base, stalk 20-70 mm, inserted at base. **Flowers:** Greenish. Male: in small clusters. Female: in larger spikes 20-100 mm, with leafy bracts (throughout year). **Fruit:** 4-7 mm, orange. **Similar species:** *C. mucronata* (see p. 52).

Albertisia (*isia* - connection, with Prince Albert of Belgium) **-** Shrubs, scrambling or lianas (for description see p 140).

Albertisia delagoensis [= *Epinetrum delagoense*] cudodo, cumbato (Th); umgandaganda (Z)
(see p. 140)

PAPAVARACEAE - Poppy Family Herbs, often with milky or yellow latex (for description see p. 52).
Argemone **-** (*argemos* - white spot, hence eye cataract, which the plant was believed to cure) Annual or biennial herbs; leaves incised, segments tipped with bristlelike spines; capsules opening by slits.

★ ***Argemone mexicana*** Yellow Mexican Poppy, Devil's Fig; Geelblombloudissel (A); ugudluthukela (Z)
Erect, robust, grey-green herb up to 1 m. Weed on disturbed land at lower altitudes, from C and S America. Leaves deeply lobed, white veined. Flowers ± 50 mm diam (throughout year). Fruit a spiny capsule 30 x 15 mm. Seed reputed to be poisonous, fruit a problem in sheeps' wool. Used traditionally to treat wounds, warts, eczema.
Similar species: ★ *A ochroleuca* [= *A. subfusiformis*] White Mexican poppy; Mexikaanse Papawer (A) Flowers larger, cream (Jul-Mar). (For photograph see p. 140)

BRASSICACEAE/CRUCIFERAE - Cabbage Family Annual or biennial herbs (for description see p 140).
Rorippa - Annual or perennial herbs; flowers in terminal inflorescence. Mainly temp regions, ± 70 species, 5 in SA.

Rorippa nudiuscula
Perennial herb, up to 600 mm. In moist grassland, E SA to Zim. Hairless throughout. **Leaves:** In basal rosette, ± 150 mm, 2-9 lobed, leaflet margins lobed and/or toothed, very variable; stem leaves small. **Flowers:** In terminal inflorescence; flowers ± 9 mm diam (spring). **Fruit:** Podlike, erect, 12-33 x 2-3 mm.

CAPPARACEAE - Caper family Woody or herbaceous, some climbing. ***Cleome*** (*cleoma* - a plant name used in the Middle Ages)- Mostly annual herbs (for descriptions see p. 142).

Cleome angustifolia [= *C. diandra*] Yellow Cleome; Peultjiesbos (A)
Erect, grey-green herb, up to 1,5 m. On sandy or rocky soil, KZN to Trop Afr. Stems simple or branched, pale whitish green. **Leaves:** 3-9 foliate, stalks ± 60 mm; leaflets 10-40 x 0,4-1 mm, becoming smaller upwards. **Flowers:** In terminal inflorescences; petals yellow with purplish red blotch, 2 larger petals ± 24 x 12 mm, 2 smaller ± 20 x 3 mm, flowers close at midday (Nov-Jun). **Fruit:** 40-110 x 3-4 mm. **General:** Two subspecies differ in distribution, number of leaflets, length of petals.

Ranunculus meyeri   *Ranunculus multifidus*   *Albertisia delagoensis*

Lal Greene   *Lal Greene*   *C J Ward*

Ranunculus meyeri   *Ranunculus multifidus*   *Cissampelos torulosa*

Lal Greene   *Martin von Fintel*   *Martin von Fintel*

★ *Argemone mexicana*   *Rorippa nudiuscula*   *Cleome angustifolia*

Mark Ward   *Martin von Fintel*   *Rosemary Williams*

253

CRASSULACEAE - Crassula Family Herbs or soft shrubs, usually succulent. Leaves often joined round stem, or in basal rosette. ± Cosmop, ± 33 genera, ± 1100 species, 6 genera in SA. *Kalanchoe* (from the Chinese for one of these species) - Succulent herbs or small shrubs; 4 petals, tube round or angled. Cosmop, ± 200 species, 14 in SA.

Kalanchoe brachyloba
Succulent herb, up to 2 m. On sandy soil, in woodland, N KZN, widespread in S Afr. Rootstock swollen. **Leaves:** 100-180 x 40-80 mm, grey-green, folded, margins ± red, with blunt teeth, clasping stem at base. **Flowers:** In loose, flat topped inflorescence; flowers ± 8 mm diam, yellow, tube square, yellowish green (Apr-Aug).

Kalanchoe crenata   Yellow Hairy Kalanchoe; Plakkie (A); ibohlololo elimpofu, ikhambi-ncolosi, umahogwe (Z) (*crenata* - scalloped, notched)

Sparse shrub, up to 1,5 m. Moist areas in bushveld or on forest margins, E Cape to KZN. 1-several stems. **Leaves:** 40-110 x 30-90 mm, margins folded, with blunt teeth, stalks 10-30 mm, clasping at base. **Flowers:** In rounded inflorescence; flowers ± 10 mm diam, 10-12 mm, yellow-orange, tube with long neck (winter). **General:** Used in traditional medicine to treat sprains, swellings and as protective charms.

Kalanchoe paniculata   Large Orange Kalanchoe; Hasie-oor, Krimpsiektebos (A); sehlkwahlakwane (SS); indabulaluvalo (Z) (*paniculata* - branched inflorescence)

Robust, downy, perennial herb, up to 2 m. On rocky outcrops, in bushveld, Free State, NE Cape, N KZN. Rootstock swollen. **Leaves:** Very large at base, 100-160 x 60 -100 mm, grey-green with bloom, blunt tipped, margins tinged red, stalks 0-30 mm. **Flowers:** In widely branched inflorescence, ± 450 mm diam; flowers ± 8 mm diam, deep yellow, tube 4 angled to round (May-Aug). **General:** Takes 2-3 years to develop, dying back after flowering, to reshoot from same rootstock. Used as a love charm.

Kalanchoe thyrsiflora   White Lady, White Bird's Brandy; Geelplakkie, Meelplakkie, Voëlbrandewyn (A); serilile (SS); utywala bentaka (X); utshwala benyoni (Z)
(*thyrsiflora* - bunchlike inflorescence)

Erect, robust succulent, up to 1,5 m, **covered with silvery bloom**. On rocky outcrops, in grassland, bushveld, NE Cape to Mpum. **Leaves:** In basal rosette, 80-120 x 30-70 mm, flat, grey-green, tinged red. **Flowers: In tightly packed inflorescence**; lobes almost square, **deep yellow**, tube grey-green (Feb-Sep), sweetly scented. **General:** Leaves in basal rosette in 1st year, flowering stem arises in 2nd year, dies down after flowering to reshoot from rootstock. Popular garden plant. Used traditionally to treat earache, colds, intestinal worms and as a charm. **Similar species:**
K. luciae Flowers smaller, lobes greenish yellow, no scent. (For photograph see p. 384)

Crassula (*crassus* - thick, refers to fleshy leaves) - Annual or perennial herbs, shrubs (for description see p. 142).

Crassula vaginata   Yellow or White Crassula; umdumbukane, umakhulefingqana (Z)
(*vaginata* - sheathed)

Perennial herb, up to 500 mm. In moist grassland, E Cape to Trop Afr. **Leaves:** In basal rosette, 5-250 x 3-20 mm, sharp tipped, flat, margins fringed with transparent teeth, **base of leaves fused. Flowers:** Inflorescence ± 100 mm diam; flowers ± 8 mm diam, **yellow** or white (Sep-May), scented. **General:** Ground roots used in sour milk as famine food (Z). Used traditionally to treat earache, bruises and as a love charm. Grown from seed. Subsp. *minuta*, Swaz; miniature; leaves narrow, opposite; 2-5 inflorescences. (See p. 148.) **Similar species:** *C. alba* (see p. 54, 386).

ROSACEAE - Rose Family Trees, shrubs or herbs, often prickly (for description see p. 148). *Duchesnea* (named after Antoine Duchesne, 1747-1827, French horticulturalist) - Perennial, trailing herbs. S Asia, 2 species.

★ Duchesnea indica   False Strawberry; Wilde-aarbei (A) (*indica* - of Indian origin)
Prostrate, perennial herb. Garden escape, in damp shade. Leaves 3 foliolate, dark green, margins toothed. Flowers yellow, ± 12 mm diam (summer). Fruit round, ± 10 mm diam, bright red, like a small strawberry. Edible, flavour insipid.

Geum (*geuo* - tasty) - Roots astringent, some species pleasantly aromatic. Temp regions, ± 71 species, 1 in SA.

Geum capense
Perennial herb, 300-600 mm. In damp mountain grassland. Plant softly hairy. **Leaves:** Basal, ± 75 x 50 mm, thick, dark green, margins toothed; stem leaves small. **Flowers:** In few-flowered, branched inflorescences; flowers ± 35 mm diam, yellow (spring).

Kalanchoe crenata

Martin von Fintel

Kalanchoe brachyloba

Martin von Fintel

Wayne Matthews

Kalanchoe crenata

Kalanchoe paniculata

Van Wyk & Malan

Kalanchoe thyrsiflora

Martin von Fintel

Kalanchoe thyrsiflora

Martin von Fintel

Crassula vaginata

Trevor Coleman

★ Duchesnea indica

Martin von Fintel

Geum capense

Martin von Fintel

Agrimonia - Perennial herbs; leaflets incised, toothed. N temp, ± 25 species, 1 introduced in SA (from Europe, Asia).

★ *Agrimonia procera* **Agrimony; Akkermonie, Geelklits (A); bohome, mo-sinoana-o-monyenyane (SS); umakhuthula (Z)** (*procerus* - stretched out, long)

Invasive herb, up to 1 m, in mountain grassland. Leaves ± 250 mm, main leaflets ± 60 x 30 mm, 1-2 pairs tiny leaflets, woolly white beneath. Inflorescence ± 400 mm, flowers ± 12 mm diam, yellow (Oct-Mar). Bristly fruit distributed by people and animals. Used in traditional medicine to treat coughs and intestinal worms.

FABACEAE (LEGUMINOSAE) **- Pea or Legume Family** Second largest flowering plant family (see p 388).
Neptunia (named after Neptune, god of the sea, rivers, fountains) - Leaves often sensitive. Trop, ± 11 species, 1 in Afr.

Neptunia oleracea (*oleracea* - resembling herbs)

Low-growing aquatic herb. In or near fresh water rivers, lakes, swamps, N KZN to Trop Afr. Stems swollen, creeping, floating or prostrate, rooting at nodes. **Leaves:** 10-45 mm, 2-4 pinna pairs, stalks 20-65 mm; 7-22 pairs leaflets, 5-16 x 1-4 mm **Flowers:** Solitary, 10-20 mm, yellow, stem 6-200 mm, hairless. **Fruit:** Pods clustered, ± 28 x 12 mm, splitting. **General:** Leaves sensitive to touch.

Tylosema (*tylos* - swelling; *sema* - mark, refers to twisted, knobby seeds) - Shrubs with trailing or climbing stems; large, woody, underground tuber; tendrils usually forked. E and C Trop Afr, 4 species, 2 in SA.

Tylosema fassoglense [= *Bauhinia fassoglensis*] **Creeping Bauhinia; Gemsbokboontjie, Maramaboontjie, Rankboerboon (A); khubakhulu (Sw)** (*fassoglense* - coming from Fazoghli, a place in the Sudan where it was first collected)

Robust trailing shrublet, up to 6 m. On woody slopes, in grassland, N KZN to Trop Afr. Tuber ± 3 x 0,15 m. **Young parts covered in velvety reddish hairs.** Tendrils 40-80 mm. **Leaves:** 60-110 x 50-120 mm, **shallowly bilobed,** ± rusty velvety hairs beneath, stalks ± 70 mm. **Flowers:** Inflorescences ± 170 mm, stems 50-230 mm; flowers yellow, ± 60 mm diam, petals crinkly (Oct-Feb). **Fruit:** Pods woody, 50-100 x 30-60 mm. **General:** Browsed by game and stock. Pods and seeds cooked in rural areas.

Chamaecrista (*chamae* - on the ground; *crista* - crest) - Mostly herbs. Trop, ± 265 species, 9 in SA.

Chamaecrista comosa [= *Cassia comosa*] **Trailing Dwarf Cassia** (*comosa* - hairy tufts)

Perennial herb, up to 550 mm. In grassland, E Cape to Tanz. Rhizome woody. Stems pinkish. **Leaves:** 30-150 x 10-35 mm; 11-35 pairs leaflets, 5-18 x 1-7 mm, rachis grooved above, **gland without a stalk, sunk in groove** at base. **Flowers:** 2-3, **large,** 16-25 mm diam, golden yellow, calyx reddish, in leaf axils, stipulelike bracts (Jul-Mar). **Fruit:** Pod 40-65 x 4-8 mm. **General:** Variable, a number of subspecies.

Chamaecrista mimosoides [= *Cassia mimosoides*] **Fishbone Dwarf Cassia; Boesmans-tee (A); umnyana (X); unobothungwana (X,Z); imbubu, umbonisela (Z)** (*mimosoides* - resembles *Mimosa*)

Annual herb, up to 0,7(1,6) m. In grassland, E Cape to Trop Afr, Asia. Very variable. **Leaves:** 40-80 x 3-12 mm, leaflets **clasping at base,** ± 8 x 1 mm, sensitive to touch, **gland stalked, round to oval,** rachis crested. **Flowers:** Yellow, ± 20 mm diam, calyx, persistent bracts, reddish brown (throughout year). **Fruit:** Pods ± 50 x 5 mm. **General:** Atttracts butterflies. Used traditionally to induce sleep, recall dreams, treat skin complaints, dysentery and loss of appetite in children. **Similar species:** *C. plumosa* [= *Cassia plumosa*] **ihlalanyosi (Z)** Perennial herb, up to 250 mm; E Cape to Moz; rhizome woody; stems annual; leaves narrow, tapering, pale to blue-green; flowers large, 15-34 mm diam, (Aug-Apr). On hills - usually short, branched, leaves green. On flats - usually tall, sparsely branched, leaves bluish; grazed by cattle.

Senna (*sena* - a plant found in Egypt, used as a purgative) - Trees, shrubs. About 350 species, 16 in SA, many aliens.

Senna italica [=*Cassia italica*] **Wild Senna; Elandsertjie, Kalwerbossie (A); impengu (Z)** (*italica* - from Italy)

Perennial shrublet, up to 600 mm. In bushveld, SA to India. Stems ± sticky hairy. **Leaves:** 40-100 mm, stalks ± 35 mm; leaflets in 4-6 pairs, 10-35 x 1-25 mm, base asymmetric, **tips rounded,** margins with orange hairs. **Flowers:** Inflorescences 20-150 mm; flowers ± 25 mm diam, yellow, calyx dark brown (Sep-Apr). **Fruit:** Pod ± 30 x 15 mm, papery, tip beaked. **General:** Seeds used as a coffee substitute and in traditional medicine to treat pain, roundworm, as a charm against evil spirits and as a snakebite remedy.

Tylosema fassoglense

Van Wyk & Malan

★ *Agrimonia procera*

Martin von Fintel

★ *Agrimonia procera*

Martin von Fintel

Chamaecrista comosa

Wally Menne

Neptunia oleracea

Darrel Plowes

Chamaecrista mimosoides

Wally Menne

Senna italica

Geoff Nichols

Chamaecrista plumosa

Tony Abbott

257

Rafnia (named after the Danish botanist C G Rafn) - Shrubs hairless, often blue-green; leaves simple, entire; flowers yellow. Endemic to SA, ± 22 species, mostly in SW Cape.

Rafnia elliptica (elliptica - like an ellipse, oval)

Stout, erect or spreading shrub, up to 1 m. In grassland. Stems angular. **Leaves:** Shape variable on the same plant, ± 75 x 30 mm, blue-green, succulent. **Flowers:** Solitary, in axils, **pair of leafy bracts under flower,** calyx lobes as long or longer than tube (Oct-Apr). **Fruit:** Pod stalkless, black (see p. 576).

Lotononis (a combination of two genus names, *Lotus* and *Ononis*) - Herbs or shrublets, prostrate or forming a small round bush; leaves 3(5) foliolate; flowers 1-3, clustered on long stems or massed in inflorescence. Mostly Afr, ± 150 species in SA.

Lotononis calycina Hairy Lotononis; namele (SS) (calycina - in the form of a calyx)

Low-growing perennial herb. In grassland, bushveld, widespread in S Afr. Much branched, covered in long spreading hairs. Variable in shape of leaflets and hairiness, size and shape of pods. **Leaves:** 3 foliolate, stipules leaflike. **Flowers:** Solitary or in small inflorescences near ends of branchlets, yellow tinged brown, **calyx as long as, or longer than keel** (Aug-Feb). **Fruit:** Pod broadly oval, tip sharply down-curved.

Lotononis corymbosa   ihlamvusenhla, incinci, umamatheka, umhlambululi, umusa, uvelabahleke (Z) (corymbosa - arranged in corymbs)

Low-growing perennial herb, up to 300 mm. In grassland, coast to 2450 m. Woody rootstock. **Stems usually unbranched,** ribbed, silky hairy. **Leaves:** Leaflets ± 35 x 15 mm, oval, narrowing to pointed tips, stalks short, ± 4 mm, **stipules leaflike. Flowers:** In dense, **domelike, terminal inflorescences surrounded by leaves;** flowers ± 15 mm, yellow turning orange-red, **hairy** (blooms throughout year). **General:** Rootstock has cucumber smell. Used in traditional medicine to treat women who have lost suckling babies, as a tonic and as love charms.

Lotononis eriantha Russet Lotononis; lefehloane, molomo-monate (SS) (eriantha - woolly anthers)

Perennial shrublet, up to 300 mm. In grassland. Rootstock woody. **Stems much branched,** straggling, curved upwards from base. **Leaves:** Leaflets ± 12 x 4 mm, pale green, **narrow** with short point at tip, stalks very short, stipules as long as leaflets, spreading hairs. **Flowers:** Few, in terminal inflorescences surrounded by leaves; flowers ± 8 mm, yellow turning reddish brown, densely hairy (Sep-Mar). **Fruit:** Pods hairless. **General:** Used traditionally as a charm.

Lotononis foliosa Bookleaved Lotononis, Golden Orb Lotononis; isisinini sentaba (Z)
(foliosa - leafy)

Small, low-growing perennial herb, up to 150(300) mm. Rocky areas in grassland. Tap root woody. Stems erect, usually unbranched, hairy. **Leaves: Leaflets tapering at both ends,** ± 15 x 5 mm, stalks very short, **stipules leaflike, ± 12 mm,** covered with long hairs. **Flowers:** In dense, **domelike,** terminal inflorescences; flowers ± 15 mm, **hairless** (Oct-Feb). **General: All parts of the plant blacken with age.** Used traditionally to ensure good healthy crops, whole dried plants ground and mixed with maize seed at sowing. **Similar species:** *L. grandis* Endemic to KZN; robust, flowers hairy. *L. lanceolata* Branches longer; leaves almost hairless, shiny, almost fleshy; flowers smaller.

Lotononis listii

Creeping perennial herb, often forming dense mats. In moist grassland, widespread in W areas of S Afr. Stems root at nodes. Plant hairless. **Leaves:** 3-4 leaflets, ± 20 x 5 mm, stalks slender, ± 20 mm. **Flowers:** Flowers small, petals yellow tinged brown (summer-autumn). **Fruit:** Pod flattened, twisted, **straight or folded. General:** Weed in lawns, on sidewalks.

Lotononis procumbens (procumbens - prostrate)

Prostrate herb. In grassland. Woody rootstock. Stems annual. **Leaves:** Leaflets ± 10 x 4 mm. **Flowers:** In round, terminal inflorescences; flowers yellow **aging red to brownish copper** (Nov-Jan).

Rafnia elliptica

Lotononis calycina

Lotononis corymbosa

Rafnia elliptica

Lotononis eriantha

Lotononis foliosa

Lotononis listii

Lotononis procumbens

259

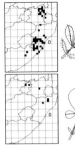

Lotononis pulchra (*pulchra* - beautiful)

Semi-prostrate herb. In rocky grassland, up to 1800 m. Woody rootstock. Annual stems. Very variable in habit, hairiness and size of flowers. **Leaves:** Leaflets ± 18 x 6 mm, stalks ± 5 mm. **Flowers:** In terminal inflorescences, ± 35 mm diam; flowers ± 10 mm, yellow, **hairless** (Dec-Jan).

Lotononis solitudinis (*solitudinis* - refers to the isolated inland distribution which distinguishes this species from others more or less confined to coastal areas)

Prostrate herb. On rocky ground. Stems slender, plant **hairless**. **Leaves:** Leaflets roundish, 5-25 x 4-15 mm, stalks ± 10 mm. **Flowers:** Solitary, opposite leaves, ± 12 mm.

Pearsonia (named after Dr Harold Pearson, 1870-1916, first Director of National Bot Gardens, Kirstenbosch) - Perennial herbs or shrublets; leaves 3 foliolate; standard petal erect, concave in the lower part, keel small, narrow, usually pointed; fruit flattened, straight, hairy, beaked. Similar to *Lotononis* which has standard petal reflexed, keel ± boat-shaped. Mostly S Trop Afr, ± 11 species, 7 in SA.

Pearsonia aristata Frilly Pea (*aristata* - having an awn)

Shrublet, up to 500 mm. In rocky grassland, KZN to Zim. Woody rootstock. Annual, leafy shoots, stems much branched, covered in sparse loose white hairs. **Leaves:** Leaflets 8-30 x 2-8 mm, conspicuously net veined beneath, margins thickened, **tip a sharp, hard point**, stalks short. **Flowers:** In loose terminal inflorescences; **flowers ± 20 mm**, yellow turning orange, calyx ± 15 mm, lobes tapering, sparsely hairy (Oct-Mar). **Fruit:** ± 30 x 5 mm, tipped with slender style, silky hairy.

Pearsonia sessilifolia Silwerertjietee (A) (*sessilifolia* - stalkless leaves)

Perennial shrublet, 0,5-1,2 m. In rocky grassland, KZN to Zim. Woody rootstock. **Leaves:** Leaflets very variable, 15-50 x 1-10 mm, sparsely hairy to velvety, stalkless or stalks ± 10 mm. **Flowers:** In terminal inflorescences; flowers ± 15 mm, yellow turning reddish brown, bracts 4-7 mm, stalks very short, calyx 5-8 mm, hairy (Sep-Apr). **Fruit:** Pod narrow, pointed, ± 25-50 mm, hairy. **General:** Subsp. *sessilifolia*, **leaflet stalks 1 mm**; flowers in small inflorescences. Subsp. *marginata*, slender shrub, 0,8-1,6 m, branching in upper parts; leaves broader, **dense silvery hairs**, stalks ± 8 mm; flowers in small to large terminal inflorescences. Subsp. *filifolia*, up to 200 mm, with soft, loose hairs; **leaflets very slender with long thin points; inflorescences long**. Subsp. *swaziensis*, **bracts round**, similar to subsp. *marginata*.

Aspalathus (*aspalathos* - a scented bush from Greece, now in the related genus *Astragalus*) - Shrubs or shrublets, sometimes spiny; leaves usually 3 foliolate, clustered, often needlelike; flower bracts often leaflike. Some species used to brew tea, particularly Rooibos tea *A. linearis*, now commercially produced and exported worldwide. Largest endemic genus in SA with ± 278 species, mostly in winter rainfall areas of the Cape.

Aspalathus chortophila Tea Bush; impishimpishi (Z)

Perennial shrublet, 100-900 mm. In grassland, E Cape to KZN (S Moz). **Stems slender, erect or trailing**, young stems velvety white. **Leaves:** Very variable, leaflets spreading, needlelike, 1,5-8 x 0,3-0,5 mm with sparse, spreading silky white hairs. **Flowers:** On short side shoots; flowers ± 15 mm, yellow, with reddish hairs, calyx 1,5-3,5 mm (throughout year). **Fruit:** Attractive pod, **woolly, grey**. **General:** Used traditionally for protection against lightning. Three forms described, mostly confined to geographic regions. Attractive garden plants. (See p. 150)

Aspalathus gerrardii (named after William Gerrard, naturalist, traveller, who collected in KZN in 1860)

Erect, sparsely branched shrub, 0,4-3 m, in small groups. In coastal grassland. **Young branches sometimes white woolly. Leaves:** Leaflets 5-11 mm, needlelike, 0,3-0,4 mm thick, soft, pointed, densely covered with long white spreading hairs. **Flowers:** Solitary or on short side shoots, **small**, ± 10 mm, pale lemon yellow, standard petal round, densely white hairy outside, calyx velvety white, 3-5 mm (throughout year). **Fruit:** Pod ± 6 x 4 mm, woolly above, dark, hairless on lower parts. **General:** Grows as a small tree at Umtamvuna.

Martin von Fintel

Lotononis solitudinis

Lotononis pulchra   *Lorraine van Hooff*

Lotononis pulchra   *Tony Abbott*

Pearsonia aristata   *I C Nel*

Aspalathus chortophila   *Martin von Fintel*

Pearsonia sessilifolia   *Van Wyk & Malan*

Pearsonia sessilifolia   *Jo Onderstall*

Aspalathus chortophila   *Lorraine van Hooff*

Aspalathus gerrardii   *Tony Abbott*

Aspalathus spinosa **Dancing Thorn; Dansdoring, Ystervarkbossie (A)** (*spinosa* - with spines)

Perennial, erect shrub, 0,2-1(2) m. Widespread, mostly at low altitudes in scrubby grassland, fynbos, SW Cape to KZN. Branches rigid, side branches **ending in spines**. **Leaves:** Leaflets needlelike, flattish, 2-20 x 0,4-1 mm, tips blunt or pointed, bright to grey-green, sparsely hairy. **Flowers:** 1-2, in leaf clusters at base of spines; flowers 4-8 mm, yellow to reddish purple, calyx tube ± hairless (Aug-May). **Fruit:** Pod 7-10 x 3-5 mm, partly woolly. **General:** Very variable. Three subspecies described. Thorns straight or more usually hooked, flowers larger in northern areas. Attracts butterflies, including Montagu Coppers *Poeclimitis uranus*.

Melolobium (*melos* - a joint; *lobos* - pod) - Shrubs or shrublets, often spiny, sticky; leaves 3 foliolate; flowers in terminal inflorescences, small, yellow. S Afr, ± 20 species.

Melolobium alpinum (*alpinum* - alpine)

Slender herb, 300-900 mm. In montane grassland, 1200-2300 m. Many unbranched stems, curved, erect, thinly hairy, sticky. **Leaves:** Leaflets narrow, hairless or slightly hairy, stipules shorter than stalks. **Flowers:** In leafless, slender terminal inflorescences, ± 100 mm; flowers yellow, red with age (Nov-Jan). **Fruit:** Curved, constricted between seeds.

Crotalaria (*krotalon* - rattle, an allusion to the seeds rattling in the pod when ripe) - **Rattle Pods** Erect herbs, shrubs, usually spineless; leaves usually 3 foliolate, stipules free, equal; flower wings shorter than keel which usually ends in an upward pointed beak; pods inflated. Attracts Blues butterflies (Lycaenidae), also *Deudorix antalus*, *Euchrysops barkeri*, *Lampides boeticus*. Widespread in warm and temp regions, ± 600 species, + 70 in SA.

Crotalaria dura **Wild Lucerne; Jaagsiektebossie, Wildelusern (A)** (*dura* - hard)

Shrublet up to 600 mm. In grassland from coast to 900 m, KZN to S Moz. Woody rootstock. Annual branches. **Leaves:** Leaflets 10-35 x 3-12 mm, thinly hairy, stalks 3-10 mm, grooved above, **stipules small**, narrow, recurved. **Flowers:** In loose or dense terminal inflorescences; flowers 6-10 mm, calyx 6-8 mm, **lobes slender, longer than tube**, finely hairy (Sep-Feb). **Fruit:** Pods roundish to oblong, very oblique, 5-9 x 5-8 mm, **black with white or yellow hairs**. **General:** Poisonous to stock.

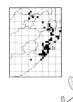

Crotalaria globifera **Round Pod Rattle Bush; Jaagsiektebossie, Klawer (A); ubhub-hubhu-wegceke (Z)** (*globifera* - bearing balls, globose)

Rounded shrublet, 0,2-1 m. In grassland, coast to 1500 m. Woody rootstock. Stems annual, erect, pale yellowish green, downy. **Leaves:** Leaflets 10-30 x 3-10 mm, hairless or finely hairy beneath, dark blue-green, stalks 4-15 mm, stipules narrow, 1-3 mm. **Flowers:** In terminal inflorescences 50-160 mm; flowers ± 10 mm, bright yellow, coppery when old, calyx 4-6 mm, downy hairy (Aug-May). **Fruit:** Pod 7-13 x 4-7 mm, **mauve**. **General:** Although very similar and occurring with *C. dura*, this plant is NOT poisonous to stock. Roots used in traditional medicine. A rewarding garden plant.

Crotalaria laburnifolia **Brown-and-yellow Birdflower; Bruin-en-geel-voëltjieblom (A)** (*laburnifolia* - leaves resemble *Laburnum*)

Erect shrubby herb, 0,6-2 m. In grassland, bushveld, disturbed areas, KZN to E Afr, Seychelles, India, Malaysia, Austr. Mostly hairless. **Leaves:** Leaflets 15-65 x 7-32 mm, tips rounded to notched, stalks 40-90 mm. **Flowers:** In loose terminal inflorescences, 150-500 mm; **flowers large**, ± 40 mm, yellow marked reddish brown outside, keel 20-30 mm, calyx bell-like, 10-15 mm (Jan-May). **Fruit:** Pod ± 100 x 12 mm. **General:** A number of subspecies have been described, three of which are found in this area, differing in length of leaf stalks and pod. Hardy garden plant.

Crotalaria lanceolata **Twin-leaved Rattle Bush; izaza (Z)** (*lanceolata* - lancelike)

Erect annual shrublet, 0,2-2 m. In grassland, woodland, disturbed areas, E Cape to Trop Afr. Branches ribbed, young parts downy. **Leaves:** Leaflets ± 80 x 10 mm, stalks slender, stiff, 40-100 x 3-20 mm. **Flowers:** Inflorescences 80-350 mm; flowers small, ± 10 mm, stalks very short, standard erect (throughout the year). **Fruit:** Pod 18-35 x 4-6 mm, blackish, tips curved upwards, downy, stalk very short. **General:** Used traditionally as a love charm. Pioneer, used as green fodder. Attracts butterflies, including *Actizera lucida*.

262

Aspalathus spinosa

Tony Abbott

Melolobium alpinum

Tony Abbott

Aspalathus spinosa

Wally Menne

Crotalaria globifera

Geoff Nichols

Crotalaria globifera

Wally Menne

Crotalaria dura

Lorraine van Hooff

Crotalaria laburnifoia

Wally Menne

Crotalaria lanceolata

Geoff Nichols

263

Crotalaria macrocarpa Golden Birdflower (*macrocarpa* - large fruit)

Bushy shrublet 0,3-1,5 m. Thicket, woodland, rocky areas, E Cape to Nam, E Afr. Branches finely hairy. **Leaves:** Leaflets 15-40 x 8-20 mm, furry beneath, **stalks 8-35 mm, slender**, stipules narrow, ± 2 mm. **Flowers:** In many-flowered inflorescences; **flowers large**, ± 20 mm, calyx 10-13 mm, furry, lobes longer than tube (Oct-May). **Fruit: Pod large**, 25-45 x 14-18 mm. **General:** A hardy, attractive shrub for the garden. **Similar species:** Closely related to *C. natalensis*.

Crotalaria monteiroi uhashazi (Z)

Much branched shrub, 0,5-3 m. In woodland, on streambanks. Finely hairy. **Leaves:** Often clustered, leaflets oval, ± 15 x 6 mm, tips blunt, no stipules, **stalks slender, ± 20 mm**. **Flowers:** In small inflorescences; **flowers large**, ± 20 mm, yellow, ± with red streaks, **tip of keel erect, pointed** (throughout year). **Fruit:** Pod cylindrical, ± 30 x 13 mm, **greatly inflated**. **General:** Heavily parasitised by wasps. Browsed by game. Suitable for gardens.

Crotalaria natalensis Forest Rattle Pod

Erect shrub, 0,5-2 m. In grassland, on margins of forest. Branches slender, angular, finely hairy or not. **Leaves:** Leaflets 15-40 x 10-20 mm, sparsely hairy beneath, **stalks slender 10-40 mm**. **Flowers:** In loose inflorescences; flowers ± 15 mm, pale yellow, calyx ± 10 mm (Oct-Apr). **Fruit:** 25-30 x 10-12 mm. **Similar species:** Closely related to *C. macrocarpa*.

Crotalaria natalitia Pioneer Rattle Pod

Erect shrub, 1-2,5 m. In grassland, KZN to Eritrea. Branchlets **slender, erect**, downy. **Leaves: In tufts**; leaflets 15-35 x 4-15 mm, finely downy beneath, tips blunt, notched, often with fine point; stalk shorter than leaflets, **leafy stipules** shortly stalked, asymmetrical, ± 5-14 x 1-4 mm. **Flowers:** In short, crowded, terminal inflorescences; flowers ±15 mm, yellow turning orange-red, keel round tipped (Mar-Aug). **Fruit:** Pod ± 45 x 13 mm. **General:** Flowers attract bumble-bees and honey-bees. Attractive in the garden, easily grown from seed.

Crotalaria obscura Prostrate Rattle Pod (*obscura* - dull, undistinguished)

Perennial herb, 200-600 mm, in clumps ± 1 m wide. In open, rocky grassland. Woody rootstock. Stems mostly prostrate, **covered in long golden hairs**. **Leaves:** ± 12 x 10 mm, held erect, stalks ± 15 mm. **Flowers:** ± 10 mm, standard petal yellow with purple markings, wings yellow, keel greeny yellow, **rounded, with incurved beak** (Nov-Mar) **Fruit:** Hairy, papery pods. **General:** Grazed by stock.

Crotalaria pallida Broad-leaved Rattle Pod (*pallida* - pale)

Robust, erect, well branched herb, 0,4-2 m. Common along coast, in open scrub, grassland, floodplains, pantrop. **Branches densely covered with silvery hairs**. **Leaves:** 3-4 foliolate; leaflets 30-130 x 25-70 mm, dark green above, grey downy beneath, stalks ± 60 mm. **Flowers:** In long, **narrow, closely packed inflorescences, ± 250 mm**; flowers ± 15 mm, pale yellow, calyx ± 7 mm (Aug-May). **Fruit:** Pods hanging, ± 35 x 5 mm. **General:** Used elsewhere in Afr as a green manure and fodder crop. Fruit heavily parasitised.

Crotalaria macrocarpa

Crotalaria natalensis

Crotalaria pallida

264

Crotalaria macrocarpa

Crotalaria monteiroi

Crotalaria natalensis

Crotalaria natalitia

Crotalaria obscura

Crotalaria pallida

265

Argyrolobium (*argyros* - silver; *lobos* - pod) - Herbs or shrublets; leaves 3 foliolate, often with silky silvery hairs; flowers usually in many-flowered inflorescences. Medit, India, mostly Afr, ± 70 species, ± 47 in SA.

Argyrolobium harveyanum (named after William Harvey, 1811-66, botanist who spent time in SA between 1835 and 1842; contributed the major part of the first 3 volumes of Flora Capensis)

Very slender, erect perennial herb, up to 650 mm. Widespread in grassland, up to 2600 m. Root carrotlike. Stems unbranched, softly downy. **Leaves:** Few; leaflets ± 30 x 3 mm, **almost stalkless**, 1-2 leaflets (often missing), stalks ± 18 mm, stipules small. **Flowers:** 1-2, opposite the leaves; flowers ± 10 mm, silky behind, almost stalkless (Jul-May). **Fruit:** Pod ± 40 x 3 mm. **General:** Grazed by stock.

Argyrolobium robustum   Liquorice Bean; Soethout-bossie (A); umuzimuka (Z)
(*robustum*-large, refers to leaves)

Perennial herb, 300-750 mm. In wooded grassland. Stems annual, sparsely branched, ± hairless. **Leaves: Large, slightly fleshy**, leaflets 50-170 x 20-80 mm, grey-green, stalks stout, 15-40 mm, **stipules leafy**, 40 x 10 mm. **Flowers: In dense, erect inflorescences, ± 400 mm**, stem 10-100 mm; flower petals roundish, ± 13 mm, yellow with reddish brown veins, stalks short (Sep-Jan). **Fruit:** Pod ± 60-85 x 4 mm, erect. **General:** Used in traditional medicine to treat impotence. **Similar species:** *A. speciosum* E Cape; leaves in basal clusters, leaflets shorter, narrower; inflorescence with fewer flowers, longer stem.

Argyrolobium molle (*molle* - velvety)

Dwarf, slender, erect, up to 120 mm. Stems **thinly covered with long silky hairs**. **Leaves:** Leaflets ± 25 x 12 mm, broadly oval, **strongly netveined**, stalks short, stipules longer than stalks. **Flowers:** 3-5 in inflorescences, stem much longer than leaves; flowers small, stalks shaggy hairy.

Argyrolobium pauciflorum (*pauciflorum* - few flowers)

Small, slender, erect herb, up to 150 mm. In rocky grassland. Tap root woody. **Densely covered in short silvery hairs. Leaves:** Leaflets ± 30 x 10 mm, stalks very short, **stipules triangular. Flowers:** 1(2), on **distinct stalks calyx 2 lipped**, nearly equal to stalk, upper lobes long, narrow (Nov-Feb). **Fruit:** Pods densely hairy.

Arygyrolobium sandersonii [now A. baptisioides]

Shrublet, branching from base, 300-450 mm. In grassland. Stems annual, hairless, angular or ribbed. **Leaves:** Leaflets 75-90 x 20-40 mm, stalks ± 25 mm, **stipules slender**, ± 15 mm. **Flowers:** In terminal, erect inflorescences; flowers yellow, standard petal oval, **edges strongly inrolled towards base** (Sep-Oct). **General: This species and** *A. sutherlandii* **have recently been placed in** *A. baptisioides*. (See p. 268)

Argyrolobium sankeyi (named after J H Sankey, collector from Tokai, Cape)

Trailing herb, up to 120 mm. In tall grassland, 1375-2440 m. Stems soft, hairy. **Leaves:** Leaflets ± 20 x 15 mm, stalks short, ± 10 mm, silky hairy, stipules narrow. **Flowers:** In terminal inflorescences; flowers ± 12 mm, yellow, hairy (Dec-Feb). **Fruit:** Pods ± 12 x 6 mm.

Argyrolobium sericosemium (*sericosemium* - silver seeds)

Perennial herb, 150-300 mm, stems trailing. In rocky grassland, 1500-2200 m. Stems loosely branched, silky hairy throughout. **Leaves:** Leaflets ± 20 x 7 mm, stalks ± 10 mm, stipules 10-15 x 4-8 mm. **Flowers:** In sparse terminal inflorescences; flowers ± 10 mm, yellow (Sep-May). **Fruit:** Pod ± 15 x 4 mm, hairy.

Argyrolobium harveyanum   *Argyrolobium robustum*

Argyrolobium molle   *Argyrolobium pauciflorum*

Argyrolobium sericosemium   *Argyrolobium sandersonii*

Argyrolobium sericosemium   *Argyrolobium sankeyi*

Argyrolobium stipulaceum (*stipulaceum* - with stipules)
Perennial herb up to 400 mm. On grassy slopes, up to 2000 m. **Stems erect, plant thickly covered with silky hairs.** Leaves: Leaflets ± 30 x 10 mm, stalks 2-5 mm, **stipules leaflike**, ± 25 x 12 mm. **Flowers:** 1-5 in inflorescences, stems ± 500 mm; flowers ± 15 mm, yellow turning orange brown, silky behind, calyx silky, upper lip 2 lobed, lower 3 lobed (Sep-Jan). **Fruit:** Inflated pod, ± 30 mm. **General:** Leaves more or less hairy.

Argyrolobium sutherlandii [now *A. baptisioides*] (named after James Sutherland, 1639-1719, first superintendent of Edinburgh Bot Gardens)
Erect shrublet, up to 700 mm. In sparse grassland. Tuber well developed. Stems annual, **well branched below**, hairy. **Leaves:** Leaflets 28-45(90) x 5-20(40) mm, ± hairy beneath, stalks 3-8 mm, stipules 6-25 x 2-5 mm, **broad at base, tips pointed. Flowers:** In slender inflorescences; flowers yellow, standard petals ± 13 mm, oval, edges strongly inrolled towards base (early spring). **Fruit:** Slender, erect, 40-60 x 4-5,5 mm. **Similar species: This species and *A. sandersonii* have recently been placed in *A. baptisioides*** (see p. 266).

Argyrolobium tomentosum Velvety Yellow Bush Pea; umadlozana, umlomomnandi (Z) (*tomentosum* - densely covered with short hairs)
Erect, much branched, slender scrambling shrub or semi-prostrate herb, ± 0,45(2) m. In damp grassland, scrub, on forest margins, disturbed areas. **Young branchlets densely golden downy or not. Leaves:** Leaflets 10-50 x 6-25 mm, **margins conspicuously hairy**, tips hairlike, stalks 5-25 mm, stipules small. **Flowers:** Usually in **long stalked, sparse inflorescences**; flowers ± 15 mm, bright yellow turning orange, calyx ± 9 x 3 mm (throughout year). **Fruit:** Pod 60-100 x 5-8 mm, flattened. **General:** Used by sangomas (diviners) to sharpen their divining powers.

Argyrolobium tuberosum Little Russet Pea; lebesa; lekolomache, tsoetsoetlala (SS); uvemvane olubomvu (Z) (*tuberosum* - resembling tubers)
Slender perennial herb, 0,45-1 m. In swampy ground, on grassy slopes, up to 2100 m, E Cape to Zim. **Tuberous roots.** Single stemmed, branching above. **Leaves:** Leaflets 35-60 x 3-5 mm, sparsely hairy, stalks 8-20 mm, stipules ± 7 x 1 mm. **Flowers:** Solitary or in sparse inflorescences, stems 30-90 mm; flowers ± 12 mm, **yellow inside, red-brown outside**, stalks very short, calyx ± 8 mm with very short tube (Sep-Feb). **Fruit:** Pod 40-60 mm. **General:** Tubers sucked by children for sweetish taste. Leaves eaten as spinach.

Melilotus (*meli* - honey; *lotus* - clover, flowers resemble clover, smell of honey) - Annual or biennial herbs. Asia, Europe, N Afr, ± 20 species, 2 naturalised in SA.

★ *Melilotus indica* Yellow Sweet Clover; Geelstinkklawer, Bitterklawer (A) (*indica* - of Indian origin)
Widespread annual shrublet, up to 1 m. In moist conditions, disturbed areas. Leaflets with shallowly toothed margins in upper two thirds, clear side veins beneath, stipules erect. Flowers yellow, in crowded inflorescences (spring-summer).

Stylosanthes (*stylos* - style; *antho* - flower, flower has long style) - Perennial herbs or shrublets, often sticky; leaves 3 foliolate, often prominently veined beneath; flowers in dense inflorescences or solitary, in axils of leafy bracts. Trop Asia, Afr, America, ± 50 species, 1 in SA.

Stylosanthes fruticosa Wild Lucerne (*fruticosa* - shrubby)
Much branched herb, up to 600 mm. In grassland, woodland, widespread in Afr, Arabia, Madag, India, Sri Lanka. Woody rootstock. Stems sparsely to densely hairy. **Leaves:** 3 foliolate, stalks ± 15 mm; leaflets 5-33 x 1-9 mm, silky, veins **white beneath**, stipules ± 15 mm, **united round stem. Flowers:** In short dense inflorescences; flowers in pairs, one fertile and one sterile, ± 7 mm, within bracts, ± 20 mm (Aug-May). **Fruit:** Pod flattened, ± 9 mm, 1-2 jointed.

Argyrolobium stipulaceum

Lal Greene

Argyrolobium stipulaceum

Lal Greene

Argyrolobium tomentosum

Martin von Fintel

Argyrolobium tuberosum

Lal Greene

Argyrolobium sutherlandii

Martin von Fintel

★ *Melilotus indica*

Van Wyk & Malan

Stylosanthes fruticosa

Van Wyk & Malan

269

Zornia (named after Johannes Zorn, 1739-99, Bavarian apothecary, author of Icones Plantarium Medicalium) - Mostly prostrate herbs, with tap root; leaves digitately 2-4 foliolate; stipules leaflike; flowers within conspicuous bracts. In warm regions, ± 80 species, ± 14 in Afr, 4 in SA.

Zornia capensis Caterpillar Bean; umkhondo (Z)

Perennial herb, up to 100-600 mm. In grassland, bushveld, E Cape to Bots, Nam to Kenya. Stems mostly wiry, prostrate. **Leaves:** 3-4 leaflets, ± 20 x 6 mm, gland dotted beneath; stipules ± 12 mm. **Flowers:** ± 8 mm, within large hairless bracts (Aug-May). **Fruit:** Pod flat, ± 18 mm, breaking into 1-seeded segments. **General:** Very variable. Visited by bees for nectar and pollen. Used traditionally as a charm to protect the unborn baby from disease. **Similar species:** *Z. milneana* Bracts with hairy margins. *Z. glochidiata* 2 leaflets.

Zornia linearis Narrow-leaved Caterpillar Bean (*linearis* - uniform width)

Much branched herb, up to 350 mm. In grassland and bushveld, on disturbed ground. Stems slender. **Leaves:** 4 foliolate; **leaflets narrow** 0,5-1,5 mm, minutely black gland dotted, stipules large. **Flowers:** In small inflorescences, ± 75 mm; flowers ± 8 mm, from within large bracts, margins hairy, with minute glands (Sep-Mar). **Fruit:** Pods **spiny**.

Dumasia (named after French naturalist M. Dumas) - Climbing herbs; leaves 3 foliolate; calyx tube cylindrical, ± pouched at base on upper side, lobes almost absent. Trop, 6-10 species, 1 in SA.

Dumasia villosa (*villosa* - shaggy, hairy)

Twining herb, stems 1,5-3 m. In woodland, forest, coast to 2550 m, KZN to Ethiopia, India, China. **Leaves:** 3 leaflets, thin oval to round, 13-60 mm diam, ± heart-shaped at base, hairy beneath, stalks 20-65 mm. **Flowers:** Inflorescences 20-40(120) mm, stems ± 60 mm; **petals with narrow stalks**, standard ± 20 mm, eared at base, keel ± 20 mm, calyx tube oblique, ± 10 mm, pouched at base on upper side (summer). **Fruit:** Narrow, flattened, curved, 20-40 x 8 mm, densely hairy.

Rhynchosia (*rhynchos* - beak, refers to style) - Prostrate, creeping or scrambling herbs or shrublets, usually with resinous dots; leaves 3 foliolate; flowers in axillary inflorescences, mostly yellow. Attracts butterflies, including *Cupidopsis iobates, Actizera lucida, Syntarucus telecanus*. Trop, subtrop, ± 200 species, ± 65 in SA.

Rhynchosia adenodes monya-mali (SS); ungazini (Z) (*adenodes* - with glandular knots)

Erect or spreading creeper, up to 400 mm. In grassland. Perennial rootstock. Stems ± 1 m, downy. **Leaves:** Leaflets ± 15 mm, firm, with **tiny red gland dots beneath**, stalks ± 25 mm. **Flowers:** Clustered towards tips of inflorescences, stems slender, ± 50 mm; flowers yellow, striped brown (Sep-Jun). **Fruit:** Pod with scattered hairs. **General:** Browsed by stock. Used traditionally to treat dysentery in calves.

Rhynchosia caribaea monya-mali, morarana-oa-liphepa, thara (SS) (*caribaea* - from the Caribbean, Leeward Islands)

Perennial, twining, scrambling herb, up to 1 m. In open woodland, forest, near streams, grassland. **Leaves:** Leaflets ± 50 mm, tips pointed, stipules long, narrow. **Flowers:** In small inflorescences, stems ± 50 mm; flowers **widely spaced**, yellow, **brown veins** when old (blooms throughout year). **Fruit:** Pods flat, covered in silky, golden hairs. **General:** Used in traditional medicine to treat rheumatic pains and headaches. A decoction of the plant was formerly used to wash sheepskin garments.

Rhynchosia cooperi (named after Thomas Cooper, 1815-1913, English plant collector and cultivator who came to SA in 1859)

Trailing herb. In grassland. Stems prostrate. **Leaves: Held erect**, stalks ± 40 mm; leaflets **oval to roundish**, ± 25 x 22 mm, hard, veins conspicuous beneath, terminal leaflet on short stalklet. **Flowers: In erect inflorescences, ± 180 mm, clustered in upper third**; flowers, conspicuous, 14-18 mm, orange-yellow (Nov-Mar).

Rhynchosia harmsiana (named after Herman Harms, 1870-1942, German botanist)

Prostrate to twining herb. On forest margins, in woodland, disturbed areas. Many slender stems, with reddish brown hairs. **Leaves:** Terminal leaflets 20-30 x 15-25 mm, roundish to broadly oval, stalk downy. **Flowers:** 5-7, in loose inflorescences, in leaf axils, stems 50-100 mm; flowers 10-15 mm, yellow with purple-brown lines, calyx bell-like, 8-10 mm, lobes longer than tube. **Fruit:** Pod ± 20 mm, roughly hairy.

270

Zornia capensis

Zornia linearis

Dumasia villosa

Rhynchosia adenodes

Rhynchosia caribaea

Rhynchosia cooperi

Rhynchosia harmsiana

Lawrence Peacock

Van Wyk & Malan

Martin von Fintel

Geoff Nichols

Van Wyk & Malan

Martin von Fintel

Lal Greene

271

Rhynchosia minima iyeza lesisu (X) (*minima* - very small)

Perennial twining or prostrate herb, 0,3-1 m. In grassland, woodland, widespread in trop. Rootstock woody. Stems long, radiating, hairy or hairless, covered with tiny glands. **Leaves:** Stalks ± 40 mm; leaflets oval to **bluntly triangular,** 10-60 x 8-50 mm, tipped with tiny point, gland dotted beneath. **Flowers:** Inflorescences ± 100 mm, stems slender, ± 50 mm; flowers well spaced, 6-10 mm, yellow, streaked red-brown, dotted with tiny glands, close in afternoon (Sep-Apr). **Fruit:** Pod ± 20 x 5 mm, slightly inflated. **General:** Two subspecies in this region.

Rhynchosia monophylla (*monophylla* - single leaf)

Trailing perennial herb. In rocky places. Woody rootstock. Stems thinly hairy, glandular. **Leaves:** Well spaced, usually only **1 leaflet** (occasionally 2 smaller side leaflets), broadly oval, ± 60 x 45 mm, heart-shaped at base, veins prominent beneath, thinly hairy above, stalks very short. **Flowers: Solitary or a few clustered,** ± 15 mm, red and orange, red and yellow or red and pink, calyx ± 60 mm, very glandular hairy (Jul-Nov). **Fruit:** Oval pod, flattened, ± 10 x 7 mm.

Rhynchosia nitens Silver Rhynchosia Bush; Vaalboontjie (A) (*nitens* - shining, smooth)

Erect shrub, up to 1 m. In grassland and bushveld. **Covered in soft silvery grey hairs.** **Leaves:** Stalks short, distinct; leaflets 40 x 30 mm, side leaflets narrower, blunt tipped, thinly hairy above, densely hairy beneath. **Flowers:** In short, few-flowered **inflorescences, in leaf axils**; flowers yellow ± 20 mm, downy behind (Oct-Dec). **Fruit:** Pods small, ± 15 mm, hairy.

Rhynchosia sordida (*sordida* - dirty in tint, dirty white)

Erect, leafy shrublet, up to 600 mm. In grassland, bushveld, E Cape to N Prov. Stems faintly ribbed, more or less **grey downy** in all parts. **Leaves:** Leaflets ± 50 x 20 mm, almost stalkless. **Flowers: In small inflorescences, shorter than leaves,** in axils; flowers small, yellow, calyx ± 12 mm, lobes long, narrow, hairy (Oct-Mar). **Fruits:** Pods flat, ± 15 x 7 mm, silky hairy.

Rhynchosia totta Yellow Carpet Bean; malintsoetla, sebalibetla (SS); igugude (Sw); ingqungqumbe, isikhonde (Z)

Slender, twining creeper. In grassland, open woodland, forest margins, up to 2400 m, S Afr to Ethiopia, Arabia. Tuberous root. Stems very slender, hairless or slightly downy. Very variable. **Leaves:** Stalks ± 30 mm; leaflets ± 35 x 5-10 mm, hairless when mature, veins prominent. **Flowers:** 1-4 on slender stem; flowers 6-12 mm, yellow, aging reddish (Aug-May). **Fruit:** Pod ± 15 x 5 mm, hairy, seeds small, grey-brown to purple. **General:** Sweet tubers eaten raw or roasted.

Rhynchosia villosa Giant Hairy-leaved Rhynchosia (*villosa* - shaggy)

Robust, prostrate, trailing herb. In grassland. Stems with long, soft hairs. **Leaves: Large,** terminal leaflet 70-110 x 60-120 mm, thick, velvety, veins deeply indented, stalks short. **Flowers:** In erect inflorescences, stems ± 80 mm; flowers densely clustered in upper half, 12-15 mm, yellow, with red veins, calyx 7-9 mm, long hairy, lobes longer than tube (Oct-Dec). **Fruits:** Pods sickle-shaped, 20-28 mm, stalkless, hairy.

Rhynchosia minima

Van Wyk & Malan

Rhynchosia monophylla

Tom de Waal

Rhynchosia nitens

Van Wyk & Malan

Rhynchosia sordida

Tony Abbott

Rhynchosia totta

Tony Abbott

Rhynchosia villosa

Wally Menne

Eriosema (*erion* - wool; *sema* - sign, refers to the woolly standard petal) - Herbs or shrubs; usually with resinous dots; petals pouched, glandular. Attracts butterflies. Warm regions, S America, Afr, ± 150 species, ± 36 in SA.

Eriosema cordatum Heart-leaved Eriosema; Iesapo, Ieshetla (SS); ubangalala, umhlambankunzi, uqonsi (Z) (*cordatum* - heart-shaped, refers to leaves)

Perennial herb, up to 150-400 mm. In grassland. Rootstock large, woody. Stems prostrate, tips erect. **Plant covered with loose to rigid reddish hairs. Leaves: Few, large,** ± stalkless; 1-3 leaflets, terminal leaflet ± 100 x 80, stalklet ± 20 mm, gland dots on both sides. **Flowers:** In terminal inflorescences, ± 50 mm, stems 50-150 mm; flowers ± 10 mm, yellow, orange with **reddish brown stripes** (throughout year). **Fruit:** Pods round, ± 15 mm, flat. **General:** Used in traditional medicine to treat impotence and to stimulate bulls in spring. Commonly hybridises with *E. salignum*.

Eriosema kraussianum Pale Yellow Eriosema (named after Christian Krauss, 1812-90, German scientist, traveller, collector)

Erect herb, 90-350 mm, in clumps. In grassland. Woody rootstock. Several stems, **covered in silvery silky hairs. Leaves:** Stalks short; leaflets 30-60 x 12 mm, stipules brown. **Flowers:** Inflorescences ± 40 mm, stems ± 50 mm; flowers ± 12 mm, **pale yellow** (Sep-Nov). **Fruit:** Pod ± 15 x 8 mm, hairy.
Similar species: *E. simulans* ined Erect shrublet, in grassland; flowers large, ± 20 mm, wing and keel petals the same length, **bright golden yellow.**

Eriosema preptum (*preptos* - distinguished)

Perennial herb or shrublet, 200-600 mm. In sandy grassland. Stems covered in short white hairs. **Leaves:** Leaflets 45-60 x 20-30 mm, sparsely hairy above, **densely woolly beneath,** veins prominent, stipules 8-14 mm. **Flowers:** 25-35 in inflorescences, stems ± 120 mm, **held well above leaves; flowers small,** 6-7 mm, orange or yellow, with red veins (Sep-Feb). **Fruit:** Pods 10-13 x 8-10 mm, silky. **General:** Used as an aphrodisiac. **Similar species:** *E. rossii* (see p. 60).

Eriosema psoraleoides Shrubby Yellow Eriosema, Yellow Seed; Geelkeurtjie (A); uthongololo (Z) (*psoraleoides* - like *Psoralea*)

Tall, erect shrub, 0,5-2(3) m, often in large colonies. In grassland, woodland, on floodplains, KZN to Trop Afr, Madag. Stems densely grey hairy. **Leaves:** Stalks very short; leaflets ± 20-90 x 8-30 mm, veins prominent, velvety silvery grey beneath. **Flowers: In dense terminal inflorescences,** stems 25-75 mm; flowers ± 14 mm, yellow (Oct-May). **Fruit:** Pod ± 18 x 10 mm, shaggy hairy, heavily parasitised, seeds yellow. **General:** Seeds cooked with maize meal. Used in traditional medicine to cure internal disorders and as protection against lightning. Hardy, garden shrub.

Eriosema salignum Narrow-leaved Eriosema, Brown Bonnets; Iesapo (SS); ubangalala, uluphondongozi, uqonsi (Z) (see p. 62)

Eriosema umtamvunense (named after the Umtamvuna River Gorge)

Perennial shrublet, up to 500 mm. In grassland. Stems densely recurved, densely hairy above. **Leaves:** Stalks short; terminal leaflets 57-70 x 28-40 mm, side leaflets smaller, asymmetrical, dull green, finely hairy above, woolly grey-white beneath, with small yellow glands, stipules 13 x 6 mm. **Flowers:** Inflorescence ± 125 mm, flowers clustered in upper third, **bracts shorter than flowers, dropping; flowers large,** 13-14 mm, dull red and yellow, calyx covered in golden hairs (Nov-Dec). **Fruit:** 15-16 x 10-11 mm, beak 3-4 mm, densely covered in long golden hairs.

Vigna (named in honour of Italian botanist Domenico Vigna, died 1647) - Usually twining herbs (for description see p.464).

Vigna luteola Yellow Wild Sweetpea; isikhwali, ithangela-omhlange (Z) (*luteola* - yellow)

Perennial climber, stems 1-2,4 m. In seasonally wet grassland, lake shore, swamp forest, E Cape to Trop Afr, Trop Asia, America. Stems covered with spreading hairs or hairless. **Leaves:** Stalks 20-100 mm; leaflets 25-90 x 4-30 mm, veins raised, dark spot at base. **Flowers:** In few-flowered inflorescences, stems 50-400 mm; flowers ± 25 mm, **pale yellow with bright yellow at base** (throughout year). **Fruit:** Pod 40-80 x 5-6 mm. **General:** Used in traditional medicine for fever and as a love charm.

Macrotyloma (*makros* - long; *tylos*- swelling) - Annual or perennial climbing herbs (for description see p. 152).

Macrotyloma axillare umhlanzo wenhliziyo (Z) (see p. 152)

Eriosema cordatum

Lawrence Peacock

Eriosema kraussianum

Martin von Fintel

Eriosema psoraleoides

Martin von Fintel

Eriosema salignum

Wally Menne

Eriosema preptum

C J Ward

Eriosema umtamvunense

Tony Abbott

Eriosema simulans ined

Martin von Fintel

Vigna luteola

Geoff Nichols

Macrotyloma axillare

Tony Abbott

275

OXALIDACEAE - Sorrel Family Annual or perennial herbs. *Oxalis* (for descriptions see p. 402).

★ *Oxalis corniculata* Jimson weed, Creeping Yellow Sorrel; Tuinsuring (A); bolila (SS); isithathe (Z) (*corniculata* - small horn)

Creeping herb up to 100 mm. Cosmop weed. Roots fibrous. Leaflets heart-shaped. Flowers ± 7 mm diam, in small inflorescences. Flowers and leaves eaten raw as a relish.Used in traditional medicine to treat snakebite.

LINACEAE - Flax family Herbs or shrubs. Stipules often glandlike. Petals twisted. Economically important for Flax *Linum usitatissimum*, to make linen and linseed oil. Cosmop, ± 14 genera, ± 250 species, 2 genera in SA.
Linum (*linon* - flax) - Herbs or undershrubs; flowers usually in branched inflorescences. About 5 species in SA.

Linum thunbergii Wild Flax; Wildevlas (A); bohlokoana (SS); ithalelimpofu (Z)
(named after Carl Thunberg, 1743-1828, pupil of Linnaeus, collector at Cape, author of Flora Capensis)

Perennial herb, up to 700 mm. In moist grassland, up to 2300 m. Stems slender, branched towards tips. **Leaves:** Narrow, ± 10 mm, **tips pointed,** stalkless, stipules brown, glandlike. **Flowers:** In branching inflorescences; flowers ± 15 mm diam, yellow, buds reddish (Sep-Mar). **General:** Used in traditional medicine to purify the blood, treat fever, pain, cure snakebite and as a charm to prevent accidents.

ZYGOPHYLLACEAE - Devil-thorn Family Herbs, shrubs. Branches often jointed at nodes. Stipules paired. Stamens with appendage at base. Mostly warm, arid regions, ± 27 genera, ± 285 species, 8 genera in SA. *Tribulus* (*tri* - three; *bolos* - a point) - Leaves opposite, one usually longer than the other. Attracts butterflies. About 54 species, ± 5 in SA.

Tribulus terrestris Devil-thorns; Dubbeltjie (A); inkunzane (Z) (*terrestris* - ground dwelling)

Annual, prostrate herb, stems up to 3,5 m. In disturbed areas, grassland, widespread in Afr. Covered with whitish hairs. **Leaves:** Opposite, compound, lower surface white hairy. **Flowers:** Solitary, 6-9 mm diam, yellow, held above leaves (Sep-May). **Fruit:** Small, **woody, with sharp spines. General:** Spiny fruit successfully distributed by readily attaching to people and animals.

MALPIGHIACEAE - Barbados Cherry Family Scrambling or erect shrubs. 2 large fleshy glands on leaf stalk. Fruit winged. Trop, subtrop, ± 67 genera, ± 1100 species, 3 genera in SA. *Sphedamnocarpus* (*sphedamnos* - name of the Maple; *karpos* - fruit) - Young branches covered in greyish brown down; fruit 3-4 winged. Afr, 12 species, 2 in SA.

Sphedamnocarpus pruriens Lesser Moth-fruit Creeper; isinambuzane, ubangalala (Z)
(*pruriens* - causing itching)

Slender, twining creeper, up to 2 m. In thicket, woodland, KZN to Angola, Moz, Malawi. Semi-woody. **Leaves:** Opposite (whorled), 35-75(135) x 10-25(100) mm, tip pointed or rounded, base lobed or rounded, stalks 2-36 mm. **Flowers:** 8-25 mm diam, **petals crumpled,** yellow (Dec-May). **Fruit: Wings** 15-20 x 11-15 mm, coppery red. **General:** Lovely in bloom. Hairs can be itchy. Used in traditional medicine. Subsp. *pruriens,* leaves densely hairy; flowers in clusters, bright yellow. Subsp. *galphimiifolius,* leaves ± hairless; flowers solitary, pale yellow.

EUPHORBIACEAE - Rubber/Euphorbia Family Herbs, shrubs, trees, twiners, succulent or not, often with milky sap. Male and female flowers within cuplike structure (cyathium) or in a regular inflorescence. Fruit usually a 3 chambered capsule. Economically important species include Rubber, Tung Oil, Castor Oil, Cassava, Tapioca and ornamentals such as Poinsettia, Crown of Thorns and Croton. Cosmop, ± 313 genera, ± 8100 species, 49 genera in SA.
Dalechampia (named after Jacques Dalechamp, 1513-88, French botanist) - Twining herbs or undershrubs; male and female flowers on same plant, clustered within 2 large, simple or lobed bracts. Trop, ± 110 species, ± 5 in SA.

Dalechampia capensis Dalechampia, Wild Hop; imbabatane (Sw); inzula (Z)

Twining perennial herb, stems up to 3,5 m. In open woodland. Rootstock woody. Plant sparsely hairy. **Leaves:** 3-5 lobed, lobes 30-100 x 10-40 mm, grey-green beneath, margins wavy, stalks ± 70 mm. **Flowers:** Clustered within **conspicuous petal-like floral bracts,** ± 30 x 45 mm, 3-5 lobed, cream or yellow, green veined, stems ± 170 mm (Aug-May). **Fruit:** ± 20 mm diam, calyx lobes with stinging hairs. **General:** Visited by small bees, attracts butterflies. Used in traditional medicine.

Jatropha (*jatros* - physician; *trophe* - food, refers to medicinal properties) - Herbs, shrubs or trees, often with large perennial rootstock; leaves alternate, simple or lobed; sexes on same plant, in compact terminal inflorescence. Trop, subtrop, especially America and Afr, ± 175 species, ± 20 in SA.

Jatropha hirsuta Hairy-leaved Jatropha; ugodide, ugodile (Z) (*hirsuta* - hairy)

Up to 450 mm. In shade. **Very variable.** Softly hairy throughout. Woody rootstock. Stem stout, solitary. **Leaves:** ± 150 x 15- 50 mm, margins shallowly toothed, each tooth gland tipped. **Flowers:** In terminal inflorescence, within leaves; flowers creamy yellow (Sep-Dec). **Fruit:** Lobed, ± 13 mm diam, hairy. **General:** Used in traditional medicine to treat fever, wounds and as protective charm against lightning.

★ *Oxalis corniculata*   *Linum thunbergii*   *Tribulus terrestris*

Sphedamnocarpus pruriens   *Jatropha hirsuta*

Dalechampia capensis   *Jatropha hirsuta*

Tony Abbott   Van Wyk & Malan   Van Wyk & Malan   Martin von Fintel   Martin von Fintel   Tony Abbott   Tony Abbott

277

Jatropha natalensis Guineafowl-foot Jatropha

Erect herb, up to 300 mm. In wooded grassland, KZN midlands. Stems from woody base. **Leaves:** Alternate, simple or **occasionally irregularly 1-4 or more lobed**, lobes widely spreading when present, margins entire to irregularly toothed, veins conspicuous, hairy, stalks ± 12 mm, swollen at base, stipules small bristles. **Flowers:** In terminal inflorescences; flowers pale yellow (Jan-Mar). **General:** Shape of leaves varies even on the same plant.

Jatropha variifolia Glossy-leaved Jatropha (variifolia - leaves variable)

Shrub up to 1,5 m. In thicket, forest. Stem stout, softly woody, **branching in upper third. Leaves: Clustered at tops of branches, irregularly 3-5 lobed**, midlobe ± 120 x 45 mm, shiny dark green above, paler beneath, stalks ± 40 mm. **Flowers:** In branched terminal inflorescences, just above leaves; flowers small, petals yellow-green (Sep-May). **Fruit:** 15 mm diam. **General:** Decorative shade plant.

Clutia (named after Outgers Cluyt, 17th century Dutch botanist, curator of Leyden Bot Gardens) - Shrubs and herbs with woody rootstock; leaves simple, alternate, usually stalkless; flowers small, in leaf axils, male in small clusters, female solitary, on separate plants. Afr, Arabia, ± 70 species, ± 33 in SA.

Clutia hirsuta Lightning Bush; ubuhlungu bedila, ungwaleni (Z) (hirsuta - hairy)

Shrublet, 0,6-1,2 m. Widespread. Stems erect, often branched, twigs angular, sparsely to densely hairy. Very variable. **Leaves:** ± 25 x 12 mm, margins slightly recurved, midrib and veins distinct beneath, stalks short. **Flowers:** Male and female on separate plants, stalks very short, finely hairy (Sep-May). **Fruit:** Capsule ± 3 mm diam. **General:** Used in traditional medicine to treat fevers, as a tonic, a purge to treat stomach troubles and protective sprinkling charms. Used with other plants to treat anthrax and gall sickness in cattle.

Euphorbia (named after Euphorbus, 1st Century physician to King Juba of Mauritania) - Herbs, shrubs, trees, usually with milky sap, sometimes succulent; flowers reduced, within a cyathium or 'cup' rimmed with glands. Cosmop, ± 2000 species, ± 200 in SA.

Euphorbia sp. nov.

In rounded clumps, up to 400 mm diam. In rock crevices, on hot dry mountainsides, N KZN to N Prov. Branches greyish green, 3 angled, tubercles spiralled. Spine shields small with short spines. Cyathia and glands yellow.

Euphorbia clavarioides [= *E. truncata*] Lion's Spoor; Melkpol, Vingerpol (A); sehlehle, sehloko, thethebale (SS); isantilele, isihlekehleke (Z) (clavarioides - means Clavaria-like because it resembles a fungus of that name)

Flat to cushionlike succulent, 20-75 x 150-300 mm. In rocky grassland, midlands to mountains, 1500-2750 m. Older branches and stems buried, closely massed stems branched or unbranched, 10-20 mm diam, olive-green to brownish, rounded at tips. **Leaves:** Small, fleshy, ± 2 mm, few at tips of branches, soon falling. **Flowers:** Cyathia solitary, stemless, with 3-5 bracts, glands greenish yellow (Sep-Feb). **Fruit:** Capsule ± 8 mm diam. **General:** Used to prepare bird lime. Children eat the dried sap as 'chewing gum'. Used in traditional medicine to bathe swollen feet and, with other species, to treat leprosy. Two subspecies.

Euphorbia grandicornis Rhino Thorn; umhlonhlo (Sw); isihlehle, isiphapha (Z) (grandicornis - large thorns)

Much branched, spiny, succulent shrub, 1-2 m. In thicket in hot dry areas, KZN to Kenya. Stems erect to sprawling, **3 angled, deeply constricted into segments**, 50-120 x 5-150 mm, central core 20-30 mm thick, green with paler green markings, with continuous pale grey margin. **Spines:** In pairs, stout, 15-70 mm with small spines or prickles on either side of flower clusters. **Flowers:** Cyathia in clusters, yellow (Apr-Aug). **Fruit:** 3 lobed, ± 13 mm diam, shiny mauve to red-brown. **General:** Flowers attract many insects, especially wasps. Fruit and flowers eaten by vervet monkeys. Plant browsed by black rhino. Thorns raise a painful bump on the skin. Introduced into horticulture in Britain and Europe in 1870s. A most decorative plant for a frost-free garden. (See p. 576)

Jatropha variifolia

Geoff Nichols

Jatropha natalensis

Tony Pooley

Clutia hirsuta

Martin von Fintel

Euphorbia clavarioides

Pam Cooke

Euphorbia clavarioides

Trevor Coleman

Euphorbia sp. nov.

Tony Abbott

Euphorbia grandicornis

Nolly Zaloumis

Euphorbia grandicornis

David Johnson

279

Euphorbia kraussiana usingalwesalukazi (Z) (named after Christian Krauss, 1812-90, German scientist, traveller and collector, who visited SA 1839-40)
Succulent shrub, up to 1,4 m. On forest margins. Stems thick, woody, leafless below, branching above, leafy. **Leaves:** Alternate to whorled at base of flowers, spreading, 30-100 x 4-15 mm, tapering to short stalks. **Flowers:** In terminal branching inflorescences, bracts ± 12 mm (Dec-Feb).

Euphorbia pseudocactus
Spiny, succulent shrub forming clumps up to 1 x 2 m (scrambling to 2 m in shade). In hot, dry, rocky areas, thicket, C KZN. Stems buried. **Branches:** Semi-erect, (3)4-5 angled, irregularly constricted into segments, 20-150 x 25-45 mm, grooved or nearly flat between angles, green with yellowish green V-shaped markings (or without), continuous white horny margins. **Spines:** Stout, in pairs ± 10 mm, grey-brown. **Flowers:** Cyathia 1-3 in clusters, yellow (Jul-Aug). **Fruit:** 3 angled, ± 14 mm diam. **General:** Forming very large colonies in some areas.

Euphorbia woodii Wood's Euphorbia; Vingerpol, Wood-euphorbia (A); isihlehle (Z) (named after John Medley Wood, 1827-1915, botanist, collector, first curator of Natal Herbarium)
Spineless dwarf succulent, up to 450 mm diam. In coastal grassland. Rare. Swollen underground stem ± 150 mm diam. **Branches:** 20-40, ± 200 x 10-15 mm, bright green, cylindric, spreading out from flat central area. **Leaves:** Each branch tipped with deciduous small leaf. **Flowers:** Cyathia clustered on central branches, stalks ± 15 mm, yellow (Sep-May). **General:** First cultivated England in 1862. Popular garden or container plant, likes plenty of water.
Similar species: *E. franksiae* Further inland; plant smaller; branches slender.

ICACINACEAE - White Pear Family Trees, shrubs and climbers. Leaves simple, margin entire, toothed or lobed. Flowers small, regular. Fruit fleshy or dry, 1 seeded. Mostly Trop, ± 52 genera and 300 species, ± 3 genera in SA.
Pyrenacantha (pyren - a fruit stone; akanthos - thorn, fruit has projecting pegs from inner walls) - Climbing shrubs; male inflorescence a long spike, female short, small. Trop, subtrop, ± 20 species, 3 in SA.

Pyrenacantha scandens Blouboktoutjie (A); umkhokhothwane, umnakile, umsekelo, umthongakazana (Z) (scandens - climbing)
Climber. In forest, Cape to Moz. Young branches densely hairy, bark rough, grey.
Leaves: 50-100 x 25-65 mm, shape variable, oval to 3-5 lobed, tips pointed, sparsely hairy above, densely hairy beneath, margins toothed, hairy, stalks ± 20 mm, very hairy. **Flowers:** Male spikes ± 50 mm, stem ± 25 mm. Female flowers in short few-flowered spikes (Aug-Apr). **Fruit:** ± 18 mm, pale yellow. **General:** Leaves cooked as spinach in winter. Used in traditional medicine to prevent miscarriage, ensure an easy birth, treat impotence and barrenness, and as a love charm.
Similar species: *P. grandiflora* velabahleke (Sw); unakile (Z) Twiner or scrambling shrub; stems with raised white dots; leaves large, ± 140 x 110 mm, heart-shaped at base, margins double toothed, teeth glandlike, hairy throughout, 5-7 veins from base, stalks 25-50 mm; male flowers in spikes ± 160 mm; female flowers solitary; fruit fleshy, ± 20 x 10 mm, 1 seeded, yellowish green, in clusters of 2-4 (Sep-Jan).

VITACEAE - Vine or Grape Family Climbers or shrubs with tendrils. Fruit fleshy. Includes the grape vine *Vitis vinifera* and ornamentals such as Boston Ivy and Virginia Creeper. Trop and warm countries, ± 14 genera, ± 850 species, 5 genera in SA. *Cyphostemma* (kyphos - bent; stemma - wreath) - Prostrate or climbing herbs, usually hairy. About 150 species, ± 34 in SA.

Cyphostemma cirrhosum Droog-my-keel, Wildedruif (A) (see p. 66)

Cyphostemma hypoleucum Double-barrel Vine; Tambesiebessie (A); udekane, umbombo (Z) (hypoleucum - leaves white beneath)
Deciduous climbing shrub. In woodland, thicket, dune forest, KZN to Zim. Stems long, robust, **distinctively 'double-barrelled'**, with tendrils, young stems velvety.
Leaves: 3-5 leaflets, ± 100 x 60 mm, slightly fleshy, margins toothed, velvety or hairless above, **velvety grey beneath**, central leaflet stalklet ± 10 mm, stalks 35-50 mm. **Flowers:** In branched inflorescences, stems ± 70 mm, velvety grey; flowers yellowish, buds velvety (Oct-May). **Fruit:** Velvety, red. **General:** Flowers visited by flies, large black ants and honey-bees. Fruits eaten by birds. Used in traditional medicine. Attractive outdoor container plant, from seed and cuttings.
Similar species: *C. flaviflorum* Succulent climber, in coastal bush; 3 leaflets, 20-55 x 15-35 mm, succulent, margins toothed, tip rounded.

Euphorbia kraussiana

Euphorbia pseudocactus

Euphorbia franksiae

Euphorbia woodii

Pyrenacantha scandens

Pyrenacantha grandiflora

Cyphostemma cirrhosum

Cyphostemma hypoleucum

281

Cyphostemma natalitium idambiso, idololenkonyane, ingquza yenkonyane (Z)

Prostrate or trailing succulent scrambler. In grassland. Stems sparingly branched, with tendrils, stalked glands. **Leaves:** 5-7 leaflets, ± 25 x 18 mm, **regularly toothed from base to tip**, stalklets 5-10 mm. **Flowers:** Small, inflorescences opposite leaves (Oct-Dec). **Fruit:** 10 x 8 mm, bluish red, hairless. **General:** Used traditionally for poultices and in pregnancy, to ensure a safe delivery . Used to treat colic in cattle.

Cyphostemma schlechteri (named after Friedrich Schlechter, 1872-1925, German botanist and traveller)

Much branched scrambler, up to 1 m. In forest, rocky places, open woodland, KZN to Moz, Zim, Bots. Stems succulent, with reddish tendrils, hairless except on inflorescences. **Leaves:** 3-5(7) leaflets, fleshy, midleaflet ± 120 x 35 mm, **grey-green**, side leaflets smaller, margins toothed, stalklets short, stalks ± 20 mm. **Flowers:** In small, open, side inflorescences (Sep-Nov). **Fruit:** 14 x 8 mm, reddish. **General:** Fruit reputed to be both edible and poisonous! Attractive plant for dry rock gardens.

TILIACEAE - Jute or Linden Family Trees, shrubs or herbs (for description see p. 156). ***Corchorus*** (*koreo* - to purge), refers to the laxative properties of some species) Shrubby herbs; flowers in 3s, petals yellow, numerous stamens. Commercially valuable for Jute *C. olitorus, C. capsularis,* used for fibre. Trop, ± 100 species, 15 in SA.

Corchorus asplenifolius igusha (Sw); ubangalala, igusha (Z) (*asplenifolius* - leaves like *Asplenium*)

Perennial herb, prostrate shrublet. In woodland, on margins of marshes. Woody rootstock. **Stems usually hairless. Leaves:** 15-80 x 2-15 mm, blue-green above, **grey beneath**, margins toothed, veins deeply indented, looking like a compound leaf, hairless to densely, roughly hairy, stalks ± 10 mm, stipules ± 10 mm. **Flowers:** Petals and sepals yellow, ± 10 mm (Nov-May). **Fruit: Capsule** 20-30 mm, **stalk twisted. General:** Very variable. Leaves eaten as spinach. Used in traditional medicine, with other plants, as an aphrodisiac and to treat impotence.
Similar species: *C. junodii* **Capsule roundish, bristly,** ± 20 x 15 mm.

Triumfetta (named after Giovanni Trionfetti, 1658-1708, Italian botanist) - Shrubs or herbs; fruit dry, covered in bristles. Often weeds of cultivation. Attracts butterflies. Trop, mostly Afr, ± 170 species, 12 in SA.

Triumfetta pilosa uvemvane (Z) (*pilosa*- covered with soft hairs)

Erect woody shrublet, up to 1,5 m. On forest margins, in grassland, thicket, disturbed damp areas. Stems hairy, reddish. **Leaves:** 50-120 x 30-70 mm, margins toothed, dark green above, paler beneath, **hairy throughout**, stalks 5-50 mm. **Flowers:** In small, leafy clusters, crowded at nodes; flowers yellow, open in afternoon (Feb-May). **Fruit:** 10-25 mm diam, with slender, hooked prickles, turning black. **General:** Flowers visited by bees. Burr-like fruit distributed by animals. Stems used to make twine. Used traditionally to wash hair when it is to be dressed.

MALVACEAE - Hibiscus Family Trees, shrubs or herbs. Flowers often with epicalyx (leafy whorl below calyx); stamens partly united into tube around style, branched above. Economically important for cotton, Okra *Hibiscus esculentus,* and ornamentals such as Hollyhocks and Hibiscus. Cosmop, ± 111 genera, ± 1800 species, 21 genera in SA. ***Abutilon*** (from the Arabic name) - Herbs or shrubs; leaf blade usually heart-shaped at base; with no epicalyx, stamen tube divided at top into many filaments, usually open in afternoon. Trop, subtrop, ± 400 species, ± 20 in SA.

Abutilon angulatum (*angulatum* - angled, with corners)

Erect shrub, 1-3 m. In scrub, on riverbanks, roadsides, KZN to Trop Afr. Stems branched towards tips, semi-woody. **All parts covered in velvety hairs. Leaves:** ± 300 x 250 mm, dark green above, paler beneath, margins slightly toothed, stalks as long as blade. **Flowers:** ± 30 mm diam, yellowish orange, calyx 10-15 mm, stalk ± 30 mm. **Fruit:** 9-12 x 8 mm, velvety. **General:** Subsp. *angulatum*, in drier places; **blue-grey velvety.** Subsp. *macrophyllum*, moist places; **yellow to brownish velvety.**

Abutilon sonneratianum Forest Abutilon, Butter and Cheese; lecheane (SS)

(named after Pierre Sonnerat, 1745-1814, French naturalist, draughtsman, who had several expeditions to SA)

Shrubby perennial, 0,5-1,5(2) m. On forest margins, in scrub, coast to 2000 m, Cape to Zim, Moz. Stems slender, bark grooved. **Leaves:** 20-100 x 10-50 mm, **velvety dark green, paler beneath, blade drooping**, slightly lobed, margins shallowly toothed, stalks long, slender, ± 30 mm. **Flowers:** ± **30 mm diam**, yellow or orange, stalk ± 60 mm (throughout year). **Fruit:** ± 15 x 25 mm. **General:** Used traditionally as a stimulant for bulls in the spring. Easily cultivated, in shade.
Similar species: *A. grantii* **Leaves smaller,** ± 40 x 30 mm, **thin, firm,** broadly toothed, velvety or almost hairless; fruit ± 12 x 18 mm.

Richard Symmons

Martin von Fintel

Cyphostemma natalitium

Cyphostemma schlechteri

Martin von Fintel

Wayne Matthews

C J Ward

Corchorus asplenifolius

Corchorus junodii

Triumfetta pilosa

Geoff Nichols

Martin von Fintel

Tony Abbott

Abutilon angulatum

Abutilon grantii

Abutilon sonneratianum

283

Malvastrum (*malvastrum* - false mallow) - Herbs or small shrubs; epicalyx 3 lobed. America, ± 3 species, 1 in SA.

★ **Malvastrum coromandelianum** **Prickly Malvastrum** (named after the Coromandel coast of India) Annual or biennial shrublet up to 1 m. On roadsides, old fields, disturbed areas. Pantrop weed. Sparsely hairy. Leaves 30-60 x 10-40 mm, margins coarsely toothed, tips blunt, stalks short, stipules ± 5 mm. Flowers solitary, ± 16 mm diam, yellow-orange (summer). Fruit ± 6 mm diam. **Similar species:** *Sida cordifolia* , no epicalyx.

Sida (name used by Theophrastus for a water plant) - Herbs, shrublets; epicalyx absent, flowers open in morning, unlike *Abutilon* which opens in the afternoon or evening, petals not much longer than calyx. Trop, ± 200 species, 11 in SA.

Sida cordifolia **Flannel Weed; Hartblaartaaiman, Verdompsterk (A)** (*cordifolia* - heart-shaped leaves) Soft shrub, up to 1 m. Pantrop, a weed of cultivation, disturbed areas. Softly grey velvety throughout. **Leaves:** ± 60 x 40 mm, ± heart-shaped at base, tips rounded to blunt, margins toothed, velvety, stalks ± 15 mm. **Flowers: In dense clusters** at end of stems and side branches; flowers ± 15 mm diam, white to yellow (throughout year). **General:** Browsed by cattle.

Sida dregei **Spider-leg, Sutherland's Curse; umdiza wethafa (Z)** (named after Johann Drège, 1794-1881, German horticulturalist, botanical collector, traveller, came to the Cape in 1826 with brother Carl and set up as collectors) Slender, much branched shrublet, up to 800 mm. In grassland, scrub, in moist places, E Cape to Zim, Moz. **Leaves:** ± 15 x 10 mm, margins with few, blunt teeth, tips blunt or square, stalks short. **Flowers: Solitary,** + 25 mm diam, orange, **stalk long, ± 50 mm** (Aug-Apr). **General:** Used in traditional medicine to treat sores. **Similar species:** *S. rhombifolia* Taaiman (A); uvevane (Sw,Z) Perennial weed, 1-2 m; leaves ± 40 x 20 mm, upper half finely toothed; flowers small, in clusters.

Pavonia (named after José Antonia Pavon, 1754-1840, Spanish botanist and traveller) - Herbs or shrubs; epicalyx of 5 or more bracts; stamen tube 5 toothed at tip. Attracts butterflies. Warm countries, ± 240 species, 13 in SA.

Pavonia burchellii [= *P. patens*] **Dainty Pavonia; indola empofu (Z)** (named after William Burchell, 1781-1863, naturalist, traveller, artist, author, who collected in SA 1810-1815) Erect to spreading herbaceous shrublet, up to 1 m. In light shade, in dry areas, KZN to Trop Afr, Ethiopia. **Plant hairy throughout,** sometimes sticky, with offensive smell. **Leaves:** 20-80 x 10-70 mm, pale green above, very pale beneath, 3-5 lobed, margins toothed, stalks slender, 20-80 mm. **Flowers: Solitary,** ± 30 mm diam, white to orange, **epicalyx with 5-6 bracts,** ± 10 x 5 mm, **stalk long, slender,** ± 50 mm (Aug-Jun). **Similar species:** *P. dregei* Slender herb, branches spreading; leaves small, widely spaced, ± 25 mm; flowers yellow.

Hibiscus (Greek name for marsh mallow) - Trees, shrubs or herbs, often with star-shaped hairs; flowers showy, often with dark centres, epicalyx of 5-20 bracts, usually as long as calyx. Attracts butterflies including Koppie Charaxes, *Charaxes jasius safurnis* and Mountain Sandman *Spialia spio*. Trop, subtrop, ± 300 species, ± 59 in SA.

Hibiscus aethiopicus **Common Dwarf Wild Hibiscus; lereletsane, se-seholo (SS); ibunda elimpofu, ihlalanyosi elimhlophe, uvemvane (Z)** (*aethiopicus* - from Ethiopia) Low-growing perennial herb, 140-350 mm. In grassland, marshy areas, open scrub, up to 1800 m, KZN to Ethiopia. Woody rootstock. Stems erect to prostrate, covered in **rough hairs. Leaves:** 10-80 x 6-45 mm, margins entire or toothed towards **blunt tips,** 3-5 veins from rounded base, hairy to hairless, stalks 5-15 mm. **Flowers:** Solitary, in leaf axils, ± 50 mm diam, white, cream to yellow, aging pink, rarely deep pink, epicalyx of **7-9 short, narrow bracts,** hairy, calyx 10-20 mm, stalk ± 45 mm (Sep- April). **General:** Very variable over the range. Used in traditional medicine to treat swollen joints, sprains and colic.

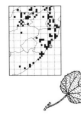

Hibiscus calyphyllus **Large Yellow Wild Hibiscus; Wildestokroos (A)** (*calyphyllus* - leafy calyx) Perennial shrub, up to 1,5(3) m. Widespread in thicket, forest, E Cape to Trop Afr, Madag. **Leaves:** ± 120 mm diam, rarely 3-5 lobed, velvety, margins toothed, stalks 50-90 mm. **Flowers:** Solitary, large, ± 120 mm diam, bright yellow with deep red centre, close in early afternoon, do not re-open, epicalyx and calyx with 5 broad bracts, ± 20 mm, tips long, pointed, stalk short (throughout year). **Fruit:** Capsule, 25 x 15 mm. **General:** Browsed by antelope. Excellent, hardy garden plant.

★ *Malvastrum coromandelianum*   *Sida cordifolia*   *Sida dregei*

Pavonia burchellii   *Pavonia dregei*

Hibiscus aethiopicus   *Hibiscus calyphyllus*   *Hibiscus calyphyllus*

285

Hibiscus cannabinus Indian Hemp-leaved Hibiscus; Wildestokroos (A); umhla-kanye (Sw); udekane (Z) (*cannabinus* - like hemp or dagga)
Annual shrubby herb, up to 3 m. Pioneer or problem plant in disturbed areas, widespread in tropics; country of origin uncertain. **Short, sharp prickles on stems, leaves, epicalyx. Leaves:** ± 150 mm diam, deeply 3-7 lobed, margins toothed, tips, pointed, stalks ± 220 mm. **Flowers:** Solitary, closely packed up tall stems, ± 100 mm diam, pale yellow with purple centre, sometimes suffused with purple, closed by midday; epicalyx of 7-8 bracts, ± 18 mm, calyx ± 25 mm, lobes long, slender (Nov-Apr). **General:** Flowers visited by ants. Grown as a fibre plant in India.

Hibiscus dongolensis Dongola Hibiscus (named after Dongola, a game reserve in the northern Transvaal, now N Prov, proclaimed to link Kruger National Park with Zimb and Bots; later deproclaimed)
Shrub, up to 2 m. In woodland, riverine thicket, SA to Trop Afr. Stems rough, not bristly, becoming smooth. **Leaves:** ± 100 x 70 mm, ± hairless, margins toothed, stalks ± 60 mm. **Flowers:** Solitary, **drooping,** ± 80 mm diam, yellow, deep golden yellow at base, deep red in centre, **only briefly fully open, epicalyx lobes 5,** ± 15 x 2 mm, calyx lobes ± 20 mm, stalk ± 10 mm (Oct-May). **Fruit: Capsule round. General:** Host to the pink bollworm, a serious cotton pest. Proclaimed a noxious weed in Zim. **Similar species:** *H. vitifolius* (p. 288).

Hibiscus microcarpus (*microcarpus* - small fruit)
Low-growing herb, up to 300 mm. In grassland and disturbed places. Rootstock woody, perennial, plant covered with rough hairs. **Leaves:** Long, narrow, 1-15 mm wide, margins entire or with few teeth, hairy. **Flowers:** Large, yellow or pink, with or without deep maroon centre, epicalyx of 7-8 bracts (Oct-Apr). **General:** Both colours found in the same colony.

Hibiscus pusillus Dwarf Hibiscus; uguqukile, uvuma (Z) (*pusillus* - small, slender)
Low-growing herb, 50-300 mm. In woodland, rocky grassland, a pioneer in disturbed places, Cape to Nam, Bots to Moz. Woody rootstock. Annual shoots, stems roughly hairy. **Leaves:** 50-60 x 20-45 mm, deeply 3-5 lobed or not lobed, hairless to hairy, margins toothed, stalks ± 15 mm. **Flowers:** Solitary, ± 60 mm diam, yellow or mauve with deep purple or red centre, epicalyx of 8-11 bracts, calyx lobes 7-25 x 3-8 mm, stalk 15-120 mm (Oct-May). **General:** Used traditionally to treat bad dreams and as love charms by men (*uvuma* (Z) - the one that agrees). (See p. 408)

Hibiscus surattensis Prickly Wild Hibiscus Creeper; isigezo, ucathucathu, uvem-vane (Z) (*surattensis* - from Bombay, India)
Annual prostrate or scrambling herb, up to 3 m. In moist areas, widespread in trop. **Covered in reddish brown, small, sharp, hooked prickles. Leaves:** ± 100 mm diam, 3-5 lobed, margins toothed, stalks ± 110 mm, stipules broad, leaflike. **Flowers:** Solitary, ± 100 mm diam, yellow with deep red centre, outer edge of petals tinged orange, epicalyx emerald green, 8-9 bracts, calyx lobes ± 25 x 10 mm, bright pink or green, stalks ± 70 mm (Mar-May). **General:** Visited by bees, small flies, browsed by game. A weed in cultivated lands near the coast. Used in traditional medicine to treat penile inflammation and venereal disease. Good garden subject.

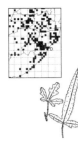

Hibiscus trionum Bladder Hibiscus; Terblansbossie (A); iyeza lentshulube (X); uvemvane olukhulu (Z) (*trionum* - flower of an hour)
Annual, straggly herb, up to 1,5 m. Widespread weed in warm regions, SA to S Europe, Asia, Austr, origin uncertain. Sparsely hairy. **Leaves:** 20-60 mm diam, not lobed to deeply 3-5 lobed, margins toothed to lobed, stalks 10-40 mm. **Flowers:** Solitary, hidden amongst leaves, 25-40 mm diam, white to yellow with deep red centre, close by early afternoon, epicalyx of 12 bracts, calyx ± 25 mm, papery, veins green to purple, lobes united almost to tip, stalk ± 55 mm (Sep-Jun). **Fruit: Calyx becomes inflated,** enclosing fruit. **General:** Very variable. Used in traditional medicine to treat worms/internal parasites.

Rick Taylor

Hibiscus cannabinus

Darrel Plowes

Hibiscus dongolensis

Tom de Waal

Hibiscus cannabinus

Hibiscus microcarpus

Van Wyk & Malan

Hibiscus pusillus

Martin von Fintel

Martin von Fintel

Hibiscus surattensis

Martin von Fintel

Hibiscus trionum

Lawrence Peacock

Hibiscus trionum

287

Hibiscus vitifolius Wildestokroos (A) (*vitifolius* - leaves like a grape vine)

Shrub or perennial herb up to 1,5 m. In woodland, near watercourses, widespread. Velvety, roughly hairy or hairless. **Leaves:** 30-150 mm diam, not lobed or 3-5 lobed, margins toothed, 5-9 veins from base, stalks 20-70(180) mm, hairy. **Flowers:** Solitary, sometimes clustered towards ends of stems, 50-90 mm diam, yellow with dark red centre, **epicalyx with 10 bracts**, calyx lobes ± 15 x 10 mm, stalk 10 -15 mm (Oct-Apr). **Fruit: Capsule winged. Similar species:** *H. dongolensis* (p. 286).

Cienfuegosia (named after Bernardi Cienfuegos, Spanish botanist) - Epicalyx with 3-12 small bracts, sepals prominently ribbed, oil glands on ribs; seeds densely silky or woolly. America, Austr, Afr, ± 20 species, 3 in SA.

Cienfuegosia hildebrandtii Small Cotton Bush, Wedge-leaved False Hibiscus
(named after Johan Hildebrandt, 1847-1881)

Stiff, erect shrub, up to 1,5 m. Wooded grassland, on rocky hills, near water courses, KZN to Kenya. Hairless or thinly hairy. **Leaves:** ± 60 x 70 mm, bright **green above, grey beneath,wedge-shaped,** 3-5 veins from base, margins sharply toothed in upper half, densely hairy to almost hairless. **Flowers:** Solitary, 60-80 mm diam, yellow with dark red centre, stalk ± 25 mm (Nov-Jun). **Fruit: Seeds covered in silky golden brown floss. General:** Heavily browsed. **Similar species:** *C. gerrardii* Leaf blade rounded, heart-shaped at base, margins shallowly lobed not toothed.

Gossypium (*gossypium* - ancient name for cotton) - Herbs or shrubs, usually dotted all over in small black oil glands; leaves 3-9 lobed; epicalyx with 3 leaflike bracts; seeds densely woolly. Warm countries, ± 10 species, 3 in SA.

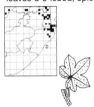

Gossypium herbaceum subsp. africanum Wild Cotton; Wildekatoen (A); kotini, litjinda (Sw); ugampokwe, umgawuma (Z) (*herbaceum* - succulent stem)

Scrambling shrub, up to 1,5(2) m. In woodland, thicket, KZN to Zim, Moz. **All parts covered in small black gland dots. Leaves:** ± 60 mm diam, 5-7 lobes, **rounded,** velvety, stalks 20-25 mm. **Flowers:** 50-60 mm diam, yellow with deep red centre, epicalyx of 3 bracts, ± 20 mm diam, calyx 8-10 mm (throughout year). **Fruit:** Capsule ± 20 mm diam. **General:** Used by birds to line nests. Extensively cultivated in the past for cotton, replaced by cultivars of *G. hirsutum*. **Similar species:** *Gossypioides kirkii* Leaf lobes narrowing to pointed tip; seeds not so woolly.

STERCULIACEAE - Cocoa/Sterculia Family Herbs, shrubs or trees. Star-shaped hairs usually present. Petals usually twisted in bud. Fruit dry, splitting into carpels when ripe. Economically important as the source of cocoa from the fermented seeds of the S American tree *Theobroma cacao* and ornamentals such as *Dombeya*, Bottle Tree *Brachychiton* and Chinese Parasol Tree *Firmiana*. Trop, warm regions, ± 67 genera, ± 1500 species, 7 genera in SA.
Melhania (from Mt Melhan in Arabia where one of the species grows) - Small shrubs; leaves often hairy; flowers solitary or in 2s, epicalyx 3 lobed, persistent. Afr, Madag, Arabia, ± 190 species, 13 in SA.

Melhania prostrata (*prostrata* - lying flat on ground)

Perennial shrublet, 0,2-0,6(1) m. In open woodland, grassland. Stems branched from near base, grey velvety with **reddish brown dots** (tiny clusters of hairs). **Leaves:** ± 90 x 5-20 mm, **thinly hairy to hairless above,** grey velvety beneath, margins entire to toothed, stalks ± 10 mm. **Flowers: Solitary or in pairs,** ± 30 mm diam, pale yellow, open in afternoon, epicalyx bracts grey velvety, long-pointed, ± 13 x 8 mm, sepals narrower, ± 13 mm (summer), scented at night. **General:** Browsed by game. **Similar species:** *Melhania didyma* Leaves broader, 25-40 mm, hairy above, margins shallowly toothed.

Melhania suluensis

Weak shrublet, 600-900 mm. On rocky slopes, in bushveld. New growth covered in pale brownish hairs. Stems annual. **Leaves:** 10-45 x 7-25 mm, **thin,** finely hairy, **silvery grey beneath,** tip broadly rounded, margins shallowly toothed, stalks 5-15 mm. **Flowers:** ± 20 mm diam, lemon yellow, 1-2 on stalks ± 12 mm (Sep-Jan).

Hermannia (named after Paul Herman, 1646-1695, professor of botany in Leyden, one of the first travellers and collectors to visit the Cape) - Herbs, shrubs; leaves alternate, stipules often leaflike; petals twisted, no epicalyx, calyx papery, sometimes ribbed; fruit dry, bristly. Attracts butterflies. Afr, Arabia, Austr, S America, ± 240 species, ± 150 in SA.

Hermannia auricoma isincamncame (Z) (*auricoma* - golden haired)

Stems prostrate. In grassland. Covered in glands and rough hairs. **Leaves:** Erect, ± 100 x 30 mm, square to heart-shaped at base, margins finely toothed; stalks ± 5 mm. **Flowers:** 1-2, nodding, calyx ± 12 mm, petals slightly longer, stem erect, ± 80 mm (Oct- Dec).

288

Hibiscus vitifolius

Darrel Plowes

Gossypium herbaceum

Darrel Plowes

Melhania didyma

Tony Abbott

Cienfuegosia hildebrandtii

Martin von Fintel

Melhania prostrata

Martin von Fintel

Melhania suluensis

Lorraine van Hooff

Hermannia auricoma

Lal Greene

Hermannia gerrardii **Gerrard's Yellow Hermannia; Bitterblaar (A)** (named after W T Gerrard, English naturalist and traveller who collected in Natal in 1860)
Coarse, prostrate herb, up to 900 mm. On rocky, grassy slopes, 1200-2250 m. **Stems** simple or branched, roughly hairy. **Leaves:** ± 120 x 75 mm, hairy, margins slightly toothed, stalks short. **Flowers:** In branched inflorescences; flowers pale yellow to orange, calyx lobes pointed (Mar-May).

Hermannia grandistipula **Yellow Granny Bonnets; ishongwe (Z)** (*grandistipula* - big stipules)
Shrublet up to 300 mm. In open grassland, Cape to Moz. Woody rootstock. **Stems** annual, **velvety**. **Leaves:** 40-70 x 18-30 mm, **densely, softly hairy**, margins ± toothed, stalks short, **stipules ± 10 x 3 mm, deeply divided**. **Flowers:** Nodding, in pairs, stem erect; petals ± 10 x 3 mm, yellow, calyx ± 12 mm diam, **inflated** (Sep-Apr). **General:** Infusions sprinkled on eggs to keep dogs from eating them.

Hermannia sandersonii **umakotegoyile (Z)** (named after John Sanderson, 1820-81, journalist, plant collector, honorary secretary, Natal Agricultural & Horticultural Society)
Low-growing shrublet. In grassland. Woody rootstock. Annual stems, ± leafless in lower half. **Leaves:** 20-50 x 7-35 mm, variable, sparsely hairy, velvety yellowish beneath, stipules ± 7 x 3 mm. **Flowers:** In terminal clusters, very hairy; petals recurved in upper half, ± 9 x 6 mm, calyx ± 7 mm, lobed (Sep-Mar).

HYPERICACEAE (sometimes included in CLUSIACEAE) - **Hypericum Family** Trees, shrubs, herbs, with clear or black dots. Includes ornamentals (St John's Wort), noxious weeds, some poisonous to livestock. Common in the Americas, ± 8 genera, ± 350 species, 1 genus in SA. *Hypericum* (Latin for St John's Wort) - Herbs or shrubs. Plants of this genus have been used for medicinal and magical purposes since earliest times. Now considered effective in treatment of depression. Introduced weed in the foothills of the Drakensberg is *H. patulum*. About 350 species, ± 7 in SA.

Hypericum aethiopicum subsp. *sonderi* **Small Hypericum; Vlieëpisbossie (A); bohoho, hoila, tabane (SS); isimayisane, isimonyo, isivumelwane, unsukumbili (Z)**
(*aethiopicum* - from Africa; *sonderi* named after Otto Sonder, 1812-81, German apothecary and botanist)
Tufted perennial herb, 200-450(600) mm. In open grassland, coast to 1900 m, E Cape to Trop Afr. **Stems** erect, mostly unbranched, with black dots. **Leaves:** In opposite pairs, stalkless, ± 20 x 15 mm, margins usually with black dots. **Flowers:** Flowers ± 25 mm diam, yellow tinged reddish, sepals reddish brown, black dotted (Sep-Jan). **General:** Conspicuous after veld fires. Attracts many insects. Used in traditional medicine for girls at puberty and to treat backache, kidney and abdominal complaints, heal sores and venereal diseases. Pretty, delicate garden plant.

Hypericum lalandii **Spindly Hypericum, Laland's St Johns Wort; Laland-se-Sint Janskruid (A); bohlokoana (SS)** (named after Pierre Delalande, 1787-1823, French naturalist)
Erect herb, 40-500 mm. In grassland, marshy areas, coast to 2100 m, from SW Cape to Sudan. **Stems** slender, **4 angled**. **Leaves:** 8-20 x 5 mm, held erect, margins recurved, stalkless. **Flowers:** Solitary or few in terminal clusters, 20-30 mm diam, yellow or orange, no dark dots, sepals tapering to fine point, ribbed (Sep-Mar).

PASSIFLORACEAE - **Granadilla Family** Climbers with tendrils (for description see p. 538). *Adenia* (for description see p. 68).

Adenia digitata **Finger-leaved Adenia; Bobbejaangif (A); isifulwane, umaphatha, umbulelo, utshwala benyoni (Z)** (see p. 68)

CACTACEAE - **Cactus/Prickly Pear Family** Spiny succulents. Leaves rudimentary. Flowers regular. Fruit usually fleshy. Popular container and garden plants. Widespread in Americas, ± 97 genera, ± 1400 species, 7 genera in SA, only 1 indigenous. *Opuntia* (named after a town in Greece) - **Prickly Pear/Jointed Cactus** Succulent shrubs. A number have become invasive pests around the world. N and S America, ± 240 species, 11 in SA, all aliens.

★ *Opuntia stricta* **Australian Pest Pear; Suurturksvy (A)** (*stricta* - straight, erect)
Spreading, much branched shrub, up to 1,5(2) m. **Declared weed** (from Central and South America). Joints longer than broad, green to blue-green, spines ± 40 mm or absent; flowers ± 70 mm, yellow (Nov-Jan). Fruits red turning purple, ± 50 mm, narrowing at base, smooth, spineless. (See p. 466) **Similar species:** ★ *O. ficus-indica* [= *O. megacantha*] **Sweet Prickly Pear; Turksvy (A); umthelekisi (Z)** Succulent shrub 1,5-3(5) m. **Declared weed. Joints thick, grey-green**, spines ± 30 mm or absent. Flowers ± 70 mm, yellow or orange (Oct-Dec). Fruit ± 80 mm, oval, **yellowish to reddish, covered in spines**. Planted for edible fruits, fodder, security hedging. (See p. 68)

Pereskia (named after N F Pieresc, 1580,1637, French patron of botany) - Trees, shrubs, scramblers (for description see p. 158).

★ *Pereskia aculeata* **Barbados Gooseberry; Barbadosstekelbessie (A)** (see p. 158)

Hermannia gerrardii

Hypericum aethiopicum

Hermannia grandistipula

Hermannia grandistipula

Hermannia sandersonii

Hypericum lalandii

Adenia digitata

★ Opuntia stricta

★ Pereskia aculeata

291

THYMELAEACEAE - **Fibre-bark/Gonna Family** Shrubs or small trees. Flowers in terminal inflorescences, calyx tubular, sepals petal-like, petals small or absent. Cosmop, ± 53 genera, ± 750 species, 9 genera in SA. *Gnidia* (after the Greek city, Knidos) - Perennial herbs or shrubs; sepals erect, spreading or reflexed, coloured, petals alternating with calyx lobes or sometimes missing. Mostly Trop and S Afr, ± 140 species, ± 100 in SA.

Gnidia anthylloides [= *Lasiosiphon anthylloides*] **Brandbossie (A); indolo, intozwane, isidikili esikhulu (Z)** (resembling *Anthyllis*)

Shrublet, up to 600 mm. In grassland, scrub, coast to midlands. Stems softly hairy at first. **Leaves: Alternate, soft, silky, closely overlapping, crowded on younger parts of stems.** Flowers: In dense, terminal inflorescences, ± 50 mm diam; flowers shiny, bright lemon yellow, petals tiny or absent, **calyx tube densely woolly** outside, sepals blunt (blooms throughout year), sweetly scented. **General:** Poisonous to stock. Used in traditional medicine to treat coughs, fevers, bad dreams and snakebite.

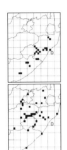

Gnidia baurii (named after Rev Leopold Baur, 1825-1889, pharmacist, bot collector; came to Cape in 1847)

Tufted perennial, up to 1 m. In grassland. Stems slender, hairy at first, leaf scars prominent. **Leaves:** Opposite, ± 15 x 3 mm, tips pointed, silky beneath. **Flowers:** At ends of branches, calyx tube ± 10 mm, pale yellow, silky outside, sepals oval, tips pointed, petals 8, blunt, thick (Oct-Jan).

***Gnidia burchellii* Harpuisbossie (A)** (named after William Burchell, 1781-1863, naturalist, traveller, artist, author; in SA 1810-15, published 'Travels in the Interior of Southern Africa')

Much branched shrub, up to 1 m. In dry woodland. Stems woody, branched, young branches softly hairy. **Leaves:** Alternate, ± 15 x 2 mm, broader above, finely hairy. **Flowers:** In terminal, stalkless inflorescences, + 25 mm diam, calyx tube ± 18 mm, **densely hairy outside,** sepals oval, 5 x 2 mm, petals tiny (Jul).

Gnidia caffra [= *Lasiosiphon caffer*] **Gifbossie (A); umshanyelo (Sw)** (*caffra* - from Kaffraria, old name for E Cape)

Erect, slender shrublet, up to 0,5(1) m. In grassland, on rocky outcrops. Underground tuber. Stems woody at base, sparsely, softly hairy. **Leaves:** Alternate, overlapping, narrow, ± 30 x 6 mm, tips **sharply pointed. Flowers:** In loose, many-flowered inflorescences; flowers shiny, lemon yellow, ± 10 mm diam, sepals large, petals tiny (Aug-Jan). **General:** Conspicuous after fires. Used as a broom.

Gnidia capitata [= *Lasiosiphon capitatus*] **Gifbossie, Kerriebossie (A); setele, thopa-e-nyenyane (SS); isidikili (Z)** (*capitata* - head-shaped)

Branching shrublet, 200-750 mm. In rocky grassland. Stems woody, red-brown, leafy. **Leaves: Narrow,** ± 30 x 6 mm, sharply pointed, green to **blue-grey. Flowers:** In terminal inflorescences, surrounded by wider leaves, stems 50-80 mm; flowers ± 6 mm diam, calyx tube 15-25 mm, silky hairy, sepals mustard yellow above, silky beneath, petals small, scalelike (blooms throughout year). **General:** Conspicuous after fires. Used to cure headaches and as a divining torch to discover thieves.

Gnidia cuneata [= *Lasiosiphon meisnerianus*] **Koorsbossie (A); isidikili (Z)** (*cuneata* - wedge-shaped)

Much branched shrub, up to 2(3) m. In tall mixed grassland, on forest margins. Branches stout, finely hairy at first. **Leaves:** Alternate, ± 25 x 5 mm, narrowing to base, silky. **Flowers:** In terminal inflorescences, calyx tube 20-30 mm, long straight hairs below, finely hairy above, lobes blunt, ± 5 x 2 mm, petals tiny (Aug-Apr).

Gnidia kraussiana [= *Lasiosiphon kraussii*] **Lesser Yellow Head; Harige Gifbossie (A); thobeha, thopa (SS); umsilawenge (Sw,Z); inhlashane, isidikili, umfukuzane, umfuzane (Z)** (named after Christian Krauss, 1812-90, German scientist, traveller, collector; in SA 1839-40)

Robust shrublet, up to 500 mm. In grassland, coast to 2130 m, E Cape to Trop Afr. Rootstock woody, tuberous. **Stems yellow aging red-brown,** unbranched; plant, hairless or densely hairy. **Leaves:** Variable, ± 30 x 10 mm, **grey to yellow-green,** upper leaves narrower, tips pointed. **Flowers:** In compact, terminal inflorescences, ± 40 mm diam, **surrounded by ring of overlapping leaves, stems 30-100 mm;** flowers ± 15 mm diam, yellow, calyx tube slender, silky (Jun-Dec), scented. **General:** Conspicuous after burns. Poisonous to stock. Used in traditional medicine to treat stomach and chest complaints, lumbago, toothache, snakebite and also to heal fractured limbs in stock. Used during pregnancy to ensure easy childbirth.

Gnidia anthylloides

Wally Menne

Gnidia burchellii

Lorraine van Hooff

Gnidia capitata

Lorraine van Hooff

Gnidia cuneata

Ld Greene

Gnidia caffra

Tom de Waal

Gnidia baurii

Tony Abbott

Gnidia kraussiana

Godfrey Symons

Gnidia kraussiana

Tom de Waal

Gnidia kraussiana

Tony Abbott

293

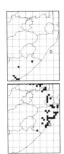

Gnidia racemosa [= *Lasiosiphon racemosa*] (*racemosa* - simple, elongate inflorescence)

Shrublet, up to 600 mm. Sparsely branched, stems long, green, branchlets erect, straight, slender. **Leaves:** ± 15 x 7 mm, erect to spreading. **Flowers:** In axils towards tips of branches; flowers yellow, calyx with long hairs (summer).

Gnidia splendens [= *Lasiosiphon splendens*] **Lesser Yellow Head; umshanyelo (Sw); umfukuzane (Z)** (*splendens* - shining)

Slender branching shrub, up to 1(3) m. In scrubby grassland. Woody at base. Stems densely leafy in upper parts, bark reddish. **Leaves:** Alternate, well spaced, **narrow**, ± 25 x 6 mm, **silvery hairy**, soft, grey-green. **Flowers:** In small clusters, held beyond leaves; flowers ± 10 mm diam, lemon yellow, calyx tube ± 15 mm, white hairy, sepals ± 5 mm, petals tiny (Jun-Mar). **General:** Flowers turn red when old. Used in traditional medicine to treat lumbago, sore throats and snakebite. Used as a broom.

Gnidia triplinervis [= *Lasiosiphon triplinervis*] (*triplinervis* - three-nerves)

Much branched, spindly shrub, up to 2 m. In grassland, coast to mountains. Stems slender, leaf scars small but prominent, **leaves and stems hairless**. **Leaves:** Alternate, narrowing to pointed tips, midrib prominent beneath. **Flowers:** In terminal clusters; flowers yellow, petals oval, **calyx tube silky**, ± 25 mm (Aug-May).

ONAGRACEAE - Evening Primrose Family Herbs. Cultivated as ornamentals, including the Fuchsias. Cosmop, especially Americas, ± 18 genera, ± 650 species, 4 genera in SA. *Ludwigia* (named after D G Ludwig, died 1773, German botanist) - Usually in swamps; petals 3-5 or absent, calyx 3-5 lobed. N America, ± 43 species, 10 in SA.

Ludwigia octovalvis **Shrubby Ludwigia** (*octovalvis* - 8 valved)

Robust, erect shrub, up to 1,2 (3) m. In damp, swampy areas, also in floating rafts of vegetation, widespread in the trop, coast to 1500 m. Stems fluted, hairy or not. When submerged, slender, erect, pink breathing roots emerge, ± 270 mm. **Leaves:** 7-140 x 1-40 mm, grey-green, finely veined, stalks ± 10 mm. **Flowers:** Yellow, ± 20 mm diam, open in the morning (blooms throughout year). **Fruit:** Capsule ± 45 x 8 mm, ribbed, with persistent calyx. **General:** Subsp. *sessiliflora*, densely hairy. Visited by butterflies of Lycaenidae and Hesperidae families.

Ludwigia stolonifera **Creeping Ludwigia** (*stolonifera* - runners or shoots)

Herb with prostrate or erect stems up to 500 mm. In damp places or floating on water, Afr to Iraq. Stems root at nodes, some slightly inflated. **Breathing roots erect, white when floating. Leaves:** 20-90 x 5-17 mm, floating leaves broader, dark green, shiny, finely veined, stalks ± 20 mm. **Flowers:** Solitary, in leaf axils, ± 35 m diam, pale yellow, dark spot at base of petals, closed in early afternoon (blooms throughout year). **Fruit:** Capsule 10-30 x 3-4 mm, ribs dark. **General:** Visited by ants, thrips.

Oenothera (*oinos* - wine, *thera* - imbibing) - Annual, biennial or perennial herbs; flowers usually open in evening, close before midday. Popular ornamentals. N and S America, naturalised in Old World, ± 110 species, 15 in SA.

★ ***Oenothera stricta*** **Yellow Evening Primrose; Geelaandblom (A)** (*stricta* - stiff, upright)

Perennial herb, 0,3-1m. Weed on roadsides, disturbed areas, from S Chile, Argentina. Stout tap root. Stems usually unbranched, tinged red. Leaves mostly basal, ± 200 m, margins with widely spaced, shallow teeth. Flowers ± 60 mm diam, bright yellow fading pinkish red, opening at sunset (Sep-Jan), lovely scent at night. Fruit a cylindrical capsule ± 30 x 4 mm. Visited by moths. Cultivated as a garden plant.

APIACEAE (UMBELLIFERAE) - **Carrot Family** Mostly herbs, usually aromatic. Stems often with pith or hollow internodes. Leaves usually much divided, stalk sheathing at base. Flowers in flat-topped inflorescences. Fruit carpels dry, often ribbed, winged, hairy or prickly. Economically important as food plants, Carrots, Parsnips, Celery, Parsley and herbs - Aniseed, Dill, Chervil, Fennel. Cosmop, ± 446 genera, ± 3540 species, 47 genera in SA. *Lichtensteinia* (named after Prof von Lichtenstein, German botanical explorer in the Cape, 1803-06) - Perennial herbs with aromatic juice; flowers in compressed terminal inflorescences. 7 species in SA.

Lichtensteinia kolbeana

Herb, up to 750 mm. In grassland. **Leaves:** Basal, ± 75-100 x 50-75 mm, **fresh green until fruiting**, deeply cut, leaflets oval, toothed, rachis winged, toothed, stalks sheathing stem. **Flowers:** In slender branching inflorescences, 8-12 rays. **Fruit:** Roundish oval. **Similar species:** *L. interrupta* Basal leaves wither after flowering.

Gnidia racemosa

Gnidia splendens

Gnidia triplinervis

Ludwigia octovalvis

Lichtensteinia kolbeana

Ludwigia stolonifera

★ *Oenothera stricta*

★ *Oenothera stricta*

Ludwigia stolonifera

295

Sium (*sion* - Greek name for a marsh plant) - Robust herbs; fruit conspicuously ribbed. About 14 species, 1 in SA.

Sium repandum Water Parsnip; Tandpynwortel (A) (*repandum* - uneven, undulating margin)

Robust herb, up to 1,5 m. In water and on banks of streams, SA to Tanz. Rhizome creeping, **stem ribbed, hollow. Leaves:** ± 300 mm; ± 12 leaflets, **each ± 100 x 20 mm,** stalkless, curved forwards, margins finely, regularly toothed, **stalks short, stout, hollow, partially sheathing stem. Flowers:** In terminal branched inflorescences; flowers white or yellowish (Jan-Apr). **General:** Leaves resemble a fern.

Berula (Latin name for Water Cress) - Fruit ribs not conspicuous. Afr, Eurasia, N America, 1 genus, 1 species.

Berula erecta Toothache Root, Giant Water Parsnip; Tandpynwortel (A); ibophwani (Z)
(*erecta* - upright)

Robust herb, up to 2,5 m. In marshy areas, on streambanks. Stem hollow, grooved. **Leaves:** ± 500 mm; 7-12 pairs leaflets, **10-80 mm,** margins irregularly toothed, **stalks ± 120 mm, narrowly sheathing stem. Flowers: In leafy inflorescences** ± 60 mm diam; flowers white (Dec-Mar). **General:** Used in traditional medicine, roots held in mouth for toothache. Reputed to poison cattle at certain times of the year.

Peucedanum (Greek name for *Ferula* - Fennel) - Perennial herbs; leaves mostly basal, compound or finely divided; flowers in compound inflorescence; fruits flattened, ribbed and winged. Europe, Asia, Afr, ± 200 species, ± 30 in SA.

Peucedanum caffrum Wild Parsley; Pietersielietabak, Tamboekietwak (A); tloro-eangoale (SS); isingcina, nhlashane (Z)

Herb, up to 1 m, in dense clumps. In grassland, on rocky slopes. **Leaves:** In basal cluster, 75-150 mm, much divided into lobed segments, 15-25 mm, stalks ± 150 mm. **Flowers:** In terminal inflorescences, stalks/rays long, flowers yellow (Oct-Jan). **Fruit:** Large, 15 x 8 mm. **General:** Used in traditional medicine to treat diarrhoea.

Peucedanum capense Large Wild Carrot; Lidbossie (A); tloro-ngoale (SS)

Stiffly erect shrub, up to 1,2 m. In rocky mountain grassland. Stem slightly ribbed, brittle, hollow, leaves along its length. **Leaves:** Compound, ± 120 mm, leaflets ± 50 x 20 mm, lobed, margins ± entire. **Flowers:** In branching inflorescences, clusters with very slender stalks/rays, flowers yellow (Dec-Mar). **Fruit:** Flat, 6 x 4 mm.

Peucedanum thodei Mountain Wild Carrot; umphondovu (Z) (named after Justus Thode)

Robust herb, up to 2 m. Streambanks, 1600-2440 m. Stems square, grooved, hollow, green to purplish red. **Leaves:** Compound, lower ± 600 mm; leaflets lobed, lobes 20-60 x 10-20 mm, irregularly toothed, stalks sheathing stem, purplish red; upper stem leaves smaller. **Flowers:** In terminal, branched inflorescences; flowers tiny, yellowish green (Dec-Feb). **Fruit:** 5-6 mm, ridged. **General:** Reputed to be used by sangomas to bring rain, but only in times of extreme drought.

EBENACEAE - Ebony Family Trees, shrubs. Flowers bisexual, or unisexual, with sexes on different plants. Petals twisted in bud. Fruit fleshy, soft or tough skinned. Economically important for timber, especially Macassar Ebony, also for Persimmon fruit. Mainly trop, ± 2 genera, ± 485 species, 2 genera in SA. ***Diospyros*** (*dios* - divine; *pyros* - grain of wheat - an edible plant) - Calyx usually persisting and enlarging in fruit. Trop, subtrop, ± 500 species, ± 21 in SA.

Diospyros galpinii Dwarf Hairy Jackalberry; siphiphabantwana (Sw); impishimpishi, indodemnyama, inqwambi (Z) (named after Ernest Galpin, 1858-1941, banker, amateur botanist)

Shrublet, up to 600 mm. In woodland, KZN to Moz. **Young stems covered in tawny hairs,** older stems smooth. **Leaves:** Alternate, 4-130 x 3-65 mm, thick, hairy at first, smooth above later, **densely velvety reddish brown beneath,** veins prominent, stalks short. **Flowers:** Solitary, ± 13 mm, creamy white, calyx densely hairy, ± 10 mm, stalk ± 25 mm (Sep-Jan), scented. **Fruit:** Roundish, ± 20 x 15 mm diam, densely hairy, enlarged calyx ± 30 mm. **General:** Fruit edible. Stems used to clean teeth.

OLEACEAE - Olive/Jasmine Family Trees, shrubs, climbers. Leaves usually opposite. Flower parts in 2s, petals united into tube at base. Fruit dry or fleshy. Economically important for olive oil, ash timber and ornamentals such as Privet, Lilac, Jasmine, Forsythia. Subcosmop, ± 24 genera, ± 615 species, 6 genera in SA.
Menodora (*menos* - force, vigour; *dora* - skin) - Leaves toothed, entire or lobed. Americas, Afr, ± 24 species, 3 in SA.

Menodora africana Balbossie (A)

Slender herb, up to 150 mm in flower (maturing 250 mm). In grassland, KZN to Bots. Woody base, many stems, slender, ridged, rough. **Leaves:** ± 15 mm, **narrowly divided. Flowers:** Solitary, red in bud, yellow tinged reddish when open, ± 20 mm diam, **calyx rough, lobes finely divided** (Oct-Jan). **Fruit:** 2 lobed papery capsule, ± 9 mm, (sometimes only 1 lobe develops), splitting in half when ripe.

Trevor Coleman

Tony Abbott

Sium repandum

Berula erecta

Tony Abbott

Geoff Nichols

Martin von Fintel

Peucedanum caffrum

Peucedanum capense

Peucedanum thodei

David Johnson

Van Wyk & Malan

Martin von Fintel

Diospyros galpinii

Menodora africana

Menodora africana

297

GENTIANACEAE - Gentian Family Herbs, sometimes aquatic (for description see p. 414). *Sebaea* (named after Albert Seba, 1665-1736, Dutch naturalist and author) - Herbs; leaves often stalkless, eared at base; flowers twisted in bud, calyx segments keeled or winged. Afr, Madag, India, Austr, New Zealand, ± 115 species, ± 45 in SA.

Sebaea grandis **Large-flowered Sebaea, Primrose Gentian; liphalana, mipa, petle, phalana (SS); umalopha omncane (Z)** (*grandis* - large, refers to the flowers)
Annual herb, up to 350 mm. In grassland, marshy areas, SA to Trop Afr. Stems 4 angled, narrowly winged, simple or branched. **Leaves:** ± 40 x 15 mm. **Flowers:** Few, terminal, ± 30 mm diam, white to creamy yellow, petals pointed, **tube ± 23 mm**, stamens not protruding, stigma 2 lobed, calyx lobes ± 25 mm, tips pointed, **wings ± 2 mm wide near base** (Dec-May). **General:** Used as a love charm emetic. (See p. 164)

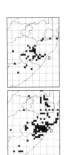

Sebaea natalensis
Erect herb, up to 250 mm. In vleis, damp grassland, up to 2100 m. Branched from base. **Leaves:** ± 13 x 15 mm, tips rounded or pointed. **Flowers:** In dense inflorescences; flowers ± 15 mm diam, **petals rounded at tip, tube short 5-7 mm**, yellow, anthers tipped with short, small, round gland, calyx dries strawlike (Nov-Apr).

Sebaea sedoides **isivumelwane esikhulu, umanqweyana, umsolo (Z)** (*sedoides* - resembles *Sedum*, Stone Crop)
Herbs, 200-650 mm. In damp grassland, marshes, SA to Zim. Woody rootstock. Stems simple or branched. **Leaves:** ± 25 mm diam, or ± 15 x 6 mm. **Flowers:** In dense, small or large inflorescences, **bracts numerous**, erect; **flowers small**, 5-15 mm diam, tube 3-8 mm, **usually longer than petals, tips mostly rounded**, yellow, creamy white, calyx lobes brittle when dry, joined at base, keeled (Dec-May). **General:** 3 varieties, differing in size and shape of flowers and inflorescences. Used in traditional medicine as enemas for children and as a love charm emetic.

MENYANTHACEAE - Cosmop, 4 genera, ± 40 species, 1 genus in SA. *Nymphoides* (resembling *Nymphaea*) - Aquatic herbs; leaves floating; flowers solitary, on long stalks, lobes fringed; fruit a capsule. Trop and temp, 5 species in SA.

Nymphoides thunbergiana **Small Yellow Waterlily; Geelwaterlelie (A)**
Perennial aquatic herb. In pools, rivers, up to 1600 m, Cape to Zam. Rhizome short, erect. **Leaves:** 30-100(200) mm diam, firm, shiny yellow-green, red-brown beneath. **Flowers:** In clusters of 5-20, **attached some distance away from leaf blade**; flowers 15-30 mm diam, yellow, stalks 20-60 mm (Oct-May), closed at midday. **Roots from base of cluster. Fruit:** Capsule **oval, blunt tipped. General:** Excellent small pond subject. **Similar species:** *N. indica* subsp. *occidentalis* Flowers white with yellow throat. *N. rautanenii* Annual; stolons floating; leaves thin, blue-green; flowers 8-10 mm diam, stalks 5-25 mm; capsule round. *N. forbesiana* S KZN Drakensberg (Moz); leaves leathery, blue-green; less than 10 flowers in clusters.

APOCYNACEAE - Impala Lily Family Trees, shrubs, woody climbers (for description see p. 416). *Strophanthus* (*strophe* - twist; *anthos* - flower) - Scrambling shrubs or lianas. Seeds poisonous, used as an arrow poison in some regions. The plants also have powerful medicinal properties. Afr, Trop Asia, ± 50 species, 5 in SA.

Strophanthus gerrardii **Spider Flower Poison Rope/Strophanthus; ukukhukhumeza (X); ubuhlungubendlovu (Z)** (named after William Gerrard, naturalist; collected in KZN in 1860)
Slender climber, up to 2 m. In dry woodland or forest, KZN to Moz. Bark reddish brown, with raised white dots, **older stems grey, forming irregular, corky outgrowths. Leaves:** 25-55 x 10-20 mm, pale silvery beneath. **Flowers:** Solitary, on short side branchlets, tube pink to mauve, ± 14 x 10 mm, **petal lobes yellow, spreading**, ± 50 mm, calyx 5-9 mm (Sep-Nov). **Fruit:** 2 lobed, widely spreading, 150-200 x 20-30 mm, tapering to point, rough, brown, with raised dots. **General:** Grown from seed. Used in traditional medicine and as a charm to ensure good crops.

Strophanthus petersianus **Sand Forest Poison Rope/Strophanthus; ubuhlungubendlovu (Z)** (named after Prof Wilhelm Peters, 1815-1863, German botanist who collected in Moz)
Scrambling shrub. In dry woodland, coastal scrub, KZN to Zim, Moz. Bark brown to grey, with raised dots. **Hairless. Leaves:** 30-80(110) x 15-40 mm. **Flowers:** 1-3 on side twigs, tube 10-20 mm, creamy white within, pinkish outside, petal lobes slender, **dangling**, spirally twisted, 60-140 mm, orange to reddish brown, calyx 10-15 mm (Sep-Nov). **Fruit:** Lobes spreading, 200-300 x 30-40 mm, smooth, brown. **General:** Used in traditional medicine and as a charm against evil. (See p. 166) **Similar species:** *S. luteolus* **Golden Strophanthus** Leaves faintly hairy along margins; flowers smaller, petal lobes 50-80 mm, trailing; fruit ± 220 x 15 mm, tapering to thickened tip.

Sebaea grandis   *Sebaea natalensis*   *Sebaea sedoides*

Sebaea natalensis   *Nymphoides thunbergiana*

Strophanthus gerrardii   *Strophanthus gerrardii*   *Strophanthus luteolus*

Strophanthus petersianus   *Strophanthus petersianus*

PERIPLOCACEAE - Periploca Family Perennial herbs, shrubs, lianas, with milky latex (for description see p. 542).
Cryptolepis (*crypto* - hidden; *lepis* - scale, refers to hidden corona) - Scrambling twiners; latex red; leaves thin, hairless; flower tube bell-like with small pocketlike flaps in sinus of lobes. Trop, subtrop Afr, India, 12 species, 5 in SA.

Cryptolepis oblongifolia Red-stemmed Cryptolepis; Bokhoring (A) (*oblongifolia* - oblong leaf)

Erect, **much branched shrub**, 0,5-1 m. Among rocks in open, dry grassland, KZN to Kenya. Stems slender, reddish brown. **Leaves:** Erect, ranked along stems, 12-50 x 12 mm. **Flowers:** 3-15 in branched clusters; flowers yellowish green, lobed more than halfway, tube 1,5-2,5 mm, **lobes short, ± 3 x 1 mm**, reflexed, with tiny tooth between lobes; corolline corona fused ± half way up, lobes clublike, fleshy, ± 1 mm (Nov-Feb). **Fruit:** Paired, erect, ± 80 x 2-10 mm. **General:** Leaves eaten as food.

ASCLEPIADACEAE - Milkweed Family Herbs, shrubs, vines, epiphytes or succulents, with milky latex (for description see p. 578). ***Xysmalobium*** (*xysma* - thread; *lobos* - lobes) - Perennial, non-climbing herbs (for description see p.542).

Xysmalobium tysonianum Sulphur Cartwheel (named after plant collector William Tyson, 1851-1920)

Herb, up to 230 mm. In open grasslands, on mountain slopes, 1200-2600 m. Deep cylindrical rootstock. **Stems reclining or prostrate. Leaves:** 35-53 x 12-20 mm, ± leathery. **Flowers: Solitary, terminal roundish inflorescences, stems 50-100 mm**; flowers **yellowish**, lobes erect, oval, ± 35-25 mm, tips curved inwards, **corona lobes longer than petals** (Nov-Feb), sweet smelling. **Fruit:** Spindle-shaped. **General:** Leaves described as smelling like 'smelly feet'.

Schizoglossum (*schizo* - cut or split; *glossa* - tongue) - Herbs with carrotlike stem tuber (for description see p. 544).

Schizoglossum flavum Yellow Split-tongue/Schizoglossum (*flavum* - yellow)

Erect, unbranched herb, 70-270 mm. In stony grassland, (90)900-2250 m, SA endemic. Simple stem tuber or with swollen branches. **Leaves:** In pairs, 30-70 x 10-20 mm, hairy. **Flowers:** 5-10 in 3-5 inflorescences, stems 10-50 mm; flowers erect, lobes oblong 7-9 x 3-4 mm, **bright yellow, flat, outer surface hairless, corona simple**, much longer than style tip, no appendages on inner face (Sep-Feb).

Schizoglossum stenoglossum Simple Split-tongue/Schizoglossum (*stenos* - narrow; *glossa* - tongue, refers to narrow corona lobes)

160-510 mm. In mountain grassland, 300-2700 m. Stems usually solitary. **Leaves:** In pairs, 45-58 x 5-15 mm. **Flowers:** Lobes **oblong, 8-9 x 3 mm, flat, hairless,** dark brown or maroon, **corona lobes simple** (Oct-Jan). **Fruit:** Solitary, erect, 45 mm. **General:** Subsp. *flavum*, 1500-2100 m; leaves ± 15 mm wide, **greenish yellow with brown stripes**; flower lobes hairy, corona lobe tips inflexed. *Subsp. latifolium*, 1050-2700 m; flower lobes **dark maroon or brown and striped (greenish yellow)**, corona lobe tips reflexed. Subsp. *stenoglossum,* **300-1500 m**; leaves ± 9 mm wide; flower lobes **dark maroon or purplish brown, striped**. (See p. 578)

Aspidonepsis - Corona lobes with central recess. SA endemic, 5 species (for description see p. 168).

Aspidonepsis cognata [= *Asclepias cognata*] Large Suncup (*cognitus* - now understood, refers to the confusion in identifying it as a species separate from *Aspidonepsis flava* and *A. diploglossa*)

Slender, erect, unbranched herb, 180-550 mm. Scattered, in mountain grassland, in damp areas near streams, (60)1200-2100 m. Stem tuber ± 7 mm diam. **Leaves:** Spreading to erect, 10-68 x 0,5-6 mm, margins smooth or rolled under. **Flowers:** 1-7 in clustered, stalkless inflorescences; flower lobes spreading, 6-10 x 2,5-6 mm, **yellow, brownish, purple outside, corona lobes large, bonnet-shaped, overtopping style tip** and tonguelike sinus appendage (Nov-Jan). **Fruit:** Usually solitary, erect. (See p. 168)

Aspidonepsis flava [= *Asclepias flava*] Small Suncup (*flavus* - pale yellow)

Erect, slender herb, 180-475 mm. In grassland, (450)600-2000 m. Stems 1(3), unbranched. **Leaves:** 7-80 x 0,5-7 mm. **Flowers:** 4-20 in 1-3 clustered, stalkless inflorescences; flower lobes spreading, reflexed, ± 5 x 3 mm, **pale yellow, corona lobes small, boxing glove-shaped, with reflexed armlike upper appendages and sausage-shaped sinus/recess appendage** (Nov-Jan). **Fruit:** Solitary, erect, smooth. **Similar species:** *A. diploglossa* Up to 500 mm; at 1500-2400 m; flowers larger, 4-9 x 6-13 mm, corona lobes larger, cup-shaped, with broad central appendage in the sinus/recess, not exceeding the flower centre, anther appendages deeply cleft.

Pachycarpus (*pachys* - thick; *karpos* - fruit) - Erect perennial herbs (for description see p. 580).

Pachycarpus grandiflorus Grand Pachycarpus, Grand Thick-fruit (see p. 580)

Cryptolepis oblongifolia

Xysmalobium tysonianum

Schizoglossum flavum

Van Wyk & Malan

Wally Menne

Martin von Fintel

Xysmalobium tysonianum

Schizoglossum stenoglossum

Tony Abbott

Pam Cooke

Aspidonepsis cognata

Aspidonepsis diploglossa

Aspidonepsis flava

Lal Greene

Rosemary Williams

Lal Greene

Pachycarpus grandiflorus

Trevor Coleman

Asclepias (named after Aesculapius, immortalised as god of medicine)- Perennial herbs (for description see p. 416).

Asclepias aurea Golden Star Drops; mohlatsisa (SS) *(aureus* - golden yellow)
Herb, 145-520 mm. In unburnt grassland, on stony hillsides, 1000-2000 m, KZN to Zim. 1-6 annual, **slender, erect** stems, branched in basal half. **Leaves:** 6-85 x **± 1 mm, margins strongly rolled under**, midrib prominent below. **Flowers: 2- 4**, in 1-7 inflorescences, **stems long, 44-140 mm; flowers star-shaped**, held at same level, **yellow**, lobes ± 5 x 2 mm (Sep-Feb). **Fruit:** Spreading-erect, **slender, sickle-shaped**, 45-80 x **3-6 mm**, tip beaked. **General:** Flowers visited by ants. Rootstock eaten. Sotho name means 'he who causes vomiting' and it is used as an emetic.

Stapelia (named after Dutch physician and botanist Johannes von Stapel,died 1636) - Perennial succulent herbs; roots fibrous; flowers large, upper surface wrinkled, trembling hairs, lobes triangular, curling and twisting when old, inner staminal corona divided into 2 long hornlike appendages which overtop the style tip, with unpleasant smell to attract pollinating flies. Widely cultivated with many horticultural hybrids.

Stapelia gigantea Giant Stapelia, Giant Carrion Flower; Aasblom (A); ililo elikhulu, isihlehle, uzililo (Z) *(giganteus* - gigantic, refers to very large flowers)
75-200 mm. In arid, sparsely vegetated areas, in thicket, E Cape to Bots, Zim, Zam, Malawi. Stems much branched, 11-32 mm diam, 4 angled, velvety, angles flattened, edged with small teeth. **Flowers: Very large**, 250-400 mm, **wrinkled**, dull yellow to light reddish purple with reddish lines, covered with long purplish hairs, lobes spreading, 70-160 x 30-70 mm (Mar-May), strong, foetid smell. **Fruit:** Paired, erect, spindlelike, 125-165 x 17-20 mm, tapering to blunt, hooked tip. **General:** Used in traditional medicine to treat hysteria and pain. Used in sorcery as a poison, reportedly capable of causing death. One of the largest flowers in the plant kingdom.

Orbeopsis (resembles *Orbea*) - No corolline corona or cushion ring. Trop, subtrop Afr, 10 species, 8 in S Afr.

Orbeopsis lutea [= *Caralluma lutea*] Yellow Carrion Flower; Geelaasblom, Kopseerblom, Slang-gwaap (A) *(lutea* - golden yellow)
Perennial succulent herb. 40-150 mm. In thorn and mopane veld, KZN to Zim. Stems tightly clustered, freely branched, 12-20 mm wide, 4 angled, angles with short stout, sharply pointed ± horizontally spreading-erect tubercles tipped with a pointed tooth, green mottled with dull purple. **Flowers:** 6-26, in stalkless inflorescences, 38-65 mm diam, upper surface wrinkled, **yellow, lobes long**, spreading, **tips tapering to long point**, margins with vibrating purple hairs (Jan-Mar). Evil smelling, like rotten fish. **Fruit:** Erect, spindle-shaped, ± 90 mm, stout. **General:** Stems and roots eaten raw.

CONVOLVULACEAE - Morning Glory Family Herbs, shrubs, with trailing or twining stems (for description see p. 176). ***Cuscuta*** (name for dodder) - Twining, parasitic; stems yellow; no leaves. Warm, temp regions, ± 80 species, ± 15 in SA.

★ *Cuscuta campestris* Dodder; unyendenyende (Z) *(campestris* - growing in fields)
Stems very slender, twining, **yellowish**. Forms dense masses, parasitic. Cosmop, a noxious weed, from N America. Leaves absent. Flowers ± 4 mm diam, white, **in clusters** (Nov-Apr). Fruits greenish yellow capsules. **Similar species:**
C. cassytoides Stems whitish, succulent; flowers solitary or in groups of 2-3.

Hewittia (named after John Hewitt, 1880-1961, naturalist, director of Albany Museum for 40 years) - Twining, hairy herb; leaves heart-shaped, entire, angled or 3 lobed; 1-3 flowers. Trop, Afr, Asia, Malaysia, Polynesia, 1 species.

Hewittia malabarica (= *H. sublobata*) Hewitt's Dwarf Morning Glory; ihlanzandulo (Z)
Perennial, twining herb, stems 1-2 m. In valleys, on floodplains, widespread. Velvety hairy throughout. **Leaves:** 30-120 x 40-100 mm, triangular to 3 lobed, margins entire or toothed, stalks ± 60 mm. **Flowers:** In small clusters, stem 10-100 mm; flowers 40-50 mm, pale yellow with **deep red centre, calyx lobes leafy**, 2 outer larger than 2 inner, ± 15 mm (throughout year). **General:** Visited by small bees.

Merremia (named after B Merrem, 1784-1824, prof of physics, maths, patron of zoology) - Perennial herbs, sometimes twining; leaves sometimes with toothed wing at base. Widespread in warm regions, ± 80 species, 10 in SA.

Merremia tridentata [now *Xenostegia tridentata*] Miniature Morning Glory, Merremia; ulonja (Z) *(tridentata* - three teeth)
Annual prostrate (twining) herb, stems up to 3 m. In grassland, KZN to Trop Afr. Stems slender, ribbed, **hairless**. **Leaves:** 20-80 x 2-6 mm, **with small, shortly lobed wings at base**, stalks short, ± 3 mm. **Flowers:** 1-3 in small clusters, stem 40-60 mm; flowers 12-20 mm, yellow with or without reddish centre, calyx lobes pointed (Sep-May). **Fruit:** Round, ± 10 mm diam. **General:** Used in traditional medicine to treat stomach complaints.

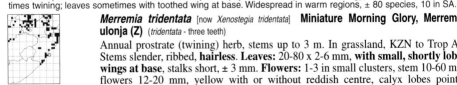

Orbeopsis lutea

Darrel Plowes

Cuscuta cassytoides

C J Ward

Stapelia gigantea

Martin von Fintel

Hewittia malabarica

Geoff Nichols

★ *Cuscuta campestris*

C J Ward

Asclepias aurea

Martin von Fintel

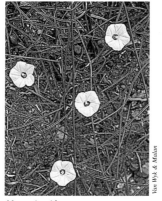

Merremia tridentata

Van Wyk & Malan

★ *Cuscuta campestris*

C J Ward

303

Ipomoea (*ips* - worm; *homoios* - like, refers to the creeping habit) **-** Mostly twiners; leaves often heart-shaped at base, sometimes lobed; flowers showy, broadly funnel-shaped, folded. Cosmop, ± 400 species, ± 50 in SA.

Ipomoea obscura Yellow Ipomoea, Wild Petunia; Wildepatat (A); ijalambu, umdzandzabuka, (Sw); usiboniseleni (Z) (*obscura* - hidden, indistinct)

Slender perennial twiner, 1-2 m. In grassland, SA to E Afr, Trop Asia, Malaysia, N Austr, Fiji. Slender tap root. Stems green when young, grooved and woody with age, ± hairy. Very variable. **Leaves:** 20-50(100) x 2-45(90) mm, broadly heart-shaped, softly hairy, margins wavy, stalks erect, 15-40(90) mm. **Flowers:** Solitary or in small clusters, stem 30-80 mm; flowers 12-30 mm diam, tube 20-40 mm, pale yellow, with or without deep red centre, calyx lobes ± 10 mm (Sep-Jun). **General:** Leaves cooked as a relish. Used in traditional medicine as an hallucinogenic.

LAMIACEAE (LABIATAE) **- Sage or Mint Family** Herbs or shrublets (for description see p. 470). ***Plectranthus*** (*plektron* - spur; *anthos* - flower)- Herbs or shrubs, often fleshy (for description see p. 472).

Plectranthus esculentus African Potato, Wild Potato; Wilde-aartappel (A); tapole emahlo (SS); itapile (X); ujangu, ujilo, umbondwe, umhlaza (Z) (*esculentus* - edible)

Erect, aromatic shrublet, up to 1,2 m. In woodland, disturbed areas, KZN to C Afr. **Tuberous roots.** Stems woody at base, slightly branched, hairy. **Leaves:** 50-80 x 13-25 mm, roughly hairy, brown dotted beneath, margins toothed, almost stalkless. **Flowers:** In slender terminal inflorescences, ± 600 mm; flowers 14-16 mm, **yellow**, produced after leaves have dropped, calyx 9-10 mm, glandular (Jul-Nov). **General:** Tuberous roots edible, similar in taste to sweet potato, planted and stored in some rural areas in the past. Attracts butterflies including the Gaudy Commodore *Junonia octavia sesamus*. Becoming rare in the wild.

SOLANACEAE - Tomato/Potato/Tobacco Family Herbs, shrubs, climbers, often spiny (for description see p. 478). ***Physalis*** (*physalis* - bladder; *physa* - bellow, refers to inflated calyx) - America, ± 140 species, ± 5 naturalised in SA.

★ *Physalis viscosa* Wild Gooseberry; Klewerige Appelliefie (A) (*viscosa* - sticky)

Bushy herb, up to 300 mm. In disturbed places, grassland (Trop America). Annual stems, densely covered in short sticky hairs. Leaves yellowish green. Flowers solitary, nodding, yellow (Oct-Jun). Berry completely enclosed in inflated calyx. Leaves, fruits reputedly edible. Visited by honey-bees. A troublesome weed.

Solanum (ancient Latin name for these 'Nightshade' plants) - Shrubs, herbs, small trees or climbers, spiny or not; leaves entire, lobed or divided; flowers in clusters; fruit a berry. Abundant in trop, ± 1700, ± 60 in SA.

Solanum acanthoideum Bitter Apple, Prickly Apple; Bitterappel, Doringappel (A); setlwane, tholana (SS); inluma, intfuma (Sw); intuma, intuma-encane (Z)

Shrublet, up to 1,2 m. In forests. Branches soft, brown, hairy, with straight yellowish brown, shiny spines. **Leaves:** ± 150 x 100 mm, deeply, irregularly lobed, tapering onto stalk, hairy, reddish hairs beneath, short yellow spines on veins, stalks short ± 30 mm, spiny. **Flowers:** In small clusters, hairy, calyx cup-shaped, 20 mm, hairy, prickly (Feb-Apr). **Fruit:** A berry, 30 mm diam, yellow. **General:** Bark stringy when torn. Used in traditional medicine to treat sandworm, ringworm.

Solanum incanum Bitter Apple, Bitter Thorn; Bitterappel, Gifappel, Grysbitterappel (A); intfuma (Sw) (*incanum* - velvety white)

Erect perennial shrublet, 0,6-1,5 m. In woodland, grassland. **Stems, leaves with prickles. Leaves:** ± 180 x 100 mm, thinly downy above, **white velvety beneath, margins broadly lobed**, stalks ± 50 mm. **Flowers:** ± 25 mm diam, mauve, calyx cone-shaped, lobes pointed, ± 10 mm (Oct-Feb). **Fruit:** Round, fleshy, ± 20 mm diam, yellow, mottled green. **General:** Used in traditional medicine to treat ringworm, chest complaints, toothache and sore throats. A weed in sugar cane fields.

SCROPHULARIACEAE - Snapdragon Family Annual or perennial herbs, shrubs, rarely trees or climbers, some parasitic (for description see p. 72). ***Melasma*** (*melas* - black, plants turn black on dying) - Herbs with rough stems; flowers solitary in axils of upper leaves, drop early; calyx inflated in fruit. Trop Afr, Trop America, ± 5 species, 1 in SA.

Melasma scabrum (*scabrum* - rough)

Erect perennial herb, up to 600 mm. In swamps, grassland. Covered with rough hairs. **Leaves:** Opposite, ± 70 x 10 mm, margins faintly toothed, tapering to both ends, stalkless. **Flowers:** Solitary, ± 30 mm diam, white or yellow with reddish purple centre, calyx tube 10 ribbed, ± 20 x 12 mm, lobes pointed, stalk ± 60 mm (Jan-Mar). **Fruit: Calyx inflated in fruit.**

Ipomoea obscura

Plectranthus esculentus

Plectranthus esculentus

Solanum incanum

★ *Physalis viscosa*

Solanum acanthoideum

Melasma scabrum

305

Alectra (*alektor, alektruon* - a cock, resembles a cock's comb) - Annual or perennial semi-parasitic herbs, roots bright orange; flowers in dense spike. Afr, Madag, India, ± 40 species, ± 20 in SA.

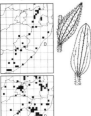

Alectra capensis sono (Sw)

Erect herb, up to 450 mm. In grassland, rocky areas, coast to 2200 m. Stems seldom branched, roughly hairy. **Leaves:** Overlapping, ± 15 x 5 mm, stalkless, blunt tipped, **margins entire.** **Flowers:** In short, dense, terminal inflorescences, 25-75 x 25-35 mm; flowers ± 20 mm diam, yellow with reddish brown veins, calyx ± 10 mm 5 lobed, tips pointed (Feb-Mar). **Similar species:** *A. thyrsoidea* Leaves hairy, larger, ± 30 x 15 mm, clasping; inflorescences longer.

Alectra orobanchoides (resembles the genus *Orobanch* - a parasitic plant)

Erect, annual herb, up to 600 mm. In grassland, bushveld, E Cape to Bots, Nam. Stems branched or not, angular, smooth or rough. **Leaves: Scalelike,** roughly hairy. **Flowers:** In spikelike inflorescence, bracts narrow, ± 4 mm, finely hairy; flowers small, in axils of bracts, orange-yellow with **red veins** (Nov-Feb).

Alectra sessiliflora Verfblommetjie (A); sono (Sw) (*sessiliflora* - stalkless flowers)

Branching herb, up to 600 mm. In grassland, damp places, coast to 1900 m, SW Cape to Malawi, Madag. Stems purple, plant sparsely hairy. **Leaves:** ± 30 x 20 mm, margins purplish, with irregular blunt teeth, stalkless or with short stalks. **Flowers:** In terminal inflorescences, **bracts leaflike with prominent teeth**; flowers pale yellow, just protruding from short calyx (Sep-May). **General:** Parasitic on grass.

LENTIBULARIACEAE - Bladderwort Family Perennial herbs, aquatic or in swamps. *Utricularia* (*utricullus* - little leather bottle)- Perennial herbs, in water or in damp places, usually with traps (for descriptions see p. 198).

Utricularia prehensilis Large Yellow Bladderwort; Blaaskruid (A); iphengulula (Z)

(*prehensilis* - seizing, taking hold)

Terrestrial herb, up to 200 mm, in colonies. In marshy ground, seasonally flooded places, coast to 2000 m, E Cape to Ethiopia. Stolons fine, branching, traps ± 1,5 mm. **Leaves:** Scattered, ± 10 x 3 mm, narrowing to stalk. **Flowers: Large,** 1-8, stem **twining** (erect), 30-350 mm; flowers 8-20 mm, yellow (Dec-Jul). **General:** Leaves not noticeable at time of flowering. Used as a love charm emetic.

ACANTHACEAE - Acanthus Family Herbs, shrubs or climbers (for description see p. 76). *Thunbergia* (named after Carl Thunberg, 1743-1828, pupil of Linnaeus, collector at the Cape, author of 'Flora Capensis') - Herbs, sometimes climbing; flowers solitary, with 2 large bracts clasping base. Afr, SE Asia, Mascarene Is, ± 200 species, ± 12 in SA.

Thunbergia atriplicifolia Natal Primrose; isiphondo esincane (Z) (*atriplicifolia* - leaves like *Atriplex*)

Perennial shrublet, up to 400 mm. **In grassland,** Cape to N Prov. Woody rootstock, milky sap. Stems twining or not; **plant densely covered with soft hairs. Leaves:** 20 -60 x 10-35 mm, **oval, almost rounded at base, margins entire,** almost stalkless. **Flowers:** ± 50 mm wide, creamy yellow, tube ± 25 mm, whitish cream, bracts 15 -25 mm, stalks ± 70 mm (Oct-Mar). **Fruit:** 15-20 x 7-10 mm. **General:** Used in traditional medicine as a love potion, green fruits for a hair wash. Good garden plant.

Thunbergia dregeana Haarbossie (A); isiphondo (Z) (named after Johan Drège, 1794-1881)

Scrambling herb, up to 1 m. In coastal scrub, on forest margins. Softly, sparsely hairy. **Leaves:** 13-50 x 14-50 mm, **base deeply heart-shaped, margins toothed, stalks 15-60 mm. Flowers:** ± 55 mm wide, white to dull orange, tube ± 20 mm, bracts 13-90 x 8-20 mm, stalks ± 50 mm (Oct-Apr). **General:** Visited by small bees. Used in traditional medicine to treat venereal diseases and for a hair wash. **Similar species:** *Thunbergia neglecta* Creeper, in grassland, woodland, Cape to Bots; plant roughly short hairy; leaf base square, margins entire, lobed or with 2 blunt teeth towards base, stalks 9-30 mm; flowers ± 40 mm wide, creamy white, yellowish inside

Justicia (named after James Justice, 1698-1763, Scottish horticulturalist)- Herbs or shrublets (for description see p. 438).

Justicia flava Yellow Justicia; Geelgarnaalbos (A); impela (Z) (*flava* - yellow)

Slender, erect to trailing herb, 0,5-1 m. In grassland, woodland, KZN to Trop Afr. Thinly hairy throughout, rooting at nodes. **Leaves:** 12-120 x 4-46 mm, stalks ± 25 mm. **Flowers: In terminal inflorescences, ± 120 mm**; flowers ± 10 mm, yellow (Sep-Jun). **General:** Used in traditional medicine to treat coughs. **Similar species:** *J. odora* Woody shrublet; in dry stony areas, KZN to Nam; leaves smaller, stalks short; flowers in small clusters in axils, yellow, veined red or purple in tube. Roots rolled into perfumed 'beads', which remain fragrant for years.

Alectra capensis

Alectra orobanchoides

Alectra sessiliflora

Martin von Fintel

Jo Arkell

Lal Greene

Utricularia prehensilis

Lal Greene

Alectra thyrsoidea

Thunbergia neglecta

Hilliard & Burtt

Van Wyk & Malan

Thunbergia dregeana

Martin von Fintel

Thunbergia atriplicifolia

Justicia flava

Trevor Coleman

Wally Menne

Tony Abbott

307

CUCURBITACEAE - Cucumber/Pumpkin Family Prostrate, trailing or climbing herbs with spirally coiled tendrils. Leaves simple or lobed. Flowers unisexual on same or separate plants, 5 lobed, ovary inferior, stigma 2-3 lobed, fleshy. Fruits usually fleshy. Important as a food source - pumpkins, squashes, cucumbers, gherkins, watermelons and as ornamental gourds and luffas. Trop, ± 119 genera, ± 775 species, 18 genera in SA.
Cucumis (Latin for cucumber) - Herbaceous climbers or creepers; rootstock woody; leaves more or less lobed; male and female flowers mostly on same plant, calyx tube bell-shaped; fruit fleshy or dry, smooth, bristly, spiny or knobbed. Includes the cultivated Cucumber, *Cucumis sativus*. Mostly Afr, ± 25 species, ± 14 in SA.

Cucumis hirsutus **Wild Cucumber; Suurkomkommertjie (A); monyaku (SS); uselwa-lwemamba, uthangazane (Z)** (*hirsutus* - hairy)
Perennial straggling creeper, stems up to 2,5 m. In woodland, grassland, Cape to Trop Afr. Rootstock woody, fibrous. Stems woody at base, hairy throughout. **Leaves:** ± 80 x 30 mm, shallowly 3-5 lobed, surface rough, stalks ± 60 mm. **Flowers:** Male and female on separate plants; flowers ± 20 mm, pale yellow, veined (Oct-Feb). **Fruit:** Round, ± 50 mm diam, hairy, spineless, yellow to brownish orange. **General:** Leaves and fruits eaten (pleasant, lemony taste). Fruits considered poisonous by some. Used in traditional medicine to treat coughs and as a purgative.

Cucumis zeyheri **Wild Cucumber; Wilde-agurkie, Wildekomkommer (A); Ierakana, monyaku (SS); inhlakahlela, iselwa-lenja (Z)** (named after Carl Zeyher, 1799-1858, German botanical collector who came to the Cape in 1822)
Perennial trailing herb. In grassland, Cape to Zam. Rootstock woody, fibrous. **Stems, leaves coarsely hairy. Leaves:** 25-90 x 20-60 mm, deeply 3-7 lobed, margins toothed, stalks 5-40 mm. **Flowers: Male and female on same plant,** ± 10 mm (Nov-Mar). **Fruit:** 30-50 x 20-35 mm, **oval, softly spiny, dark and light green stripes ripening yellow. General:** Leaves used as spinach. Fruit poisonous, killing cattle. Used in traditional medicine to treat chest complaints, diarrhoea. Must be used with care due to poisonous qualities.

Peponium (*pepo* - a melon) - Prostrate or scrambling herbs, often very hairy; rootstock tuberous; tendrils unequally forked; fruit fleshy with firm outer layer. Afr genus ± 20 species, ± 2 in SA.

Peponium mackenii (named after Mark McKen, 1823-72, first curator, Bot Gardens, Durban)
Robust climber, stems up to 10 m. On forest margins, in thicket. Stems grooved, densely covered with soft hairs when young. **Leaves:** 60-130 x 60-160 mm, lobes triangular, thinly hairy above, hairy beneath, margins toothed, stalks 30-80 mm. **Flowers:** Male and female on separate plants, ± 35 mm, yellow, stems long, 40-180 mm (May-Aug). **Fruit:** Oval, 60-90 x 30-40 mm, green mottled white maturing yellow. **General:** Monkeys eat fruit when food is scarce.

Coccinia (*coccinus* - scarlet; *kokkos* - berry) - Herbaceous climbers or creepers. Usually with tuberous rootstock; tendrils simple or forked; flowers usually yellow, male in short clusters, female solitary, on separate plants; fruit fleshy, elongated, red or mottled. Mainly Afr, ± 30 species, ± 7 in SA.

Coccinia adoensis (*adoensis* - from Aden, Arabia)
Climber, stems up to 6 m. In rocky grassland, woodland, KZN to Trop Afr. Tuberous rootstock. Stems annual, **sparsely to densely hairy. Leaves:** 25-125 x 25-150 mm, broadly 3-5(7) lobed, **margins finely toothed,** surface rough, stalks ± 50 mm, tendrils simple. **Flowers: Male:** ± 20 mm, dull creamy yellow, in elongated clusters, stems ± 90 mm. Female: smaller, solitary (Sep-Dec). **Fruit:** 30-80 x 10-30 mm, oval, smooth, red. **General:** Leaves have disagreeable smell but are cooked as spinach.

Coccinia hirtella (see p. 80)

Coccinia palmata **Wild Cucumber; Bospampoentjie (A); uthangazane omncane, uthangazane lwehlathi (Z)** (see p. 80)

Coccinia rehmannii **Wild Cucumber; uselwa-lwenyoka (Z)** (named after Anton Rehmann, 1840-1917, Polish botanist and geographer, collector, who visited SA twice)
Slender creeper, stems up to 8 m. In sandy soil, in grassland, woodland, Cape to Zim, Moz. Rootstock large, tuberous. Stems annual, densely hairy when young, smooth, whitish with age, tendrils simple. **Leaves:** 20-80 x 25-130 mm, shortly hairy, shallowly to deeply lobed, margins entire, sharply toothed, stalks ± 60 mm. **Flowers:** Cream or yellowish. Male: in small clusters, ± 15 mm, stem ± 30 mm. Female: solitary (Sep-Mar). **Fruit:** Roundish, 30-50 x 20-35 mm, tip pointed, green with whitish spots in longitudinal bands, red when ripe. **General:** Fruit, tubers edible.

Cucumis zeyheri   *Martin Kunhardt*

Cucumis zeyheri   *Van Wyk & Malan*

Cucumis zeyheri   *Van Wyk & Malan*

Peponium mackenii   *Geoff Nichols*

Cucumis hirsutus   *Van Wyk & Malan*

Coccinia adoensis   *Van Wyk & Malan*

Peponium mackenii   *Geoff Nichols*

Coccinia hirtella   *Neil Crouch*

Coccinia palmata   *Rosemary Williams*

Coccinia rehmannii   *C J Ward*

ASTERACEAE (COMPOSITAE) - **Daisy Family** (for description see p. 208). *Felicia* Herbs (for description see p. 210).

Felicia mossamedensis Yellow Felicia (named after the Mossamedes district, Angola)
Much branched herb, up to 300 mm. In dry grassland, open scrub, on roadsides and overgrazed areas, KZN to Angola, Bots, Zim, Moz. Tough tap root, woody at base. **Twigs and leaves harshly hairy. Leaves:** ± 35 x 6 mm. **Flowerheads:** Solitary, ± 20 mm diam, **yellow**, stems 30-100 mm (Oct-Apr).

Nidorella (*nitor* - strong smell) - Annual or perennial herbs. Afr, ± 13 species, ± 11 in SA.

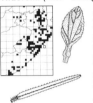

Nidorella auriculata inhlanga (Z) (*auriculata* - ear-shaped)
Perennial herb, 0,35-1,7m, **in colonies**. On grassy slopes, disturbed ground. Stems simple, thinly hairy. **Leaves:** Variable, ± 90 x 35 mm, margins entire, toothed or lobed, **veins strongly raised beneath, base conspicuously eared. Flowerheads:** In widely branched inflorescences; 2-5 mm diam, pale to deep yellow (Dec-Jun). **General:** Attracts small bees. **Similar species: *N. anomala*** Stiffly erect, ± 600 mm; 1200-2000 m; stems sticky, closely leafy; leaves ± 40 x 4 mm, roughly hairy, sticky. ***N. undulata*** Up to 1 m; in marshy places, 600-2450 m, S Cape to Zim; mostly hairless; leaves in basal rosette, ± 300 x 40 mm; inflorescences glandular hairy.

Conyza (*konyza* - a strong smelling plant) - Annual or perennial herbs. Trop, subtrop, ± 50 species, ± 13 in SA.

Conyza ulmifolia umacakaza (Z) (*ulmus* - elm tree; *folia* - leaves)
Straggling herb, up to 400 mm. In damp places, on forest margins, near streams, coast to 1200 m, SW Cape to Zim. Stems branching, **downy, glandular, aromatic. Leaves:** Soft, ± 70 x 20-30 mm, **margins irregularly toothed and lobed**, eared at base. **Flowerheads:** In loose inflorescences, on slender stems; ± 10 mm diam, bracts in 3 rows (throughout year). **General:** Visited by flies. Used traditionally to treat coughs.

Chrysocoma (*chrysos* - gold; *kome* - hair) - Bushy shrublets; leaves sometimes ericoid. S Afr, ± 18 species, 1 in KZN.

Chrysocoma oblongifolia [= *C. ciliata*] Bitter Karoo Bush; Bitterkaroobossie (A); sehalahala (SS) (*oblongifolia* - oblong leaves)
Bushy, ericoid shrublet, 0,3-1,2 m. Open rocky places, in scrub, up to 2440 m, SW Cape to Mpum. Branches bare below, closely leafy towards tips. **Leaves:** Alternate, 8-15 x 5 mm, tips recurved, gland dotted, hairless. **Flowerheads:** In profusion, 6 x 10 mm, yellow (throughout year), very sweetly scented. **General:** Fuel plant in mountain areas, collected and sold, green or dry. Becomes weedy in disturbed areas.

Pseudognaphalium ('false' *Gnaphalium*) - Herbs. SE Asia, Europe, the Americas, ± 50-60 species, 3 in SA.

Pseudognaphalium luteo-album [= *Gnaphalium luteo-album*] Jersey Cudweed; Roerkruid, Vaalbossie (A); manku, mosuoane, toane (SS); umgilane (Z) (*luteo-album* - yellowish white)
Spreading herb, up to 600 mm. Near streams, marshes, widespread weed in warmer parts of the world. Stems thinly grey woolly. **Leaves:** ± 80 x 12 mm, margins wavy. **Flowerheads:** In tight clusters, in branched inflorescences; ± 3 mm, yellowish, bracts woolly (Dec-Apr). **General:** Used traditionally to fumigate a room in which a child is feverish, and to make a 'mattress' on which skins are cured.

Helichrysum (*helios* - sun; *chrysos* - gold) - Herbs, shrubs, sometimes dwarf and cushion forming (for description see p. 212).

Helichrysum acutatum Sticky Everlasting; Taaisewejaartjie (A); uzangume (Z)
(*acutatum* - somewhat sharp)
Perennial, silvery grey herb, up to 800 mm. In grassland, coast to 1950 m, E Cape to N Prov. Stems simple, **cobwebby to woolly**, very variable. **Leaves:** Basal ± 250 x 50 mm, with sticky yellow glands, 3 veined, **narrowing to long, winged base, clasping stem. Flowerheads:** Dense, branched inflorescences, ± 60 mm diam; ± 7 x 3 mm, yellow, bracts overlapping (Aug-Apr). **General:** Used in traditional medicine.

Helichrysum appendiculatum Sheep's Ears Everlasting (see p. 82)

Helichrysum aureonitens Golden Everlasting; Gouesewejaartjie (A); toane-ntja (SS); impepho-emhlophe, indondokazane, inkondlwane (Z) (*aureonitens* - golden lustre)
Silvery grey perennial herb, up to 400 mm, **in colonies**. In damp grassland, E Cape to Angola, Moz. Rootstock creeping, stems slender, greyish white woolly. **Leaves:** ± 20 x 3 mm, base half clasping. **Flowerheads:** In compact inflorescences; 4 x 3 mm, bracts yellow to pale brown (Jul-Feb). **General:** Used in traditional medicine to invoke goodwill of ancestors and by diviners to induce trances.

Felicia mossamedensis

Nidorella anomala

Nidorella undulata

Van Wyk & Malan

Martin von Fintel

Martin von Fintel

Nidorella auriculata

Chrysocoma oblongifolia

Helichrysum aureonitens

Lal Greene

Rosemary Williams

Lal Greene

Conyza ulmifolia

Pseudognaphalium luteo-album

Tony Abbott

Lal Greene

Helichrysum acutatum

Helichrysum appendiculatum

Sheila Peacock

Trevor Coleman

311

Helichrysum aureum Yellow Everlasting; leabane (SS) (*aureum* - golden)
Perennial herb, 100-400(800) mm. In grassland, scrub, coast to 3000 m. Crown ± 25 mm diam, 1-several leaf rosettes. **Several flowering stems to each rosette, white woolly.** Leaves: Basal rosette 30-100(270) x 10-25(60) mm, glandular hairy on both surfaces, sometimes woolly on margins, midvein. **Flowerheads: Solitary,** 17-45 mm diam, glossy yellow (white) (Jul-Mar). **General:** 6 varieties, differing in habitat, woolly hairiness and size.

Helichrysum cephaloideum ibhade (Z) (*cephaloideum* - headlike)
Perennial herb, up to 400 mm. In grassland, up to 2600 m, E Cape to N Prov, Zim. Several flowering stems from crown, **loosely grey woolly, leafy throughout.** Leaves: In basal rosette, ± withered at flowering, 20-50 x 10-20 mm, with coarse, spreading hairs. **Flowerheads: In compact, roundish inflorescences,** ± 30 mm diam, often webbed together with wool at base; ± 5 mm diam, bracts glossy bright yellow (Oct-Mar).
Similar species: H. auriceps 300-800 mm, coast to 2000 m; leaves long, narrow, 65-150 x 8-15 mm, grey woolly, upper surface also with long coarse hairs; inflorescences tight, congested, ± 45 mm diam; flowerheads ± 8 mm diam, bract tips pointed. *H. longifolium* Leaves 100-250 x 7-20 mm, hairless above, white woolly beneath; flowerheads in open, branched inflorescences.

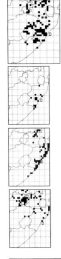

Helichrysum cooperi Yellow Everlasting; Geelsewejaartjie (A); umadotsheni (Z)
(named after Thomas Cooper, 1815-1913, English plant collector and cultivator who came to SA in 1859)
Biennial, aromatic herb, up to 1,5 m. In grassland, near forest margins, up to 2450 m. Stems simple, stout, ± 10 mm diam, leafy, bristly glandular. **Leaves: Large,** in rosette in first year, ± 150(250) x 60 mm, **bright green, tapering to broad base, clasping stem,** margins woolly (KZN); stem leaves ± 65-130 x 20-45 mm, tips pointed, margins white woolly. **Flowerheads: In large, leafy, horizontally spreading inflorescences,** branches thinly cobwebby; 15-25 mm, bracts glossy bright yellow (**Dec-May**). **General:.** Used as a love charm. **Similar species:**

H. ruderale In dense stands, in disturbed areas; leaves rough, sticky, with short, winging stem; **inflorescence branches obliquely ascending, white woolly to well below first forking;** flowerheads 25-30 mm diam (**Sep-Nov**).

H. decorum impepho (Z) Coast to 900 m, E Cape to Moz; stems thinly grey-white woolly; leaves in rosette in first year, narrowing to base, **upper surface cobwebby, thinly grey-white woolly beneath;** flowerheads ± 30 mm diam (Nov-Apr).

H. setosum bohloko, phefo-ea-thaba, toane-balingoana (SS) Bushy, branched from base; in rocky grassland, KZN to Zim, Malawi; stems brittle, woody, sticky; leaves 20-50 x 10-20 mm, green, sticky, margins, main vein ± woolly, base broad, clasping; flowerheads 20-30 mm diam, **solitary, at tips of long leafy branches** (Mar-Aug).

Helichrysum cymosum impepho (Z) (*cymosum* - in flat topped flower cluster)
Spreading subshrub, up to 1 m. **In straggling clumps,** in moist places, SW Cape to KZN. Branches reclining at base, then erect, thinly greyish white woolly, densely leafy. **Leaves:** Small, variable, 8-15(45) x 2-4(15) mm, **thin silvery grey above, closely white woolly beneath,** tapering to sharp, hairlike tips. **Flowerheads: In compact terminal inflorescences; cylindrical,** 3-4,5 x 1-3 mm, bracts transparent, glossy, yellow (Sep-Apr). **General:** Useful garden groundcover. Subsp. *cymosum*, coast to 600 m, E Cape to KZN. Subsp. *calvum*, 1200-3170 m; leaves narrower, more crowded; flowerheads smaller.

Helichrysum glomeratum (*glomeratum* - club-shaped, clustered into a head)
Perennial herb, up to 450 mm, in large colonies. In open grassland. Rhizomatous. Stems, erect, simple, loosely grey cottony. **Leaves: In spreading basal rosette,** ± 30 x 10 mm, tapering to pointed tip, base broad, covered in silvery silky hairs, **stem leaves smaller, erect, overlapping. Flowerheads:** In congested, flattish inflorescences, 20-50 mm diam, matted with wool at base; ± 4 x 1,5 mm, bracts brownish outside, tipped yellow inside (Feb-May).

Helichrysum aureum

Helichrysum auriceps

Lal Greene

Helichrysum cephaloideum

Rosemary Williams

Helichrysum cooperi

Lal Greene

Helichrysum decorum

Lorraine van Hooff

Helichrysum ruderale

Tony Abbott

Helichrysum setosum

Martin von Fintel

Helichrysum cymosum

Geoff Nichols

Helichrysum glomeratum

Martin von Fintel

313

Helichrysum herbaceum Monkey-tail Everlasting; impepho-yamakhosi (Z)
(*herbaceum* - succulent stem, herblike)

Perennial herb, up to 400 mm. In grassland, S Cape to Tanz. Stems simple or forked. **Leaves:** In rosette, ± 50 x 20 mm, white felted beneath; **stem leaves narrow**. **Flowerheads:** Solitary, **large**, ± 20 x 28 mm, **bracts merging onto stem**, outer glossy brown, inner lemon yellow (Oct-Apr). **General:** Flowers often galled. Plant burnt to invoke goodwill of ancestors. **Similar species:** *Relhania pungens* (see p. 316).

Helichrysum hypoleucum (*hypoleucum* - white beneath leaves)

Softly woody shrublet, up to 2 m. On forest margins, steep grassy slopes, 1200 -2000 m. Branches white felted. **Leaves:** ± 80 x 50 mm, **heart-shaped at base**, white felted beneath, 5 veined from base, stalks ± 25 mm, **narrowly winged, clasping**. **Flowerheads:** In congested clusters in branched inflorescences; 2 x 2 mm, outer bracts woolly, inner glossy, silvery transparent (Feb-Apr).

Helichrysum kraussii Straw Everlasting; Sewejaartjie (A); isithangwazi (Th); isiphe-shane, isiqoqo (Z) (named after Christian Krauss, 1812-90, German scientist and collector; in SA 1839-40)

Aromatic shrublet, up to 1 m, in colonies. In coastal grassland, open woodland, E Cape to Angola, Zim, Moz. **Leaves:** ± 20 x 2 mm, sharp tipped; **margins rolled under, white felted beneath. Flowerheads:** In dense, branched inflorescences; cylindrical, 3,5 x 1 mm, bracts pale yellow (Jun-Sep). **General:** Fluffy white galls sometimes at branch tips. Visited by honey-bees. Grown from seed, needs full sun.

Helichrysum nanum (*nanus* - dwarf)

Mat-forming perennial herb, 50-120 mm. In poor stony grassland or on rock sheets, 1575-1800 m. Main branches stoloniferous. **Leaves:** Stiff, erect, ± 35 x 1 mm, **margins strongly rolled under, midrib raised beneath**, silvery felted, base broad, clasping. **Flowerheads:** In small clusters, felted together in congested inflorescences; 4-5 x 1,5 mm, bracts brownish outside, inner tipped bright yellow (Nov-Apr).

Helichrysum nudifolium Hottentot's Tea; Hottentotstee (A); letapiso, mohlomela-tsie-oa-thaba (SS); ludvutfane (Sw); icholocholo (X,Z); isidwaba-somkhovu, uma-gada-emthini (Z) (*nudifolium* - hairless leaves)

Perennial herb, up to 1,5 m. In grassland, Cape to Trop Afr. **Leaves:** In basal rosette, ± 600 x 130 mm, **rough, shiny above**, white woolly beneath, 3-7 veins, protruding below, narrowing to broad, stalklike base. **Flowerheads:** In **crowded inflorescence**; 4-5 x 2-3 mm, bracts woolly at base, **blunt tipped, pale yellow** (Oct-May). **General:** Delicate aromatic leaves, eaten in some areas. Used traditionally as a tea, a poultice to treat chest complaints, headaches, fevers, wounds and burnt to invoke goodwill of ancestors. Grown from seed. **Similar species:**

H. allioides Up to 650 mm, in colonies; coast to 1250 m; leaves **long, narrow**, ± 600 x 20 mm, leathery, dark green, thinly woolly above, white **woolly felted beneath**, 3 veined, **narrowing to long thin wiry stalks**; flowerheads ± 6 x 4-6 mm, pale yellow, bracts overlapping, outer purplish (Aug-Dec).

H. inornatum Up to 500 mm, in damp marshy grassland, 1800-2100 m; leaves ± 150 x 10 mm, **thin, soft**, flat, rough above, lightly cobwebbed, thinly greyish white felted beneath, 3 veined; inflorescences 20-30 mm diam, stem white felted, flower-heads ± 4 x 2,5 mm, bracts **light golden brown** (Dec-Jan).

H. krookii Up to 400 mm, in small colonies; in moist grassland, 1500-2800 m; leaves basal, ± 100 x 50 mm, glandular hairy, abruptly narrowed to broad, clasping stalklike base, ± 30 x 6 mm; **inflorescence 20-70 mm diam**, flowerheads 3-4 x 2-3 mm, **felted together**, bracts bright yellow (Jan-Feb).

H. pallidum Up to 650 m; leaves ± 400 x 120 mm, rough, harshly hairy above, thinly grey white woolly beneath, **5-7 veined, net veining visible, gradually contracted to long, flat, stalk**; inflorescence large, spreading with age, flowerheads 6-7 mm, bract tips rounded, creamy to pale yellow (Aug-Feb).

H. pilosellum isicwe (X,Z); umadotsheni, umaphephesa (Z) Up to 450 mm; E Cape to Malawi; **crown brown silky woolly; leaves few, spreading**, ± 150(230) x 40(60) mm, **rough,** long hairs above, white felted beneath, 5-9 veined; flowering stem woolly felted, flowerheads 5 x 5 mm, bracts curly, clear pale brown (Aug-Mar).

Helichrysum herbaceum

Helichrysum hypoleucum

Helichrysum kraussii

Lal Greene

Martin von Fintel

Barry James

Helichrysum kraussii

Helichrysum kraussii

Tony Pooley

Geoff Nichols

Helichrysum nanum

Helichrysum nudifolium

Helichrysum allioides

Tony Abbott

Lorraine van Hooff

Martin von Fintel

Helichrysum inornatum

Helichrysum pallidum

Helichrysum pilosellum

Helichrysum krookii

Martin von Fintel

Tony Abbott

Lal Greene

Tony Abbott

315

Helichrysum odoratissimum impepho (SS,Sw,X,Z); phefo-ea-setlolo, tooane (SS)
(*odoratissimum* - very sweet smelling)
Much branched, straggling, aromatic, perennial herb, up to 0,6(1) m, in large clumps. On grassy or rocky slopes, Cape to Zim, Mal, Moz, up to 2000 m. **Leaves:** 5-60 x 1-15 mm, thinly or thickly woolly, **base clasping, in long wings on stem.** **Flowerheads:** In terminal inflorescences; 2-3 mm, **matted with wool at base**, bracts closely overlapping, outer pale brown, inner yellow (Aug-Dec). **General:** Essential ingredient for herbalists. Leaves pleasantly scented, burnt to fumigate a sick-room, treat coughs, colds and to invoke the goodwill of the ancestors. Mixed with fat for a scented, soothing ointment. **Similar species:** *H. gymnocomum* At higher altitudes, up to 3000 m; flowerhead bracts loosely overlapping; leaves strongly scented.

Helichrysum oreophilum (*oreophilum* - mountain loving)
Perennial herb, up to 300 mm. In grassland, invades eroded areas, 1550-2450 m. Flowering stems leafy, simple, thinly **grey silky woolly. Leaves:** ± 80 x 15 mm, only main vein visible beneath, base half clasping. **Flowerheads:** In compact inflorescences; ± 7 x 5 mm, bracts cobwebby at base, tips pointed, lemon yellow (Sep-Feb).

Helichrysum splendidum Cape Gold; Geelsewejaartjie (A); phefo-ea-loti, toane-moru (SS); impepho (Sw) (*splendidum* - shining)
Slender, sprawling shrub, 0,6-1,5 m. In rocky places, on forest margins, S Cape to N Prov. **Leaves:** 10-30 x 1-2 mm, grey woolly above, whitish woolly beneath, margins rolled under. **Flowerheads:** In compact or open branched inflorescences; 4-5 x 5-8 mm, bracts glossy bright yellow (orange) (Oct-Feb). **General:** Aromatic to lavender scented. Used in traditional medicine to treat rheumatism. A good fuel plant in the mountains. Useful garden groundcover, grown from cutting or seed. **Similar species:** *H. montanum* Mat-forming dwarf shrub, 0,1-0,45 x 1 m; on rocky outcrops, 1800-2500 m; branches short, congested; leaves thickly white woolly, 3-5 veined.

Helichrysum umbraculigerum Kerriekruie (A) (*umbraculigerum* - bearing woolly umbrellas)
Tufted perennial herb, up to 1 m. In rough grassland, scrub, on forest margins, up to 2500 m, E Cape to Zim. Young parts thinly grey woolly, leafy. **Leaves:** Variable, 20-80 x 3-25 mm, ± cobwebby or thinly to thickly greyish white woolly above, ± thickly woolly beneath, abruptly narrowing to stalklike, clasping base. **Flowerheads:** In many crowded clusters, webbed together with wool, **forming 'umbrellalike' inflorescences**; 3 x 1 mm, bracts golden yellow (Jan-Apr). **General:** Heavily grazed.

Relhania (named after Rev Richard Relhan FRS, 1754-1823, author *Flora Cantab*) - Shrubs, often sticky, rarely herbs; leaves narrow, rigid, often ending in stiff point. Endemic to SA, ± 28 species, mostly in coastal belt, 1 in KZN.

Relhania pungens (*pungens* - piercing)
Bushy perennial herb, up to 300 mm. In rocky grassland, SW Cape to KZN. Woody rootstock. Stems simple below, branched above, closely leafy, older stems bare. **Leaves:** Spreading to suberect, ± 20 x 1 mm, sharp tipped, margins in-rolled, white woolly, 3 veined beneath. **Flowerheads:** Solitary, **narrow**, ± 17 x 8 mm, **bracts light brown** (Dec-Feb). **Similar species:** *Helichrysum herbaceum* (see p. 314).

Macowania (named after Peter MacOwan, 1830-1909, Director Cape Town Bot Gardens, first prof botany at SA College) - Tall or dwarf shrubs, often intricately branched and glandular; leaves overlapping. Afr, 11 species, 9 in SA.

Macowania corymbosa (*corymbosa* - arranged in flat topped inflorescence)
Erect, spindly shrub, up to 1,5 m. In shrub communities along streams, on steep slopes, 1525-2590 m. KZN Drakensberg endemic. Young branches covered in overlapping leaves. **Leaves:** ± 40 x 3 mm, **margins rolled under**, thinly woolly beneath, bristly above and on midrib below. **Flowerheads:** Crowded terminally; ± 25 mm diam, ray florets yellow, **bracts edged dark brown, bristly** (Mar-Jul).

Geigeria (named after Prof Geiger, German prof of pharmacy) - Perennial herbs. Afr, ± 28 species, ± 21 in SA.

Geigeria burkei Vermeersiektebossie (A) (named after Joseph Burke, 1812-1873, botanical and zoological collector for Lord Derby)
Perennial herb, up to 600 mm. In woodland, poor grassland, KZN to Bots, coast to 1660 m. Stems simple below, branching above. **Leaves:** Variable, ± 100 x 6 mm, rough or smooth, margins entire or slightly toothed, tapering to stalklike base. **Flowerheads:** ± 15 mm diam, **stalkless, at each fork of stem**, yellow, outer bracts with short leaflike appendage (Dec-Jun). **General:** Plants erect or prostrate, more or less leafy.

Helichrysum odoratissimum

Tony Abbott

Helichrysum oreophilum

Trevor Coleman

Helichrysum gymnocomum

Lorraine van Hooff

Helichrysum splendidum

Tony Abbott

Helichrysum umbraculigerum

Darrel Plowes

Relhania pungens

Tony Abbott

Relhania pungens

Tony Abbott

Macowania corymbosa

Martin von Fintel

Geigeria burkei

Geoff Nichols

317

Aspilia (*a* - without; *spilos* - a spot) - Annual or perennial herbs; leaves opposite; flowerheads solitary, in loose inflorescences or stalkless in condensed inflorescences. S America, Trop, subtrop Afr, Madag, ± 125 species, 3 in SA.

Aspilia natalensis Wild Creeping Sunflower; ikhambi-lenyongo, ubuhlungwana, umahoqo, umphamephuce (Z)

Straggling perennial herb, up to 600 mm. In grassland, up to 600 m, E Cape to Tanz. Rhizomatous; **rough hairy**. **Leaves:** ± 120 x 30 mm, margins entire to toothed. **Flowerheads:** Solitary, ± 40 mm diam, orange-yellow, close at night (throughout year). **General:** Used in traditional medicine to treat chest complaints, diarrhoea, nausea and as poultices for wounds. Good garden plant for damp areas.

Tithonia (from Tithonis, another name for Aurora, goddess of dawn) - Coarse, ± annual herbs; leaves entire or lobed; flowerheads on long stalks, thickened near tip. C America, W Indies, ± 10 species, 2 widespread weeds in SA.

★ *Tithonia diversifolia* Mexican Sunflower; Mexikaanse Sonneblom (A); umbabane (Z)

(*diversifolia* - leaves of more than one kind)

Bushy annual or perennial herb, 1,5-3,5 m. Invasive alien weed, coast to 600 m, from C America. Woody at base. Leaves ± 150 x 120 mm, pale velvety beneath, deeply 3-5 lobed. Flowerheads ± 100 mm diam, yellow, stalks swollen, velvety beneath heads, in terminal inflorescences (Apr-Jun). Brown fruits in rounded spiky heads.

Melanthera (*melas* - black, anthers) - Herbs. Trop, subtrop America, Afr, India, ± 50 species, ± 5 in SA.

Melanthera scandens ikhaphanyongo, isihiyapice, ulimi-lwenkomo (Z) (*scandens* - climbing)

Erect or scrambling herb, 0,45-2 m. In damp places, on forest margins, coast to 600 m, E Cape to Moz. Stems pale silvery green. **Leaves:** ± 120 x 80 mm, rough, margins lobed, toothed, stalks ± 30 mm. **Flowerheads:** ± 30 mm diam, orange, solitary, stems ± 150 mm (Oct-Apr). **General:** Visited by small bees and butterflies, (including Acraeidae). **Similar species:** ★ *Wedelia trilobata* Trailing herb, garden escapee; flowerheads ± 25 mm diam, yellowish orange.

Coreopsis (*cor* - bedbug; *opsis* - appearance, refers to seed) - Herbs. Americas, Trop Afr, ± 120 species, 2 in SA.

★ *Coreopsis lanceolata* Tickseed (*lanceolata* - lancelike, swordlike)

Perennial herb, up to 600 mm. Garden escape, now naturalised, from USA. Basal leaves crowded, ± 200 x 30 mm, margins entire, tapering to base, half clasping; flowering stems leafy, lower leaves divided, upper entire. Flowerheads ± 60 mm diam, yellow, solitary, on very long bare stems (Oct-Dec).

Bidens (*bidens* - 2 toothed, refers to seed) - **Black-jacks or Cosmos** - Herbs. Cosmop, ± 250 species, ± 7 in SA.

★ *Bidens bipinnata* Spanish Black-jack (see p. 218)

★ *Bidens biternata* (see p. 218)

Tagetes (named after the mythical Tages, grandson of Jupiter, who taught the art of ploughing to the Etrurians) - Branched annual or perennial herbs; strongly scented. America, ± 50 species, 1 naturalised weed in SA.

★ *Tagetes minuta* Tall Khaki Weed, Mexican Marigold; Kakiebos, Langkakiebos (A); insangwana, unukani (Z) (*minuta* - small)

Strongly scented annual herb, 0,5-3 m. Widespread weed, from S America. Leaves ± 100 mm, compound; leaflets ± 50 x 5 mm, margins sharply toothed, half clasping at base. Flowerheads small, in congested terminal inflorescences, dull yellow bracts, ray florets creamy white (Feb-Jun). Pungent smelling leaves. Used to treat nematode infestations, fleas on dogs, and in the perfume industry.

Inulanthera [= *Athanasia*] - Shrubs or shrublets. S Afr, 10 species.

Inulanthera calva [= *Athanasia calva*] (*calva* - hairless)

Softly woody shrub, up to 1,5(3) m. In scrub, damp grassland, on forest margins. Stems simple or branched, thinly white woolly. **Leaves:** Tufted, **oblong**, ± 40 x 4 mm, hairless to densely hairy, glandular, **margins entire to sharply toothed in upper half**, stalkless, stipulelike lobes at base. **Flowerheads:** In compact, terminal inflorescences, 60-150 mm across; ± 6 mm diam, yellow (Mar-May). **General:** Crushed leaves smell like eucalyptus.

Similar species: *I. leucoclada* [= *Athanasia leucoclada*] Leaves alternate, ± 30 x 13 mm, rigidly leathery, gland dotted, margins sharply toothed, upper leaf margins sometimes entire; inflorescences dense, woolly, flowerheads ± 10 mm diam.

Aspilia natalensis   ★ *Tithonia diversifolia*   *Melanthera scandens*

Lawrence Peacock   *Martin von Fintel*   *Wayne Matthews*

★ *Coreopsis lanceolata*   ★ *Bidens bipinnata*   ★ *Bidens biternata*

Geoff Nichols   *Anne Rennie*   *C J Ward*

★ *Tagetes minuta*   *Inulanthera calva*   *Inulanthera leucoclada*

Anne Rennie   *Martin von Fintel*   *Tony Abbott*

319

Phymaspermum (*phyma* - swelling; *sperma* - seed) - Shrubs or shrublets. S Afr, 18 species.

Phymaspermum acerosum [= *Athanasia acerosa*] Geelblombos (A); isibhaha-Segceke, umhlonishwa (Z) (*acerosum* - needle-shaped, like a pine needle)

Well branched shrublet, up to 1,5 m, in colonies. In grassland, on forest margins, coast to 2000 m. Perennial rootstock. Stems woody, simple, leafy. Leaves: Variable, ± 45 x less than 1 mm, simple or 5-7 lobed, segments 3-30 mm, rigid or soft, sparsely hairy, large glandlike swelling at base of midrib beneath, stalkless. Flowerheads: In dense, branched, terminal inflorescences; 5 x 2-3 mm, narrowly cylindrical, yellow (throughout year). General: Used in traditional medicine and as charms to ward off lightning. Similar species: *P. villosum* [= *Athanasia villosa*] Shrublet, up to 450 mm, in grassland, on stony slopes; stems densely grey silky hairy, closely leafy, lower leaves with dwarf shoots, leaves not decreasing upwards; ± 20 mm, lobes ± 15 mm, feathery; flowerheads 6 x 5 mm, yellow (Jan-May).

Cotula (*kotule* - a cup, refers to receptacle) - Herbs; leaves usually compound, finely dissected, rarely simple; stems sometimes swollen beneath flowerheads. Mainly S Hemisp, ± 90 species, ± 40 in SA, 1 a widespread weed.

Cotula hispida (*hispida* - with stiff hairs or bristles)

Tufted perennial herb, up to 400 mm. On steep grassy slopes, at base of cliffs and rock outcrops, 900-3000 m. Rhizomatous. Stems slightly woody, reclining at base. Leaves: Basal, ± 30 x 15 mm, lobes narrow, expanded, half clasping, stalks ± 80 mm; upper stem leaves with spreading hairs. Flowerheads: Solitary, 10-15 mm, yellow, reddening with age, depressed in centre, stems bare, slightly swollen below flowerheads (Jan-Apr).

Schistostephium (*schizo* - cut; *stephos* - crown, refers to deeply toothed florets) - Woody perennials, often aromatic. Afr, ± 11 species, ± 7 in SA.

Schistostephium crataegifolium Golden Flat-flower; Bergkruie (A); kobo-ea-mare-na, kobo-kholo, leapi-lehakanya (SS) (*crataegifolium* - leaves like *Crataegus*)

Tufted, aromatic perennial herb, 300-900 mm. Stony grassy slopes, up to 1950 m. Woody rootstock. Stems long, grey silky hairy throughout. Leaves: ± 45 x 30 mm, deeply lobed or cut to midrib, lobes pointed, bristle tipped, margins entire or toothed. Flowerheads: In terminal flattish inflorescences; ± 10 mm diam, yellow (Dec-Apr). General: Used in traditional medicine to treat chest complaints, sore eyes, cases of excess bile and as a charm to chase away hail clouds. Similar species: *S. heptalobum* Slender shrublet; in grassland, on forest margins, up to 1200 m; thinly hairy; leaves with 3-4 pairs lobes, margins entire or 1-2 lobed, gland dotted. *S. rotundifolium* imadliwazimbuzi (Z) Up to 1,2 m; on forest margins, coast to 1550 m; leaves ± 30 x 35 mm, silky hairy, margins broadly lobed, teeth rounded, stalks 5-10 mm; many inflorescences, flowerheads small, ± 4 mm diam (Nov-May).

Cineraria (*cinerarius* - light grey, refers to leaf colour of some species) - Herbs or subshrubs. Afr, ± 50 species, ± 35 in SA.

Cineraria dieterlenii (named after Anna Dieterlin, 1858-1945, who collected widely in Lesotho)

Perennial, straggling herb, up to 1 m or more. In damp, shady places, on forest margins, along watercourses. Stems woody at base, branching, thinly hairy, leafy. Leaves: Kidney-shaped, ± 60 x 80 mm, lobed, margins coarsely toothed, sometimes cobwebby below, young buds white woolly, stalks ± 50 mm, ears toothed, large at base. Flowerheads: In few to many, open inflorescences; ± 20 mm diam, yellow (Jan-May).

Senecio (*senex* - old man, refers to whitish grey hairy pappus) - Herbs, shrubs, rarely trees; flowerheads solitary or in inflorescences, bracts in a single row, margins interlocking. Largest genus of flowering plants, ± 2000 species worldwide, ± 300 in SA.

Senecio barbertonicus Succulent Bush Senecio (named after Barberton, the Mpun town)

Much branched, scrambling, succulent shrub, up to 2(4) m. In dry, sandy areas, on rocky outcrops or in thicket, KZN to Zim, Moz. Old stems woody, brittle, with leaf scars, pale, shiny. Leaves: Cylindrical, slightly curved, ± 80 x 5 mm, bright to dark green, narrowing to pointed tip. Flowerheads: In small terminal inflorescences; narrow, ± 18 mm, yellow-orange (Aug-Sep), sweetly scented. General: Browsed by game. Habit variable, leaves closely clustered or very slender, shorter, sparsely scattered. Useful garden plant, grown from cuttings.

320

Phymaspermum acerosum

Phymaspermum villosum

Schistostephium crataegifolium

Martin von Fintel

Tony Abbott

Van Wyk & Malan

Cotula hispida

Schistostephium rotundifolium

Martin Kunhardt

Tony Abbott

Schistostephium heptalobum

Cineraria dieterlenii

Senecio barbertonicus

Van Wyk & Malan

Martin von Fintel

Geoff Nichols

321

Senecio brachypodus (*brachypodus* - short foot)

Scrambling, succulent shrub, up to 2 m. On forest margins, in thicket, woodland, coast to 1100 m, E Cape to Moz. Stems weak, ± 10 mm diam, leafy. **Leaves:** ± 120 x 50 mm, margins entire to wavy, toothed, tapering to stalks, ± 20 mm. **Flowerheads: In congested clusters in large, terminal, branched inflorescences**; yellow, **2-5 ray florets** (Apr-Jul). **General:** Pungent scent. Hardy garden plant, attracts butterflies, dies back in early summer.
Similar species: S. pleistocephalus Old stems corky, pale creamy brown; flowerheads without ray florets, heavily honey scented.

Senecio bupleuroides Yellow Starwort; lehlongoana, lereko (SS); idwarane (X); indabula-luvalo, insangansanga yentaba, isiqandamatshana, unsonkonsoko (Z) (*bupleuroides* - resembles *Bupleurum*, family Apiaceae)

Perennial herb, up to 750 mm, in colonies. In grassland. Rootstock woody. Stems rigid, hairless throughout. **Leaves:** 3-6, **long, narrow**, ± 225 x 20 mm, leathery, veins ± prominent, margins thickened, entire or with a few teeth, often rolled under. **Flowerheads:** In loose, much branched inflorescences; ± 20 mm diam, yellow, 5-6 ray florets (Aug-Jan). **General:** Generally blooms after fires. Used in traditional medicine to treat chest and heart complaints and to ensure easy childbirth.
Similar species: S. glaberrimus Leaves broader; flowerheads with or without ray florets.

Senecio coronatus Woolly Grassland Senecio; Sybossie (A); lehlomane, moremoholo, motabo (SS); ikhubalo lesikhova, indlebe yebokwe (X); izonkozonko, ubulibazi (Z) (*coronatus* - crowned)

Perennial herb, up to 750 mm, in colonies. In grassland, coast to 2100 m, Cape to Zam, Malawi, Tanz. **Rootstock silky woolly, roots woolly**. 1-several leafy flowering stems. **Leaves:** In basal rosette, 100-400 x 5-80 mm, lightly cobwebby to hairless, **margins finely toothed**, tapering to long broad, clasping, stalklike base. **Flowerheads:** In branched inflorescence, **stems stout, loosely woolly**; ± 25 mm diam, butter yellow, bracts thinly woolly (Aug-Dec). **General:** Used in traditional medicine as poultices, purification purgatives, enemas for infants during weaning and to treat stomach ache.

Senecio decurrens isikhathazo esimhlophe (Z) (*decurrens* - running down)

Stout herb, up to 1(2) m. In grassland, damp areas, coast to 2000 m. Stems simple, cobwebby to hairless, leafy. **Leaves:** In basal rosette, ± 600 x 70 mm, tapering to tip, gradually narrowed to stalklike base; stem leaves smaller, stalkless, **wings running onto stem**. **Flowerheads:** In branched inflorescence; ± 35 mm diam, yellow (Oct-May). **General:** Used in traditional medicine as an emetic.

Senecio deltoideus undenze (X) (*deltoideus* - triangular)

Much branched, slender, **herbaceous scrambler**. On forest margins, in open scrub, SW Cape to Malawi, Moz. **Stems zigzag**, ± finely hairy. **Leaves:** Widely spaced, 50-80 x 30-70 mm, thin, soft, dark green above, paler beneath, margins irregularly toothed, stalks ± 30 mm, **leaflike ears clasping at base**, or absent. **Flowerheads:** In widely branched inflorescences; small, yellow, ± 1-4 ray florets (Apr-Sep), sweetly honey scented. **General:** Used in traditional medicine to treat sore eyes. Good bee plant. Easily grown from cuttings, useful sand stabiliser on coastal dunes.
Similar species: Delairea odorata [= *Senecio mikanioides*] At 800-1900 m in this region, Cape to KZN; stems, leaves slightly succulent, not zigzag, leaves sharply 3-5 lobed on each side, stalks ± 70 mm, often twisted, ± 2 small leaflike ears at base.

Senecio haygarthii (named after Walter Haygarth, 1862-1950, who collected in Natal and E Griqualand; botanical artist who had illustrations in 'Natal Plants' by Wood & Evans)

Robust, erect, perennial, shrubby herb, up to 1 m, in colonies. Along watercourses, in shrub communities on mountain slopes, 1500-2450 m. Many densely leafy stems, **unbranched** below inflorescences. **Leaves:** ± 60 x 25 mm, decreasing in size upwards, deeply, narrowly lobed, margins rolled under, green, **hairless** (cobwebby) **above, white felted beneath. Flowerheads: In branched inflorescences**; ± 10 mm diam, yellow (Sep-Dec).

Senecio brachypodus

Martin von Fintel

Senecio pleistocephalus

Geoff Nichols

Senecio glaberrimus

Tony Abbott

Senecio bupleuroides

Martin von Fintel

Lal Greene

Senecio deltoideus

C J Ward

Senecio coronatus

Martin von Fintel

Senecio decurrens

Martin von Fintel

Senecio haygarthii

Geoff Nichols

323

Senecio helminthioides **ihlozi elincane (Z)** (*helminthioides* - like a worm)
Succulent climber, up to 3 m. On dry forest margins, in woodland, coast to 900 m, E Cape to N Prov, Moz. **Leaves:** ± 60 x 70 mm, shallowly lobed, **margins toothed,** stalks ± 60 mm. **Flowerheads:** Solitary, or few in terminal inflorescences; ± 10 mm diam, orange, **leafy calyx-like bracts** (Apr-Jul), sweetly scented. **General:** Dies back in winter, useful garden plant.
Similar species: *S. quinquelobus* **uchantikhulu (X)** E Cape to KZN midlands, on forest margins; no leafy calyx-like bracts.

Senecio heliopsis (*heliopsis* - like the sun)
Perennial herb, up to 1 m, in colonies. **In well drained grassland,** up to 2400 m. Woody rootstock, crowned with **coarse, fibrous leaf bases. Leaves:** In basal rosette, **broad,** ± 300 x 90 mm, usually less, fleshy, margins ± entire to toothed, tapering to broad, stalklike, clasping base. **Flowerheads:** 3-9 **on long stalks,** in branched terminal inflorescences; ± 30 mm diam, yellow (Sep-Dec). **Similar species:** *S. caudatus* In very marshy ground; basal leaves narrow; flowers on short stalks; both species found together at times.

Senecio hygrophilus **Blouvleibossie (A)** (*hygrophilous* - moisture loving)
Perennial herb, up to 1 m, in colonies. In valley bottoms, **in damp grassland.** Rootstock thick, woody. Stem simple, leafy, **blue-green. Leaves:** 90-160 x (20)30-75 mm, margins entire to slightly toothed, slightly fleshy, aging leathery, narrowing to half-clasping, stalklike base. **Flowerheads:** In crowded, flat topped inflorescences; long, narrow, 1-2(3) ray florets, yellow (Nov-Dec). **Similar species:** *S. adnatus* On dry, grassy hill tops, leaves long, narrow.

Senecio inornatus **lehlongoana-le-leholo (SS); inkanga, uhlabo (Z)** (*inornatus* - modest)
Perennial herb, up to 2 m, in colonies. In moist grassland, coast to 3000 m, Cape to Tanz. Rootstock stout, woody. **Stems solitary,** leafy, lightly cobwebby at first, hairless later. **Very variable in leaf size, texture, margins, flowerheads. Leaves:** In basal rosette, **long,** ± 600 x 50 mm, thin or leathery, margins toothed; stem leaves broad, eared and clasping at base, running onto stem, sometimes winged. **Flowerheads:** In branched, crowded, flat topped inflorescences; **small, 5 ray florets,** yellow, shortish, curled back (Dec-Mar). **General:** Visited by ants and stingless bees. Used in traditional medicine to treat palpitations and phthisis.

Senecio isatideus **Dan's Cabbage; Blouvleibossie (A); lebato, lehlomane-le-leputsoa (SS)** (*isatideus* - resembles the genus *Isatis*, family Cruciferae/Brassicacae)
Perennial herb, up to 1,5 m, in colonies. In grassland. Rootstock stout, woody, **crown woolly.** Stems solitary, leafy, wool in axils. **Leaves:** ± 200 x 65 mm, decreasing in size upwards, **bluish green,** margins thickened, toothed, side veins sharply ascending, narrowed into broad, flat, winged stalks. **Flowerheads:** In congested clusters, in branched inflorescence; yellow (Dec-Jan). **General:** Poisonous to stock. New leaves appear before grass in spring.
Similar species: *S. isatidioides* Up to 2,4 m; on forest margins, in damp grassland, 1600-1800 m, KZN to N Prov. Crown not woolly; stem closely leafy throughout, hairless. Leaves leathery, broad, ± 200 x 115 mm, margins finely toothed, side veins abruptly ascending then spreading at right angles to midrib before looping upwards near margins, base rounded, running onto, and slightly winging, stem.

Senecio latifolius **Molteno-disease Plant; idwara, iyeza lasekaya (X); idwakala, ingcobangcoba, uhlambahlanyana, uqedizwe (Z)** (*latifolius* - broad leaved)
Robust, perennial herb, up to 1,5 m, in colonies. In grassland or open woodland, E Cape to Malawi, Moz, up to 800(1200) m. Rootstock stout, woody, crown woolly. 1(2) stems, **simple, leafy throughout, leaves hardly reducing upwards,** hairless (woolly hairs in axils). **Leaves:** ± 90(140) x 40(80) mm, leathery, margins thickened, widely toothed or entire, heart-shaped, half-clasping at base. **Flowerheads:** In large, much branched, flattish inflorescences; small, yellow (Sep-Dec). **General:** Weedy at times. **Similar species:** *S. retrorsus* At higher altitudes; stem branching near base; leaves more widely spaced, decreasing in size upwards.

Senecio helminthioides

C J Ward

Senecio quinquelobus

Tony Abbott

Senecio heliopsis

Lal Greene

Senecio hygrophilus

Olaf Wirminghaus

Senecio inornatus

Pam Cooke

Senecio isatideus

Martin von Fintel

Senecio isatidioides

Martin von Fintel

Senecio latifolius

Lawrence Peacock

Senecio latifolius

Lorraine van Hooff

325

Senecio macroglossus Flowering Ivy *(macroglossus - large tongue)*
Slender, succulent climber. On forest margins, sandy to rocky places, S Cape to Zim. Stems root from nodes. Hairless throughout. **Leaves:** ± 45 x 80 mm, usually 3 lobed, shiny dark green, stalks 15-30 mm. **Flowerheads:** 1-3, **large, 40-50 mm diam, pale creamy yellow**, stalks ± 100 mm (mainly Mar-Jul). **General:** Popular garden plant, grown in Europe since 1875.
Similar species: *S. macroglossoides* 600-1700 m; leaves 3-5 lobed; ± 12 yellow flowerheads in open inflorescences, on short leafy side branches, bracts leafy.

Senecio macrospermus *(macrospermus - long seeds)*
Stout perennial herb, up to 1 m, in large colonies. On steep, damp, mountain slopes, up to 3000 m. Thick, woody rootstock. **Large clump of leaf rosettes,** flowering stems stout, leafy, plant **pale grey woolly. Leaves:** Basal, ± 600 x 80 mm, tapering to broad, clasping, stalklike base (remaining as fibrous crown), margins with tiny teeth, wavy. **Flowerheads:** ± 8, in branched inflorescences; ± 13 ray florets, yellow (Dec-Mar).

Senecio madagascariensis
Annual herb, up to 800 mm. S Cape to Moz, Madag, Mascarene Is, coast to 1500 m. Stems simple, leafy, hairless. **Leaves:** ± 120 x 25 mm, usually smaller, margins toothed, ± finely lobed, tapering to narrow, stalklike, half-clasping base. **Flowerheads:** In clusters in open branched inflorescences; small, yellow, ± 13 ray florets, **often rolled under** (throughout year). **General:** Visited by flies, bees, wasps, small moths, beetles and thrips. Common weed in disturbed areas.
Similar species: *S. harveianus* Canary Weed; Geelopslag (A); khotolia (SS) **Perennial, bushy herb,** up to 1,2 m; on rocky outcrops, bare places, on mountains, 1400-3000 m; leaves narrow, ± 100 x 10 mm, stalkless, margins entire or toothed; flowerheads larger, yellow, 3-4 rows calyxlike bracts, dark tipped, overlapping (Feb-May). *S. inaequidens* Perennial, much branched herb, not found below 1400 m in KZN; more woody; flowers smaller.

Senecio medley-woodii *(named after John Medley Wood, 1827-1915, botanist, collector, first curator of Natal Herbarium, who published widely on Natal flora)*
Well branched succulent shrub, up to 2 m. In scrub on cliff edges, granite outcrops, up to 600 m. Rare. Stems thick, white felted at first, hairless later. **Leaves:** ± 60 x 30 mm, white felted on both surfaces, margins entire to coarsely toothed in upper half, tips blunt or pointed, base narrowed, flat, stalklike. **Flowerheads:** ± 50 mm diam, yellow, white felted bracts, stems long, ± 150 mm, white felted (Jun-Jul). **General:** Good container and garden plant for hot dry places.

Senecio napifolius *(napifolius - leaves like a turnip)*
Perennial herb, up to 800 mm, in colonies. In open grassland, moist depressions, 1300-2300 m (at lower altitudes in Cape). Rhizomatous, stem solitary, erect, simple, hollow, ± 10 mm diam, leafy in lower part, harshly hairy to hairless. **Leaves:** ± 200 x 90 mm, **deeply lobed,** margins coarsely, sharply toothed, lower leaves tapering to broad, flat, half-clasping, stalklike base; upper leaves eared, reducing in size upwards. **Flowerheads:** In congested clusters in compact inflorescence; ± 25 mm diam, yellow (Nov-Jan).

Senecio natalicola
Perennial herb, up to 600 mm. **In coastal grassland,** sometimes marshes, up to 350 m. Rootstock woody, ± 10 mm diam. Stems **hollow,** simple, thinly sticky hairy throughout. **Leaves:** In basal rosette, ± 300 x 50 mm, soft, margins coarsely toothed or lobed, narrowed to broad, flat, stalklike, clasping base. **Flowerheads:** In slightly branched inflorescences; ± 40 mm diam, pale yellow, stalks long (**Aug-Nov**).
Similar species: *S. ingeliensis* High Drakensberg, Ngeli Mountain, 1850-2500 m; summer flowering (Dec-Mar).

Senecio macroglossus

C J Ward

Senecio macroglossoides

Tony Abbott

Senecio macrospermus

Koos Roux

Senecio madagascariensis

Tom de Waal

Senecio harveianus

Lal Greene

Senecio medley-woodii

Geoff Nichols

Senecio medley-woodii

Geoff Nichols

Senecio napifolius

Tony Abbott

Senecio natalicola

Tony Abbott

Senecio panduriformis Bosdissel (A) (*panduriformis* - fiddle-shaped leaves)
Robust herb up to 2,4 m, colonies. On forest margins, up to 1600 m. Stem woody, simple, mostly leafless below, leafy above; ± woolly throughout. **Leaves:** ± 220 x 110 mm, margins thickened, toothed, base broad, **abruptly contracted to broadly winged, stalklike base,** eared and half-clasping. **Flowerheads:** In much branched inflorescence; yellow (Mar-May).

Senecio paucicalyculatus (*paucicalyculatus* - few bracts, resembling outer calyx)
Perennial herb, up to 700 mm. In grassland in black, peaty, waterlogged soil, 1200-2800 m. Rhizome stout, crown woolly, roots thonglike. Flowering stems simple, from centre of each leaf rosette. **Leaves:** In basal rosette, ± 150 x 50 mm, margins toothed, narrowing to broad, flat, stalklike clasping base. **Flowerheads:** Few to many in branched inflorescence; ± 40 mm diam, yellow (Sep-Jan).

Senecio polyanthemoides (*polyanthemoides* - many flowers)
Bushy annual herb, up to 1,8 m. On forest margins, weed of disturbed ground. Stems woody at base, leafy throughout, **rough, resinous. Leaves:** ± 150 x 100 mm, margins entire, sharply toothed or deeply divided, white felted beneath, **base narrowed, stalklike. Flowerheads:** In large, branched inflorescences; ± 10 mm diam, yellow, ± **8 ray florets** (throughout year). **General:** Visited by flies, bees, wasps, butterflies, small beetles. Reputed to cause the death of horses.

Senecio rhomboideus lekoto-la-litsoene, lelutla-la-pula (SS) (*rhomboideus* - diamond-shaped)
Fleshy, perennial herb, up to 1 m. In grassland, on rocky outcrops, 1300-3000 m, S Cape to N Prov. Elongated tubers ± 80 x 15 mm. **Leaves:** ± 200 x 80, **blue-green,** margins widely toothed in upper part, lobed or sharply toothed, **tapering to broad, flat, stalklike, half-clasping base. Flowerheads:** In branched inflorescences; yellow (Nov-Mar).
Similar species: *S. oxyriifolius* **False Nasturtium; Kappertjieblaar (A); idumbe, idumbe lasendhle, ihlula (Z)** Coast to 2300 m, S Cape to Tanz; leaves basal, round, 50-90 mm diam, margins toothed or sharply angled, stalks long, slender, ± 150 mm, often ± peltate (attached inside blade); flowering stem long, ribbed. Used traditionally to treat fever, barrenness in women, swellings in animals and to prevent sorcery.

Senecio rhyncholaenus Ruikbossie (A); mahoaneng, mahoanyana (SS); imfenyane (Sw,Z) (*rhyncholaenus* - snoutlike)
Perennial herb, up to 600 mm, in colonies. In grassland, rock outcrops, up to 1400 m. Rootstock stout, woody. Stems leafy, thinly **sticky** hairy. **Leaves:** Basal ± 200 x 70 mm, **finely lobed,** margins ± toothed, **narrowing to stalklike base. Flowerheads:** In branched inflorescences; creamy white, **bracts with sticky glands** (throughout year). **General:** Characteristic sweet or spicy smell, persists after drying. Used in traditional medicine to treat colds, colic pains, sore hands, feet and to repel stalk borer. Used to make the *isicholo,* traditional married woman's headdress.

Senecio serratuloides Two-day Cure; ichazampukane, insukumbili, umaphozisa umkhuthelo (Z)
Stiffly erect, perennial herb, up to 1 m, in large colonies. **In grassland, open woodland,** up to 2000 m, E Cape to N Prov. **Leaves:** ± 120 x 25 mm, **finely lobed,** 1-4 pairs, **terminal lobe very large, ± folded lengthwise,** margins ± double-toothed, ± thinly cobwebby beneath, often with blackish red sticky gland dots. **Flowerheads:** Many, in congested inflorescences, ± 120 mm diam, or in looser inflorescences, fewer flowers (Mar-May), scented. **General:** Used in traditional medicine to treat infected sores and burns, and brewed as a tea for infections. Grown from suckers.

Senecio tamoides Canary Creeper; Kanarieklimop (A); ihlozi elikhulu, uqobaqoba (Z) (*tamoides* - resembling *Tamus*)
Succulent climber, to top of canopy. On forest margins, E Cape to Zim. Mature stems corky. **Leaves:** ± 80 x 80 mm, **unequally lobed,** margins toothed, stalks ± 90 mm. **Flowerheads: In large inflorescences 120-150 mm diam;** ± 15 mm diam, ± 5 yellow ray florets (Mar-Jul), sweetly scented. **General:** Visited by butterflies (Pieridae). Used in traditional medicine to treat flatulence, and anthrax in cattle. Lovely garden plant. Dies back in colder areas.

Senecio oxyriifolius

Van Wyk & Malan

Senecio panduriformis

Martin von Fintel

Senecio paucicalyculatus

Lal Greene

Senecio oxyriifolius

Lal Greene

Senecio rhomboideus

Tony Abbott

Senecio serratuloides

Richard Symmonds

Senecio polyanthemoides

Lorraine van Hooff

Senecio rhyncholaenus

Tony Abbott

Senecio tamoides

Trevor Coleman

Senecio tamoides

Lorraine van Hooff

329

Solanecio (possibly a combination of *Solanum* and *Senecio*) - Climbers, herbs (trees); fast growing, used for hedging in Kenya. Trop Afr, Madag, Yemen, 16 species, 1 in SA.

Solanecio angulatus [= *Crassocephalum bojeri, C. subscandens*] (*angulatus* - angled)

Robust semi-succulent scrambling shrub or climber, up to 30 m. In coastal and dry forest, KZN to Ethiopia. **Stems branching at right angles**, faintly grooved. **Leaves:** Alternate, ± 120 x 80 mm, paler beneath, lobed, margins with irregular teeth, red edged, **stalks ± 50 mm, narrowly winged, pair of broad, rounded, toothed ears at base.** **Flowerheads:** In compact inflorescences, stems bare, with leafy bracts at base; yellow (Apr-Sep), **foul smelling. General:** Grown from cuttings.

Euryops (*eurys* - large; *ops* - eye, refers to showy flowerheads) - Shrubs or shrublets; leaves alternate, often crowded, shape variable; flowerheads large to small on short or long stalks. Afr, ± 98 species, majority in S Afr.

Euryops chrysanthemoides Daisy Bush (*chrysanthemoides* - chrysathemumlike)

Evergreen shrub, 0,5-2 m. In coastal areas, on forest margins, in scrub, grassland, disturbed areas. Main stems bare, young branches closely leafy. **Leaves:** Close set, **soft, flat, spreading**, 30-100 x 10-30 mm, deeply lobed, narrowing to stalklike base. **Flowerheads:** Solitary, ± 35 mm diam, yellow, stems 50-200 mm, several at tips of branches (Mar-Sep). **General:** Hardy garden plant, weedy in places.

Euryops evansii sehlakoana (SS) (named after Maurice Evans, 1854-1920, English businessman, plant collector, who came to Natal in 1875; joint author with Medley Wood of 'Natal Plants' vol 1)

Sparingly branched shrub, up to 1,8 m, in colonies. In scrub along rocky watercourses, alpine grassland, 1200-3000 m. Main stems bare, rough with leaf scars, leaves clustered at tips. **Leaves:** 10-100 x 2-20 mm, **grey-green, leathery, flat, tips 3 toothed. Flowerheads:** 2-5 in terminal clusters, ± 15 mm diam, yellow (Jul-Apr). **General:** Plants project above snow. Used in traditional medicine to treat headaches.

Euryops laxus Resin Bush; Harpuisbossie (A) (*laxus* - loose, limp)

Perennial herb, up to 600 mm. In open or rocky grassland, coast to 2000 m. Stems annual, simple or little branched, leafy towards base. **Leaves:** Variable in size and shape, erect to spreading, 10-110 mm, entire or with ± 4 pairs lobes, soft, flat or thickish to roundish. **Flowerheads:** Solitary, ± 40 mm diam, yellow, ray florets widely spaced, stalks ± 250 mm (Aug-Dec). **General:** One of the first plants to shoot after grass fires.

Euryops tysonii sehlakoana (SS) (named after William Tyson, born Jamaca 1851, died Grahamstown 1920, teacher, plant collector)

Much branched shrub, up to 1,5 m, in colonies. On rocky mountain slopes, boulder beds of streams, 1200-2500 m. Stems leafy towards tips, rough with leaf scars below. **Leaves: Closely set, often overlapping**, erect to spreading, 10-30 x 2-8 mm, glossy green, flat, leathery, margins entire or ± toothed, white wool in axils. **Flowers:** Solitary in upper leaf axils, creating a crowded terminal cluster; ± 10 mm diam, stalks ± 40 mm (Sep-May), sweet scent. **General:** Attractive garden shrub.

Othonna (*othonne* - linen, perhaps refers to soft leaves of some species) - Shrubs, subshrubs or herbs, often semi-succulent. Afr, ± 140 species, mainly in the Cape.

Othonna natalensis Geelbossie (A); naka, phela (SS); incamu (Z)

Perennial fleshy herb, up to 550 mm, in colonies. In grassland, among rocks, coast to 2700 m, E Cape to Zim. Woody rootstock, crown cushionlike, ± 200 mm diam, with few to many leaf tufts, woolly at base. **Leaves:** Erect, in basal rosette, ± 150 x 40 mm, thick, **blue-green**, flushed reddish purple at base, margins entire or toothed, tapering to stalklike base. **Flowerheads:** Solitary, terminal, 30-40 mm diam, yellow, stem simple or forked, ± 400 mm (Aug-Oct). **General:** Eaten by people and stock when food is scarce. Used as a salad vegetable. Roots rich in oil. Used in traditional medicine to treat nausea, tapeworm, and also worm infestations in calves.
Similar species: *O. carnosa* Succulent, herb, up to 600 mm, in sandy grassland, near sea; foul smelling; leaves ± 150 x 10 mm, cylindrical in upper parts; flowerheads less than 10 mm diam, yellow, no ray florets (var. *discoidea*), or with ray florets (var. *carnosa*) stems long, bare, branching (Mar-Oct). Visited by flies and bees, immature fruits eaten by the Yelloweyed Canary; useful garden plant. Var. *carnosa* is mostly confined to the Cape.

Solanecio angulatus

Euryops tysonii

Euryops chrysanthemoides

Euryops evansii

Euryops evansii

Othonna natalensis

Othonna carnosa

Euryops laxus

Osteospermum (*osteon* - bone; *sperma* - seed, refers to hard seeds) - Mostly SA, ± 37 species. Attracts butterflies.

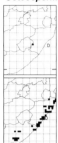

Osteospermum attenuatum (*attenuatum* refers to tapering leaf bases)

Mat-forming perennial herb, stems up to 400 mm long. In moist, grassy places, **1675-2300 m**. Rootstock thin, creeping. **Leaves:** Alternate, ± 55 x 10 mm, margins toothed, **tapering to stalklike base. Flowerheads:** Solitary, ± 25 mm diam, yellow, ray florets purplish red beneath, stalks ± 40 mm (Dec).

Osteospermum grandidentatum Yellow Trailing Daisy; uqoboquba (X,Z); umadinsane (Z) (*grandidentatum* - large teeth)

Sprawling to scrambling perennial herb, stems up to 1 m. In grassland, on forest margins, **coast to 1500 m**. Rootstock woody. Stems rough. **Leaves: Alternate**, ± 60 x 40 mm, **thick**, margins toothed, **stalkless. Flowerheads:** Solitary, 20-30 mm diam, orange-yellow (Jul-Feb). **General:** Used traditionally as a strong emetic. **Similar species:** *O. imbricatum* **inkhupuhlana, umasigcolo (Z)** Slender shrublet, up to 1,5 m; **leaves overlapping**, thick, leathery, margins hard, entire.

Ursinia (named after Johann Ursinus, 1608-66, author of Arboretum Biblicum) - Herbs. Mostly SA, ± 40 species.

Ursinia tenuiloba umuthi wezifuba (Z) (*tenuiloba* - narrow lobes)

Perennial herb, in clumps, up to 300 mm. In grassland, coast to 2130 m. Stems annual, **leafy. Leaves:** ± 50 mm, **upper part finely lobed**, lobes ± 10 mm, narrow, white hairy at first, lower half stalklike or with reduced lobe. **Flowerheads:** Solitary, ± 30 mm diam, ray florets yellow above, often reddish below, stalks ± 150 mm (Jul-Dec). **Fruit:** Pappus of **broad white petal-like scales. General:** First to bloom after fires. Pollinated by a pale green fly. Used traditionally to treat coughs.

Arctotis (*arktos* - a bear; *otis* - an ear, a Linnaean flight of fancy) - Woolly or glandular herbs. Mostly SA, ± 50 species.

Arctotis arctotoides putswa-pududu (SS); ubushwa (X)

Mat-forming perennial herb. In marshy places, up to 2745 m, Cape to KZN. **Leaves:** Basal, 100-200 x 20-80 mm, margins wavy, lobed or faintly toothed, **white felted beneath**, narrowing to half-clasping stemlike base. **Flowers:** Solitary, 25-40 mm diam, ray florets yellow, purplish brown beneath, bracts white woolly, stalks ± 200 mm, white cobwebby or hairless (Sep-Mar). **Fruit:** 2 mm, **not woolly**.

Arctotheca (*arktos* - bear; *theke* - a case or capsule, densely woolly fruit) - Perennial herbs. SA, 4 species.

Arctotheca populifolia Beach Pumpkin; Seepampoen (A) (*populifolia* - leaves like a Poplar)

Fleshy, perennial herb, up to 300 mm. **Colonises shifting beach sand**, Cape to S Moz coastline. Stems ± 10 mm diam, branched, leafy, **white felted** throughout. **Leaves:** ± 70 x 70 mm, stalks flat, ± 80 mm, half clasping at base. **Flowerheads:** 15-20 mm diam, yellow, inconspicuous, bracts white felted, stalks ± 100 mm (Aug-Dec).

Gazania (named after Theodor of Gaza 15th Century translator of botanical works) - Perennial herbs. SA, ± 16 species.

Gazania krebsiana Common Gazania; Bruingousblom (A); mabone, shoeshoe, tsikitlane (SS); isapokwe, umkwinti (X); ubendle (X,Z); impephotshani, isiphephane (Z) (named after Georg Krebs, 1792-1844, German apothecary, plant collector who came to SA in 1817)

Perennial herb, up to 300 mm. In grassland, coast to 3000 m. **Leaves:** ± 100(200) x 2-5(10) mm, lobed or not, white felted beneath. **Flowerheads:** Solitary, 30-70 mm diam, ray florets yellow with greenish or reddish line below, sometimes a dark reddish blotch at base, open in bright sunlight, close at night to reopen next day (throughout year). **General:** Flowers eaten raw. Felt on back of leaves rolled into twine to make skirts in Lesotho. Used traditionally to treat sickly babies, earache and sterility in women. Popular garden plant, in cultivation since 1755, many hybrids.

Haplocarpha (*haplo* - single, spread out; *karphos* - small dry body, refers to pappus) - Endemic to Afr, ± 8 species.

Haplocarpha scaposa False Gerbera; Bietou, Melktou (A); khutsana, lengoako, leshala, lisebo, moarubetso, sesweu (SS); isikhali, umkhanzi (X) (*scaposa* - leafless stems)

Perennial herb, up to 350(600) mm. In grassland, Cape to CE Afr, 1525-2000 m (in KZN). **Leaves:** In basal rosette, ± 150 x 70 mm, leathery, margins entire or toothed, downy above, **white felted beneath**, veins almost parallel beneath. **Flowerheads:** Solitary, 40-80 mm diam, pale yellow (Aug-Mar). **General:** Crushed leaves used by women during menstruation. Used by sangomas when consulting the divining bones. White felt of leaves once used as tinder for tinder boxes. Garden plant.

Osteospermum attenuatum   Hilliard & Burtt

Osteospermum grandidentatum   Lawrence Peacock

Osteospermum imbricatum   Tony Abbott

Arctotis arctotoides   Lal Greene

Ursinia tenuiloba   Lal Greene

Arctotheca populifolia   Trevor Coleman

Gazania krebsiana   Darrel Plowes

Haplocarpha scaposa   Martin von Fintel

Gazania krebsiana   Lal Greene

333

Gazania rigens Trailing Gazania; Rankbotterblom (A); ubendle (Z) *(rigens - stiff)*

Creeping perennial herb, 200-300 mm. **Common sand coloniser**, S Cape to Moz. **Stems 4-5 mm diam, branched, rooting at nodes. Leaves:** ± 120 x 15 mm, leathery, glossy above, white felted beneath, margins entire, occasionally lobed. **Flowerheads:** Solitary, ± 40 mm diam, yellow, stalks 100-150 mm (throughout year). **General:** Visited by small beetles, bees. Used for a love charm emetic.

Berkheya (named after Jan le Francq van Berkhey, 1729-1812, Dutch botanist) - Perennial herbs or shrubs, often thistlelike; leaves spiny; flower bracts usually spiny. Mostly SA, ± 75 species.

Berkheya bergiana (named after Peter Bergius, 1730-90, superintendent of Company's garden at the Cape)

Stout perennial herb, **up to 2,5 m, in colonies.** On forest margins, weedy in disturbed areas, up to 1800 m. Stem branching above, downy, winged. Milky juice. **Leaves:** ± 150 x 50 mm, lobed, rough above, white cobwebby beneath, margins sharply hairy, coarsely, deeply toothed, teeth spine tipped, **running onto stem in broad, spiny wings. Flowerheads:** In branched inflorescences; 40-60 mm diam, yellow, bracts ± 3 mm wide, tips and margins spiny, lightly cobwebby beneath (Mar-Jun).

Berkheya cirsiifolia mohata-o-mosoeu, ntsoantsane-e-kholo, tsehlo-ea-thaba (SS)
(cirsiifolia - leaves like Cirsium)

Stout perennial herb, up to 1,5 m, in colonies. On moist, grassy slopes, streambanks, 1800-2500 m. Stems softly hairy, winged, leafy. **Leaves:** ± 300 x 80 mm, ± 6 lobes each side, rough above, white felted beneath, margins coarsely, deeply toothed, **upper leaves broad, clasping, running onto stem in spiny wings. Flowerheads:** Solitary or few in branched terminal inflorescences; ± 80 mm diam, **ray florets white or yellow, bracts leafy,** ± 10 mm wide, **spines ± 10 mm** (Jan-Mar). **Similar species:** *B. onopordifolia* Bract spines shorter, ± 4 mm. (See p. 446)

Berkheya echinacea iphungula (Z) *(echinacea - prickly)*

Stout, perennial herb, up to 1 m, in colonies. In stony grassland, KZN to N Prov, 1300-1830 m. Tuberous roots. **Leaves:** Basal (often missing), ± 80 x 50 mm; stem leaves, ± 50 x 8 mm, **upper surface and margins densely covered in straw coloured bristles,** margins **running onto stems in broad, toothed, bristly wings. Flowerheads:** 1-5 in inflorescences; ± 60 mm diam, yellow, bracts ± 2 mm wide, tips and margins spiny (Dec-Feb). **General:** Used in traditional medicine.

Berkheya erysithales

Robust, erect, perennial herb, up to 1,8 m. In damp, shady places, up to 1200 m. Stems leafy, sometimes cobwebby at first. **Leaves:** ± 350 x 180 mm, rough above, thinly white felted beneath, wavy, irregularly lobed, coarsely toothed or cut, spine tipped, lower leaves narrowed to a stalklike base, upper leaves broad, half clasping, all with spiny basal ears. **Flowerheads:** In large, open, branched inflorescences; 30-50 mm diam, yellow, few ray florets, bracts ± 3 mm broad, **margins fringed with hairs** (Dec-May). **General:** Can become weedy in overgrazed areas.

Berkheya insignis (*insignis* - remarkable)

Perennial herb, up to 400(600) mm, in clumps. On rocky hillsides. Stems, downy. **Leaves:** ± 80 x 15 mm, bristly above, white felted beneath, **bristle tipped,** margins with **long, flexible bristles, ± 10 mm. Flowerheads:** Solitary, ± 80 mm diam, yellow-orange, bracts ± 15 mm, white felted on back, margins and tip spiny (**Aug-Dec**). **General:** Very showy, especially after fires.

Berkheya macrocephala ntsoantsane, sehohlo-se-seholo (SS) *(macrocephala - large head)*

Perennial herb, up to 500 mm. On grassy hillsides, 1525-2450 m. Stems stout, lightly cobwebby. **Leaves:** In spreading basal rosette, ± 400 x 120 mm, 10-12 **lobes each side, more or less overlapping,** margins spiny. **Flowerheads: Solitary, large,** ± 100 mm, yellow, bracts ± 8 mm broad, tips and margins spiny (Oct-Jan). **Similar species:** *B. multijuga* (see p. 336).

Martin von Fintel

Tony Abbott

Tony Abbott

Gazania rigens   *Berkheya bergiana*   *Berkheya erysithales*

Darrel Plowes

Rosemary Williams

Martin von Fintel

Berkheya cirsiifolia   *Berkheya onopordifolia*   *Berkheya echinacea*

Tom de Waal

Olaf Wirminghaus

Berkheya insignis   *Berkheya macrocephala*

335

Berkheya mackenii (named after Mark McKen, 1823-1872, first curator Bot Gardens, Durban)
Shrub, up to 1 m, in colonies. In grassland, 1330-1500 m. **Leaves:** ± 50 x 10 mm, rigid, white felted beneath, lobes triangular, spine tipped, margins fringed with spines, **running onto stem in narrow wings.** Flowerheads: 1-2 at tips of branchlets, 20-30 mm diam, yellow, rarely with ray florets, bracts ± 2,5 mm broad, margins, tips spiny, white felted (Mar-Apr). **General:** Invades overgrazed grassland.

Berkheya montana mohatollo, ntsoa-ntsane-ea-loti (SS) (*montana* - of mountains)
Robust herb, up to 2 m, in dense stands. On forest margins, in swampy ground, 1370-1850 m. Stem covered with slender spines ± 7 mm, **leafy throughout. Leaves:** ± 200 x 100 mm, harshly hairy above, cobwebby beneath, margins toothed, bristly. **Flowerheads:** In spreading inflorescences; 30-40 mm diam, yellow, bracts ± 2,5 mm broad, tips, margins spiny (Feb-Apr). **General:** Used traditionally to treat bruises. **Similar species: *B. maritima*** Leaves more deeply cut, white felted beneath, running onto stem in narrow wings, teeth in 2s or 3s; flower bracts white felted beneath.

Berkheya multijuga Spiny Berg Thistle; Doringrige Bergdissel (A); mohatollo, ntsoa-ntsane-ea-loti (SS); imboziso emhlophe, ukhakhasi (Z)
Perennial herb, up to 1,8 m, in colonies. On steep grassy slopes, 1800-3200 m. **Leaves:** In rosette, ± 400 x 150 mm, usually cut almost to midrib, ± overlapping, margins toothed, spine tipped, softly hairy above, **cobwebby below**; stem leaves half-clasping at base. **Flowerheads:** ± **8,** in terminal inflorescences; ± 60-100 mm diam, bract tips, margins spiny (**Dec-Mar**). **Similar species;** *B. macrocephala* (see p. 334).

Berkheya rhapontica ntsoa-ntsane, pepetloane-e-meutla (SS); ikhakhasi, iphungula (Z) (*rhapontica* - like garden rhubarb)
Perennial herb, up to 1,2(2) m, in small colonies. In grassland, on rocky outcrops. Stem stout, hairless, downy or cobwebby. **Leaves:** In basal rosette, ± 300 x 100 mm, spiny, harshly hairy above, downy to white felted beneath, margins entire or lobed, lobed to coarsely toothed, narrowed to stalklike base; stem leaves **run onto stem in broad or narrow spiny wings.** **Flowerheads:** Scattered, forming narrow inflorescences, stalks 10-100 mm, usually winged; 20-40 mm diam, yellow, bracts ± 2 mm wide, tips and margins spiny, cobwebby beneath (Dec-Apr, subsp. *platyptera* Mar-Jul). **General:** Used traditionally for dry coughs. Three subspecies.

Berkheya setifera Buffalo-tongue Berkheya; Rasperdisseldoring (A); lelelemla-khomo, ntsoantsane (SS); mavambuka (Sw); indlebe-lenkomo (X); ulimi-lwenkomo (Sw, Z); ikhakhasi, ulimi-lwenyathi (Z) (*setifera* - bristles)
Perennial herb, up to 1,2 m, in colonies. In grassland, up to 2000 m, E Cape to Zim. Rootstock woody, sap milky. **Leaves:** Basal, ± 550 x 80-120 mm, **green on both surfaces, upper surface with coarse, straw coloured bristles**, lower, cobwebby when young, later harshly hairy; margins entire to shallowly lobed. **Flowerheads:** In branched inflorescences, ± 60 mm diam, yellow, bracts narrow, 1 mm wide, tips and margins spiny (Sep-Feb). **General:** Used for brushing hair, as a pot herb and in traditional medicine to treat stomach complaints and repel evil spirits.

Berkheya speciosa Skraaldisseldoring (A); ntsoantsane (SS); ikhakhasi elikhulu, umaphola (Z) (*speciosa* - beautiful)
Perennial herb, up to 1 m, in colonies. In open grassland. Rootstock woody. **Leaves:** Basal, ± 300 x 250 mm, green, harshly hairy above, **white felted beneath**, margins entire, wavy, coarsely toothed, spiny, stalks 20-300 mm. **Flowerheads:** In forking inflorescences; ± 70 mm diam, yellow, bracts ± 2 mm wide, tips and margins spiny, sometimes cobwebby beneath (Aug-Feb). **General:** Used traditionally to treat abdominal disorders, bilharzia and to bathe sore eyes. Attractive garden plant.

Berkheya umbellata Geelklossiedissel, Klossies, Vleidissel (A); ikhakhasana elincane (Z) (*umbellata* - flowerheads in flat topped inflorescence)
Perennial herb, up to 80 mm. In grassland. **Leaves:** In basal rosette, ± 350 x 150 mm, **deeply cut or lobed,** covered in bristles above, downy beneath, margins toothed, spiny; stem leaves **running onto stem forming long spiny wings. Flowerheads: In terminal inflorescence,** stem simple; **no ray florets,** bracts ± 1 mm wide, tips, margins spiny (Aug-Dec). **General:** Used as scented body lotion by girls.

Berkheya multijuga
Lal Greene

Berkheya mackenii
Martin von Fintel

Berkheya maritima
Martin von Fintel

Berkheya montana

Berkheya setifera
Rosemary Williams
Geoff Nichols

Berkheya speciosa
Lawrence Peacock

Berkheya umbellata
Lawrence Peacock

Berkheya rhapontica
Tony Abbott

Hypochaeris (Greek name for 'succory'; *hypo* - beneath; *chaeris* - young pig) - Herbs; leaves mostly basal; flower-heads solitary or in sparsely branched inflorescences. Europe, N Afr, S America, 50-100 species, 5 introduced in SA.

★ *Hypochaeris radicata* **Hairy Wild Lettuce, Spotted Cat's Ear; Harige Skaapslaai, Katoor (A); umkhothane (X)** (*radicata* - with tap root)

Perennial herb, up to 600 mm. Cosmop weed, from Europe, widespread in disturbed areas. Leaves in rosette, ± 200 x 30 mm, margins wavy, toothed and or lobed, hairy or hairless. Several flowering stems, branching above, flowerheads ± 25 mm diam, yellow, solitary at tips of long branches (Sep-Mar). Used as a spinach.

Tragopogon (*tragos* - he-goat; *pogon* - beard, refers to hairy pappus crowning each seed) - Biennial or perennial herbs; leaves alternate; flowerheads solitary, terminal. Europe, W Asia ± 45 species, 3 introduced in SA.

★ *Tragopogon dubius* **Yellow Goat's Beard; Geelbokbaard (A)** (*dubius* - doubtful)

Perennial herb, up to 1 m. Common weed, ± 1500 m, from Americas. Sparsely branched from base, stems thick, sap white. Leaves grasslike, ± 250 x 15 mm, base broad, half-clasping, forming sheath. Flowerheads 80-120 mm diam, solitary, yellow, stems inflated, swollen at top, bracts pointed, 50-60 mm in fruiting heads (Nov-Dec) **Similar species:** *T. porrifolius* Purple Goat's Beard, Salsify; Persbokbaard (A) Smaller; flowerheads pinkish purple, stems hardly inflated, bracts ± 30 mm.

Taraxacum (*tarassein* - to confuse, alter, refers to culinary, medicinal properties of leaves) - Stemless perennial herbs; thick tap root; leaves in basal rosette; flowering stems hollow. N Hemisp, ± 32 species, ± 15 introduced in SA.

★ *Taraxacum officinale* **Common Dandelion; Perdeblom, Platdissel (A); irwabe lenyoka (X); umashwababa (Z)** (*officinale* - of practical use to people)

Perennial herb, up to 250 mm. Weed, on roadsides, disturbed areas. Leaves in basal rosette, margin deeply cut, toothed, tips triangular. Flowerheads solitary, ± 45 mm diam, stems usually longer than leaves (Sep-Nov, throughout year). Leaves used in cooking, roots medicinal. Roots dried and used as a coffee substitute.

Launaea (named after J Mordant de Launay, 1750-1816, French lawyer, librarian at Museum d'Histoire Naturelle in Paris, author and editor of horticultural works) - Herbs; stems erect or prostrate, simple or branched; leaves crowded in rosettes, toothed or lobed. Trop, subtrop, Medit, Aust, New Zealand, ± 40 species, ± 4 in SA.

Launaea sarmentosa (*sarmentosa* - bearing long slender runners)

Perennial **slightly succulent herb, prostrate runner**, stems several metres long. **Strand pioneer**, on sandy beaches, in salt spray zone, E Cape to Egypt, Madag, Seychelles, Mauritius, India, Sri Lanka, Indo China, Java. Rooting at nodes, internodes long, stems long, slender, simple or branched, from crown. **Leaves:** In basal rosette, ± 100 x 30 mm, **blue-green**, margins entire or toothed, narrowing into long stalklike base. **Flowerheads:** Solitary or few on short branched stems; ± 15 mm diam, yellow (Aug-May). General: Visited by small bees and beetles.

Sonchus (*sonchos* - cow thistle) - Herbs, sometimes woody at base; leaves in rosettes or alternate; flowerheads in irregular branched inflorescences. Europe, Asia, Afr, ± 60 species, a few have become cosmop weeds.

Sonchus nanus **Thistle; leshoabe, sentlokojane, sethokojane (SS)** (*nanus* - dwarf)

Dwarf perennial herb, up to 200 mm. In short, open grassland, not in coastal areas in KZN. Several leaf rosettes from woody crown, milky sap. **Leaves:** In rosette, ± 80 x 25 mm, **often blue-green**, margins entire, toothed or lobed. **Flowerheads: Solitary**, ± 20 x 10 mm, yellow, almost stemless at flowering, stem maturing ± 200 mm (Sep-Jan). **General:** Young leaves used as a pot herb. **Similar species:** *S. integrifolius* Stems with widely spaced leaves; ± 5 flowerheads. ★ *S. oleraceus* inwabe, ihlaba (X) ± 1,5 m; stem stout, erect, hollow; stem leaves clasping at base, inflorescences branched. A widespread weed. Young leaves used as a pot herb.

Lactuca (Latin word for lettuce; *lact* - milky, refers to juice from plant when pressed) - Herbs, usually hairless; leaves in rosettes or alternate; flowerheads usually in branched inflorescences. Temp Eurasia, Afr, ± 100 species, ± 6 in SA.

★ *Lactuca indica* **Wild Lettuce; Wildeslaai (A)**

Stout, leafy, **annual herb**, up to 4 m. Along roadsides, weed of cultivation, KZN to India, China, Indonesia. Stem simple, branched above, milky sap. Leaves ± 200 x 50 mm, often much narrower, greyish beneath, margins entire, toothed or lobed, narrowed to winged, stalklike base. Flowerheads many, yellow, in long, narrow, branched inflorescences (Dec-Apr). Young leaves used as a pot herb.

Similar species: *L. tysonii* Perennial herb, ± 350 mm; rootstock slender, creeping; leaves basal, ± 200 x 60 mm; flowerheads ± 20 mm, yellow, a few in branched inflorescence (Sep-Dec).

Lawrence Peacock

★ *Hypochaeris radicata*

Lal Greene

★ *Tragopogon dubius*

Van Wyk & Malan

★ *Taraxacum officinale*

C J Ward

Launaea sarmentosa

Martin von Fintel

Sonchus nanus

Jo Arkell

Sonchus integrifolius

Lorraine van Hooff

★ *Lactuca indica*

Rosemary Williams

Lactuca tysonii

339

MONOCOTYLEDONS - Single seed leaf, parallel veins; flower parts in threes or multiples of three.
ARACEAE - Arum Lily Family The 'petal' is a modified leaf called a spathe. Tiny male and female flowers are carried on the central 'column' or spadix. One of the most important groups of ornamental plants, including *Anthurium, Dieffenbachia, Philodendron, Monstera, Caladium.* The thickened rootstocks of some species are cultivated as a starchy food; fruits of *Monstera* are prized for their delicate flavour. Mostly in humid trop, ± 105 genera, ± 2550 species, 6 genera in SA. *Zantedeschia* (named after Francesco Zantedeschi, 1773-1846, Italian physician and botanist) - First introduced to horticulture in Europe from the Cape in the 1600s. Genus endemic to S Afr, 8 species.

Zantedeschia rehmannii Pink Arum; Pienkvarkoor (A); umfana-kamacejane (Sw)
(named after Anton Rehmann,1840-1917, renowned Polish botanist from Cracow)

Deciduous, up to 450 mm, in small groups. In grassland, on rocky hillsides, up to 2135 m. **Leaves:** ± 550 x 50 mm, **lance-shaped, base tapering not lobed. Flowers:** Spathe slender, ± 100 mm, mouth narrow, pink, red, deep maroon or greenish white, turns green with age (Oct-Mar). **Fruit:** Green, firm; flowering stalk with fruit bends towards ground. **General:** Popular garden plant.

COMMELINACEAE - Commelina Family Herbs. Nodes swollen, stems slightly succulent. Leaves with closed basal sheath. Flowers often within spathes and valves. Trop, ± 39 genera, ± 640 species, 7 genera in SA.
Murdannia (named after Murdan Aly, plant collector and keeper at Saharanpore Herbarium) - Inflorescence branched, terminal, 3 equal sized petals and sepals. Cosmop in trop and subtrop climates, ± 50 species, 1 in SA.

Murdannia simplex Murdannia (*simplex* - simple)

Herb, up to 600 mm, in clumps. In moist areas, grassland, KZN to Trop Afr. **Leaves:** Basal, erect, ± 200 x 10 mm, dark green. **Flowers: In branched inflorescences,** ± 13 flowers open at once, **3 equal sized mauve petals,** ± 10 mm, **stamens feathery, dark blue,** opening in mid-afternoon, closing at sunset (Sep-May). **General:** Pleasing horticultural subject, easily propagated by seed and root division.

Coleotrype (*coleotrype* - sheath borer, refers to inflorescence piercing through sheath) - Afr, Madag, 9 species, 1 in SA.

Coleotrype natalensis Forest Commelina

Perennial herb, up to 500 mm, in colonies. In forest, warm, moist areas, E Cape to Zim. Rhizomes creeping, shallow. **Leaves:** ± 150 x 20 mm; sterile shoots perennial with basal cluster of ± 7 leaves; fertile shoots, annual, reclining. **Flowers:** 4-6 in inflorescences, in leaf axils, piercing the leaf sheath; tepals ± 16 mm, mauve, stamen filaments feathery, open in early morning, close in afternoon (Sep-Apr). **General:** Attractive groundcover in shade but can become rampant.

Cyanotis (cyanotis - refers to blue flowers) - Succulent perennial herbs; bulb, corm, rhizome or tuber, often with separate fertile and sterile shoots. Warm regions of Europe, Asia, Afr, ± 50 species, 7 in SA.

Cyanotis speciosa [= *C. nodiflora*] Doll's Powderpuff; Bloupoeierkwassie (A); khopo, theepe-balingoana (SS); umagoswana (X); ingonga, inkombo, insonga, udabulamafu, umakotigoyile (Z) (*udabulamafu* - cloud breaker, used to ward off lightning)

Perennial herb, up to 500 mm. In summer rainfall areas, SA to Tanz. **Rhizome swollen, U-shaped. Leaves:** Basal, ± 170 x 8 mm, **long hairs beneath,** sheaths purple. **Flowers:** 1-3 erect inflorescences; 3 equal sized tepals, pink, mauve, purple or blue, **size variable, stamens densely hairy,** closing at midday (throughout year). **General:** Grazed by cattle. Roots used in traditional medicine to treat infertility and as love and protective charms. Garden plant for sunny situations. (See p. 448)
(See p. 448)
Similar species: *C. lapidosa* In colonies on rocky areas; N KZN to N Prov; roots thin, branching; leaves hairy on both surfaces; inflorescences reclining.

Floscopa (*flos* - flower, *scopa* - broom) - Herbs, always in wet areas; flowers in dense inflorescences, usually with fine glandular hairs, 3 tepals, 1 smaller than the others. Cosmop, warm regions, ± 20 species, 3 in SA.

Floscopa glomerata (*glomerata* - clustered into heads)

Perennial, up to 600 mm. Along streams, in water, in warmer areas, E Cape to Trop Afr, Madag. Stems sparsely branched, reclining. **Leaves:** ± 80 x 12 mm, basal sheath ± 12 mm. **Flowers: In compact, terminal, sticky inflorescences,** ± 40 mm; **flowers small,** ± 6 mm, tepals mauve, open in mornings only (Mar-Jul). **General:** Sometimes growing in large masses.

★ *Tradescantia fluminensis* Wandering Jew; Wandelende Jood (A) (named after John Tradescant, gardener to Charles I in the 1600s; *flumensis* - running water)

Prostrate herb. A garden escape in coastal areas. Leaves ± 40 x 20 mm, striped purple and white, purple beneath. Tepals ± 8 mm, stamens feathery (summer). Used to treat warts. Commonly cultivated shade plant in SA.

Zantedeschia rehmannii

Martin von Fintel

Murdannia simplex

Wally Menne

Coleotrype natalensis

Geoff Nichols

Floscopa glomerata

Van Wyk & Malan

Cyanotis speciosa

Trevor Coleman

Cyanotis speciosa

Lawrence Peacock

★ Tradescantia fluminensis

Geoff Nichols

341

COLCHICACEAE - Formerly part of Liliaceae. Herbs with buried, starchy corms, sometimes with runners. Stems erect or twining. Leaves sheathing at base. Flowers with 6 tepals of similar size and shape, free or basally joined, 6 stamens, free. Fruit a capsule. Afr, Medit, W Asia, Austr, ± 15 genera, ± 165 species, 12 genera in SA.
Wurmbea (named after F von Wurm, Dutch merchant in Java) - Afr, Austr, ± 25 species, 19 in SA, mostly in the Cape.

Wurmbea kraussii (named after Christian Krauss, 1812-1890, German scientist, traveller and collector)
Up to 150 mm. In damp places, on streambanks, also in grassland, coast to 2400 m. **Leaves:** Basal leaf solitary, narrow, 25-150 x 10-20 mm, 1-2 stem leaves short, broad based, 10-30 x 3-7 mm. **Flowers:** 1-6 in spike, ± 35 mm; flowers 10-20 mm diam, white or pink, lobes distinctly veined, **nectary elevated, with free tip** (Aug-Dec).

ASPHODELACEAE - Formerly part of Liliaceae (for description see p. 224). *Aloe* - Succulents (for description see p. 228).

Aloe greenii icena (Z)
Up to 1,3 m, in colonies. In shade of thicket, hot dry areas, C KZN to Moz. **Leaves:** In dense rosette, ± 500 x 80 mm, flattish at base, erect and arching in upper third, bright green with whitish spots forming irregular bands on both surfaces, margins with pale pinkish brown teeth. **Flowers:** Inflorescence 150-250 mm, stem with 5-7 branches; flowers ± 30 mm, light to dark pink, with bloom (Jan-Mar). **General:** Inconspicuous flowers, elegant leaves. Grow in shade, protect from afternoon sun.

Aloe minima Pink Grass Aloe; inhlatjana (Sw); isiphuthumane, isiphukuthwane, isiphukhutshane (Z)
Up to 500 mm, solitary. Scattered in grassland, coast to midlands. **Leaves:** Swollen at base, 250-350 x 4-6 mm, spotted white and purple at base beneath, some spots forming tough spikelike protuberances, margins with very fine white teeth on lower half. **Flowers:** Inflorescence 30 x 40 mm; buds erect, flowers pale pink (Oct-Apr). **General:** Young shoots and flowers eaten as a raw vegetable.

Aloe myriacantha umakhuphulwane (Z) (*myri* - countless; *acantha* - spine or prickle, although this species does not have leaves more prickly than any other grass aloe)
Up to 300 mm, solitary. Widespread in grassland, coast to 600 m, E Cape to C Afr. **Leaves:** Swollen at base, ± 250 x 10 mm, sparsely to copiously spotted, some spots with a spikelike little bump, margins with small white teeth. **Flowers:** In small inflorescence ± 45 x 60 mm; buds erect, flowers ± 20 mm, dull mauve-pink, rarely greenish white, **2 lipped** (Jan-Apr).

Gasteria (*gaster* - belly, refers to swollen base of flower tube) - Leaves spineless; flowers curved with bulbous base. SA, mostly in the Cape, ± 67 species.

Gasteria croucheri Gasteria, Variegated Aloe; Bosaalwyn (A); impundu, iqhomololo (Z)
Succulent herb, up to 600 mm. On shady, moist or dry cliff faces. **Leaves:** In rosette, ± 600 mm diam, 200-360 x 30-100 mm, triangular, ± 20 mm thick, **smooth**, dark green to purplish, **often with bloom**, dense white spots in bands, margins hard. **Flowers:** Inflorescences usually horizontal; flowers ± 40 mm, pink tipped white with green stripes (Nov-Feb). **Fruit:** Capsule ± 25 mm. **General:** Northern plants in dense clusters, inflorescences simple or with ± 2 branches. Southern plants solitary, inflorescence spreading, much branched. Used in traditional medicine to treat hysteria and for protective charms. Popular container and garden plants with a number of cultivars. **Similar species:** *G. batesiana* Up to 100 mm, in groups; N KZN to N Prov; leaves in a fan at first, later forming rosette ± 300 mm diam, brittle, rough, with small and large green or white tubercles; inflorescences unbranched, flowers large, 35-40 mm; capsules ± 43 mm.

Haworthia (named after Adrian H Haworth, 1768-1833, English botanist and writer on succulents) - Small plants, like miniature aloes; flowers dull white, 2 lipped. SA, most in SW Cape, ± 140 species, 1 extending to Zim and Ang.

Haworthia limifolia indvololwane (Sw); isihlalakahle, umathithibala (Z) (*limifolia* - leaves with distinct margins)
Up to 750 mm, solitary or in groups. On rocky outcrops, mountains, KZN to Mpum, Moz. **Leaves:** In rosette, 50-80 x 20 mm, dull green to coppery, covered with small white raised spots. **Flowers:** In branched inflorescences, stems slender; flowers ± 12 mm, pink (May, throughout the year). **General:** Used in traditional medicine to treat stomach complaints and as a protective charm, particularly against lightning. A variety of the Lebombo mountains has no spots on leaves. Good container plant.

Wurmbea kraussii

Martin von Fintel

Aloe minima

Tony Abbott

Aloe myriacantha

Neil Crouch

Aloe greenii

Cynthia Gidds

Haworthia limifolia

Neil Crouch

Geoff Nichols

Gasteria croucheri   *Gasteria croucheri*   *Gasteria batesiana*

343

ALLIACEAE - Onion Family Perennial herbs with bulbs, bulblike corms or a rhizome (in SA species). Leaves basal, sometimes sheathing the flowering stem. Inflorescence with membraneous bracts at base; stamens 6; ovary superior. Some species have an onion smell (*Tulbaghia*). Fruit a capsule. Subcosmop, ± 30 genera, ± 850 species, 4 genera in SA.
Tulbaghia (named after Ryk Tulbagh, Governor at the Cape, 1751-71, who sent specimens to Linnaeus) - Perennial herbs; compact tuberous rhizomes, often smelling of garlic when bruised; flowers with a corona or fleshy ring at mouth of tube. Afr, mostly SA, ± 20 species.

Tulbaghia natalensis Sweet Wild Garlic, Pink Wild Garlic; iswele lezinyoka (Z)

Up to 400 mm. On rocky or marshy ground, 800-1800 m. **Leaves:** ± 250 x 7 mm. **Flowers:** 6-10 in inflorescence, opening in succession; flowers palest pink or white tinged purple; fleshy ring irregularly 3 lobed, green to yellowish orange (Aug-Feb). **General:** Used as a culinary herb. Cultivated to keep snakes away.

HYACINTHACEAE - Formerly part of Liliaceae. Perennial herbs. Bulbs sometimes with free scales. Inflorescence elongated, stamens 6, ovary superior. Fruit a capsule. Subcosmop, ± 41 genera, ± 770 species, 27 genera in SA.
Drimiopsis (resembling *Drimia*) - Bulbous herbs, without papery outer scales; leaves few, usually with a stalk, often spotted; flower stem without bracts, flowers held upwards, crowded in short inflorescence. Afr, ± 15 species, 5 in SA.

Drimiopsis lachenalioides Lachenalia Drimiopsis (*lachenalioides* - resembling *Lachenalia*)

Up to 150 mm. In grassland, on forest margins, up to 2100 m. Bulb ± 40 mm. **Leaves:** Semi-erect, smooth to hairy, 100-200 x 25-40 mm, sometimes blotched on upper surface, purplish wavy bars on undersurface near base. **Flowers:** In dense inflorescence, stem slightly longer than leaves; flowers ± 15 mm, bright pink to purple, **tepals erect-spreading** (Oct-Dec).

Ledebouria (named after Carl Ledebour, 1785-1851, German prof of botany) - Bulbous herbs; outer bulb scales papery; leaves with reddish or green spots on upper surface. Afr, Asia, ± 30 species, 15 in SA.

Ledebouria cooperi [=*Scilla cooperi*] Cooper's Squill; lepjetlane (SS); icubudwana, icukudwane (Z) (named after Thomas Cooper, 1815-1913, English plant collector and grower)

Up to 250 mm. In damp grassland. Bulb **roundish**, 10-25 mm diam, scales loosely arranged. **Leaves:** 200-250 x 16-18 mm, glossy green, dark green or purplish spots above, ± **longitudinal purple stripes beneath**, erect. **Flowers:** 1-3 dense inflorescences, 50-80 x 20-30 mm, stem ± 150 mm; flowers bright pink (Oct-Feb). **General:** Used in traditional medicine to ease pregnancy and treat internal ailments in cattle. **Similar species:** *L. sandersonii* [= *Scilla sandersonii*] In shallow soil in damp montane grassland; bulb oval, leaves ± oval, 15-75 x 18-30 mm, purplish beneath, prostrate.

Ledebouria ovatifolia [= *Scilla ovatifolia*] icubudwana, untanganazibomvu (Z)
(*ovatifolia* - oval leaves)

Up to 80 mm, solitary. In grassland, woodland, widespread. Bulb 35-70 x 30-50 mm, live scales fleshy, **loosely arranged**, copious threads when torn. **Leaves:** Usually **flat on ground**, 50-120 x 36-60 mm, fleshy, **glossy**, ± with purple spots above, **purplish below**, margins white to purple, ± after flowers. **Flowers:** 1-4 dense inflorescences, 30-50 x 25-30 mm, stems 50-70 mm; flowers pink to purple, tepals recurved (Aug-Nov). **General:** Leaves erect or suberect in shade, eaten by porcupines. Used in traditional medicine to treat diarrhoea, flu and backache. **Similar species:** *Ledebouria* sp. In grassland; leaf leathery, veins prominent.

Ledebouria stenophylla (*stenos* - straight, narrow; *phyllon* - leaves)

Plants solitary. In open grassland, woodland. Bulb 40-60 x 20-30 mm, live scales fleshy, tightly arranged. **Leaves:** 60-150 x 2-5 mm, erect to spreading, **spirally twisted**, partly emerged at flowering, with threads when torn, grey-green with dull purple spots below, veins prominent. **Flowers:** 1-3 inflorescences, 25 x 15 mm, longer than leaves; flowers pink with green keel, **tepals long, narrow** (Aug-Jan).

Veltheimia (named after Count August von Veltheim, 1741-1801, German patron of botany) - Bulbous plants. SA, 2 species.

Veltheimia bracteata [= *V. undulata, V. viridifolia*] Glossy Forest Lily; Sandui (A) (*bracteata* - bracts)

Up to 600 mm, in large colonies. In thicket, coastal bush, amongst rocks. Bulb oval, ± 70 mm diam, purplish, covered in papery brown old leaf bases. **Leaves:** ± 450 x 70 mm, **margins wavy to crisped**, shiny pale to deep green. **Flowers:** In compact inflorescence, stem stout, purplish spotted; flowers tubular, pale to deep pink, speckled, green tipped (Jul-Oct). **Fruit:** Attractive **inflated capsules**, lemon yellow, tinged pink, seeds black. **General:** A well known garden plant, grown in shade.

Tulbaghia natalensis   *Drimiopsis lachenalioides*   *Ledebouria stenophylla*

Ledebouria ovatifolia

Ledebouria sp.   *Ledebouria cooperi*

Veltheimia bracteata   *Ledebouria sandersonii*

345

AMARYLLIDACEAE - Bulbous herbs, rarely rhizomatous. Inflorescence an umbel, ovary inferior. Fruit a berry (*Clivia, Scadoxus, Haemanthus*) or a capsule. Popular horticultural subjects, attract the *Amaryllis* caterpillar pest. Trop and warm regions, ± 65 genera, ± 725 species, 19 genera in SA.

Haemanthus (haima - blood; *anthos* - flower) - Bulbous herbs; few, fleshy leaves, in two ranks, no stem; flowers small, in dense inflorescence. S Afr endemic, ± 21 species in SA.

Haemanthus humilis subsp. *hirsutus* [= *H. hirsutus*] Rabbit's Ears; Bobbejaanoor, Velskoenblaar (A); sekitla, tsebe ea phofu (SS) (*humilis* - low growing)

Deciduous, up to 300 mm, solitary or in clumps. On rocky outcrops, 1220-2350 m. Bulb ± 80 mm wide. **Leaves:** 150-300 x 55-130 mm, smooth or hairy, lower surface usually hairy, ± erect, produced with flowers. **Flowers: In stiff inflorescence,** 50-120 mm diam; **flowers ± 25 mm, white to pale pink, stamens protrude well above tepals,** 7-10 bracts (**Nov-Dec**, Sep-Feb). **Fruit:** White to orange, oval, ± 10 mm diam, fruity smell when ripe. **General:** Used in traditional medicine to treat stomach complaints, wounds and asthma. Requires partial shade.

Haemanthus montanus Mountain Haemanthus (*montanus* - growing on mountains)

Deciduous, up to 400 mm. In grassland, seasonal wetlands. **Leaves: Erect,** 150-250 x 15-50 mm, **hairless,** margins smooth, produced with flowers. **Flowers: In spreading inflorescence,** 40-90 mm diam, stem green to reddish, **hairless;** flowers ± **14 mm,** white, **5-8 bracts, spreading to reflexed, pale pink,** ± 13 mm (Oct-Dec), pleasant scent. **General:** Requires partial shade. (See p. 106, 232)

Boophone (bous - ox; *phonos* - slaughter, refers to poisonous qualities of bulb) - Bulb covered in loose papery tunics; leaves erect, in a fan; flowers in dense inflorescence. Mostly S Afr, 5 species.

Boophone disticha Fan-leaved Boophone, Poison Bulb, Sore-eye Flower, Tumblehead; Gifbol, Perdespook, Seerooglelie (A); kxutsana-ya-naha, leshoma, lesoma, motlatsisa (SS); incumbe, siphahluka (Sw); incotho, incwadi (X,Z); ibhade (Z) (*disticha* - in 2 rows, refers to leaves)

Deciduous, up to 450 mm. In dry grassland, rocky areas, Cape to Trop Afr. Bulb half above ground, ± 170 x 150 mm diam, thick covering of dry scales. **Leaves: In conspicuous fan,** ± 450 x 50 mm, grey-green, margins flat or wavy. **Flowers:** Inflorescence ± 150 mm diam, stem short; flowers ± 50 mm diam, deep pink, stalks 50-80 mm lengthening to 150 mm in fruit (Jul-Oct), sweetly scented. **Fruit:** 3 angled. Inflorescence matures into large ball ± 400 mm diam, breaking off when dry, blowing in the wind, dispersing seed. **General:** Used to plug sour milk containers. Leaves stripped for fringes and decorative body ornaments. Bulb poisonous to stock, used for arrow poison by the San. Used in traditional medicine to treat pain, wounds and as a narcotic. Auriol Batten (1988) comments on headache, drowsiness and sore eyes from close proximity to the flower when painting. Fire induces flowering.

Nerine (Nerine - a sea nymph, daughter of sea gods Nereus and Doris) - Bulbous herbs; few leaves; flowers without tube (or very short tube), lobes narrow, spreading, sometimes wavy. Many horticultural hybrids. S Afr, ± 22 species.

Nerine angustifolia Ribbon-leaved Nerine; Berglelie (A); lematlana (SS) (*angustifolia* - narrow leaves)

Up to 0,6 (1,2) m. In marshy areas, grassland. Bulb ± 20 mm diam. **Leaves:** ± 300 x 8 mm, **flattish. Flowers:** Inflorescence with less than 10 flowers, bracts narrow, folded back; tepal lobes ± 40 x 3 mm, pink, spreading, wavy, with midrib, dark stamens, stalks ± 50 mm, ± erect (Feb-Apr). **Fruit:** Less than 10 mm. **General:** Used as a protective charm against lightning and illness. A well known garden plant.

Nerine appendiculata Nerine; umlukulo (Z) (*appendiculata* - having appendages)

Up to 900 mm, evergreen. In marshy areas, up to 1800 m. Bulb oval, ± 25 x 20 mm. **Leaves:** 1-3, ± 450 x 5 mm, **deeply channelled,** with flowers. **Flowers:** 10-20, in crowded inflorescence, 2 reddish papery bracts ± 35 mm, stem twisted; tepal lobes ± 30 x 5 mm, pale to deep pink, middle vein darker, **stamens with conspicuous white appendages ± 10 mm at base** (Dec-Apr). **General:** Good garden plant.

Nerine bowdenii Large Pink Nerine; Grootpienknerina (A)

Robust, up to 700 mm, deciduous. In moist ground, at base of cliffs, up to 3200 m. **Leaves:** Up to 8, ± 470 x 25 mm, **flat. Flowers:** Up to 7, in inflorescence ± 200 mm diam; flowers **large,** ± 50 mm diam, bright pink, lobes recurved, margins wavy (Jan-**Apr-May**). **General:** Frost resistant. Popular garden plant, flowers long lasting.

Boophone disticha

Darrel Plowes

Haemanthus humilis subsp. *hirsutus*

Darrel Plowes

Nerine angustifolia

Godfrey Symons

Haemanthus montanus

Geoff Nichols

Nerine appendiculata

Martin von Fintel

Nerine bowdenii

Lal Greene

347

Brunsvigia (honours the House of Brunswick) - Large bulbs; leaves widely spreading or prostrate; inflorescence large, round, flowers on long stalks, stamens curving down and up at ends, stalks elongate as fruit ripens, fruiting head breaks off as a whole and rolls in the wind, distributing seed. Mainly S Afr, ± 16 species.

Brunsvigia grandiflora Giant Candelabra Flower; Kandelaarblom (A); isichwe (X); umqhele-wenkunzi (Z) (*grandiflora* - larger than normal flowers)

Robust, up to 800 mm. Scattered in grassland, 1200-2300 m. Bulb large, oval, ± 200 x 140 mm with thick papery outer layer. **Leaves: 10-15, erect** or soft and bending, 200-450 x 25-45 mm, flat, margins wavy, produced with flowers. **Flowers:** 30-60 in spreading inflorescence; flowers 50-70 mm, light to dark pink, tepal lobes ±12 mm wide, wavy, slightly recurved, stalks 150-250 mm, pale red (Jan-Mar). **General:** Bulb used in traditional medicine to soothe and heal wounds, particularly after circumcision. Good feature or container plant.

Brunsvigia natalensis Natal Candelabra Flower; Kandelaarblom (A); lilula (Sw); umbhola (Z)

Up to 450(900) mm. Scattered in grassland, on rocky outcrops, up to 2280 m. Bulb 50-120 x 200 mm diam. **Leaves: 2-6, flattish to semi-erect,** 150-300 x 70-120 mm, rough on upper surface, blunt tipped, produced with flowers. **Flowers:** 30-60, inflorescence ± 300 mm diam, bracts ± 60 x 40 mm, stem 180-250 x 15-20 mm; flowers ± 40 mm, deep pink (red), stalks 40-120 mm (**Oct-Jan**). **Fruit:** Fruit 3 angled, ± 40 mm, stalks ± 300 mm. **General:** Habitat reduced due to draining of marshy areas. Zulu name refers to the rotten smell around the bulb. Used in traditional medicine to 'straighten bones of children'. Good feature or container plant.

Brunsvigia radulosa Candelabra Flower; Kandelaarblom, Misryblom (A); lematla (SS); lilula (Sw) (*radulosa* - rough, rasping)

Up to 800 mm, solitary. In grassland, NW Cape to N Prov, Bots. Bulb ± 200 mm diam, outer layer hard. **Leaves: Spreading, prostrate,** 250-500 x 100-200 mm, **thick, rough,** with or after flowers. **Flowers:** 30-60, in inflorescence, bracts ± 80 mm, stem 300-500 x 25-35 mm; flowers 45-55 mm, pink to red, tepal lobes 10-15 mm wide, stalks 200-300 mm (Jan-Feb). **Fruit:** Stalks lengthen up to 300 mm. **General:** Bulb used to seal leaking clay pots. Used in traditional medicine to 'straighten bones of children', treat barrenness in women and ease birth. Good feature or container plant.

★ *Zephyranthes grandiflora* Storm Lily, Flower of the West Wind; Stormlelie (A)

Up to 300 mm. Garden escape, naturalised in many coastal areas (from C America). Leaves blue-green, ± 200 x 15 mm. Flowers ± 170 mm diam, pale pink. Blooms before or with rain.

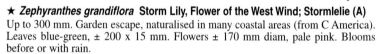
Crinum (*krinon* - lily) - Robust, deciduous bulbous plants; flowers very large, tube long, trumpet-shaped, tepal lobes spreading or reflexed; seeds large, without hard coat. Rewarding garden plants. Mainly Afr, ± 130 species, ± 21 in SA.

Crinum acaule Maputaland Grass Crinum (*acaule* - without stalks, or seemingly so)

Up to 400 mm. Scattered in sandy grassland, in low-lying and coastal areas, N KZN to S Moz. Bulb ± 120 x 80 mm, neck ± 90 mm. **Leaves:** Long, narrow, 200-500 x 4-14 mm, deeply channelled, shiny dark green, margins finely hairy. **Flowers:** 1-3, tube ± 100 mm, tepals ± 120 x 25 mm, upper third recurving, **stalk mostly underground,** ± 50 mm, open late afternoon, closing early morning (Sep-Jan, in response to rain), **lovely strong scent. Fruit: Develops at or below ground level. General:** Flowers and leaves browsed by game; bushpigs eat the bulbs.

Crinum bulbispermum Orange River Lily, Vaal River Lily; Oranjerivierlelie, Vaalrivierlelie, Vleilelie (A); lelutla, mototse (SS); umnduze (Z) (*bulbispermum* - bulblike seed)

Up to 900 mm, solitary or in large colonies. Near rivers, streams, seasonal pans, NW Cape to N Prov. Bulb ± 130 mm diam at base. **Leaves:** ± 800 x 80-110 mm, **bluish grey-green, soft,** folded upwards, **arching,** margins **wavy, sheathing at base forming 'stem', ± 450 mm. Flowers:** 6-16, in inflorescence; flowers **drooping,** narrow, tube ± 110 mm, tepal lobes ± 100 x 30 mm, white to red with darker red keel, stamens white to deep pink (Sep-Dec), faintly scented. **Fruit:** Roundish, ± 70 mm diam, green tinged reddish purple, **tipped with a ring. General:** Used in traditional medicine to treat colds, rheumatism, varicose veins, reduce swelling and as poultices for septic sores. Used to ensure easy delivery in pregnancy and to stimulate breast milk. Planted to protect home from evil. Popular garden plant.

Martin von Fintel

Brunsvigia grandiflora

Darrel Plowes

Brunsvigia radulosa

Godfrey Symons

Brunsvigia natalensis

Geoff Nichols

Crinum acaule

Lorraine van Hooff

★ *Zephyranthes grandiflora*

Trevor Coleman

Crinum bulbispermum

349

Crinum delagoense **Candy-striped Crinum; umnduze (Z)** *(delagoense* - from Delagoa Bay)
Up to 500 mm. Scattered in grassland, bushveld, on sandy soils, **low altitudes,** N KZN to Moz. Bulb ± 220 mm diam, abruptly narrowing to neck. **Leaves: Broad, flat,** spreading, ± 1000 x 210 mm, margins finely hairy. **Flowers:** ± 50 in inflorescences, stems arching upwards; flower tube ± 100 mm, tepal lobes ± 90 x 25 mm, curling back, white with deep magenta keel, sometimes entirely deep pink, **stalks long, ± 50 mm** (Oct-Nov), sometimes scented. **Fruit:** Roundish, large, ± 70 mm diam, **shiny pinkish red, not beaked. General:** Used in traditional medicine for urinary tract problems and to treat cattle. Attractive garden plant in flower and fruit.

Crinum graminicola **Grass Crinum, Grass Vlei Lily; Graslelie (A)** *(graminicola* - dwelling in grass)
Up to 400 mm. In grassland. Bulb ± 140 mm diam, neck ± 100 mm. **Leaves:** ± 140 mm wide, broad, spreading, **margins with brown hairs. Flowers:** 8-30 in inflorescences, stems erect to **reclining**; flower tube curved, ± 110 mm, tepal lobes ± 90 x 25 mm, deep pink, **stalks short, ± 25 mm** (Oct-Feb). **Fruit:** Round to oval, **beaked.**

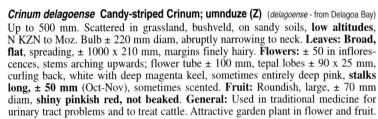

Crinum macowanii **River Lily; Rivierlelie (A); intelezi (X); umnduze (Z)** (named after Peter MacOwan, 1830-1909, botanist, teacher, started SA Bot Exchange Society, a large private herbarium)
Up to 900 mm. Coast to mountains, in grassland, rocky areas, near rivers, E Cape to Zim. Bulb 60-250 mm diam, narrowed into short neck. **Leaves:** ± 800 x 160 mm, deeply channelled, spreading or arching, margins ± wavy, leaves **forming short stem,** becoming very large and long (± 2 m) in hot, humid areas in shade. **Flowers:** ± 25, in inflorescences, opening upwards, stems erect at first, reclining later; flowers bell-shaped, tube short, tepal lobes ± 220 mm, tips curl back, palest pink to dark pink and white, **pollen black** (Oct-Feb), lovely scent. **Fruit:** ± 60 mm diam, **beaked. General:** Used in traditional medicine to treat urinary infections, itchy rashes and for poultices, bandages and as protective charms. Lovely garden plant, producing more than three inflorescences in succession. Variable growth habit over the wide range.

Crinum moorei **Moore's Crinum, Natal Lily; Boslelie, Natal-lelie (A); umnduze (Z)** (named after Dr D Moore, director of the Bot Garden, Dublin, who obtained seed from Mr Webb who collected it while serving in the army in Natal in the 1860s)
Up to 1,6 m, in clumps, also in large colonies. In damp, marshy areas, in shade, near streams, coastal areas. Bulb ± 190 mm diam, **narrowing into long stemlike neck ± 1,2 m. Leaves: Narrowing to tip and base,** 650-1500 x 60-130 mm, bright green, **midrib thickened,** margins slightly wavy. **Flowers:** 5-10 in inflorescence; tepal lobes ± 100 x 40 mm, drooping by day, **erect and wide open at night,** white to pale pink (Sep-Jan), strongly scented at night. **General:** Used in traditional medicine for urinary tract infections and to treat cattle. Lovely, hardy garden and container plant.

Crinum paludosum **Vlei Lily** *(paludosum* - growing in marshy places)
Up to 550 mm, in large colonies. In seasonal pans, marshy areas, N KZN to N Prov, Nam. Bulb ± 200 mm diam, narrowing to long neck. **Leaves:** Soft, pale green, **gracefully arching,** margins wavy. **Flowers:** 5-11 in inflorescence; flower tube ± 120 mm, tepal lobes ± 100 x 30 mm, suberect to spreading, **white** to pale pink with darker pink keel, **stigma red,** open fully only at midday (Dec-Jan), slightly scented. **Fruit:** ± 35 mm diam. **General:** Usually blooms whilst submerged in ± 300 mm water. Leaves browsed by stock. (See p. 106)

Ammocharis *(ammos* - sand; *charis* - delight) - Leaves perennial, in 2 rows, flat on ground; inflorescence on short stem, stalks not elongating in fruit. Afr, 5 species, 3 in SA.

Ammocharis coranica **Ammocharis, Ground Lily; Berglelie, Gifbol, Seeroogblom (A); boka (SS); icukudo, incukudwane, isidiya, umbhodiya (Z)** *(coranica* - refers to the Korana San)
Up to 200 mm, in large communities. Hot, dry, flat areas, widespread in S Afr. Bulb ± 200 mm diam. **Leaves: In 2 rows, flat on ground,** ± 300 x 40 mm, grey-green, **blunt tipped. Flowers:** Inflorescence ± 250 mm diam, stem **flat,** reclining, ± 200 mm; flower tube ± 15 mm, tepal lobes ± 50 x 6 mm, glossy pink maturing reddish, stalks ± 30 mm, erect to spreading (Oct-Jan), sweetly scented. **Fruit:** Seeds fleshy. **General:** Wonderful when fields of these plants bloom after rain. They do not bloom every year. Leaves heavily browsed by stock. Bulb ground to a paste to waterproof pots. Once used for men's head rings. Used to treat ailments caused by witchcraft.

Trevor Coleman

Crinum delagoense

Martin von Fintel

Van Wyk & Malan

Crinum graminicola

Geoff Nichols

Crinum moorei

Wally Menne

Crinum paludosum

Trevor Coleman

Crinum macowanii

Trevor Coleman

Ammocharis coranica

351

HYPOXIDACEAE - Star Flower Family Tuberous rhizome or corm, covered in papery fibres. Leaves usually in 3 ranks, fibrous, often with long hairs, lasting 1-2 years. Tepals often green and hairy beneath, ovary inferior. Fruit a capsule which splits in half, seeds small, shiny, black. S Hemisp, 8 genera, ± 220 species, 6 genera in SA.
Rhodohypoxis (*rhodo* - rose, red; genus *Hypoxis*) - Small herbs; rhizome tuberous, erect, fibrous; flowers white or pink, inner lobes covering centre of flower before spreading outwards. SA endemic, 6 species.

Rhodohypoxis baurii Red Star; Rooisterretjie (A) (named after Rev Leopold Baur, 1825-1889, pharmacist and missionary, plant collector who came to the Cape in 1847)

Up to 150 mm, forming colourful carpets. In grassland, rocky places, up to 2400 m. Tuber with few bristles. **Leaves:** 25-110 x 5 mm, **with sparse long hairs. Flowers:** 1-2, tube short with long spreading hairs, also on midrib of outer tepals, lobes ± 15 x 6 mm, spreading flat, white, pink, red, stem hairy (Oct-Jan), faintly scented. **General:** Cultivated in Europe and Japan, hardy, requiring well drained soil. Var. *baurii*, in damp, shady, rocky places up to 2400 m; flowers mostly deep red. Var. *confecta*, on moist grassy slopes, damp turf amongst rock sheets, 1900-2900 m; flowers white, pink, red (sometimes opening white then turning deep red). Var. *platypetala*, in short dry rocky grassland up to 2100 m; flowers mostly white, occasionally pink. Hybridises with *R. milloides* and *Hypoxis parvula*.
Similar species: *R. milloides* Usually near running water, leaves hairless, flowers pink to deep red.

VELLOZIACEAE - Black-stick Lily or Bobbejaanstert Family Fibrous perennials, stems protected by non-inflammable leaf bases. Leaves in tufts. Afr, Madag, S America, 8 genera, ± 288 species, 2 genera in SA.
Xerophyta (*xeros* - dry; *phytos* - plant) - Ovary rough, hairy. Afr, Madag, Brazil, ± 50 species, ± 9 in SA.

Xerophyta retinervis [= *Vellozia retinervis*] Black-stick Lily, Monkey's Tail; Aapstert, Besembos, Bobbejaanstert (A); sifunti (Sw); isigqumana, isiphemba (Z) (*retinervis* - net veined)

Deciduous, up to 1,8 m. On rocky outcrops in hot dry areas. Stems irregularly branched, robust, black, rough, fibrous, made up of old leaf bases, with thick root system beneath. **Leaves:** Grasslike, ± 250 mm, keeled, in terminal tufts. **Flowers:** Tepals ± 50 x 13 mm, deep to pale mauve or white, on slender stems ± 150 mm, in abundance amongst leaves (Sep-Nov, especially after fire), lovely scent. **General:** Stems used as pot scourers and to make rope for hut and screen building. Used in traditional medicine to treat asthma and as a charm against lightning. The rough stems are sometimes host to an epiphytic orchid. Fascinating feature plant with 'life-less' but interesting blackened stumps, transformed when in bloom. (See p. 108)

Xerophyta viscosa [= *Vellozia viscosa*] Small Black-stick Lily; Bobbejaanstert (A); lefiroane, lethepu, mariroane (SS) (*viscosa* - sticky)

Up to 600 mm. On rocky outcrops, up to 2400 m, Cape to Zim. Stems blackened, rough with **recurved leaf bases. Leaves:** ± 180 mm, keel and margins with short stiff hairs. **Flowers:** ± 80 mm diam, mauve, stems ± 390 mm, **speckled with black glands** on stems, ovary and tepal tips beneath (Nov-Apr). **General:** Leaves plaited into rope. **Similar species:** *X. longicaulis* Up to 300 mm; Tugela Gorge, KZN Drakensberg, 1800 m; stem with leaf base tips not recurved; flowers white with pale violet markings (Oct).

IRIDACEAE - Iris Family Corms or rhizomes. Leaves sword-shaped, in 2 ranks. Flowers regular or irregular, stamens 3, ovary inferior. Cosmop, ± 82 genera, ± 1700 species, over half the species occur in SA, 38 genera.
Schizostylis (*schizostylos* - split style) - Flower with well developed tube. Single species genus, E Cape to Zim.

Schizostylis coccinea Scarlet River Lily; Rooirivierlelie (A); khahlana (SS) (see p. 42)

Hesperantha (*hesperos* - evening; *anthos* - flower) - Corm flat bottomed; style branches simple. Sub-Saharan Afr, ± 65 species, mostly SA.

Hesperantha baurii khahla-e-nyenyane, khukhu-e-nyenyane, qelo (SS); isidwa (Z) (named after Rev Leopold Baur, 1825-89, pharmacist, missionary, amateur botanist; arrived in the Cape in 1847)

Slender, erect, perennial herb, 150-750 mm. Common in moist open grassland, coast to 2450 m. Corm ± 20 mm diam. **Leaves:** 2 basal, 200-550 x 4-7 mm, straight, firm, margins thickened, midrib raised, side veins raised, 2 upper leaves sheathing flowering stem. **Flowers:** 5-15, stem erect, zigzag; flower tube 6-12 mm, tepals ± 16 x 5 mm, bright magenta, occasionally white, open in sunlight (Nov-Mar). **General:** Corms eaten by children.

Wally Menne

Rhodohypoxis baurii

Wally Menne

Rhodohypoxis baurii

Lal Greene

Rhodohypoxis milloides

Tom de Waal

Geoff Nichols

Xerophyta retinervis

Xerophyta retinervis

Rosemary Williams

Xerophyta viscosa

Martin von Fintel

Schizostylis coccinea

Lawrence Peacock

Hesperantha baurii

353

Hesperantha scopulosa (scopulosa - rocky)

Hanging, up to 250 mm. Often in long horizontal lines, in crevices of wet cliffs, 1500-2200 m, endemic to KZN. **Leaves:** Flat, limp, 45-370 x 5-10 mm. **Flowers:** 1-8, stem hanging, tip erect; flowers ± 40 mm, bright magenta, tube long, 32-42 mm, tepal lobes 16-25 x 5-7 mm, anthers 5-6 mm, opening in daylight (Feb-May).
Similar species: H. grandiflora Erect, 150-700 mm; **on damp, grassy stream-banks**, forest margins, 1600-3000 m; leaves 2-6 mm wide; 1-6 flowers, tube 26-40 mm, **curved at tip on opening**, tepal lobes 25-37 x 6-12 mm, unequal, open during the day, anthers 8-13 mm (Jan-Apr).
H. huttonii E Cape mountains; corms developing cormlets on lower part of stem; flower tube short, 20-39 mm, anthers large, 8-10 mm.
H. longituba E Karoo mountains; erect, flowers white, pale pink beneath (Aug-Sep).

Dierama (*dierama* - a funnel) - **Hairbells, Wand-flowers; Grasklokkies** Fibrous-coated corms; leaves grasslike; flowering stem tall, slender, usually branched, arching, flowers hanging on slender stalks, bracts dry, papery. Lovely plants for the garden. Afr, ± 38 species in SA.

Dierama dracomontanum (refers to the Drakensberg Mountains)

In large clumps, up to 1 m. In mountain grassland, 1525-2800 m. Corms 10-20 mm diam. **Leaves:** 300-650 x 3,5-6,5 mm. **Flowers:** Inflorescences drooping, 2-4 branches, ± 2-5 flowers each, lowest branch 30-65 mm; flowers 19-29 mm, tepals light to dark rose or purplish pink; bracts 13-20 x 6-12 mm, solid dark or red-brown at least in lower part between veins, shoulders broad, white, or heavily flecked, 5 main veins each side, fading in upper half (Nov-Feb). **General:** First introduced to horticulture in Britain as *D. pumilum*. **Similar species:** *D. floriferum* (see p. 454).

Dierama erectum (erectum - upright)

In clumps, up to 1,5 m. In rough, wet grassland near streams. **Leaves:** Several, 80-950 x **6-12 mm. Flowers: Inflorescences erect,** ± 10 branches, 5-10 flowers each, crowded; flowers ± 27 mm, light magenta-pink with **'eyes' at base of each tepal; bracts robust,** ± 20 x 8 mm, veins joining to form an almost solid patch at base, light green drying light buff, flecked red-brown, midline to tip red-brown or ochre, the remainder papery, whitish (Apr).

Dierama igneum Fairy Bell, Small Hairbell; lethepu (SS) (ignescens - flame coloured)

Solitary or in small clumps, 0,45-1,15 m. In open grassland, coast to 1500 m. **Leaves:** 300-900 x 2-6(9) mm. **Flowers:** Inflorescences with 4-8 branches, 2-10 flowers each, stems **drooping down to tips of leaves**; flowers 16-31 mm, light to dark lilac, white to pale pink; bracts 10-25 x 5-8 mm, well flecked all over or fading outwards towards white margins (Jun-**Aug-Dec-**Apr). **General:** Used in traditional medicine for enemas. **Similar species:** *D. pendulum* Occurs further west in E Cape; inflorescences held well above leaves. *D. pulcherrimum* (see p. 356).

Dierama insigne [= D. davyi, D. rupestre] litsembu (Sw) (insigne - outstanding or notable)

Solitary or in small clumps, 0,65-1,3 m. In grassland, on rocky outcrops. **Leaves:** 350-750 x 2-4 mm. **Flowers:** Inflorescences with 2-4 branches, 3-12 flowers each, crowded, stems ± 1,5 m, drooping; flowers 24-30 mm, tepals 15-20 x 7-10 mm, light pink to magenta; bracts 20-30 x 6-10 mm, light green drying buff to brown, margins almost pure white to flecked or brown (Oct-Nov-Feb). **General:** Leaves plaited into ropes for hut building.

Hesperantha grandiflora *Hesperantha grandiflora* *Hesperantha scopulosa*

Pam Cooke

Tom de Waal

Dierama dracomontanum *Dierama insigne*

Darrel Plowes

Hilliard & Burtt

Dierama dracomontanum

Darrel Plowes

Dierama igneum *Dierama erectum*

Auriol Batten

Godfrey Symons

355

Dierama latifolium (*latifolium* - broad leaves)

In large clumps, up to 2,5 m. In open grassland. **Leaves:** 550-1500 x **5-15 mm.**
Flowers: Inflorescence with 6-11 branches, 5-16 flowers each, often crowded,
stem long, drooping to suberect; flowers ± 33 mm, pale to deep pink, rarely deep
wine red; **bracts white,** or with light flecking, 18-27 x 7-10 mm (Oct-Jun). (See p. 42)

Dierama pauciflorum (*pauciflorum* - few flowers)

In **dense clumps**, 300-600 mm. **In standing water** in marshes, 1500-2400 m,
E Cape to Mpum, a gap then E Zim. **Leaves:** 100-400 x 1-4 mm. **Flowers:**
Inflorescence solitary, erect or with ± 5 drooping branches, lowest 25-40 mm, 1-5
flowers each; flowers 20-28 mm, **pink** or reddish; bracts 12-18 x 7-10 mm, **bright
rust brown**, flecked, **6-8 veins each side of midvein, nearly to margins** (Nov-
Dec). **General:** Few flowers in each inflorescence, but massed plants bloom
profusely. **Similar species:** *D. trichorhizum* (see p. 456)

Dierama pulcherrimum East London Hairbell; Oos-Londengrasklokkie (A) (*pulcher-
rimus* - very beautiful)

Solitary or in small clumps, up to 1,6 m. In grassland. **Leaves:** 500-900 x 5-9 mm.
Flowers: Inflorescence with 4-8 branches, 2-5 flowers each, crowded, stems
drooping; flowers 35-54 mm, **nearly cylindrical, tepal lobes not spreading,** light
to dark magenta or deep purple-red; bracts 23-34 x 10-12 mm, brown (Nov-Feb).
General: Beautiful garden plant. **Similar species:** *D. igneum* (see p. 354).

Dierama tysonii (named after William Tyson, 1851-1920, teacher and plant collector)

In **small clumps**, 450-850 mm. In open grassland, 1370-1650 m. **Leaves:** 300-600
x 3-8 mm. **Flowers:** Inflorescence with 4-8 branches, **4-7 flowers** each, crowded,
stems erect; flowers ± 23 mm, light to deep bright pink; bracts 14-20 x 4-6 mm,
translucent whitish to pale orange-buff lightly flecked all over, midline light
orange-brown, 5-6 veins each side, fading about half way (Sep-Oct).

Gladiolus (*gladiolus* - small sword, refers to leaf shape) - Bracts green; style branches short, undivided or shortly
divided in 2; seeds winged. Hybrids created since the early 1800s have produced the cut-flowers and garden plants
popular worldwide. The Xhosa call them '*itembu* ' - 'fruits of the earth', and the corms are dug up and eaten. Mostly
S Afr, also Trop Afr, S Europe, Middle East, ± 259 species, over 126 in SA.

Gladiolus crassifolius Thick-leaved Gladiolus; khahla-e-nyenyane (SS); sidvwana (Sw);
igulusha, ingangulazi (Z) (*crassifolius* - thick leaves)

Up to 1 m, in small groups. In grassland, coast to 1950 m, E Cape to Trop Afr.
Corm roundish, 20-30 mm diam. **Leaves:** Erect, ± 700 x 12 mm, **margins and
midrib yellow,** forming **sheathing fan. Flowers:** In dense inflorescence, **stem
curving out from leaves**, with 1-3 branches; buds in two rows, 12-22(40) flowers,
turned to one side, small, 25-40 mm, pink, orange, pale lilac, lower 2 lobes with
dark blotch (blooms throughout year). **Fruit:** Capsule roundish, ± 8 mm, reddish
brown. **General:** Pollinated by proboscid flies. Used in traditional medicine to cure
headaches. (See p. 456)

Gladiolus gueinzii (named after Wilhelm Gueinzius, 1814-74, first resident botanist in Natal, apothecary,
naturalist, botanical and zoological collector)

300-550(750) mm. **On coastal dunes**, S Cape to KZN. Corm roundish, ± 25 mm
diam, tunics thin reddish brown. **Leaves:** Basal, ± 5 mm wide, **thick, fleshy** margins
and midrib thickened, taller than flowering stem. **Flowers:** Small, ± 40 x30 mm, pink
with purple to mauve and red markings with white stripe on 3 lower lobes; bracts
slightly fleshy, ± 18 mm, stem slender, erect, sheathed with leaves (Oct-Dec).

Gladiolus microcarpus (*microcarpus* - bearing small fruit)

Hanging, up to 1 m. In moist crevices in cliffs, 1800-2700 m. **Corm roundish,**
± 20 mm diam. **Leaves:** 3-5 in a soft fan, ± 600 x 10 mm, **spreading golden hairs
on prominent ribs,** forming a sheathing stem, 2 bractlike leaves sheathing base.
Flowers: 5-11, **stem and spathes hairless**; flowers ± 45 mm, tepal lobes 25-
40 mm, pointed, white to pink or mauve with darker stripes on lower half (Jan-
Feb). **Fruit:** Capsule 15 mm. **Similar species:** *G. scabridus* (see p. 358).

Dierama latifolium

Dierama pulcherrimum

Dierama pauciflorum

Gladiolus gueinzii

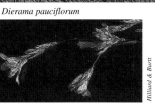

Dierama paucifllorum

Gladiolus microcarpus

Dierama tysonii

Gladiolus microcarpus

Gladiolus crassifolius

357

Gladiolus oppositiflorus [= *G. salmoneus*] **Salmon Gladiolus, Transkei Gladiolus; Transkeiswaardlelie (A)** (*oppositiflorus* - flowers inserted on stem opposite to each other)
Up to 1,5 m, in small clumps. In open grassland, marshy areas. Corm roundish, old corms persist. **Leaves:** ± 1000 x 20-30 mm, raised yellow ribs, very finely hairy, sheathing below, in a fan above. **Flowers:** 20-35, inflorescence with ± 15 open at a time; bracts ± 60 x 10 mm; flowers ± 100 mm, white to pale or deep pink, dark lines on tepals, blotches in throat (Nov-Mar). **General:** Grown in Europe since late 1800s. Subsp *oppositiflorus*, coastal areas, E Cape to S KZN; hairless; ± 30 flowers, in 2 ranks, pale white to pink. Subsp. *salmoneus*, on rocky slopes, KZN Drakensberg, up to 2500 m; finely hairy; ± 20 flowers in single row, to one side, deep pink.

Gladiolus parvulus (parvulus - small)
Up to 300 mm. On grassy mountain slopes, up to 3300 m. **Leaf:** Solitary, **sheathing stem. Flowers:** 2-4 in simple spike, stem slender, wiry, with papery **bractlike leaf immediately below lowest flower**; flowers delicate, ± 20 mm, pink (Oct-Nov). **Similar species:** *G. pubigerus* (see p. 240).

Gladiolus scabridus [= *G. microcarpus* subsp. *italaensis*] **Itala Gladiolus**
Erect, in rock crevices on steep slopes, in light shade, at lower altitudes, about 250 m. **Leaves: Hairless. Flowers: Stem and spathes densely downy**; flowers delicate, pale pink, lower lobes with dark pink midrib edged white, fading to dark lilac (Dec-Jan). **Similar species:** *G. microcarpus* (see p. 356).

Gladiolus sericeovillosus **Large Speckled Gladiolus; Bloupypie (A); sidvwana (Sw); udwendweni, isidwi esincane, umlunge (Z)** (*sericeovillosus* - grey haired)
Solitary or in small colonies, 0,35-1,5 m. In grassland, near coast to 1750 m, E Cape to Zim. Corm round, ± 30 mm diam, old corms persist, densely covered in thick fibres. **Leaves:** Forming a stem at base, fanning out, ± 6(35) mm wide, firm, margins prominent, yellow ribs. **Flowers:** ± 20(40) flowers, overlapping, in 2 ranks, stem sturdy, with **woolly, curly white hairs**; flowers ± 45 x 20 mm, pale green or cream, sometimes speckled pink or mauve, lower tepal lobes with dark edged yellow-green blotches; **bracts woolly**, ± 30 mm (Dec-May). **Fruit:** Capsule oval, ± 20 mm. **General:** Pollinated by a bee species. Used in traditional medicine to treat dysentery, swollen joints, menstrual pain, help expel afterbirth and treat sterility in women, also as a charm to ensure a good harvest. (See p. 112)

Watsonia (*Watsonia* - named after English scientist Sir William Watson, 1715-1787) - Flattened corm with persistent fibrous tunics; leaves firm, basal and sheathing stem leaves; inflorescence a spike, flower tube curved, widening to funnel shape, lobes spreading, ± equal, 6 stigmas, bracts rigid, usually brown. Mostly SA, ± 52 species, 1 in Madag.

Watsonia confusa (confusa - refers to the species often being confused with other KZN species with similar dry bracts, especially *W. densiflora*)
Large, robust, **up to 1,5 m**, solitary or in small clumps. In **damp sites** or in grassland on south facing slopes, coast to 1000 m. **Leaves: 15-25 mm wide**, pale blue-green; stem leaves ± overlapping, sheathing, **slightly inflated. Flowers:** ± 30, stem unbranched; **bracts dry brown**, 20-35 x 14-18 mm, overlapping, clasping in lower two thirds; flowers large, ± 25 mm, tepal lobes ± 32 x 11 mm, pink to purple, often with dark pink line in middle of 3 lower tepals (Oct-Mar).

Watsonia densiflora [= *W. neglecta, W. plantii*] **Natal Watsonia; kxahla (SS); sidvwa (Sw); incembuzane, intshumo, isidwa, umlunge (Z)** (densiflora - densely flowered)
In clumps, up to 1,2 m. In open grassland, usually well watered. **Leaves:** ± 15 mm wide, grey-green, midvein and margins thickened, yellow. **Flowers:** ± 42, **in dense inflorescence, 3 or more stems, inclining at base**; bracts dry, brown, margins **dark, veins pale**; flower tube ± 30 mm, lower part enclosed in bracts, upper part ± 12 mm, tepal lobes ± 24 x 9 mm, pink with dark pink streak in middle of each tepal (Nov-Jun). **General:** Corm edible. Used in traditional medicine to treat diarrhoea and as a charm to ensure good harvests. Easy to grow from seed, difficult to maintain, requires plenty of water, rich garden soil. White and deep red colour forms occur. (See p. 114) **Similar species:** *W. pulchra* Solitary or in small clumps, up to 1,2 m; in grassland, woodland, NE KZN to Mpum escarpment; leaves broader, 15-30 mm, midrib not thickened, margins strongly thickened; bracts dark brown.

Gladiolus oppositiflorus

Tom de Waal

Gladiolus oppositiflorus

Darrel Plowes

Gladiolus scabridus

Martin von Fintel

Gladiolus parvulus

Trevor Coleman

Watsonia confusa

Wally Menne

Watsonia confusa

Wally Menne

Gladiolus sericeovillosus

Martin von Fintel

Watsonia densiflora

Lal Greene

Trevor Coleman

359

Watsonia inclinata (*inclinata* - refers to stem which is bent at base, inclined at a 45 degree angle)

Solitary, up to 600 mm. In **rocky grassland**, Pondoland endemic. **Leaves:** 2 basal, **pale green**, 4-14 mm wide; upper stem leaf or leaves bractlike. **Flowers:** 6-11 in widely spaced inflorescence, **stem bent at base, inclining**; bracts ± 30 mm, **not dry and brown, not overlapping**; flower tube ± 28 mm, tepals ± 28 x 12 mm, **pink**, paler in throat and tube (Aug-Oct), sweetly scented.

Watsonia lepida khahla (SS) (*lepida* - attractive or pleasing)

Up to 650 mm, **solitary** (occasionally in small clumps). In grassland, rocky areas, 1500-1980 m. **Leaves:** 2-3, basal, 5-15 mm wide, margins and midrib strongly thickened; flowering stem leaves large, overlapping, sheathing. **Flowers:** ± 22, in **crowded** inflorescence, **stem short, sturdy, erect**; bracts ± 25 x 10-12 mm, **narrow, only clasping stem near base, dry, uniformly dark brown**; flowers bright pink to purplish pink, tube ± 30 mm, funnel-shaped above, tepal lobes ± 20 x 9 mm (Nov-Feb). **General:** Flowers sucked for nectar by children. Leaves plaited for rope. Used traditionally to treat diarrhoea in calves. **Similar species:** *W. confusa*, *W. densiflora*, *W. pulchra* (see p. 358).

Watsonia mtamvunae (named for the Mtamvuna Nature Reserve in S KZN)

Slender, **short, 200-450 mm**. On grassy, stony slopes, Pondoland endemic. **Leaves:** 3-5, basal, **narrow**, ± 3 mm wide, sometimes broken and dry by time of flowering; flowering stem with sheathing bract leaves. **Flowers:** ± 12, stem unbranched; bracts ± 16 mm, dry, brown in upper half, purplish below, overlapping; **flowers small**, pale pink, tube ± 20 mm, upper part horizontal, funnel-shaped, tepal lobes ± 16 x 7 mm (Aug-Oct). **General:** Blooms well after fires.

Watsonia pondoensis (from Pondoland)

Up to 600 mm, in small clumps, occasionally in dense colonies. **In marshes**, Pondoland endemic. **Leaves:** 2, basal, half as long as stem, **4-12 mm wide**, blue-green; flowering stem with sheathing bract leaves. **Flowers:** 3-8, in widely spaced inflorescence, stem unbranched; bracts ± 27 mm, clasp stem below, **not overlapping**, dry, brown tipped, purplish at base; **flowers large, purple**, paler in throat, tube ± 30 mm, tepal lobes ± 22 x 7 mm (Sep-Oct).

ZINGIBERACEACE - Ginger Family Well known for its spice plants including ginger *Zingiber officinale*, cardamom *Elettaria cardamomum* and turmeric, *Curcuma longa* which is not uncommon in gardens in KZN. Trop, ± 52 genera, ± 1100 species, 3 genera in SA. *Siphonochilus* (*siphono* - tube; *chilos* - lip) - Rhizomatous herbs; rhizome fleshy; flowering stem separate from leaf shoot. Mainly Old World Trop, a few in S and C America, ± 2 species in SA.

Siphonochilus aethiopicus [= *Kaempferia aethiopica, K. ethelae*] Wild Ginger; Wildegemmer(A); sidvungulu (Sw); indungulu, isiphephetho (Z)

Up to 1 m. In forests. Extinct in the wild in KZN, Mpum. Rhizome aromatic. Shoots 300-1000 mm. **Leaves:** 30-400 x 50-90 mm, deciduous. **Flowers:** 2-6, in inflorescence separate from leaf shoot; flowers white to bright pink, yellow on lip, tube 30-40 mm, white, tepal lobes 60-80 mm wide (Oct-Feb), faintly scented. **General:** Female plants smaller than male plants. Cultivated traditionally to provide protection from lightning and snakes. Used in traditional medicine to treat coughs, colds and influenza. In demand as a container plant; now grown by tissue culture.

ORCHIDACEAE - Orchid family Highly specialised, flowers in two whorls, outer 3 sepals and inner 3 petals often all the same colour. One of the sepals can be differently shaped and is called the median, dorsal or odd sepal. One of the petals is usally lobed and crested and called the lip. Either the median sepal or the lip may have a sac or spur. Single stamen, stigma and style are united to form a structure called the column. Pollen grains are collected into waxy or grainy pollinia which are attached to a sticky gland. Cosmop, ± 788 genera, ± 18500 species, 54 genera in SA.

Stenoglottis (*stenos* - narrow; *glotta* - tongue) - Terrestrial or epiphytic; leaves in basal rosette. SE Afr, ± 4 species in SA.

Stenoglottis fimbriata Fringed Stenoglottis; Fraiing-stenoglottis (A) (*fimbriata* - fringed)

Small, 100-400 mm. In forest, on rocks, mossy banks, tree trunks, coast to 1925 m, E Cape to Tanz. Roots thickened, hairy. **Leaves:** In basal rosette, ± 150 x 20 mm, ± marked with dark purple spots, **margins wavy**, very variable. **Flowers: 5-70 in erect inflorescence**, stem slender; flowers small, ± 15 mm, lilac-pink (white) with darker spots, **lip 3 lobed, without spur** (Jan-Apr). **General:** A good container plant. **Similar species:** *S. longifolia* Known only from a few inland areas of KZN; much more robust; leaves unspotted; lip 5 lobed, unspurred (May-Jun).

Watsonia inclinata

Watsonia lepida

Watsonia mtamvunae

Siphonochilus aethiopicus

Watsonia pondoensis

Stenoglottis fimbriata

Stenoglottis fimbriata

Stenoglottis longifolia

361

Stenoglottis woodii (named after John Medley Wood, 1827-1915, first curator of Natal Herbarium, botanical collector who published widely on KZN flora)
Small, up to 200 mm. In rocky areas. **Leaves:** In basal rosette, ± 150 x 30 mm, unspotted, dull green, pointed tip. **Flowers:** Inflorescence with **5-40** flowers, stem slender, erect; flowers white or pink with few darker spots on **3 lobed lip, small spur at base** (Oct-May).

Holothrix (*holos* - entire; *thrix* - hair, meaning hairy all over) - Terrestrial herbs with 2 leaves flat on ground; flowering stem leafless and bractless, flowers white to yellowish green. Afr, ± 55 species, 22 in SA.

Holothrix scopularia [= *H. multisecta*] (*scopulinus* - bearing small brushes)
Slender to robust, up to 330 mm. In rocky grassland, 1200-2800 m. **Leaves:** ± 52 mm broad, with scattered long thin hairs near margins above. **Flowers:** In dense inflorescence, stem with long thin hairs; flowers small, white to dull yellow or pink, lip ± 9 mm, deeply divided into ± 11 lobes (Oct-Jan).
(See p. 240)

Brachycorythis (*brachy* - short; *koros* - helmet, refers to the uppermost of the 3 sepals which is convex and smaller than the other two) - Terrestrial herbs; densely leafy from ground level, with large leaflike bracts; flowers pink, purple or greenish, lip stretches forward. Afr, ± 35 species, 7 in SA.

Brachycorythis pubescens (*pubescens* - slightly hairy, downy)
Slender to robust, up to 450 mm. In grassland, coast to 1500 m, KZN to Trop Afr. **Leaves: Finely hairy,** ± 50 x 17 mm, conspicuously veined. **Flowers:** In dense inflorescence; flowers brownish purple**, hairy on reverse of segments,** lip ± 10 x 11 mm, pink with **red spotted yellow patch** at base, no spur (Oct-Dec). **Similar species:** *B. ovata* (see p. 456).

Satyrium (*Satyros* - refers to the 2 horned satyr, half man half goat - the two spurs are said to resemble a satyr's horns) - Terrestrial herbs with underground tubers; ovary not twisted, lip forms a hood, 2 conspicuous spurs or 2 pouches. Used in traditional medicine, mixed with other medicines, to help with illnesses that are difficult to cure. Mostly Afr, a few in Mascarene Is, India and S China, ± 140 species, 33 in SA.

Satyrium hallackii (named after Russell Hallack, 1824-1903, businessman and amateur botanist who arrived in SA in 1843)
Robust, 0,19-1 m, solitary or in large colonies. In marshy ground, in water, 600-2000 m, E Cape to Trop Afr. **Leaves:** 4-6, sheathing stem, 70-200 mm, tips pointed. **Flowers:** ± 70, densely or well spaced, inflorescence ± 180 mm; flowers **white, pink to deep pink,** ± 15 mm wide, spurs ± 30 mm (Nov-Mar), faintly scented. **General:** Subsp. *ocellatum* [= *S. ocellatum*], E Cape to Trop Afr. Subsp. *hallackii*, SW and SE Cape endemic. (See p. 118)

Satyrium longicauda **Blushing Bride Satyrium, Long-tailed Trewwa; Langstert-trewwa (A); Iekoesha (Ss); uklamkleshe, unoklamu, unokleshe (Z)** (*longicauda* - long tailed)
Slender, 170-800 mm, in small groups and large colonies. In grassland, rocky areas, marshes, coast to 3000 m, S Cape to Trop Afr. **Leaves:** 1-2, basal, ± 200 mm, prostrate or partly erect, **on separate shoot from flowering stem or absent. Flowers:** Inflorescence ± 200 mm, with ± 60 flowers, stem with sheathing leaves, bracts deflexed; flowers ± 20 mm, white to pink, veins and tips often darker pink, **flap above lip entrance hairy,** spurs slender, ± 46 mm (Sep-Apr), sweetly scented. **General:** Tuberous roots edible. Used as protective and love charms. Var. *longicauda*, up to 2100 m; flowers large. Var. *jacottetianum*, up to 3000 m; flowers smaller, pink to red, spurs + 26 mm. (See p 118)
Similar species: Hybrid, *S. longicauda* x *S. neglectum* subsp. *woodii* [= *S. rhodantha*] **ilabatheka elibomvu (Z),** possibly a valid species; extremely localised; deep pink to red.

Tom de Waal

Stenoglottis woodii

Ray Boardman

Holothorix scopularia

Bob Duckworth

Brachycorythis pubescens

Pam Cooke

Satyrium hallackii

Godfrey Symons

Satyrium hallackii

Johan Bodenstein

Satyrium longicauda

Lal Greene

Satyrium longicauda

David Johnson

Satyrium longicauda x neglectum

363

Satyrium macrophyllum **uklamkleshe, unoklamu, unokleshe (Z)** *(macrophyllum* - large leaves)*

Robust, up to 1 m, in groups or colonies. In marshy ground, moist grassland, 350-1800 m. **Leaves:** 2-3, up to 400 x 70 mm, erect, sheathing at base; stem leaves clasping. **Flowers:** ± 90, held horizontally, in dense inflorescence ± 400 mm, bracts ± 30 mm, reflexed when flowers open; flowers white to deep pink, hood flattish, merging with broad based spurs, ± 26 mm, tapering gradually (Nov-Apr), faintly scented . **General:** Tuberous roots eaten by people. **Similar species:** *S. cheirophorum* Moz to E Afr.

Satyrium neglectum **Pink Candle Satyrium** *(neglectum* - overlooked, insignificant)*

Slender to robust, 140-950 mm. In moist grassland, up to 3000 m, E Cape to Tanz. **Leaves:** ± 350 mm, spreading, **on separate short shoot**, absent or fully grown at flowering. **Flowers:** 12-130, inflorescence ± 550 mm; flowers small to medium, **pink to deep red, orange to orange-yellow, mauve, yellowish white,** 10 mm wide, spurs ± 20 mm (Oct-Apr), sweetly scented. **General:** Subsp. *neglectum*, in upland grassland, on moist slopes, 100-300 m, NE Cape (N Transkei) to Tanz; spike ± 20 mm diam, lip small, opening 2-4 mm (Jan-Mar). Subsp. *woodii*, localised in moist grassland, 300-1500 m, E Cape to KZN midlands; spike ± 30 mm diam, lip medium sized, opening 6-9 mm.

Schizochilus (*schizein* - splinter or split; *cheilos* - a lip) - Terrestrial herb; leaves few, narrow, near base of stem; inflorescence dense, usually drooping over at tip. Afr genus, ± 20 species, 8 in SA.

Schizochilus gerrardii (named after William Gerrard, died on Madag 1866, professional collector who discovered 150 new species)

Slender, up to 250 mm. On margins of rocky outcrops, in grassland, 1200 m, restricted distribution. **Leaves:** ± 25, **lower 6-10 in basal cluster**. **Flowers:** In dense, cylindrical inflorescence; flowers white to pink with greenish spot on lip, sepals 5-8 mm, petals ± 3 mm, spur 1 mm, straight (Dec-Feb).

Brownleea (named after Rev John Brownlee, 1791-1871, Scottish missionary, gardener, linguist, theologian, a plant collector who collected the type species of the genus, *B. coerulea*, in E Cape) - Terrestrial (rarely epiphytic or lithophytic) herbs; few leaves; median/odd sepal joins with two lateral petals to form trumpet-shaped hood which tapers gradually into curved spur, lip very small. Afr, ± 15 species, 5 in SA.

Brownleea macroceras *(macroceras* - large horns)*

40-80(200) mm. On damp rock ledges, grassy slopes 1800-3000 m. **Leaves:** 1(3), **narrow,** less than 10 mm wide, scattered on stem. **Flowers: 1-3(6)**, whitish to deep lilac blue; dorsal sepal ± 13 mm, spur slender, 25-40 mm, horizontal then curving downwards (Jan-Apr), sweetly scented. **General:** Cultivated as an alpine species.

Disa (possibly from *dis* - rich or opulent, alluding to the beauty and magnificence of the first species described in this genus, *D. uniflora*) - Underground tubers; several leaves; median sepal hooded, prolonged into a spur or pouch, direction in which spur points is useful in identification. Afr, Madag, ± 130 species, ± 94 in SA.

Disa aconitoides **Oumakappie (A); ihlamvu, umashushu (Z)** *(aconitum* - like a monk's hood)*

Slender, up to 600 mm. In grassland, on stony slopes, coast to 2000 m, S Cape to Mpum. **Leaves:** Many, overlapping, on stem. **Flowers:** 15-70, in slender inflorescence; flowers white to pale mauve with darker spots, **spur ± 10 mm, upward pointing, thick, almost as broad as the hood** (Oct-Jan). **General:** Infusion of roots used in traditional medicine to promote fertility in women.

Disa cooperi (named after Thomas Cooper who collected plants in KZN and the Cape in the 1850s)

Robust, up to 700 mm. In stony, moist or dry grassland, 1500-2200 m. **Leaves:** Basal, and with sheathing stem leaves. **Flowers:** ± 50, large, overlapping, in dense inflorescence; flowers whitish to pale pink (purple) with **triangular green lip, spur 30-40 mm, pointing upwards** (Dec-Feb). **Similar species:** *D. scullyi* (see p. 368).

Satyrium neglectum

Martin von Fintel

Satyrium neglectum

Sheila Peacock

Satyrium neglectum

Martin von Fintel

Satyrium macrophyllum

Martin von Fintel

Schizochilus gerrardii

Martin von Fintel

Brownleea macroceras

Darrel Plowes

Disa aconitoides

Martin von Fintel

Disa cooperi

Tessa Hedge

Disa cooperi

Darrel Plowes

365

Disa crassicornis [= *D. jacottetiae*] (*crassus* - thick; *cornis* - horn, refers to single spur)

Robust, up to 1,25 m, solitary or in small groups. Widespread but uncommon in damp grassland, on forest margins, rock ledges, up to 2200 m. **Leaves:** 3-5, basal, ± 130 x 30 mm, from separate shoot; stem leaves sheathing, usually withered at time of flowering. **Flowers:** ± 5-25, large, inflorescence ± 300 mm, bracts papery, reddish brown; flowers creamy white to pale pink with purple or pink mottled spots, **sepals 20-40 mm, spur 30-40 mm, curving out then down,** tip slender, greenish (Nov-Mar), strongly scented. **General:** Cultivated in Europe since the 1800s, but difficult to maintain. Withstands both snow and high summer temperatures. (See p. 120) **Similar species:** *D. thodei* (see p. 120).

Disa fragrans Fragrant Disa; Lekkerruik-disa (A) (*fragrans* - fragrant)

Robust, 150-500 mm. In damp grassland, on cliff edges, 1800-3000 m, E Cape to Tanz. **Leaves:** 4-6, on stem, ± 100 mm, purple barred. **Flowers: In dense, cylindrical inflorescence**, ± 100 mm; flowers small, ± 8 mm diam, white to deep pink, mottled, spur slender, 5-10 mm, pointing upwards (Jan-Mar), strongly scented.

Disa maculomarronina (*macula* - a blotch; *marroninus* - maroon, refers to blotches at the base of lateral sepals)

Slender (robust), 300-450 mm. In swampy grassland 1500-1680 m. **Leaves:** Sterile shoot slender, 30-60 mm, with 2 leaves 200-300 x 10-20 mm; stem leaves overlapping, 35-90 x 7-12 mm. **Flowers:** Inflorescence cylindrical, 50-90 mm; 12-35 flowers, bracts 12-18 mm drying quickly; flowers purple-pink, lateral sepals lighter with basal blotch, petals and lip maroon-pink to purple-maroon, spur usually horizontal or deflexed from middle, ± 8 mm (Dec-Jan). **Similar species:** Closely related to *D. versicolor* (see p. 368).

Disa nervosa (*nervosa* - veins/nerves)

Conspicuous, robust, 400-800 mm. Widespread, in dry, rocky grassland, forest margins. **Leaves:** Narrow, sheathing, overlapping, 130-200 x 20-30 mm, veins prominent beneath. **Flowers:** In dense cylindrical inflorescence; flowers bright pink, sometimes with purple spots, sepals ± 25 mm, **spur horizontal, ± 20 mm** (Dec-Mar).

Disa patula (*patulus* - spread out, extended)

Slender to robust, 250-650 mm. In grassland, 200-2000 m, E Cape to Zim. **Leaves:** ± 100 x 15 mm, sheathing stem. **Flowers:** Inflorescence ± 200 mm; flowers pale to bright pink with purplish spots, **spur round, pointed, 5-12 mm, horizontal** (Nov-Mar). **General:** Var. *patula,* E Cape; inflorescence wider than 30 mm, flowers larger. Var. *transvaalensis;* widespread, inflorescence narrower, flowers smaller.

Disa pulchra (*pulchra* - beautiful)

Up to 600 mm. In stony grassland, 1200-2300 m. **Leaves:** ± 200 mm, rigid. **Flowers:** In loose, crowded inflorescence; flowers large, bright pink, sepals ± 30 mm, **spur 15-20 mm, slender, horizontal, curved down at tip** (Dec-Jan).

Disa crassicornis

Martin von Fintel

Disa crassicornis

Martin von Fintel

Disa fragrans

Darrel Plowes

Disa maculomarronina

Martin von Fintel

Disa nervosa

Geoff Nichols

Disa fragrans

Martin von Fintel

Disa patula

Martin von Fintel

Disa patula

Martin von Fintel

Disa pulchra

Trevor Coleman

367

Disa rhodantha (*rhodantha* - bearing red flowers)

Slender, 300-600 mm. In swampy areas, on streambanks, E Cape to Zim. **Leaves:** Up to 4, on separate shoot; stem leaves sheathing. **Flowers:** 15-30, overlapping, in crowded, narrow, spikelike inflorescence; flowers pink to dark red, lip narrow, hanging, spur 7-17 mm, pointing upwards with down curving tip (Dec-Feb).

Disa scullyi (named after William Charles Scully, 1855-1943, magistrate, author, collector, who came to Cape Town in 1867, died in Mbogintwini, KZN)

Slender to robust, up to 600 mm. In swampy areas, 1500-2700 m. **Leaves:** Basal, on separate shoot; stem leaves sheathing. **Flowers:** ± 20, in inflorescence; flowers white to pink, **lip green, oblong, spur 30-40 mm, pointing upwards then curving downwards** (Dec-Feb). **Similar species:** *D. cooperi* (see p. 364).

Disa stachyoides   ihlamvu elimpofu lasenkangala (Z)   (*stachyoides* - resembling *Stachys*, Wound Wort)

Robust, 100-400 mm. Widespread, in dry grassland. **Leaves:** Few, pointed, ± 80 x 10 mm. **Flowers:** In dense inflorescence, ± 100 mm; flowers small, purple with white lip, **spur 2-6 mm, broad, flat, almost horizontal** (Nov-Jan). **General:** Traditionally used to ward off evil spirits and storms. (See p. 458)

Disa versicolor [= *D. macowanii*] **Apple-blossom Orchid; ihlamvu elibomvu (Z)** (*versicolor* - variously coloured, changing colour)

Robust, up to 600 mm. Widespread in marshy areas, moist grassland, coast to 2400 m, E Cape to Zim. **Leaves:** 3-5, basal, ± 200 x 20 mm, folded, from separate shoot; a few sheathing stem leaves, ± 100 x 15 mm. **Flowers:** In dense inflorescence, ± 150 mm, bracts longer than flowers; flowers dull red to pink, fading greenish brown, **spur 5-7 mm, hooked** (Dec-Feb), vanilla scented. **General:** Infusion from plant used for charm against evil. **Similar species:** Closely related to *D. maculomarronina* (see p. 366).

Disperis (*dis* - double; *pera* - pouch, refers to spurs on side sepals) - **'Granny Bonnet' Orchids** Slender perennial herbs; undergound tubers; with few leaves; petals joined to median sepal to form helmet-shaped hood, side sepals with noticeable spur or pouch. Afr, India, New Guinea, Mascarene Is, ± 75 species, ± 26 in SA.

Disperis concinna (*concinna* - pretty, neat, elegant)

Slender, 100-500 mm. In marshy grassland, 1500-2400 m, KZN to Zim. **Leaves:** 1-3, clasping, 10-20 mm. **Flowers:** 1-4, small, pale to deep pink, sometimes spotted green inside, **hood shallow, rounded**, ± 3 mm deep, **side sepals 6-7 mm**, spreading, pointed (Jan-Mar).

Disperis cooperi (named after Thomas Cooper, 1815-1913, English plant collector and grower who visited SA in 1859)

Stout, 150-400 mm. In marshy grassland, 1500-2000 m. **Leaves:** 2-4, alternate, 25-35 mm, stalkless, clasping, tips pointed. **Flowers:** 5-12, white to pinkish purple, tinged green, **hood deep, rounded**, 8-10 mm, green and purple spotted on the rim, **side sepals 7-10 mm**, spreading, pointed (Feb-Apr). **Similar species:** *Disperis wealii* (see p. 122).

Disa scullyi

Emile Plumstead

Disa rhodantha

Lal Greene

Disa rhodantha

Martin von Fintel

Geoff Nichols

Disa scullyi

Emile Plumstead

Disa stachyoides

Trevor Coleman

Disa versicolor

Anne Rennie

Disperis concinna

Martin von Fintel

Disperis cooperi

Lal Greene

369

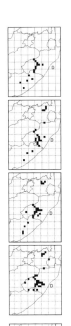

Disperis oxyglossa (oxyglossa - pointed tongue)

Slender, 150-300 mm. In damp grasslands, 1400-2500 m. **Leaves:** 3-4, clasping, 20-40 mm. **Flowers:** 1-5, pinkish purple, **petals with green spots on lower half,** hood narrow, compressed, ± 10 mm, **side sepals ± 17 mm, spreading, spurs facing backwards,** with long pointed tip (Feb-Mar).

Disperis renibractea (renibractea - kidney-shaped bracts)

150-300 mm. In grassland, 1400-2700 m. **Leaf:** Solitary, roundish, 10-30 mm. **Flowers:** ± 10, greenish, pinkish or brownish, all facing one way, **hood broad, shallow,** ± 17 mm, **inside of hood visible, spotted purple,** side sepals 6-8 mm, spreading, **bracts kidney-shaped** (Dec-Mar), pungent odour. (See p. 520) **Similar species:** *D. cardiophora* (see p. 122).

Disperis stenoplectron (stenoplectron - with narrow spurs)

Stout, 150-300 mm. In grassland, 1700-2200 m. **Leaves:** 2-4, alternate, clasping, 20-40 mm. **Flowers:** 5-10, dark purple and green or pale white to pink, **hood ± 10 mm deep,** side sepals ± 12 mm, spreading and pointing downwards (Jan-Apr).

Disperis tysonii (named after William Tyson, born Jamaica 1851, died Grahamstown 1920, teacher and plant collector)

Slender, 150-400(650) mm. Widespread in grassland, 1500-3100 m. **Leaves:** 3-6, clasping, ± 30 x 10 mm. **Flowers: 2-14,** pink to deep pinkish red, marked green, **hood deep, ± 8 mm tall, inclined backwards,** side sepals 4-7 mm, spreading (Jan-Apr).

Disperis woodii (named after John Medley Wood, 1827-1915, first curator of Natal Herbarium, botanist, collector, who published widely on KZN flora)

Small, 50-100 mm. In grassland. **Leaves:** 2, at base or on stem, 8-15 mm, closely alternate, dark green with silvery veins. **Flowers:** Solitary, pink, in axil of small bract on red stalk, hood extends into tall, narrow, deep pink spur, 10-15 mm, side sepals 4-6 mm with shallow spur at about the middle, marked deep pink, petals paler, dotted green, lip with basal claw and long slender appendage which extends into spur (Apr-May, Jul-Oct).

Cheirostylis (*cheiro* - hand; *stylis* - style) - Terrestrial herbs, leaves narrowed to stalklike base; flower small, sepals, petals, lip united to form funnel-shaped flower, lip united with the column in lower third. One species in SA.

Cheirostylis gymnochiloides

Herb, 200-400 mm. In humid swamp forests, KZN northwards, also Malagasy Is. **Leaves:** 30-50 x 12-25 mm. **Flowers: Small,** pinkish-brown, **slightly hairy,** sepals 3-4 mm (Sep-Oct). **General:** Habit more or less resembles a *Commelina.* **Similar species:** *Platylepis glandulosa* (see p. 124).

Eulophia (*eu* - well; *lophos* - crest, refers to the crested lip) - Terrestrial herbs; rhizomes thickened into fibrous tubers, some with pseudobulbs; leaf-bearing shoot separate from flowering stem, leaves narrow, often folded, in 2 ranks; flowers usually showy, sepals ± equal, lip with ridges on upper surface, spur very shallow or up to half length of flower. Trop, subtrop regions of Old World, most common in Afr, ± 200 species, ± 42 in SA.

Eulophia aculeata lekholela, 'mametsana (SS) (aculeata - thorns, prickly, pointed)

Slender to stout, 60-650 mm. In grassland, SW Cape to Mpum. **Leaves:** Stiff, ± 600 x 17 mm, partly to fully grown at flowering. **Flowers:** 3-30, in **dense, crowded inflorescence**; petals and sepals ± 18 mm, same colour, ivory to greenish white, pink or purple, **spur absent** (Sep-Apr), faintly scented. **General:** Subsp. *aculeata,* SW Cape to Mpum; flowers small, median sepal 5-9 mm, sepals, petals and lip ivory to white or greenish white (Nov-Jan). Subsp. *huttonii,* E Cape to Mpum; median sepal 9-18 mm, sepals, petals, lip greenish white to pink to dark reddish purple, lip crests usually yellowish green to white (Sep-Apr). (See p. 126)

Disperis oxyglossa

Ray Boardman

Disperis renibractea

Emile Plumstead

Disperis stenoplectron

Ray Boardman

Disperis tysonii

Trevor Coleman

Disperis tysonii

Lal Greene

Disperis woodii

CJ Ward

Cheirostylis gymnochiloides

CJ Ward

Cheirostylis gymnochiloides

CJ Ward

Eulophia aculeata

Tony Abbott

Eulophia clavicornis lekholela, maholohanya, 'mametsana (SS); imfeyamasele eluhlaza (Z) (*clava* - club; *cornis* - horn)

Slender, 0,10-1 m. Widespread in grassland, coast to 1700 m, S Cape to N Prov. **Leaves:** 50-730 mm, partly to fully developed at flowering. **Flowers:** Widely spaced, sepals green to purplish brown, ± 19 mm, petals and lip white to purple or yellow, **spur cylindrical, 14-89 mm, crests tall to end of lip** (Jul-Feb). **General:** Grazed by stock. Tubers eaten by people. Infusion from tubers used in traditional medicine as protection from evil and to treat infertility. Flower colour, size and leaf development very variable. Subsp. *clavicornis,* flowers white, pale pink to pale blue, lip as long as median sepal, 9-18 mm (Aug-Sep). Subsp. *inaequalis,* lip often shorter than median sepal (Sep-Oct). Subsp. *nutans,* leaves fully developed at flowering, 100-730 mm; flowers white to pale or deep purple or yellow (Dec-Feb). (See p. 126) **Similar species:** *E. ovalis* (see p. 126, 244).

Eulophia cucullata amabelejongosi, uhlamvu lwabafazi, udwendweni (Z) (*cucullata* - hooded)

Slender, 250-500 mm, solitary or in small groups. In grassland, on edge of marshes, woodland, widespread, KZN to Trop Afr, Madag. **Leaves:** Absent or partly grown at flowering, maturing ± 300 x 10 mm. **Flowers:** 3-15, large, ± 30 mm diam, petals and sepals ± 27 mm, petals much broader, petals and lip bright pink to white tinged pale purplish pink, inner surface of lip yellow with orange and purple spots, sepals purplish brown (Sep-Jan), sweetly scented or not scented at all. **General:** Used in traditional medicine to treat impotence, barrenness and as a love charm.

Eulophia horsfallii Purple Vlei Orchid; Persvlei-orgidee (A) (named after J B Horsfall, horticulturalist who grew the type material)

Tall, robust, 0,6- 2(3) m. In marshes, on margins of swamp forest, widespread but not common, KZN to Trop Afr. **Leaves:** 2-4, up to 1500 x 90 mm, pleated, tapering to sheathing stalk at base, midrib yellow, protruding beneath. **Flowers:** 10-40, large, in inflorescence; flowers ± 50 mm wide, sepals purplish red-brown, petals pink, lip side lobes mottled green, midlobe purple with white ridges, spur mottled dark green (Sep-Jul). **General:** One of the largest and most beautifully coloured African orchids, successfully grown as a container plant in E Afr.

Eulophia petersii isaha (Z) (named after Prof Wilhelm Peters of Berlin who collected in Mozambique in the 1800s)

Robust, up to 2 m, in large clumps. In thicket, among rocks, in hot, dry areas , KZN to E Afr. **Pseudobulbs,** 60-150 mm, yellowish with dry white sheaths, mostly above ground. **Leaves:** Thick, spreading, ± 400 x 44 mm, **margins rough. Flowers:** In well spaced inflorescence, stem branching, growing up through vegetation to the light; flowers large, sepals 19-33 mm, **petals and sepals curled back,** greenish purplish brown, lip ± 30 x 15 mm, white with purplish pink crests, spur 2-8 mm (Nov-Apr), sweetly scented. **General:** Used as a love charm. Lovely garden plant, easily grown, dormant in winter.

Oeceoclades (*oikos* - house; *cladus* - branch, shoot) - Terrestrial herbs; aerial pseudobulbs, each with a single, folded, leathery leaf; flowering stem from base of pseudobulb, with 1-2 branches, lip 4 lobed, 2 central lobes often curved at tip. 3 species in SA.

Oeceoclades mackenii [= *Eulophia mackenii*] impimpi encane (Z) (named after Mark McKen, 1823-1872, greatest of early colonial plant hunters, curator Durban Bot Gardens 1851-53 and 1860-72)

Up to 300 mm. In forest in deep shade. Rare. Pseudobulbs dark purplish green. **Leaves:** Thick, **horizontal,** blade ± 150 x 15 mm, **mottled grey-green, stalk short. Flowers:** ± 30, in simple or branched inflorescence; flowers cream and pink, lip side lobes marked pinkish red with 2 red blotches in front, spur club-shaped (Feb-Apr). **General:** Traditionally used as a love charm. Easily grown in sandy leaf litter. (See p. 520)

Eulophia clavicornis

Eulophia cucullata

Eulophia cucullata

Eulophia horsfallii

Eulophia horsfallii

Oeceoclades mackenii

Oeceoclades mackenii

Eulophia petersii

Eulophia petersii

373

DICOTYLEDONS - Two seed leaves, net veins; flower parts in fours, fives or multiples of these.
PROTEACEAE - Protea Family Woody plants. Leaves leathery. Flowers in dense heads, sometimes surrounded by showy bracts, sepals 4, petal-like, petals absent or reduced to scales, stamens fused to sepals, ovary with long style. Mostly Austr, SA, ± 75 genera, ± 1600 species, 16 genera in SA, including exotics *Hakea* and *Macadamia*.
Protea (named after the Greek god Proteus) - **Sugarbush** Shrubs, small trees; flowers massed in heads surrounded by coloured bracts; fruits woody, hairy. Mostly SW Cape, ± 115 species in Afr, ± 83 in SA.

Protea dracomontana Drakensberg Dwarf Sugarbush or Protea; Drakensbergse Dwergsuikerbos (A) (*dracomontana* - from the Drakensberg)
Dwarf shrub 0,5-1(1,5) m, up to 1 m diam, in colonies. In subalpine *Themeda* grassland, 1600-2600 m, E Cape to Zim. Rootstock large, woody. Stem stout, 5-10 mm diam, bark reddish. **Leaves:** 80-140 x 25-45 mm, leathery, with horny margin. **Flowerheads:** 40-60 mm diam, white to dark pink to red, **bracts hairless,** rounded (Nov-Mar). **General:** Fire adapted. Flowering related to frequency of fire. (See p. 132)

Protea parvula Dainty Sugarbush or Protea (*parvula* - very small)
Dwarf shrub up to 160 mm, trailing stems up to 1 m. In rocky grassland, 1300-2150 m. Woody rootstock. **Leaves:** Closely spaced, **all held vertically,** 60-140 x 5-20 mm, margin and stalk reddish. **Flowerheads:** Round in bud, **flattened when open,** 35-60 mm diam, white to pink, bracts hairless (Nov-Mar). **General:** Stems usually wither in winter.

Protea simplex Dwarf-grassveld Sugarbush or Protea, Mountain Rose Sugarbush; sidlungu (Sw) (*simplex* - simple, refers to unbranched stems)
Dwarf shrub, 0,3-1 m, solitary or in colonies. In grassland, coast to 1950 m. Woody rootstock. Multi-stemmed, erect, **slender, 2-5 mm diam**, green to pink or red. **Leaves:** 60-120 x 7-30 mm, **thin**, tips pointed to rounded. **Flowerheads:** Solitary, terminal, 30-60 mm diam, greenish, whitish to deep pink, bracts hairless (Dec-May). **General:** Blooms after fires. Stems wither in winter, or are burnt off by fire. Hybridises with *P. caffra* making separation of species difficult.

LORANTHACEAE - Mistletoe Family Partially parasitic shrubs, rootless, attached to host by suckers (for description see p. 48). *Erianthemum* (*erion* - wool; *anthemon* - flower) - Large, partially epiphytic shrubs; younger stems and leaves densely covered in brownish or whitish down; flowers with conspicuous whitish hairs, tube without split, lobes usually longer or equal to length of tube, opening explosively; berries with long silky hairs, calyx tube persistent. Central to S Afr, ± 15 species.

Erianthemum dregei [= *Loranthus dregei*] Hairy Mistletoe, Wood Flower; Voëlent (A); inovu (Sw); idumba (X,Z); inevu emhlophe, inomfi, iphakama (Z) (named after Johann Drège, 1794-1881, German horticulturalist, collector, traveller, who visited the Cape with his brother in 1826)
In large clumps, up to 2 x 1,5 m. Widespread, parasitic on a large number of tree species, E Cape to Trop Afr. Very variable. **Leaves:** Usually alternate, on side branches, 40-100 x 20-30 mm, leathery, **hairless,** side veins conspicuous, stalk 6-10 mm; **young parts velvety brown. Flowers:** Massed, in small clusters; flowers 40-50 mm, greyish white to pale pink, densely hairy, lobes long, folded back (blooms throughout year). **Fruit:** 11-12 mm, red. **General:** Used for bird lime. Flowers, fruits attract birds. Fruits eaten by children. Used in traditional medicine to treat stomach complaints in children and cows. **Similar species:** *E. ngamicum* N KZN to Bots; leaves smaller, covered in hairs, in dense clusters on older stems, young stems velvety white; flowers orange. (See p. 50)

POLYGONACEAE - Rhubarb Family Herbs, shrubs, climbers. Base of leaf stalk often forming a sheath. Flowers within dry bracts. Cosmop, ± 46 genera, ± 1100 species, 4 genera in SA.
Rumex (Latin name for the culinary sorrel) - Herbs (shrubs); leaves alternate; flowers in whorls; fruit 3 angled, enclosed within the 3 inner enlarged and persistent sepal lobes. Mostly N temp, ± 200 species, ± 20 in SA, some introduced.

Rumex lanceolatus Smooth Dock; Gladdetongblaar (A); khamane, molokoli, potaka-leleme (SS); idolonyana (X); idolenkoyane (Z) (*lanceolatus* - lancelike)
Erect perennial herb, up to 900 mm. In moist, disturbed areas. Stems grooved, branched. **Leaves:** Alternate, margins rolled under, with tiny teeth, tapering to base. **Flowers:** In whorls, in dense, erect, terminal, sparsely branched inflorescence; flowers small, 3-4 mm, yellow (spring). **Fruit:** 3 angled, green turning pinkish brown. **General:** Leaves chopped, boiled and mixed with porridge, planted for food by the Xhosa. Used in traditional medicine as a blood purifier and to treat diarrhoea, intestinal worms, wounds, bruises and gall sickness in cattle.

Protea dracomontana

Trevor Coleman

Protea dracomontana

Trevor Coleman

Protea simplex

Lal Greene

Protea simplex

Cameron McMaster

Protea parvula

Jo Onderstall

Rumex lanceolatus

Martin von Fintel

Erianthemum dregei

Martin von Fintel

Erianthemum dregei

Trevor Coleman

375

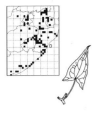

Rumex sagittatus **Climbing Rumex, Climbing Dock; Ranksuring (A); bolila-bo-boholo (SS); umdende (Z)** (*sagittatus* - arrowlike)

Low scrambler. In scrub, woodland, forest margins, widespread. **Leaves:** Arrow-shaped, on long slender stalks. **Flowers:** In large, dense inflorescences; flowers ± 10 mm (Feb-Apr). **Fruit:** Segments 7-8 mm diam, pale green to coppery red, papery. **General:** Flowers visited by honey-bees. Eaten as a relish or spinach. Used in traditional medicine to treat pain, constipation and tuberculosis. Planted as a protective charm. Related to the Coral or Honolulu Creeper of horticulture. (See p. 526)

Rumex woodii **Paper Hearts, Wood's Rumex; Tongblaar (A); bolila-ba-likhomo (SS)** (named after John Medley Wood 1827-1915, botanist, founding curator of Natal Herbarium)

Perennial herb, up to 1 m. In grassland, up to 2200 m. Tuberous rootstock. Stem stout, ± 10 mm diam, erect, ribbed. **Leaves:** ± 150 x 4 mm, tapering to both ends, some-times with short, blunt, basal lobes, on long erect stalks or nearly stalkless. **Flowers:** In few-flowered whorls in terminal, branched inflorescences (Oct-Jan). **Fruit: Lobes heart-shaped**, ± 13 mm wide, coppery red. **General:** Very decorative. Eaten raw. Used traditionally to dose calves with diarrhoea, and as a charm to protect grain crops.

Persicaria (*persicum* - peach; *aria* - like) - Perennial (annual) herbs or shrubs; leaf base stem-clasping; flowers in terminal inflorescences; fruit angled or flattened. Cosmop, ± 300 species, ± 18 in SA, some introduced.

Persicaria attenuata [= *Polygonum pulchrum*)] **Bristly Snakeroot, Bristly Polygonum; Slangwortel (A)** (*attenuata* - narrowing to a point)

Robust, hairy perennial, up to 2 m, in large colonies. In moist areas, near swamps, rivers, widespread. Stems sometimes floating, rooting at lower nodes, reddish green with dense brown hairs, **sheath ± 35 mm, with fringe of long, hard bristles. Leaves:** ± 120-180 x 25-55 mm, finely hairy above, sometimes whitish velvety beneath, margins wavy, edged with short bristly hairs, stalks short. **Flowers:** Inflorescence 50-80 mm, stem softly hairy or not; flowers 3-4,5 mm, pink (throughout year). **Fruit:** Small nut, 2-3 mm. **General:** Bees and flies attracted to nectar and pollen.

★ ***Persicaria lapathifolia*** [= *Polygonum lapathifolium*] **Spotted Knotweed, Spotted Polygonum; Hanekam (A); khamane-ea-noka, tolo-la-khongoana (SS); idolo-lenkonyane, umancibikela, umancibilika (Z)** (*lapathifolia* - leaves like Dock *Rumex*)

Robust, mostly annual herb, up to 1(2) m. In swamps, widespread. Stem sheaths brownish, hairless. Leaves ± 100 x 20 mm, marked with dark blotches, hairs on midvein beneath, ± stalkless. Inflorescences slender, branching, drooping, flowers widely spaced, pink (Mar-Jun). Used traditionally to treat venereal disease.

Persicaria senegalensis [= *Polygonum senegalensis* forma *albotomentosum*] **Silver Polygonum, Silver Snakeroot** (for description see p. 250).

Persicaria serrulata [= *Polygonum salicifolium, P. serrulatum*] **Knotweed, Snake Root; Duisend-knoop, Hanekam, Slangwortel, Snotterbel (A); tolo-la-khongoana-le-lenyenyane (SS)** (*serrulata* - minute teeth)

Erect, slender annual, up to 1 m. In damp areas, on floodplains, coast to 2400 m. Widespread in S Afr, throughout Trop. Stems reddish, rooting at lower nodes; sheaths ± 20 mm, fringed with stiff bristles, 10-25 mm. **Leaves:** 80-150 x 10-20 mm, tapering to both ends, stalkless. **Flowers:** In slender, branched, dense inflorescences, 20-90 mm; flowers pink (throughout year). **General:** Used in traditional medicine to treat sores.

AMARANTHACEAE - Amaranthus Family Mostly herbs. Inflorescence with flowers hidden within persistent bracts, often stiff, translucent, sharply pointed or hooked. Trop, ± 71 genera, ± 750 species, 24 genera in SA.
Pupalia (from eastern name *pupali*) - Herbs or undershrubs. Afr, India, Malaysia, Philippines, 4 species, 3 in SA.

Pupalia lappacea [= *P. atropurpurea*] **Forest Burr; Bosklits, Klits (A); isinama esibomvu (Z)** (*lappacea* - burrlike)

Slender shrub, 300-900 mm, scrambling up to 2,5 m. In thicket, woodland, forest margins. Stems, leaves finely hairy. **Leaves:** Opposite, variable in shape and size, 20-140 x 15-50 mm, stalks ± 10 mm. **Flowers:** In terminal inflorescences, compact at first, lengthening, stems ± 150 mm; flowers in clusters, ± 10 mm diam, each surrounded by hooked spines, woolly hairs between (Oct-Jul). **Fruit:** Forms a burr. **General:** Used in traditional medicine to cure fever. (See p 528)

Rumex sagittatus   *Rumex woodii*   *Persicaria attenuata*

Rumex woodii   *Persicaria serrulata*

★ *Persicaria lapathifolia*   *Persicaria senegalensis*   *Pupalia lappacea*

NYCTAGINACEAE - Bougainvillea/Four-o'clock family Flowers surrounded by green or coloured bracts. Trop, mainly Americas, ± 30 genera, ± 390 genera, 2 genera in Afr. *Mirabilis* **- Four-o'clock's/Vieruurtjies** Perennial herbs; flowers large, conspicuous. Warm Americas, ± 60 species, introduced elsewhere.

★ *Mirabilis jalapa* Four-o'clocks; Vieruurtjies (A)

Shrubby herb, up to 1,5 m. Garden escape, naturalised in disturbed areas. Leaves 35-100 x 20-80 mm. Flowers ± 30 mm diam, tube 40-55 mm, purple, red, yellow, white, sometimes on the same stem (Nov-Jul), open late afternoon. Leaves used as poultices.

Commicarpus (*kommi* - gum; *carpus* - wrist joint) **-** Perennial herbs with long, slender stems. Mostly Afr, ± 20 species, 9 in SA.

Commicarpus pentandrus Cerise Stars; Veldpatats (A) (*pentandrus* - 5 stamens)

Robust herb, prostrate, forming wide mats in the open or scrambling up to 2 m. In open grassland, on forest margins, floodplains, up to 1400 m. Stems annual, woody at base. **Leaves:** Slightly succulent, ± 40 mm diam, **stalks short**, 1-15 mm. **Flowers:** In **well spaced whorls** at tips of long unbranched stems; flowers ± 15 mm diam, dark pink, close at night (Oct-Jun). **Fruit: Broader at tip, with 5 large, raised sticky brown glands**, smaller glands below. **General:** Good food for livestock. **Similar species:** *C. chinensis* Leaf stalks 5-35 mm; inflorescence usually flat; fruits narrow at both ends, covered with sticky glands. *C. plumbagineus* Flowers white.

Boerhavia (named after Herman Boerhaave, 1668-1738, great Dutch physician) - Herbs. Trop, ± 30 species, ± 7 in SA.

★ *Boerhavia diffusa* Spiderling (*diffusa* - spreading)

Sprawling weed, up to 1 m. Widespread. Leaves slightly succulent, olive green above, white beneath, 15-60 x 8-50 mm. Flowers small, 2-7 mm, pink or white (Sep-May). Fruit sticky. Leaves cooked, roots eaten raw or cooked. Fruit dispersed by animals.

MESEMBRYANTHEMACEAE - Vygie Family Succulent herbs or shrublets. Leaves opposite. Flowers brightly coloured, petals many, free, stamens numerous, free. Fruit a many seeded capsule. *Mesembryanthemum* comes from Greek for midday, or noon flowering, the flowers usually open only in full sunlight. Mainly S Afr (Karoo, Namaqualand and Nam), ± 22 genera with a few thousand species.
Aptenia (*apten* - wingless, refers to the valves of the capsule) - Short lived, prostrate, perennial herbs; branches elongated; leaves opposite, flat; flowers solitary. 2 species in SA.

Aptenia cordifolia Aptenia; Brakvygie (A); ibohlololo, umjuluka, uncolozi omncane (Z) (*cordi* - heart; *folia* - leaves)

Prostrate or semi-scrambling, succulent herb. In low thicket, on rocky outcrops, coastal dunes. **Stems elongated, forking at intervals. Leaves:** In widely spaced pairs, ± 60 x 20 mm. **Flowers:** Solitary, magenta (Sep-Jul). **General:** Visited by bees. Used in traditional medicine as a poultice, anti-inflammatory, deodorant, love charm and as protection against sorcery. Popular groundcover, tolerant of salt spray.

Carpobrotus (*karpos* - fruit; *brotos* - edible) - Succulent herbs; leaves erect, 3 angled. Afr, Austr, Tasmania, S America (probably introduced into these latter areas), ± 18 species in SA, mostly in coastal strip.

Carpobrotus dimidiatus Natal Dune Vygie; Strandvygie (A); ikhambi-lamabulawo, umgongozi (Z) (*dimidiatus* - halved or divided, half the organ smaller than the other)

Perennial, trailing succulent. In sand, on the coastal strip, down to the high tide mark. Stems fleshy at first, becoming woody with age. **Leaves:** 70-80 x 10 mm, joined at base, bright green tinged red. **Flowers:** Solitary, up to 60 mm diam, magenta (summer/throughout year). **Fruit:** Large, fleshy. **General:** Forms large mats on open sand. Fruit eaten by people and by blue duiker. Flowers visited by bees, beetles and Lycaenid butterflies. Leaf sap effective against bluebottle stings and severe sunburn. Used in traditional medicine to treat allergies, diabetes, sore throats, thrush and stomach complaints. Good groundcover, sand stabiliser, salt spray tolerant.

Delosperma (*delos* - visible; *sperma* - seed) - Succulent shrublets or herbs; leaves opposite. Popular garden plants. Afr, ± 140 species, mostly SA.

Delosperma ashtonii (named in 1922, after H Ashton who collected it)

Low, succulent shrublet, up to 80 mm. In grassland. **Roots tuberous**, branches crowded, erect, tufted, ± 45 mm thick, all soft parts green, softly hairy. **Leaves:** Spreading, ± 45 x 12 mm, 4 mm thick, slightly narrowed to base, **flattened**, sheath 2 mm. **Flowers:** 1-3, **large**, ± 45 mm diam, bright pink, white at base, sepals 5, 6-9 mm, stalk 20-40 mm, bracts near middle, ± 30 x 5 mm (summer).

★ *Mirabilis jalapa*

Geoff Nichols

★ *Boerhavia diffusa*

C J Ward

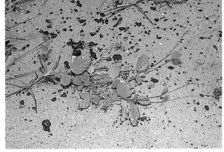

★ *Boerhavia diffusa*

C J Ward

Commicarpus pentandrus

Martin von Fintel

Delosperma ashtonii

Godfrey Symons

Commicarpus pentandrus

Martin von Fintel

Aptenia cordifolia

Tony Abbott

Carpobrotus dimidiatus

Geoff Nichols

379

Delosperma caespitosum (*caespitosus* - tufted like the grass of a sod)
Succulent shrublet. In grassland. Stems creeping, 4 mm thick, producing slender flowering branches from base. **Leaves:** Spreading to recurved, ± 40 x 4 mm by 3 mm thick, upper surface concave. **Flowers:** Terminal, ± 22 mm diam, white (pink), stalks 15-20 mm.

Delosperma carterae
Loosely branched, slender shrublet up to 200 mm. Branches prostrate to spreading, 1-2 mm thick, hairless, internodes 25-40 mm, covered in prominent, tiny protuberances/bumps. **Leaves:** Erect, joined, ± 30 mm, 3-4,5 mm thick, upper surface concave, lower surface rounded, tip pointed. **Flowers:** In repeatedly forking inflorescences; flowers ± 15 mm diam, white or pink, stalks 10-35 mm. (See p. 134.)

Delosperma hirtum (*hirtus* - rough)
Low-growing, slightly succulent herb, 50-80 mm. Branches spreading, ± 3,5 mm diam, flowering branchlets erect, densely leafy, internodes invisible. **Leaves:** Erect to spreading, ± 50 x 7 mm, broadest at base, concave to flat above, keeled, covered with tiny bumps, ending in short bristle, margins fringed with longer, almost rigid bristles. **Flowers:** Solitary, ± 33 mm diam, magenta, white towards base, petals in 3 whorls, stalks 5-30 mm (summer). **Fruit:** Open capsule ± 16 mm diam. **General:** Open in full sun. (See p. 136)

Delosperma obtusum **Mountain Vygie; Bergvygie, Kransvygie (A)** (*obtusum* - blunt, rounded at tip)
Succulent shrublet, up to 50 mm. On rock sheets and outcrops, mountains, up to 2350 m. Branches prostrate, 1,5 mm thick, internodes 5-30 mm, covered in small, crowded protruberances. **Leaves:** Spreading, round to 3 angled, 5-17 x 3 mm, green to blue-green, **blunt tipped. Flowers:** In much branched inflorescences; flowers ± 18 mm diam, glossy magenta, stalks 5-15 mm (Nov-Mar).

Delosperma sutherlandii (named after James Sutherland, 1639-1719, first superintendent, Edinburgh Bot Gardens)
Succulent, sprawling, perennial herb, up to 120 mm. In grassland, 1525-2100 m. Woody rootstock. Annual stems roughly hairy. **Leaves:** Flat, slightly joined at base, 50-80 x 15-20 mm, bright green, tapering to slender point, keeled beneath, margins with short hairs. **Flowers:** 1-3, terminal, 35-60 mm diam, magenta to white at base, pink to white, stamens white, stalks 50-100 mm (Oct-Dec). **General:** Quick to flower after veld fires.

Khadia (*Kgadi* - Tswana name for a drink made from roots of this plant) - Dwarf, tufted, succulent perennials; fleshy rootstock; very short branches; leaves opposite, united at base, crowded; flowers solitary. 6 species in SA.

Khadia acutipetala **Khadivygie (A)** (*acutipetala* - pointed petals)
Low-growing, tufted perennial succulent herb, up to 60 mm. On grassy, rocky ridges, often on white quartz. Rootstock fleshy. **Leaves: Close set, erect,** 3 angled, tapering to pointed tip, covered in transparent dots, joined at base. **Flowers:** Solitary, on short, ± flattened stalk (Aug-Dec). **General:** Beer made from roots.

Lampranthus (*lampros* - bright, shining; *anthos* - flower) - Succulent herbs. S Afr, ± 200 species.

Lampranthus stipulaceus (*stipulaceus* - stipules)
Succulent shrublet, up to 250 mm. In rocky grassland near coast. Branches spreading. **Leaves:** Erect or spreading, 30-40 x 2-5 mm, round or flat on upper surface, tips pointed, ± tapering towards base. **Flowers:** 1-3, ± 40 mm diam, brilliant magenta, open in full, hot sun (Aug-Mar). **Fruit:** Capsule ± 15 mm diam. **General:** In cultivation in England since before 1732.

Delosperma caespitosum

Tony Abbott

Delosperma carterae

Lawrence Peacock

Delosperma hirtum

Lal Greene

Delosperma obtusum

Lal Greene

Delosperma sutherlandii

Hilliard & Burtt

Khadia acutipetala

Van Wyk & Malan

Lampranthus stipulaceus

Tony Abbott

381

PORTULACACEAE - Purslane Family Herbs with succulent leaves. Calyx with 2 sepals, 4-6 petals. Fruit a capsule which opens by means of valves or a lid. The family includes a number of popular ornamentals. Cosmop, ± 32 genera, ± 380 species, 7 genera in SA.

Talinum (from the native name of a species from Senegal) - Perennial rootstock, annual stems; flowers open in afternoon, close at night; fruit splits in 3 parts. Cosmop, 5 species in SA.

Talinum portulacifolium Pink Bush Talinum *(portulacifolium - leaves like Portulaca)*

Low shrub, up to 1 m. In open woodland, KZN to Trop Afr, Arabia, India. **Leaves:** 20-90 x 10-30 mm, dark green, tips rounded or bluntly pointed, stems pale yellow. **Flowers:** In loose, many flowered inflorescences; flowers ± 25 mm diam, pale pink to purplish (summer). **General:** Browsed by antelope. Hardy garden plant.

CARYOPHYLLACEAE - Carnation Family Annual or perennial herbs. Leaves in opposite pairs, joined at base, nodes more or less swollen. Flowers with 5 petals, tips often notched or lobed. The family includes a large number of horticultural ornamentals including the Carnation, Gypsophila, Silene and Maltese Cross. A number of species have become naturalised weeds in SA. Cosmop, ± 87 genera, ± 2300 species, 18 genera in SA.

Silene (*sialon* - saliva, refers to some species having sticky stems) - Annual or perennial herbs or shrubs; leaves opposite; flowers with inflated tubular calyx. Mostly in N Hemisp, ± 500 species, 15 in SA.

Silene burchellii Gunpowder Plant; Kruitbossie (A); ho-batla, kopane, lithokoano, motebane (SS); iyeza lehashe (X); igwayintombi elincane, injuju, umthusi (Z)

(after William Burchell, 1781-1863, great English botanist, author of 2 vol classic "Travels in the Interior of S Afr")

Soft herb, up to 700 mm. In grassland, on rocky slopes, coast to mountains, widespread in S Afr. Tap root perennial, swollen. Plant hairy, **not sticky**, stems unbranched above base. **Leaves:** 10-80 x 10-13 mm, lower leaves oval, upper smaller, narrower. **Flowers:** In terminal inflorescences, unbranched, **all flowers on one side**, ± 10 mm diam, white to pink or purple, petals deeply lobed, calyx 10-25 mm, green or red veined, open in evening (blooms throughout year). **Fruit:** Inflated capsule, small brown seeds rattle. **General:** Two varieties, differences mostly in leaf shape and growth form. Used in traditional medicine to treat scrofula, as a tonic and for love charms.

Dianthus (*dios* - divine; *anthos* - flower, refers to the scent of some species) - Tufted annual or perennial herbs; leaves opposite, narrow; petals entire, toothed or fringed, calyx tubular, base surrounded by bracts. Europe, Asia, Afr, ± 300 species, 15 in SA.

Dianthus basuticus Lesotho Dianthus, Lesotho Carnation; Lesothose Grootblom-wilde-angelier (A); hlokoa-la-tsela (SS) *(basuticus - from Basutuland, now Lesotho)* (see p. 138)

Dianthus mooiensis Frilly Dianthus, Frilly Carnation; Wilde-angelier (A); tjanis-bezwe (Sw); utshanibezwe (Z)

Perennial herb, up to 900 mm. In grassland, on rocky slopes, up to 2200 m. Rootstock woody. Stems straggling. **Leaves:** In basal rosette, stem leaves in pairs, widely spaced, ± 80 x 3 mm, tapering to long point, blue-green, stalks tinged purple. **Flowers:** Solitary, terminal, ± 25 mm diam, white to deep pink, petals fringed, calyx ± 26 mm, basal bracts ± 10 mm (Oct-Feb). **General:** Two subspecies differ in texture of stems, size of leaf sheaths and size of calyx. Used in traditional medicine.

Dianthus zeyheri Wild Dianthus, African Carnation; Grasangelier (A); iningizimu, isidala, umzima (Z) *(named after Carl Zeyher, 1799-1858, botanical collector; came to the Cape in 1822)*

Perennial herb, up to 750 mm. In grassland, coast to 2300 m, KZN to Zam. Carrotlike root. Stems robust, erect, woody at base. **Leaves:** 20-90 x 2-12 mm, blue-green, on lower parts of stem. **Flowers:** ± 50 mm diam, white to pink, petals fringed, calyx 25-45 mm (Sep-May). **General:** Used in traditional medicine for love charms, as charms to keep lightning away and by diviners to improve their divining faculties. **Similar species:** *D. crenatus* Stems much branched or simple, angular; leaves long narrow, 3 veined, ± 75 x 5 mm; **petals very shortly toothed**.

RANUNCULACEAE - Buttercup Family Herbs or woody climbers. Leaves compound, often palmate, **bases forming a sheath.** Flowers with sepals commonly petal-like, petals equal to, or larger than sepals, or absent. Includes a large number of well known ornamentals including Anemone, Delphinium and Ranunculus. Mostly N Hemisp, ± 62 genera, ± 2450 species, 7 genera in SA.

Anemone (from Greek *anemos* - wind; also of older, Semitic origin, from *nahamea* - handsome, equivalent of Adonis) - Perennial rhizomatous herb (for description see p. 138).

Anemone caffra Anemone; Anemoon, Syblom (A); iyeza elimnyama (X); intingwe, umanzamnyama (Z) (see p. 138)

Talinum portulacifolium   *Silene burchellii*   *Dianthus basuticus*

Dianthus crenatus   *Silene burchellii*   *Dianthus zeyheri*

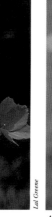

Dianthus mooiensis   *Anemone caffra*

383

FUMARIACEAE - Herbs with fibrous or tuberous roots. Stems weak, prostrate or scrambling, often with watery juice. Leaves much dissected, stalk ending in a tendril. Mostly N Hemisp, ± 17 genera, ± 530 species, 4 genera in SA.

Cysticapnos [= *Phacocapnos*] (*kystis* - bladder; *kapnos* - smoky, refers to the bladderlike capsules) - Annual, climbing herbs; leaves dissected, tipped with tendrils; back petal spurred. Endemic to SA, 5 species.

Cysticapnos pruinosa [= *Phacocapnos pruinosus*] Wild Fumaria; 'musa-pelo-la-noka (SS)
(*pruinosa* - waxy powdery secretion on surface)

Straggling, climbing, bushy herbs, up to 600 mm. In boulder beds, damp rocky places, 1200-3000 m. **Leaves:** Finely dissected, tips tendril-like, grey-green. **Flowers:** 2 lobed, pink, **lower lip with narrow claw, pitted in the middle, upper lip expanded, with a wide, blunt, reflexed spur** (Dec-Apr). **Fruit:** Hanging pod, narrowing to tip. **General:** Used as a charm to comfort the sorrowing.

Fumaria (*fumus* - refers to smoky scent of some species) - Annual herbs; upper petal spurred; fruit a round nut. N Hemisp, ± 60 species, introduced weed in SA.

★ *Fumaria muralis* [= *F. officinalis*] Pink Weed, Fumitory; Duiwekerwel (A) (*muralis* - on walls)

Straggling annual herb, stems up to 500 mm. On disturbed ground, in cultivated fields. Leaves deeply divided and lobed, ending in tendrils. Flowers 7-12 mm, pink to purple, tipped dark purple-red (Aug-Jan). Originally from Europe.

CAPPARACEAE - Caper Family Woody or herbaceous, some climbing. Leaves alternate, simple or 3-5 foliate. Ovary usually on long stalk (gynophore). Fruit a long, narrow capsule opening by means of 2 valves, or a berry. Economically important as Capers to season food (dried flower buds of *Capparis spinosa*). Warm areas, ± 39 genera, ± 650 species, 8 genera in SA.

Cleome (*cleoma* - a plant name used in the Middle Ages) - Mostly annual herbs, sometimes shrubby; leaves simple or 3-9 foliate; flowers in terminal inflorescences, 4 sepals, 4 petals. Warm regions, ± 150 species, 25 in SA.

Cleome monophylla Spindlepod; Enkelblaar-cleome, Rusperbossie (A); munyenyae, musa pelo (SS); isiwisa esiluhlaza (Z) (*monophylla* - one leaf)

Annual herb, 0,3-1 m. Common, often a weed, in warm dry areas, E Cape to Trop Afr, Madag, India and Ceylon. Much branched from short main stem, covered in sticky glandular hairs. **Leaves: Simple**, 20-70 x 3-25 mm, stalks ± 40 mm. **Flowers:** In compact, terminal inflorescences, elongating in fruit; flowers pale pinkish mauve with yellow band edged with purple at base, petals ± 10 mm (Sep-Apr). **Fruit:** 50-110 x 3 mm. **General:** Leaves used as a pot herb, seeds like mustard. Used as a love charm emetic and, in the East, to treat intestinal parasites.

DROSERACEAE - Sundew Family Small insectivorous herbs, in damp places. Leaves usually rolled in bud, covered in sticky, glandular hairs which trap small insects, then secrete enzymes which dissolve the prey and absorb the fluid into the plant. Petals 5, free. Fruit a capsule. Remarkable for the insectivorous character of the leaves. The family includes the famous Venus Flytrap *Dionaea*. Cosmop, 4 genera, ± 110 species, 2 genera in SA.

Drosera (*droseros* - dewy, refers to the dewy leaf glands) - Annual or perennial herbs; leaves with sticky, gland tipped hairs; tip of inflorescence bent over. Mostly Austr, New Zealand, ± 125 species, ± 20 in SA.

Drosera burkeana Sundew; Doublom, Slakblom, Sondou (A); tholo-ea-metsi (SS)

Small herb. In marshy areas, KZN to Trop Afr, Madag. Roots few, thin, long. **Leaves:** In basal rosette, ± 20 mm, **including stalk**, hairy above, hairless beneath. **Flowers:** 3-10, clustered close together, stem erect, 50-200 mm; flowers ±10 mm diam, pale pink (summer). **Similar species:** *D. dielsiana* Leaves with rounded tip, tapering below, no stalk, lower surface sparsely hairy, hard marginal tentacles, blade tentacles softer; flowers small, seldom open, stem sturdy, hairy near base.

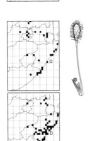

Drosera madagascariensis Sundew; Doublom, Sondou (A); tholo-ea-metsi (SS)

Perennial herb, up to 250 mm. In marshes in warmer areas, E Cape to Trop Afr. 1-2 swollen roots. **Stem erect. Leaves: Alternate**, 10-15 x 7 mm, lower surface smooth, upper with knob-shaped tentacles, stalks ± 30 mm. **Flowers:** 4-12, in terminal cluster, stem 200-400 mm, wiry; flowers, small, ± 15 mm diam, pink to bluish (throughout year). **General:** Plants grow taller to reach the light.

Drosera natalensis Sundew; Doublom, Sondou (A)

Small herb, up to 250 mm. In marshes, coast to 2150 m, E Cape to Trop Afr. Roots long, thin. **Leaves:** In rosette, ± 20 x 5 mm, **soft, thin**, tip rounded, tapering to base, **no stalk. Flowers:** ± 10 flowers, stem wiry, erect or curved; **flowers not often open**, white, pink or purple (Aug-Apr).

CRASSULACEAE - Crassula Family Herbs or soft shrubs, usually succulent. ***Kalanchoe*** (for descriptions see p. 254).

Kalanchoe luciae (see under *K. thyrsiflora* p. 254)

Cysticapnos pruinosa

★ *Fumaria muralis*

Cleome monophylla

Drosera burkeana

Drosera madagascariensis

Drosera natalensis

Drosera natalensis

Kalanchoe luciae

Kalanchoe luciae

385

Crassula (*crassus* - thick, refers to fleshy leaves) **-** Delicate annuals or perennial herbs, shrubs, softly woody to succulent, very variable, including aquatics. Mostly S Afr, ± 300 species, ± 255 in SA.

Crassula alba [= *C. rubicunda*] feko, khato (SS); impakatha, isidwe, isikhelekhehlane (Z)
(*alba* - white)

Perennial or biennial, up to 500 mm. In grassland, up to 2500 m, E Cape to Ethiopia. Variable in growth form, hairiness, flower colour. **Leaves:** In basal rosette, 60-170 x 5-15 mm, sometimes with reddish purple markings or purple beneath, in pairs on stem. **Flowers:** Inflorescence ± 150 mm diam; flower tube deep red, pink, white or yellow, lobes 3-6 mm (throughout year). **General:** Used as a charm to make one invisible. Rewarding garden plants, blooming for weeks, dying back after flowering to reshoot from the old base. Grown from seed. (See p. 54) **Similar species:** *C. vaginata* (see p. 254)

Crassula multicava Fairy Crassula; Skaduplakkie (A); umadinsane (Z) (*multicava* - many hollows)

Perennial, up to 400 mm. On rocky outcrops, in shade. Stems reclining to erect. **Leaves:** 20-60 x 15-40 mm, yellowish grey-green, tinged pink, finely pitted on both sides, narrowing abruptly to stalks ± 20 mm. **Flowers:** In rounded inflorescences, stem ± 80 mm; flowers small, 4-5 petals, cream, white, tinged red (May-Nov). **General:** Used in traditional medicine as a strong emetic. Two subspecies, differing mostly in flower size and number of petals. Popular garden plant, suitable for shady, dry or damp spots. Roots from stems and produces 'brood-buds' from inflorescence. **Similar species:** *C. streyi* (see p. 56)

Crassula natalensis bohobe-ba-setsomi, bohohoana (SS)

Up to 450 mm, solitary, unbranched. In mountain grassland, among rocks, on streambanks, up to 2250 m, N Cape, Free State, Les, C KZN. No fleshy rootstock. **Leaves:** In basal rosette, 15-60 x 5-15 mm, short hairs on margins, sheaths ± 6 mm. **Flowers:** In flattened to rounded inflorescences; flowers small, white tinged pink (Jan-May). **General:** Used in traditional medicine to treat sore throats and eyes.

ROSACEAE - Rose Family Trees, shrubs, herbs, often prickly. Leaves simple or compound, usually alternate with pair of stipules at base of leaf stalk. Fruits variable, many edible. Economically valuable fruits such as Apple, Pear, Quince, Cherry, Plum, Prune, Peach, Nectarine, Apricot, Almond, Blackberry, Raspberry, Loganberry, Strawberry and many ornamentals such as the Cotoneaster, Firethorn (*Pyracantha*), Flowering Quince and the Rose. Subcosmop, ± 95 genera, ± 2825 species, 18 genera in SA.

Rubus (*ruber* - red, also the old Latin name for the plant) - Prickly, mostly scrambling shrubs; fruits edible. Leaves of many species used to make a tea. Mostly N Hemisp, ± 3000 species, ± 20 in SA, many introduced, invasive plants.

Rubus ludwigii Silver Bramble; Wildebraam (A); monoko-metsi, monokotsoai-oabasali (SS); imencemence, itshalo, unomhloshane (Z) (named after Carl von Ludwig, 1784-1847, German-born pharmacist, business man, patron of natural science who came to SA in 1805)

Sprawling shrub up to 2 m. On rocky outcrops on grassy hillsides, 1500-2400 m. **Leaves:** 3-9 leaflets, upper surface green, hairless, except along sunken veins, **lower surface white woolly**, stalks 12-40 mm. **Flowers:** Branched inflorescence; flowers ± 13 mm diam, **pale pink to red** (Oct-Dec). **Fruit:** Oval, 6-10 mm diam, purple with white down. **General:** Fruit is collected and eaten. Used in traditional medicine to ease stomach ache, treat pain, fits and snakebite. **Similar species:** Hybrid **Rubus x proteus** - a fairly widespread hybrid between ★ *R. cuneifolius* and *R. longipedicellatus*, an indigenous species. ★ *R. cuneifolius* American Bramble Midlands to 1800 m; 3-5 leaflets, green above, downy grey beneath on new growth, terminal leaflet usually wedge-shaped at base; flowers large, white, petals much longer than sepals; fruit red turning black, shiny. Declared weed.

Rubus rigidus Wild Bramble; Braambos (A); monoko-metsi (SS); umgcunube (X); ijikijolo, ugagane (Z) (*rigidus* - stiff)

Scrambling shrub. In woodland, scrub, coast to 2100 m, SW Cape to Ethiopia. Stems with recurved prickles. **Leaves:** 1-5 leaflets, **densely woolly white beneath**, margins toothed. **Flowers:** In many-flowered inflorescences; flowers small, **petals slightly shorter than calyx lobes**, pink (Aug-Feb-Jul). **Fruit:** Round, orange to black. **General:** Flowers visited by bees. Fruit edible, makes good jelly. Used in traditional medicine to treat diarrhoea, dysentery, pain, toothache and to bathe eyes affected by *Euphorbia* latex. **Similar species:** *R. pinnatus* 3-9 leaflets, shiny, hairless, green on both surfaces; petals shorter than woolly calyx lobes, pink; fruit yellow to orange-red.

Crassula multicava

Lorraine van Hooff

Rubus ludwigii

Geoff Nichols

Rubus rigidus

Van Wyk & Malan

Crassula natalensis

Lal Greene

Crassula alba

Godfrey Symons

Rubus x proteus

Rosemary Williams

387

FABACEAE (LEGUMINOSAE) - **Pea/Legume Family** Second largest flowering plant family. Leaves usually bipinnately compound. Fruit usually a pod. Family divided in 3 subfamilies, Mimosoideae: flowers tiny, in dense heads or spikes (eg *Acacia*). Caesalpinioideae: flowers large, petals irregular, never in the 'butterfly' pea pattern (eg *Cassia*). Papilionoideae: petals in typical 'butterfly' pea flower, the largest subfamily. Economically important, producing food, fodder, dyes, gums, resins, oils and many ornamentals. Cosmop, ± 642 genera, ± 18000 species, ± 144 genera in SA.
Mimosa (*mimos* - to mimic) - Herbs or shrubs (trees), sometimes scrambling; with or without prickles; leaves sensitive to touch, bipinnate; flowers in roundish heads. Trop, ± 500 species, 1 species possibly indigenous to SA, 1 introduced.

Mimosa pigra Sensitive Weed; Kruidjie-roer-my nie (A); imbuna, umazifisa (Z)
(*pigra* - slow, sluggish)

Sprawling shrub, up to 2 m. In floodplains, swamps, KZN to Trop Afr. Stems hairy, with prickles. **Leaves:** 20-120 mm, **4-14 pinna pairs, prickle ± 10 mm at join of each pinna pair**; leaflets ± 9 x 1 mm, stalks ± 14 mm, rachis much longer. **Flowers:** 1-2 heads, ± 10 mm diam, pink (throughout year). **Fruit:** Pod ± 70 x 12 mm, clustered, breaking into segments. **General:** Leaves collapse on touching. Origin uncertain. Invasive weed in Australia. **Similar species:** ★ *Mimosa pudica* Pantrop weed; leaves with 1-2 pinna pairs, rachis much shorter than leaf stalk, no prickles on leaves.

Hoffmannseggia (named in honour of Ioannis de Hoffmannsegg) - Herbs or low shrubs, often covered in dark scattered glands; flowers in spikelike inflorescence. Texas, Mexico, Afr, ± 47 species, 3 in SA.

Hoffmannseggia sandersonii (named after John Sanderson, 1820-1881, plant collector)

Shrublet, up to 400 mm. In grassland. Stems annual, **covered in reddish hairs**. **Leaves:** 20-80 mm; 3-7 pinna pairs; 3-10 pairs leaflets, 5-14 x 2-6 mm, dotted with dark glands. **Flowers:** Inflorescences erect, ± 300 mm; flowers ± 20 mm diam, red to salmon pink, **calyx with short tube, gland dotted** (Aug-Oct). **Fruit:** Pod oblong, slightly curved, ± 45 x 16 mm, dark brown, covered in dense, shaggy, pinkish hairs.

Podalyria (named after Podaleirios, son of Asklepios, Greek god of healing) - Silky hairy shrubs. Endemic to SA, ± 29 species, mostly in SW Cape.

Podalyria velutina Hairy Podalyria; Keurtjie (A) (*velutina* - velvety)

Shrub up to 2,5 m. On streambanks. **Stems with shaggy or silky hairs. Leaves:** Simple, alternate, 25-45 x 6-8 mm, **thick**, finely hairy above, **densely velvety beneath**, narrowing to pointed tip. **Flowers:** 1-2(4), shorter than leaves, calyx with shaggy, rusty hairs (May-Sep). **Fruit:** Pod covered with **shaggy, long, rufous hairs**.

Trifolium (*tri* - three; *folium* - leaf) - **Clover** Herbs; leaves 3-7 foliolate. Attracts butterflies, including Common Blue *Cyclyrius pirithous* and *Syntarucus telicanus*. Temp and subtrop regions, ± 300 species, ± 19 in SA, mostly introduced.

Trifolium burchellianum Wild Clover; Wildeklawer (A); moqophi, moroko (SS); usithathi (Z) (named after William Burchell, great English botanist, travelled SA in 1811-15)

Low growing, perennial herb, up to 400 mm. In wet areas, on forest margins. Plant ± hairless. **Leaves: Leaflets heart-shaped**, ± 25 x 19 mm, strongly veined, stalks ± 25-70 mm, stipules triangular. **Flowers:** Inflorescences compact, ± 30 mm diam, stems ± 150 mm; flowers 13 mm, pink to red (Aug-Mar). **Similar species:** *T. africanum* Plant hairy; leaflets oblong. Inflorescences eaten raw by children, used traditionally to treat sore throats, heart trouble, as a diuretic and a charm.

Indigofera (bearing indigo, a blue dye that is obtained from several species of this genus) - Annual or perennial herbs, shrubs; leaves pinnately 1-9 foliolate; pods cylindrical. Economic potential for forage crops, green manure, soil stabilisers, chemical compounds, traditional medicines, poisons, insecticides, dyes, seed gums and horticultural ornamentals. Attracts butterflies. Cosmop, ± 750 species, ± 200 in SA.

Indigofera confusa [= *I. arrecta*] Verfbossie (A); umphekambhedu (Z) (*confusa* - confused)

Shrubby, up to 2,2 m. On floodplains, in open scrub, KZN to Angola, Moz. Stems downy. **Leaves:** ± 70 mm; 8 pairs leaflets, ± 20 x 6 mm, often folded, terminal leaflet stalkless. **Flowers:** Inflorescences, ± 25 mm; flowers dull red to pink (Feb-May). **Fruit:** Pod straight, ± 30 mm. **General:** Roots used as blue dye for woven mats, baskets. Cultivated here and in the Far East in the early 1900s for dye. Garden plant.

Indigofera dimidiata Trifoliate Indigofera; 'musa-peloa-thaba (SS) (*dimidiata* - halved)

Low growing, perennial herb, 100-700 mm. In grassland, coast to 2600 m, E Cape to Malawi, Moz. Stems 300-600 mm. **Leaves: 3 foliolate**, stalks 10-25 mm, stipules large; leaflets 25-40 mm. **Flowers:** Compact inflorescences, stems ± 250 mm; flowers ± 6 mm, pink, hairless (Sep-Feb). **Fruit:** Pod ± 25 mm, hairless. **General:** Used traditionally to treat fevers, used in mourning rites and as a good luck charm.

Mimosa pigra

Martin von Fintel

★ *Mimosa pudica*

David Johnson

Podalyria velutina

Geoff Nichols

Rosemary Williams

Hoffmannseggia sandersonii

Indigofera confusa

Geoff Nichols

Rosemary Williams

Hoffmannseggia sandersonii

Trifolium burchellianum

Darrel Plowes

Indigofera dimidiata

Darrel Plowes

Indigofera hilaris Red Indigo Bush; chubhujeje (Sw); igqokisi, isikhubabende, uhlomantethe (oluncane) (Z) *(hilaris - cheerful, gay)*

Perennial shrublet, up to 600 mm. In open grassland, widespread, E Cape to Malawi. Woody rootstock. Annual stems, covered with silky hairs. **Leaves:** Crowded, ± 5 leaflets, ± 8 x 2 mm, grey-green, tip a fine point. **Flowers:** In short dense inflorescences, in profusion, **stems short**; flowers ± 10 mm, pink, red (Jul-Jan). **Fruit:** Pod ± 20 mm. **General:** Blooms in response to fire, habit becomes taller, more straggly in the absence of fire. (See p. 58) **Similar species:** *I. rubroglandulosa* E Cape to KZN; glandular red hairs; leaflets 12-17 x 5-9 mm; calyx lobes longer.

Indigofera longebarbata *(longebarbata - long bearded)*

Herbaceous perennial or slightly woody annual, up to 1,3 m. In mountain grassland, on forest margins, 1300-2500 m, E Cape to Ethiopia. Covered in loose white hairs. **Leaves:** ± 80 mm, stalk short, stipules long, narrow; 9-13 leaflets, stalkless, ± 20 x 10 mm, tips finely pointed, rachis softly brown hairy. **Flowers:** Inflorescences ± 80(250) mm, dark brown hairy; flowers small, ± 12 mm, pink, lobes very slender, calyx ± 8 mm, brown-black hairy (Mar). **Fruit:** Pods ± 8 x 1,8 mm, black hairy.

Indigofera schimperi

Shrublet, up to 1 m. KZN to E Afr. Rootstock woody. Stems, leaf rachis, inflorescences silvery hairy. **Leaves:** ± 60 mm, stipules ± 9 mm; **leaflets alternate**, 5-10, ± 25 x 20 mm, shortly hairy. **Flowers:** Inflorescence ± 200 mm, stem 10-20 mm; flowers pink, **glistening yellow hairy behind**, **calyx white hairy**. **Fruits:** Pods straight, curved sharply at base, ± 28 mm.

Indigofera spicata Indigo; Verfbossie (A); uhlomantethe (oluncane) (Z) *(spicata - spike-like)*

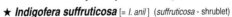

Perennial, **low-growing or creeping** herb. In grassland, on sand dunes and disturbed areas, KZN to Ethiopia, Madag, India, SE Asia, introduced to Americas. Stems ridged, ± flattened, hairy. **Leaves:** ± 30(50) mm, stipules broad at base, tapering to narrow tip; 5-7(11) **alternate leaflets**, 3-10 mm. **Flowers:** In dense inflorescences, stems 10-40 mm; flowers red, pink (Sep-Jun). **Fruit:** Pod, ± 18 x 2 mm. **General:** Browsed. Visited by honey-bees and Lycaenid butterflies.

★ Indigofera suffruticosa [= *I. anil*] *(suffruticosa - shrublet)*

Much branched shrub, up to 1,5 m. Widespread, on disturbed ground, SA to Trop Afr, reputed to originate in Trop America. Branches straight, woody, thinly silvery. **Leaves:** 50-100 mm, stalks short, firm, stipules small; 6-8 pairs leaflets, ± 25 x 12 mm, stalklets short, thinly silvery at first. **Flowers:** Inflorescence dense, 25-50 mm, ± stalkless; flowers small (summer). **Fruit:** Reflexed, sickle-shaped pods, ± 20 x 2 mm. **General:** One of the species most commonly cultivated.

Indigofera tristis Velvety Indigo; mothimo-kholo, 'musa-pelo (SS) *(tristis - sad, dull coloured)*

Erect, slender shrub, 0,4-2,5 m. In grassland. Stems pale brown. **Leaves:** Widely spaced; 3-5 pairs leaflets, 10-20 mm, deep green above, paler beneath, velvety. **Flowers:** Inflorescences ± 70 mm; flowers pink, mauve, red, **covered in silky dark brown hairs behind and on buds**, calyx white hairy (Oct-Feb). **Fruit:** Pods ± 35 x 2 mm. (See p. 58)

Indigofera velutina Grey-leaved Indigo; isikhubabende, isiphungo, umphendulobomvu (Z) *(velutina - velvetlike)*

Reclining shrublet 0,15-1 m. In grassland. Rootstock woody. Stems covered in soft white hairs. **Leaves:** ± 75 mm; 2-4 pairs leaflets, grey-green, oval, hairy beneath. **Flowers:** Inflorescences spikelike, stems 50-100 mm; flowers pink to rose-red, downy (Aug-Mar). **Fruit:** Pod ± 12 x 2 mm, hairy when young.

Indigofera hilaris

Indigofera spicata

Indigofera suffruticosa

Indigofera longebarbata

Indigofera suffruticosa

Indigofera schimperi

Indigofera tristis

Indigofera velutina

391

Tephrosia (*tephros* - ashen, refers to grey-green or silvery leaves of many species) - Herbs or shrubs; leaves pinnate, with close parallel veins; pods flattened. Some species used as a fish poison and insecticide. Trop, subtrop, ± 400 species, mostly Afr, ± 40 in SA.

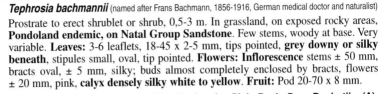

Tephrosia bachmannii (named after Frans Bachmann, 1856-1916, German medical doctor and naturalist)

Prostrate to erect shrublet or shrub, 0,5-3 m. In grassland, on exposed rocky areas, **Pondoland endemic, on Natal Group Sandstone.** Few stems, woody at base. Very variable. **Leaves:** 3-6 leaflets, 18-45 x 2-5 mm, tips pointed, **grey downy or silky beneath,** stipules small, oval, tip pointed. **Flowers:** Inflorescence stems ± 50 mm, bracts oval, ± 5 mm, silky; buds almost completely enclosed by bracts, flowers ± 20 mm, pink, **calyx densely silky white to yellow. Fruit:** Pod 20-70 x 8 mm.

Tephrosia grandiflora Large Pink Tephrosia, Pink Bush Pea; Rooiertjie (A); ihlozane, iqwense, udabane (Z) (*grandiflora* - large flower)

Erect annual or biennial shrub, 0,3-1,5 (2) m. In woodland, on roadsides. Woody at base, stems finely hairy. **Leaves:** ± 40 mm, **stipules small, oval, flat against stem;** 3-5 pairs leaflets, ± 15 x 6 mm, silvery grey hairy beneath, with stalklets. **Flowers:** Inflorescences on long stems, 30-120 mm, **bracts** 10-32 mm, **sparsely hairy; flowers large,** ± 20 mm, brilliant magenta-pink, calyx silky, white to yellowish, lobes narrow, shorter than tube (throughout year). **Fruit:** Pod ± 30 x 8 mm. **General:** Used in traditional medicine to treat chest ailments, also as a fish poison; potential as an insecticide. Popular, evergreen garden plant, from seed. **Similar species:** *T. inandensis* Stipules narrow, spreading away from stem; bracts very hairy, flowers white. *T. glomeruliflora* Stems ± downy white when young; leaves blue-green, 7-9 leaflets, silky beneath; young inflorescences in dense clusters, bracts enclose young buds completely, flowers ± 15 mm, deep pink, calyx and bracts downy white.

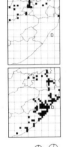

Tephrosia lupinifolia Vingerblaarertjie (A) (*lupinifolia* - leaves like Lupin)

Creeping perennial herb. In grassland. Covered in yellowish hairs. **Leaves: 4-5 foliolate, palmate;** leaflets 15-85 x 4-18 mm, thick, grey-green, downy beneath, stalks 18-50 mm, stipels at end of stalk beneath leaflets. **Flowers:** Inflorescences ± 300 mm; flowers small, ± 7 mm, pink (Sep-Dec). **Fruit:** Pod 25-35 x 3-5 mm, downy.

Tephrosia macropoda Creeping Tephrosia; Visboontjie, Vishoutbossie (A); intozane (X); ilozane, ugwengu (Z) (*macropoda* - large foot or base)

Straggling **perennial,** up to 1 m, sometimes in mats. In open and rocky grassland, coast to mountains. Covered in soft white hairs. Size and number of leaflets variable. **Leaves:** ± 200 mm, stalks ± 70 mm, stipules broadly clasping at base, ± 12 x 7 mm, **maturing dark brown, curling away from stems;** (5-9)3-7 leaflets, flat, 20-65 x 6-30 mm, veins well marked. **Flowers:** Inflorescences ± 250 mm; 2-5 flowers crowded at tip, ± 20 mm, pink, hairy outside, calyx lobes narrow, abruptly tapering (Oct-May). **Fruit:** Pod ± 50 x 7 mm, hairless. **General:** Used traditionally to treat chest complaints, fevers, lice, intestinal parasites and as a fish poison. **Similar species:** *T. brummittii* Stipules flat on stem, 7-11 leaflets, smaller, narrower, greygreen beneath; flower bracts ± 15 x 10 mm, enclosing young buds, reddish brown.

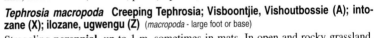

Tephrosia multijuga Multi-coloured Tephrosia (*multijuga* - many pairs of leaves)

Small, **much branched shrublet,** up to 1,5 m. In rocky grassland. Stems stiff, with short hairs. **Leaves:** 25-55 mm; 3-10 leaflets, ± 25 x 3 mm, veins usually reddish brown beneath, stipules 2-7 mm. **Flowers:** In slender inflorescences, ± 160 mm; flowers ± 8 mm, pink or red on same plant (Aug-Apr). **Fruit:** Pods 35 x 3 mm, finely hairy. **Similar species:** *T. capensis* Prostrate habit.

Tephrosia polystachya Pioneer Tephrosia (*polystachya* - many spikes)

Erect shrub, 0,6-1 m. In moist, shady places, on forest margins. Stems **covered in short spreading yellowish hairs.** Very variable. **Leaves:** 30-85 mm, stalks short; 3-9 pairs leaflets, 7-30 x 3-9 mm, stipules 5-10 mm, slender. **Flowers:** Irregularly scattered in **branched inflorescences,** ± 270 mm; flowers ± 10 mm, pale to deep pink, calyx lobes oval to pointed (Jan- Apr). **Fruit:** Pods ± 40 x 3 mm. **General:** Var. *hirta*, covered in rusty down; inflorescences shorter, more dense. Var. *longidens*, calyx lobes long, narrow. Var. *latifolia*, 5-8 pairs leaflets, ± 32 x 13 mm, longer, broader, thinner, less hairy; pink and white flowers on same plant.

Tephrosia grandiflora

Tephrosia lupinifolia

Tephrosia bachmannii

Tephrosia macropoda

Tephrosia multijuga

Tephrosia polystachya

Tephrosia polystachya

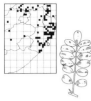

Tephrosia purpurea Silver Tephrosia; ilozane (Z) *(purpurea - purple)*

Erect shrublet, up to 600(900) mm, or prostrate herb. On forest margins, on coastal sand dunes, cosmop. Much branched, covered in short rough hairs. **Leaves:** Grey-green, 50-90 mm; 7-17 pairs **broad, oval leaflets**, 18-25 x 5-20 mm, stipules narrow. **Flowers:** 6-20, well spaced in slender inflorescences, stems 7-150 mm; flowers ± 8 mm, pink to red-purple, calyx silky (Sep-Jun). **Fruit:** Pods ± 30 x 5 mm, slightly curved, hairy, seeds mottled. **General:** Used in traditional medicine to kill vermin on people and animals. Very variable. A number of subspecies described.

Tephrosia shiluwanensis [= *T. medleyi*] *(shiluwanensis* - first described from the Shilovane district, Mpumalanga)

Erect shrub, sparsely branched, 0,4-2 m. On forest margins, E Cape to N Prov. Stems woody, young stems softly hairy. **Leaves:** 55-130 mm, stalks 30-70 mm; 3-8 pairs leaflets, 14-50 x 5-13 mm, grey-green beneath, stipules ± 10 mm, sword-shaped, densely hairy along margins. **Flowers:** Few, clustered at tips of inflorescences, ± 110(200) mm; flowers ± 15 mm, bright pink, calyx covered with golden brown hairs (Jan-Apr). **Fruit:** Pods ± 40 x 7 mm. **General:** Stems, leaf stalks, veins on underside of leaflets, stipules and bracts are **dark reddish pink**. Ornamental, suitable for the garden.

Ophrestia (anagram of *Tephrosia*) - Leaves pinnate, leaflets with 4-5 prominent veins, thick. Closely related to *Tephrosia*. Endemic to SA, 2 species.

Ophrestia oblongifolia *(oblongifolia* - oblong leaves)

Creeping herb. In grassland. Woody rootstock. **Leaves:** ± 75 mm; 1-5 pairs **oblong leaflets**, 25-70 x 9-25 mm, densely hairy beneath, **veins very noticeable**. **Flowers:** Inflorescences ± 320 mm; flowers ± 10 mm, white, pale pink, lilac, calyx densely golden hairy (Dec-Feb). **Fruit:** Pod ± 40 x 5 mm.

Lessertia (named after Jules de Lessert, 1773-1847, French industrialist, banker, amateur botanist with a private herbarium) - Herbs or shrubs; leaves pinnate; pods papery, flat or slightly inflated. Afr, ± 60 species, ± 30 in SA.

Lessertia perennans Lessertia; 'musa-pelo (SS) *(perennans* - growing throughout the year)

Herbaceous shrublet, up to 1,5 m, in colonies. In grassland, on boulder beds, 450-2400 m. Stems pale, simple or branched, erect. **Leaves:** ± 50 mm; 8-10 pairs leaflets, grey-green, silky hairy. **Flowers:** Inflorescences with straight stems, 75-150 mm; flowers ± 6 mm, pale pink, buds deep pink (Nov-Mar). **Fruit:** Pod flat. **General:** A number of subspecies described. A lovely plant.
Similar species: *L. stricta* Blaasertjie (A) In grassland, rocky or damp areas; 4-6 pairs leaflets; flowers pale to dark pink, white or blue **on same plant**.

Desmodium (*desmos* - bond or chain, refers to jointed pod which resembles the links of a chain. Also said to refer to the joined or 'bonded' stamens) - Herbs or shrubs; usually 3 foliolate; flowers in slender or dense inflorescences; pods flat, separating into 1 seeded segments. Warm regions of the world, ± 300 species, 12 in SA.

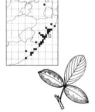

Desmodium incanum Sweethearts; isinama (Z) *(incanum* - like grey felt, hoary)

Spreading herb or shrublet, up to 1 m. In disturbed grassland, forest, up to 1000 m. **Leaves:** Leaf stalk ± 30 mm, covered in grey hairs, terminal leaflet ± 100 mm, shiny dark green, lighter in centre along midvein. **Flowers:** In loose, slender, terminal inflorescences; flowers deep pink, mauve to purple (Sep-Jun). **Fruit:** Pods ± 25 x 8 mm with 5-8 segments, **covered in sticky hairs. General:** Pods dispersed by people and animals. **Similar species:** *D. setigerum* (see p. 464).

Tephrosia purpurea

Ophrestia oblongifolia

Ophrestia oblongifolia

Geoff Nichols

Tony Abbott

Van Wyk & Malan

Tephrosia purpurea

Geoff Nichols

Tephrosia shiluwanensis

Martin von Fintel

Lessertia perennans

Geoff Nichols

Lessertia stricta

Van Wyk & Malan

Desmodium incanum

C J Ward

395

Pseudarthria (*pseudo* - false; *arthron* - joint, refers to the constriction between seeds) - Herbs or shrubs, softly woolly; leaves 3 foliolate; flowers in terminal, branched inflorescences. Asia, India, Afr, ± 6 species, 1 in SA.

Pseudarthria hookeri Velvet Bean, Bug-catcher; Fluweelboontjie (A); uphandosi, uqhonqo, uqwashu (Z) (named after Sir Joseph Hooker, first Director, Royal Bot Gardens at Kew in 1841)
Robust, deciduous shrub, up to 3 m. On forest margins, damp hillsides, coast to 2000 m, E Cape to Trop Afr. Rootstock woody. **Stems angular, velvety. Leaves:** Leaflets ± 70 x 40 mm, **rough, leathery above, velvety, with protruding veins beneath. Flowers:** Crowded inflorescences ± 350 mm; flowers pink (white), ± 8 mm (Sep-Jun). **Fruit:** Pods straight, 12-38 x 3-4 mm, velvety mauve, **sticky hairy. General:** Curved hairs stick to other surfaces. Branches placed around sleeping mats in Zim, reputedly used to catch bed bugs! Ornamental garden plant. (See p. 576)
Similar species: *Desmodium salicifolium* (see p. 150)

Derris (*derris* - skin, leather covering, refers to pods) - Woody climbers (trees, shrubs); flowers much longer than calyx, white pink or purplish; pods flattened, papery, not splitting. Trop, subtrop, ± 50 species, 1 in SA.

Derris trifoliata (*trifoliata* - three leaves or leaflets)
Woody climber, 3-15 m. In coastal thicket, along rivers, in mangrove swamps, KZN, Moz, Madag, Asia, Austr. Bark brown, with pale raised dots. **Leaves:** 80-200 mm; 3-5 leaflets, 50-110 x 25-65 mm. **Flowers:** Clustered on very short side stalks, in slender terminal inflorescences, 100-280 mm; flowers ± 12 mm, white to pale mauve tinged pink, calyx bell-shaped (Sep-Oct). **Fruit:** Pods ± kidney-shaped, 30-45 x 20-30 mm.

Canavalia (from the Malabar common name 'Kanaval' for these herbs) - Climbers or creepers; leaves 3 foliolate, stipules small. Attracts butterflies. Trop, subtrop, mainly American, ± 50 species, 5 in SA.

Canavalia bonariensis Forest Canavalia (from Bonaria, in Buenos Aires, S America)
Robust climber. In low-lying swamp or riverine forest, E Cape to KZN, S America. **Leaves:** Leaflets ± 75 x 30 mm, stalklets sparsely white hairy. **Flowers:** In short, hanging clusters; flowers ± 30 mm, magenta when new, red when older, held 'upside down' (Sep-May). **Fruit:** Pods cylindrical, ± 150 x 35 mm, seeds brown turning black, floating, impermeable to water for at least 2 years. **General:** Located by the fallen flowers on forest floor. Good garden or container plant, does well in shade.

Canavalia rosea [= *C. maritima*] Beach-bean Canavalia; Strandboontjie (A) (*rosea* - rose red)
Robust climber or trailer, stems up to 10 m. On coastal sand dunes and estuaries, throughout the tropics. **Leaves:** Leaflets **almost round**, 25-95 x 15-90 mm; stalks 20-70 mm. **Flowers:** In erect inflorescences, ± 180 mm; flowers ± 25 mm, pink to purple with whitish patch at base (Dec-Aug), sweetly scented. **Fruit:** Pods 110-150(200) x 25-35 mm, velvety at first, maturing hairless. **General:** Very common, growing with *Ipomoea pes-caprae*. Cultivated in Europe since 1795. (See p. 576)

Canavalia virosa Savanna Canavalia (*virosa* - poisonous, refers to supposedly poisonous seeds)
Perennial trailer or climber, up to 15 m. In savanna, forest, thicket, Trop Afr, S Arabia, India. **Leaves:** Stalk 40-120 mm; leaflets 70-150 x 50-100 mm, shiny dark green, **sparsely to densely hairy**, rachis 15-30 mm, stalklets 5-10 mm. **Flowers: In long, hanging inflorescences**, 120-430 mm; flowers ± 30 mm, magenta at first, aging deep red, held 'upside down' (Dec-Aug). **Fruit:** Pods velvety, ± 170 x 30 mm, ± 20 mm thick, splitting, twisting when ripe, seeds brown marbled black, not impermeable to water. **General:** Seeds reputed to be poisonous. Grown by seed.

Sphenostylis (*sphenostylis* - wedge-shaped, refers to the style) - Herbs or shrublets; 3 foliolate leaves, terminal leaflet stalked; flowers large, in small cluster on end of long stem, calyx lobes rounded; pods narrow. Can be separated in the field from *Vigna* by the more compact habit of growth. Afr, 2 species in SA.

Sphenostylis angustifolia Wild Sweetpea Bush; Wilde-ertjie (A); insololo, ithethe (Z)
(*angustifolius* - narrow leaves)
Erect, compact **shrublet**, 250-450 mm. In grassland. Stems woody at base, leafy. **Leaves:** Stalks 20-80 mm, stipules small; **leaflets narrow**, ± 40 x 5-10 mm, stipels small. **Flowers:** 1-4, stems 40-80 mm; flowers ± 30 mm, brilliant magenta, purple, rarely creamy white, yellow blotch at base, **keel twisted, forming a bulge** (Aug-Apr), **sweetly scented. Fruit:** Pods ± 80 mm. **General:** Good fodder. Used in traditional medicine to cleanse stomach and blood. (See p. 152) **Similar species:** *S. marginata* Stems sometimes twining; few leaves, conspicuous stipules and stipels, leaflets broad, ± 80 x 30 mm; flowering stems ± 300 mm, flowers smaller, pink.

Pseudarthria hookeri

Derris trifoliata

Pseudarthria hookeri

Canavalia rosea

Canavalia virosa

Canavalia rosea

Canavalia virosa

Canavalia bonariensis

Sphenostylis angustifolia

Vigna (named in honour of Italian botanist Domenico Vigna, died 1647) - Usually twining herbs (for description see p. 464)

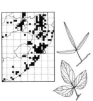

Vigna unguiculata Wild Cow Pea; atimbawini (Th); imbumba, isihlumaya, isikhwali, umcwasibe (Z) (*unguiculata* - long claws)

Trailing herb, stems up to 2 m. In grassland, woodland, throughout tropics. Tubers on roots. **Leaves:** Thin, dark green, stalks ± 20 mm; leaflets very variable, ± 70 x 40 mm, **unequal sided, terminal leaflet bulging on both sides at base**, stalklets ± 20 mm. **Flowers:** 1-2, on erect stems ± 300 mm; flowers ± 25 mm, greenish white, pale pink to purple (Sep-Mar). **Fruit:** Pod erect, 50-100 x 3-11 mm. **General:** Seeds an important staple food. Tubers on roots eaten, leaves used as spinach. Used traditionlly to treat fever and as a love charm. The cultivated Cow Pea, subsp. *unguiculata* and the Yard-long Bean also belong to this species. Plants visited by ants. Very variable, as indicated by a number of subspecies and varieties. (See p. 464)

Vigna vexillata [= *V. davyi*, *V. hispida*] Narrow-leaved Wild Sweetpea; Wilde-ertjie (A); mgcenga (Sw); isikhwali, ubombo, umcwasibe, umnxwasibe (Z) (*vexillata* - flag or standard)

Slender trailing creeper. In grassland, woodland, widespread in tropics. Tuberous rootstock. Stems roughly hairy. **Leaves:** Stalks ± 30 mm; **terminal leaflet large,** ± 100 x 40 mm. **Flowers:** Stems ± 300 mm; flowers ± 25 mm, hairless, pale lilac to purple (Aug-Mar), sweetly scented. **Fruit:** Pod ± 90 x 4 mm, hairy. **General:** A number of varieties described. Plants visited by ants. Seeds and root tubers eaten by people. Used in traditional medicine to treat fever and as love charms. (See p. 466)

Lablab (origin unknown) - Very variable, single species genus, widely cultivated in the trop, originating in Asia.

★ *Lablab purpureus* [= *Dolichos lablab*, *D. purpureus*] Bonavist Bean, Egyptian Kidney Bean, Hyacinth Bean, Indian Butter Bean, Lablab Bean

Perennial, slender climber or erect herb, stems 1-5 m. In partial shade, originally from Asia. Leaflets heart-shaped, terminal leaflet ± 40 x 30 mm. Inflorescences on long stems ± 100 mm, flowers 10-15 mm, magenta to purple (Feb-Apr). Pods flat, 30 x 11 mm, seeds small, white, red or black. Useful food and fodder plant. Leaves, young pods, red and white beans cooked as a side dish, black beans too bitter to eat.

GERANIACEAE - Geranium Family Herbs or soft wooded shrubs, often aromatic. Leaves usually lobed or divided, with stipules. Flowers regular or slightly irregular, ovary superior. Fruit beaked, splitting into five 1 seeded sections, each separating with part of the persistent dry style. Economically important for aromatic oils, the florist trade, horticulture, especially the garden plants known as 'Geraniums', which belong to the genus *Pelargonium* and not *Geranium*. Temp, few trop, 11 genera, ± 800 species, 5 genera in SA. *Geranium* (*geranos* - a crane) - Annual or perennial herbs, shrubs; flowers symmetrical, solitary. Attracts butterflies. Cosmop, mainly temp, ± 400 species, 27 in SA.

Geranium caffrum khoara, makorotsoane (SS) (named after Kaffraria, now the Eastern Cape)

Sprawling perennial herb. In damp areas in rough grassland or low scrub, on margins of marshes, up to 1500 m. Tap root long. Stems slender, woody at base, rooting at nodes. **Leaves:** ± 70 mm diam, deeply 3-5 lobed, **each lobe deeply dissected**, sparsely hairy above, **downy on veins beneath, margins rolled under**, stalks more than 70 mm. **Flowers:** Petals ± 13 x 8 mm, entire or shallowly notched, white or pale pink, calyx finely hairy (Sep-Jan). **General:** Hybridises with *G. flanaganii*.

Geranium flanaganii bolila-ba-litsoene, chechane (SS) (after Henry Flanagan, 1861-1919, Komga, E Cape farmer, plant collector; whose garden and herbarium were bequeathed to the nation)

Perennial, scrambling herb, in clumps. On damp forest margins, in marshy places. Stems straggling, hairy. **Leaves:** ± 90 mm diam, 5 lobed, more than half way to base, lobes mostly with 2 coarse teeth on each side, **shortly hairy** above, stalks 35-150 mm, stipules deeply dissected. **Flowers: Large,** petals ± 16 x 11 mm, light to dark pink, veins darker (Aug-Feb). **General:** A commonly used Zulu household remedy.

Geranium multisectum (*multisectum* - many incisions)

Perennial herb, **in clumps**, 200-400 mm. In open marshy areas, 1400-3300 m, E Cape to N Prov. Stems downy, well branched, woody at base. **Leaves:** ± 50 mm diam, 5 lobed, **cut to base**, each lobe divided into **narrow segments 1-2 mm broad**, margins rolled under, ± hairless above, more densely hairy beneath, bicoloured or not; **lower leaves with very long stalks, ± 300 mm**. **Flowers:** Petals ± 17 x 13 mm, shallowly notched, purple to magenta, calyx downy, stalks hairy (Oct-Mar). **General:** At high altitudes, leaves smaller, lobes short, often incurved. Plants at lower altitudes, leaves larger, lobes longer, more spreading. **Similar species:** *G. incanum* SW Cape to E Cape; not in clumps; leaves always bicoloured.

Vigna unguiculata

Neil Crouch

Vigna vexillata

Lorraine van Hooff

★ *Lablab purpureus*

Geoff Nichols

Vigna vexillata

Lorraine van Hooff

Geranium caffrum

Lorraine van Hooff

Geranium flanaganii

Olaf Wirminghaus

Geranium caffrum

Geoff Nichols

Geranium multisectum

Martin von Fintel

399

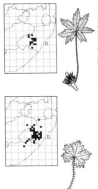

Geranium pulchrum (*pulchrum* - beautiful)

Robust shrublet, up to 1,2 m. In marshy areas, on streambanks, 1500-2200 m, Drakensberg endemic. Stems woody at base, ± 10 mm diam, silky. **Leaves:** ± 120 mm diam, deeply 5-7 lobed, lobes sharply lobed and toothed, hairy above, **thick, silvery silky velvety beneath**, stalks longer than leaves. **Flowers: In loose terminal clusters**, petals ± 22 x 19 mm, shallowly notched, light purple or deep pink, sometimes white at centre, stalks ± 60 mm, covered in white hairs (Oct-Apr). (See p. 466)

Geranium schlechteri Pink Baby (after Friedrich Schlechter, 1872-1925, German botanist and traveller)

Fragrant, straggling, perennial herb. In moist grassland, near rocks, 800-2590 m. Stems ± 1 m, loosely branched, with long silvery hairs. **Leaves:** ± 60 mm diam, 5 lobed to 4-10 mm of base, lobes sparsely toothed, thinly hairy above, long spreading hairs below, **often gland tipped**; lower leaf stalks ± 180 mm, stipules deeply dissected. **Flowers: Opposite upper leaves**, petals ± 13 x 7 mm, entire or **shallowly notched**, white fading pink or white veined pink, calyx lobes maroon tipped, stalks 10-40 mm, with spreading **gland tipped hairs** (Oct-Apr). **General:** Plants can become robust and scrambling, with larger flowers. **Similar species:** *G. wakkerstroomianum* (see p. 152)

Monsonia (named for Lady Anne Monson, 1714-76, great granddaughter of Charles II; known for her botanical knowledge; visited Cape about 1775) - Herbs or undershrubs; often with simple stem from woody rootstock or deep tap root; leaves toothed or divided; flowers regular, petals 5, separate, tips broad, blunt or slightly notched, stamens in 5 groups with 3 stamens in each, 1 longer than others, ovary 5 lobed; fruit beaked. Afr, W Asia, E India, ± 40 species, ± 21 in SA.

Monsonia angustifolia Pink Monsonia; Angelbossie (A) (*angustifolia* - narrow leaves)

Slender, **annual herb**, 100-300 mm. In grassland, bushveld, often in disturbed areas. Stems branched, reddish purple, hairy. **Leaves:** ± 25 x 6-10 mm, **margins irregularly toothed**, stalks ± 10 mm, stipules often spiny. **Flowers:** Usually solitary, petals ± 12 mm, pink, mauve (white) with **5 dark blue or grey main veins**, calyx lobes with slender tips, stalks slender, erect, ± 50 mm (Nov-Mar). **Fruit:** Erect, ± 50 mm.

Pelargonium (*pelargos* - stork's beak, refers to fruit) - Perennial (annual) herbs or soft woody shrubs; leaves usually lobed or divided, often aromatic; flowers asymmetrical. The horticultural varieties, generally (incorrectly) known as Geraniums, popular garden and container plants since the 1700s. Attracts butterflies. Mostly S Afr, ± 250 species.

Pelargonium acraeum Horseshoe Pelargonium; Wildemalva (A) (*acraeum* - dweller on heights)

Scrambling, soft wooded shrub up to 1(2) m. In mountains, on forest margins, 1300-1500 m, KZN to N Prov. Softly downy. Stems slightly succulent. **Leaves:** 50-100 mm diam, **deeply lobed**, lobes bluntly toothed, stalks 25-80 mm, stipules ± 10 mm. **Flowers:** 7-15, inflorescence stems 90-150 mm; petals nearly equal, ± 24 x 14 mm, pink, stalks ± 30 mm (Mar-Dec). **General:** Grows well in cooler areas.

Pelargonium capitatum Rose-scented Pelargonium (*capitatum* - head, refers to inflorescence)

Sprawling shrub, 0,25-1 m. In sandy soils along coast, in disturbed areas, SW Cape to KZN. Stems, leaves softly hairy, **fragrantly scented when bruised. Leaves:** ± 45 x 60 mm, shallow to deeply 3-6 lobed, margins toothed. **Flowers:** Small, 8-20, in compact inflorescences; flowers pale pink to deep purple with stripes on 2 upper petals (throughout year). **General:** Cultivated in Europe to produce Oil of Geranium. Bruised leaves used in traditional medicine to soothe skin rashes and in a tea to treat kidney and bladder ailments, nausea, diarrhoea and stomach cramps. Easily grown.

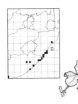

Pelargonium luridum Stalk-flowered Pelargonium, Stork's Bill, Waving Pelargonium; Wildemalva (A); inyonkulu, isandla sonwabu, umsongelo, unyawolwenkuku, uvendle (Z) (*luridum* - smoky or drab)

Deciduous, low-growing herb, up to 0,6(1) m. Widespread in grassland, E Cape to Tanz. Woody tuber. Plant hairy throughout. **Leaf, flower colour, size very variable. Leaves: In basal rosette**, ± 270 mm diam, shallowly to deeply lobed or threadlike, stalks ± 300 mm. **Flowers:** 5-60, in large **solitary** inflorescence, ± 130 mm diam, stem erect; flowers pink, cream or white, **not blotched** (Aug-Apr). **General:** Eaten raw as a vegetable. Grazed. Used in traditional medicine to treat dysentery, nausea, vomiting, fever, sick calves and as a love charm. Easily grown from seed, woody tubers. **Similar species:** *P. schlechteri* Two-tiered Pelargonium Leaf margins toothed, net veins strongly raised; inflorescence usually 2 tiered, petals greenish yellow, each with purplish red blotch. (For photograph see p. 62)

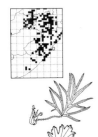

Geranium pulchrum   Lal Greene

Geranium pulchrum   Tony Abbott

Geranium schlechteri   Lal Greene

Geranium schlechteri   Lal Greene

Pelargonium acraeum   Tony Abbott

Pelargonium capitatum   Tony Abbott

Monsonia angustifolia   Van Wyk & Malan

Pelargonium luridum   Lorraine van Hooff

Pelargonium luridum   Lorraine van Hooff

Pelargonium multicaule (*multi* - many; *caule* - stems)

Low-growing, soft shrublet, up to 300 x 1000 mm. On rocky hillsides. Stems **trailing**. **Leaves:** 30-40(65) x 20-30(40) mm, irregularly cut, with sparse glandular hairs, segments blunt, margins entire, stalks 30-130 mm, stipules ± 5 x 4 mm. **Flowers: 3-5 on unbranched stem**; **4 petals**, two at back, ± 18 x 8 mm, with dark purple markings and white blotch at base (throughout year). **General:** Fast growing, useful groundcover (dies back at end of growing season), from seed or cuttings.

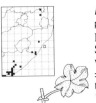

Pelargonium peltatum [= *P. lateripes*] Ivy-leaved Pelargonium; Kolsuring (A) (*peltatus* - peltate, refers to the shieldlike leaves, stalk attached to centre of the blade)

Perennial scrambler, up to 2 m. In coastal or succulent thicket, SW Cape to Mpum. Stems smooth, zigzag, becoming woody at base. **Leaves:** Succulent, 30-70 mm diam with 5-7 shallow lobes, with or without central reddish marking, usually hairless, stalks ± 55 mm. **Flowers:** 2-10, inflorescence stem ± 65 mm; petals ± 20 x 9 mm, pale pink to mauve with darker purple markings (Aug-Jan). **General:** The ancestor of the hybrid 'ivy-leaved geraniums' first introduced to horticulture in Holland in 1700 by Willem Adriaan van der Stel and in Britain by Masson in 1774. Rewarding garden plant.

OXALIDACEAE - Sorrel Family Herbs. Leaves simple or usually with 3 leaflets. Petals stalked, often twisted. Fruit a capsule or berry. Trop, Temp, 6 genera, ± 775 species, 2 genera in SA. *Oxalis* (*oxys* - acid, sour; *als* - salt, refers to the sharp taste of the plant) - Herbs; many with enlarged vertical or horizontal underground stems; leaves in basal rosette; flowers bell-shaped. About 200 species in SA, mostly in winter rainfall area.

★ *Oxalis latifolia* Pink Garden Sorrel; Suring (A) (*latifolia* - broad leaves)

Low-growing deciduous herb, up to 250 mm. In grassland, disturbed areas, SA to Ethiopia (from Mexico). Runners and bulbils. Leaves large, folded. 5-20 flowers, light pink or mauve with green throat (Aug-Apr). Flowers visited by honey-bees.

Oxalis obliquifolia Oblique-leaved Sorrel; Skuinsblaarsuring (A); simunyane (Sw)
(*obliquifolia* - leaves slanting sideways)

Up to 100 mm, in small colonies. In damp grassland, rocky areas, on disturbed soil, SA to Ethiopia, up to 2000 m. Slender, horizontal underground stem, brown bulbils ± 10 mm. **Leaves:** Leaflets 3-15 mm, tips broad sometimes notched. **Flowers: Solitary**, 10-23 mm diam, petals ± 20 mm, bright pink or white, **yellow** or white in throat, tube yellow (Oct-May). **General:** Flowers visited by butterflies, honey-bees.

Oxalis semiloba Common Sorrel, Folded-leaved Sorrel; Suring (A); bolila (SS); incangiyane, isibungu, isimuncwane, isimunyane (Z) (*semiloba* - half lobed)

Perennial, deciduous herb, up to 200(600) mm, in small colonies. In grassland, open scrub, on forest margins, SA to Kenya. Swollen, vertical underground stem, also with bulbils. **Leaves:** Leaflets bilobed, variable. **Flowers: 3-12, in small inflorescences**, ± 15 mm, bright pink, ± with yellow centre (Oct-May). **General:** Leaves, flowers, bulbs eaten by people. Grazed by stock. Used traditionally to treat thrush in babies.

Oxalis smithiana Narrow-leaved Sorrel; Klawersuring (A); bolila (SS); izotho (X); umuncwane (bulb), inkolowane (X,Z); incangiyane (Z)

Deciduous herb, up to 250 mm. In damp grassland, on rock outcrops, coast to 2300 m. Swollen underground stems ± 35 mm. Very variable. **Leaves:** Leaflets **deeply divided**, lobes oblong, **narrow**, ± 20 x 3 mm. **Flowers: Solitary**, petals ± 20 mm, pale lilac, mauve, white, stalk slender ± 120 mm (Aug-Jan). **General:** Grazed. Leaves, bulbs eaten by children. Used in traditional medicine as a tapeworm remedy.

RUTACEAE - Lemon Family Trees, shrubs (herbs), often aromatic. Leaves simple, dotted with transparent oil glands. Economically important for citrus fruit, cork and hop trees and a number of ornamentals. Cosmop, especially trop, ± 156 genera, ± 1800 species, 21 genera in SA. *Agathosma* (*agathos* - good; *osme* - scent) - **Buchu** Erect woody shrublets; leaves usually very small, flat or 3 angled. Endemic to SA, mostly SW Cape, ± 140 species.

Agathosma ovata Oval-leaved Buchu, False Buchu; Basterboegoe, Bosboegoe (A); umahesaka-omhlophe (Z) (*ovata* - oval, broader at base)

Much branched shrublet, up to 0,5 m in KZN (up to 1,5 m in the Cape). Widespread on grassy hillsides. **Leaves:** Leathery, oval to roundish, ± 15 mm, flat on both sides, dull green above, shiny bright green beneath, margins recurved. **Flowers:** ± 10 mm diam, white to lilac (throughout year). **General:** Very variable over its wide range. Crushed leaves have lovely citrus scent. Used traditionally to treat nervous complaints. Avoided by grazing animals. A popular, fairly fast growing garden plant.

Pelargonium multicaule

Tony Abbott

Oxalis obliquifolia

Darrel Plowes

Pelargonium peltatum

Martin von Fintel

★ *Oxalis latifolia*

Lorraine van Hooff

Oxalis semiloba

Neil Crouch

Oxalis smithiana

Lal Greene

Agathosma ovata

Tony Abbott

403

POLYGALACEAE - Milkwort Family Herbs or shrubs. Flowers superficially resemble 'pea' flowers, inner 2 sepals are petal-like wings, petals reduced, one forms a 'keel' with a brushlike crest below the tip. Fruit usually a capsule, seeds often covered in short hairs. Subcosmop, ± 17 genera, ± 950 species, 4 genera in SA. *Polygala* (*poly* - much; *gala* - milk, refers to the old belief in Europe that grazing certain species of these plants would increase the milk yield of cows) - Herbs or shrubs; seeds often distributed by ants. Many popular garden plants. Cosmop, ± 600 species, ± 88 in SA.

Polygala amatymbica **Dwarf Polygala, Thembu Polygala; mohlabeho-o-monyenyane, nkokolotsane (SS)** (named after the amaThembu tribe)

Dwarf, tufted perennial, up to 150(300) mm. In grassland, thicket. Tap root woody. Stems branching from base, very leafy. Variable leaf, flower size and colour. **Leaves:** ± 25 x 15 mm, oval, nearly stalkless, tapering to **sharply pointed tip**. **Flowers: Solitary or in pairs in leaf axils,** small, wings ± 6 x 3 mm, brilliant magenta or purple (Sep-Feb). **General:** Used in traditional medicine as a stimulant for cattle.

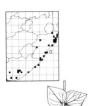

Polygala fruticosa **Heart-leaved Polygala; ithethe (Z)** (*fruticosa* - shrubby)

Deciduous shrublet 0,4(1) m. In grassland, dry rocky areas, coast to 2000 m, SW Cape to S Moz. Rootstock woody. **Leaves:** Opposite, 8-40 x 6-30 mm, **firm, shiny but glaucous, 3 veined from base,** hairless or velvety, margins red, **stalkless; young leaves shiny coppery pink. Flowers:** ± 20 x 25 mm, magenta, in dense inflorescences (Aug-May). **General:** Used in traditional medicine to purify the blood, treat poor circulation, ulcers and venereal diseases. Introduced into horticulture in 1790. **Similar species:** *P. confusa* **ungqangendlela (Z)** Spreading herb, up to 300 mm; in forest, Cape to KZN; leaves ± 30 x 18 mm, soft, stalks short; flowers smaller.

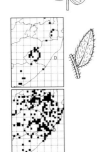

Polygala hispida (*hispidus* - shaggy, rough)

Spreading, cushion-forming herb, stems 200-300 mm. On mountainsides. Rootstock woody. Stems spreading to erect, branching towards tips, leafy, **plant covered in long, silky hairs. Leaves:** Alternate, ± 18 x 5 mm, almost stalkless. **Flowers:** In terminal, compact to elongating inflorescences; flowers pink (Sep-Dec).

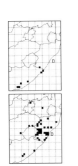

Polygala hottentotta **Small Purple Broom; lehlokoa-la-tsela (SS); umanqandi, uzekane (Z)** (pertaining to the land of the Hottentots, the Khoi-khoi, who occupied a region in the Cape)

Slender, **perennial**, deciduous herb, 0,2-1 m. In grassland, woodland, SA to Zim, Moz, coast to 2100 m. Rootstock woody. Stems erect, arching, wiry, sparsely branched. **Leaves:** Few, slender, 10-25(40) x 1-2 mm. **Flowers:** In widely spaced inflorescences ± 200 mm; wings ± 8 x 6 mm, pale greenish yellow, magenta, pink or purple, conspicuously veined (Aug-May). **General:** Used in traditional medicine to treat abdominal complaints, anthrax and as charms. Roots, stems scented.

Polygala refracta **Narrow-leaved Polygala** (*refractus* - broken)

Slender, up to 300 mm. In grassland. Woody at base. **Leaves:** Alternate, erect, 6-25 x 1-2 mm, tips pointed, margins translucent, stalkless. **Flowers:** 2-3 in small clusters, **almost at right angles to the stem, stalks almost as long as flowers**; flowers ± 12 mm (Oct-Dec).

Polygala rehmannii **bolao-bo-boholo, lesira, mohale-oa-bopeli, setetea (SS)** (named after Anton Rehmann, 1840-1917, Polish botanist who visited KZN)

Perennial, **erect, tufted herb,** 100-300 mm. In grassland, up to 2300 m, KZN to Zim. Woody rootstock. Stems slightly winged, **leafy. Leaves:** 10-35 x 2-6 mm, tips usually blunt, stalkless. **Flowers:** In slender inflorescences, 30-70 mm; wings ± 8 x 4 mm, purple, blue, magenta (Nov-Apr). **General:** Used traditionally as a love potion and charm.

Polygala serpentaria **Slangwortel (A); inhlanhlenkulu, uncinci-wafika-umthakwethu, ungqangendlela (Z)** (*serpentaria* - like a serpent, refers to its use in treating snakebite)

Trailing herb, up to 200 mm. In rocky grassland, open woodland, Cape to KZN. Woody rootstock. Stems simple or branched, slender, leafy. **Leaves:** ± 20 x 5-10 mm, paler beneath, margins rolled under, stalkless. **Flowers:** Small, in small clusters, in axils (Sep-Dec). **General:** Used in traditional medicine as purgative enemas for children, as a love charm and to treat snakebite. **Similar species:** *P. rhinostigma* Erect, tufted herb, 100-300 mm; in mountain grassland; many stems from base, slightly branched, leafy; leaves 10-15 x 4-8 mm; flowers small, in dense inflorescences (Oct-Dec).

Polygala amatymbica

Lawrence Peacock

Polygala confusa

Tom de Waal

Polygala fruticosa

Geoff Nichols

Polygala hispida

Martin von Fintel

Polygala hottentotta

Tony Abbott

Polygala refracta

Tony Abbott

Polygala rehmannii

Martin von Fintel

Polygala rhinostigma

Martin von Fintel

Polygala serpentaria

Tony Abbott

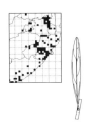

Polygala virgata Purple Broom, Bumble-bee Polygala; Bloukappies (A); ithethe, ujulwezinyosi, umphehlwana, unohlonishwayo obomvu (Z) (*virgata* - twiggy)

Slender shrub, 1,5-3 m. In grassland, on forest margins, up to 1850 m, SA to Tanz, Congo. Single main stem, **branching in upper third**. Variable in size, shape, texture of leaves (velvety or not) and flower colour. **Leaves:** ± 20-90 x 1-20 mm, stalks short, usually dropping before flowering. **Flowers:** In long, dense, terminal inflorescences, 30-200 mm; flowers large, wings ± 13 x 9 mm, pink to magenta, with darker veins (Oct-Feb, throughout year). **General:** Heavily browsed. Used in traditional medicine as a blood purifier. Popular garden plant, hardy and free flowering, self seeding, good cut-flower.

Muraltia (named after John von Muralt, Swiss botanist and author) - Shrubs or shrublets; leaves small, dense, sharp tipped, often pungently scented; flowers small, solitary, lower petal with two winglike lobes; fruit a flattened capsule, often tipped with horns. Afr, ± 115 species, mostly SW Cape.

Muraltia lancifolia Purple Heath; umahesaka-onsundu (Z) (*lancifolia* - lancelike leaves)

Perennial, up to 400 mm. In grassland, coast to 1500 m. Branching near ground, young stems softly or harshly hairy. **Leaves:** Crowded in clusters, 5-11 mm, flat, spine tipped, margins and midrib roughly hairy. **Flowers:** ± 10 mm, pink, stalkless (Sep-Mar). **General:** Roots used in traditional medicine. **Similar species:** *M. saxicola* Up to 200 mm; leaf margins thickened; flowers smaller.

BALSAMINACEAE - Balsam Family Soft, perennial herbs, usually in damp places. Flowers asymmetrical, 3-5 sepals, back sepal petal-like, extended into honey spur, side petals 2 lobed. Fruit splits elastically. Popular ornamentals. Trop, 2 genera, ± 850 species, 1 genus in SA.

Impatiens (*impatiens* - impatient, refers to bursting of pod and forceful scattering of seeds) - Genus description as for family, 5 species in SA.

Impatiens flanaganiae Mrs Flanagan's Impatiens (discovered by Mrs Flanagan, wife of Henry Flanagan, 1861-1919, E Cape farmer, whose garden and herbarium were bequeathed to the nation)

Soft perennial herb, up to 1 m, in colonies. In shade, usually on boulders on steep slopes or near the base of waterfalls, mostly on sandstone. Rare. **Tubers large**, pink. Stems fleshy, erect, branched, **reddish**, dying back in winter. **Leaves:** Large, oblong, 100-240 x 45-110 mm, tapering to narrow tip, margins toothed, stalks 10-45 mm. **Flowers:** 6-12 in erect inflorescences, **stems long** 170-390 mm; flowers **large**, **deep pink**, spur yellow, lower sepal ± 17 mm, gradually tapering to curved spur, ± 40 mm, side petals ± 28 x 34 mm (early to midsummer). **General:** Forms large clumps in cultivation. Prone to eelworm.

Impatiens hochstetteri [= *I. duthiae*] Common Wild Impatiens, Mauve Impatiens; Kruidjie-roer-my-nie (A); ihlula, umadolwane (Z) (named after C G Ferdinand von Hochstetter, 1829-1884, German geologist and anthropologist who collected at the Cape in 1857)

Soft herb, 100-400 mm, in colonies. In damp shade of forest. Stems erect, semi-transparent. **Leaves:** Blade 50-100 x 50 mm, margins toothed, tufts of hairs between teeth, **tapering to long, narrow tip**, stalks slender, 15-50 mm, **Flowers:** In groups of 1-3, small, front petal and spur ± 10 mm, pink or mauve, stalks slender, ± 50 mm (throughout year). **Fruit:** Explodes open. **General:** Used in traditional medicine to treat eczema. Attractive groundcover for moist shady areas. **Similar species:** *I. sylvicola* Flowers cup-shaped with deeper pink eye.

MALVACEAE - Hibiscus Family Trees, shrubs or herbs. Flowers usually conspicuous, often with epicalyx (a leafy whorl below calyx), stamens partly united into tube around style, branched above. Fruit splitting into segments or a capsule. Economically important for cotton, edible fruits of Okra *Hibiscus esculentus*, and ornamental Hollyhocks, Hibiscus and many others. Cosmop, especially trop, ± 111 genera, ± 1800 species, 21 genera in SA.

Anisodontea (*aniso* - unequal; *odon* - toothed, refers to irregularly toothed leaves) - Woody perennials or shrubs; leaves simple or lobed; flowers solitary or in clusters, epicalyx with 3-5 bracts. S Afr, ± 190 species, mainly Cape.

Anisodontea julii

Straggling shrub up to 2 m. In scrub, often among boulders, on roadsides, 1200-2300 m. Young parts velvety, stems very hairy towards base. **Leaves: 3-7 lobed**, ± 75 mm, coarsely toothed, hairy at first, stalks long. **Flowers:** 2-3 in axils of leaves, ± 40 mm diam, deep pink to purple (Feb-Mar).
Similar species: *A. scabrosa* Pink Mallow; Harigemalva (A) Evergreen shrub, up to 1,8 m; in thicket, grassland, in frost-free coastal areas; leaves 50-75 mm, **3 lobed**, aromatic, sticky hairy; flowers ± 35 mm diam, pale to deep mauve or pink (Aug-Dec). Popular, long flowering garden plant.

Polygala virgata

Polygala virgata

Muraltia lancifolia

Muraltia lancifolia

Impatiens flanaganiae

Impatiens hochstetteri

Anisodontea julii

Anisodontea scabrosa

407

Pavonia (named after José Antonia Pavon, 1754-1840, Spanish botanist, traveller) - Herbs or shrubs; epicalyx of 5 or more bracts close to 5 lobed calyx. Attracts butterflies. Warm countries, ± 240 species, especially in America, 13 in SA.

Pavonia columella Pink Pavonia; indola ebomvu (Z) (*columella* - small pillar)

Robust, herbaceous shrub, 1-2 m. In moist areas, in thicket, on forest margins, E Cape to C Afr. Stems stout, plant hairy. **Leaves:** ± 120 x 150 mm, heart-shaped at base, 3-5 lobed, margins toothed, stalks ± 60 mm. **Flowers: In clusters** on side branches, ± 50 mm diam, white, pale pinkish mauve, epicalyx with 5 narrow bracts, **stalks short,** ± 10 mm (Sep-Feb-Jun). **General:** Potential garden plant.

Hibiscus (Greek name for marsh mallow) - Trees, shrubs or herbs; often with star-shaped hairs; flowers often large, showy, many with dark centres, epicalyx of 5-20 bracts, usually as long as calyx, 5 calyx lobes; fruit surrounded by calyx, splitting along carpel walls. Attracts butterflies, including *Charaxes* species. Trop, subtrop, ± 300 species, ± 59 in SA.

Hibiscus pedunculatus Forest Pink Hibiscus; Pienkhibiskus (A); indola ebomvu (Z)
(*pedunculatus* - stalked)

Slender, straggling, perennial herb, 1-2 m. In light shade, low-lying forest, thicket, E Cape to Moz. Stems, leaves roughly hairy. **Leaves:** 20-80 mm diam, 3 lobed, rounded at tips, margins bluntly toothed, 5-7 veins from base. **Flowers:** Solitary, **drooping,** ± 70 mm diam, pale to deep pink or lilac, epicalyx with 7-8 bracts (Nov-May). **General:** Bark used for twine in hut building and in traditional medicine to treat urinary complaints. Long-flowering garden plant, in semi-shade and sun.

Hibiscus pusillus Dwarf Hibiscus; uguqukile, uvuma (Z) (see p. 286)

VIOLACEAE - Violet Family Herbs or shrubs. Petals 5, unequal, front petals larger, sometimes with spur or pouch. Popular ornamentals Violet and Viola. Cosmop, ± 20 genera, ± 800 species, 3 genera in SA. **Hybanthus** (*hybos* - a hump; *anthos* - a flower) - Herbs. Trop, subtrop, mostly S and C America, ± 100 species, 4 in SA.

Hybanthus enneaspermus Lady's Slipper (*enneaspermus* - 9 seeds)

Perennial herb, trailing or erect, 200-500 mm. In damp grassland, Afr, Asia, Austr. Stems annual. **Leaves:** Alternate, very variable, 10-90 x 10-25 mm, soft, hairy, margins entire or toothed. **Flowers:** 5-20 mm, lilac, pink, **lowest petal pouched at base** (throughout year). **Fruit:** Capsule 6-10 mm. **General:** Attracts butterflies.

BEGONIACEAE - Begonia Family Herbs or shrublets, often succulent. Leaves often with unequal sides. Male and female flowers separate. Fruit dry or fleshy. Popular ornamentals. Trop, mostly Americas, 2 genera, ± 900 species, 1 genus in SA. **Begonia** (named after Michael Begon,1638-1710, French governer of San Domingo, patron of botany).

Begonia dregei Dwarf Wild Begonia; Wildebegonia (A) (named after J F Drège, 1794-1881)

Soft, succulent herb, up to 300 mm. In forest, on rocky cliffs, steep banks. Rare. **Swollen stem base (caudex).** Thick, fleshy, **perennial** stems. **Leaves: Smallish,** ± **50-80 x 20-35 mm,** white spotted when young, **narrow, margins usually lobed and widely toothed,** stalks ± 40-90 mm, green or reddish; juvenile leaves entire or slightly lobed. **Flowers:** ± 30 mm diam, white to pink, male tepals 2, female 5 (Dec-Aug). **Fruit:** 10-20 mm across wings. **General:** Good container and shade plant. (See p. 156)

Begonia homonyma Large-leaved Wild Begonia; Wildebegonia (A); idlula (Z)
(*homonyma* - with the same name)

Soft, succulent herb, up to 1 m. On cliffs in forest, coast to 900 m. Rare. **Swollen stem bases (caudex).** Stems perennial, tinged red. **Leaves:** ± **70-130 x 30-70 mm, margins entire or broadly, shallowly lobed,** young leaves white spotted, stalks 30-50(130) mm. **Flowers:** ± 30 mm diam, white to pink, male tepals 2, female 5 (Dec-Mar). **Fruit:** ± 20 mm across wings. **General:** Used traditionally to treat chest ailments, as protection against poisoning of food, for protective charms. Good container and shade plant. **Similar species:** *B. rudatisii* Pondoland, S KZN; stems shorter, stronger; leaves larger, ± 250 mm, brownish, thinner, lobes sharply angled.

Begonia sonderiana Sonder's Wild Begonia; Wildebegonia (A) (named after O W Sonder,
1812-1881, German apothecary and botanist, co-author with Harvey of 'Flora Capensis')

Soft, succulent herb, up to 1 m. On cliffs, rock falls in forest, rocky outcrops in grassland, 1000-1850 m, Swaz to Zim, Moz. **Tuber.** Annual stems stout, pink to reddish, nodes swollen and rooting. **Leaves:** ± 120-180 x 140-160 mm, margins 5-7 lobed, irregularly toothed, waxy above, veins reddish, stalks ± 150 mm. **Flowers:** ± 30 mm diam, pink or white tinged pink, male tepals (2)4, female 5 (Jan-Mar). **Fruit:** ± 20 x 20-30 mm. **General:** Good container and shade plant. (See p. 156)

Pavonia columella — Lorraine van Hooff

Pavonia columella — Martin von Fintel

Hibiscus pedunculatus — Martin von Fintel

Hibiscus pusillus — Jo Onderstall

Hybanthus enneaspermus — Lorraine van Hooff

Hibiscus pedunculatus — Lorraine van Hooff

Begonia dregei — Geoff Nichols

Begonia homonyma — Martin von Fintel

Begonia sonderiana — Neil Crouch

LYTHRACEAE - Pride-of-India Family Herbs, shrubs or trees. Leaves usually in opposite pairs. Flowers regular. Fruit dry, splitting. Mostly trop, ± 27 genera, ± 600 species, 6 genera in SA. *Nesaea* (*nesos* - island, refers to Mauritius where it grows) - Herbaceous shrublets. Afr, Austr, Madag, India, S America, ± 44 species, ± 28 in SA.

Nesaea radicans Marsh Nesaea (*radicans* - striking root)

Perennial herb, 0,2-0,6(1,2) m. In moist places, E Cape to Moz, Zanzibar. Stems and leaves hairy, stems rooting at nodes especially when aquatic. **Leaves:** Opposite, almost stalkless, 10-55 x 4-25 mm. **Flowers: In compact, rounded inflorescences;** ± 10 mm diam; flowers mauve (Mar-May). **General:** Good garden plant for damp places. **Similar species:** *N. sagittifolia* **Leaves arrowhead-shaped**; small flowers.

MELASTOMATACEAE - Lasiandra/Tibouchina Family Trees, shrubs or herbs. *Dissotis* (for description see p. 466).

Dissotis canescens Pink Marsh Dissotis, Pink Wild Tibouchina; sichobochobo (Sw); imfeyenkala, imfeyesele, uhlazifukwe oluncane (Z) (*canescens* - greyish white hairs)

Shrub up to 1,5 m. **In marshy areas**, E Cape to Trop Afr. Branches square, reddish brown. **Leaves:** 14-80 x 3-30 mm, velvety whitish beneath, 3-5 veins from base. **Flowers:** In branched inflorescences; flowers **35-45 mm diam, brilliant magenta,** 5 petals, calyx velvety red-brown, scarlet within (Nov-May). **General:** Reportedly eaten in times of famine. Used traditionally to treat dysentery and hangovers. A beautiful shrub for damp spots or as a container plant. Grown from seed.

Dissotis phaeotricha Dwarf Dissotis; sichobochobo (Sw) (*phaeotricha* - reddish brown bristles)

Perennial herb up to 600 mm. On edge of marshes, SA to Trop Afr. Stems usually unbranched, reddish with long, pale hairs. **Leaves:** 10-60 x 5-20 mm, 3-5 veins from base, densely hairy. **Flowers: In dense terminal inflorescences, amongst leaves;** flowers 20-30 mm diam, **4 petals**, mauve to pink, calyx densely bristly (Oct-May). **Similar species:** *D. debilis* Annual; less hairy; flowers in small, dense, bristly clusters.

ONAGRACEAE - Evening Primrose Family Perennial or annual herbs (for description see p. 160). *Epilobium* (*epi* - upon; *lobos* - pod, flowers seem to grow on seed pod) - Perennial herbs; fruit a capsule, splitting lengthwise, seeds with terminal tuft of hairs. Cosmop, except trop, ± 450 species, 5 in SA.

Epilobium hirsutum Salt of the Shepherds; mosika-nokana, noha (SS); icikiciki, itswayi lentaba (Z) (*hirsutum* - rough hairy)

Erect, perennial herb, up to 2 m. In moist grassland, marshy areas. Stems covered in **dense whitish hairs**. **Leaves:** Opposite, alternate towards ends of stems, **clasping at base**, margins coarsely toothed. **Flowers:** Petals ± 15 mm, purplish pink, **tips deeply notched** (summer). **Fruit:** Capsule 30-80 mm, densely hairy. **General:** Herdsmen lick the plant for the salty taste (*itswayi lentaba* (Z) - salt of the mountain). Used in traditional medicine to cure warts and for bathing sick babies.

Oenothera (*oinos* - wine, *thera* - imbibing) - Annual, biennial or perennial herbs; flowers usually open in evening, close before midday. Popular ornamentals. N and S America, naturalised in Old World, ± 110 species, 15 in SA.

★ Oenothera rosea Rose Evening Primrose; Pienkaandblom, Rooskleurige Nagblom (A) (*rosea* - rose coloured)

Much branched perennial or annual herb, 200-500 mm. In damp, disturbed areas, naturalised in SA (from S America). Leaves 20-50 mm, stalks 4-30 mm. Flowers nodding before opening, ± 20 mm diam, bright pink, open near sunrise (Sep-Feb). Fruit a club-shaped capsule, ± 20 x 4 mm, narrowly winged.

ERICACEAE - Erica/Heath Family Large or small shrubs, often on acid soils. Leaves usually small, firm, in whorls. Flowers with 4-5 petals, ± united into tube. Rhododendrons, Azaleas and Heather (*Erica*) cultivated as ornamentals, Blueberries and Cranberries (*Vaccinium*) for fruit. Cosmop, ± 107 genera, ± 3400 species, 20 genera in SA. *Erica* (*ereiko* - to rend, refers to the reputed ability of some species to break down gallstones, according to the ancient Greeks) - Leaves in whorls, margins recurved; flowers in terminal inflorescences or clustered in upper leaf axils. Hardy, attractive garden plants and cut-flowers. Mainly Afr, Europe, ± 650 species, 600 in SA, mainly in SW Cape.

Erica aestiva (*aestiva* - flowering in summer)

Much branched, slender shrublet, up to 600 mm, mat forming. In grassland, on rock sheets, high mountains, 1800-2750 m. **Leaves:** 2-4 mm, fine, on short side shoots, spreading to erect, overlapping. **Flowers:** In masses, 3 mm, purple to pink, bell-shaped, **narrowing to mouth, sticky**, style protruding (Jan-Aug).

410

Nesaea radicans — Trevor Coleman

Dissotis canescens — Martin von Fintel

Dissotis canescens — Martin von Fintel

Dissotis debilis — Wayne Matthews

Dissotis phaeotricha — Nolly Zaloumis

Epilobium hirsutum — Lal Greene

★ *Oenothera rosea* — Lal Greene

Erica aestiva — Martin von Fintel

Erica aestiva — Trevor Coleman

411

Erica algida lekhapu-le-lenye-nyane, sehalahala (SS) *(algida* - cold loving, refers to the habitat of the plants)

Dwarf shrub, up to 300 mm. On grassy slopes, valley bottoms, 1800-3000 m. Stems erect, downy. **Leaves:** Clustered, ± 5 mm, needlelike. **Flowers:** Pale pink to whitish, downy (Oct-Feb). **General:** Grey-brown when dry. Favoured fuel plant.

Erica alopecurus Foxtail Erica; chalbeke-e-nyenyane, chesa-litelu, molomo-oa-lekolu-kotoane (SS) *(alopex* - refers to the leafy branches that resemble a fox's tail)

Compact, rounded dwarf shrub, up to 300 mm. In open grassland, damp grassy streambanks, marshy places, up to 3000 m. **Leaves:** In 3s, erect, incurving, midrib visible beneath. **Flowers:** Massed in **dense, terminal, cylindrical inflorescences** (Jan-Jul). **General:** Used as fuel.

Erica aspalathifolia *(aspalathifolia* - leaves like *Aspalathus)*

Slender, semi-erect shrublet, 300-450 mm. In shrubby grassland. **Leaves:** In clusters of 3-4, crowded, very narrow, sharp tipped, flattish, with long white hairs. **Flowers:** In clusters of 3-4, crowded on short branchlets forming dense inflorescences ± 180 x 12 mm, white, segments rounded (Nov-Jul).

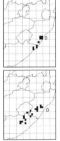

Erica cooperi (named after Thomas Cooper, 1815-1913, English plant collector and cultivator who came to SA in 1859)

Stout, rigid, much branched shrub, up to 1 m. In riverside grassland, 1800 m. Branches rough with spreading hairs. **Leaves:** In 4s, mostly spreading, rough hairy, paler beneath. **Flowers:** In 4 flowered inflorescences; white to pale pink, hairy, lobes spreading (Jan-Sep).

Erica cubica *(cubica* - cubic, refers to the boxlike shape of the lower half of the flowers)

Erect shrublet, up to 450 mm. On damp grassy flats. Branches straight or spreading. **Leaves:** In 4s or scattered, very variable size, crowded, strongly incurved or longer and straighter. **Flowers:** In dense clusters at ends of branches, pink (throughout year).

Erica schlechteri (named after Rudolph Schlechter, 1872-1925 who came to the Cape from Berlin in 1893 as gardener to H M Arderne in Cape Town. Collected plants extensively between 1891 and 1897 before returning to Germany to attend university)

Shrub up to 1 m, often in conspicuous stands. On high mountain slopes and in valleys, near streams, 1500-2600 m. **Leaves:** In 4s, erect to spreading, overlapping, narrow, blunt, grooved, ± 5 mm. **Flowers:** In terminal clusters of 3-4, pink or whitish, 5-7 mm, sticky (Nov-Jun). **General:** Sometimes found growing with *E. algida.*

Erica algida

Martin von Fintel

Erica alopecurus

Martin von Fintel

Erica aspalathifolia

Tony Abbott

Erica cooperi

Auriol Batten

Erica cubica

Tony Abbott

Erica schlecteri

Dolf Schumann

413

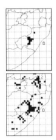

Erica straussiana (named after Berlin gardener Obergartner Strauss)
Spreading, leafy shrub up to 1 m, often in conspicuous stands. On rocky grass slopes and valley bottoms, 1600-2500 m. **Flowers:** Pink, ± 6 mm, sepals as long or longer (almost throughout year). **General:** Sometimes found growing with *E. algida*.

***Erica woodii* Pink Heath; Pienkheide (A)** (named after John Medley Wood, 1827-1915, botanist, founder of Natal Herbarium, who published widely on flora of KZN)
Spreading shrublet, up to 600 mm. On rocky hills, widespread, 1000-2500 m. Branches glandular hairy. **Leaves:** Crowded on short side branches. **Flowers:** Massed, in axils, 2 mm, white, pale pink or red, lobes straight, sepals dark red, stigma swollen, stalks dark red (Jan-Jul). **Similar species:** *E. drakensbergensis* (see p. 162).

GENTIANACEAE - Gentian Family Herbs,sometimes aquatic. Leaves mostly opposite or basal. Flowers in loose or compact inflorescence or solitary, 4-5 petal lobes, often twisted in bud, 4-5 stamens, ovary superior, calyx 4-5 lobed. Fruit usually dry, splitting lengthwise. Cultivated as ornamentals. Cosmop, especially temp, subtrop, ± 78 genera, ± 1225 species, 9 genera in SA.

Chironia (named after Chiron, a centaur, who studied medicine, astronomy, music and arts) - Annual and perennial herbs; leaves opposite, usually stalkless; flowers solitary or in loose inflorescences, anthers sometimes spirally twisted; fruit a capsule, dry or berrylike. Afr, Madag, ± 30 species, ± 15 in SA.

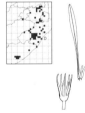

***Chironia baccifera* Wild Gentian, Christmas Berry; Agdaegeneesbos, Bitterbos, Perdebossie (A)** (*baccifera* - bearing berries)
Much branched shrublet, up to 0,5(1) m. In dry sandy soils, mostly coastal. Stems rigid, angled or narrowly winged. **Leaves:** 5-20 x 1-2 mm, thin or slightly fleshy, semi-clasping at base, tips hooked. **Flowers:** Solitary, terminal, massed, close at night to re-open; flowers ± 20 mm diam, magenta, tube ± 15 mm, anthers yellow, **style simple** (Feb-Aug). **Fruit:** Berry, red when ripe, turning black, splitting irregularly. **General:** Fruit eaten by birds. Used in traditional medicine as a blood purifier, purgative, to treat skin complaints, diarrhoea and as a leprosy remedy. Poisonous to sheep. A well known garden plant, easily grown from seed. (See p. 70)

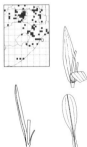

***Chironia krebsii* Kreb's Chironia/Gentian; khomo-ea-sepha-tla, lehlapahali, mamorulane, mosia (SS); umanqunduswazi, umbangwangwa (Z)** (named after Georg Krebs, 1792-1844, apothecary and naturalist, collector, visited SA in 1817)
Herb, 400-700 mm. In marshy ground, up to 2450 m. **Creeping rhizome.** Stems simple, erect. **Leaves:** Long, **clustered at base,** 90-300 x 6-17 mm; stem leaves smaller. **Flowers:** In **narrow, terminal clusters,** stalks erect, 10-30 mm; flowers ± 26 mm diam, lobes pointed, tube 10-20 mm, deep pink (white), **stigma 2 lobed** (Oct-Jan). **Fruit:** Oval, pointed, ± 10 mm. **General:** Used in traditional medicine to treat colic and diarrhoea in children, uneasiness in pregnant women.

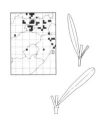

***Chironia palustris* Marsh Chironia, Cerise Stars; Bitterwortel (A); khomo-ea-sepha-tla, lehlapahali, lepshetlane, mosia, thatjane (SS)** (*palustris* - swamp loving)
Erect herb, 300-700 mm, in clumps. In marshy areas, near rivers, E Cape to Zim, Zam. Stems branched above, die back in winter. **Leaves:** In **basal rosette** (sometimes not persisting), broad at base, slightly tapering to tip, sometimes blue-green, slightly succulent or not, depending on moisture in ground. **Flowers:** In terminal, **well spaced** inflorescences; flowers broad, ± 25 mm diam, pale to **bright rose pink,** tube 20-30 mm, anthers yellow, slightly twisted after pollination, style 2 lobed, calyx as long as or shorter than flower tube, **calyx lobes short, sticky, triangular** (Oct-Mar). **General:** Ants attracted to sticky calyx. Used in traditional medicine to treat colic and diarrhoea, reputed to be poisonous to animals. Lovely, hardy, garden plant. Three subspecies described, differing in persistence and colour of leaves, size of flowers, extent to which anthers twist.

***Chironia purpurascens* Chironia** (*purpurascens* - purplish)
Slender biennial or perennial, 200-800 mm, often in large colonies. In damp areas, SA to Zim. Stems angled, sometimes narrowly winged. **Leaves:** Basal, not always persistent, blue-green, stem leaves widely spaced. **Flowers:** In branched inflorescences; flowers ± 30 mm diam, tube ± 25 mm, deep magenta-pink, **anthers strongly twisted,** calyx longer than flower tube, **calyx lobes longer than calyx tube, tapering to long fine points** (Nov-Dec). **General:** Lovely garden plant, grown from seed. Two subspecies, differing in size of plant, flower and stalk length.

Erica straussiana — Trevor Coleman

Erica woodii — Martin von Fintel

Chironia krebsii — Martin von Fintel

Chironia baccifera — Trevor Coleman

Chironia baccifera — Trevor Coleman

Chironia palustris — Wayne Mathews

Chironia palustris — Van Wyk & Malan

Chironia palustris — Martin von Fintel

Chironia purpurascens — Darrel Plowes

Chironia purpurascens — Martin von Fintel

415

APOCYNACEAE - Impala Lily Family Trees, shrubs, woody climbers, sometimes succulent, usually with milky latex. Flowers conspicuous, often scented, parts in 5s, usually twisted in bud. Fruits often fleshy, sometimes 2 lobed, seeds often with tufts of hairs. Well known ornamentals, Oleander, Periwinkle, Allamanda, Frangipani, Mandevilla, Dipladenia. A number of SA genera have been investigated for poisonous or medicinal properties. Mostly trop, ± 165 genera, ± 1900 species, 20 genera in SA.

Catharanthus (*katharos* - pure; *anthos* - flower) - From India, 1 species a widespread weed, naturalised in SA.

★ ***Catharanthus roseus*** [= *Vinca rosea*] **Periwinkle, Vinca; ikhwinini, isishushlungu (Z)**
Herb, up to 1 m. In disturbed areas. **Flowers pink or white**, ± 40 mm diam. Widely used in traditional medicine to treat diabetes, rheumatism and insect bites, warts and gonorrhoea. Extracts used to treat various forms of cancer.

Adenium (*adenium* - a glandular enlargement) - Succulent shrubs; stems swollen; leaves fleshy; petal lobes showy, overlapping, with small scales forming pockets in throat. Afr, Arabia ± 12 species, 4 in SA.

Adenium multiflorum [= *A. obesum* var. *multiflorum*] **Impala Lily, Sabi Star; Impalalelie (A); sisila-semphala (Sw); isigubengubu (Z)** (*multiflorum* - many flowered)
Succulent shrub, 0,6-1,5(3) m. In dry woodland, KZN to Trop Afr. Rootstock large, swollen. Branches swollen, bark smooth, grey. **Leaves:** 70-120 x 30-80 mm, slightly succulent, shiny grey-green, after flowers. **Flowers:** ± 50 mm diam, lobes white with dark pink margins, tube ± 30 x 16-24 mm, velvety pinkish brown (May-Sep). **Fruit:** 2 lobed pods, ± 150 x 12 mm, velvety. **General:** Browsed by game. Lovely garden or container plant in frost-free areas. **Similar species:**
A . swazicum Summer Impala Lily; sisila-semphala (Sw) Up to 450 mm; in bushveld, N KZN to Mpum, S Moz; leaves ± 130 x 30 mm, with flowers; flowers ± 60 mm diam, tube ± 50 mm, pink to deep reddish purple throughout (Dec-May).

ASCLEPIADACEAE - Milkweed/Butterflyweed Family Herbs, shrubs, vines, epiphytes or succulents (shrublike trees), with milky latex. Leaves usually opposite, sometimes whorled, or absent. Flowers regular, bisexual, petal lobes 5, free or fused, sometimes with a corona, stamens 5, forming a column with simple to complex fleshy basal corona in 1(2)3 whorls, pollen in waxy masses (pollinia), attached in pairs, ovary superior. Fruit solitary or paired follicles. Sometimes placed with Apocynaceae which it resembles vegetatively and florally (not sexually). Also similar to Periplocaceae, differing in pollination mechanism. Cosmop, ± 253 genera, ± 2000 species, 63 genera in SA.

Asclepias (named after the Greek doctor *Aesculapius* who was immortalised in ancient mythology as a god of medicine) - Perennial herbs with milky latex; leaves opposite, entire; flowers divided to base, lobe margins fringed with hairs, corona lobes with a central cavity; fruits solitary (paired), spindlelike. The genus is undergoing revision at present and will be restricted to the New World. SA species, ± 52, will soon be transferred to other genera.

Asclepias adscendens **Pompom Cartwheels** (*adscendens* - ascending)
Herb 100-200 mm. In grassland, 100-1600 m, E Cape to NW Prov, Mpum. Annual stems, **reclining at first, tips erect, usually much branched, forking from near base. Leaves:** 13-45 x 4-14 mm, leathery, margins ridged, veins prominent below, harshly hairy. **Flowers: 12-20 in round, solitary, terminal inflorescences**, stems 13-65 mm; flowers reflexed, lobes 4-5 x 3-4 mm, **corona lobes compressed sideways, square** (Oct-Feb), scented towards evening. **Fruit:** 60 x 20 mm, tip curved to a narrow beak, covered in erect long bristles. **General:** Leaves edible.

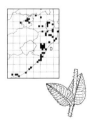

Asclepias albens [=*A. affinis*] **Cartwheels; idoyi, ishongwe, umadoye (Z)** (*albens* - whitened)
Herb, 200-500 mm. In annually burnt grasslands, rocky areas, coast to 1800 m, E Cape to N Prov. **3-5 stems, unbranched or forking from base, reclining, tips erect. Leaves:** 20-75 x 12-18 mm, leathery, veins prominent beneath, harshly hairy. **Flowers: 15-40 in solitary, terminal inflorescences**, 35-75 mm diam, **stems** 12-100 mm; flower lobes reflexed, tips turned up, ± 8 x 4 mm, **corona lobes square** (Oct-Mar), sweetly scented. **Fruit:** ± 50 mm, with long, bumpy, fleshy ridges, tip beaked. **General:** Leaves cooked as a spinach (*imifino*). **Similar species:** *A. vicaria* (See p. 172)

Asclepias cucullata [= *Trachycalymma cucullatum*] **Hooded Meadow-star; udambisa, udelunina (Z)** (*cucullatus* - hooded, refers to corona lobes)
Herb, 170-350 mm. In open, usually burnt grassland, 1000-2400 m. Annual stems 1(3), erect to reclining, tips erect. **Leaves:** ± erect, 7-10 x **0,3-4 mm**, margins rolled under, midrib prominent below, covered in short, harsh hairs. **Flowers: In 4s in erect inflorescences**, stems 20-80 mm; flowers starlike, lobes speading with tips turned up, 6-7,5 x 3-5 mm, corona lobes helmet-shaped (Sep-Dec, throughout year). **General:** Visited by beetles, bugs and ants. Hybridises with *A. stellifera, A. brevipes.*

Asclepias flexuosa **umampofu (Z)** (see under *A. multicaulis* p. 170)

★ *Catharanthus roseus*

Geoff Nichols

Adenium swazicum

Jo Onderstall

Adenium multiflorum

Tom de Waal

Asclepias adscendens

Trevor Coleman

Asclepias adscendens

Van Wyk & Malan

Asclepias flexuosa

Pam Cooke

Asclepias cucullata

Tom de Waal

Asclepias albens

Martin von Fintel

Asclepias cucullata

Martin von Fintel

417

Asclepias navicularis Pouched Turret-flower *(navicularis - boat, refers to pouched corona lobes)*

Herb, 105-290 mm. In open grassland on sandy soils, flowering when grass still short, 20-900 m. Stems annual, 2-6, **reclining**, tips erect, a few harsh hairs. **Leaves:** Spreading to ± erect, 8-85 x 1-5 mm, hairless or sparse short, harsh hairs, stalks 0-5 mm. **Flowers:** 4-8, in erect, **solitary, terminal inflorescences**, stems 9-30 mm; flowers held on same level, **lobes spreading**, tips turned up, 8-11 x 3-5 mm, **corona lobes with sinus blocked at upper end, anther wing with distinct notch along its length** (Nov-Feb), pleasant, ± heady scent at sunset. **Fruit:** 85 x 6,5 mm, tip beaked, streaked with darker markings. **Similar species:** *A. brevicuspis* (see p. 550).

Asclepias stellifera Common Meadow-star; mohlatsisa, moholantja (SS) *(stella - star)*

Herb, 120-290 mm. In open grassland, stony ground, 1000-2100 m, E Cape to Bots. Annual stems spreading-erect. **Leaves:** 10-105 x 0,5-2 mm, margins rolled under, covered in short, harsh hairs. **Flowers:** In 4s at **nodes and terminally**; flowers held at same level, **starlike, large**, lobes reflexed, tips turned up, **4,5-7 x 3-4 mm**, corona lobes **slipper-shaped** (Sep-Apr). **Fruit:** Erect, narrow, straight to sickle-shaped, 60-100 x 5-12 mm, tip narrowly beaked. **General:** Natural hybrids with *A. meyeriana* or *A. brevipes* are known. **Similar species:** *A. brevipes* (see p. 550).

Xysmalobium sp. nov. Red-flowered Cartwheel

Herb, 150-210 mm. In open grasslands, on hilltops, 600-2100 m, KZN endemic. Stems reclining, tips erect. **Leaves:** 20-36 x 12-22 mm, leathery, softly, sparsely hairy, veins prominent beneath. **Flowers:** ± 18, in erect, round, inflorescences, ± 35 mm diam, stems 35-42 mm; flower **lobes mauvish red**, spreading-erect, ± 8 x 3 mm, **corona lobes simple, solid, erect at base, tip reflexed outwards** (Dec).

Pergularia *(pergula - trellis work, refers to the climbing pattern of these plants)* - Perennial, herbaceous climbers; milky latex; leaves heart-shaped; flowers hairy, lobes spreading. Trop, subtrop Afr, Madag, Arabia, India, 5 species, 1 in SA.

Pergularia daemia Trellis Vine; intungu (Z)

Stems twining up to 4(9) m. On forest margins, up to 1000 m, E Cape to Trop Afr, Asia. Stems usually downy. **Leaves:** 25-150 x 30-127 mm, stalks 18-90 mm. **Flowers:** 20-30, **hanging**, inflorescence elongating with age, **stems 50-160 mm**; flowers 10-18 mm diam, dusty pink/mauve (white), lobes spreading, **upper surface with long white woolly hairs along margins, open at night**, closed in daylight (all year), faintly scented. **Fruit:** Erect, 50-75 x 10-20 mm, tapering to short, curved tip, ± covered in soft recurved bristles. **General:** Grown in Europe since 1777. Eaten as a spinach. Used in traditional medicine to treat blood pressure. Var. *daemia*, **stems hairy**; leaves 20-120 mm. Var. *leiocarpa*, **stems hairless**; leaves 15-60 mm.

Tenaris *(teina - to stretch, refers to flower lobes)* - Perennial herbs; stem tuber roundish; stems grasslike; flowers in 2s (up to 7), lobes long, narrow or spoon-shaped. Included in *Brachystelma* by some authors. SA to Kenya, 5 species, 4 in SA.

Tenaris rubella Pink Tenaris *(rubellus - reddish)*

Herb, 150-790 mm. In open grassland, savanna, up to 1800 m, S Afr and E Afr, but nowhere in between. Stems annual, thin, wiry, ± unbranched below inflorescence, **flowering part of stem leafless. Leaves:** Recurved, 19-75 x **1-3,4 mm, margin rolled under. Flowers:** In 1-4 inflorescences, stems 12-100 mm, at upper nodes, in pairs or whorled; flowers **pink, tube shallow**, lobes spreading, **narrow, spoon-shaped**, 8-16 x 1-3 mm, ± recurved, covered in minute bumps beneath, **stalks 4-18 mm** (Oct-Feb). **Fruit:** Erect, spindle-shaped, spreading, smooth. **Similar species:** *T. chlorantha* Up to 460 mm; in rocky areas, 1500-1850 m, KZN to Mpum; leaves 50-75 mm; 3-7 flowers clustered at upper nodes, green to browny purple, lobes slender, long, 5-7 mm, margins recurved, stalks 0-9 mm. (For photograph see p. 554)

CONVOLVULACEAE - Morning Glory Family Herbs, shrubs, stems trailing or twining (for description see p. 176). **Astripomoea** *(astron - star, plus Ipomoea, refers to star-shaped hairs)* - Herbs or subshrubs. Afr, ± 12 species, 3 in SA.

Astripomoea malvacea Common Star-ipomoea *(malvacea - resembles a type of mallow)*

Perennial herb, stems 0,6-2 m. In grassland, woodland, KZN to W Trop Afr, Ethiopia. Rootstock woody. Stems annual, erect or reclining, densely hairy. Very variable. **Leaves:** 30-80(120) x 20-50(80) mm, margins entire, sparsely hairy above, matted white hairy beneath. **Flowers:** Leafy inflorescences, stems slender, ± 120 mm; flowers ± 50 mm diam, magenta, pink, calyx lobes 6-8 mm (Sep-Jan). **Fruit:** Round to oval, 6-12 x 6-9 mm. **General:** Used in traditional medicine.

Asclepias navicularis — Tony Abbott

Asclepias stellifera — Lal Greene

Xysmalobium sp. nov. — Lal Greene

Xysmalobium sp. nov. — Lal Greene

Pergularia daemia — Martin von Fintel

Tenaris rubella — Rosemary Williams

Pergularia daemia — Martin von Fintel

Pergularia daemia — C J Ward

Tenaris rubella — Tony Abbott

Astripomoea malvacea — Darrel Plowes

419

Ipomoea (*ips* - worm; *homoios* - like, refers to the creeping habit) - Mostly twiners; leaves often heart-shaped at base, sometimes lobed; flowers showy, broadly funnel-shaped. Cosmop in trop, temp regions, ± 400 species, ± 50 in SA.

Ipomoea aquatica Water Ipomoea (*aquatica* - found in water)

Perennial herb, up to 500 mm. In moist, marshy areas, circumtrop. **No tubers.** Stems hollow to spongy, ± 3 m, rooting at nodes, trailing on moist soil or floating on water. **Leaves:** Variable, 30-150 x 10-90 mm, margins entire or toothed, stalks thick, 30-200 mm. **Flowers:** ± 50 mm, tube 30-50 mm, pink to mauve with purple centre (white) (May-Oct). **General:** Leaves cooked as a pot herb, cultivated for food and ornament. **Similar species:** ★ *I. batatas* Sweet Potato Cultivated for its tubers.

Ipomoea bolusiana Narrow-leaved Pink Ipomoea; seakhoe (SS) (named after Harry Bolus, 1834-1911, founder of the Bolus Herbarium at UCT, author of several books on orchids)

Perennial herb, up to 300 mm. In grassland, SA to Trop Afr. Tuberous rootstock. Stems erect or prostrate, very short or ± 3 m. **Leaves:** 3 lobed, ± 60 x 3 mm, or simple, 40-100 x 2-4 mm, **stalks** ± 10 mm. **Flowers: Solitary, held erect,** ± 40 mm diam, tube ± 40 mm, pink to mauve, calyx ± 10 mm (Sep-Mar). **General:** Raw roots chewed by shepherds in Lesotho. **Similar species:** *I. simplex* (see p. 178).

Ipomoea cairica Common Ipomoea; ihlambe, ijalamu, intana, umaholwana (Z)
(*cairica* - from Cairo)

Slender, vigorous twiner. In riverine and disturbed areas, SA to Trop Afr. **Leaves:** 30-100 mm diam, deeply dissected, 5-7 lobes, grey beneath, **pseudostipules leaflike. Flowers:** 40-60 mm diam, deep mauve, close mid-afternoon (blooms throughout year). **Fruit:** Capsules 8-12 mm diam. **General:** Monkeys eat shoots, flowers, fruits. Used in traditional medicine to treat rashes and for purification rites after a funeral. Often cultivated. Can become a weed, suffocating vegetation with its luxuriant growth.

Ipomoea crassipes Leafy-flowered Ipomoea; Wildewinde (A); maime, mothokhoana, sekutle, seletjane-se-setona (SS); ubhoqo, uvimbukhalo (Z) (*crassipes* - thick stem)

Trailing perennial, stems up to 1 m. In grassland, disturbed areas, E Cape to Bots, E Afr. Tuberous roots. **All parts softly hairy. Leaves:** Very variable, 15-80 x 8-30 mm, margins entire, purplish. **Flowers:** 35-60 mm diam, tube 30-45 mm, magenta, pale mauve or creamy white with dark purple centre, **calyx lobes leaflike,** outer, ± 20 x 11 mm, stems slender, ± 40 mm, **leaflike bracts at middle** (Sep-May). **Fruit:** Oval capsule ± 10 mm diam. **General:** Roots eaten raw. Used in traditional medicine to treat dysentery, sores, hiccups and as charms against lightning. (See p. 178)

Ipomoea ficifolia Fig-leaved Ipomoea; ikhambilesihlungu, umkhokha wehlathi (Z)
(*ficifolia* - leaves like *Ficus*)

Perennial twiner. In grassland, scrub, on forest margins, E Cape to E Afr. Stems **hairy. Leaves:** 20-90 x 15-80 mm, thin, **white hairy beneath when young,** yellow hairs on veins. **Flowers:** 40-60 mm diam, tube 40-60 mm, magenta-pink, calyx lobes equal, ± 15 mm (Sep-May). **General:** Browsed by bushbuck. Used in traditional medicine for stomach disorders and to treat snakebite. Cultivated in Europe.

Ipomoea magnusiana Small Pink Ipomoea (*magnus* - great)

Slender twiner or prostrate herb, stems hairy, up to 2 m. In grassland, woodland, KZN to Zim. **Leaves: Blade deeply divided into 3-7 lobes,** 60-110 mm, pale green, thinly hairy above, **white woolly beneath,** veins yellow hairy. **Flowers: Small,** 12-25 mm diam, tube ± 25 mm, baby pink, close at midday, calyx lobes narrow, tapering to slender point, ± 15 mm (Nov-May). **General:** Grown from seed.

Ipomoea mauritiana [= I. digitata] Large Forest Ipomoea, Natal Cotton Plant; Garingtou (A)
(*mauritiana* - from Mauritius)

Robust, deciduous climber, up to 20 m. In riverine and swamp forest, KZN to E Afr. Tuberous root. Stems branched, becoming woody towards base. **Leaves: Large, round to heart-shaped or deeply dissected into 5-7 lobes,** 60-140 x 60-150 mm, veins raised beneath, stalks 30-100 mm. **Flowers:** In clusters, stems 30-100 mm; flowers 60-90 mm diam, tube 50-80 mm, pinkish mauve with deep mauve centre, close early afternoon, calyx 6-11 mm (Jan-Apr). **Fruit:** Capsule, 8-10 x 12-14 mm, seeds covered in white wool. **General:** Visited by large ants and flies. Attractive climber, easily grown from seed.

Ipomoea aquatica

Darrel Plowes

Ipomoea bolusiana

Martin von Fintel

Ipomoea cairica

Wally Menne

Ipomoea crassipes

Darrel Plowes

Ipomoea ficifolia

Tom de Waal

Ipomoea magnusiana

Martin von Fintel

Ipomoea crassipes

Lal Greene

Ipomoea magnusiana

Tony Abbott

Ipomoea mauritiana

Trevor Coleman

421

Ipomoea pellita Grassland Ipomoea; ubhoqo (Z) *(pellita - skin, filmlike)*

Perennial, prostrate creeper, stems up to 2 m. On roadsides, in grassland, woodland. Rootstock thick. Stems covered in bristly hairs. **Leaves:** 40-100 x 20-65 mm, margins wavy, **densely covered in golden yellow bristly hairs,** less or absent in mature leaves. **Flowers:** In clusters; 40-70 mm diam, deep magenta, calyx lobes 18-25 mm, **narrow, tapering to point, bracts very narrow,** 12-25 mm (Nov-Mar). **Fruit: 4 lobed capsule,** 12-15 mm diam, splits open. **General:** Tuberous root eaten in time of famine. Used as love charms and protective charms against lightning.
Similar species: *Turbina oblongata* E Cape to Moz; 1-2 flowers, not so bristly, bracts and sepals broad at base, tapering to tip, ± 25 mm; fruit leathery, not splitting open.

Ipomoea pes-caprae Dune Morning Glory; Strandpatat (A); isende lengulube, bulili bengulube (Z) *(pes-caprae - foot of goat)*

Perennial trailing herb, 5-30 m. **On sandy beaches,** Cape to E Afr, circumtrop. Rootstock thick, woody. Stems stout, firm, often hollow, rooting at nodes. **Leaves: Held erect,** 30-100 mm, smooth, leathery, appearing 2 lobed, stalks ± 120 mm. **Flowers:** Solitary or in small clusters, stems stout, 30-160 mm; flowers ± 60 mm diam, tube 30-50 mm, pink, magenta with darker centre (Dec-Mar). **Fruit:** Capsules 12-15 mm. **General:** Flowers visited by bees. Easily propagated from cuttings.

Ipomoea sinensis umdzandzabuka (Sw); ijalambu (Z)

Annual, prostrate to twining herb. In woodland, disturbed places. Thinly hairy. **Leaves:** ± 40 x 20 mm, thin, stalks ± 20 mm. **Flowers:** Solitary or in small clusters, stems slender, ± 50 mm; flowers ± 25 mm diam, pale mauve or pink, deep magenta in centre, calyx ± 14 mm, shaggy hairy (Jan-Apr). **General:** Considered a weed in some areas.

BORAGINACEAE - Forget-me-not/Borage Family Herbs, shrubs or trees, often roughly hairy. Leaves mostly alternate. Flowers often in 1 sided inflorescences, often coiled. Fruit fleshy or dry. Grown as ornamentals, including herbs Borage and Comfrey. Widely distributed, ± 130 genera, ± 2300 species, 17 genera in SA.

Heliotropium *(helios - sun; tropos - turn)* - Herbs, shrublets; leaves alternate; inflorescence solitary or forked into 2 elongated spikes, coiled at tip, flowers on 1 side. Attracts butterflies. Trop, temp regions, ± 150 species, ± 19 in SA.

★ **Heliotropium amplexicaule** Blue Heliotrope *(amplexicaule - stem clasping)*

Low-growing herb, in disturbed areas. Stems long, trailing. Leaves ± 50 x 10 mm, margins toothed, veins hairy. Flowers mauve, yellow (Dec-Mar). Visited by honey-bees, wasps, flies, moths and butterflies (Pieridae, Lycaenidae). A garden escape.

VERBENACEAE - Verbena/Teak Family Herbs, shrubs, trees. Stems often 4 angled. Leaves opposite or clustered. Flowers regular or 2 lipped. Fruit often slightly fleshy, sometimes dry. Economically important for teak timber and for a number of ornamentals such as *Clerodendrum, Duranta, Holmskioldia, Lantana, Petrea* and *Verbena.* Mostly trop, ± 1 000 species, ± 9 genera in SA.

Lantana (Italian dialect name for *Viburnum* which has similar leaves) - Aromatic shrubs; usually roughly hairy; leaves in pairs or 3s; flowers in dense round clusters; fruit slightly fleshy, 2 lobed. Mostly trop Americas, ± 150 species, ± 6 in SA.

★ **Lantana camara** Common Lantana, Birds' Brandy, Tickberry; Gewone Lantana (A); ubutywala bentaka (X); ubukhwebezane (Z) *(camara - vaulted chamber)*

Scrambling shrub, up to 2 m. In disturbed areas, on forest margins, noxious weed (from C and S America). Stems with short stiff hairs, recurved prickles. Leaves rough, foul smelling when crushed. Flowers pink, red, orange, yellow, white (throughout year). Fruits fleshy, purplish black. Introduced as an ornamental. **Invasive weed.** Poisonous to cattle. Young stems browsed by bushbuck. Flowers visited by bees and butterflies; fruits eaten by birds and monkeys, visited by fruit moths and flies.

Lantana rugosa Birds' Brandy, Wild Grassland Lantana; Voëlbrandewyn (A); mabele-mabutsoa-pele, molutoane (SS); bukhwebeletane, inkobe (Sw); utyani-ben-taka, utywalabentaka (X); impema, ubukhwebezane, ubungungundwane, ugugu-vama, umkhukhuthwane, utshwala benyoni (Z) *(rugosa - wrinkled)*

Much branched, aromatic shrub, up to 1(1,8) m. In thicket, woodland, SA to Trop Afr. **Stems and leaves roughish. Leaves:** ± 35 x 20 mm, veins protrude beneath, margins toothed. **Flowers:** In dense, small round inflorescences, stems ± 40 mm; flowers 6-12 mm, pink to purple (Sep-May). **Fruit:** Clustered within bracts, juicy, purple. **General:** Fruits eaten by people, monkeys, birds. Flowers attract butterflies. Used in traditional medicine to treat abdominal complaints in children, sore eyes, coughs, sprains and rheumatism. Burnt in fields to hasten ripening of grain.

Darrel Plowes

Ipomoea pellita

Martin von Fintel

Ipomoea pes-caprae

Martin von Fintel

Ipomoea sinensis

Ipomoea sinensis

Tony Abbott

Heliotropium amplexicaule marked with ★

Lawrence Peacock

★ *Heliotropium amplexicaule*

Lal Greene

★ *Heliotropium amplexicaule*

Darrel Plowes

Turbina oblongata

Lal Greene

★ *Lantana camara*

Trevor Coleman

Lantana rugosa

423

Phyla (*phylum* - a division; or misspelling of *phyllon* - a leaf) - Trop and warm regions, ± 11 species, 1 introduced to SA.

★ *Phyla nodiflora* Lawn Daisy (*nodiflora* - conelike flowers)

Prostrate, creeping herb. On floodplains, rocky riverbeds. Leaves ± 30 x 12 mm, margins sharply toothed in upper half. Flowers in dense inflorescences ± 14 x 7 mm, flowers tiny, mauve to white (Oct-Mar). Good groundcover for exposed places.

LAMIACEAE (LABIATAE) - **Sage/Mint Family** Aromatic herbs or shrublets. Leaves in opposite pairs. Flowers irregular, usually 2 lipped. Economically valuable for aromatic essential oils, herbs Sage, Lavender, Rosemary, Mint, Marjoram, Basil, Thyme and ornamentals such as Salvia, Stachys. Cosmop, ± 252 genera, ± 6700 species, 41 genera in SA.

Stachys (*stachys* - spike, ear of corn) - Herbs, shrubs; flowers in clusters, in terminal or axillary inflorescences, usually hairy, tube narrow, upper lip erect or arched, lower lip longer, spreading, 3 lobed. Cosmop, ± 450 species, ± 40 in SA.

Stachys tubulosa Mauve Sage, Mauve Stachys (*tubulosa* - hollow cylinder or tube)

Soft, straggling herb, up to 400 mm. On forest margins, in shade. Stems sparsely branched; softly hairy throughout. **Leaves:** 35-70 x 25-65 mm, margins toothed, stalks 18-40 mm. **Flowers:** 4-6 in clusters, in short terminal inflorescences; flowers ± 12 mm, pink flecked mauve, tube straight, slender, ± 18 mm, calyx 4-8 mm, lobes long pointed (Nov-Apr). **General:** Attractive groundcover for shady places.

Satureja (Latin for savoury herb) - Herbs or subshrubs. Temp and warm regions, ± 200 species, ± 4 in SA.

Satureja reptans (*reptans* - creeping and rooting)

Straggling perennial herb, 250-600 mm. In mountain grassland, 1200-2500 m. Stems slender, hairy. **Leaves:** 16-24 x 12-20 mm, margins toothed, **strongly aromatic**. **Flowers:** 1-3(5) in clusters; flower tube bell-like, ± 10 mm, white, flushed pink or pale violet with middle yellow stripe, stalks slender, 10-25 mm (Dec-Apr). **Similar species:** *S. grandibracteata* Only at high altitudes, rare; more robust, flowers large.

Mentha (Latin for mint) - Aromatic herbs; flowers small, in congested inflorescences. Some grown for essential oils or as culinary herbs, such as Peppermint, Spearmint, Pennyroyal. Cosmop, mostly N Hemisp, ± 25 species, ± 3 in SA.

Mentha aquatica Water Mint; Waterment (A); koena-e-nyenyane, koena-ya-libida (SS); ityaleba (X); amabunu, imbozisa, umaliwane, umayime, umnukani (Z) (*aquatica* - living in water)

Perennial herb, erect up to 800 mm, or trailing stems up to 1,5 m. In marshes, damp places, SW Cape to Trop Afr, Europe. Thinly hairy, gland dotted. **Leaves:** 20-55 x 5-26 mm, margins obscurely toothed. **Flowers:** In terminal **roundish** clusters ± 25 mm diam; flowers 5 mm, pale mauve to purple (Jan-Mar). **General:** Delicious culinary herb. Also used for fragrant, relaxing bath. Used in traditional medicine to treat colds, respiratory problems and as a protective charm against evil spirits. Easily propagated.

Plectranthus (*plektron* - a spur; *anthos* - flower)- Herbs or shrubs, often fleshy (for description see p. 472).

Plectranthus ecklonii Large Spur-flower Bush; Persmuishondblaar (A) (see p. 474)

Rabdosiella (*rabdos* - taken from another closely related genus *Rabdosia*) - Closely related to *Plectranthus*. Stems more woody; leaves often in 3s; bracts leaflike, flowers in dense, terminal inflorescence. Afr, India, 2 species, 1 in SA.

Rabdosiella calycina Upland Fly Bush; Spoorblom (A) (*calycina* - in the form of a calyx)

Coarse herb or soft shrub, up to 1,5 m. In grassland, rocky places, E Cape to N Prov. Woody rootstock. Stems annual, hairy. **Leaves:** 40-100 x 20-45 mm, leathery, rough to hairless above, hairless to densely velvety beneath with orange gland dots, margins toothed, stalk very short. **Flowers:** In **dense, leafy, branched inflorescences**, 100-300 mm; flowers white to mauve, 8-11 mm, hairy, calyx ± 9 mm, erect at fruiting (Dec-Jun). **General:** Unpleasantly scented. Attractive, hardy garden plant.

Syncolostemon (*syn* - united; *kolos* - stunted; *stemon* - pillar, refers to filaments) - Herbs, rarely woody; leaves on short leafy branchlets; flowers in dense, branched inflorescences, calyx 2 lipped, 5 lobed. S Afr endemic, 10 species.

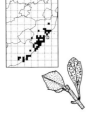

Syncolostemon densiflorus Pink Plume; isidlekesenqomfi, isolelemamba (Z) (*densiflorus* - densely covered with flowers)

Shrub 1-2,2 m. In grassland, on forest margins, up to 1000 m. Stems velvety white, sparsely branched, woody at base. **Leaves:** 5-15 x 4-10 mm, margins toothed above the middle. **Flowers: 4-6, in clusters**, in **dense terminal, branching inflorescences**, 60-160 x 40-65 mm; flowers 18-23 mm, stamens exserted 8-10 mm, bright pink (crimson), **calyx lobes long, narrow**, reddish mauve (Oct-Jun). **General:** Strongly aromatic. Used traditionally as a love charm emetic. Excellent garden plant, in full sun.

Phyla nodiflora CJ J Ward

Phyla nodiflora Tony Abbott

Stachys tubulosa Lal Greene

Satureja reptans Tom de Waal

Mentha aquatica Geoff Nichols

Plectranthus ecklonii Lorraine van Hooff

Rabdosiella calycina Lal Greene

Rabdosiella calycina Martin von Fintel

Syncolostemon densiflorus Martin von Fintel

425

Syncolostemon macranthus Long-flowered Pink Plume (*macranthus* - long flowers)

Much branched, aromatic shrub, 1-2,5 m. On forest margins, along streams, 1600-2200 m. Stems bristly hairy. **Leaves:** 20-45 x 12-20 mm, **rough**, margins faintly toothed, stalks short, 2-8 mm. **Flowers:** 4-6 in clusters, in branched inflorescences, 80-180 mm; flowers 25-30 mm, pink to purple, calyx cylindrical, ± 10 mm, densely hairy, **upper lobe larger** than lower narrow lobes (Nov-May). **General:** Lovely, but not easy to cultivate.

Syncolostemon ramulosus (*ramulosus* - many small branches)

0,6-1,2 m. In grassland, Pondoland, S KZN. **Leaves:** 5-7 x 3-6 mm. **Flowers: Small, 16-20 mm**, pale pink, lilac (white), **stamens exserted by 5-6 mm**.

Syncolostemon rotundifolius Round-leaved Pink Plume (*rotundifolius* - round leaves)

Soft, sparsely branched shrub, 0,8-1,8 m. Prominent in grassland and scrub on rocky slopes, up to 400 m. Stems velvety white. **Leaves:** 6-15 x 4-12 mm, hairy, tips rounded, margins entire or faintly toothed above centre. **Flowers: In 2s**, in **fairly dense** branched inflorescences, 50-80 x 60 mm; flowers 23-27 mm, mauve, pink or magenta, calyx 9-10 mm, **lobes triangular** (Sep-Apr). **General:** Lovely, difficult to grow.

Hemizygia (*hemi* - half; *zygon* - joined, refers to 2 lipped flowers) - Herbs, shrublets; leaves opposite or in 3s; flowers in clusters of 2-6, in well spaced groups, in terminal or axillary inflorescences, bracts small, sometimes coloured, falling off, terminal ones sometimes enlarged, calyx upper lobe broadly oval to roundish. Closely related to *Syncolostemon* with calyx upper lobe not broadly oval. Mostly Afr, ± 35 species, ± 28 in SA.

Hemizygia pretoriae Dwarf Sage Bush

Erect, perennial shrublet, up to 500 mm. In grassland, among rocks. Woody rootstock. Stems annual, simple, slender. Plant with short rough hairs throughout. **Leaves:** 8-24 x 2-15 mm, **gland dotted**, often folded along midrib, margins entire or with few teeth. **Flowers:** 14-16 mm, whitish to pale mauve, **tube long, narrow**, calyx ± 11 mm, lobes short, purplish (Oct- Mar). **General:** Attracts butterflies.

Hemizygia teucriifolia (leaves like *Teucrium*)

Bushy herb, 150-300 mm. In grassland, 600-1500 m. Woody rootstock. Annual stems slender, greyish hairy. **Leaves:** 8-18 x 3-6 mm, slightly leathery, upper surface blackish, rough hairy, greyish velvety beneath, margins entire, rolled under. **Flowers:** 4-6 in clusters, in axils of **leaflike bracts**, **in simple unbranched inflorescences**, 40-80 mm; flowers 10-12 mm, mauve, calyx ± 6 mm, harshly hairy (Sep-Apr). **General:** Said to make cattle sick.

Hemizygia transvaalensis Large Hemizygia

Soft, sticky, aromatic shrublet, up to 1 m. In grassy flats, among rocks, 1000-1700 m. Woody rootstock. Stems annual, branched, sparsely hairy. **Leaves:** 15-40 x 8-22 mm or 12-20 x 4-8 mm, sparsely hairy, margins toothed in upper parts, stalks very short. **Flowers:** 3-6 in clusters in loose inflorescences, 70-200 mm, bracts pinkish purple, 12-24 x 4-10 mm; flowers **18-22 mm**, white to mauve, lilac-pink, calyx ± 14 mm, hairy (Aug-Dec). **General:** Lovely in the garden.

Becium (ancient name for Sage) - Slightly woody herbs; often with deep tap roots; leaves opposite or clustered, gland dotted; flowers in terminal spikelike inflorescences. Mainly Afr, Arabia, India, ± 10 species, ± 4 in SA.

Becium obovatum [= B. grandiflorum] Cat's Whiskers; Katsnor (A); idada, iziba, ufukuzela, umathanjane (Z) (*obovatum* - egg-shaped, attached at smaller end)

Low growing herb, up to 300 mm. In grassland, E Cape to Bots. Woody rootstock. Stems annual, erect, sometimes branching. **Leaves:** Variable, 15-40 x 5-20 mm, sparsely hairy to very hairy, gland dotted, margins entire or with few shallow teeth, stalks short. **Flowers:** In well spaced clusters, in terminal inflorescences; flowers 10-17 mm, white to pale mauve, **upper lip frilly, with violet lines, stamens protruding**, calyx 5 mm, wide open, enlarging to 10 mm in fruit, net veined (Sep-Feb). **General:** Used in traditional medicine as a hair restorer, and as enemas for children with stomach complaints. Attracts Blues butterflies. (See p. 188)

Syncolostemon macranthus   *Martin von Fintel*

Syncolostemon ramulosus   *Martin von Fintel*

Syncolostemon rotundifolius   *Martin von Fintel*

Hemizygia pretoriae   *Van Wyk & Malan*

Hemizygia transvaalensis   *Godfrey Symons*

Hemizygia teucriifolia   *Tony Abbott*

Hemizygia teucriifolia   *Tony Abbott*

Becium obovatum   *David Johnson*

427

Orthosiphon (*ortho* - erect; *siphon* - tube, refers to flower tube) - Aromatic herbs or shrublets; leaves in pairs or 3s; flowers in well spaced clusters of 1-4, in terminal inflorescences, upper lip 3-4 lobed, lower entire, calyx upper lobe broad, 4 slender sharply pointed lobes below. About 50 species, ± 9 in SA.

Orthosiphon labiatus Shell Bush (*labiatus* - lipped)

Much branched shrublet, 0,6-1,8 m. On dry, rocky, wooded hillsides, KZN to Zim. Thinly hairy throughout. **Leaves:** 30-80 x 20-60 mm, sparsely hairy above, long hairs beneath, margins coarsely toothed, **stalks slender, 5-30 mm. Flowers:** In clusters of 6-8, 10-20 mm apart, inflorescences 50-180 mm; flowers 10-20 mm, pink to mauve, stamens well exserted, calyx ± 15 mm, reddish mauve (Dec-Mar). **General:** Leaves mint scented or unpleasantly aromatic. Popular, hardy, long flowering garden plant.

Orthosiphon serratus Small Shell Bush (*serratus* - saw teeth)

Shrub up to 900 mm. In grassland, on stony slopes. Woody rootstock. Stems erect, hardly branched, densely bristly hairy. **Leaves:** In 3s, 40-90 x 20-35 mm, densely hairy or nearly hairless, margins **with distinct, even, sharp teeth,** stalks short. **Flowers:** 4-12 in clusters ± 30 mm apart, inflorescences 80-320 mm; flowers 9-16 mm, mauve to purple, calyx ± 15 mm, maroon, enlarged in fruit (Oct-May).

SCROPHULARIACEAE - Snapdragon Family Annual or perennial herbs, shrubs (for description see p. 72, 480).
Diascia (*di* - two; *askion* - bladder, wine skin; refers to the two flower pouches in the first species described) - Herbs; flower usually with 1 or 2 translucent yellow patches forming shallow pouches behind, tube very short or absent; fruit a capsule. Cultivated as ornamentals in Europe, much hybridised. Used as pot herbs when young. S Afr, ± 30 species.

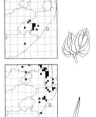

Diascia cordata (*cordata* - heart-shaped)

Straggling, branched, perennial herb. On damp slopes, in rough vegetation along streams, 1400-2440 m. **Leaves:** 12-30 x 8-20 mm, **margins sharply toothed, tips rigid,** stalks short. **Flowers:** In long slender inflorescences, 50-200 mm; flowers ± 18 mm wide, pink, **spurs blunt, conspicuous** (Nov-Mar).

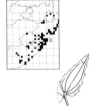

Diascia integerrima Twinspur; Pensies (A); bolao-ba-litoeba, leilanenyana (SS)
(*integerrima* - perfect)

Perennial, tufted herb, 200-500 mm. On cliffs, rocky areas, near streamlets, 2100-2865 m. Stems slender, erect, branched near base. **Leaves: Narrow,** ± 20 x 10 mm, **margins entire,** tips sharp, stalks short. **Flowers:** In terminal inflorescences; flowers ± 10 x 20 mm, petal lobes rounded, pink with raised keel usually covered in dark gland dots on mouth, window yellow-maroon, spurs conspicuous, **incurved,** calyx lobes spreading (Dec-Mar). **General:** Hardy garden plant, long flowering season. **Similar species:** *D. barberae* Leaves heart-shaped, margins toothed; flowers larger, with two patches of gland dots in mouth, calyx lobes reflexed.

Nemesia (from *Nemesion*, name used by Dioscorides for similar plant) - Annual or perennial herbs; flower tube short with spur, with or without bosses in mouth of spur (seen as inverted bumps on underside of tube), upper lip 4 lobed, lower entire or slightly notched; fruit flattened, halves boat-shaped, seeds winged. SA endemic genus, ± 70 species.

Nemesia denticulata Wild Nemesia; Leeubekkie, Maagpynblommetjie (A) (*denticulata* - toothed)

Erect, **tufted** perennial **herb,** up to 600 mm. In grassland, open scrub, coast to 1100 m. Annual stems from woody rootstock. **Leaves clustered towards base. Leaves: Broad,** ± 30 x **5-10 mm, margins toothed. Flowers:** In small, flattish, terminal clusters; flowers ± 15 mm, pink, mauve, fading blue or white, yellow or orange on crest of mouth, 2 **flat** orange bosses at mouth of spur, spur 5-6 mm (throughout year). **General:** Used as a pot herb. Attractive when massed, grown from seed or cuttings. Often misidentified in the past as *N. fruticans*. (See p. 480)

Diclis (*diclis* - double folding, or 2 winged, possibly refers to flower lobes) - Annual or perennial herbs; leaves opposite; flowers in axils, tube short, spur 2 lobed; fruit a capsule. Afr, Madag, ± 10 species, ± 5 in SA.

Diclis reptans Dwarf Snapdragon, Toadflax; koenana, ponye (SS); isinama (Z)
(*reptans* - creeping and rooting)

Sprawling, mat-forming herb, up to 200 mm. In damp, shady, rocky places, or open dry grassland, coast to 2000 m. **Roots thin, fibrous. Stems reddish, tips erect, hairy. Leaves:** ± 30 x 35 mm, **margins deeply, sharply toothed, stalks long,** ± 25 mm. **Flowers:** Solitary, ± 10 mm, white to pale mauve, upper lip 2 lobed, lower 3 lobed, spur straight, slender, 2,5-3 mm, calyx lobes pointed, upper lobe narrow, stems slender, ± 30 mm (Sep-May). **Fruit:** Dry, rounded, notched at tip. **General:** Plant edible. Used in traditional medicine to treat distemper in dogs. (See p. 190)

Orthosiphon labiatus   *Orthosiphon serratus*   *Diascia barberae*

Diascia cordata   *Diascia cordata*

Nemesia denticulata   *Diclis reptans*   *Diascia integerrima*

Nemesia denticulata   *Nemesia denticulata*   *Diascia integerrima*

429

Selago (*sel* - sight; *jach* - salutary, refers to supposed medicinal properties) - Herbs or shrublets; leaves usually alternate or in clusters; small, in dense, round, or broad, branching sometimes irregular inflorescences; fruit not splitting, 2 nutlets. Attracts Blues butterflies of the *Lepidochrysops* genus. Afr, ± 150 species, mostly SA.

Selago longipedicellata (*longi* - long; *pedicellata* - little foot)

Much branched, perennial shrublet, up to 500 mm. In grassland. Branches downy. **Leaves:** In clusters, 4-10 mm, margins with 2 pairs of sharp teeth near pointed tips, ± bristly hairy. **Flowers:** In short inflorescences (elongating ± 50 mm in fruit); flower tube ± 4 mm, pink.

Selago trauseldii (named after William Trauseld, 1911-1989, game ranger with Natal Parks Board in Drakensberg, photographer and amateur botanist, author of 'Wild Flowers of the Natal Drakensberg')

Perennial herb, up to 750 mm. On moist, grassy slopes, 1800-2200 m. Few erect stems from woody base. **Leaves:** In clusters, 4-10 x 1-2 mm, margins entire, thickened, finely hairy. **Flowers:** In compact clusters, 7-10 mm diam, terminating a leafy twig ± 60 mm, arranged in narrow inflorescences; flowers ± 5 mm diam, tube ± 5 mm, white flushed mauve, hairy outside (Jan-Mar).

Veronica (the name of a plant, Speedwell) - Herbs; leaves opposite; flowers in terminal or axillary inflorescences, 4 unequal petals, calyx deeply divided.

★ Veronica anagallis-aquatica (*anagallis* - a plant genus; *aquatica* - found in water)

Annual or short lived perennial, 300-600 mm. In moist, shady places, along streams. Introduced from Europe. Branched from base, stems erect, fleshy, hollow, rooting at lower nodes, hairless. Leaves 20-100 mm, lower margins entire, upper irregularly toothed towards tip, clasping stem at base. Flowers in long, slender inflorescences; flowers 5-10 mm diam, on short stalks (spring-autumn).

Buttonia (named after Edward Button, 1836-1900, geologist, who wandered round south east Africa in search of gold and plants) - Slender, climbing, parasitic shrub (on grasses, herbs); leaves opposite, deeply lobed, stalked; flowers solitary, in axils, calyx leathery; fruit woody, dry. Afr, 3 species, 2 in SA.

Buttonia superba Large-flowered Climbing Foxglove; umhlanhlaze enkulu (Z)
(*superba* - superb)

Scrambling climber, up to 2 m. In thicket. Stems woody at base, young parts purplish. **Leaves:** Opposite, **deeply 3-5 lobed**, slightly succulent, shiny bright green, stalks 10-25 mm. **Flowers:** Massed in upper parts of stems, **bracteoles small, narrow**, ± 10 x 3 mm, dropping early; **flowers large**, ± 60 mm, ± 50 mm diam, pink with deeper pink veins, fading almost white, calyx ±15 mm, stalks 20-40 mm (Nov-Jun). **Similar species:** *B. natalensis* Leaves deeply 5-7 lobed; bracteoles larger, flowers smaller, ± 35 mm.

Graderia (anagram of *Gerardia*, which was the genus to which Linnaeus first allocated these plants) - Perennial herbs or subshrubs; flowers solitary, in upper leaf axils, almost stalkless; fruit a capsule. Afr, SA, 3 species.

Graderia scabra Wild Penstemon, Pink Ground-bells; impundu, isimonyo, ugweja, umphuphutho (Z) (*scabra* - rough, refers to hairs on leaves and stem)

Erect perennial shrublet, up to 600 mm. In grassland, coast to 2100 m, E Cape to Zim. Woody rootstock. Stems hairless to hairy. **Leaves:** Overlapping, ± 50 x 15 mm, margins entire or with few teeth, stalkless. **Flowers:** ± 30 mm, pink to deep mauve or reddish, whitish, thinly hairy, calyx 5 lobed, ± 15 mm (Aug-Dec). **General:** Used in traditional medicine (with other plants) to treat stomach complaints, fevers, rashes, sores, to prevent miscarriage, relieve menstrual pain and as love charm emetics.

Sopubia (Indian common name) - Perennial herbs; leaves narrow or deeply dissected; flowers regular, solitary in upper leaf axils, forming slender, elongate inflorescences. Afr, Madag, Himalayas to Indo China, ± 40 species, 5 in SA.

Sopubia cana Silvery Sopubia; leilane, pulumo-tsoeu (SS) (*cana* - grey)

Erect parasitic shrublet, up to 450 mm. In grassland, 1200-2000 m, E Cape to Trop Afr. **Covered in velvety, silvery grey hairs throughout. Leaves:** ± 25 x 2 mm, with short leafy shoots in axils. **Flowers:** In dense, terminal inflorescences, often branched; flowers ± 20 mm diam, pink, petal lobes delicate, crinkly, tube short, within calyx (Oct-Mar). **General:** Conspicuous after burns. Parasitic on grasses. Used in traditional medicine to relieve menstrual pain and prevent miscarriage. **Similar species:** *S simplex* Up to 600 mm; **nearly hairless.**

Selago longipedicellata

Selago trauseldii

★ *Veronica anagallis-aquatica*

Buttonia superba

Graderia scabra

Sopubia cana

Sopubia cana

Sopubia simplex

431

Buchnera (named after 18th Century German naturalist J Buchner) - Perennial herbs, often parasitic; flowers regular, in axils of bracts, forming spikelike inflorescences. Trop, subtrop, mostly Old World, ± 100 species, ± 9 in SA.

Buchnera simplex [=*B. glabrata*] **False Verbena; umusa omkhulu (Z)** (*simplex* - simple)

Slender, erect, perennial herb, up to 600 mm. In damp grassland, coast to 2100 m. Woody rootstock. Stems unbranched. **Leaves:** Basal, ± 70 x 15 mm, 3 veined, margins with few small teeth; stem leaves few. **Flowers:** In slightly branched, **small, congested terminal inflorescences** (elongate in fruit), 6-50 mm; flowers ± 5 mm diam, blue to lilac, white, tube ± hairless outside (Sep-May). **General:** Used as a love charm emetic. **Similar species:** *B. dura* Stems leafy; leaves 12-35 mm; inflorescence dense above at first, elongating, 25-175 mm, flower tube softly hairy.

Cycnium (*kyknos* - swan, probably refers to slender, elongated, furry flower tube) - Perennial parasitic herbs; flowers nearly regular, large, in axils, forming terminal inflorescences. Afr, ± 40 species, ± 3 in SA.

Cycnium racemosum **Large Pink Ink Plant; Berginkplant (A); injanga (X); uhlaba-hlangane (Z)** (*racemosum* - inflorescence of flowers with stalks)

Erect, usually unbranched herb, up to 750 mm. In grassland, rocky places, up to 2600 m. Stem ribbed, **rough. Leaves: Large, ± 80 x 20 mm, rough**, margins purplish red, with **prominent teeth. Flowers: In terminal inflorescence**, sometimes with 1-2 branches; flowers solitary or in pairs, **large**, ± 60 mm wide, tube ± 25 mm, white to deep pink, calyx ± 12 mm, lobes short, narrow, tips hooked, **stalks short** (Dec-Jun), fragrantly scented. **General:** Flowers turn black when bruised. Used in traditional medicine to treat pain, ease childbirth.

Similar species: *C. tubulosum* [= *Rhamphicarpa tubulosa*] In marshy ground; less robust, stems slender, hairless, semi-erect; leaf margins entire; flower stalks long, ± 15 mm.

Striga (*striga* - Latin: furrow, Italian: witch) - Parasitic herbs; leaves opposite or alternate, sometimes reduced; flowers solitary in axils of bracts. Afr, Asia, Austr, ± 40 species, ± 7 in SA.

Striga bilabiata **Small Witchweed; seona (SS); sono (Sw); isinone esimhlophe, isona (Z)** (*bilabiata* - divided into two lips)

Slender, erect, up to 300 mm. In grassland, coast to 1800 m. Stems sometimes branched, purplish at base, roughly hairy throughout. **Leaves:** Erect or spreading, ± 20 x 1 mm. **Flowers:** In dense terminal spikes; flowers **2 lipped**, lilac, greyish white, calyx ± 8 mm, with 5 prominent veins (Dec-Jan).

Striga gesnerioides **Bloublom (A); seona (SS); sono (Sw); igalo (X)** (*gesnerioides* - like *Gesnera*)

Erect, up to 100 mm. In thicket, grassland, E Cape, N Prov, Nam. Branching from base, slightly succulent, dull pale pink, almost hairless. **Leaves:** Scalelike, ± 7 x 3 mm, close to stem, softly hairy. **Flowers:** Small, ± 8 mm, magenta, pink (Jan-Jun). **General:** Parasitic on grass, tobacco.

Striga junodii (named after Rev Junod, Swiss missionary to Moz in early 1900s, author of 'Life of a SA Tribe', anthropological work on the amaThonga people)

Herb up to 450(600) mm. In low-lying areas, N KZN to Moz. Stems branched from base, bristly hairy. **Leaves:** Narrow, ± 20 mm. **Flowers:** In simple, loose inflorescence; flowers 20 mm, pinkish orange, calyx ± 8 mm, ribbed, lobes pointed, narrow (summer).

Buchnera simplex

Lal Greene

Buchnera simplex

Tom de Waal

Cycnium racemosum

Martin von Fintel

Striga bilabiata

Darrel Plowes

Cycnium tubulosum

Lorraine van Hooff

Cycnium racemosum

Tom de Waal

Striga bilabiata

Darrel Plowes

Striga gesnerioides

C J Ward

Striga gesnerioides

Godfrey Symons

Striga junodii

Braam van Wyk

433

Harveya (named after Dr William Harvey, 1811-1866, chief author of early volumes of Flora Capensis, prof of botany in Dublin, Ireland) - Parasitic herbs; leaves reduced to scales. Afr, Mascarene Is, ± 40 species, ± 25 in SA.

Harveya leucopharynx (*leucopharynx* - white throat)

Parasitic herb, 150-450 mm. In damp, grassy, rocky places or damp scrub, 1800 -2550 m. Glandular hairy throughout. **Flowers:** Inflorescence with 5-10 flowers, ± 30 x 40 mm, **pink with white throat**, tube ± 45 mm, calyx ± 30 x 15 mm, stalks ± 35 mm (Nov-Feb), pleasant fruity scent. **Similar species:** *H. pulchra* Smaller, ± 200 mm; at high altitudes, 1900-3000 m; flowers smaller, with yellow throat (Jan-Mar). *H. huttonii* Restricted to E Cape; flowers smaller, pink with white throat.

Harveya silvatica (*silvatica* - growing in woods)

Parasitic herb, 400-600 mm. In forest, woodland, E Cape to N Prov. **Leaves:** Scalelike, ± 15 x 4 mm. **Flowers:** 7-20 in loose inflorescence; flowers ± 30 mm wide, pink with yellow throat, tube ± 35 mm, calyx ± 19 mm (Nov-Dec). **Similar species:** *H. coccinea* Up to 350 mm; in coastal grassland (with *Hyphaene coriacea* palm clumps), stems, scales, bracts reddish; flowers ± 24 mm wide, pinkish white.

Hyobanche - Parasitic herbs; flowers in thick dense spikes, small, oblique, tube cylindrical. S Afr, ± 8 species.

Hyobanche fulleri (named after Claude Fuller born 1872 Austr, died 1928 in car accident in Moz, entomologist who worked on tsetse fly, collected mainly fungi)

Parasitic herb, up to 130 mm. In dune scrub. Parasitic on roots of *Chrysanthemoides monilifera*. **Leaves:** Pressed close to stem, glandular hairy. **Flowers: In oblong spike,** ± 130 x 30 mm; flowers slightly curved, ± 35 x 7 mm, hairy in upper half, mouth slit ± 10 mm (Aug). **Similar species:** *H. rubra* On stony ground, at high altitude; flowers in dense, flat topped spike, ± 60 x 6 mm, pink to red.

BIGNONIACEAE - Bignonia Family Trees, shrubs, woody climbers (for description see p. 76). **Podranea** (anagram of related Austr genus *Pandorea* in which Podraneas were first classified) - Afr, 2 species, 1 in SA, 1 in Zim.

Podranea ricasoliana **Port St John's Creeper** (named after V Ricasoli)

Robust, scrambling shrub, on forest margins. Stems with raised white dots. **Leaves:** 140-190 mm, ± 9 leaflets, ± 30-60 x 20-30 mm, margins toothed. **Flowers:** In large, loose, nodding inflorescences; flowers ± 40 x 60 mm, pink, tube ± 75 mm, mouth compressed, calyx inflated, 5 lobed (throughout year). **Fruit:** Pods ± 300 x 10 mm. **General:** Popular garden plant, cultivated in Europe since the 1870s.

PEDALIACEAE - Sesame Family Annual or perennial herbs (for description see p. 76). **Sesamum** (Greek and Latin name for Sesame) - Annual or perennial herbs. Afr, Mascarene Is, S Europe, Asia, ± 37 species, ± 12 in SA.

Sesamum alatum **Wing-seeded Sesame; ludvonca-loludliwako (Sw); udonqa (Z)** (*alatum* - winged)

Erect annual herb, up to 1 m. On floodplains, in woodland, KZN to Trop Afr. Stems hairless. **Leaves:** Basal leaves irregularly lobed or with 3-5 leaflets, lobes 20-70 x 2-10 mm, stalks 20-70 mm; upper leaves simple. **Flowers:** Solitary, in axils, ± 15 mm wide, tube ± 30 mm, pinkish red (Dec-Mar). **Fruit:** Capsule 20-40 x 4-12 mm, **tapering abruptly to terminal beak, seeds winged. General:** Seeds edible.

Ceratotheca (*kerato* - horned; *theke* - a case, refers to horned fruit) - Annual herbs. Afr, ± 8 species, 4 in SA.

Ceratotheca triloba **Wild Foxglove; Wildevingerhoedjie (A); ludvonca (Sw); udonqa (Sw, Z); udoncalwabathwa, udonqabathwa (Z)** (*triloba* - three lobed)

Annual or biennial herb, up to 1,5 m. In disturbed places, E Cape to Zim. **Leaves:** Opposite, ± 50 x 40 mm, deeply 3 lobed, margins toothed, stalks ± 40 mm. **Flowers:** Hanging, ± 75 mm, pale pink to mauve, finely hairy (Oct-Apr). **Fruit:** ± 25 mm, erect, tip 2 horned. **General:** Visited by carpenter and honey-bees. Unpleasant smell when crushed. Used in traditional medicine to treat painful menstruation, stomach cramps, nausea, fever and diarrhoea. Hardy garden plant, grown from seed.

ACANTHACEAE - Acanthus Family Herbs, shrubs, climbers (for description see p. 76). **Dyschoriste** (*dys* - with difficulty; *choristos* - separate, refers to capsule valves which stick together) - Afr, America, Asia, ± 108 species, 11 in SA.

Dyschoriste depressa (*depressa* - flattened, lying flat)

Spreading shrublet, up to 500 mm. In disturbed scrub, grassland, near rivers. **Leaves:** ± 25 x 8 mm, dark green, margins entire, stalks 6-8 mm. **Flowers:** 3-8 in clusters in axils; flowers ± 12 mm, bracteoles short, narrow, calyx ± 8 mm, teeth rough hairy (Sep-Feb). **Fruit:** Capsules 6-12 mm, suberect. **General:** Browsed by bushbuck.

Harveya leucopharynx
Lal Greene

Harveya silvatica
Braam van Wyk

Hyobanche fulleri
C J Ward

Podranaea ricasoliana
Geoff Nichols

Sesamum alatum
Martin von Fintel

Sesamum alatum
Martin von Fintel

Ceratotheca triloba
Tom de Waal

Ceratotheca triloba
Martin von Fintel

Dyschoriste depressa
Geoff Nichols

Barleria (after Jacques Barrelier, 1606-1673, Dominican monk and botanist) - Herbs or shrubs (for description see p. 488).

Barleria greenii Green's Barleria, Wild Bush Petunia (named after Dave Green, farmer and amateur botanist from Estcourt, KZN, who first collected this species, described in 1984)

Perennial, much branched shrub, up to 0,8(1,8) m. On black clay in open rocky areas. Stems robust, woody at base, bark pale grey-brown; young stems green, softly white hairy. **Leaves:** ± 30 x 10 mm, thick, smooth, shiny dark green above, yellowish green beneath, tips with recurved hook, stalks short. **Flowers:** 4-6, in axils; flowers **large, conspicuous,** ± 40 mm, white to deep pink, bracteoles ± 20 x 3 mm, stiff, spiny, pale green with reddish purple tip, 4 lobed calyx, outer ± 30 x 20 mm, **ending in stiff spine,** finely hairy outside, veins conspicuous, margins entire or with fine short spines, inner lobes smaller (Feb-Mar). **Buds sweetly scented at night. General:** Copious nectar, attracts bumble-bees. Pollinated by moths. A lovely garden plant.

Barleria obtusa Bush Violet; Bosviooltjie (A); idololenkonyane (Z) (see p. 490)

Peristrophe (*peri* - around; *strophos* - a twisted band, refers to the twist in the flower stalk) - Herbs, shrubs; rooting at nodes; flowers in axils, bracts enclose calyx; fruits do not split elastically. Afr, Madag, E Indies, ± 25 species, ± 9 in SA.

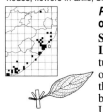

Peristrophe cernua [= *P. natalensis*] False Buckwheat; umhlolowane (X); uhlalwane oluncane (Z) (*cernua* - nodding, drooping)

Slender, sprawling, perennial shrub, up to 1 m. In valley bushveld, dry woodland. **Leaves: Well spaced,** 18-35 x 8-15 mm. **Flowers: In small clusters in axils**; flower tube ± 9 mm, lips ± 16 x 5 mm, magenta to purple with dark purple markings, white on upper lip, bracts unequal, ±12 x 1 mm, downy, spine tipped (Mar-Sep, throughout year). **General:** Leaves mostly fallen when in full flower. Heavily browsed by game, goats, visited by sunbirds, honey-bees and butterflies (Pieridae). Used in traditional medicine to treat sore eyes. Good garden plant, in full sun.

Dicliptera (*di* - two; *kleio* - to shut; *pteros* - winged) - Herbs; leaves stalked, well spaced; flowers in 1-3 clusters in axils; fruits split elastically. Trop, subtrop regions, ± 70 species, ± 12 in SA.

Dicliptera clinopodia (*clinopodia* - leaning foot, limp)

Erect or straggling shrublet, up to 1 m. In thicket, near streams, E Cape to Bots. Stems grooved. Thinly hairy throughout. **Leaves:** ± 60 x 25 mm, stalks ± 20 mm. **Flowers: In dense, short stalked clusters in axils and terminally**; flowers ± 20 mm, tube ± 15 mm, violet or magenta, calyx small, **bracts ± 10 mm, narrow, tapering to fine point,** pale yellow with green veins (Mar-Aug), faintly scented. **General:** Browsed by game. Easily grown from cuttings.

Dicliptera heterostegia (*heterostegia* - on different planes, perhaps refers to different sized bracts)

Straggling perennial shrublet, up to 700 mm. On forest margins, in damp places. Thinly hairy throughout. **Leaves:** ± 90 x 30 mm, stalks ± 40 mm. **Flowers:** In stalkless clusters; flowers ± 25 mm, **white to pink, outer bracts oval to round,** ± 15 x 10 mm, with long hairs, calyx short (Mar-Sep). **General:** Attracts larvae of butterflies including Mother-of-Pearls, *Protogoniomorpha parhassus aethiops*. Good garden shade plant. **Similar species:** *D. zeylanica* Low growing; bract tips rounded.

Hypoestes (*hypo* - beneath; *estia* - house, Greek for undergarment; refers to calyx being covered by bracts) - Evergreen herbs or shrubs; flowers 2 lipped, tube long, upper lip notched, lower 3 lobed, anthers 1 chambered; fruit stalked, non-elastic. Afr, Mascarene Is, Austr, E Indies, China, ± 150 species, ± 3 in SA.

Hypoestes aristata Ribbon Bush; Lintbos, Seeroogblommetjie (A); idololenkonyane-elimhlophe, uhlonyane (Z) (*aristata* - bearded awns, like ear of barley)

Shrub up to 1,5 m. In dry thicket, forest, damp places, E Cape to Trop Afr. Softly hairy, stems brittle, pale brown. **Leaves:** 35-110 x 17-69 mm, **veins pale, clearly marked,** margins wavy. **Flowers: In axils of leaves, appearing to be in whorls**; flowers ± 32 mm, pink to bright magenta with darker purple speckles, bracts with threadlike tips, calyx tube short, 4 lobed (Mar-Aug). **General:** Used as spinach in some areas. Visited by small bees and flies. Popular, hardy garden plant, blooms best in full sun, frost tender. Var. *alba*, N KZN to N Prov; leaves and flowers smaller, white. Var. *thiniorum*, Cape to Port St John's; restricted to coastal sand dunes; leaves succulent. **Similar species:** *H. triflora* [= *H. phaylopsoides*] Slender, loosely branched shrublet, carpeting forest floor, E Cape to Trop Afr; thinly hairy throughout; leaves ± 70 x 30 mm, tapering to both ends; flowers in loose clusters of 3-5, ± 25 mm, pink, mauve or white, sometimes with streaks, bracts leaflike, ± 10 mm (Feb-Dec).

Barleria greenii

Tom de Waal

Barleria greenii

Godfrey Symons

Barleria obtusa

Lorraine van Hooff

Peristrophe cernua

Tony Abbott

Dicliptera clinopodia

Martin von Fintel

Dicliptera clinopodia

Martin von Fintel

Dicliptera heterostegia

Geoff Nichols

Hypoestes aristata

Trevor Coleman

Hypoestes triflora

Lal Greene

437

Rhinacanthus (*rhine* - file or rasp; *acanthus* - a genus of Acanthaceae) - Scrambling herbs; leaves with stalks, margins wavy; flowers in clusters in inflorescence. Afr, Madag, India, China, America, ± 22 species, 2 in SA.

Rhinacanthus gracilis Dainty Spurs (*gracilis* - slender, slim)

Scrambling herb, up to 1,2 m. In woodland, forest. Stems grooved. **Leaves:** ± 60 x 20 mm, narrowing gradually to long tip, margins slightly wavy. **Flowers:** In loosely branched inflorescences, stems slender; flowers ± 15 mm wide, tube very slender, ± 20 mm, white or mauve, thinly hairy, calyx ± 7 mm (Mar-Sep). **Fruit:** On long stalk. **General:** Browsed by antelope. Good garden plant.

Isoglossa (*iso* - equal; *glossa* - tongue) - Herbaceous or slightly woody shrubs; flowers in compact or slender inflorescences, 2 lipped, tube long or short, bell-shaped. Afr, India; ± 15 species in SA.

Isoglossa cooperi (named after Thomas Cooper, 1815-1913, English plant collector and cultivator who came to SA in 1859)

Soft shrub, 0,2-1 m. In forest understorey. **Sticky hairy throughout. Leaves:** ± 50 x 20 mm, stalks ± 25 mm. **Flowers:** Loose clusters towards ends of branches; flowers ± 20 mm, lilac, tube long, slender, **bracts, calyx sticky hairy** (Feb-Mar), scented. **General:** Browsed by bushbuck. **Similar species:** *I. hypoestiflora* Shrub up to 3 m; leaves larger, ± 75 x 25 mm; bracts, calyx with white, non-sticky hairs.

Justicia (named after James Justice, 1698-1763, Scottish horticulturalist) - Herbs, shrublets; flowers solitary or in dense terminal inflorescences, 2 lipped, tube broad or bell-shaped. Attracts butterflies. Pantrop, 22 species in SA.

Justicia capensis Money Plant; Sakemansplant (A); ihlalanyosi, ikhokhela (Z)

Shrub or woody herb, 0,2-2 m. In shade, woodland, thicket. **Leaves:** Small, 14-80 x 5-35 mm, shiny green, densely velvety, slightly fleshy when young, hairless when mature. **Flowers:** ± 15 mm, magenta with white mouth, bracts leafy, ± 17 x 9 mm (throughout year), scented. **General:** Used in traditional medicine to attract customers to business or improve chances of employment. Hunters rub leaves on snares to mask human scent. Easily grown from seed, in sun or shade.

DIPSACACEAE - Scabiose Family Annual or perennial herbs. Leaves mainly in basal rosette. Flowers clustered in dense heads surrounded by a whorl of small bracts (involucre), 2 lipped, those on outer edge have lengthened petals, calyx papery, cup-shaped. Popular ornamentals. Mostly Medit and East, also Europe, Afr, Asia, ± 11 genera, ± 290 species, 2 genera in SA. **Scabiosa** (named after scabies, a complaint treated with the use of some species) - Annual or perennial herbs; leaves opposite, often in basal rosette, entire, toothed, lobed or divided; flowerheads surrounded at base by 1-2 rows of bracts, calyx lobes with long bristles. About 100 species, 9 in SA.

Scabiosa columbaria Wild Scabiosa; Bitterbos, Meerjarige Skurfkruid (A) ; hlakuea-pitsi, 'mamokhale, moholungoane, selomi (SS); ilelemimoya, isilawu esikhulu, iyeza lamehlo, makgha (X); ibheka, ubucubele, udoloqina, uxhaphozi (Z) (*columbaria* - dovelike)

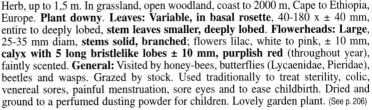

Herb, up to 1,5 m. In grassland, open woodland, coast to 2000 m, Cape to Ethiopia, Europe. **Plant downy. Leaves: Variable, in basal rosette**, 40-180 x ± 40 mm, entire to deeply lobed, **stem leaves smaller, deeply lobed. Flowerheads: Large**, 25-35 mm diam, **stems solid, branched**; flowers lilac, white to pink, ± 10 mm, **calyx with 5 long bristlelike lobes ± 10 mm, purplish red** (throughout year), faintly scented. **General:** Visited by honey-bees, butterflies (Lycaenidae, Pieridae), beetles and wasps. Grazed by stock. Used traditionally to treat sterility, colic, venereal sores, painful menstruation, sore eyes and to ease childbirth. Dried and ground to a perfumed dusting powder for children. Lovely garden plant. (See p. 206)

Scabiosa tysonii Wild Scabiosa; isilawu esikhulu (X) (named after William Tyson, 1851-1920, teacher and collector, born in Jamaica, died Grahamstown)

Perennial, prostrate to straggling bushy herb, 1-2 m. On forest margins, in damp places. Stems much branched. **Leaves:** 25-150 mm, margins scalloped. **Flowerheads:** ± 15 mm diam, stalks slender, ± 100 mm (Dec-May).

LOBELIACEAE - Lobelia Family Herbs, often with milky sap (for description see p. 208). **Cyphia** (*kyphos* - a twiner) - Perennial herbs, erect or twining; leaves alternate; flowers 1-2 lipped; fruit a capsule. Afr, ± 50 species, ± 32 in SA.

Cyphia tysonii (named after William Tyson, 1851-1920, teacher and collector)

Perennial twining herb. In grassland, 1250-2300 m. Stems hairless. **Leaves:** 20-50 x 1-4 mm, margins entire or with tiny, widely separated teeth, narrowing to short stalk. **Flowers:** In loose, twining inflorescence; flowers solitary (or in clusters of 2-5), ± 18 mm, white, lilac (Jan-Mar).

438

Rhinacanthus gracilis

Isoglossa cooperi

Justicia capensis

Justicia capensis

Scabiosa columbaria

Cyphia tysonii

Scabiosa columbaria

Scabiosa tysonii

Scabiosa tysonii

439

ASTERACEAE (COMPOSITAE) - **Daisy Family** The largest family of flowering plants (for description see p. 208).
Ethulia - Erect, branching herbs; leaves alternate; flowerheads small, in flattened, much branched inflorescences. Afr, Madag, Asia, S America, ± 10 species, 1 naturalised in SA.

Ethulia conyzoides Blue weed, Carter's Curse; umsokosoko (Z) *(conyza - strong smelling)*

Erect, weedy herb, 0,75-1,5 m. In low-lying, damp places. **Stems, leaves downy. Leaves:** ± 120 x 25 mm. **Flowerheads:** In much branched inflorescences; 3-4 mm diam, **purple fading to white**, bracts whitish, tipped with dark gland (throughout year). **General: Leaves give off strong odour when crushed.** Visited by wasps and bees. Used in traditional medicine to treat colic, intestinal parasites and madness.

Vernonia (named after William Vernon, died 1711, botanist)- Herbs, shrubs, climbers or trees (for description see p. 496).

Vernonia adoensis [= *Baccharoides adoensis*] linyatselo (Sw); inyathelo, uhlonyane (Z)
(adoensis - from Aden, Arabia)

Shrubby, up to 2,3 m. In open grassland, scrub, KZN to Ethiopia, up to 800 m. Thinly downy throughout. **Leaves:** ± 120 x 30 mm, roughly hairy, grey hairy beneath, margins irregularly toothed, tapering to narrowly winged base. **Flowerheads:** In terminal inflorescences, ± 40 mm diam; purple, mauve, fading white, bracts broad, loose, ± 20 mm, whitish with wavy margins (Aug-Oct, Apr-Jun), scented. **General:** Used in traditional medicine to treat stomach, chest and skin complaints, head lice and back pain. Used to annoint dogs before hunting.

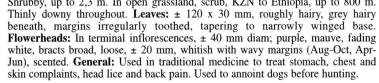

Vernonia angulifolia [also known as *Distephanus angulifolius*] Trailing Vernonia; impoqompo-qwane (Z) *(angulifolia - angular leaves)*

Scrambling shrub or climber. On forest margins, E Cape to Moz. **Leaves:** ± 50 x 40 mm, **margins widely toothed**, dark green. **Flowerheads: Small, massed in branched inflorescences**; ± 4 mm diam, lilac-pink to whitish, no ray florets (May-Aug), sweetly scented. **General:** Bark stripped. Used traditionally to treat stomach ailments. Attracts butterflies, moths, flies, bees, wasps and beetles. Hardy garden plant for frost-free areas. **Similar species:** *Microglossa mespilifolia* (see p. 210).

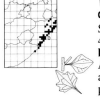

Vernonia crataegifolia *(krataigos - thorny flowering shrub; folia - leaves)*

Perennial herb or shrub, 0,3-2 m. In dry, open woodland, on forest margins, up to 1200 m, E Cape to N Prov. Stems **downy throughout. Leaves:** Erect, ± 90 x 20 mm, hairless above or cobwebby on both surfaces, **wedge-shaped. Flowerheads:** In **large, flat, branched inflorescences**; less than 5 mm wide, mauve to white, bracts blunt, downy (Dec-May). **Similar species:** *V. tigna* [= *V. neocorymbosa*] **Swarttee-bossie (A); uhlunguhlungu (Sw, Z); umzane-wehlati (Z)** Leaves half erect, ± 60 x 40 mm, margins toothed in upper half, **grey, silky hairy beneath**. Used traditionally to treat colds, stomach ache, hysteria, epilepsy and to ensure an easy birth.

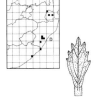

Aster (*astron* - a star, refers to flower shape) - Perennial herbs, soft shrublets; flowerheads solitary, on long stems, ray floret tips 3 toothed; pappus of rough, easily detached bristles. Mainly N Hemisp ± 250 species, ± 16 in SA.

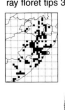

Aster bakerianus phoa (SS); noxgxekana, umthekisana (X); udlatshana, umaqhun-sula, umhlungwana (Z) (named after J G Baker, 1834-1920, British botanist and keeper of the herbarium of the Royal Bot Gardens, Kew)

Perennial herb, up to 450(600) mm. In open grassland, coast to 2285 m, S Cape to Tanz. **Herbaceous stems roughly hairy throughout. Leaves:** ± 80 x 20 mm, margins more or less toothed, base half-clasping. **Flowerheads:** ± 25 mm diam, deep pink to whitish, bract margins tinged purplish, **long spreading hairs**, at least on mid-line (Aug-Dec). **General:** Used in traditional medicine to treat stomach complaints, coughs, urinary infections, eye infections, headaches, sores, internal parasites, syphilis, snakebite, psychiatric disturbances and as protective charms. Slow growing, from seed. **Similar species:** *A. harveyanus* **Stems and bracts hairless.**

Aster perfoliatus Grey-leaved Aster; Grysblaar-aster (A) *(perfoliatus - stem as if it were passing through the leaf)*

Perennial herb, up to 600 mm, in colonies. In short, rocky grassland, 1500-2300 m. **Single to several stems from base, hairless throughout**, leaves mostly on lower half. **Leaves:** ± 50 x 40 mm, **leathery, grey-green, veins prominent, basal lobes clasping stem**, margins entire. **Flowerheads:** ± 40 mm diam, ray florets blue, mauve (white), disc florets yellow, bracts dark keeled, margins papery (Oct-Dec).

440

Ethulia conyzoides

Martin von Fintel

Vernonia adoensis

Martin von Fintel

Vernonia angulifolia

Wally Menne

Vernonia crataegifolia

Tony Abbott

Vernonia tigna

Rosemary Williams

Vernonia angulifolia

Martin von Fintel

Aster bakerianus

Martin von Fintel

Aster harveyanus

Martin von Fintel

Aster perfoliatus

Martin von Fintel

441

Felicia (named after Herr Felix, a German official, died 1846) - Much branched shrubby herbs (for description see p. 210).

Felicia filifolia   Fine-leaved Felicia; Draaibos, Wilde-aster (A); sehalahala-seseholo (SS)   *(filifolia - leaves like fern fronds)*

Branched shrub, up to 1 m. In rocky places, **a weed on overgrazed areas**, up to 1800 m, SW Cape to N Prov. **Twigs creamy brown. Leaves:** ± 25 mm, **needlelike. Flowerheads:** ± 20 mm diam, ray florets mauve to white (throughout year), **aromatic. General:** Poisonous to sheep. Used for firewood. Hardy garden plant.

Felicia wrightii

Perennial, mat-forming herb. On earth banks along streams. **Leaves:** In flat, basal rosettes, ± 40 x 10 mm, thick, hairless, margins entire, with stout hairs. **Flowerheads:** Solitary, ± 20 mm diam, stems ± 25 mm, hairy, ray florets mauve (white), disc florets yellow (Sep-Oct).

Blumea (named after Karl Blume, died 1862, Dutch botanist) - Often aromatic. Old World trop, ± 75 species, 5 in SA.

Blumea mollis   *(mollis - soft)*

Erect herb, up to 900 mm. In damp grassland, widespread in trop. **Young parts, inflorescences covered in long white hairs. Leaves:** ± 100 x 50 mm, tapering to stalklike base ± 20 mm. **Flowerheads:** Inflorescences **drooping in bud**; ± 5 mm diam, pale pink to purple (Aug-Apr). **General:** Visited by honey-bees.

Helichrysum *(helios* - sun; *chrysos* - gold) - Herbs, shrubs, sometimes cushion forming (for description see p. 212).

Helichrysum adenocarpum   Pink Everlasting; Pienksewejaartjie (A); senko-toana, toane-balingoana (SS); uhlambahloshane obomvu (Z)   *(adenocarpum - glandular fruits)*

Perennial herb, up to 450 mm. In grassland, coast to 3000 m, E Cape to Zim. **Leaves: In rosettes**, 20-40(140) x 15-25(40) mm, **grey woolly. Flowerheads:** Simple or **branched inflorescences**; 15-20 x 25-35 mm, bracts red, pink or white (Sep-May). **General:** Lovely garden plant. Subsp. *adenocarpum*, bracts red to pink. Subsp. *ammophilum*, coastal KZN, Moz; bracts white. (See p. 212)

Helichrysum caespititium   Speelwonderboom (A); boriba, botsiki-nyane, lelulaphooko, moriri-oa-lefatse, phate-ea-naha (SS)   *(caespititium - spreading in carpetlike patches)*

Perennial, **mat-forming** herb. On sparsely grassed areas, Cape to N Prov. **Leaves:** 5-10 x 0,5 mm, **covered in silvery hairs** (tissue-papery). **Flowerheads:** 5 x 2 mm, tips white or pink (Aug-Dec). **General:** Used traditionally to treat colds and cure nausea.

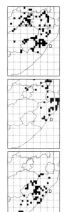

Helichrysum candolleanum   umaphipha (Z)   *(candolleanum - like Candollea)*

Perennial herb, 150-450(900) mm. In grassland, sometimes a weed, KZN to Zim, Moz, Nam. Very variable. **Leaves:** 10-35 x 1-8 mm, **greyish woolly. Flowerheads: Inflorescences** ± 20 mm diam; ± 6 x 4 mm, bract **tips pointed, shiny, transparent**, silvery white, **tinged pink, disc florets yellow** tipped red (throughout year).

Helichrysum ecklonis   [= *H. lamprocephalum, H. scapiforme*]   umuthi wechanti (X)   (named after Christian Ecklon, 1795-1868, apothecary, traveller and plant collector)

Perennial herb, up to 500 mm. On grassy slopes, coast to 2750 m. **Leaves: In basal rosette**, 100-200 x 20 mm, soft, loosely cobwebby, **sometimes hairless above, 3-5 veined**, persistently woolly beneath. **Flowerheads: Solitary**, 25-30 x 40 mm, bracts glossy white to deep pink (Sep-Jan). **Similar species:** *H. adenocarpum* (see p. 212).

Athrixia (*thrix* - hair) - Erect perennial herbs or shrubs. Afr, Madag, ± 25 species, 13 in SA, mainly summer rainfall areas.

Athrixia gerrardii   (after William Gerrard, died 1866, naturalist, traveller, who collected in Natal in 1860)

Perennial herb, up to 600 mm. In stony grassland, above 1200 m. **Leaves:** ± 35 x 2 mm, white felted beneath, margins rolled under. **Flowerheads: Solitary**, ± 25 mm diam, ray florets magenta, disc florets yellow, **bracts tapering to long bristle points**, margins, midveins dark, loosely white woolly, gland dotted (Nov-Jan).

Athrixia phylicoides   Bushman's Tea; Boesmanstee (A); luphephetse, sephomolo (Sw); icholocholo (X,Z); iphephetha, ishanela, ishayelo (Z)   *(phylicoides - resembles Phylica)*

Aromatic shrub, up to 1 m. In grassland, forest margins, coast to mountains. **Leaves:** ± 30 x 10 mm, smooth, shiny above, white felted beneath. **Flowerheads:** ± 15 mm diam, ray florets mauve, disc florets yellow (throughout year). **General:** Used to make 'hard' brooms and a tea. Used traditionally to treat coughs, sores and boils.

Felicia filifolia

Felicia filifolia

Blumea mollis

Hilliard & Burtt

C J Ward

Van Wyk & Malan

Felicia wrightii

Helichrysum adenocarpum

Helichrysum candolleanum

Lal Greene

Lal Greene

Van Wyk & Malan

Helichrysum caespititium

Helichrysum ecklonis

Athrixia gerrardii

Van Wyk & Malan

Tony Abbott

Lal Greene

Athrixia phylicoides

Athrixia phylicoides

Geoff Nichols

Tony Abbott

443

Bidens (Latin for 2 toothed, refers to 2 hooks on seed) - **Black-jacks or Cosmos** Herbs; leaves opposite, entire or compound; flowerheads solitary or in loose inflorescences. Cosmop, mostly America, ± 250 species, ± 7 in SA.

★ *Bidens formosa* [= *Cosmos bipinnata*] Cosmos; Kosmos, Mieliepes (A)

Bushy annual herb, up to 2,5 m. Naturalised weed, on roadsides, disturbed places, introduced as fodder in late 1890s from USA. Leaves opposite, ± 100 x 50 mm, deeply lobed. Flowerheads ± 100 mm diam, solitary on long bare stems, ray florets white, pink to deep red (Feb-May). **Often in spectacular stands.**

Senecio (*senex* - old man, refers to whitish grey hairy pappus) - Herbs, shrubs; flowerheads solitary or in inflorescences, bracts in a single row, margins interlocking. Largest genus of flowering plants, ± 2000 world wide, ± 300 in SA.

Senecio polyodon ihubo (Z) (*polyodon* - many toothed)

Perennial herb, up to 750 mm. In grassland, **marshes or seasonally flooded grassland**, up to 3000 m, E Cape to Zim. Stem solitary, leafy, sticky hairy, often reclining, rooting at base. **Leaves: Long, narrow**, in basal rosette, ± 100(300) x 20(40) mm, margins coarsely toothed, narrowing gradually to longish, flat stalks; stem leaves broadly clasping at base. **Flowerheads:** In branched inflorescence; var. *polyodon*, white to purple, **no ray florets**; var. *subglaber*, pink, magenta to bluish, **with ray florets** (Oct-Jan). **General:** Whole plant sweet smelling.

Senecio poseideonis (*poseideonis* - after Poseidon, god of the sea)

Branching herb, up to 1,5 m, in colonies. Along streams, on damp banks in forest. Stems leafy, sticky hairy. **Leaves:** ±150 x 65 mm, **finely lobed**, with enlarged terminal lobe, margins toothed, base eared, stem-clasping. **Flowerheads:** ± 20 mm diam, ± 8 ray florets (or absent), lilac, purple or white, disc florets mauve to whitish (Dec-Jan). **General:** Flower colour variable.

Senecio speciosus Beautiful Senecio; sebea-mollo-se-senye-nyane (SS); idambiso (X,Z); ibohlololo, inzwabuhlungu (Z) (*speciosus* - beautiful)

Fleshy, perennial herb, up to 700 mm, **forming clumps**. In damp grassland, marshy places, Cape to Moz. Several stems from crown, softly hairy to nearly hairless. **Leaves:** In basal rosette, 100-200(400) x 20-40(110) mm, **margins lobed, wavy or coarsely, widely toothed, narrowing to flat, stalklike, clasping base. Flowerheads: In flattish, branched inflorescences**; ± 40 mm diam, magenta to deep purple or pale pink (Jul-Jan). **General:** Used in traditional medicine to treat

chest complaints, dropsy, headaches and for poultices. Decorative even when not in flower, dies back briefly. Good in frost-free gardens, grown from seed. **Similar species:** *S. macrocephalus* Mountain Senecio; ngoakoana-ea-loti, sebea-mollo (SS) In open grassland, up to 2500 m; leaf margins entire, wavy to shallowly toothed, narrowing to broad flat base (stalkless); flowerheads in narrow to flattish inflorescences, bracts and branches with long, gland tipped hairs.

Emilia - Old World, ± 100 species, 3 pantrop weeds, 6 in SA.

Emilia transvaalensis [=*Senecio transvaalensis*]

Bushy annual herb, up to 450 mm. In poor rocky ground, on roadsides, along Lebombo mountains, KZN to Mpum. **Stems woody,** leaves clustered midway. **Leaves:** Slightly fleshy, ± 60 x 15 mm, grey, thinly cobwebby at first, maturing hairless, tapering to broad, clasping base. **Flowerheads:** Solitary, ± 12 mm diam, pink, on slender stalks, ± 250 mm (throughout year). **General:** Pretty, grown from seed.

Garuleum (corruption of *coeruleus* - refers to deep blue colour of marginal female florets) - Shrubs with sticky rough hairs. SA endemic, ± 8 species.

Garuleum latifolium (*latifolium* - broad leaves)

Slender, leafy, aromatic shrublet, up to 1,3 m. On margins of bush clumps, up to 800 m. **Leaves:** Alternate, ± 60 x 30 mm, coarsely toothed or deeply cut, margins toothed, stalkless or narrowing to stalklike base, often with pair of stipulelike basal ears, sticky, woolly hairs on stems and beneath leaves. **Flowerheads:** Showy, in loose terminal inflorescences; ± 25 mm diam, ray florets pink, lilac to blue, disc florets yellow, **outer bracts shorter than inner,** stalks ± 150 mm (Feb-Apr). **Similar species:** *G. sonchifolium* 915-1800 m, E Cape to KZN; plants sticky, aromatic; **bracts ± the same length** (Nov-May). *Garuleum* sp. nov. E Cape, S KZN mountains; low growing, from woody base; leaves sharply toothed; flowers (Oct).

444

★ *Bidens formosa*
Senecio polyodon

Senecio poseideonis *Senecio speciosus* *Senecio polyodon*

Emilia transvaalensis *Garuleum sonchifolium* *Garuleum latifolium*

Lal Greene

Lal Greene

Tony Abbott

Martin von Fintel

Lal Greene

Martin von Fintel

Lal Greene

Tony Abbott

445

Dimorphotheca (*dis* - twice; *morph* - shape; *theka* - a fruit, refers to two kinds of fruit found in same fruiting head) - Herbs, shrubs or subshrubs; hairless or hairy, often sticky glandular. Afr, ± 19 species.

Dimorphotheca jucunda [= *Osteospermum jucundum*] Trailing Mauve Daisy; Bergbietou, Bloutou (A); umasigcolo-nkonekazi (Z) (*jucunda* - lovely)

Spreading, perennial herb, up to 450(600) mm, in clumps. In rocky grassland, over low cliffs, up to 3200 m. Stems erect or trailing, young parts leafy, thinly downy throughout. **Leaves:** 60-150 x 20 mm, margins entire or faintly toothed. **Flowerheads:** Solitary, ± 60 mm diam, **pink, magenta, ray florets coppery below, disc florets tipped black**, stalks ± 150 mm (Sep-Jun). **General:** Used in traditional medicine to treat stomach complaints. Lovely plant for gardens. The common garden plant is derived from *D. barberae*, E Cape coast, known as 'Bloem Erf Beauty'.

Berkheya (named after Jan le Francq van Berkhey, 1729-1812, Dutch botanist) - Perennial herbs or shrubs, often thistlelike; leaves in rosette or alternate, spiny; flowerheads medium to large, solitary or in terminal inflorescences, bracts usually spiny. Mostly SA, ± 75 species.

Berkheya onopordifolia mohato, ntsoantsane (SS) (see under *B. cirsiifolia* p. 334)

Berkheya purpurea Purple Berkheya; Bloudisseldoring (A); sehlohlo, sehloohlo (SS)

Stout, perennial herb, up to 900 mm, in large colonies. On steep, grassy mountain slopes, in rough vegetation along streams, 1525-3050 m. **Leaves:** Basal, crowded, ± 250 x 100 mm, harshly hairy above, woolly white beneath, margins wavy, toothed or shallowly lobed, spiny. **Flowerheads:** In terminal inflorescence; 50-80 mm diam, **ray florets pale to deep mauve** (white), **disc florets purple**, bracts ± 5 mm broad, tips, margins spiny (Jan-Apr). **General:** Topmost flower opens first.

Platycarpha (*platys* - broad, flat; *karphos* - scale, refers to the pappus) - Perennial herbs. Afr, ± 5 species, 3 in SA.

Platycarpha glomerata usiphahluka (Z) (*glomerata* - club-shaped)

Perennial herb, in colonies. On poor, stony, sandy soils. Fleshy, stout, underground runners, ± 10 mm diam, **crown woolly white**. **Leaves:** In basal rosette, ± 300 x 100 mm, white felted beneath, margins coarsely, deeply toothed, teeth spiny. **Flowerheads: In crowded, stalkless inflorescence**, ± 100 mm diam; purple, bracts straw coloured, sharply pointed (Nov-Feb). **General:** Grows easily from seed.

Cirsium (*kirsion* - a kind of thistle) - N Hemisp, ± 300 species, a few weed species introduced into SA.

★ *Cirsium vulgare* Scotch Thistle; Disseldoring, Skaapdissel, Skotsedissel, Wildekarmedik (A); hlaba, ntsoa-ntsane (SS)

Robust, spiny, biennial herb, up to 2 m. Widespread **declared weed** of moist areas and disturbed places, coast to 1830 m. Leaves in large, flat rosette in first season, ± 450 x 100 mm. Stems develop in second year, much branched, leaves ± 150 x 70 mm, with stiff hairs above, grey-white woolly beneath, deeply lobed, segments ending in strong spines. Flowerheads in terminal inflorescences, 35 x 25 mm, pink to reddish purple, bracts with long recurved spiny tips (Sep-Jul).

Gerbera (after Traugott Gerber, died 1743, German naturalist) - Perennial herbs (for description see p. 82).

Gerbera aurantiaca x *G. kraussii* Hilton Daisy Natural Hybrids (see under *G. aurantiaca* p. 82).

Dicoma (*di* - two; *kome* - tuft of hairs, refers to double pappus of first species of *Dicoma* described) - Woody perennial herbs, erect or prostrate; leaves alternate, simple, usually felted below; flowerheads usually solitary, stalkless, bracts sharp pointed, ray florets absent, pappus mostly bristly rough or feathery. Mostly Afr, ± 32 species, ± 25 in SA.

Dicoma zeyheri Doll's Protea, Toy Sugarbush; Jakkalsbossie, Maagwortel (A); mahlabane, somanheva (Sw); umlunge, umqele (X); isihlabamakhondlwane, ububendle (Z) (named after Carl Zeyher, 1799-1858, botanical collector who came to the Cape in 1822)

Perennial herb, up to 400 mm. In grassland or wooded grassland on rocky soil. Stems branching above, cobwebby. **Leaves:** ± 110 x 30 mm, leathery, hairless above, **white felted beneath**, margins entire or faintly toothed. **Flowerheads:** Solitary or in few-flowered inflorescences; 40-60 mm diam, purplish, **bracts ± 25 x 10 mm, sharp pointed, silvery**, ± tinged purple (Jan-May). **General:** Used in traditional medicine to treat chest ailments, as blood strengtheners to mothers after a long, difficult birth. Hardy garden plant, long lasting cut-flower. **Similar species:** *D. argyrophylla* [= *D. zeyheri* subsp. *argyrophylla*] Coast to 1200 m; lower leaves large, narrowing to stalklike base; **stem leaves densely overlapping, sharp tipped, resembling flowerhead bracts** (Dec-Apr). *D. speciosa* (see p. 220).

Dimorphotheca jucunda

Pam Cooke

Berkheya onopordifolia

Tony Abbott

Berkheya purpurea

Darrel Plowes

Dimorphotheca jucunda

Wally Menne

Gerbera (hybrid)

Wally Menne

Dicoma zeyheri

Tony Abbott

Dicoma argyrophylla

Tony Abbott

★ *Cirsium vulgare*

Martin von Fintel

Platycarpha glomerata

Wally Menne

447

MONOCOTYLEDONS Single seed leaf, parallel veins; flower parts in threes or multiples of three.

COMMELINACEAE - Commelina Family Herbs. **Commelina** - Flowers within boat-shaped bracts (for description see p. 222).

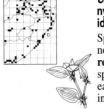

Commelina benghalensis Benghal Commelina; Blouselblommetjie (A); khopo-e-nyenyane, khotsoana (SS); uhlotshane (X); idambiso, idangabane, idemadema, idlebendlele (Z) (*benghalensis* - of Benghal)

Spreading herb, up to 500 mm. Widespread weed. Origins uncertain, probably indigenous. Plant hairy. **Leaves:** ± 80 x 30 mm, shiny, **abruptly narrowed at base, long reddish brown hairs** at mouth of leaf sheath. **Flowers: Small**, pale to deep blue, spathes ± 10 x 15 mm, **clustered** towards ends of stems (Aug-Jun). **General:** Leaves eaten as spinach in times of drought. Browsed by bushbuck. Used traditionally to treat infertility, burns, sore throats, sore eyes, dysentery, rashes and leprosy.

Commelina eckloniana Ecklon's Blue Commelina; idangabane elincane (Z) (after Christian Ecklon, 1795-1868, German collector, in renowned partnership with Carl Zeyher; collecting in SA from 1823)

Annual, up to 350 mm, spreading. In rocky areas, SA, to Trop Afr. Rootstock knobbly. **Leaves:** 60-100 x 8-25 mm, pale grey-green, **long, narrow. Flowers:** Blue, **spathes solitary**, recurved, 10-15 mm, stalks ± 25 mm (Aug-Apr). **General:** Sometimes eaten as spinach.

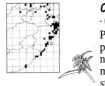

Commelina erecta Blue Commelina; Blouselblommetjie (A); idangabane (Z) (*erecta* - upright)

Perennial, erect or spreading, up to 500 mm. In sandy coastal areas and in wet places, E Cape, widespread in Afr, America, Asia, Austr. **Leaves:** 60-120 mm, narrow, oval, folded upwards. **Flowers:** Blue, close mid-morning, spathes15-30 mm, margins joined at base, **wet inside** (throughout year). **General:** Spathes usually stalked, solitary but also stalkless and clustered, particularly along KZN coast.

Aneilema (*aneilema* - without sheaths) - Herbs; inflorescences loosely branched. Cosmop, ± 80 species, 11 in SA.

Aneilema dregeanum Blue Aneilema (named after Johann Drège, 1794-1881, German traveller, plant collector, horticulturalist, who came to the Cape with his brother Carl in 1826)

Perennial herb, up to 300 mm, mostly low growing. In thicket, on forest margins, in coastal, low-lying areas, up to 940 m, E Cape to Moz. Stems pale lemon, trailing. **Leaves:** Spirally arranged, 30-110 x 10-45 mm. **Flowers:** In terminal inflorescences; flowers ± 18 mm wide, blue or lilac, close before 14h00 (Aug-Apr).

Cyanotis (*cyanotis* - refers to blue flowers) - Succulent perennials; with bulbs, corms, rhizomes or tubers, often with separate fertile and sterile shoots. Warm regions, Europe, Asia, Afr, ± 50 species, 7 in SA.

Cyanotis speciosa [= *C. nodiflora*] Doll's Powderpuff; Bloupoeierkwassie (A); khopo, theepe-balingoana (SS); umagoswana (X); inkombo, insonga, udabulamafu, umakotigoyile (Z)

Solitary or in small groups, up to 500 mm. Widespread in summer rainfall areas, SA to Tanz. **Rhizome swollen, U-shaped. Leaves:** Basal, ± 170 x 8 mm, dark green with long hairs beneath, sheaths purple. **Flowers:** 1-3 **erect** flowering stems, tepals pink, purple or blue, **stamens densely hairy**, close at midday (blooms throughout year). **General:** Grazed by cattle. Roots used in traditional medicine to treat infertility and as a love charm. Container plant, in the sun. (See p. 340)

PONTEDERIACEAE - Aquatic herbs, rooted or free floating. Trop and warm regions, 6 genera, ± 32 species, 4 genera in SA. **Eichhornia** (after Johann Eichhorn, died 1856, Prussian official) - Mostly America, 6 species, 1 Afr (*E. natans*).

★ *Eichhornia crassipes* Water Hyacinth; Waterhiasint (A) (*crassipes* - thick)

Aquatic herb, 40-600 mm. Widespread (from S America). Leaf blade ± 100 mm, stalks ± 500 mm, inflated. Flowers ± 50 mm diam, mauve-blue and yellow (Nov-May). **A serious problem in open fresh water.** Decorative plant which should NOT be grown.

ASPHODELACEAE - Formerly part of Liliaceae (for description see p. 224). **Caesia** (named after Frederico Cesi, 1585-1630, Italian naturalist)- Grasslike plants; flower stalks erect, curved in fruit. Afr, Austr, Madag, ± 12 species, 2 in SA.

Caesia contorta (*contorta* - contorted)

100-700 mm, grasslike. In grassland, W Cape to S KZN. Roots woody. **Leaves:** 5-35 x 1-4 mm, ribbed, in a fan. **Flowers:** In loose, much branched or long and simple inflorescence; **flowers blue, spirally twisted when faded**, lobes 3 veined, stalks 3-10 mm, lengthening in fruit (Dec).

Commelina eckloniana   *Tony Abbott*

Commelina erecta   *Tom de Waal*

Aneilema dregeanum   *Tony Abbott*

Cyanotis speciosa   *Rosemary Williams*

Commelina benghalensis   *Martin von Fintel*

Aneilema dregeanum

Caesia contorta   *Tony Abbott*

Cyanotis speciosa   *Lawrence Peacock*   *Van Wyk & Malan*

★ *Eichhornia crassipes*   *CJ Cilliers NBI*

ALLIACEAE - Onion Family Perennial herbs with bulbs, bulblike corms or rhizomes (in SA species). Leaves basal. Inflorescence with membraneous bracts at base, stamens 6, ovary superior. Some species have an onion smell (*Tulbaghia*). Fruit a capsule, seeds black. Subcosmop, ± 30 genera, ± 850 species, 4 genera in SA.

Agapanthus (*agape* - love; *anthos* - flower) **-** Rootstock tuberous; inflorescence enclosed in two bracts in bud, flowers mostly tubular. Excellent garden plants, first grown in Holland in the 1680s. Endemic to SA, 10 species.

Agapanthus campanulatus Bell Agapanthus; Bloulelie (A); leta-laphofu (SS); ugebeleweni (X); ubani (Z) (*campanulatus* - bell-shaped)

Slender deciduous perennial, up to 700 mm, in colonies. In moist grassland, on rocky hillsides, up to 2400 m, E Cape to N Prov. **Leaves:** Narrowing to **stemlike base**, 150-500 x 10-25 mm, greyish green, purplish at base. **Flowers:** Inflorescence with 10-30 flowers, **less than 35 mm**, light to dark blue with darker blue stripe, **tepal lobes spreading**, stalks 20-70 mm (Dec-Mar). **General:** Used traditionally as a protective charm. Popular garden plant, good cut-flower. Subsp. *campanulatus*, flower tube long, tepal lobes less spreading. Subsp. *patens*, tepal lobes more spreading.

Agapanthus caulescens hlakahla (Sw) (*caulescens* - producing stems)

Deciduous, 0,6-1,8 m. In rocky areas. **Leaves: Forming short stem**, 250-600 x 15-50 mm, bright green, margins transparent. **Flowers: ± 50 mm**, tube shorter than tepal lobes, **lobes spreading widely, sometimes curving back**, bright blue (white), stalks 30-70 mm, spreading to drooping (Jan-Feb). **General:** Used in traditional medicine. Good garden plant. Subsp. *angustifolius*, stiffly erect; leaves narrow; flowers often smaller, tepal lobes not recurving. Subsp. *caulescens*, leaves broad, ± 50 mm wide, tips blunt; flowers larger. Subsp. *gracilis*, leaves floppy; tepal lobes strongly recurved.

Agapanthus inapertus Drakensberg Agapanthus, Drooping Agapanthus; Bloulelie (A); hlakahla (Sw) (*inapertus* - closed)

Deciduous, up to 1,5(2) m. On forest margins, in grassland, in mountains. **Leaves:** Forming stem at base, more or less in fan, 450-670 x 30-60 mm, often arching, grooved, grey-green, tips more or less pointed. **Flowers:** 30-60 mm, **tubular, drooping**, violet to deep blue (white), stalks 20-55 mm, erect to spreading at first (Jan-Mar). **General:** Used traditionally as a good luck charm. Good garden plant, deciduous or evergreen. 5 subspecies, differing in shape and size of flowers.

Agapanthus praecox Common Agapanthus; Bloulelie, Gewone Agapant (A); ubani (Z) (*praecox* - appearing early)

Evergreen perennial, up to 1,5 m, in clumps. In grassland, on rocky hillsides, S Cape to KZN. **Leaves: Not forming stem at base**, 200-700 x 15-55 mm, grooved, arching. **Flowers: ± 100, in dense inflorescence;** flowers 30-70 mm, tepal lobes widely spreading, mauve to pale blue (white), stalks 40-120 mm, spreading (Dec-Feb). **General:** Used traditionally to ensure easy birth and healthy children, as an aphrodisiac and for protective charms. Popular garden plant, in cultivation since 1680s. Subsp. *minimus* Dwarf Agapanthus, small, slender, ± 600 mm, not in dense clumps, few-flowered inflorescence. Subsp. *orientalis*, in dense clumps; leaves shorter, more rigid; inflorescence dense, stem sturdy, flowers less than 50 mm, stalks very stiff. Subsp. *praecox*, leaves erect, leathery; flowers 50 mm or longer.

HYACINTHACEAE - Formerly part of Liliaceae. Mostly perennial herbs. Bulbs sometimes with a number of free scales. Inflorescence elongated, ovary superior. Fruit a capsule, seeds black. Subcosmop, ± 41 genera, ± 770 species, 27 genera in SA.

Scilla (*squilla* - the sea squill) - Bulbous herbs, flowering with or without leaves. Afr, Europe, Asia, ± 40 species, 6 in SA.

Scilla dracomontana Miniature Blue Scilla (*dracomontana* - dragon mountains, the Drakensberg)

Small, up to 110 mm, in colonies. On cliffs, rock platforms, 1675-2100 m. **Leaves: Flat on ground**, produced **with flowers**. **Flowers:** Inflorescence 25-45 mm; flowers blue (Sep-Nov). **General:** Previously incorrectly placed under *S. natalensis*. Hybrids and white flowered forms can be found in the Loteni/Sani Pass areas.

Scilla kraussii Dwarf Scilla; ichitha, inguduza (Z) (named after Christian Krauss, German scientist and collector who travelled in SA from 1838-1840)

Up to 250 mm. On rocky hillsides, below 1000 m. Bulb roundish, ± 50 mm diam. **Leaves:** Spreading, 50-75 mm, firm, strongly ribbed, softly hairy, green above, purplish beneath, after flowers. **Flowers:** Inflorescence 45-150 mm, stem slender, purple; flowers ± 10 mm diam, bracts purple (Jan). **General:** Has been placed under *S. natalensis* in the past.

450

Darrel Plowes

Agapanthus campanulatus

Pam Cooke

Agapanthus caulescens

Martin von Fintel

Agapanthus campanulatus

Lorraine van Hooff

Agapanthus praecox

Jo Onderstall

Agapanthus inapertus

Hilliard & Burtt

Scilla dracomontana

Martin Kunhardt

Scilla kraussii

451

Scilla natalensis **Large Blue Scilla; Blouslangkop (A); kherere (SS); ichitha, imbizenkulu, ubulika, inguduza (Z)**
Up to 1 m, solitary or in large colonies. Very variable. In damp grassland, cliffs and rocky slopes, coast to 2000 m. Bulb ± 300 mm diam, half above ground, papery, purplish brown. **Leaves:** Erect, ± 500 mm, grey-green, hairless or velvety, produced after flowers. **Flowers:** Inflorescence ± 300 x 100 mm, stem sturdy, arching; flowers ± 10 mm diam, pale to deep purplish blue (Sep-Dec). **General:** Poisonous to sheep. Used to make soap. Traditional treatment for internal tumours, boils, fractures and for lung disease in cattle. Frost resistant garden plant, cultivated from seed.

Ledebouria (named after Carl F Ledebour, 1785-1851, German prof of botany) - Bulbous herbs, outer bulb scales papery; leaves with reddish or green spots on upper surface. Afr, Asia, ± 30 species, 15 in SA.

Ledebouria revoluta (= *Scilla revoluta* S. *carnosula*) **Common Ledebouria, Wavy-leaved Ledebouria; bokhoe (SS); inqwebebane, ubuhlungu (X); icubudwana (Z)** (*revoluta* - rolled back from margin, refers to tepal lobes)
Up to 150 mm, solitary. In woodland. Bulb 60-80 x 40-60 mm, outer scales purplish brown. **Leaves:** 80-130 x 30-90 mm, with dark green or purplish spots, threads when torn. **Flowers:** 30-70 in dense inflorescences, 70-120 x 30-40 mm; flowers greenish mauve, filaments maroon (throughout year). **General:** Leaves used to make twine for mats. Used traditionally to treat skin irritations, wounds, lumbago and gall sickness in animals. Interesting garden plant. **Similar species:** *L. floribunda* (see p. 512).

IRIDACEAE - Iris Family (for description see p. 236). ***Moraea*** (named after Robert More, 1703-80, a cultivator of flowers in England. Linnaeus altered the spelling to honour his father-in-law, J Moraeus, a Swedish physician) - End of style branches petal-like. Afr, Madag, Austr, ± 90 species, ± 101 species in SA, mostly in SW Cape.

Moraea ardesiaca (*ardesiaca* - slate coloured, refers to dull slate blue flower colour)
Slender, up to 700 mm, solitary. In damp grassland near streams, 1800-2200 m, KZN Drakensberg endemic. Corm ± 15 mm diam. **Leaf:** Solitary, erect below, trailing above, 5-10(25) mm wide. **Flowers: Large,** outer tepals ± 75 mm, limb ± 50 x 35 mm, inner tepals ± 60 mm, **slate blue to purple, brown beneath** with **narrow, pale yellow nectar guides** on outer tepals (Nov-Jan).

Moraea elliotii **Blue Tulp; Bloutulp (A)** (named after George Scott Elliot, Scottish botanist who collected in SA in the late 1800s)
Up to 550 mm, solitary. In moist grassland, on rocky hillsides, S Cape to Malawi. Corm ± 20 mm diam, dark brown tunics forming fibrous neck. **Leaf: Solitary,** round, inserted near or well above the ground, **appears with flowers. Flowers:** Blue-violet, nectar guides yellow-orange, outer tepals ± 30 mm, spreading, inner ± 24 x 4 mm, limb ± 18 x 12 mm, open in evening (Aug-Mar). (See p. 110)

Moraea inclinata **Nodding Wild Iris; Knikkende Wilde-iris (A)** (*inclinata* - inclined, refers to stem)
Up to 900 mm. In damp grassland, 1525-2400 m. Corm ± 15 mm diam, fibrous brown tunics. **Leaf:** Solitary, **much longer than flowering stem**, round, margins inrolled, **inserted on upper part of stem just below flowers. Flowers: Large,** outer tepals ± 30 x 10 mm, blue-violet with yellow nectar guides, inner tepals ± 25 x 6 mm, limbs reflexed, **stem long, slender**, smooth or sometimes woolly, **usually leaning,** 2-4 branches (Nov-Mar, depending on altitude). **Fruit:** Capsule **round.**

Moraea natalensis **teele-roka, tele, tele-ea-thaba (SS); incembe (Z)**
Up to 450 mm. In seasonally wet exposed areas, coast to midlands KZN to Trop Afr. Corm ± 15 mm diam, covered in dark brown fibres. **Leaf:** Solitary, round, **well up flowering stem, as short as spathes or ± 200 mm. Flowers:** Lilac to blue-violet, nectar guide yellow, edged with dark mauve, outer tepals ± 20 mm, inner tepals ± 15 mm, opening late morning, **stem erect** (Dec-Jan). **Fruit:** Capsule **oval.**

Moraea stricta **Bloutulp (A)** (*stricta* - very straight or upright)
Up to 450 mm. In open grassland, widespread in Afr. Corm ± 30 mm diam, with dark brown fibres. **Leaf:** Solitary, ± 600 x 15 mm, round, **dead or absent at flowering. Flowers: Small,** pale lilac to **blue-violet**, nectar guides yellow, orange spotted, outer tepals ± 24 mm, limb ± 14 x 8 mm, inner tepals erect or drooping, ± 18 x 4 mm, ± 3 flowers open at once, closing at sunset, stem erect, with 3-6 **short branches**, bracts brown, **dry, papery** (Jul-Nov). **General:** Common on recently burnt grassland.

Scilla natalensis

Ledebouria revoluta

Moraea ardesiaca

Moraea elliotii

Moraea inclinata

Moraea inclinata

Moraea inclinata

Moraea stricta

Moraea natalensis

453

Aristea (*aristos* - best, noblest) - Perennial; rhizome creeping or erect; leaves in fan; flowers blue, twist into tight spiral after blooming; open early and close by midday except on overcast days. Afr, ± 49 species, 39 in SA.

Aristea angolensis

Slender to robust, up to 1 m. In mountain grassland, on marshy areas, streambanks, coast to 2200 m, mostly at higher altitudes, E Cape to Nigeria. **Leaves:** Basal, ± 600 x 10 mm, stem leaves, 30-335 mm. **Flowers:** In clusters, within bracts, ± 9 mm, inflorescence well branched, stem ± 6 mm wide; flowers ± 20 mm diam, **bright sky-blue**, also mauve, dark purple-blue (Sep-Feb). **Fruit:** Capsule slightly oblong. **General:** A number of subspecies described in S Afr. Hardy garden plant.

Aristea abyssinica [= *A. cognata*] **Blue-eyed Grass, Miniature Blue Iris; lethepu-le-lenyenyane (SS); phayimashimane (Sw); icebethwane (Z)**

Slender, 100-330 mm, in tufts. Widespread on rocky outcrops, in sparse grassland, marshy areas, coast to 2100 m, E Cape to Trop Afr. **Leaves: Narrow, all clustered at base,** ± 300 x 3 mm. **Flowers: In a terminal cluster, stem narrow**, unbranched, flattened, without midrib, margins translucent, white; flowers ± 15 mm diam, **sky-blue**, violet, deep red, pink (Sep-Mar). **Fruit:** Oblong capsule. **General:** Used in traditional medicine to treat sprains and as a protective charm.

Aristea ecklonii **Blue Stars; Blousterre (A); phayimashimane (Sw); ikhambi eliluhlaza, ikhwanyana, umabhanjana, umafosi, umhushuza (Z)** (named after Christian Ecklon, 1795-1868, born in Denmark, apothecary, traveller and plant collector)

Up to 1 m, in clumps. On forest margins, streambanks, grassland, scrub, E Cape to Tanz. **Leaves:** Basal, in a fan, ± 600 x 14 mm, curved, outer edge white; stem leaves 36-400 x 3-12 mm, narrow, bases keeled. **Flowers:** Inflorescence stem flattened, branched or not, upper part zigzag, bracts rusty brown; flowers ± 20 mm diam, pale to deep mauve-blue (Aug-Mar). **Fruit:** Oblong 3-angled capsule. **General:** Used in traditional medicine to treat fever, coughs, venereal disease, internal sores and as a protective charm. Popular garden plant, requires morning sun. Flowers close early, but provide a wonderful display for a few weeks.

Aristea schizolaena (*schizo* - cleave; *laena* - a cloak)

Robust, 360-930 mm. In damp places, coast to 1670 m. **Leaves:** Basal, ± leathery, spreading, narrowing to pointed tip, margins translucent white to brown, veins noticeable, 210-520 x 3-12 mm; stem leaves curved, keeled. **Flowers:** 2-3 in clusters, inflorescence slightly branched, **bracts oval, with dark rusty brown triangle** at base, prominently veined, **midvein raised**, tips pointed, torn; flowers ± 20 mm diam, blue to deep purple (Dec-Mar). **Fruit:** Capsule oblong.

Aristea woodii **Wood's Aristea; Blousuurkanol (A); khahla, lethepu-le-lenyenyane (SS); phayimashimane (Sw); umluzi omncane (Z)** (named after John Medley Wood, 1827-1915, botanist, first curator Natal Herbarium)

Evergreen perennial, up to 850 mm. In grassland, coast to 2500 m, E Cape (Transkei) to Zim. **Leaves:** ± 450 x 10 mm, in basal fan, narrowly spreading, tips, margins translucent white; stem leaves ± 470 x 4 mm, **tips fringed, translucent white. Flowers:** Stem branched, oval, ± 9 mm wide, **bracts** ± 10 mm, **oval, deeply torn,** dark brown in centre, sheathing the stem; flowers ± 20 mm diam, dark blue, pale blue or deep mauve (Sep-Mar). **Fruit:** Oblong, dark brown, angled, ± 8 x 4 mm. **General:** Used as protective and good luck charms. Garden plant for semi-shady areas.

Dierama (*dierama* - a funnel) - **Hairbells, Wand-flowers; Grasklokkies** - Fibrous coated corms; leaves grasslike; flowering stem tall, slender, usually branched, arching, flowers with dry papery bracts, hanging on slender stalks. Lovely plants for the garden. Afr, ± 38 species in SA.

Dierama floriferum (*floriferum* - bearing flowers)

In clumps, 400-750 mm. In grassland, marshy ground, 800-1675 m. **Leaves:** 380-700 x 2-5 mm. **Flowers:** In crowded, drooping inflorescence with **4-9 branches**, each with 4-8 flowers, bracts ± 17 x 8 mm, **tip of each bract just reaching next bract**, flecked in lower half, upper half with broad pure white margin; flowers ± 20 mm, deep mauve to pinkish purple or whitish (Aug-Dec). **Similar species:** Often misidentified as *D. medium* Dainty, solitary or in small clumps, confined to Mpum, Swaz; inflorescence with 2-3 branches, bracts overlapping, dark brown in lower half with light flecking, white margins. *D. dracomtanum* (see p. 354).

Aristea angolensis

Aristea schizolaena

Aristea woodii

Aristea angolensis

Aristea abyssinica

Aristea ecklonii

Dierama floriferum

455

Dierama trichorhizum *(trichorhizum - hairy roots)*
Solitary or in small tufts, 100-600 mm. Often in colonies in damp grassland, 1200-2700 m. **Leaves:** ± 4, 150-400 x 2-3 mm, **on a separate shoot, often not developed at flowering, basal internode** 5-20 mm between top of corm and lowest stem leaves, **1-2 cormlets in axil of lower leaf sheaths. Flowers: In solitary inflorescence, erect or with 1-4 drooping branches, few flowers, bracts small**, 6-14 x 5-8 mm, tips 3 toothed, **speckled to golden brown**; flowers 18-25 mm, pale mauve to light purple (Sep-Jan). **Similar species:** *D. pauciflorum* (see p. 356).

Gladiolus *(gladiolus - small sword, refers to leaf shape)* - Corms (for description see p. 110).

Gladiolus crassifolius Thick-leaved Gladiolus; khahla-e-nyenyane (SS); sidvwana (Sw)
(crassifolius - thick leaves)
Up to 1 m, in small groups. Widespread, in grassland, coast to 1950 m, E Cape to Trop Afr. Corm roundish, 20-30 mm diam, covered in brown fibres, deeply buried. **Leaves:** Erect, ± 700 x 12 mm, **margins and midrib yellow**, forming **sheathing fan. Flowers:** In densely packed inflorescence, **stem curving out from leaves**, with 1-3 branches, buds in two rows; 12-22(40) flowers, turned to one side, small, 25-40 mm, pale lilac, pink, orange or mauve, lower two lobes with dark blotch (throughout year). **Fruit:** Capsule small, roundish, ± 8 mm, reddish brown. **General:** Pollinated by long proboscid flies. Used in traditional medicine to cure headaches. (See p. 356)

Gladiolus densiflorus *(densiflorus - densely covered with flowers)*
Up to 1,3 m, solitary or in small clumps. In grassland, up to 1300 m. Corm ± 30 mm diam, tunics of wiry brown fibres. **Leaves:** 6-8 forming a spreading fan, 250-500 x 10-35 mm, **soft**, blue-green, midvein raised, yellow, **many fine, closely spaced veins**; stem leaves 3-4, bractlike, sheathing. **Flowers:** In dense spike, 15-30 flowers on one side, overlapping, rarely with side branches; flowers small, 30-40 mm, **funnel-shaped, densely spotted** with dark red, maroon or pink raised dots on whitish or greyish background, lower tepal lobes ± 15 mm, with yellowish mid line near tips, stamens purple (Feb-Apr). **Fruit:** Woody capsule, 10 mm diam, red-brown. **General:** Flowers can seem pure red or mauve when spotting is very dense. (See p. 44)

Gladiolus elliotii *(after George Scott Elliot who first collected this plant in the Bethal district in the 1890s)*
Plants up to 800 mm. In grassland, 1000-1600 m, Free State to Zim. Corm ± 25 mm diam, fibrous brown tunics. Hairless. **Leaves:** In compact fan, clasping at base, ± 700 mm x 20 mm, midrib and marginal veins raised, yellow, veins close set, leaves not always fully developed at flowering. **Flowers:** ± 25, in dense inflorescence, in two rows, pointing in opposite directions; flowers ± 50 mm, pale blue or mauve, densely speckled maroon or pink, forming a dark midline, yellowish patch on lower lobes (Nov-May). **Fruit:** Capsule ± 25 mm, oval, within bracts at first.

Gladiolus wilsonii (see p. 112)

ORCHIDACEAE - Orchid Family Highly specialised flowers (for description see p. 240).
Brachycorythis *(brachy - short; koros - helmet, refers to the uppermost of the 3 sepals)* - Terrestrial herbs; densely leafy from ground level, with large leaflike bracts; flower lip stretches forward. Afr, ± 35 species, 7 in SA.

Brachycorythis ovata imfeyamasele yentaba (Z) *(ovata - egg-shaped)*
Slender to robust, up to 450 mm. In grassland. **Leaves:** Crowded, ± 70 x 22 mm, sharp tipped. **Flowers:** In crowded inflorescence, lower flowers hidden within long bracts; flowers pale pink to purple with **white keel, lip purple spotted**, ± 13 mm, **3 lobed at the tip**, no spur (Oct-Jan), strongly scented. **General:** Used in traditional medicine to treat madness and as protective charm. **Similar species:** *B. pubescens* (see p. 362).

Disa (possibly from *dis* - rich or opulent) - Underground tubers; several leaves; median sepal hooded, prolonged into a spur or pouch, direction in which spur points is useful in identification. Afr and Madag, ± 130 species, ± 94 in SA.

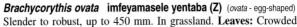

Disa cornuta Golden Orchid *(cornuta - horned or spurred)*
Robust, up to 1 m. Widespread in well drained grassland, coast to 2400 m, W Cape to Zim. **Leaves:** Densely leafy, basal and stem leaves overlapping, lower ones purple spotted. **Flowers:** In dense cylindrical spike, stem stout; flowers silvery purple, yellow and green, **spur 10-20 mm, facing upwards or backwards** (Sep-Feb), scent faintly spicy.

Dierama trichorhizum
Lal Greene

Gladiolus crassifolius
Tony Abbott

Gladiolus crassifolius
Geoff Nichols

Gladiolus densiflorus
Geoff Nichols

Gladiolus elliotii
Wally Menne

Gladiolus wilsonii
Geoff Nichols

Brachycorythis ovata
Auriol Batten

Brachycorythis ovata
Auriol Batten

Disa cornuta
Trevor Coleman

Disa sagittalis (*sagitta* - an arrow)

Up to 300 mm. On rocks, along streams, in shade, coast to 1000 m. **Leaves:** Basal, 5-10, strap-shaped, spreading; upper leaves dry sheaths. **Flowers:** In small, dense inflorescence; flowers white to mauve, petals darker, strap-shaped, from broad base, spur slender, 2-3 mm (Sep-Nov).

Disa similis (*similis* - like)

Slender, up to 500 mm. In swamps, E Cape to KZN, also in Angola, Zam. **Leaves:** 3-8, 120 x 15 mm near base stem. **Flowers:** Inflorescence with 10-30 horizontal flowers; pale violet to blue, sepals 7-9 mm, hood with short, flattened spur, 3 mm, lip oblong with yellow tip (Sep-Nov).

Disa stachyoides ihlamvu elimpofu lasenkangala (Z) (*stachyoides* - resembles *Stachys*, Wound Wort)

100-400 mm. Widespread in upland dry grassland, up to 2000 m. **Leaves:** Few, pointed, ± 80 x 10 mm. **Flowers:** In dense inflorescence, ± 100 mm; flowers small, purple with white lip, **spur 2-6 mm, broad, flat, almost horizontal** (Nov-Jan). **General:** Used to ward off evil and storms. (See p. 368)

Disa stricta (*strictus* - straight)

Slender, erect, up to 450 mm. On grassy slopes, damp floodplains, 1800-2400 m. **Leaves:** Narrow, rigid, ± 200 mm. **Flowers:** In dense inflorescence; flowers pink to lilac or bluish, lip darker, **spur ± 5 mm, horizontal or pointing upwards** (Nov-Jan).

Brownleea (after Rev John Brownlee, 1791-1871, Scottish missionary who collected the type species of the genus in E Cape) - Terrestrial (rarely epiphytic or lithophytic) herbs; few leaves; median/odd sepal joins with two lateral petals to form trumpet-shaped hood which tapers gradually into curved spur, lip very small. Afr genus, ± 15 species, 5 in SA.

Brownleea coerulea (*coerula* - heavenly blue, dark blue)

100-600 mm. In shade of forest, on mossy tree trunks and rock ledges, coast to 1500 m. **Leaves:** 2-3, large, **oval**, ± 110 x 40 mm, soft. **Flowers:** **6-15**(30) in inflorescence; flowers bluish mauve, purple spots on hood, ± 10 mm, dorsal sepal ± 10 mm, spur ± 26 mm, **horizontal**, gradually curving downwards (Feb-Apr).

Herschelianthe (named after Sir John Frederick Herschel, eminent astronomer who spent some time at the Cape in the 1830s and collected and illustrated some of the wild flowers) - Lip fringed. Afr, 13 species in SA.

Herschelianthe baurii [= *Herschelia baurii*] Bloumoederkappie (A) (named after Leopold Richard Baur, German pharmacist, missionary and botanical collector who worked in the Transkei in the 1800s)

Slender, up to 400 mm. In grassland, damp spots near streams, coast to 2440 m, E Cape to Tanz. **Leaves:** Slender, grasslike, ± 300 mm, after flowers. **Flowers:** 2-14, pale mauve, pale blue, bright blue or purplish blue, **lip margins deeply dissected, fringed**, mauve to purple, spur greenish with slightly enlarged tip, ± 5mm, pointing upwards (Jul-Nov). **General:** Tubers eaten by bushpigs.

Calanthe (*kalos* - beautiful; *anthos* - flower) - Terrestrial, pseudobulbs in rows; leaves pleated; sepals and petals similar in shape and colour. Most common in Trop Asia, reaching Japan, Austr, ± 120 species, 1 in SA.

Calanthe sylvatica [= *C. natalensis*] (*sylvatica* - growing in woods and forests)

Up to 750 mm. On forest floor, in deep shade near streams, at low to medium altitudes, E Cape to Trop Afr. **Leaves:** Thin, pleated, ± 600 x 150 mm, stalklike base ± 150 mm. **Flowers:** Inflorescence held above leaves; flowers ± 50 mm wide, whitish mauve fading apricot, tinged turquoise-blue when bruised, lip 3 lobed, midlobe with two large rounded lobes at tip, spur 20-40 mm (Nov-Mar).

Eulophia (*eu* - well; *lophos* - crest, refers to the crested lip) - Terrestrial herbs; rhizomes thickened into fibrous tubers, some with pseudobulbs; leaf-bearing shoot separate from flowering stem, leaves in two ranks; sepals more or less equal, lip with ridges on upper surface, spur very shallow or up to half length of flower. Mostly trop and subtrop regions of Old World, over 200 species, ± 42 species in SA.

Eulophia zeyheriana (named after Carl Zeyher, 1799-1858, botanical collector who came to Cape in 1822)

Slender, up to 400 mm. In sandy, stony or marshy grassland, 1200-2000 m. **Leaves:** Stiff, erect, 200-400 x 3-7 mm. **Flowers:** Inflorescence with ± 17 small flowers; sepals 7-10 mm, green and purplish brown, petals and lip pale blue tinged purple or completely dull red, lip crests white, spur 2-3 mm (Nov-Feb).

Disa sagittalis — Tom de Waal

Disa similis — Rick Taylor

Brownleea coerulea — Geoff Nichols

Disa stachyoides — Lal Greene

Disa stricta — Wally Menne

Brownleea coerulea — Geoff Nichols

Eulophia zeyheriana — Tom de Waal

Herschelianthe baurii — C J Ward

Calanthe sylvatica — C J Ward

459

DICOTYLEDONS Two seed leaves, net veins; flower parts in fours, fives or multiples of these.
NYMPHAEACEAE - Waterlily Family (for description see p. 138). *Nymphaea* (*nymphaios* - sacred to the nymphs; *nymphe* - goddess of springs) - Aquatic herbs; rhizome often tuberous; leaves large; flowers with 4 sepals, many petals; fruit fleshy ripening under water, seeds small, often with pulpy, saclike aril. Sometimes known as the Blue and White Lotus, not to be confused with the Lotus Lily of the East, *Nelumbium*, which has leaves and flowers raised well out of the water on long emergent stalks. Cosmop, ± 45 species, 2 in SA.

Nymphaea nouchali [= *N. caerulea, N. capensis, N. petersiana, N. stellata*] **Blue Waterlily; Blouwaterlelie (A); ikhubalo lechanti, intekwane (X); amazibu, izeleba, izubu (Z)**
(*nouchali* - probably from a wrongly interpreted English plant name)
Robust aquatic. In rivers, lakes and pools, SA, Trop Afr to Egypt. Tuberous rhizome. **Leaves:** 80-350 x 75-420 mm, blade smooth above, veins protruding beneath, under surface purple to green, margins toothed. **Flowers:** ± 120 mm diam, petals ± 50 x 15 mm, close at midday to re-open next day or remain open for a number of days (throughout year), scent lovely, stronger at night. **Fruit:** 20-30 mm, develops underwater. **General:** Tubers exposed on mudflats eaten by hippos, monkeys; collected in the shallows by local people, cooked as a vegetable. Flowers visited by beetles, flies and bees. Fruit eaten by Purple Gallinule. Used in traditional medicine to treat coughs, colds and as love charms. Commonly cultivated in garden ponds.

BRASSICACEAE (CRUCIFERAE) - **Cabbage or Mustard Family** Annual or biennial herbs (for description see p. 140).
Heliophila (*helios* - sun; *philein* - to love) - Annual or perennial herbs or shrubs (climbers); flowers with 4 petals; fruit with style short or long, slender or stout. Endemic to SA, ± 90 species, mostly in winter rainfall areas.

Heliophila rigidiuscula **Grassland Blue Cross Flower, Blue Cress; Bloubekkie (A); uvemvane oluncane (Z)** (*rigidiuscula* - rigid)
Slender, erect, perennial herb, 250-900 mm, solitary or in groups. In grassland, coast to 2800 m. Woody base with a few annual stems. **Leaves:** 20-120 x 1-4 mm, thin or slightly fleshy. **Flowers:** In long inflorescences on leafless stem; flowers drooping, 10-20 mm diam, pink, mauve, blue, purple, petals often with white or light 'eye' (Oct-Mar). **Fruit:** 30-70 x 3-8 mm. **General:** Leaves used as spinach.

FABACEAE (LEGUMINOSAE) - **Pea or Legume Family** (for description see p. 388).
Lotononis (combination of two genus names, *Lotus* and *Ononis*) - Woody or herbaceous herbs or shrublets; leaves 3(5) foliolate; flowers usually yellow (white, blue, violet). Mostly Afr, ± 150 species in SA.

Lotononis amajubica [= *Buchenroedera amajubica*] (*amajuba* - named for Majuba mountain, KZN)
Shrublet, up to 700 mm. In stony mountain grassland, 1200-2000 m. Woody rootstock. Stems annual, erect, branching at base, leafy, silvery hairy. **Leaves:** 5-35 mm, stalks short. **Flowers:** 10-80, in slender, crowded, terminal inflorescence, bracts long, slender; flowers small, ± 7 mm, blue fading to white at base, calyx long, densely silvery hairy (Nov-Jan). **Fruit:** Oval, 5-6 mm, silvery.

Lotononis bachmanniana (named after Frans Bachmann, 1856-1916, German medical doctor, naturalist)
Slender, perennial herb, up to 450 mm. In damp places, in grassland. Rootstock woody. Stems reclining to erect, hairless. **Leaves:** 9-15 x 2-4 mm, stalks ± 10 mm. **Flowers:** In loose, terminal clusters; flowers ± 10 mm, purple, blue (May).

Lotononis eriocarpa [= *L. wylei*] (*erio* - wool; *carpa* - fruit)
Robust shrublet, up to 1,2 m. In thicket near streams. Stems sturdy, branched, closely leafy, mostly hairless. **Leaves:** ± 14 x 5 mm, broadly rounded to pointed tip, narrowing to base, **midrib conspicuous, margins thickened**, stalks ± 6 mm. **Flowers:** In small clusters, in axils, ± 8 mm, blue (throughout year).

Lotononis galpinii (named after Ernest Galpin, 1858-1941, banker, amateur botanist)
Prostrate to erect shrublet, up to 150(600) mm diam. On rocky streambeds, rocky slopes, at high altitude. Much branched, silvery grey. **Leaves:** Small, leaflets 3-5 x 3 mm, stalks ± 3 mm. **Flowers: Solitary**, ± 10 mm, blue with white eye with yellow spot (Dec-Feb).

Lotononis lotononoides
Perennial shrublet, up to 1,2 m, sometimes in colonies. In moist rocky grassland, 1500-2650 m. Stems sturdy, branched, leafy. **Leaves:** Leaflets **oval**, ± 20 x 8 mm, grey-green, **hairlike tip recurved, sparsely hairy**, stalks ± 8 mm. **Flowers:** In axils towards ends of branchlets, dark blue, ± 10 mm (Dec-Apr).

Nymphaea nouchali

Heliophila rigidiuscula

Lotononis bachmanniana

Lotononis amajubica

Lotononis galpinii

Lotononis lotononoides

Lotononis eriocarpa

461

Lotononis sericophylla [= *L. trisegmentata*] **khonyana-stohana, motoaitoai (SS)** (*serico-phylla* - silky leaves)

Slender, erect shrub up to 1,5 m. In boulder beds, rocky streams and on riverbanks and disturbed areas, 1525-2400 m. Stems silky, much branched, bark greenish brown. **Leaves:** Leaflets small, ± 10 x 4 mm, **covered in silvery hairs. Flowers:** Solitary, ± 15 mm, pale blue, wings and keel pale greenish yellow or whitish (Dec-Mar). **General:** Very variable. **Similar species:** *L. divaricata* Less hairy; leaves smaller.

Pearsonia (named after Dr Harold Pearson, 1870-1916, first Director of the National Bot Gardens, Kirstenbosch) **-** Perennial herbs or shrublets; leaves 3 foliolate; standard petal erect, concave in the lower part, usually hairy outside, keel small, narrow, usually pointed; fruit flattened, straight, hairy, beaked. Similar to *Lotononis* which has the standard petal reflexed and the keel ± boat-shaped. S Trop Afr, ± 11 species, 7 in SA.

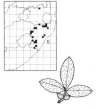

Pearsonia grandifolia **Mauve Frilly Pea** (*grandifolia* - large leaves)

Perennial herb, prostrate, forming mats. In montane grassland, often on steep, rocky ground, 1200-2100 m, KZN to Zim. Woody tap root. Stems zigzag, covered in short silvery hairs. **Leaves:** Very variable in size and shape, leaflets 35-70 x 20-35 mm, hairy, tapering to hairlike tip, stalks 3-15 mm, stipules 2-9 mm. **Flowers:** In terminal inflorescences, 50-150 mm; **flowers crumpled,** ± 20 mm, mauve or white with purple centre, calyx ±15 mm, densely hairy (Oct-Mar), scented. **Fruit:** ± 17 x 3 mm, densely hairy, just extending out of calyx. **General:** Two subspecies have been described, differing in size of bracts, flower stalks and calyx.

Psoralea (*psoraleos* - scabby, refers to glandular dots on leaflets) - Shrubs or herbs, mostly found in damp areas; leaflets slender. 24 species in SA.

Psoralea abbottii (after Tony Abbott, farmer, expert amateur botanist, specialising in the Pondoland flora)

Reclining shrublet, up to 1,5 m, in colonies. In grassland near marshy areas, on margins of swamp forest, 300-1500 m. Stems branching near base, arching above. **Leaves:** 3-5(7) leaflets, 20-25 x 0,5 mm, dull dark green, stalks short. **Flowers:** Solitary in axils, ± 14 mm, on short stalks, mauve with purple patch, **buds elongate** (Dec-Apr).

Otholobium (*otheo* - to burst forth; *lobos* - pod, fruit of *O. caffrum* seems to be 'pushing out of calyx') **-** Leaflets entire, oval, tips hairlike, recurved; flowers in 3s, with bract at base. Found in drier areas than *Psoralea* species. Restricted to S and SE Afr, ± 40 species in SA.

Otholobium caffrum [= *Psoralea caffrum*] (*caffrum* - from Kaffraria, E Cape)

Erect shrub, up to 6 m. On forest margins. Stems leafy, with prominent glands, hairy at first. **Leaves:** Leaflets 10-45 x 7-30 mm, thickly gland dotted, terminal leaflet stalklets ± 10 mm, stalks ± 18 mm. **Flowers:** In loose or dense inflorescences, stems ± 50 mm; flowers 5-7 mm, lilac, calyx woolly, densely gland dotted, lobes long, pointed (May-Sep). **Fruit:** Pods ± 7 x 4 mm, hairy, within calyx. **Similar species:** *O. fumeum* insiphili (Z) Slender, deciduous shrubs, 0,9-1,5(3) m; 1600-3200 m; leaflets very slender, young leaflets covered in black hairs; strong smelling; flowers larger, white tinged lilac, calyx velvety black, teeth hairless within; pods covered in short, spreading black hairs.

Otholobium polystictum [= *Psoralea polystictum*] **Vlieëbos (A); mohlonecha, mohlonepshoa (SS)** (*polystictum* - many spots)

Perennial shrub, up to 1,5 m. In rocky grassland. Stems covered with short white hairs. **Leaves:** Stalkless, leaflets 9-36 x 3-15 mm, covered in gland dots, tips rounded, midrib ending in short, hard, recurved tip. **Flowers:** In clusters, in axils of upper leaves, stalkless, pale blue, ± 8 mm (Aug-Apr). **Fruit:** Roundish, ± 5 mm, hairy. **General:** Used in traditional medicine to treat head colds and as a body wash by chiefs.

Otholobium stachyerum [= *Psoralea stachyera*] (*stachyerum* - spikelike)

Shrub up to 2 m. In damp places, near rivers, streams. Much branched. **Leaves:** Leaflets ± 15 mm, **wedge-shaped,** clear gland dots, recurved fine point at tip, young leaves finely hairy, ± stalkless. **Flowers:** In **dense terminal inflorescences,** ± 30 x 20 mm; flowers small, blue to purple or white (Sep-Oct).

Lotononis sericophylla

Psoralea abbottii

Otholobium caffrum

Psoralea abbottii

Otholobium polystictum

Otholobium stachyerum

Pearsonia grandifolia

463

Desmodium (*desmos* - bond or chain, refers to jointed pod which resembles the links of a chain, also said to refer to the joined or 'bonded' stamens) - Herbs or shrubs, usually 3 foliolate; flowers in slender or dense inflorescences, pods flat, separating into 1 seeded segments. Warm regions of the world, ± 300 species, 12 in SA.

Desmodium dregeanum Marsh Desmodium (named after Johann Drège, 1794-1881, German horticulturalist, botanical collector, traveller; came to Cape in 1826 with brother Carl, set up as professional collectors)

Erect to straggling woody herb, usually low-growing. In moist grassland, widespread in E S Afr, mostly coastal, up to 1800 m. Silvery hairy. **Leaves:** 3 foliolate, stalks ±10 mm; leaflets ± 30 mm, stipules ± 8 x 1 mm, green to reddish, stipels beneath terminal leaflet. **Flowers:** In **dense small, compact inflorescence**, calyx with conspicuous yellow hairs (Sep-Jun). **Fruit:** Pod ± 25 mm.

Desmodium setigerum [= *D. hirtum*] (*setigerum* - bearing bristles)

Prostrate herb. In moist grassland, on forest margins, E Cape to Trop Afr, coast to 2000 m. Straggling silky stems. **Leaves:** 3(5) leaflets, ± 20 mm, blunt tipped, roundish, thin, silky hairy beneath, stipules ± 10 mm, stalks ± 10 mm. **Flowers:** In terminal slender inflorescences, ± 300 mm; flowers ± 4 mm, widely spaced, pale blue or mauve, stalks slender, ± 15 mm (Nov-May). **Fruit:** Flat pod with 4-5 segments. **Similar species:** *D. incanum* (see p. 394).

Abrus (*abros* - soft, refers to leaves) - Twining herbs; leaves pinnate, terminal leaflet replaced by a bristle; flowers in inflorescence; fruit a pod, seeds round, shiny red and black. Roots used as a substitute for liquorice; seeds used as rosary beads. Widespread in trop, 6 species, 2 in SA.

Abrus laevigatus   umphitsi (Sw) (*laevigatus* - smooth, slippery)

Slender, trailing creeper. On rocky hillsides, in grassland. Stems scrambling over grasses, **flowering branches leafy. Leaves:** ± 70 mm, stalk ± 20 mm; ± 9 pairs leaflets, ± 15 x 8 mm, blunt with tiny pointed tip. **Flowers:** Clustered towards tip of terminal inflorescences; flowers ± 9 mm, mauve to cream (Sep-May). **Fruit:** Single flat pod ± 35 mm with several seeds.

Abrus precatorius Luckybean Creeper; umphitsi (Sw); umuthi wenhlanhla (X,Z); umkhokha (Z) (*precatorius* - used in worship, refers to use of seeds in rosaries)

Vigorous, deciduous creeper. In grassland, woodland, E Cape to Trop Afr, Asia, S America. Flowering branches often bare of leaves. **Leaves:** ± 100 mm; more than 10 pairs leaflets, ± 15 x 5 mm. **Flowers:** In short, terminal inflorescences; flowers lilac (Sep-Apr). **Fruit:** In clusters, ± 100 mm diam, pods 25-30 mm, square at base, seeds shiny red and black. **General:** Pods remain conspicuous for months. Seeds used as beads to decorate ceramic pots and for sound effects in musical instruments. Extremely toxic if **chewed**. Roots, leaves (seeds) used in traditional treatments for chest complaints and, across its range, for a wide variety of ailments. (See p. 60)

Vigna (named in honour of Italian botanist Domenico Vigna, 1647) - Usually twining herbs; rootstock often tuberous; leaves 1-3 foliolate, terminal leaflet stalked; flowers large, petals stalked or pouched, keel often twisted, tip recurved; pod usually straight. A number of species cultivated as 'Kidney Beans'. Cosmop, ± 100 species, ± 16 in SA.

Vigna frutescens [= *V. decipiens*] **Wild Sweetpea** (*frutescens* - shrubby)

Perennial prostrate or twining herb, 0,5-1,5 m. In grassland, woodland, SA to Ethiopia. Woody tuber, ± 50 mm. Stems, calyx, pods velvety. **Leaves:** Stalks 10-55 mm; leaflets 15-75 x 10-47 mm, entire to deeply 3 lobed. **Flowers:** ± 26 x 28 mm, pale mauve, greyish outside, yellow at base inside, with darker purple edge, on tip of stem 12-190 mm (Aug-Sep), scented. **Fruit:** Pods 50-110 x 4-5 mm, held erect. **General:** Develops thick stems when not burnt regularly.

Vigna unguiculata [= *V. hispida*] **Wild Cow Pea; Boontjie, Koertjie (A); atimbawini (Th); imbumba, isihlumaya, isikhwali, umcwasibe (Z)** (*unguiculata* - long claws, refers to floral parts)

Straggling, trailing herb, stems up to 2 m. In grassland, woodland, throughout the tropics. Tubers on roots. Slightly hairy. **Leaves:** Thin, stalks ± 20 mm; leaflets very variable, ± 70 x 40 mm, **unequal sided, terminal leaflet bulging on both sides at base**, stalklets ± 20 mm. **Flowers:** ± 25 mm, greenish white, pale pink to purple, on tip of erect stem, ± 300 mm (Sep-Mar). **Fruit:** Pods erect, 50-100 x 3-11 mm. **General:** Very variable with a number of subspecies and varieties. Plants visited by ants. Seeds an important staple food. Tubers on roots eaten, leaves used as spinach. The cultivated Cow Pea, subsp. *unguiculata*, has pods ± 300 mm. The Yard-long Bean also belongs to this species. Used in traditional medicine to treat fever. (See p. 398)

Desmodium dregeanum

Desmodium setigerum

Abrus laevigatus

Desmodium dregeanum

Vigna frutescens

Vigna unguiculata

Abrus precatorius

465

Vigna vexillata [= *V. davyi*] **Narrow-leaved Wild Sweetpea; Wilde-ertjie (A); mgcenga (Sw); isikhwali, ubombo, umcwasibe (Z)** (see p. 398)

GERANIACEAE - Geranium Family Herbs or softly woody shrubs, often aromatic. ***Geranium*** (*geranos* - a crane) - Annual or perennial herbs or shrubs (for description see p. 398).

Geranium robustum (*robustum* - big, strong)

Robust subshrub, up to 1 m, in dense stands. On moist, shrubby mountain slopes, near streams, 1600-2590 m. Several stems from base, silky leafy above, bare, woody at base. **Leaves:** ± 50(100) mm diam, (3)5(7) lobed to base, each lobe deeply divided, silky silvery hairy above, thickly hairy beneath, stalks long, ± 100 mm. **Flowers:** In terminal clusters; petals ± 20 x 12 mm, tips shallowly notched, light purple, stalks ± 60 mm, calyx lobes ± 9 x 3 mm, glandular hairy (Nov-Mar).

Geranium pulchrum (see p. 400)

STERCULIACEAE - Cocoa/Sterculia Family Herbs, shrubs or trees. Star-shaped hairs usually present. ***Hermannia*** (after Paul Herman, 1640-1695, botanist, collector) - Herbs, shrubs, with perennial rootstock (for description see p. 66).

Hermannia coccocarpa **Moederkappie, Opslag, Oumakappie (A)**

Much branched shrublet, up to 300 mm. In grassland. Tap root woody. Plant hairless to glandular hairy. **Leaves:** 25-40 mm, margins toothed to deeply lobed, reddish, stalks short, stipules shorter than stalk. **Flowers:** In 2s, in terminal inflorescences, stems slender; flowers purplish blue, stalks long, slender (summer). **Fruit:** Capsule ± 25 mm.

CACTACEAE - Cactus/Prickly Pear Family Spiny, succulents. Leaves rudimentary. ***Opuntia*** (for descriptions see p. 290).

★ *Opuntia stricta* **Australian Pest Pear; Suurturksvy (A)** (*stricta* - straight, erect)

Spreading, much branched shrub, up to 1,5(2)m. **Declared weed** (from Central and South America). Joints longer than broad, green to blue-green, spines ± 40 mm or absent; flowers ± 70 mm, yellow (Nov-Jan). Fruits red turning purple, ± 50 mm, narrowing at base, smooth, spineless. (See p. 290)

MELASTOMATACEAE - Lasiandra/Tibouchina Family Softly woody trees, shrubs, herbs. Leaves with more or less parallel veins. Flowers showy, stamens equal or unequal, filaments with simple or lobed appendage. Cultivated as ornamentals. Trop and warm regions, especially S America, ± 188 genera, ± 4950 species, 5 genera in SA. ***Dissotis*** (*dissos* - two-fold, anthers of two different types) - Herbs or shrubs, usually hairy; leaves opposite, 3-5 veined. Afr, ± 84 species, ± 5 in SA.

Dissotis princeps **Purple Wild Tibouchina, Royal Dissotis; Kalwerbossie (A); sichobochobo, umpongamponga (Sw)** (*princeps* - distinguished, princely)

Perennial softly woody shrub, 1,8-3 m. **In marshy areas**, KZN to Trop Afr. Young stems angular, plant covered in short, bristly hairs. **Leaves:** 2-3 at nodes, **large**, 30-145 x 10-55 mm, dark green above, paler to whitish beneath, 5-7 veins from base, stalks ± 30 mm; old leaves turn red. **Flowers:** In clusters in terminal inflorescences, ± 230 x 160 mm; **flowers ± 60 mm diam**, 5 petals, lilac to **dark purple** (white), calyx ± 15 mm (Jan-Oct). **General:** Used in traditional medicine. Beautiful garden plant for damp places.

PLUMBAGINACEAE - Plumbago Family Herbs or shrubs. Leaves clustered or alternate. Calyx tubular, ribbed, often with glandular hairs. Fruit enclosed in persistent calyx tube. A number of species cultivated as ornamentals. Cosmop, ± 27 genera, ± 730 species, 3 genera in SA. ***Plumbago*** (*plumbum* - lead, supposed cure for lead poisoning and eye disease) - Perennial herbs or shrubs; leaf stalk eared at base. Warmer regions, N and S Hemisp, ± 10 species, 5 in SA.

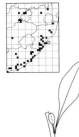

Plumbago auriculata [= *P. capensis*] **Plumbago; Blousyselbos (A); umabophe, umatshintshine, umuthi wamadoda (X,Z); umasheleshele, umasweliseweli, umat-shwilitshwili (Z)** (*auriculata* - ear-shaped, refers to leaf base)

Scrambling shrub, up to 2 m. In scrub, thicket, in valley bushveld. Brittle stemmed, much branched. **Leaves:** Oblong or wedge-shaped, ± 100 x 25 mm, **thin, dark green above, greyish green beneath**, stalks short, slightly winged, stem clasping, eared at base. **Flowers:** In terminal inflorescences, 30-100 mm; flowers pale blue, ± 20 mm diam, tube ± 30 mm, calyx ± 13 mm, sticky hairy (Sep-Apr). **Fruit:** Capsule, 5 grooved, sticky hairy, the top splitting open like a lid. **General:** Visited by butterflies. Used in traditional medicine to treat warts, broken bones, wounds, as snuff for headaches, as an emetic to dispel bad dreams and as protective charms. Popular garden and hedging plant worldwide. Easily cultivated from suckers and cuttings. White and deep purplish blue forms are in cultivation.

Vigna vexillata

Geranium robustum

Geranium pulchrum

Hermannia coccocarpa

★ *Opuntia stricta*

Dissotis princeps

Plumbago auriculata

Dissotis princeps

467

PERIPLOCACEAE - Periploca Family Perennial herbs, shrubs, lianas. ***Raphionacme*** - (for descriptions see p. 542).

Raphionacme hirsuta [= *R. divaricata*, *R. velutina*] False Gentian; Khadiwortel (A); intsema (X); umathangane, umathanjana (Z) (*hirsuta* - hairy, although many plants are hairless)

Much branched herbs, 50-200 mm. In grassland, E Cape to N Prov, S Moz, coast to 2600 m. Stem tuber ± 380 mm. **Leaves:** Hairy or not, 12-50 x 6-25 mm, **midvein prominent beneath, secondary veins parallel. Flowers: Often before leaves, purple**, lobes oblong, 4-9 x 1,5-3,5 mm; corona lobes variable, white or purple (Aug-Dec). **Fruit:** Solitary, 25-75 x 7-13 mm. **General:** Said to be poisonous although tubers are used to help brew beer. Used in traditional treatment of chronic ulcers.

CONVOLVULACEAE - Morning Glory Family Herbs, shrubs, stems trailing or twining (for description see p. 176). ***Evolvulus*** (*e* - without, *volvulere* - to roll or twist, these plants do not twine) - Mostly America, ± 97 species, 2 in SA.

Evolvulus alsinoides Blue Haze, Wild Evolvulus (*alsinoides* - resembles the genus *Alsine*)

Perennial herb, up to 200(600) mm. In grassland, woodland, a weed of cultivation, throughout tropics, subtropics. **All parts silky hairy. Leaves:** 10-26 x 2-10 mm. **Flowers:** 1-5 in small clusters; flowers ± 10 mm diam, bright blue (white) (Sep-May). **Similar species:** *E. nummularius* Prostrate groundcover; flowers white.

Ipomoea (*ips* - worm; *homoios* - like, refers to the creeping habit) - Mostly twiners (for description see p. 178, 420).

★ *Ipomoea purpurea* Common Morning Glory; Purperwinde (A); imbotyika-tsana (X); ijalamu, ijalapha, ubhoqo (Z)

Annual twiner. Naturalised weed (from Trop America). Leaves 40-150 mm. Flowers ± 60 mm diam, purple, blue, pink, white or variegated. Used in traditional medicine for stomach disorders, blood purifiers and as protective and love charms. (See p. 178)

Ipomoea wightii Small Blue Ipomoea

Perennial twiner. In low-lying, moist places. Stems stout, firm, with brownish yellow hairs. **Leaves:** 30-120 x 25-100 mm, heart-shaped, entire to 3 lobed, **thin, hairy above, downy grey beneath**, stalks 20-100 mm. **Flowers: In dense clusters**, stem 30-130 mm; flowers 20-40 mm diam, blue, pink or purple, **calyx very hairy, lobes broad** (Jan-Apr). **General:** Essential organs eaten by small black beetles.

BORAGINACEAE - Forget-me-not/Borage Family (for description see p. 178). ***Trichodesma*** (*trichos* - hair; *desmos* - bond, hairs unite the stamens) - Calyx enlarging around fruit. Trop, subtrop, Asia, Afr, Austr, ± 12 species, ± 6 in SA.

Trichodesma angustifolium Hairy Bluebells (*angustifolium* - narrow leaves)

Shrublet, up to 500 mm. In grassland, open woodland, up to 1500 m, N KZN to Bots, Nam. Covered with small raised bristles. **Leaves:** ± 60 x 1-9 mm, thick, **narrow**, veins pale bright green. **Flowers:** 2-8, in small inflorescences; flowers ± 20 mm, deep blue, calyx pinkish green, enlarging ± 25 x 20 mm in fruit (Mar-Jul).

Cynoglossum (*kyon* - dog; *glossa* - tongue) **-** Fruit covered in small hooked spines. Temp, subtrop, ± 60 species, ± 8 in SA.

Cynoglossum geometricum (*geometricum* - geometric shape)

Erect biennial herb, up to 1 m. On damp forest margins, in disturbed places, E Cape to KZN, Malawi to Ethiopia. **Leaves:** In rosette at base at first, rosette absent at time of flowering, leaves harshly hairy, grey-green. **Flowers:** Crowded in large flat clusters; flowers 2-8 mm diam, white to pale blue (Nov-Mar). **Fruit: Nutlets with scattered, hooked spines. General:** Flowers bright blue in E Afr.

Myosotis (*myos* - mouse; *otis* - ear) - Flower tube almost closed by 5 scales. Temp Eurasia, ± 50 species, 2 in SA.

Myosotis semiamplexicaulis [=*M. afropalustris*] Forget-me-not; Vergeet-my-nie (A) (*semiamplexicaulis* - half stem-clasping)

Erect, bushy herb, up to 600 mm. In damp ground, in scrub or among rocks, 1400-3000 m. Bristly hairy. **Leaves:** Lower leaves tapering to short stalks. **Flowers: In** much branched inflorescences; flowers small, blue, white or pink, throat scales yellow (Nov-Mar). **Fruits:** Burrlike. **General:** Used in traditional medicine to treat hysteria and for training traditional healer initiates to develop memory.

Echium (*echis* - viper, seeds, stem resemble snake head and skin) - Europe, Asia, N Afr, ± 40 species, 2 introduced in SA.

★ *Echium plantagineum* Purple Echium; Blou-echium, Bloudisseldoring (A)

Erect biennial, up to 1 m. In disturbed areas, originally a garden escape. Covered in coarse white hairs. **Basal rosette leaves large, narrowing to a stalk. Terminal inflorescences**, ± 300 mm; flowers open pink, age blue to purplish (Oct-Apr).

468

Raphionacme hirsuta

Raphionacme hirsuta

Evolvulus alsinoides

★ *Ipomoea purpurea*

Ipomoea wightii

Trichodesma angustifolium

Cynoglossum geometricum

Myosotis semiamplexicaulis

★ *Echium plantagineum*

Martin von Fintel

Lorraine van Hooff

Lawrence Peacock

Lorraine van Hooff

Geoff Nichols

Darrel Plowes

Lal Greene

Martin von Fintel

Martin von Fintel

469

VERBENACEAE - Verbena/Teak Family Herbs, shrubs, trees. Stems often 4 angled. Leaves opposite or clustered. Flowers regular or 2 lipped. Fruit often slightly fleshy, sometimes dry. Economically important for teak timber and for a number of ornamentals such as *Clerodendrum, Duranta, Holmskioldia, Lantana, Petrea* and *Verbena*. Mostly trop, ± 41 genera, ± 950 species, 9 genera in SA.
Verbena (verbene - sacred boughs of olive, myrtle or laurel) - Herbs or low shrubs; inflorescences densely crowded, elongate or flat topped. Trop, ± 260 species, ± 6 introduced in SA.

★ *Verbena bonariensis* **Tall Verbena, Purple Top; Blouwaterbossie (A)** (from Bonaria, Buenos Aires, S America)

Erect, robust, sparsely branched annual, up to 1,6 m. On floodplains, in grassland, disturbed areas. Widespread weed (from S America). Short, rough hairs throughout. Leaf margins toothed. Flowers in large, branched, flat topped, congested inflorescences of small, purple flowers (Oct-Jun). Visited by butterflies and wasps. **Similar species:** ★ *V. brasiliensis* Slender, branched, annual herb, up to 900 mm; inflorescences slender, smaller, pinkish mauve.

★ *Verbena aristigera* [= *V. tenuisecta*] **Fine-leaved Verbena, Moss Verbena; Fynblaar-verbena (A)** (*aristigera* - bearing beards)

Perennial herb, up to 200 mm. On disturbed ground, roadsides, naturalised garden escape (from S America). Leaves deeply, finely dissected, clasping at base, hairy. Flowers in dense terminal clusters, mauve to blue or white (Sep-Apr).

Stachytarpheta (stachys - an ear of grain, spike; *tarphos* - a thicket) - Some species widely dispersed as weeds in trop, a few cultivated as ornamentals. Mainly Trop America, ± 100 species, 2 introduced in SA.

★ *Stachytarpheta urticifolia* (*urticifolia* - leaves resembling those of *Urtica*, the nettle)

Annual or biennial herb, up to 1 m. Naturalized weed. Leaves hairless. Flowers small, deep blue. **Similar species:** ★ *S. mutabilis* Leaves densely velvety on lower surface; flowers larger, pink.

Clerodendrum (kleros - chance; *dendron* - a tree, refers to doubtful medicinal properties) - Herbs, shrubs, small trees; leaves opposite or in 3s; flowers regular or 2 lipped, stamens and style long, protruding; fruit fleshy. Warm regions of Old World, ± 430 species, ± 21 in SA.

Clerodendrum hirsutum **Wild Violet; umathanjana, usikisiki (Z)** (*hirsutum* - hairy)

Herb, up to 450 mm. In grassland. Woody rootstock. Stems angled, branched from base, hairy. **Leaves:** Opposite or 3 whorled, ± 30 x 10 mm, margins reddish hairy, ± stalkless. **Flowers:** 1-2 in axils, bright purplish blue with 2 white markings, stems slender (Sep-Dec). **General:** Used in traditional medicine to treat intestinal worms and scrofula swellings.

Clerodendrum triphyllum **Grassland Clerodendrum, Small Violet Bush; khopha, mokata (SS); sigibanyongo (Sw); umathanjana (Z)** (*triphyllum* - 3 leaved)

Shrublet or herb, up to 600 mm. In grassland, woodland. Rootstock woody. Stems almost hairless to densely hairy. **Leaves:** In 3s, ± 50 x 10 mm, margins entire, rough, stalkless. **Flowers:** In few-flowered clusters, **in leaf axils**; flower lobes ± 15 mm, unequal, pale blue to violet, **stamens prominent**, calyx lobes pointed (Nov-Mar). **General:** Used in traditional medicine to treat kidney complaints, scrofulous swellings and taken during pregnancy to ensure easy childbirth. **Similar species:** *C. louwalberts* Leaves long, narrow, 20-50 x 3-7 mm; flowers on slender stalks, a few in each axil, forming terminal inflorescence.

LAMIACEAE (LABIATAE) **- Sage/Mint Family** Aromatic herbs or shrublets. Stems usually 4 angled. Leaves opposite, each pair at right angles to the next. Flowers 2 lipped, rarely bell-shaped. Economically valuable for aromatic essential oils, herbs, including Sage, Lavender, Rosemary, Mint, Marjoram, Basil, Thyme, Savory and ornamentals such as Salvia, Stachys. Cosmop, ± 250 genera, ± 6700 species, ± 41 genera in SA.
Ajuga (ajuga - a bugle or *azygon* - without a yoke) - Perennial herbs; flowers in dense, terminal spikes, upper lip very short. Mostly N Hemisp, ± 40 species, 1 in SA.

Ajuga ophrydis **Bugle Plant; moonyane, se-nyarela (SS)** (*ophrydis* - refers to orchid genus *Ophrys*)

Perennial low-growing herb, 60-250 mm. In grassland, coast to 2700 m. Short rhizome. Several erect stems. **Leaves:** Mostly in basal rosette, 30-170 x 15-40 mm, thick, usually hairy, **margins irregularly, coarsely toothed to almost entire**, tips blunt to rounded, tapering to base. **Flowers:** In pairs, clustered in long inflorescence; flowers ± 12 x 14 mm, blue, mauve, white, calyx hairy, ± 7 mm (Oct-Feb). **General:** Used in traditional medicine to treat female sterility and painful menstruation. Easily grown, by division.

470

★ *Verbena bonariensis* ★ *Verbena brasiliensis* ★ *Verbena aristigera*

★ *Stachytarpheta urticifolia* *Clerodendrum hirsutum* *Clerodendrum hirsutum*

Ajuga ophrydis *Ajuga ophrydis* *Clerodendrum triphyllum*

471

Prunella (German word for croup, which some plants are said to cure) - Temp regions, ± 5 species, 1 naturalised in KZN.

★ **_Prunella vulgaris_ Self-heal, Heal-all** (_vulgaris_ - common)
Straggling herb, up to 300 mm. In vleis, on moist forest margins (originally from Europe). Rooting at nodes, sparsely hairy. Leaves 20-30 x 12-20 mm. Flowers in dense inflorescences, 20-40 mm, floral bracts purplish; flowers dark blue to purple, 9-10 mm. Used in traditional medicine to soothe inflamed mucous membranes.

Salvia (_salvere_ - to heal) - Herbs or shrubs; flower tube usually enlarging towards the throat, calyx 2 lipped, as long as flower tube. Attracts butterflies. Temp, trop regions, ± 900 species, 22 in SA, 4 naturalised from Europe and America.

Salvia repens Kruipsalie (A) (_repens_ - creeping)
Perennial herb, 250-600 mm. In grassland, woodland, a weed in disturbed places. Stems simple or branched. Very variable. **Leaves:** Crowded, larger at base, 30-100 x 8-45 mm, margins irregularly toothed, ± finely hairy. **Flowers:** In clusters of 6-8, inflorescence widely spaced below, closely spaced above; flowers 14-26 mm, pale blue, mauve, purple (white) (Oct-Feb). **General:** Crushed leaves aromatic.

Tetradenia (_tetra_ - four; _aden_ - a gland) - Perennial shrubs, usually leafless at flowering; leaves aromatic; male and female flowers on separate plants. Afr, ± 6 species, ± 3 in SA.

Tetradenia riparia [= _Iboza riparia_] **Iboza, Misty Plume Bush; Gemmerbos (A); iboza, ibozane (Z)** (_riparia_ - growing on banks of rivers and streams)
Robust, slightly succulent shrub, up to 3 m. On wooded hillsides in frost-free areas. **Stems branched, stout, pale brown, brittle at base, young stems 4 angled, furry. Leaves:** 35-180 x 35-140 mm, velvety on both surfaces, margins toothed. **Flowers:** In large, spreading inflorescences, ± 400 x 250 mm, mauve (white). Male spikes 20-80 mm. **Female spikes more compact**, 10-25 mm (May-Aug). **General:** Lavender scented. Used in traditional medicine to treat coughs, sore throats, stomach ache and malaria. Hardy garden plant for frost-free areas, easily grown from cuttings.

Pycnostachys (_pyknos_ - dense; _stachys_ - a spike) - Perennial herbs or soft shrubs; flowers in dense terminal spikes, lower lip large, boat-shaped, calyx with 5 rigid lobes. Afr, Madag, ± 40 species, 3 in SA.

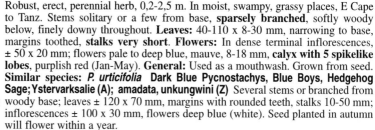

Pycnostachys reticulata Slender Pycnostachys; uhlalwane, umvuthuza (Z) (_reticulata_ - network, refers to veins)
Robust, erect, perennial herb, 0,2-2,5 m. In moist, swampy, grassy places, E Cape to Tanz. Stems solitary or a few from base, **sparsely branched**, softly downy below, finely downy throughout. **Leaves:** 40-110 x 8-30 mm, narrowing to base, margins toothed, **stalks very short. Flowers:** In dense terminal inflorescences, ± 50 x 20 mm; flowers pale to deep blue, mauve, 8-18 mm, **calyx with 5 spikelike lobes**, purplish red (Jan-May). **General:** Used as a mouthwash. Grown from seed. **Similar species: _P. urticifolia_ Dark Blue Pycnostachys, Blue Boys, Hedgehog Sage; Ystervarksalie (A); amadata, unkungwini (Z)** Several stems or branched from woody base; leaves ± 120 x 70 mm, margins with rounded teeth, stalks 10-50 mm; inflorescences ± 100 x 30 mm, flowers deep blue (white). Seed planted in autumn will flower within a year.

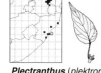

Plectranthus (_plektron_ - a spur; _anthos_ - flower, refers to base of flower tube) - Herbs or shrubs, often fleshy; flower clusters in spikelike inflorescences. Attracts butterflies. Afr, Arabia, India, Austr, ± 300 species, ± 45 in SA, mostly endemic to the area east of the Drakensberg plateau.

Plectranthus ambiguus Large-flowered Plectranthus; iboza elincane (Z) (_ambiguus_ - uncertain)
Perennial herb or shrublet, 0,4-1,2 m. On forest margins. Branching from base, stems softly hairy, rooting freely. **Leaves:** 25-120 x 20-90 mm, thinly hairy, brownish gland dots beneath, margins toothed, stalks 10-70 mm. **Flowers: In congested inflorescences**, 40-170 mm; flowers 23-30 mm, purple, **tube straight**, calyx ± 8 mm, purple (Mar-Apr). **General:** Used in traditional medicine to treat colds. Good container plant and groundcover for shady areas.

Plectranthus dolichopodus (_dolichopodus_ - long stalked)
Erect or straggling perennial herb, 0,25-1 m. In cool, moist forests. Stems branched, hairy. **Leaves:** 30-100 x 25-80 mm, slightly hairy, gland dotted beneath, margins coarsely toothed, stalks 20-60 mm. **Flowers:** 2-6 in clusters, in terminal inflorescence, 100-200 mm; flowers 8-10 mm, **bright to deep blue, purple, upper lip very short** (Jan-May). **General:** Difficult to grow, likes cool conditions.

★ *Prunella vulgaris*

Salvia repens

Tetradenia riparia ♀

Lal Greene

Martin von Fintel

Martin von Fintel

Tetradenia riparia ♂

Tetradenia riparia ♂

Pycnostachys reticulata

C J Ward

Martin von Fintel

Geoff Nichols

Pycnostachys urticifolia

Plectranthus ambiguus

Plectranthus dolichopodus

Geoff Nichols

Geoff Nichols

Lal Greene

473

Plectranthus ecklonii **Large Spur-flower Bush; Persmuishondblaar (A)** (named after Christian Ecklon, 1795-1868, German apothecary, traveller, plant collector who collected in SA with Carl Zeyher)

Erect soft shrub, 0,7-2,5 m. In forest understorey. Woody at base, much branched. **Leaves:** 60-170 x 40-100 mm, thinly hairy above, velvety beneath, margins toothed. **Flowers:** In branched, terminal inflorescences, 120-250 mm; flowers 16-20 mm, purplish blue, pink (white), **tube widening towards mouth**, calyx purplish red (Feb-May). **General:** Used traditionally to treat headaches, hayfever. Wonderful plant for shady and sunny places. Pink and white varieties found in cultivation. (See p. 424)

Plectranthus ernstii (named after Ernst van Jaarsveld, horticulturalist at Kirstenbosch and collector, authority on this genus, author of books on SA flora)

Perennial, semi-succulent herb, up to 250 mm. **In rock crevices**. Rare. Branching, stems more than 20 mm at base, **becoming swollen, brown and potatolike**. **Leaves:** 12-30 x 10-25 mm, faintly hairy, margins with few teeth. **Flowers:** Simple inflorescences, 30-100 mm; flowers small, 4-8 mm, pale blue-mauve to whitish, tube expands abruptly to form a sac-like base 4-5 mm deep, narrowing to throat (Feb). **General:** Good container plant and bonsai subject, susceptible to eelworm.

Plectranthus fruticosus **Forest Spur-flower; Spoorsalie (A); cabhozi (Sw)** (*fruticosus* - shrubby)

Soft, branching shrub, 0,6-2 m. In forest, scrub, SW Cape to N Prov. Thinly hairy with **honey coloured gland dots** throughout, stems purplish. **Leaves:** 40-140 x 35-110 mm, tinged purple beneath, margins toothed. **Flowers:** In branched inflorescences, 80-250 mm; flowers pale to deep **mauve**, 5-13 mm, tube deflexed, spurred at base, narrowing slightly towards throat, calyx 7-8 mm, glandular (Jan-May). **General:** Attracts Gaudy Commodore butterflies *Junonia octavia sesamus*. Effective as a fly repellent (stems rubbed on window sills). Lovely in deep shade of gardens.

Plectranthus hilliardiae **Hilliard's Plectranthus** (named after Olive Hilliard, SA botanist, collector and author of books on African flora)

Erect, branched perennial herb, up to 400 mm. Among rocks on margins of scrub forest. Rare. Stems shortly hairy. **Leaves: Fleshy**, 55-90 x 40-60 mm, dark green, sparsely bristly, gland dots beneath, margins shallowly toothed above middle. **Flowers: In loose, branched inflorescences**, 80-150 mm; flowers 26-30 mm, tube deflexed and expanding at base, narrowing towards throat, purplish blue with darker flecks near throat (Dec-Mar). **General:** A lovely shade plant.

Plectranthus neochilus **Lobster Flower, Blue Coleus** (*neochilus* - calyx lips)

Perennial, aromatic succulent herb, up to 500 mm. In dry thicket, open and rocky woodland, E Cape to Zim, Zam, Nam. Roots sometimes tuberous. Stems much branched, softly hairy. **Leaves:** 20-50 x 15-35 mm, succulent grey-green, sticky, **blunt tipped**, folding along midrib, downy beneath with orange gland dots, margins faintly toothed. **Flowers:** In terminal inflorescences, 70-150 mm, **keeled bracts form 4 angled tip, greenish white, edged purple**, dropping early; flowers 12-20 mm, deep blue and purple, upper lip bluish white, short, **lower lip large, boat-shaped, 8-11 mm** (Sep-Apr). **General:** Said to be an efficient air purifier. Excellent groundcover, in warm dry areas. **Similar species:** *P. tetensis* (see p. 476).

Plectranthus oertendahlii **Silver-leaved Spur-flower** (named after Ivar Anders Oertendahl, former Head Gardener of Uppsala University Bot Garden, Sweden)

Perennial semi-succulent herb, up to 200 mm. In wooded river valleys near coast. Rare. Stems branch freely, trailing, rooting at lower nodes, woolly. **Leaves:** 30-40 x 25-40 mm, sparsely hairy, **upper surface with silvery markings along veins**, purple beneath, with colourless gland dots, margins toothed. **Flowers:** In simple or branched inflorescences, 70-200 mm; flowers 8-13 mm, white or pale mauve, calyx ± 8 mm, purple tinged (Oct-Apr). **General:** First described in 1924 from specimens cultivated in Sweden, origin unknown. It was finally discovered in the wild by Hugh Nicholson and Rudolf Strey in 1971, although a herbarium specimen had in fact been made in 1936 by Lilian Britten, botany lecturer at Rhodes University from a plant cultivated in Grahamstown but originally collected in Oribi Gorge. A most attractive container plant for light shade; take new cuttings each season to deal with eelworm.

Plectranthus ecklonii

Lorraine van Hooff

Plectranthus ernstii

Geoff Nichols

Plectranthus hilliardiae

Geoff Nichols

Plectranthus fruticosus

Rosemary Williams

Plectranthus fruticosus

Wally Menne

Plectranthus neochilus

Jo Onderstall

Plectranthus oertendahlii

Neil Crouch

475

★ *Plectranthus barbatus* (*barbatus* - bearded)

Erect, semi-succulent shrub, up to 3 m. A garden escape, originally from India. Stems densely woolly. Leaves 40-90 x 25-50 mm, densely woolly, margins with rounded teeth, stalks 10-20 mm. Flowers in terminal inflorescences, 200-230 mm, enclosed in large overlapping bracts in bud; flowers 17-20 mm, pale blue-mauve, lower lip boat-shaped.

Plectranthus oribiensis (from Oribi Gorge, S KZN)

Herb or soft shrub, up to 1,5 m. In leaf litter on rocks, on forest margins, in kloofs. Rare. **Roots tuberous**. Stems erect, branched, densely hairy. **Leaves:** 50-100 x 50-90 mm, densely hairy, veins protrude beneath, white with gland dots, margins toothed, stalks 40-70 mm. **Flowers:** In branched inflorescences, ± 200 mm; flowers 10-12 mm, mauve, **hairy, upper lip 5-6 mm, unspotted**, lower lip boat-shaped, 5-7 mm, calyx purple tinged (Dec-Apr). **General:** Garden shade plant.

Plectranthus petiolaris (*petiolaris* - stalked)

Perennial herb, up to 1 m. In semi-coastal forest, on shaded rocky hillsides. Stems erect, spreading, much branched, softly hairy. **Leaves:** 40-140 x 35-110 mm, thin, **margins coarsely toothed, with small secondary teeth**, bristly hairy, colourless gland dots beneath, stalks 20-150 mm. **Flowers:** In slender inflorescences, 100-250 mm; flowers 12-15 mm, **deep purple** with bluish lips (pink), **tube narrow then expanding to wide throat**, upper lip 6-8 mm, lower lip 7-9 mm, calyx hairy (Nov-Apr). **General:** Aromatic, **mint scented**. Grown in shade.

Plectranthus saccatus Stoep Jacaranda; Stoepjakaranda (A) (*saccatus* - baglike)

Soft, erect to spreading perennial shrub, up to 1,2 m. In forest, semi-shade and in rocky places. Stems woody at base, semi-succulent, much branched, purple tinged, softly hairy. **Leaves:** 20-70 x 15-50 mm, thin to semi-succulent, hairless or faintly hairy with colourless gland dots beneath, margins with few large teeth, stalks 15-50 mm. **Flowers:** In terminal, few-flowered inflorescences, 50-120 mm; flowers large, 13-30 mm, mauve, blue (white), sometimes with purple markings, hanging on one side of stem (Nov-May). **General:** Popular, attractive, hardy, shade and container plant in frost-free areas. Var. *saccatus*, the typical plant, very variable in leaf texture and flower colour. Var. *longitubus*, leaves larger, ± 70 mm; flower tube longer and narrower at base.

Plectranthus spicatus Long-spiked Spur-flower (*spicatus* - spikelike)

Perennial succulent, spreading to scrambling, up to 1,5 m. In dry woodland, rocky places. Several stems, hairless to finely hairy. **Leaves:** 25-50 x 8-25 mm, **fleshy, clustered towards base**, red gland dots beneath, margins with few irregular teeth in upper half, reddish brown in full sun, stalks very short. **Flowers:** In compact, many-flowered clusters, in tall, spikelike inflorescences, 90-600 mm; **flowers small**, 7-8 mm, purple and deep blue (Mar-Oct). **General:** Attractive leaves and flowers, suitable for gardens, in full sun, in dry areas.

Plectranthus tetensis (*tetensis* - from Tete, Mozambique)

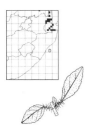

Perennial, aromatic, semi-succulent herb, up to 700 mm. In dry thornscrub, KZN to Kenya. **Stems trailing**, sparingly branched, softly hairy, with erect inflorescences. **Leaves:** 15-25 x 12-20 mm, softly succulent, hairy, orange-red gland dots beneath, narrowing to tip, margins bluntly toothed, stalks short. **Flowers:** In dense, spikelike inflorescences, 50-80 mm, **bracts fleshy, persistent,** rounded; flowers 15-18 mm, mauve-purple, calyx ± 5 mm, red gland dotted outside, hairy within (Mar-Jun). **General:** Attractive groundcover for hot dry gardens. **Similar species:** *P. neochilus* (see p. 474).

lectranthus oribiensis

★ *Plectranthus barbatus*

Plectranthus petiolaris

Geoff Nichols

Geoff Nichols

Geoff Nichols

lectranthus saccatus

Plectranthus spicatus

Plectranthus spicatus

Lorraine von Hooff

Tony Abbott

Geoff Nichols

Plectranthus saccatus var. *longitubus*

lectranthus saccatus

Plectranthus tetensis

Martin von Fintel

Trevor Coleman

C J Ward

477

Plectranthus zuluensis Zulu Spur-flower; Zoeloemuishondblaar (A)
Erect soft shrub, up to 2 m. On forest margins, near streams. Much branched, stems erect, velvety when young. **Leaves:** 30-70 x 25-55 mm, soft, semi-succulent, hairy, margins coarsely toothed. **Flowers:** Inflorescences 40-80 mm; flowers 10-16 mm, pale blue to mauvish white, with rows of mauve dots on upper lip, calyx purple tinged (throughout year). **General:** Shade and container plant in warmer areas.

SOLANACEAE - Tomato/Potato/Tobacco Family Herbs, shrubs, rarely climbers and trees, often spiny. Leaves alternate. Flowers regular, petals 5, united, calyx sometimes inflated in fruit. Fruit a berry or prickly capsule. Economically important for food plants such as the potato, brinjal, tomato, red pepper; for tobacco and drug plants such as Henbane, Belladonna and Atropine; and for ornamentals such as *Petunia*, *Cestrum*, *Datura*, *Brunfelsia*, *Solanum*. Subcosmop, ± 94 genera, ± 2950 species, 9 genera in SA.

Nicandra (named after Nikander of Colophon, 2nd century Greek physician and botanist) - Annual herbs. 1 species from Peru, now naturalised around the world.

★ Nicandra physalodes Apple of Peru, Shoo-fly Plant; Basterappelliefie, Bitter-appelliefie (A); linyooko (SS); gqwangugqangu, umpungempu (X); umgabaganga, omncane (Z) (physalis - a bladder or bubble)
Erect, branched annual herb, up to 1,5 m. On roadsides, disturbed areas, cosmop weed, widespread in SA. Leaves large, oval, shortly hairy, margins scalloped, stalks tinged purple. Flowers solitary, in leaf axils, ± 10 mm diam, pale mauve to white (Nov-Jun). Fruit a round yellow berry, enclosed in bladderlike calyx. Birds eat seeds. Leaves boiled and mixed with maize meal, but only used between May and August.

Solanum (Latin name for 'Nightshade', perhaps from *solamen* - soothing, referring to narcotic properties of some species) - Shrubs, herbs, small trees or climbers, spiny or not; leaves entire, lobed or divided; flowers in clusters; fruit a berry. Abundant in trop, ± 1700, ± 60 in SA.

Solanum sp. nov.
Creeper, up to 3 m. In thicket, N KZN. Stems and leaves thorny. Leaves shiny dark green above, paler beneath, margins deeply lobed. Flowers deep lilac (Oct-Dec). Fruit shiny red.

Solanum duplo-sinuatum Bitter Apple; Bitterappel (A) (duplo - double; sinuatum - bent)
Erect herb, up to 1,2(2,2) m. On forest margins, KZN to Trop Afr. Stems with scattered spines ± 8 mm. **Leaves:** 120-420 x 100-300 mm, covered with purple hairs, margins deeply lobed, veins with scattered spines, stalks hairy and spiny. **Flowers:** Lilac, ± 45 mm diam, calyx lobes spreading, enlarging in fruit, covered in erect spines (throughout year). **Fruit:** ± 35 mm diam, yellow, mottled green and white. **General:** Used in traditional medicine to treat ringworm.

Solanum geniculatum Rankaartappel (A); umthuma (X) (geniculatum - abruptly bent)
Scrambling shrublet. In thicket. Branches pale green, hairless, faintly winged, sometimes bent. **Leaves:** ± 55 x 40 mm, margins entire, slightly wavy, rolled under, stalks ± 30 mm. **Flowers:** In terminal clusters; flowers ± 15 mm diam, white to mauve, calyx margins white, thickened, lobes rounded (Feb-Aug). **Fruit:** Shiny black berry. **General:** Visited by a small black bee.

Solanum panduriforme Bitter Apple, Poison Apple; Bitterappel, Geelappel, Gifappel (A); setlwane, tholana (SS); inluma (Sw); intuma (Sw, Z); intuma-omncane (Z)
(panduriforme - fiddle-shaped)
Erect, perennial shrublet, up to 1 m. On floodplains, in disturbed areas, termite mounds, KZN to Zim. Stems thinly furry orange, with or without prickles. **Leaves:** Up to 100 x 40 mm, olive green above, grey beneath, margins wavy, stalks ± 30 mm. **Flowers:** Solitary or in small clusters; flowers ± 30 mm diam, mauve, calyx ± 15 mm (Sep-May). **Fruit:** Round, fleshy, shiny yellow, ± 20 mm diam. **General:** Heavily browsed, fruits eaten by nyala antelope and black rhino. Green fruits poisonous. Used in traditional medicine to treat skin infections, toothache and haemorrhoids.

★ Solanum seaforthianum Slender Potato Creeper; Aartappelranker (A); ijalamu (Z)
Slender, scrambling climber, up to 3 m. In woodland, thicket, forest, introduced weed from Trop America. Softly woody stems at base. Leaves deeply lobed into 2-4 pairs unequal leaflets, bright green. Flowers ± 20 mm diam, deep mauve to purple, in drooping, branched clusters (Dec-Jul). Fruits small, shiny red berries, 5-10 mm diam, in hanging bunches. A rampant garden escape. **Declared weed.** (See p. 72)

Plectranthus zuluensis

Lorraine van Hooff

★ *Nicandra physalodes*

Martin von Fintel

Solanum sp. nov.

Martin von Fintel

Solanum duplo-sinuatum

Geoff Nichols

Solanum sp. nov.

Martin von Fintel

Solanum geniculatum

Martin von Fintel

Solanum panduriforme

Martin von Fintel

★ *Solanum seaforthianum*

David Johnson

Solanum panduriforme

Lorraine van Hooff

SCROPHULARIACEAE - Snapdragon Family Annual or perennial herbs, shrubs, some parasitic. Flowers usually irregular, often 2 lipped, sometimes with pouches or spurs. Famous for the drug plants *Digitalis* (Foxgloves) and ornamentals such as Snapdragons, Veronicas, Penstemons, Mimulus. Cosmop, ± 269 genera, ± 5100 species, 79 genera in SA.
Nemesia (from *Nemesion*, Greek name used by Dioscorides for a similar plant) - Herbs; flower tube short with flaps, with or without bosses in mouth of spur (seen as inverted bumps in underside of tube), upper lip 4 lobed, lower entire or slightly notched; fruit dry, flattened, halves boat-shaped, seeds winged. Genus endemic to SA, ± 70 species.

Nemesia caerulea Nemesia; Leeubekkie (A) (caerula - sky-blue)

Slender perennial herb, up to 600 mm. In grassland, on rocky slopes, up to 2900 m. Rootstock creeping. Stems usually simple, leafy below, sometimes branching at base. **Leaves:** Opposite, ± 25 x 12 mm, margins with thickened teeth, stalkless. **Flowers:** In terminal clusters, 25-75 mm, 8-10 mm, blue to purple, mouth yellow or white, hairy, **2 raised orange-yellow bosses,** spur 2-3 mm, calyx hairy (Sep-Jan).

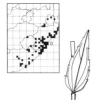

Nemesia denticulata Wild Nemesia; Leeubekkie, Maagpynblommetjie (A) (denticulata - toothed)

Erect, **tufted** perennial **herb,** up to 600 mm. In grassland, open scrub. Woody rootstock. Annual stems, leaves clustered towards base. **Leaves: Broad,** ± 30 x **5-10 mm, margins toothed. Flowers:** In small, flattish, terminal cluster; flowers ± 15 mm, pink, mauve, fading blue or white, yellow or orange on crest of mouth, spur 5-6 mm, with 2 **flat** orange bosses at mouth (throughout year). **General:** Used as a pot herb. Attractive when massed, grown from seed or cuttings. (See p. 428) **Similar species:** Often mis-identified in the past as *N. fruticans.*

Jamesbrittenia (named after James Britten, 1846-1924, British botanist) - Stamens hidden (not visible to the eye). Differs from *Sutera* which has stamens protruding. Mostly Afr, SA to Angola, Zam.

Jamesbrittenia pristisepala [= Sutera pristisepala] letswalo (SS); umahokwe(Z)
(*pristisepala* - ragged sepals, like a sawfish)

Dwarf shrublet, up to 350 mm. On rocky places, 1500-3000 m. Rootstock stout. Plant covered in glistening glands or glandular hairs, leafy. Very variable. **Leaves:** Opposite, becoming alternate on flowering part of stems, 10-30 x 5-17 mm, deeply lobed, lobes deeply cut. **Flowers:** Solitary in axils of upper leaves, forming long, crowded inflorescences; flowers ± 11 mm wide, tube ± 11 x 2 mm, mouth compressed, petal lobes creamy white, yellowish to lilac, throat white to pale yellow, tube purplish outside (Nov-Apr). **General:** Hybridises with *J. breviflora* (see p. 74).

Sutera (named after Johan Suter, 1766-1827, Swiss botanist and physician, prof of Greek and philosophy at Berne) - Stamens protude. Afr south of Cunene and Zambezi rivers, ± 49 species.

Sutera floribunda Kerriebos (A); boluma (SS); usikisiki lwehlathi (Z) (see p. 190)

Selago (*sel* - sight; *jach* - salutary, refers to supposed medicinal properties) - Herbs or shrublets; flowers small, in dense inflorescences; fruit 2 nutlets, not splitting. Attracts Blues butterflies. Afr, ± 150 species, mostly SA.

Selago flanaganii lehlomanyane (SS) (after Henry Flanagan, 1861-1919, farmer, plant collector, whose private garden, Flanagan's Arboretum is now at Union Buildings; private herbarium bequeathed to nation)

Shrublet, up to 1,5 m. In grassland or shrub communities, up to 3300 m. Stems downy. **Leaves:** Closely leafy, alternate, in clusters, 4-12 x 1-3 mm, margins entire or with 1-3 pairs small teeth, hairless or hairy. **Flowers:** In large terminal inflorescences; flowers ± 14 mm diam, white to mauve (Nov-Jan).

Selago galpinii [= S. cooperi, S. sandersonii] tsitoanenyana, tsitoanyane (SS) (named after Ernest Galpin, 1850-1941, SA banker, amateur botanist)

Perennial woody shrublet, 150-500 mm. In grassland, rocky places, 1500-2575 m. Woody rootstock. Several leafy stems, forming rounded cushion. **Leaves:** In clusters, 7-23 x 1-2 mm, midrib channelled above, raised below. **Flowers:** In terminal slender branched inflorescences, side branchlets mostly on one side; flowers ± 5 mm diam, **tube short,** 3-4 mm, in rounded clusters, ±10 mm diam (Jan-May).

Tetraselago (*tetra* - four) - Tufted, perennial herbs; fruit a capsule, splitting to release seeds. 4 species endemic to SA.

Tetraselago natalensis Natal Blue Haze; usikisiki (Z)

Erect perennial shrublet, up to 750 mm. In grassland, woodland. Stems slightly branched, from woody base, almost hairless. **Leaves:** Spreading, ± 30 x 3 mm, tips sharply pointed, margins sometimes with short sharp teeth. **Flowers:** In terminal, compact, rounded inflorescences, ± 100 mm diam; flowers small, blue or mauve (Jan-Jun). **Similar species:** *T. wilmsii* Stems straggling, leaves ± 15 x 5 mm.

Nemesia caerulea

Nemesia denticulata

Sutera floribunda

Lal Greene

Geoff Nichols

Lal Greene

Nemesia caerulea

Lal Greene

Jamesbrittenia pristisepala

Lal Greene

Selago flanaganii

Martin von Fintel

Selago galpinii

Tony Abbott

Selago flanaganii

Lal Greene

Tetraselago natalensis

Trevor Coleman

481

GESNERIACEAE - African Violet Family Herbs; flowers irregular, oblique, ± 2 lipped, 5 lobed. Fruit a dry capsule. Economically important as ornamentals such as Gloxinia, African Violet, Cape Primrose (*Streptocarpus*), *Achimenes*. Trop, subtrop, ± 130 genera, ± 2900 species, 1 genus in SA. *Streptocarpus* (*streptos* - twisted; *karpos* - fruit) - Often epiphytic, some plants die after flowering (monocarpic); rooting stem below leaves called a petiolode; leaves solitary or in rosette, continuously growing from base; fruit a capsule with spirally twisted valves. Afr, ± 135 species, ± 51 in SA.

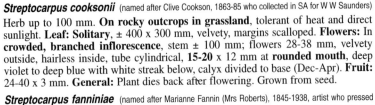

Streptocarpus cooksonii (named after Clive Cookson, 1863-85 who collected in SA for W W Saunders)
Herb up to 100 mm. **On rocky outcrops in grassland**, tolerant of heat and direct sunlight. **Leaf: Solitary**, ± 400 x 300 mm, velvety, margins scalloped. **Flowers:** In crowded, **branched inflorescence**, stem ± 100 mm; flowers 28-38 mm, velvety outside, hairless inside, tube cylindrical, **15-20** x 12 mm at **rounded mouth**, deep violet to deep blue with white streak below, calyx divided to base (Dec-Apr). **Fruit:** 24-40 x 3 mm. **General:** Plant dies back after flowering. Grown from seed.

Streptocarpus fanniniae (named after Marianne Fannin (Mrs Roberts), 1845-1938, artist who pressed and painted plants collected by her brother G F Fannin in the Dargle; mother of noted ornithologist Austin Roberts)
Perennial herb, 0,3-1 m, in large colonies. In forest, **on damp rock faces, streambanks**, 900-1500 m. **Creeping, rooting 'stems'**, ± 15 mm diam. **Leaves:** Solitary, ± 900 x 220 mm, margins scalloped, hairless to softly hairy above, veins hairy beneath. **Flowers:** 1-2 inflorescences, **stems erect**, ± 300 mm; flowers in profusion, large, 28-40 mm, white to deep blue, **tube more than 15 mm, mouth 7-9 mm wide**, floor of tube pale yellow, calyx with 5 narrow lobes, 10 x 1 mm, stalks 10-18 mm, hairy (Nov-Apr), sweetly scented. **Fruit:** 30-60 x 2 mm.

Streptocarpus formosus [= *S. primulifolius* subsp. *formosus*] (*formosus* - beautiful)
Perennial herb, ± 100 mm. **Leaves:** ± 450 x 110 mm, softly hairy, running onto clasping stalk, ± 50 x 8 mm. **Flowers:** 1-2, tube white outside, lobes whitish suffused with violet towards tips, **yellow streaked purplish brown on floor of tube**, main veins on lower lip finely spotted purple, stem 70-105 mm (Dec). **Fruit:** Capsule 110-179 mm. **Similar species:** *S. primulifolius* (see p. 484).

Streptocarpus gardenii (named after Major Robert Garden, served in Natal, 1843-1859)
Perennial herb, up to 170 mm. In forest, on rocks, steep slopes, streambanks, 900-1950 m. **Leaves:** In rosette, ± 300 x 70 mm, green or reddish brown, margins scalloped, reddish purple beneath, softly hairy, stalks ± 70 x 6 mm. **Flowers:** 1-2(6), stem ± 150 mm; flowers ± 50 mm, pale violet **lower lip with deep violet usually broken lines, tube narrow, greenish white**, hairy outside, hairless within (Nov-Apr). **Fruit:** Capsules 60-120 x 1,5 mm. **General:** Lines on lower lip of flower solid or absent. **Similar species:** *S. rexii* Cape Primrose; Tweelingsusters (A); umfazi onengxolo (X) Up to 210 mm, E Cape to S KZN; flowers large, 40-75 mm, pale violet, tube white tinged violet, mouth round, shortly hairy on floor of tube inside, lip white, marked with solid violet lines; used traditionally as a love charm. Popular container plant, the basis for many hybrids, first cultivated in Europe in the 1800s.

Streptocarpus grandis **Purple Fountain** (*grandis* - large)
Herb, up to 450 mm. **In forests**, 600-1200 m. **Leaves: Solitary, large**, ± 380 x 330 mm, softly hairy, margins scalloped. **Flowers:** Many flowers open at once; 22-45 mm, hairy outside, hairless inside, throat and base of lower lip violet with deeper violet and white markings, tube cylindrical, **throat ± 10 mm wide**, calyx lobes ± 5 x 1 mm (Oct-Mar). **Fruit:** Capsules **long, 65-110** x 1,2 mm. **General:** Plant dies after flowering. Very variable, especially flower colour, from white to medium violet (pale forms sometimes have yellow markings on floor of tube).

Streptocarpus haygarthii (named after Walter Haygarth, 1862-1950, collector, illustrator, whose sister married botanist John Medley Wood)
Herb, up to 400 mm. In forests, on earth banks or epiphytic on rocks and tree trunks. **Leaves: Solitary**, ± 400 x 350 mm, softly hairy, dark green above, purplish red beneath, margins scalloped. **Flowers:** ± 36 flowers in inflorescence, **stem curls up through leaf lobes**; flowers ± 45 mm, hairy outside, glandular round mouth, white to violet, tube abruptly deflexed, then directed forwards, mouth flattened, sometimes patterned with lines or shaded violet (Sep-Apr). **Fruit:** Capsule 25-80 x 1,5 mm. **General:** Plant dies after flowering. Flowers very variable in size, shape of two upper petal lobes, colour and pattern.

Streptocarpus fanniniae

Streptocarpus cooksonii

Streptocarpus formosus

Streptocarpus gardenii

Streptocarpus grandis

Streptocarpus haygarthii

Streptocarpus gardenii

483

Streptocarpus johannis (named after Port St John's, where it was first collected)

Perennial herb, up to 300 mm. In forest, on rock and earth banks, coast to 1650 m. **Rhizome horizontal. Leaves:** In **loose rosette, suberect,** ± 350 x 100 mm, softly hairy, blunt tipped, stalks ± 40 mm. **Flowers:** 1-12, stem ± 300 mm; flowers ± 45 mm, whitish to pale violet, white or yellowish in throat, veins on all petal lobes violet, flower tube cylindrical, bulbous at base, strongly curved, flattened at mouth (Oct-Dec). **Fruit:** Capsule 30-60 x 2,5 mm. **General:** Colour and shape variable.

Streptocarpus kentaniensis (named after Kentani, on the Transkei coast)

Perennial herb, 60-120 mm. On rocks, in dry forest. **Leaves: In rosette,** 30-200 x 18 mm, **narrow, suberect, thick, midvein remarkably prominent beneath,** tips pointed, margins scalloped. **Flowers:** Inflorescence with 2-5 flowers, 22-30 mm, tube straight, cylindrical, throat 6-10 mm wide, pale violet outside, flushed, streaked darker violet in mouth, floor of tube with pale yellow stripe, spotted violet (Jul-Sep). **Fruit:** Capsule 30-50 x 2 mm. **General: Unique midwinter flowering period.**

Streptocarpus pentherianus (named after Arnold Penther, 1865-1931, who collected in SA and Zim)

Perennial herb, up to 150 mm. On mossy rocks in forest or in moist shade of rock outcrops in grassland, 1200-2000 m. **Leaves:** 1-3, ± 120 x 80 mm, reddish beneath, sparsely hairy, margins scalloped. **Flowers:** Inflorescence with ± 12 flowers, **small,** ± 18 mm, white, sometimes tinged violet, **tube narrow, strongly curved,** glandular hairy outside, **throat flattened,** pale yellow, with glandular hairs around mouth inside, calyx lobes 2 x 0,5 mm, stalks 10-20 mm (Nov-Mar). **Fruit:** Capsules **short,** 9-20 x 2 mm, **deflexed. General:** New leaves develop on top of old ones.

Streptocarpus polyanthus (polyanthus - many flowers)

Perennial herb, or dying after flowering, up to 250 mm. On rocky outcrops, forest margins, coast to 2000 m. **Leaves:** ± 240 x 170 mm, **thick, upper surface grey-green, reddish purple beneath,** margins scalloped. **Flowers:** ± 36, a few open at a time, **stem stout;** flowers 15-45 mm, hairy outside, glandular towards throat inside, **chalky,** pale violet to mauve, **tube narrow, sharply deflexed** then directed forwards, with **keyhole opening** (Jul-Feb). **Fruit:** Capsules **stout,** 15-65 x 2 mm. **General:** In cultivation in Europe since the 1800s. Subsp. *comptonii*, leaves small; flowering stem very slender, flowers small, greenish white; capsules short. Subsp. *dracomontanus*, flowering stem short, stout, few-flowered; capsule 16-40 mm. Subsp. *polyanthus*, robust, flowering stems stout, many-flowered; capsules 30-65 mm. Subsp. *verecundus*, inflorescence slender, less than 12 flowers; capsule 17-45 mm.

Streptocarpus porphyrostachys (porphyrostachys - purple plant)

Perennial herb, up to 260 mm. On damp rock faces near streams in forested gorges. **Leaves:** 1(3), ± 300 x 180 mm, **dark green** above, **purple-red beneath,** sparsely hairy, margins scalloped. **Flowers:** ± 24, several open at once, in branching inflorescence; flowers 30-43 mm, violet with white patch below near mouth, **tube expanded** on lower side in upper half, **sparsely hairy outside,** lobes violet, patterned with white wedges and deep violet streaks, hairy on roof of throat inside, stalks 12-30 mm, reddish brown, sparsely hairy (Nov-Jan). **Fruit:** Capsule 40-65 mm.

Streptocarpus primulifolius (primulifolius - leaves like *Primula*)

Perennial herb, up to 270 mm. In forest. **Rhizome horizontal, stout. Leaves:** In rosette, ± 450 x 110 mm, stalks ± 50 x 8 mm, hairy. **Flowers:** 1-2(4), stem ± 270 mm; flowers **large, 65-90 mm,** pale bluish violet outside, hairy, floor of tube and lower lip deep violet with 5 reddish purple lines, base of lower lip with reddish flush, petal lobes whitish outside (Dec-Apr). **Fruit:** Capsule 70-180 x 2 mm. **Similar species:** *S. formosus* (see p. 482).

Streptocarpus prolixus **isikhwalisamatshe (Z)** (prolixus - of great extension)

Perennial herb, up to 200 mm. On cliff faces in kloof forests. **Leaves:** 2-3, ± 230 x 150 mm, usually prostrate, margins scalloped, **purplish red beneath,** softly hairy. **Flowers:** ± 36 mm, tube sharply deflexed, then directed forwards, pale violet to white, throat pale yellow with impressed lines, hairy outside, glandular inside around mouth, calyx lobes 3 x 1 mm, stalks 9-20 mm (Oct-Dec). **Fruit: Capsules slender,** 18-45 x 1,5 mm. **General:** Used traditionally as a purgative for cows.

Streptocarpus johannis

Martin Kunhardt

Streptocarpus pentherianus

Martin Kunhardt

Streptocarpus kentaniensis

Tracy McLellan

Streptocarpus polyanthus

Martin Kunhardt

Streptocarpus porphyrostachys

Tony Abbott

Streptocarpus polyanthus

Martin Kunhardt

Streptocarpus porphyrostachys

Lorraine van Hooff

Streptocarpus primulifolius

Elise Cloete

Streptocarpus prolixus

Lorraine van Hooff

485

Streptocarpus pusillus (*pusillus* - weak, small)

Small herb, up to 120 mm. On cliff faces, in kloof forest on banks, mossy rocks, 1200-2600 m. **Leaves:** 1 (2-3), ± 220 x 160 mm, margins scalloped. **Flowers:** ± 30, many open at once, ± 18 mm, white, sticky glandular outside, tube cylindrical (Nov-Apr). **Fruit:** Capsule 15-25 x 2 mm. **General:** Plant dies after flowering. (See p. 196)

Streptocarpus silvaticus (*silvaticus* - loving woods)

Perennial herb, up to 160 mm. In midland forests, **epiphyte or lithophyte. Leaves:** 2-5, ± 120 x 70 mm, green above, reddish beneath, softly hairy, margins scalloped. **Flowers:** ± 10, tube greenish, sharply deflexed, mouth compressed, violet inside, with impressed lines and 2 small keels from base to yellow-green throat, hairy outside, glandular inside mouth (Oct-Jan). **Fruit:** Capsule 17-54 x 1,5 mm.

Streptocarpus trabeculatus (*trabeculatus* - little beams, refers to very prominent veins beneath leaves)

Herb, 20-100 mm. On cliff faces, under rock outcrops. **Leaves:** Solitary, ± 400 x 160 mm, **very thick, veins very prominent, sticky hairy beneath. Flowers:** Many open at once, in crowded inflorescence; flowers ± 25 mm, **tube short, narrow, bent sharply downwards and forwards, mouth not compressed**, white streak on floor of tube, base of lower lip white, marked with deep violet streaks (Oct-Feb). **Fruit:** Capsule 16-35 x 3 mm. **General:** Plant dies after flowering. Good container plant.

Streptocarpus wendlandii Giant Streptocarpus; Reusestreptocarpus (A) (named after Hermann Wendland of Hanover in 1890)

Herb, up to 550 mm. On steep earth banks or epiphytic in forest. **Leaves:** Solitary, **large**, ± 450 x 350 mm, **purplish red beneath. Flowers:** 35-50 mm, **tube short, narrow, deflexed about the middle**, violet with 2 deeper violet blotches in throat, **white stripe on floor of tube**, white wedges on lower lip (Dec-Mar). **Fruit:** Capsule 45-85 x 2,5 mm. **General:** Plant dies after flowering. Endemic to Ngoye forest. Cultivated in Europe since 1890, from seed supplied by John Medley Wood.

LENTIBULARIACEAE - Bladderwort Family Perennial herbs, aquatic or in swamps. Submerged leaves modified into bladderlike pitchers with traps for catching insects. Flowers 2 lipped, spurred or pouched at base. Cosmop, ± 3 genera, ± 245 species, 2 genera in SA. **Genlisea** (named after Comtesse de Genlis, author of 'La Botanique Historique et Literature', 1810) - Rootless herb; bladders tubular with 2 spirally twisted arms. Brazil, Afr, ± 23 species, 1 in SA.

Genlisea hispidula (*hispidula* - small bristles, rough)

Erect, terrestrial herb, 100-300 mm, in colonies. In marshes, wet grassland, coast to 1500 m. **Leaves: In rosette**, 20-40 x 9 mm; traps colourless, tubular, densely clustered below on slender stalks, partly buried in mud. **Flowers:** 3-10 in simple or sparsely branched inflorescence; flowers ± 12 mm, violet, blue, mauve (yellow), sparsely hairy outside, **spur greenish or yellowish**, stalks erect (Jul-Sep).

Utricularia (*utriculus* - little leather bottle, refers to insect trapping bladders on leaves and runners) - Perennial herbs, in water or damp places; usually with traps; fruit a capsule. Cosmop, ± 40 species, ± 18 in SA.

Utricularia livida Bladderwort; Blaaskruid (A); tlamana-sa-metsi (SS); intambo (Z) (*livida* - lead coloured)

Terrestrial herb, up to 200(450) mm, in colonies. In marshy ground, seasonally wet grassland, coast to 2600 m, Cape to Trop Afr, Madag. Stems fine, ± 50 mm, much branched. **Leaves:** 10-20 x 1-5 mm, **main vein branched**; traps 1-2 mm, on leaves and stems. **Flowers:** 1-8 in terminal clusters, stems slender, erect to twining or reclining; flowers ± 10 mm, mauve or white (yellow), with or without yellow blotch on lower lip, spur short, blunt (Aug-Apr). **General:** Leaves not conspicuous at time of flowering. Used in traditional medicine to help babies keep milk down.

Utricularia sandersonii Bladderwort; Blaaskruid (A) (named after John Sanderson, 1820-1881, journalist, trader, draughtsman, president of Natal Agricultural and Horticultural Society)

Dwarf, terrestrial and aquatic herb. On wet rocks, 210-1200 m. Stems hairlike, simple or sparsely branched, ± 50 mm. **Leaves:** Few, erect, **2-3 at base of flowering stem**, otherwise scattered, ± 15 mm, tips rounded, narrowing to stalk; traps oval, 1-1,5 mm, numerous. **Flowers:** 1-6, in short, erect inflorescences, stems slender; flowers 10-15 mm, pale mauve with violet markings, **upper lip deeply lobed, spur long**, 8-10 mm, strongly curved, tip pointed (throughout year).

Streptocarpus pusillus

Tony Abbott

Streptocarpus silvaticus

Martin von Fintel

Streptocarpus trabeculatus

Martin Kumhardt

Streptocarpus wendlandii

Geoff Nichols

Streptocarpus wendlandii

Geoff Nichols

Genlisea hispidula

Tony Abbott

Genlisea hispidula

Van Wyk & Malan

Utricularia livida

Lal Greene

Utricularia sandersonii

Geoff Nichols

Utricularia sandersonii

Tom de Waal

487

ACANTHACEAE - Acanthus Family Herbs, shrubs or climbers. Leaves opposite, without stipules. Inflorescence often with large leafy bracts, flowers irregular or 2 lipped, upper lip entire or 2 lobed, lower lip 3 lobed. Fruit an explosive capsule, ± club-shaped, seeds often with water absorbent hairs. Some have become popular ornamentals. Pantrop, ± 229 genera, ± 3450 species, 43 genera in SA.

Thunbergia (after Carl Thunberg, 1743-1828, author of 'Flora Capensis') - Herbs (for description see p. 306).

Thunbergia natalensis Dwarf Thunbergia, Natal Blue Bell; Dwergthunbergia (A); isiphondo esikhulu, unohlonishwayo (Z)

Shrublet, up to 1,2 m. In grassland, on forest margins, E Cape to Kenya. Unbranched stems from woody base. **Leaves:** ± 80 x 50 mm, margins with few blunt teeth near base. **Flowers:** ± 80 mm wide, **blue-mauve**, tube ± 40 x 15 mm, pale blue outside, yellow within, bracts 15-25 x 10-15 mm, veins conspicuous (Oct-Mar). **Fruit:** Hairy, 20-30 x 8-17 mm. **General:** Stems eaten by long-tailed tree mouse. Used as a charm to ensure a happy marriage. Popular garden plant, grown from seed.

Hygrophila (*hygrophila* - water loving) - Herbs, often glandular; leaves narrow; flowers solitary or clustered in axils of leaves or bracts, 2 lipped, upper lip hooded. Afr and trop, ± 90 species, ± 9 in SA.

Hygrophila auriculata (*auriculata* - eared)

Robust, erect, annual herb, up to 0,6(1,5) m. On water's edge, KZN to Trop Afr. Thinly hairy, stems square, sparsely branched. **Leaves:** ± 150 x 25 mm, margins entire, tapering to both ends, stalkless. **Flowers:** In stalkless clusters in axils, with ± 6 straight spines, ± 40 mm; flowers ± 25 mm, pale blue to mauve to violet (Jun-Aug). **General:** Good plant for damp spots in garden.

Ruellia (named after Jean de la Ruelle of Soissons, physician to Francis 1, author of 'De Natura Plantarum', 1536) - Herbs; flowers solitary or in small groups in axils, tube widening to bell-shaped, lobes broad, calyx short, deeply 5 lobed, bracts leaflike. Attracts butterflies. Trop America, Afr, Mascarene Is, Asia, Austr, ± 150 species, ± 13 in SA.

Ruellia cordata Veld Violet (*cordata* - heart-shaped)

Perennial herb, up to 120 mm. In grassland. Stems branching at base, 4 angled, **softly grey hairy** throughout. **Leaves:** ± 32 x 17 mm, grey-green, slightly heart-shaped at base, stalks short. **Flowers:** ± 20 mm wide, tube ± 20 mm, mauve (pink or white) with purple streaks (Sep-Dec). **General:** Used traditionally as a love charm and to make someone invisible. Hardy, attractive in gardens, in full sun.

Ruellia sp. nov. 2 [incorrectly known as *R. patula*]

Perennial herb, low growing to prostrate. In woodland, grassland. Rootstock woody. Stems soft, thinly hairy. **Leaves:** ± 25 x 15 mm, margins slightly wavy, **stalks ± 12 mm**. **Flowers:** ± 20 mm wide, white or mauve with darker streaks, **tube long, ± 25 mm**, finely hairy (blooms throughout year). **General:** Attracts Brown Commodore and Christmas Forester butterflies. Hardy, attractive groundcover.

Barleria (named after Jacques Barrelier, 1606-1673, Dominican monk and French botanist) - Herbs or shrubs; leaves with 2 buds in axils, 1 sometimes developing into a spine, the other into a leafy branch or inflorescence, 2 small and 2 large calyx lobes; fruit an explosive capsule. Warmer parts of Afr, Asia, America, ± 250 species, ± 60 in SA.

Barleria gueinzii (named after Wilhelm Gueinzius, 1814-74, apothecary, botanical and zoological collector)

Scrambling shrub, up to 2 m. On forest margins, in woodland in rocky places. Much branched, thinly hairy throughout, **no spines**. **Leaves:** ± 50 x 25 mm, soft greyish olive green, stalks ± 10 mm. **Flowers:** ± 40 mm wide, blue-mauve, tube ± 30 mm, bracteoles narrow, larger calyx lobes ± 10 mm wide, papery, tapering to fine point, margins toothed (Mar-May). **Fruit:** Capsule horny, ± 15 mm, sharply pointed. **General:** Blooms in profusion, flowers drop after a day. Easily grown.

Barleria lancifolia (*lancifolia* - lancelike leaves)

Slender sprawling shrublet. In woodland, scrub, NW Cape to Bots, Nam, N Prov. Stems long hairy, **no spines**. **Leaves:** 50-60 x 20 mm, grey hairy, young leaves white woolly, stalks very short. **Flowers:** In axils, ± 30 mm wide, tube ± 30 mm, pale mauve, calyx deeply divided, lobes narrow, ±13 mm wide, glandular hairy, stalk very short (Mar-May).

Barleria meyeriana

Slender, straggling shrublet. In woodland. Irregularly branched. **Leaves:** ± 50 x 20 mm, **unequal sided at base**, stalks very short. **Flowers:** In axils, ± 40 mm wide, tube 20-30 mm, white to pale blue, mauve, with few dark streaks, **buds red**, calyx deeply divided, ± 14 mm wide, glandular hairy, stalk short (Feb-May).

Thunbergia natalensis

Tony Abbott

Thunbergia natalensis

Lawrence Peacock

Thunbergia natalensis

Tom de Waal

Hygrophila auriculata

Geoff Nichols

Hygrophila auriculata

Geoff Nichols

Ruellia cordata

Lawrence Peacock

Ruellia sp. nov. 2

Darrel Plowes

Barleria gueinzii

Geoff Nichols

Barleria lancifolia

Geoff Nichols

Barleria meyeriana

Geoff Nichols

Barleria monticola Berg Barleria (*monticola* - growing on hills)
Cushionlike herb, 150-450 mm, in colonies. In moist grassland. Woody rootstock. Stems **hardly branching, with long, silky golden hairs throughout**. Leaves: ± 45 x 12-20 mm, stalkless. **Flowers:** ± 30 mm wide, tube ± 40 mm, petal lobes only just protrude beyond calyx lobes, calyx lobes overlapping, sharply pointed, ± 20 mm (Aug-Dec). **General:** Spectacular when flowering after fires. **Similar species:** *B. ovata* Hairs long, soft; leaves often overlapping; large, terminal inflorescences ± 90 x 50 mm, flowers ± 30 mm wide, tips of petal lobes pointed, mauve to magenta (yellow) darker in throat, calyx lobes conspicuous, pinkish (Dec-Mar).

Barleria obtusa Bush Violet; Bosviooltjie (A); idololenkonyane (Z) (*obtusa* - blunt tipped)
Perennial herb to scrambling shrub, up to 2 m. On dry hillsides, rocky ground, in grassland and woodland. Stems erect or spreading, rooting at nodes, slightly woody, finely hairy throughout, **no spines**. **Leaves:** ± 50 x 30 mm, dark green, stalks very short. **Flowers:** ± 25 mm wide, blue, mauve, pink (white), bracteoles narrow, calyx deeply divided, ± 15 mm, lobes unequal (Mar-Jun). **General:** Browsed by stock and game. Attacts butterflies (Pieridae). Popular garden plant, flowering profusely in autumn. Needs a good pruning after flowering. (See p. 436)

Barleria saxatilis (*saxatilis* - found among rocks)
Straggling or erect shrub, 0,3-1,5 m, in large colonies. On dry rocky hillsides. Woody branches, with **short hairs**. **Leaves:** Variable, ± 30 x 20 mm, tapering to fine point. **Flowers: 1-4** in axils, **small**, ± 20 mm wide, tube ± 15 mm, bluish **mauve**, bracteoles firm, with spiny teeth, outer calyx lobes ± 20 x 9 mm, pale with darker veins, margins with fine spines (Mar-May). **Fruit:** Capsule **small, ± 10 x 4 mm**. **General:** Branches used to keep rats away from grain stores.

Barleria wilmsiana [= *B. wilmsii*] (named after Dr Friedrich Wilms, 1848-1919, apothecary, collector from Lydenburg)
Herb, up to 280 mm. Almost hairless. **Leaves:** ± 50 x 20 mm, **grey-green**, almost stalkless. **Flowers:** Solitary in axils; flowers ± 30 mm, lilac-purple, calyx lobes ± 20 x 5 mm.

Sclerochiton (*skleros* - hard; *chiton* - covering, refers to woody capsule) - Shrubs. Afr, ± 12 species, 6 in SA.

Sclerochiton apiculatus Blue Lips (*apiculatus* - pointed ends)
Erect or scrambling shrubs, up to 3 m. In dry sand forest, thicket, at low altitudes, KZN to Moz. Young stems sparsely hairy. **Leaves:** 30-75 x 13-35 mm, shiny very dark green, pale yellowish around finely hairy veins, stalks 1-5 mm. **Flowers: 2-14 in inflorescences**; flowers ± 22 mm, **deep blue**, silvery beneath, tube white, bracts yellowish brown to dark brown, calyx lobes hairy (Nov-Apr), **scented**. **Fruit:** Capsule ± 18 mm. **General:** Browsed by game. Easily grown, tolerates shade. **Similar species:** *S. harveyanus* mazabuka (Sw) Flowers in leaf axils, widely scattered, ± 18 mm, horizontal, blue, lilac or purple, bracts short, dark green or brown, glossy.

Blepharis (*blepharis* - eyelash) - Herbs or shrublets; leaves often in unequal pairs, or 4s, margins entire, toothed or spiny; flowers 1 lipped, 3-5 lobed, usually hairy on both surfaces, bract margins usually spiny, front calyx lobes forked or spiny; seeds covered in water absorbing hairs. Afr, Arabia, India, ± 80 species, ± 40 in SA.

Blepharis integrifolia Rankklits (A) (*integrifolia* - leaves with unbroken smooth edge)
Prostrate, trailing herb. In grassland, woodland, Cape to Nam, Bots. Woody rootstock. Stems much branched, leafy, densely hairy. **Leaves:** Small, 10-25 x 3-5 mm, leathery, white hairy, margins entire. **Flowers:** In small clusters, in leaf axils, flowers 14-25 mm, pale blue, mauve, white, 3-5 lobed, **bracts shortly spiny at tips** (Nov-Apr). **General:** Grown from cuttings. **Similar species:**
B. natalensis Sturdy, flat topped shrublet, in overgrazed, rocky areas; leaves ± 30 x 10 mm, margins with spine tipped teeth, spines in axils ± 15 mm; 2-6 flowers in spikes, ± 25 mm, dark blue, bracts with short spines towards tip (Mar-Aug).
B. obtusisepala Sturdy shrublet, prostrate or up to 300 mm; stems finely downy; leaves ± 30 x 10 mm, margins irregularly toothed; 4-6 flowers in round inflorescences, bracts with short spines in upper third (Sep-Dec). *B. maderaspatensis* Hairless; leaves 35 x 15 mm, in 4s at nodes; flowers white with yellow centre, purple stripes, bracts with long, recurved spines.

Barleria monticola

Martin von Fintel

Barleria saxatilis

Geoff Nichols

Barleria wilmsiana

Martin von Fintel

Barleria monticola

Martin von Fintel

Barleria obtusa

Lorraine van Hooff

Sclerochiton apiculatus

Wayne Matthews

Blepharis integrifolia

Van Wyk & Malan

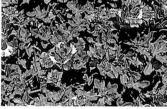

Blepharis natalensis

Geoff Nichols

Blepharis obtusisepala

Tony Abbott

491

Blepharis subvolubilis (*subvolubilis* - climbing, twining, an incorrect description of the habit)

Perennial shrublet, stems up to 600 mm. In sandy soil, in grassland. **Leaves:** 20-70 x 3-10 mm, leathery, **grey-green**, margins with spine tipped teeth. **Flowers:** Oval inflorescences, elongating to ± 90 mm; flowers ± 25 mm, lobes blue, tube creamy white, bracts ± 30 x 20 mm, veins conspicuous, margins with 5-7 long, thin, curved spines each side, tipped with 10 mm spine (Oct-Jan). **Fruit:** Capsule ± 12 x 6 mm.

Salpinctium (*salpinctium* - Greek for heralding trumpets) - Flowers strongly 2 lipped, tube long, slender. 3 species in SA.

Salpinctium natalense [= *Asystasia natalensis*]

Erect perennial, 100-500 mm. In rocky *Acacia* thicket. **Sparsely hairy** at nodes. **Leaves:** 15-65 x 9-20 mm, with sparsely scattered hairs. **Flowers:** Widely spaced, inflorescences ± 90 mm; flowers mauve-lilac, tube ± 25 x 2 mm, upper lobes reflexed, ± 8 x 5 mm, lower lobes ± 10 x 5 mm, **calyx lobes small, hairy** (Oct-Jun).

Ecbolium (*ecbole* - expulsion, refers to discharge of seeds) - Shrublets. Afr, Madag, India, ± 17 species, 3 in SA.

Ecbolium glabratum (*glabratum* - to make smooth, deprive of hair or bristles)

Erect shrublet, up to 900 mm. In thicket, on disturbed ground. Grey-green, almost hairless. **Leaves:** ± 60 x 30 mm, leathery grey-green, veins prominent, slightly clasping at base. **Flowers:** In terminal inflorescences, bracts broad, leaflike, overlapping; flowers 2 lipped, ± 20 mm wide, tube slender, ± 30 mm, blue, downy (Nov-May). **Fruit:** Stalked capsule, seeds rimmed on one side.

Justicia (named after James Justice, 1698-1763, Scottish horticulturalist, owner of two great gardens) - Herbs or shrublets; flowers 2 lipped, tube broad or bell-shaped. Attracts butterflies. Pantrop, 22 species in SA.

Justicia petiolaris **Blue Justicia** (*petiolaris* - stalked)

Perennial herb, 0,1-1m. In woodland, forest. **Leaves:** 16-145 x 9-70 mm. **Flowers:** In terminal inflorescences; flowers 8-18 mm, blue, mouth white striped mauve, **bracts 5-15 mm, hairy** (Nov-May). **General:** Subsp. *petiolaris*, in forest understorey; leaves large; inflorescences dense. Subsp. *bowiei*, E Cape; leaves ± 50 x 24 mm, stalks ± 20 mm; flowers widely spaced. Subsp. *incerta*, 100-500 mm, in woodland, KZN to N Prov; leaves ± 30 x 20 mm; flowers widely spaced, smaller.

RUBIACEAE - Gardenia/Coffee Family (for description see p. 556). ***Conostomium*** (*konos* - cone; *stoma* - mouth) - Perennial herbs or shrublets; stipules and sheath with hairs or teeth. Trop Afr, ± 9 species, 2 in SA.

Conostomium natalense [= *Oldenlandia natalensis*] **Wild Pentas; umbophe, ungcolosi (Z)**

Erect, slightly woody shrublet, 0,5-1 m. On forest margins, E Cape to N Prov. **Leaves:** 35-70 x 8-20 mm. **Flowers:** In terminal inflorescences, 20-40 mm diam, surrounded by leafy bracts; flowers ± 8 mm diam, tube ± 15 mm, pink, lilac or white, calyx lobes narrow (Oct-Apr). **Fruit** ± 7 x 6 mm. **General:** Used traditionally as love charms and to prevent lightning. Invades disturbed areas. (See p. 202)

Pentanisia (*pente* - five; *anisos* - unequal) - Perennial herbs; rootstock stout, woody. Afr, ± 15 species, 3 in SA.

Pentanisia prunelloides **Broad-leaved Pentanisia; Sooibrandbossie (A); khatoane, setima-mollo (SS); umgwamiso (Sw); icishamlilo (X,Z); isibunde, umakuphole (Z)**
(*prunelloides* - resembles *Prunella*)

Herb, up to 600 mm. In grassland, Cape to Tanz, coast to 1980 m. **Leaves:** Variable, 13-85 x 2-35 mm, very hairy to ± hairless. **Flowers: Dense inflorescences** ± 45 mm diam, stems 35-300 mm; flowers ± 8 mm diam, pale to deep purplish blue (Oct-Mar). **General:** First to bloom after fires. Afrikaans name means 'heartburn shrublet'; Zulu 'that which puts out the fire'. Traditionally used to treat a range of ailments from stomach pains to haemorrhoids. Deserves horticultural attention. **Similar species:** *P. angustifolia* Almost hairless; leaves narrow, ± 100 x 10 mm; **sparse** inflorescences.

CAMPANULACEAE - Bell Flower/Canterbury Bell Family Herbs or shrubs. Flowers 4-5 lobed. Fruit crowned with persistent calyx. Cosmop, mostly temp and subtrop regions, ± 82 genera, ± 2000 species, 12 genera in SA.
Roella (named after W Roell, prof of anatomy in Amsterdam 1737) - Shrublets. Endemic to SA, ± 24 species.

Roella glomerata **ibhosisi (X); amazombe (Z)** (*glomerata* - club-shaped)

Dwarf shrublet, up to 600 mm. On sandy flats, in grassland. Stems erect, woody below, sap milky. **Leaves:** Not crowded, 5-15 x 2-4 mm, soft, flat, margins entire or with a few teeth. **Flowers:** Inflorescences 15-30 mm diam; **flowers bell-shaped**, 10-20 mm, white, pale blue or mauve, bracts broad, toothed or lobed at top, calyx lobes longer than bracts (Dec-Apr). **General:** Used traditionally to treat lumbago.

Salpinctium natalense — *Geoff Nichols*

Ecbolium glabratum — *Martin von Fintel*

Justicia petiolaris — *Geoff Nichols*

Blepharis subvolubilis — *Wally Menne*

Pentanisia prunelloides — *Godfrey Symons*

Roella glomerata — *Tony Abbott*

Conostomium natalense — *Pam Cooke*

Pentanisia angustifolia — *Van Wyk & Malan*

Pentanisia prunelloides — *Wally Menne*

493

Wahlenbergia (named after Dr Goran Wahlenberg of Uppsala, 1780-1851, Swedish author of 'Flora Lapponica') - Herbs or shrublets; flowers bell-like, 5 lobed; fruit a capsule. S Hemisp, ± 150 species, ± 135 in SA.

Wahlenbergia cuspidata (*cuspidata* - tipped with rigid point, refers to calyx lobes)

Bushy herb, 300-500 mm. In mountains, in shelter of rocks or on damp cliffs, 1500-3000 m. **Leaves: Hairy, half clasping stem at base. Flowers:** ± 15 mm, **calyx lobe margins toothed, long, narrow, pointed** (Dec-Mar). **Similar species:** Previously often misidentified as *W. undulata* In mountain grassland, E Cape; stems loosely branched; calyx lobes short, ± 4 mm.

Wahlenbergia fasciculata (*fasciculata* - in close clusters)

Slender erect herb, 100-300 mm. In mountain grassland, rocky places, 1500-2400 m. Stems solitary, simple. **Leaves: Short, narrow, crowded, in tufts. Flowers:** ± 15 mm, stalkless, crowded in upper leaf axils, blue-mauve (Feb-Apr). **General:** Lovely garden plant.

Wahlenbergia grandiflora Giant Bell Flower; umnqantula, ushayindida omhlophe (Z)
(*grandiflora* - large flowers)

Perennial herb, 250-700 mm, in colonies. In grassland. Stems erect, robust. **Leaves:** Alternate, 30-40 x 6-8 mm, hairy, **margins wavy. Flowers:** At tips of slender, branched stems, ± 30 mm diam, blue, mauve, almost white, stalks 20-30 mm (Aug-Sep). **General:** Small flies attracted to flowers. Lovely garden plant. (See p. 206)

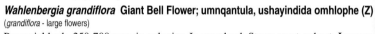

Wahlenbergia huttonii [= *Lightfootia huttonii*]

Erect, perennial herb, 100-350 mm. In rocky grassland, up to 1950 m. Woody rootstock. Stems simple or branched from base. **Leaves:** 5-15(25) x 3-8 mm, **crowded, spreading,** hairless to hairy beneath, **stalkless. Flowers: In small terminal clusters,** flowers 6-10 mm, **lobes deeply split,** blue or violet, ± **stalkless** (Dec-Apr).

Wahlenbergia krebsii [= *W. zeyheri*] tenane (SS) (after Georg Krebs, 1792-1844, apothecary, collector)

Slender perennial herb, 200-700 mm, in conspicuous groups. In grassland, damp places, up to 3000 m. Stems slender, simple below, branched above. **Leaves:** ± 55 x 10 mm, margins wavy, toothed, **crowded towards base of stems,** scattered up stem, narrow, margins toothed, **stalkless. Flowers:** In loose inflorescences; flowers 10-16 mm, violet-blue, **stalks 2-25 mm** (Nov-May). **General:** Used as a pot herb.

Wahlenbergia pallidiflora (*pallidus* - pale, pallid; *flora* - flowers)

Perennial herb, up to 600 mm. In marshy ground, 1500-2100 m. **Leaves:** 15-25 x 5-10 mm, **margins wavy,** toothed. **Flowers:** ± 25 mm diam, **chalky blue,** calyx lobes ± 13 x 4 mm, **margins toothed, stalks finely hairy** (Dec-Apr). **Similar species:** *W. appressifolia* In colonies; flowers deep blue, calyx lobes ± 9 x 4 mm, stalks hairless.

Craterocapsa (*krateros* - cup-shaped; *capsa* - capsule) - Prostrate, perennial herbs; flowers bell-like. S Afr, 4 species.

Craterocapsa tarsodes Carpet Bell Flower (*tarsodes* - mat forming)

Mat-forming herb. On rocky outcrops, in stony grassland, 1200-2500 m, E Cape to Zim. Tap root thick. Stems short, **ending in rosettes of leaves. Leaves:** 7-30 x 5(12) mm, tapering to broad, stalklike base, margins hairy. **Flowers: Solitary, in axils of rosette leaves,** ± 20 mm, **opening one at a time,** pale blue or white (Nov-Feb).

LOBELIACEAE - Lobelia Family Herbs, often with milky sap. Flowers often 2 lipped, inverted on the stalks. Fruit a capsule. Includes some well known ornamentals. Cosmop, ± 20 genera, ± 1000 species, 5 genera in SA.
Lobelia (named after Matthias de L'Obel, 1538-1616, Flemish nobleman, botanist, physician to King James I) - Herbs or shrublets; flowers 5 lobed, regular or 2 lipped; fruit a capsule. Cosmop, mostly American, ± 300 species, ± 70 in SA.

Lobelia anceps Swamp Lobelia (*anceps* - two edged, flattened)

Much branched, reclining or erect herb, up to 600 mm. In marshy ground. Stems thick, winged. **Leaves:** ± 80 x 20 mm, slightly fleshy, margins toothed. **Flowers:** ± 15 mm, pale blue with two white streaks on lower lobes, deep lilac spots on lip (Aug-Mar). **General:** Good plant for damp areas, grown from cuttings. **Similar species:** *L. chamaedryfolia* Prostrate to reclining herb; in grassland near rivers; leaves ± 30 x 20 mm, broad tipped; flowers 10-14 mm; stalks reflexed in fruit. *L. corniculata* Up to 600 mm, in moist places; rootstock woody; stems slender, triangular, winged; leaves ± 22 x 8 mm; flowers solitary, irregularly scattered, blue with 2 yellowish crests in mouth of tube.

494

Wahlenbergia cuspidata

Wahlenbergia cuspidata

Wahlenbergia fasciculata

Wahlenbergia huttonii

Wahlenbergia krebsii

Wahlenbergia pallidiflora

Wahlenbergia grandiflora

Lobelia chamaedryfolia

Lobelia anceps

Craterocapsa tarsodes

Lobelia corniculata

495

Lobelia coronopifolia [= L. caerulea] Wild Lobelia, Buck's Horn Lobelia; itshilizi, ubulawu (X); isidala esikhulu (Z) (coronopifolia - leaves like Coronopus)

Perennial shrublet, up to 600 mm. In grassland. Woody rootstock. **Leaves:** Clustered at base, 20-45 x 1-3 mm, margins toothed. **Flowers:** In terminal inflorescences, stems ± 170 mm; flowers ± 25 mm, purplish blue (throughout year). **General:** Visited by honey-bees, butterflies. Used in traditional medicine for eardrops and to treat bad luck or constant bad dreams. Hardy garden plant, grown from cuttings.

Lobelia erinus Edging Lobelia; mahlo-a-konyana, napjane-ea-phiri, tsoinyane (SS); impenjana, incamathela, isidala esiluhlaza (Z) (erinus - liver balsam)

Annual herb, 100-600 mm, in colonies. In grassland, marshy ground. Stems simple or branched near base. **Leaves:** Clustered towards base, 10-23 x 5 mm, margins entire or toothed. **Flowers:** In many-flowered inflorescences, **stems very slender;** flowers ± 15 mm, **blue and white** (throughout year). **General:** Used as a pot herb when young. Visited by butterflies. Used in traditional medicine to treat colds and to wash divining bones. Popular garden plant, with many horticultural varieties.

Lobelia flaccida Wild Lobelia; motlapa-tsoinjane (SS); itshilizi, ubulawu (X); isidala esiluhlaza (Z) (flaccida - limp)

Slender, erect, annual or short lived perennial, 50-600 mm. In grassland, on stream-banks, coast to 2450 m, E Cape to Zim, Moz. **Stems angled, narrowly winged,** simple or branching from base, hairless or finely hairy. **Leaves:** Well spaced, 20-70 x 2-10 mm, margins toothed. **Flowers:** ± 15 mm, pale blue, mauve or whitish with two crests in mouth of tube, stalks 5-50 mm (Nov-Jun). **General:** Used as a pot herb.

Monopsis (mon - one; opsis - appearance, flowers almost regular in some species) - Annual or perennial herbs; flowers split to base, 2 lipped or regular; 2 valved fruit. Mainly S Afr, ± 20 species.

Monopsis decipiens [= Lobelia decipiens] Butterfly Lobelia; Skoenlapperplant (A); isidala somkhuhlane (Z) (decipiens - deceiving, a species that closely resembles another)

Slender herb, 50-250 mm. In grassland, seasonally wet places, E Cape to Zim. **Creeping rhizome.** Stems branched. **Leaves:** Alternate, 8-15 x 1-2 mm, roughly hairy on margins and midrib beneath. **Flowers:** Solitary, ± 18 mm, blue and purple with yellow markings on lower lip (Sep-Mar). **General:** Used in traditional medicine to treat colds, skin diseases, rheumatism. Needs damp places in garden.

Monopsis stellarioides Sticky-leaved Monopsis; inamathela (Z) (stellarioides - starlike)

Annual or perennial herbs, 50-600 mm. In grassland, swampy places, E Cape to Trop Afr. Stems rooting at lower nodes. Plant **covered in tiny, rough bumps. Leaves:** Opposite, 10-35 x 2-9 mm, margins toothed. **Flowers:** Solitary, in axils, ± 11 mm, mustard yellow, dull pink, brownish purple or violet, with 2 crests in mouth, stalks 8-35 mm (Nov-Feb). **General:** Leaves and stems stick to clothing.

ASTERACEAE (COMPOSITAE) - Daisy Family The largest family of flowering plants (for description see p. 208). **Vernonia** (named after William Vernon, died 1711, English botanist who collected in USA) - Herbs, shrubs, climbers or trees. Afr, America, Asia, Madag (Austr), ± 1000 species, ± 50 in SA, absent from winter rainfall areas.

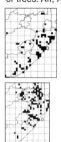

Vernonia capensis [= V. pinifolia] Cape Vernonia, Narrow-leaved Vernonia; Blounaaldetee (bossie) (A); bolou, mofefa-bana-oa-thaba, phefo (SS)

Herb, up to 1 m. In open grassland, coast to 1800 m, Cape to Zam, Malawi. Woody rootstock. Stems annual, simple (branched). **Leaves: Narrow,** 40-70 x 1-2 mm, **olive green above, silky white beneath,** tapering to hairlike tips. **Flowerheads:** In branched inflorescences; ± 10 mm wide, violet to magenta, bracts silky silvery (Jul-Jan). **Fruit:** Pappus with rough bristles. **General:** This and the following two species make excellent garden plants, grown by seed, cuttings or division. **Similar species: V. natalensis** Silver Vernonia; ileleva, isibhaha sasenkangala, umlahlankosi-omhlophe (Z) Plant silky silvery; leaves 35-60 x 4-10(20) mm; used traditionally to treat coughs, malaria, ensure healthy pregnancy and as a charm against lightning. **V. oligocephala** Bicoloured-leaved Vernonia; Bitterbossie, Groenamarabossie, Maagbossie, Wildetee (A); mofefa-bana, mofolotsane (SS); ihlambihloshane, uhlungu-hloshana (Z) Stems silvery hairy; leaves ± 40 x 25 mm, dark green above, silky white beneath, margins wavy, broadly rounded at base. Used traditionally to treat intestinal and other complaints and to drive away hail storms. Leaves used for a tea.

496

Tony Abbott

Lobelia coronopifolia

Rosemary Williams

Lobelia erinus

Tom de Waal

Lobelia flaccida

Geoff Nichols

Monopsis decipiens

Lal Greene

Monopsis stellarioides

Lorraine van Hooff

Vernonia capensis

Darrel Plowes

Vernonia natalensis

Van Wyk & Malan

Vernonia oligocephala

497

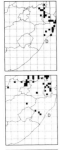

Vernonia centaureoides <small>(after a plant whose medicinal properties were said to be discovered by a centaur)</small>
Stiffly branched herb, 300-500 mm. In grassland, woodland, on sandy soils, KZN to Moz. Stems, leaves rough, gland dotted. **Leaves:** Rigid, ± 40 x 3 mm, margins rolled under. **Flowerheads:** In open branched terminal inflorescences; ± 10 mm wide, magenta-purple, **bracts abruptly narrowed to hairlike tip** (Nov-May). **Fruit:** Pappus with long, feathery bristles. **General:** Flowers attract butterflies.

Vernonia fastigiata <small>(fastigiata - narrowing toward the top)</small>
Bushy annual herb, up to 1 m. In dry, sandy places, roadsides, on coastal plain, KZN to Trop Afr. **Leaves:** ± 60 x 4 mm, margins entire. **Flowerheads:** In open inflorescences; ± 20 mm wide, purple, **bracts long, bristle tipped, recurved, woolly** (Dec-Jun).

Vernonia galpinii **Bloukwasbossie, Perskwasbossie (A)** <small>(named after Ernest Galpin, 1858-1941, banker, amateur botanist)</small>
Herb, 200-350(600) mm, in clumps. In grassland, E Cape to Zim. Perennial rootstock. Annual stems, roughly hairy throughout. **Leaves:** Crowded towards base, ± 45 x 10 mm, margins entire, stalkless. **Flowerheads:** Usually solitary (2-3) terminal, ± 25 mm wide, purple (Aug-May). <small>(See p. 210)</small>

Vernonia hirsuta **Quilted-leaved Vernonia; Wildesonsoekertjie (A); hlele-hlele, phefo-e-kholo, sethsee (SS); ijungitheka, ikhambi lenyongo, uhlunguhlungwana lwentaba, umhlazawentaba (Z)** <small>(hirsuta - hairy)</small>
Herb, up to 1 m, in colonies. In grassland, scrub, on forest margins, coast to 1900 m. Woody rootstock. Annual stems simple, **roughly hairy** throughout. **Leaves:** Thick, ± 100 x 50 mm, variable, margins entire, scalloped or toothed, **veins indented above, protruding beneath,** upper surface roughly hairy, **greyish white woolly beneath, stalkless, clasping at base. Flowerheads:** In dense, flat, branched inflorescences; ± 8 mm wide, magenta to purple, pink, bracts abruptly contracted to hairlike tips, grey hairy (Sep-Jan). **General:** Used in traditional medicine to treat colic, sore throats, coughs, headaches and rashes. Hardy garden plant, from seed.
Similar species: *V. flanaganii* In moist scrubby places, 1525-2000 m; leaves tapered into short stalks; flowerheads larger, ± 10 mm wide, bracts gradually narrowed to tip.

Vernonia thodei <small>(named after Justus Thode, 1859-1932, German naturalist, teacher, who collected in SA)</small>
Perennial herb up to 350 mm. In grassland, 900-2100 m. **Leaves: In basal rosette,** 40-50(100) x 20 mm, margins entire or obscurely toothed, narrowing to stalklike base, ± hairless. **Flowerheads:** Solitary or paired, ± 20 mm wide, magenta (Sep-Jan).

Ageratum <small>(ageraos - ageless, refers to non-fading flowers) - Trop, subtrop America, ± 30 species, 2 now cosmop weeds.</small>

★ ***Ageratum houstonianum*** **Blue Weed; Tuinageratum (A)**
Soft annual herb, up to 1 m. Common weed, probably a garden escape, in disturbed, moist places. Leaves ± 80 x 60 mm. Flowerheads in compact inflorescences; 6-7 mm wide, mauve, blue, bracts hairy, glandular. Visited by bees. Slightly aromatic. **Similar species:** ★ *A. conyzoides* Flowerheads 4-5 mm wide, bracts sparsely hairy, no glands.

Senecio <small>(senex - old man, refers to whitish grey, hairy pappus)- Herbs, shrubs, rarely trees (for description see p. 320).</small>

Senecio barbatus **Sticky-plume Senecio** <small>(barbatus - bearded)</small>
Perennial herb, up to 300 mm. In grassland, swamps, up to 3000 m. Stems **covered in long, soft, sticky, often purplish hairs. Leaves:** In basal rosette, ± 70 x 20 mm, margins entire or wavy toothed, narrowing to broad, flat, stalklike base; stem leaves erect, narrow, clasping at base. **Flowerheads:** In congested inflorescence; ±10 mm wide, dull white to yellowish, purplish maroon or blue (Nov-Jan).

Senecio discodregeanus <small>[= S. dregeanus var. discoideus]</small> **lehlomane-le-lenyanyane, mantoana, sebiloane, sebilwane (SS)**
Slender, erect, perennial herb, up to 1,5 m, in groups. In grassland, coast to 2100 m. Stem simple, solitary, leafy below, all parts **white woolly cobwebby at first, persisting in leaf axils, on flower bracts. Leaves:** Leathery, ± 400 x 40 mm, margins thickened, ± toothed, tapering to long, narrow, stalklike base. **Flowerheads:** In branched inflorescence; ± 15 mm diam, dull, deep violet, bracts ± 9 mm, red edged (Aug-Feb). **General:** Used in traditional medicine to treat chest colds and madness.

498

Vernonia centaureoides

Wayne Matthews

Vernonia fastigiata

Martin von Fintel

Vernonia galpinii

Lal Greene

Vernonia hirsuta

Darrel Plowes

Vernonia thodei

Lal Greene

★ *Ageratum houstonianum*

C J Ward

Senecio barbatus

Wally Menne

Senecio barbatus

Lal Greene

Senecio discodregeanus

Olaf Wirminghaus

499

CYCADOPSIDA Cone bearing plants with naked seeds and large compound leaves.

STANGERIACEAE (First described as a fern, until a living, cone producing plant was sent to England in 1854 by Dr W Stanger, Surveyor General of Natal, after whom it was named) - Leaflets with midrib, net veins. One genus and 1 species. Separate male and female plants. Endemic.

Stangeria eriopus **Stangeria; Bobbejaankos (A); umfingwani, umncuma (cone) (X); imfingo (Z)** (*erio* - woolly)

Perennial, 0,25-1,5 m. Widespread in coastal grassland and forest, E Cape to S Moz. **Wide variation between forest** (larger, leathery) **and grassland** (smaller, softer) **plants.** Underground stem with large, elongated tuberous roots. **Leaves: Very variable in size and shape,** 0,25-2 m, 5-20 pairs leaflets, ± 400 x 60 mm, **midrib present,** side veins forked, margins entire, serrated or lobed; new stalks velvety. **Cones:** 1 per plant, stalk ± 120 mm, covered in silvery hairs at first, maturing brownish (May-Oct). Male: 100-150 x 30-50 mm. Female: 180-200 x 80-100 mm. **Seeds:** Red. **General:** Parts of plant reputed to be eaten by people. Seeds eaten by Purple-crested Lourie, Trumpeter Hornbill, Dassies and the Red Squirrel (Ngoye forest). Used in traditional medicine to treat high blood pressure and pain, and as a charm to ward off evil spirits and protect warriors. Easily cultivated by seed.

ZAMIACEAE - Cycad Family Stems above or below ground, covered with persistent leaf bases, leaves in a palmlike crown. Separate male and female plants. Mainly S Hemisp, 8 genera, ± 125 species, 1 genus in SA.

Encephalartos (*en* - in, *kephale* - head, *artos* - bread, refers to the bread made from the pith of the upper part of the stem) - Leaflets with parallel veins, no midrib. Afr ± 45 species, ± 37 in SA.

Encephalartos ngoyanus **Ngoye Dwarf Cycad; Ngoye Broodboom (A)** (*ngoyanus* - named after Ngoye Forest)

Semi-deciduous, up to 1 m. Grassland, forest margins, often near boulders, endemic to N KZN, Swaz. Underground stem ± 300 x 200 mm. Roots tuberous. **Leaves:** 0,6-1,25 m, **leaflets well spaced,** 70-100 x 8 mm, dark green, margins entire or with 1-3 teeth, rachis straight; stalk ± 150 mm; new leaves covered in whitish wool. **Cones:** Occur singly, dark yellow. Male: 200-250 x 50-70 mm. Female: 250 x 120 -150 mm. **Seeds:** Red. **General:** Grows well in cultivation, in full sun, dryish conditions. **Similar species:** *E. caffer* E Cape; leaves softer, more compact, fresh green.

Encephalartos villosus **Poor Man's Cycad, Ground Cycad; Grondbroodboom, Stamlose Broodboom (A); umgusa, umphanga (X); lisitsa, mayiphuku, sijekwane (Sw); isidwaba-somkhovu, isigqikisomkhovu, isikomakhoma sehlati (Z)** (*villosus* - long, soft, straight hairs)

Perennial up to 2,5 m, solitary or in clumps. Widespread in moist, shady or forested areas, coastal and inland, E Cape to Swaz/Moz border. Underground stem, usually unbranched, sometimes slightly exposed, ± 300 x 200 mm. **Leaves:** Variable, 1,2-3 m, shiny dark green, outer leaves arching with tips sometimes touching the ground, leaflets 150-250 x 15-25 mm, 1-5 spiny teeth on both margins, or entire, **reduced to spines towards base;** new leaves covered in dense white hair which disappears with age, except on rachis. **Cones:** 1-4 per crown (May). Male: 600-700 x 120-150 mm, lemon yellow, unpleasant smell when ripe. Female: 300-500 x 200 -250 mm, deep shiny yellowish orange; stalk stout, ± 200 mm. **Seeds:** Shiny red. **General:** Seeds eaten by Purple-crested Lourie, Trumpeter Hornbill and maggots. Stem used in traditional medicine as a protective charm and to promote longevity. Considered a lightning conductor by Swazis. Easily cultivated, leaves may reach 4 m in length. Hybridises with *E. altensteinii* and *E. lebomboensis*. **Similar species:** *E. umbeluziensis* Swaz, S Moz; leaves straight, stalks bare; cones green at maturity.

500

Stangeria eriopus

Stangeria eriopus ♀

Stangeria eriopus ♂

Encephalartos ngoyanus

Encephalartos ngoyanus ♀

Encephalartos villosus ♂

Encephalartos villosus ♀

501

MONOCOTYLEDONS Single seed leaf, parallel veins; flower parts in threes or multiples of three.

POTAMOGETONACEAE - Pondweed Family Herbaceous aquatic perennials forming colonies in fresh or brack water. Submerged or floating leaves. Flowers held erect in a spike (in SA plants). Fruit develops underwater. Cosmop, 2 genera, ± 90 species, 1 genus with 7 species in SA, *Potamogeton* (*potomos* - river; *geiton* - neighbour).

Potamogeton crispus **Wavy-leaved Pondweed; Fonteingras (A); ikhubalo lomkhondo wempahla (X); isaswane (Z)** (*crispus* - irregularly waved and twisted, curled)
Submerged aquatic. In fresh water in frost-free areas of S Afr. Stems 0,5-1,5 m, slender, 4 angled, branched. **Leaves:** Submerged, 30-90 x 8-15 mm, translucent, bright green, blunt tipped, margins wavy, toothed. **Flowers:** Inflorescences 25-70 mm; flowers pink to white (Jul-Dec). **Fruit:** Beaked drupe 2-4 mm. **General:** Eaten by ducks and fish. A refuge for aquatic insects and molluscs. .

Potamogeton pusillis **Thin-leaved Pondweed; Smalblaar Fonteingras (A); boele, joangba-metsi-bo-boholo, ntlo-ea-hlapi-e-kholo (SS)** (*pusillus* - very small, weak)
Submerged aquatic. In fresh water, fairly common in S Afr, widespread in N Hemisp. Stems ± 1 m, branching. **Leaves:** Submerged, 20-40 x 1-2 mm, stipules tubular at first, brownish, 6-17 mm. **Flowers:** Inflorescences 10-40 mm; flowers in ± 4 whorls, above water (Oct-May). **Fruit:** Beaked drupe ± 2,5 x 1,5 mm.
Similar species: *P. pectinatus* **ulule (Z)** In fresh or brackish water, cosmop. Leaves, 40-120 x 1-2 mm, stipule united with leaf base to form folded sheath with whitish margin. Upper parts die down in very cold or very dry periods.

Potamogeton thunbergii **Broad-leaved Pondweed; Breëblaar Fonteingras (A); ntlo-ea-hlapi, sesei (SS); ikhubalo lomkhondo wempahla (X)** (named after Carl Thunberg, renowned botanist and student of Linnaeus who collected plants widely in SA)
Perennial aquatic. **In deep water or emergent**, on mudbanks, E Cape to E Trop Afr. Rhizomes, woody, orange-brown. Stems ± 1 m. **Submerged leaves:** 80-200 x 8-16 mm, linear with net veins. **Floating leaves:** 50-80 x 25-35 mm, veins indistinct. **Leaves on land plants:** usually smaller, ± 60 mm, erect. **Flowers:** Inflorescences 50-100 mm, pink (Sep-Apr). **Fruit:** Rounded drupe ± 4 mm, greenish brown. **General:** Eaten by ducks and fish. Used in traditional medicine. **Similar species:** *P. schweinfurthii* Leaves submerged or floating, 100-200 x 10-20 mm, margins wavy, net veined, midrib prominent, exposed leaves shiny, leathery.

CYPERACEAE - Sedge Family Grasslike herbs usually found near water or damp areas. Stems triangular or cylindrical, solid, mostly without joints (grass stems jointed, often hollow). Leaves present, in 3 ranks or reduced to tubular sheaths. Flowers small, clustered in spikelets on upright or spreading branches, or in heads forming collectively an inflorescence. Fruit a nutlet. An ecologically important but little studied family only now receiving attention. Apart from providing a source of food and building materials, they hold significance in land use and management. Cosmop, ± 95 genera, ± 4350 species, ± 35 genera in SA.

Cyperus (*cyperus* - sedge) - Herbs, mainly perennial, sometimes with corms, tubers. Cosmop, ± 650 species, ± 70 in SA.

Cyperus albostriatus **Forest Star Sedge; taone (SS); incoshane (Sw); ingawane ephakathi (Z)** (*albostriatus* - white striped)
Perennial, 300-500 mm. Common in shade of forest, woodland, on rocky ground, E Cape northwards. Rhizome elongated, woody. **Leaves:** Basal, ± 15 mm wide. **Flowers:** Inflorescence ± 250 mm diam, with spreading branches, bracts ± 250 mm (Oct-Jun). **General:** Used in mat making. Indoor plant overseas. Good groundcover for shady areas.

Cyperus esculentus **Yellow Nut Sedge; Geeluintjie, Patrysuintjie, Hoenderuintjie (A); indawo, insikane (Z)** (*esculentus* - good to eat)
Perennial (annual), up to 650 mm. Weed in moist, disturbed places, cosmop. Rhizomes with roundish tubers; stems 3 angled. Young plants yellowish green. **Leaves:** Grasslike, shiny. **Flowers:** In branched head with 3-5 leaflike bracts; spikelets in clusters ± 20 mm, light brown (Jul-May). **General:** Tubers edible, sweet and nutty; chewed for indigestion and used in traditional medicine to hasten the inception of menstruation. Underground parts are main organs of reproduction, seed being unimportant. Tubers have greater resistance to herbicides than is usual for herbaceous plants. Has been described as one of the most formidable weeds in KZN (and most of the world).

Potamogeton crispus

Mike Wells — NBI

Potamogeton pectinatus

Geoff Nichols

Potamogeton pusillus

Rick Taylor

Potamogeton thunbergii

Mike Wells — NBI

Potamogeton schweinfurthii

Geoff Nichols

Cyperus esculentus

C J Ward

Cyperus albostriatus

C J Ward

503

Cyperus laevigatus (*laevigatus* - smooth)
Perennial, ± 350 mm. Extremely variable throughout its pantrop range; reasonably uniform in eastern SA. Early coloniser of sandy alluvium on seashore or near estuaries. Stems solitary along rhizome or clustered. **Leaves:** Reduced to sheaths. **Flowers:** Each inflorescence with overtopping, erect bract, few to several neat spikelets. **General:** Important ecologically, saline tolerant.

Cyperus papyrus Papyrus; Papirus (A); adumu (Th); ibumi (Z) (*papyrus* - papery)
Largest sedge in Afr, up to 2,5 m. Extensive stands in coastal marshes, as far south as Mhlatuze River mouth, KZN; widespread in Afr. Rhizome large, woody, with reddish scale leaves. **Leaves:** Reduced to stem sheaths at base of 3 angled stem. **Flowers:** Inflorescence large, ± 400 mm diam, branches spreading. **General:** Stems split, dried and woven to make traditional doors. Used for making the scrolls of emergent literate civilizations. Well known in garden landscaping.

Cyperus pulcher (*pulcher* - beautiful)
Robust, tufted, leafy perennial, up to 1 m. Rooted in shallows in wet mud or in shallow water, on stream or riverbanks. Woody rhizome. Stems 3 angled, ± 3 mm diam, winged below flowering head. **Flowers:** In brown inflorescences, bracts spreading, leaflike. **General:** Suitable for water features in gardens.

Cyperus sphaerospermus (*sphaer* - ball; *spermus* - seed)
Perennial, up to 600 mm. In large stands in moist places on margins of swamps, streams. Rhizome compacted. Stems 3 angled under inflorescence, **not winged**, firm, ± 2 mm diam. **Leaves:** 3-4 mm wide. **Flowers:** Spikelets **dull green or pale brown** tinged red, 3-4 mm wide, bracts longer than inflorescence branches. **General: New plants root from vegetative buds on inflorescences. Similar species:** *Cyperus denudatus* (see p. 560).

Cyperus textilis Tall Star Sedge; Matjiesgoed (A); ingculu (X); umuzi (X, Z) (*textilis* - woven)
Perennial, up to 1 m, in large colonies. On river and streambanks, in marshy areas, Cape to KZN. **Leaves:** Leafless. **Flowers:** Inflorescence branched, bracts **less than 100 mm, sharp tipped, stem cylindrical, smooth. General:** Used to make basket-ware, twine and sleeping mats. Cultivated. Attractive garden plant. **Similar species:** *C. alternifolius* subsp. *flabelliformis* Mostly coastal, in swamp forest and open standing water; stems robust, faintly ridged, rough beneath the inflorescence. *C. sexangularis* Coast to midlands; stems slender, 6 angled, with rough ridges.

Mariscus (old name used by Pliny for a rush) - Doubtfully distinct from *Cyperus*. More or less cosmop, ± 200 species, ± 32 in SA.

Mariscus congestus qoqothoane (SS); intsasela (X); indawo (Z) (*congestus* - crowded)
Tufted perennial, 600-800 mm. In damp places in grassland, on streambanks, up to 2100 m, SW Cape to Zim, also Europe, Middle East, Austr. **Leaves:** Basal, tough, ± 10 mm wide. **Flowers:** Inflorescence branched, spikes large, reddish brown, ± 35mm diam, stalkless or stalked, bracts ± 220 mm (summer). **General:** Grazed by cattle. Used to make ropes and baskets.

Mariscus macrocarpus (*macro* - large; *carpus* - fruit)
Perennial, up to 350 mm. In sand, on margins of dune forest, or in open glades. Slender to sparsely tufted, shoot bases hard, swollen. **Flowers:** Inflorescence either a central, small head with rays, spikelets variable or more contracted into a pseudo-head. **General:** Often confused with other species, particularly the more delicate, yellower plants of the weedy *M. sumatrensis*.

Cyperus papyrus

Cyperus laevigatus

Cyperus pulcher

Cyperus sphaerospermus

Cyperus textilis

Mariscus congestus

Mariscus macrocarpus

505

Schoenoxiphium (*schoinos* - rush; *xiphos* - a sword) - About 18 species in SA.

Schoenoxiphium madagascariense
Robust, tufted perennials. In forest clearings, on rocky outcrops, streambanks and damp grassy slopes. Rhizomes short. **Leaves:** 6-10 mm wide, leaf blades and bracts very long, slender, tapering to tips, slightly blue-green. **Flowers:** In rounded heads, in long, narrow utricles, on delicate branches.

Carex (*caric* - sedge) - Evolutionary an old established genus, the fruits hardly differing at all from fossil remains identified from between 70-30 million years ago. Fairly cosmop in moist temp climates, also Arctic and Antarctic regions. Mostly N Hemisp, ± 1700 species, ± 19 in SA.

Carex austro-africana
Leafy perennial, less than 1 m. In wet areas of marshes, streamlets, usually rooted in shallow, slow-flowing water. **Flowers:** Spikes ± 70 mm, drooping, usually 5-6 per stem. **Fruit:** Nutlet.

ARACEAE - Arum Lily Family - 'Petal' is a modified leaf called a spathe. Tiny male and female flowers are carried on the central 'column' or spadix. One of the most important groups of ornamentals, including *Anthurium, Dieffenbachia, Philodendron, Monstera, Caladium*. The thickened rootstocks of some species are cultivated as a starchy food and the fruits of *Monstera* are prized for their delicate flavour. Mostly in humid trop regions, ± 105 genera, ± 2550 species, 6 genera in SA. *Zamioculcas* - Leaves compound, pinnate. E and S Afr, 1 species.

Zamioculcas zamiifolia Fern Arum (*zamiifolia* - leaves like a cycad)
Slightly succulent perennial, up to 800 mm. In coastal, swamp and sand forests, N KZN to Tanz. Woody rhizome, roots swollen. **Leaves: Deciduous, compound**; 6-8 pairs leaflets, 60-120 x 30-60 mm, stalks ± 250 mm, blue-green with horizontal purple bands, **remains of old leaf stalks die off to ± 75 mm above ground. Flowers:** Spathe yellowish brown, ± 100 x 40 mm, stem ± 150 mm (summer). **General:** Attractive shade and container plant. **Leaflets fall in autumn**. Base of leaflet swells to form bulbil, from which a new plant will grow.

Stylochiton (*stylos* - style; *chiton* - a covering) - Leaves distinctly veined. Trop Afr, ± 15 species, 1 in SA.

Stylochiton natalensis Bushveld Arum; umfana-kamacejane (Sw); insulansula, intebe encane yokhalo, umfana-embuzi, umfana-kahlanjane, umfana-kanozihlanjana, umfana-nkomo (Z)
Deciduous, up to 450 mm. In open woodland, amongst rocks on grassy hillsides, KZN to Tanz. Tuber ± 150 x 10 mm, surrounded by fibrous remains of old leaf stalks; roots stout, tuberous. **Leaves:** Solitary or several, size varies according to conditions, blade ± 180 x 150 mm, dull dark green, **conspicuous veining**. **Flowers:** 2-3, spathe 70-200 mm, **lower half tubular, bulge at base**, greenish outside, cream to purple inside, on **short stout** stalk (Oct-Dec). **General:** Roots and leaves used traditionally to treat earache and chest complaints.

Pistia (*pistos* - aquatic) - Widespread in warm regions worldwide, 1 species.

★ Pistia stratiotes Water Lettuce (*stratiotes* - layered)
Aquatic, up to 100(290) mm, floating on surface, forming large 'rafts'. E Cape to Trop and N Afr. Roots fine, in large mass. Leaves in rosette, grey-green, velvety, 5 veined. Flowers small, green, within leaves (Dec-Jun). **Invasive plant, a threat to waterways.** Known in Egypt since the time of Pliny (77 AD) who recorded its use in healing wounds.

JUNCACEAE - Rush Family - Flower petals dry and scaly rather than soft and coloured. Stems solid or hollow, leaves grasslike, soft and flat or hard and cylindrical, often reduced to an open or tubular sheath. Found in wet areas. Cosmop, 8 genera, ± 315 species, 3 genera in SA.

Juncus (*jungere* - to join, refers to ancient use in making mats, chair seats) - Leaves closely resemble grasses and sedges. Cosmop, mainly in mild and cold conditions, ± 250 species, ± 22 in SA.

Juncus effusus (*effusus* - spread out)
Tufted perennial, up to 1 m. In swamps, streambeds, SW Cape to N Prov, cosmop but more common in N Hemisp. Rhizomes horizontal, matted. **Leaves:** Stemlike, 2-3 mm diam, smooth, bright green, cataphylls sheathing 70-170 mm. **Flowers:** Very small, crowded, in loose or round inflorescence (spring-summer). **Fruit:** Capsules pale yellowish, seeds golden brown.

Tony Abbott

Tony Abbott

Trevor Coleman

Schoenoxiphium madagascariense

Carex austro-africana

Zamioculcas zamiifolia

Geoff Nichols

Trevor Coleman

Stylochiton natalensis

Zamioculcas zamiifolia

Wally Menne

C J Cilliers NBI

★ *Pistia stratiotes*

Rosemary Williams

Stylochiton natalensis

Juncus effusus

507

HYACINTHACEAE - Formerly part of Liliaceae. Mostly perennial herbs. Bulbs sometimes with a number of free scales. Inflorescence elongated, stamens 6, ovary superior. Fruit a capsule, seeds black. Subcosmop, ± 41 genera, ± 770 species, 27 genera in SA.

Bowiea (named after James Bowie, 1789-1869, a plant collector for Royal Bot Gardens at Kew) - Inflorescence develops as a much branched vine, some of the branches becoming tendrils. Tepals free, more or less reflexed. S to C Afr, 2 species, both in SA.

Bowiea volubilis **Bowiea; Knolklimop (A); gibizisila (Sw); umgaqana (X); iguleni, ugibisisila (Z)** (*volubilis* - twinging)

Deciduous climber, up to 3 m. In thicket, on forest margins, among rocks, E Cape to E Afr. Bulb large, green, ± 150 mm diam, often on surface of soil. **Leaves:** Small, 1-2 at base, dropping early. **Flowers: Stem fleshy, bright green, much branched, functions as leaves**; flowers 16-24 mm diam, green, stalks turn backwards (Oct-Apr). **Fruit:** Brownish oval capsule ± 25 mm. **General:** Bulb poisonous. Extensively used in traditional medicine to treat sore eyes, skin complaints, dropsy, headaches, barrenness and also as a love charm. Interesting ornamental container plant easily grown from seed.
Similar species: *Schizobasis intricata* **Jeukui, Volstruiskos (A); ubulilibekhonde, umthondo-wemfene (Z)** Bulb round, up to 40 mm diam; 4-10 leaves, erect, 75-100 mm, dying back before stems appear. Flowering stems erect, inflorescence 75-150 mm, very loose, zigzag, slender, spreading, flowers white with brown keel.

ASPHODELACEAE - Formerly part of Liliaceae. Mostly herbs, also woody forms such as the tree aloes. Leaves often thick, succulent, in rosette, basal or just below inflorescence, margins often toothed and spiny. Inflorescence unbranched or branched, tepals free or fused into a tube, ovary superior. Fruit a capsule, seeds black. Europe, Asia, Afr, centred in S Afr, ± 17 genera.

Kniphofia (named after J H Kniphof, 1704-1763, professor of medicine at Erfurt University) - **Red-hot Pokers** Leaves soft, basal; inflorescence usually a simple dense spike. Mostly Afr, ± 70 species, 47 in E areas of SA.

Kniphofia baurii **Baur's Poker; icacane (Z)** (named after Rev Leopold Richard Baur, 1825-1889, born in Germany, died in E Cape, a pharmacist, missionary and botanical collector)

Up to 1 m, in small groups. On streambanks, moist grassy slopes, 650-1300 m. **Leaves:** Erect or recurved, 200-700 x 12-**40 mm**, soft, **blue-green** or pale green, margins entire or **faintly serrated. Flowers: In dense, rounded inflorescence,** 40-100 x 40-60 mm; buds spreading, on **short stalks 1-2 mm**, green tinged dull red, flowers 28-38 mm, hanging, greenish to greenish yellow (Sep-Feb). **Fruit: Roundish, 5-8 mm**.

Kniphofia ichopensis **Ixopo Red-hot Poker; Ixopovuurpyl (A); icacane (Z)** (*ichopensis* - named after Ixopo, where the plant was first discovered)

Up to 900 mm, **solitary or in small groups**. In moist grassland, midlands to mountains, up to 2450 m. **Leaves:** Few, 500-800 x 5-10 mm. **Flowers:** Inflorescence 100-300 x 60-70 mm; buds dull yellow, tinged red, flowers **30-42 mm**, cream, yellow-green (salmon-pink), **bracts long, narrow, pointed** (Nov-Apr). **General:** Subsp. *aciformis*, dense tufts of 20-30 leaves, ± 1 mm diam, surrounded at base by fibrous leaf sheaths from previous year. **Similar species:** *K. angustifolia* (see p. 26), *K. laxiflora* (see p. 28).

Kniphofia latifolia (*latifolia* - broad leaves)

Up to 800 mm, in groups. On grassy slopes, riverbanks, in moist depressions, 850 -1000 m. **Leaves:** 8-12, 600-900 x 20-40 mm, **broad**, erect, yellow-green, taller than flowers, V-shaped, **tapering rapidly to tip**, margin and keel finely serrated. **Flowers:** In dense, **tapering inflorescence**, 70-220 x 45-50 mm; buds hanging, red, flowers 30-35 mm, lobes not spreading, hanging, yellowish green, bracts ± 9 x 4 mm, broad, blunt to rounded (Oct-Nov). **Fruit:** Erect, ± 5 mm (flowering stem lengthens, becoming taller than leaves at fruiting).

Kniphofia parviflora (=*K. modesta*) **ihlinzanyoka (Z)** (*parviflora* - small flowers)

250-800 mm, solitary. In grassland, marshy places, coast to 2000 m. **Leaves:** 5-8, 200-750 x 3-7 mm, recurving, keeled, forming fibres at base, margin smooth. **Flowers:** In elongate, **one sided inflorescence**, 60-280 x 12-17 mm, buds greenish brown to maroon, hanging, flowers spreading at first, creamy yellow to greenish, ± 10 x 2 mm (Aug-Jan-Mar), scented.

Schizobasis intricata

Geoff Nichols

Bowiea volubilis

Neil Crouch

Kniphofia baurii

Tom de Waal

Kniphofia baurii

Rosemary Williams

Kniphofia ichopensis

Martin von Fintel

Kniphofia latifolia

Martin von Fintel

Kniphofia latifolia

Martin von Fintel

Kniphofia parviflora

Tony Abbott

Kniphofia parviflora

Keos Roux NBI

509

Aloe (probably a Greek word allied to the Hebrew 'allal' for bitter) - Succulent plants (for description see p. 228).

Aloe striatula *(striatula - refers to the thin parallel lines on the leaf sheaths)*
Robust, straggling shrub, up to 2 m. On mountain tops. Much branched. **Leaves:** Deeply channelled, **shiny dark green, recurved. Flowers:** In dense inflorescence, ± 400 mm; buds deep red, flowers yellow-orange (Nov-Jan). **General:** Useful garden plant, forms large bushes, withstands snow and frost.

ALLIACEAE - Onion Family Perennial herbs with bulbs. **Tulbaghia** (for descriptions see p. 344).

Tulbaghia acutiloba Wild Garlic; Wildeknoffel (A); motsuntsunyane, sefotha-fotha (SS); lisela (Sw); ishaladi lezinyoka (Z) *(acutiloba - sharply pointed lobes)*
150-450 mm. In dry rocky grassland, up to 1800 m, E Cape to N Prov. **Leaves:** 50-450 x 3-8 mm, soft. **Flowers:** ± 8 x 4 mm, green, tepal lobes ± 5 x 1,5 mm, green, **conspicuously recurved**; fleshy ring orange to reddish brown (Aug-Nov, throughout year), sweetly scented. **General:** Very variable. Noticeable after fires. Used as a culinary herb. Plant parts smell of garlic. Used traditionally as a snake repellent.

Tulbaghia ludwigiana Scented Wild Garlic; ingotjwa, sikwa (Sw); umwelela-kweli-phesheya (Z) (named after Carl von Ludwig, 1784-1847, pharmacist, businessman, patron of natural science)
Up to 600 mm. In rocky grassland, on marshy streambanks, up to 1900 m. **Leaves:** 200 x 3 mm, grey, purple at base **Flowers:** Green to purplish, **fleshy ring distinctly 3 lobed**, deep cream to bright yellow (Aug-Feb), strong, sweet scent. **General:** Edible. Used traditionally as a love charm.

HYACINTHACEAE - Formerly part of Liliaceae. **Albuca** - Bulbous herbs (for descriptions see p. 92, 230).

Albuca angolensis [= *A. bainesii*] Large Yellow Albuca, Green and Gold Albuca
Deciduous, up to 1,3 m. In shade, on forest margins, KZN to Moz. Large fleshy bulb. **Leaves:** Flat, ± 1000 x 30 mm, tapering to slender point. **Flowers:** ± 20 mm, bright yellow with broad green stripe (Oct-Jan), sweetly scented. **General:** Used in traditional medicine. Attractive, thrives in shade, easily grown from seed.

Urginea (Algerian, Ben Urgen, the name of an Arab tribe) - Bulbous herbs (for description see p. 94).

Urginea delagoensis [= *Drimia delagoensis*] umahlanganisa (Sw, Z); isiklenama (Z)
Up to 450 mm. In thicket, rocky areas, KZN to Moz. Bulb coppery green, ± 60 mm diam, generally above the ground. **Leaves:** ± 500 x 10 mm, round with furrow, fleshy to tough, rubbery grey-green, produced with flowers. **Flowers:** Small, 8 mm diam, creamy green to brownish, central stripe green, purple beneath (July-Jan). **General:** Used in traditional medicine for splints for bone fractures and as a protective charm.

Galtonia (after Sir Francis Galton, 1822-1911) - Bulbous herb with drooping bell-shaped flowers (for description see p. 96).

Galtonia viridiflora Green Berg Lily (for description see p. 96).

Dipcadi (*dipcadi* - oriental name originally used for the Grape Hyacinth) - Bulbous herbs; inflorescence often with flowers on 1 side of the stem. Some poisonous, some edible. Afr, Madag, Medit, India, ± 30 species, ± 14 in SA.

Dipcadi marlothii Dronkui (A); morothoana-phookoana (SS) (named after H W R Marloth, 1855-1931, pharmacist, analytical chemist, botanist)
Up to 1 m. In grassland. **Leaves:** ± 450 mm, wiry, **spirally twisted** above, short hairs on margins. **Flowers: Inflorescence tip droops sharply in bud**; flowers ± 20 mm, tepal lobes **without tails**, spreading (Oct-Feb). **General:** Used traditionally to treat diseases of sexual organs and to induce good aim of hunters and fighters.

Dipcadi viride Dainty Green Bells, Green Dipcadi; Gifbolletjie, Grootslymuintjie, Skaamblommetjie (A); lephotoana, molubeli, morothoana-phookoana, thebeli-moro (SS); ikhakhakha eliluhlaza (Z) *(viride - green)*
Up to 1,2 m. Widespread in grassland in S Afr. Bulb ± 60 mm diam. **Leaves:** Hairless, 60-600 x 3-20 mm, grey-green, folded, narrowing to tip. **Flowers:** In long, slender inflorescence, **open flowers all face the same direction, drooping at tip**; outer tepal lobes with 'tails' ± 20 mm, with a pocket for part of the length on the inner surface, green and yellowish beige to reddish, inner lobes ± 12 mm (Oct-Apr), sometimes faintly scented, unpleasant scent at night. **General:** Bulbs and leaves eaten as culinary herbs. Used as a protective charm against storms.

Aloe striatula

Tulbaghia acutiloba

Van Wyk & Malan

Tulbaghia ludwigiana

Martin von Fintel

Trevor Coleman

Urginea delagoensis

Rosemary Williams

Albuca angolensis

Martin von Fintel

Albuca angolensis

Martin von Fintel

Galtonia viridiflora

Lal Greene

Dipcadi marlothii

Van Wyk & Malan

Dipcadi viride

Jo Onderstall

Eucomis (*eucomis* - beautiful hair or topknot) - Bulbous herbs; inflorescence topped with leafy bracts S Afr, ± 10 species.

Eucomis autumnalis [= *E. undulata*] Common Pineapple Flower; Krulkop, Wildepynappel (A); kxapumpu (SS); ubuhlungu becanti (X); umathunga, ukhokho, umakhandakansele, umakhondle (Z) *(autumnalis* - autumn, refers to flowering time)

Up to 500 mm. In damp grassland, coast to 2450 m, E Cape to Zim. Bulb ± 100 mm diam. **Leaves:** 150-550 x 40-130 mm, **± wavy, tightly scalloped or toothed. Flowers:** 10-45 terminal bracts; flowers white to pale yellow-green (Dec-Apr). **General:** Widely used in traditional medicine to treat urinary and pulmonary ailments, fever and diseases of stock. Popular garden plant. Three subspecies.

Eucomis humilis Dwarf Pineapple Flower; Beskeie Berglelie (A) *(humilis* - low)

Up to 400 mm. Below cliffs, in rocky stream beds, up to 2400 m. Large bulb, ± 150 mm. **Leaves:** ± 400 x 70 mm, keeled, **margins wavy**, tinged purple, spotted purple beneath. **Flowers:** Inflorescence 80-220 mm, tuft small, bracts edged purple, sometimes spotted; **flowers densely packed**, ± 10 mm, greenish white tinged and/or edged purple, stamens purple, stalks short (Nov-Feb), unpleasant scent. (See p. 98)

Ornithogalum (*ornis* - bird; *gala* - milk, Greek for bulbous plant with white flowers) - Bulbous herbs (for description see p. 98).

Ornithogalum graminifolium [= *O. longiscapum*] metsana-a-manyenyane, nko-ea-ntja (SS) *(graminifolium* - grasslike)

Bulbous herb, up to 450 mm. On moist, rocky mountain slopes up to 2400 m, SW Cape to KZN. **Leaves:** Few, erect, 80-250 mm, narrow, produced with flowers. **Flowers:** Many-flowered inflorescence; flowers 10-20 mm diam, white, pale yellow or pink (Dec-Feb). **General:** Wide distribution, very variable in habit and colour.

Drimiopsis (resembling *Drimia*) - Bulb with no papery outer scales; leaves usually with a stalk. Afr, ± 15 species, 5 in SA.

Drimiopsis maculata Green Drimiopsis, Spotted-leaved Drimiopsis; injobo, ucibi-cibane (Z) *(maculata* - spotted, blotched)

Up to 250 mm. In shady places. Bulb ± 40 mm, narrowing to slender tip. **Leaves:** 100-200 x 70 mm, **deeply lobed**, with **dark green spots**, margins wavy, **stalks ± 100 mm. Flowers:** In small, compact inflorescence; buds white, flowers grey-green, **inner tepals incurved**, ± 4 mm (Sep-Apr). **General:** Used traditionally for stomach trouble in children. Attractive garden and container plant for deep shade.

Drimiopsis maxima [= *Scilla schlechteri*] Large-leaved Drimiopsis *(maxima* - largest)

Up to 400 mm. In grassland, among rocks. Bulb 30-50 mm, top flattened. **Leaves:** 80-150 x 30-50 mm, **narrowing gradually to base. Flowers:** In short, dense inflorescence, erect; **tepals erect to spreading**, ± 8 mm, greyish, striped pink, white, green or brown (Sep-Dec). **General:** Good garden and container plant for shade.

Ledebouria (named after Carl Ledebour, 1785-1851, German prof of botany) - Bulbous herbs (for description see p. 344).

Ledebouria apertiflora Common Squill *(apertiflora* - exposed flowers)

Up to 350 mm. In dry woodland, S Cape to Zim. **Leaves:** 200-350 x 7-25 mm, dark green or purple spots on lower parts in N KZN, Swaz. **Flowers:** Inflorescences 50-100 x 15-20 mm, stems ± 225 mm; flowers 5-6 mm, tepal lobes recurved, **tips pointed**, pink to purple, keel green, stamens maroon (Oct-Jan). **General:** Heavily grazed.

Ledebouria floribunda [= *Scilla floribunda*] Large Ledebouria; isikholokotho (X,Z) *(floribunda* - flowering abundantly)

Up to 300 mm. In shade, seasonally damp places. **Leaves:** 200-350 x 40-50 mm, **glossy**, with spots, blotches, green to purple at base. **Flowers:** Inflorescences 150-200 x 30-50 mm, ± erect; flowers 7-9 mm, green to pink, keel green, stamens purple above, white below (Oct-Jan), strongly scented. **General:** Used in traditional medicine. Hardy garden plant. **Similar species:** *L. revoluta* (see p. 452).

Ledebouria zebrina [= *Scilla zebrina*] Giant Ledebouria *(zebrina* - refers to parallel lines on leaves)

Up to 300 mm. In moist, shady places. Bulb 100-150 mm diam. **Leaves:** 4-6, 300-500 x 90-120 mm, dull, **sometimes with longitudinal purple stripes** or large blotches, **with threads when torn. Flowers:** Inflorescences 150-200 x 30-37 mm; flowers 4-7 mm, tepals recurved, light green, stamens green (Aug-Jan).

Eucomis autumnalis

Eucomis autumnalis

Eucomis humilis

Ornithogalum graminifolium

Drimiopsis maxima

Ledebouria apertiflora

Drimiopsis maculata

Ledebouria floribunda

Ledebouria zebrina

513

ASPARAGACEAE - Asparagus Family - Subshrubs or climbers. ***Asparagus -*** (for descriptions see p. 100).

Asparagus asparagoides [= *Myrsiphyllum asparagoides*] **Cape Smilax; Breëblaarklimop, Krulkransie (A); khopananyane, likhopa, sethota-sa-matuela (SS); isicakathi (X); ibutha, inkunzimbili (Z)**

Scrambling shrublet, up to 2 m. In forest, thicket, coast to 2450 m, S Cape to Trop Afr. Stems twisting, wiry, smooth or ridged, branches usually short. **Leaves:** Soft, slightly succulent, 25-40 x 8-20 mm, bright green, flat or folded, **variable in size and shape. Flowers:** ± 15 mm diam, white, **forming tube at base, tepal lobes curving back,** stamens protruding, stalks ± 10 mm (throughout year), sweetly scented. **Fruit:** Berry round, ± 10 mm diam, black. **General:** Used in traditional medicine to treat sore eyes and as a charm to increase fertility of cattle. Popular with florists and as a container plant. Introduced into gardens in Europe in 1700s.

SMILACACEAE, *Smilax* (ancient Greek name of obscure meaning) - Spiny, scrambling shrubs (for description see p. 572).

Smilax anceps [= *S. kraussiana*] **Leg-ripper, Wild Sarsaparilla; Wag-'n-bietjieklimop, Wyfieklimop (A); inchachabutane (Sw); ingqaqabulani, ingungwa, inkunkwa, iyala, iyali, ulimi-lwenyathi (Z)** (see p. 572)

DIOSCOREACEAE - Yam Family. *Dioscorea* - Climbers; rootstock thick, woody or tuberous (for descriptions see p. 108).

Dioscorea brownii

Erect, single stemmed, up to 1 m. In tall grassland, up to 1500 m. Tuber with crown above, 3-5 fingerlike processes ± 110 x 24 mm below; new 'fingers' produced each year. **Female plants unbranched, male plants branched,** tips often twining. **Leaves:** Spirally arranged, lower leaves largest, 100-130 x 10-35 mm, 5-7 veins, stalks 10-20 mm. **Flowers:** Male inflorescence ± 70 mm. Female inflorescence 40-50 mm (Dec-Feb). **Fruit:** 20-25 mm, tipped with short beak, wings 6-7 mm wide.

Dioscorea cotinifolia **Wild Yam; Olifantsvoet (A); umtane (X); intana, unyawo-lwendlovu (Z)** (see p. 108)

Dioscorea dregeana **Wild yam; ndiyaza (Sw); ingcolo (X, Z) ilabatheka, isithund-lathundla, udakwa, undiyaza (Z)** (named after Johann Drège, 1794-1881, horticulturalist, botanical collector and traveller, who visited the Cape in 1826)

Robust climber, up to 15 m high. In woodland, E Cape to N Prov, Nam. Tubers clustered. **Leaves: 3 large leaflets, ± 100 mm,** slightly hairy, dark green above, velvety grey beneath, abruptly tapered to slender tip, stalks ± 150 mm. **Flowers:** Male: green, in slender, much branched inflorescence. Female: white, less branched (Oct-Jan). **Fruit:** ± 40 x 25 mm, finely velvety (wings closest to point of attachment). **General:** Used in traditional medicine to treat insanity, fits, sores, wounds, to ensure easy childbirth and as a charm against lightning. Decorative, grown from seed.

Dioscorea rupicola **impinyampinya, inkwa (Z)** (*rupicola* - growing in stony places)

Slender climber, up to 3 m. On forest margins, up to 1900 m. Tuber **below ground,** 1-3 branches ± 300 x 30 mm, dark brown, corky. **Leaves:** ± 70 x 60 (140 x 110) mm, **heart-shaped, 5-7 lobes,** shiny above, dull, paler beneath, narrowing to long point, **margins wavy. Flowers:** Spikes ± 80 mm (Nov-Jan). **Fruit:** Hanging bunches, fruit held erect, ± 30-20 mm, 3 winged, glossy light brown. **General:** Tubers edible when boiled (in times of famine). Used in traditional medicine and as a fish poison.

Dioscorea sylvatica **Forest Elephant's Foot, Wild Yam; Olifantsvoet, Skilpad-knol (A); lunyawo-lwendlovu (Sw); ingwevu, intane, ufudu, ufudu lwehlathi (Z)** (*sylvatica* - growing in woods and forests)

Slender climber, up to 15 m high. In scrub, forest, coast to mountains, E Cape to C Afr. Tuber **large,** ± 0,3(1)mm diam, flattened, 120 mm thick, dark brown, corky, with reticulate markings, exposed above ground or buried ± 250 mm. **Leaves:** 50-80 x 60 mm, heart-shaped, ± lobed, narrowing to threadlike point, very variable. **Flowers:** Male: yellowish green, in spikes ± 140 mm. Female: in hanging spikes, ± 90 mm (Nov-Apr). **Fruit:** ± 25 x 15 mm, yellowish green edged reddish brown. **General:** Rootstock contains diosgenin, used in preparation of cortisone. Used traditionally to treat blood problems, chest complaints and also to treat cattle. Species threatened through exploitation. Decorative container or feature plant.

514

Asparagus asparagoides

Geoff Nichols

Lawrence Peacock

Smilax anceps

John Manning

Dioscorea brownii

Tony Abbott

Dioscorea brownii

Tony Abbott

Dioscorea rupicola

Wally Menne

Dioscorea cotinifolia

Jo Onderstall

Dioscorea dregeana

Tony Abbott

Dioscorea sylvatica

Rosemary Williams

515

IRIDACEAE - Iris Family Corms or rhizomes (for description see p. 42). *Gladiolus* (*gladiolus* - small sword, refers to leaf shape) Bracts green, style branches short, undivided or shortly divided in 2; seeds winged; deciduous. Hybrids created since the early 1800s have produced the cut-flowers and garden plants popular worldwide. Known as *itembu* (X) 'fruits of the earth', the corms are dug up and eaten. A large genus of ± 259 species found mostly in S Afr, also Trop Afr, S Europe and Middle East; over 126 species in SA.

Gladiolus dalenii [= *G. dracocephalus, G. natalensis, G. psittacinus*] **African Gladiolus, Natal Lily; Papegaaigladiolus, Wildeswaardlelie (A); khahla-e-kholo (SS); sidvwana (Sw); isidwi esibomvu, udwendweni, uhlakahla (Z)** (see p. 44, 572)

ORCHIDACEAE - Orchid Family Highly specialised. Flowers in 2 whorls, outer 3 sepals and inner 3 petals often all the same colour. One of the sepals can be differently shaped and is called the median, dorsal or odd sepal. One of the petals is usually lobed and crested and called the lip. Either the median sepal or the lip may have a sac or spur. Single stamen, stigma and style are united to form a structure called the column. Pollen grains are collected into waxy or grainy pollinia which are attached to a sticky gland. Cosmop, ± 788 genera, ± 18500 species, ± 54 genera in SA.

Holothrix (*holos* - entire; *thrix* - hair, meaning hairy all over) - Terrestrial plants; 2 leaves flat on ground; flowering stem leafless and bractless, flowers white to yellowish green. Afr, ± 55 species, 22 in SA.

Holothrix thodei (named after Hans Justus Thode, 1859-1932, naturalist and plant collector)

Slender, up to 300 mm. In moist rocky areas, 1500-2600 m. **Leaves:** ± 14 mm broad, with scattered short hairs above, withered by flowering time. **Flowers:** In loose or dense inflorescence, stem with long, downward facing hairs; flowers yellowish to brownish green, lip ± 5 mm, 3 lobed, **middle lobe much longer** (Jan-Mar).

Habenaria (*habena* - strap or thong; *aria* - possessing, refers to the long spur) - Terrestrial herbs; flowers mostly green and white, median sepal joined with whole or with upper lobes of petals forming hood, lip lobed, spur long. Widely distributed in trop, subtrop regions, ± 600 species, 35 in SA.

Habenaria arenaria (*arenaria* - sand loving, growing in sandy places)

Slender, up to 400 mm, in groups. In thicket, forest, coast to 1200 m, S Cape to S Moz. **Leaves:** 2, **at base of stem**, ± 150 x 40 mm, **mottled grey**, few smaller leaves **grading into bracts up stem**. **Flowers:** In loose inflorescence; flowers small, green, petals **triangular**, sharp tipped, lip 3 lobed, spur ± 15 mm (Oct-Jan, Apr-Jul).

Habenaria chlorotica (*chlorotica* - pale green)

Slender, up to 600 mm. In marshy grassland, up to 1850 m, KZN to Trop Afr. **Leaves: Narrow,** ± 120 x 10 mm, **not grading into bracts. Flowers:** In loose inflorescence; flowers green, **petals undivided**, lip with 3 long, narrow lobes, ± 7 mm, spur 20-30 mm (Jan-Apr).

Habenaria ciliosa (*ciliosa* - fringed, eyelashlike)

Slender to robust, up to 500 mm. In marshy grassland, 700-2000 m. **Leaves:** Suberect, ± 9 x 14 mm; **basal leaf sheaths horizontally barred with black.** **Flowers:** In loose or dense inflorescence, **bracts with short scattered hairs**, as long as flowers, ± 20 mm; flowers green and dull yellow, lip 3 lobed, ± 4 mm, spur 15-20 mm (Jan-Apr).

Habenaria clavata 'mametsana **(SS)** (*clavata* - club-shaped)

Usually robust, up to 700 mm. In grassland, 600-1950 m, widespread, E Cape to Trop Afr. Fleshy tuber. **Leaves:** Sheathing at base, ± 110 x 30 mm. **Flowers:** In loose inflorescence, ± 200 x 80 mm, bracts ± 30 x 15 mm, broadly oval, tip pointed; flowers green with white stigmas, **hood 15-20 mm**, petal lobes ± 40 mm, slender, **spur long, 30-50 mm, slender, with thickened tip**, stalks ± 25 mm (Dec-Mar). **General:** Buds all open at same time.

Habenaria cornuta (*cornuta* - horned)

Slender to robust, up to 500 mm. In marshy grassland, 900-2100 m, E Cape to Trop Afr. **Leaves:** Oval to oblong, ± 100 x 30 mm. **Flowers:** In dense inflorescence; flowers pale green, lip 3 lobed, 5-12 mm, spur 14-17 mm, twisted once, inflated towards tip (Feb-Apr).

Gladiolus dalenii

Lawrence Peacock

Holothrix thodei

Martin von Fintel

Habenaria arenaria

Martin von Fintel

Habenaria clavata

Lal Greene

Habenaria clavata

Lal Greene

Habenaria chlorotica

Rosemary Williams

Habenaria ciliosa

Martin von Fintel

Habenaria ciliosa

Martin von Fintel

Habenaria cornuta

Ray Boardman

517

Habenaria dregeana Small Green Hood; 'mametsana (SS) (named after Johann Drège, 1794-1881, horticulturalist, botanical collector and traveller)
Up to 330 mm. In short grassland, on rocky hillsides, up to 2000 m, E Cape to Trop Afr. **Leaves: 2 basal, flat on ground**, ± 85 mm diam; stem leaves ± 20 mm, tapering to hairlike tip. **Flowers:** In very dense inflorescence, ± 110 mm; flowers greenish, hood, sepals ± 7 mm, **lip 3 lobed, middle lobe slightly longer**, spur ± 10 mm, **with wide mouth**, thicker at tip (Oct-Apr). **General:** Used as a charm to prevent lightning striking huts.

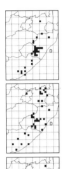

Habenaria laevigata (laevigata - smooth, slippery)
Slender, up to 400 mm. In grassland, 700-2000 m. **Leaves:** ± 65 x 14 mm, **clasping stem, grading into bracts. Flowers:** In dense inflorescence; flowers green, lip 3 lobed, two outer lobes shorter than middle one, spur 16-25 mm (Nov-Apr), scented.

Habenaria lithophila (lithos - stone; philos - loving)
Slender, up to 250 mm. In short grassland, 600-2200 m, S Cape to Malawi, Tanz. **Leaves:** Basal, ± 70 mm diam. **Flowers:** In dense, crowded inflorescence; flowers green, petal lobes subequal in length, lip 3 lobed, lobes subequal, ± 8mm, spur ± 7 mm, **mouth very narrow** (Nov-Mar).

Habenaria malacophylla (malacophylla - with soft leaves)
Slender, up to 700 mm. In forest understorey, margins, 150-1600 m, E Cape to Trop Afr. **Leaves:** ± 120 x 30 mm, spreading. **Flowers:** Inflorescence ± 120 mm; flowers spreading, green and white, petals 2 lobed, lip 3 lobed, lobes subequal, spur ± 15 mm (Dec-Apr).

Habenaria nyikana (named after the Nyika plateau in Malawi)
Robust, up to 500 mm. In grassland, 300-1300 m, KZN to Zim. **Leaves:** Narrow, ± 150 x 12 mm. **Flowers:** In loose to fairly dense inflorescence; flowers cream with pale centre, front petal lobe up to twice as long as back petal lobe, **lip 3 lobed nearly to base**, ± 11 mm, lobes subequal, spur 15-20 mm, swollen in upper part (Mar-Apr).

Habenaria schimperiana (named after Andreas Schimper, 1856-1901, professor of botany at Basle University)
Slender to fairly robust, up to 700 mm. In marshes, coast to 1350 m, KZN to Trop Afr. **Leaves:** Narrow, ± 70 x 10 mm. **Flowers:** In loose inflorescence; flowers green, **front petal lobe spreading downwards**, longer and broader than back petal lobe, **lip 3 lobed from clearly undivided base**, ± 10 mm, side lobes half as long as midlobe, spur 11-22 mm (Feb).

Habenaria tysonii (named after William Tyson, 1851-1920, teacher and collector)
Slender, up to 300 mm. On grassy, rocky hillsides, E Cape to Zim, Zam. **Leaves:** Basal, ± 50 mm diam. **Flowers:** In loose to dense, crowded inflorescence, stalks horizontal; flowers green, front petal lobe much longer than back petal lobe, lip 3 lobed, ± 10 mm, side lobes slender, as long as, or longer than midlobe, spur short, 12-14 mm, inflated towards tip.

Neobolusia - Slender herbs with small oval tubers; 1-2 large basal leaves, few smaller stem leaves; inflorescence loose or dense, no spur. Afr, ± 4 species, 2 in S Afr.

Neobolusia tysonii (named after William Tyson, 1851-1920, teacher and collector)
Slender, up to 460 mm. In moist or marshy grassland, 1200-2350 m. **Leaves:** Basal, 2, ± 80 x 20 mm with a few smaller stem leaves. **Flowers:** In loose inflorescence, 2-12 flowers, sepals brownish green, lip white, 8-12 x 4-8 mm, **widest near tip** (Dec- Feb). **Similar species:** *N. virginea* Up to 250 mm, solitary basal leaf, oval, ± 33 x 16 mm; flowers in small, dense cluster, white to pale pink, lip 6-8 x 4 mm, widest at base.

Habenaria dregeana

Habenaria dregeana

Habenaria laevigata

Tom de Waal

Tessa Hedge

Olaf Wirminghaus

Habenaria laevigata

Lal Greene

Martin von Fintel

Martin von Fintel

Habenaria lithophila

Habenaria malacophylla

Habenaria tysonii

Habenaria nyikana

Habenaria schimperiana

Neobolusia tysonii

Martin von Fintel

Lal Greene

Martin von Fintel

Martin von Fintel

519

Satyrium (*Satyros* - refers to the 2 horned satyr, half man half goat, the two spurs said to resemble a satyr's horns) - Terrestrial herbs with underground tubers; ovary not twisted; **lip forms a hood; 2 conspicuous spurs or 2 pouches.** Used in traditional medicine, mixed with other medicines, to help with illnesses that are difficult to cure. Mostly Afr, a few in the Mascarene Is, India and China, ± 140 species, 33 in SA.

Satyrium parviflorum Devil Orchid; ilabatheka elikhulu elibomvu, impimpi en-kulu (Z) (*parviflorum* - small flowers)

Slender to robust, 0,15-1,3 m. In moist or dry grassland, amongst rocks, coast to 2300 m, S Cape to Trop Afr. **Leaves:** 2-3, basal, ± 300 x 100 mm, from separate shoot or at base of flowering stem, often withered at time of flowering. **Flowers:** Inflorescence ± 300 mm; ± 100 small, densely packed flowers, **yellowish green** tinged olive to dark maroon, **drying brown soon after opening,** spurs ± 15 mm (Sep-Mar), sweetly scented. **General:** Used as protective and love charms. (See p. 572)

Disperis (*dis* - double; *pera* - pouch) - **'Granny Bonnet' Orchids** Slender perennial herbs (for description see p. 122).

Disperis cardiophora (*cardiophora* - bearing hearts)

Slender, up to 250 mm. Common but easily overlooked, in moist grassland, 400-2700 m. **Leaf:** Solitary, 10-30 mm, clasping base of stem. **Flowers:** Small, all facing same direction, white and green with purple at tips, petals only slightly extending from hood, outer surface exposed, sepals ± 7 mm, spreading, bracts heart-shaped (Dec-Mar), sweetly pungent scent. (See p. 122)

Disperis renibractea (*renibractea* - kidney-shaped bracts) (see p. 370)

Polystachya (*poly* - many; *stachys* - ear of corn or spike) - Usually epiphytic; base of stem swollen to form a pseudo-bulb; ovary not twisted, lip uppermost. Throughout the trop, mostly Afr, ± 200 species, 12 in SA.

Polystachya transvaalensis iphamba (Z)

Slender, up to 300 mm, in compact clumps. On rocks and trees, in **cooler forests,** KZN to E Trop Afr. Pseudobulbs 80-220 x 5-6 mm with black sheaths on parts. **Leaves:** 2-6, blade ± 150 x 20 mm, blunt. **Flowers:** In short, erect inflorescence, ± 60 mm, rarely branched; ± 12 flowers, yellowish green tinged reddish brown on outer surface, median sepal ± 12 mm, lip white with faint purple streaks, only on side lobes (Oct-Jan). **General:** Used as protective and love charms.

Eulophia (*eu* - well; *lophos* - crest, refers to the crested lip) - Terrestrial herbs; rhizomes thickened into fibrous tubers, some with pseudobulbs; leaf-bearing shoot separate from flowering stem, leaves narrow, often in two ranks; flowers usually showy, sepals more or less equal, lip with ridges on upper surface, spur very shallow or up to half length of flower. Mostly in trop, subtrop regions of Old World, over 200 species, most common in Afr, ± 42 in SA.

Eulophia foliosa lekholela, loetsane, 'mametsana (SS) (*foliosa* - leafy)

Stout, up to 450 mm. In grassland, bush, coast to 2500 m, E Cape to N Prov. **Leaves:** Partly to fully grown at flowering, 200-600 x 25 mm, stiff, erect, pointed tip, deeply indented veins. **Flowers:** In dense elongated cluster, ± 100 x 40 mm; 6-40 flowers, dull lime green, sepals, petals ± 16 mm, tip of lip dark purple (white to pale purple), no spur (Sep-Apr), honey scent.

Eulophia leachii (named after Leslie Leach, born 1909, businessman and amateur botanist with a particular interest in succulents and taxonomy)

Slender, up to 600 mm, in large clumps. In shade, in bushveld, KZN to Zim. **Pseudobulbs** 70-140 mm, mostly above ground. **Leaves:** Leathery, ± 300 x 15 mm, bright green, margins rough. **Flowers:** 3-24, sepals ± 22 mm, purplish brown to black, petals broad, cream to yellow-green, lip crests white, side lobes streaked purple, spur recurved (Dec-Jan). **General:** Leaves browsed by antelope. Easily grown.

Oeceoclades (*oikos* - house; *cladus* - branch, shoot) - Terrestrial herbs, on forest floor; aerial pseudobulbs, each with a single, folded, leathery leaf; inflorescence from base of pseudobulb, with 1-2 branches, lip 4 lobed, 2 central lobes often curved at tip. 3 species in SA.

Oeceoclades mackenii [= *Eulophia mackenii*] impimpi encane (Z) (named after Mark McKen, 1823-1872, greatest of early colonial plant hunters, curator of Durban Bot Gardens, 1851-53 and 1860-72)

Up to 300 mm. Rare, in forest in deep shade. Pseudobulbs dark purplish green. **Leaves:** Thick, **horizontal,** blade ± 150 x 15 mm, **mottled grey-green, stalks short. Flowers:** In simple or branched inflorescence; ± 30 flowers, cream and pink, lip side lobes marked pinkish red with 2 red blotches in front, spur club-shaped (Feb-Apr). (See p. 372) **General:** Grown in sandy leaf litter. Questionably distinct from *O. maculata*.

Satyrium parviflorum

Olaf Wirminghaus

Satyrium parviflorum

Martin von Fintel

Disperis renibractea

Emile Plumstead

Disperis cardiophora

Martin von Fintel

Polystachya transvaalensis

Geoff Nichols

Eulophia leachii

Geoff Nichols

Eulophia foliosa

Tom de Waal

Eulophia foliosa

Lal Greene

Oeceoclades mackenii

Geoff Nichols

521

Tridactyle (*tri* - three; *dactyl* - finger) - Epiphytes, without pseudobulbs; leaves thick, fleshy; flower differs from *Angraecum* in the lip which is flat, thin, divided into 3 lobes, side lobes toothed or fringed at tip, spur long, slender. Afr, ± 36 species, 4 in SA.

Tridactyle tridentata [= *Angraecum bolusii*, *A. tridentatum*] iphamba (Z) *(tri* - three; *dentata* - toothed)

Up to 300 mm, slender, erect or hanging in large, dense masses. On sandstone outcrops, high up on trees in forest or scrub, E Cape to Trop Afr. Roots grey. **Stems round,** ± 3 mm diam. **Leaves:** 10-14, **narrow, round, fleshy,** 50-100 x 2-4 mm diam, widely spaced, slightly grooved on upper surface, pointed. **Flowers:** In spikes opposite leaves; **3-5 flowers per spike,** 5-8 mm diam, pale waxy cream, lip 3 toothed, spur narrow, ± 8 mm (Nov-Mar). **General:** Used as a protective charm. Difficult to cultivate, must be kept dry in winter.

Diaphananthe (*dia, phainein* - to show through, more or less transparent; *anthos* - flower) - Epiphytes with woody stems; leaves very unequally bilobed at tips; numerous inflorescences, flowers semi-transparent (diaphanous), sepals and petals similar, spreading, lip broader than long, spur variable. Trop Afr, ± 42 species, 4 in SA.

Diaphananthe fragrantissima (*fragrantissima* - very fragrant)

In thick clumps. In hot coastal bush, riverine forest, N KZN to Trop Afr. Stems thick, woody, branched. **Leaves:** ± **300 x 20 mm, curved and hanging down, thick, leathery or fleshy,** flattened towards tip, very unequally bilobed, V-shaped towards base, yellowish green. **Flowers:** In several slender, hanging inflorescences, ± 300 mm; flowers ± 18 mm wide, in opposite pairs or groups of four, greenish white or yellowish, spur shorter than lip, inflated (Apr-May), lovely scent. **General:** Easily cultivated.

Diaphananthe xanthopollinia [= *Mystacidium gerrardii*, *M. peglerae*] iphamba (Z) (*xanthopollinia* - yellow pollinia)

Stems up to 120 mm, often branched, standing out from tangled **mass** of long, straight roots. Low-growing epiphyte at low altitudes, E Cape to Trop Afr. **Leaves:** ± 16, 40-100 x 6-9 mm, leathery, **thin, straight,** tips with rounded lobes. **Flowers:** 10-25 in horizontal or hanging inflorescences; flowers yellowish green, **6-12 mm diam,** lip very broad, spur ± 5 mm, strongly curved (Feb-May). **General:** Used as a protective charm. Easily cultivated.

Mystacidium (*mystax* - moustache; *idium* - diminutive, refers to rostellum lobes) - Small epiphytes; stems short; few leaves, many roots; flowers small to medium sized, sepals and petals curved back, pointed at tip, spur mouth wide, tapering to long, narrow point. S and E Afr genus, ± 12 species, 7 in SA.

Mystacidium aliceae (named after Alice Pegler, 1881-1929, teacher, painter, collector from E Cape)

Tiny, stemless epiphyte, up to 40 mm. In thick scrub, in shade, on twigs and small branches. Roots small, thin, soft, grey-green, stems very short. **Leaves:** 20-35 x 4-6 mm, light green. **Flowers:** In 2-4 inflorescences, 10-13 mm; 3-5 flowers, in 2 ranks, 6-8 mm wide, translucent yellowish green, sepals much longer than petals and lip, lip pointed, spur 7-11 mm (Nov-Feb).

Mystacidium flanaganii (named after Henry Flanagan, 1861-1919, Komga farmer, plant collector, whose garden and herbarium were bequeathed to the nation. The Flanagan Arboretum is now at the Union Buildings)

Dwarf, up to 40 mm, in scattered groups. On forest margins in light to heavy shade, on twigs and branches, mostly in cool, moist forests, up to 1800 m. Roots few, fine, 1 mm diam, in zigzag pattern. Short stem ± 4 mm. **Leaves:** 2-5, 15-30 x 5-7 mm, strap-shaped or slightly curved. **Flowers:** In 1-2 hanging inflorescences, ± 60 mm; 5-10 widely spaced, small flowers, ± 10 mm diam, yellowish white, **sepals pointed,** longer than petals and lip, spur 20-30 mm (May-Jun, Nov-Mar).
Similar species: *M. pusillum* Tiny; in light shade of scrub, 900-1200 m; leaves ± 25 mm; flowers pale green, **sepals rounded at tips, rostellum bearded** (Jun-Jul).

Darrel Plowes

Tridactyle tridentata

Darrel Plowes

Tridactyle tridentata

C J Ward

Diaphananthe xanthopollinia

Geoff Nichols

Diaphananthe fragrantissima

Geoff Nichols

Diaphananthe fragrantissima

Martin von Fintel

Diaphananthe xanthopollinia

Johan Bodenstein

Mystacidium pusillum

Tessa Hedge

Mystacidium aliceae

Martin von Fintel

Mystacidium flanaganii

523

DICOTYLEDONS - Two seed leaves, net veins, flower parts in fours, fives or multiples of these.
PIPERACEAE - Pepper Family Slightly succulent herbs. Flowers tiny, without petals, in dense spikes. Trop, ± 3000 species, 8 genera, 2 in SA. *Peperomia* (*peperi* - pepper; *homoios* - like) - Small, succulent herbs. Several species popular as container plants. In warmer regions of N and S Hemisp, mostly America, ± 1000 species, 4 in SA.

Peperomia blanda [= *P. arabica*]   **Large Wild Peperomia**   (*blanda* - pleasant, agreeable)
Slightly succulent herb, up to 300 mm. In forest. Rhizome horizontal, creeping, slender, rooting at nodes. Stems erect, square, slightly downy. **Leaves:** Opposite, ± 30 x 15 mm, narrowing to tip. **Flowers:** In very slender, long, erect spikes ± 80 x 1 mm, in axils (Jan-Mar). **General:** Popular container plant and suitable for groundcover in shady areas.

Peperomia retusa   **Wild Peperomia**   (*retusa* - blunted with slight notch at end)
Perennial creeping herb, 50-200 mm, in dense clumps. **Epiphyte** on mossy rocks or trees in forest. Stems root at lower nodes. **Leaves:** Slightly succulent, **alternate**, ± 20 mm, dark green above, greyish beneath, **hairless**. **Flowers:** In **terminal spikes**, ± 10 mm; flowers very small, green (throughout year). **General:** Popular container plant, attractive groundcover for shady areas. **Similar species:** *P. tetraphylla* [= *P. reflexa*] Larger, 150-450 mm; leaves 4 whorled; flower spikes ± 25 mm.

MYRICACEAE - Waxberry Family Woody or herbaceous, in damp places. Leaves with yellow gland dots, often aromatic when crushed. Flowers in spikes, without petals. Fruit often waxy, surface rough. Subcosmop, 3 genera, ± 55 species, 1 genus in SA. *Myrica* (*myrike* - riverside shrub) - Temp and warm regions, ± 35 species, ± 9 in SA.

Myrica brevifolia   **Dwarf Waxberry**   (*brevifolia* - short leaves)
Dwarf shrub, 0,3(1) m, in colonies. In grassland, up to 2100 m. Tufts of slender, mostly unbranched stems, bark grey-black, tips of stems velvety. **Leaves:** Small, 15-30 x 5-13 mm, margins entire or with 1-5 teeth, **covered with golden glands**. **Flowers:** Male and female on separate plants, in short spikes ± 12 mm (Oct-Jan). **Fruit:** Round, 2-3 mm diam, warty, waxy. **General:** New leaves highly aromatic.

URTICACEAE - Nettle Family - Herbs or shrubs, often with stinging hairs. Bark tough, fibrous. Cosmop, trop and temp, ± 48 genera, ± 1050 species, 11 genera in SA. *Urtica* (*urere* - to sting) - Herbs. About 50 species, 1 indigenous to SA.

★ *Urtica urens*   **Stinging Nettle; Bosbrandnetel, Brandblare (A); isibathi (Sw); imbabazane, ububazi (X,Z); imbathi (Z)**   (*urens* - stinging, scorching)
Annual herb, up to 600 mm. Widespread weed, in disturbed forest, up to 2300 m (from Europe). Leaves 12-60 x 10-30 mm, stalks ± 30 mm, margins deeply serrated, covered in bristly stinging hairs. Compact inflorescences, topped with stinging hairs, flowers small (Jan-Mar). Commonly eaten in Afr and Europe as a relish and used worldwide in traditional remedies. Rich in minerals, particularly calcium, potassium.

Laportea (named after Laporte) - Annual herbs, sometimes with stinging hairs. Trop, ± 13 species, trop, 3 species in SA.

Laportea peduncularis   **River Nettle; ubazi, ububasa (X); imbabazane, imbathi (Z)**
(*peduncularis* - stalked)
Erect or scrambling, up to 3 m. In damp areas, light shade. Stems much branched, with sparse, stinging hairs. **Leaves:** Alternate, ± 120 x 60 mm, silvery beneath, thin, 3 veined, **tapering to long narrow tip**, stalks ± 80 mm, very slender. **Flowers:** Inflorescences ± 50 mm, stems 30-40 mm; flowers small, greenish pink (throughout year). **General:** Pollen liberated explosively. Browsed by bushbuck. Used as a spinach. Subsp. *peduncularis*, creeping, scrambling, in montane forest, Cape to Tanz; bristly, often with stinging hairs, leaf margins finely toothed. Subsp. *latidens*, ± erect, in coastal forest, KZN to Moz; no stinging hairs, leaf margins bluntly toothed. **Similar species:** *L. grossa* **Spotted Nettle** 0,6-1 m, in forest, closed woodland; stems few, erect; hairs fiercely stinging; leaves 25-125 x 20-90 mm, triangular, margins broadly toothed, sometimes marked with large white spots; flowers (Feb-May).

LORANTHACEAE - Mistletoe Family - Partially parasitic. *Tapinanthus* (for descriptions see p. 48).

Tapinanthus lugardii [=*Loranthus lugardii*]   **Lugard's Mistletoe**   (named after Mrs Charlotte Lugard, 1859-1939, who collected and painted plants on an expedition with her husband to Ngamiland, now Botswana)
Up to 1 m. Parasitic mostly on *Acacia* species, N KZN to Bots. Stems densely hairy when young, hairless, greyish with age. **Leaves:** 20-60 x 5-15 mm, finely hairy to hairless, leathery. **Flowers:** 33-37 mm, pale greenish yellow to pink with age (Nov-Jan). **Fruit:** Oval, red-orange, 8-10 mm, persistent calyx. **General:** Birds feed on nectar and fruits.

Peperomia retusa

Peperomia blanda

Myrica brevifolia

Laportea grossa

★ *Urtica urens*

Laportea peduncularis

Tapinanthus lugardii

Tapinanthus lugardii

VISCACEAE - Mistletoe Family Perennial parasites. *Viscum* (*viscum* - bird lime) - Shrubby (for full descriptions see p. 50).

Viscum anceps Winged Mistletoe; Voëlent (A); iduma (Z) (*anceps* - flattened, compressed)

Leafless shrub 0,5-1 m. Parasitic on trees in woodland, E Cape to KZN. Stems pale yellowish green, younger branches flattened, older ones rounded, internodes 15-20 mm, **basal nodes with pale yellow margin, forming a wing on older stems.** **Flowers:** Stalkless, solitary at nodes of younger branches (Jun-Aug). **Fruit:** Oval to round, 4-5 mm, **warty on upper half when ripe**, dull yellowish orange. **General:** Fruits eaten by birds. Used traditionally to treat skin complaints and hysteria.

Viscum rotundifolium Round-leaved Mistletoe, Red-berried Mistletoe; Rooibessie Voëlent (A) (see p. 50)

Viscum verrucosum Warty Mistletoe; Voëlent (A); iphakama, iqhakama (Z) (*verrucosum* - warty)

Leafless shrub, up to 1 m high and wide. Parasitic mostly on *Acacia* and *Combretum* species, E Cape to Bots, Nam. Stems much branched, pale green, rounded, internodes 15-25 mm. **Leaves:** Reduced to scales. **Flowers:** Solitary or in small clusters (throughout year). **Fruit:** Round when ripe, 5-6 mm, slightly warty to smooth, pale yellow-orange, developing a **stalk 1-2 mm**, **young berries densely warty**. **General:** Fruit eaten by birds. Used for bird lime and in traditional medicine.

POLYGONACEAE - Rhubarb family Herbs, shrubs, climbers. *Rumex* - Herbs, rarely shrubs (for descriptions see p. 374).

★ *Rumex crispus* Curly Rumex, Narrow-leaved Dock; Suring, Tongblaar, Wilde-spinasie (A); idololenkonyane, ubuklunga (X,Z) (*crispus* - curled)

Perennial herb up to 1 m. Weed, in disturbed areas, damp places. Stem stout. Basal leaves large, crowded, margins wavy. Flowers small, crowded (Jul-Nov). Fruits 3 angled, in dense whorls, pale green to coppery pink, brown. Eaten as spinach.

Rumex sagittatus Climbing Sorrel, Climbing Rumex; bolila-bo-boholo (SS); umdende (Z) (*sagittatus* - arrowlike)

Low scrambler with long trailing stems. In woodland, on forest margins, widespread. **Leaves:** Arrow-shaped, stalks long, slender. **Flowers:** Large, dense inflorescences; flowers ± 10 mm (Feb-Apr). **Fruit:** Segments 7-8 mm diam, pale green to coppery red. **General:** Flowers visited by honey-bees. Eaten as a relish or spinach. Used in traditional medicine for toothache, pain, constipation and tuberculosis. Planted as a protective charm. Related to the Coral or Honolulu Creeper of horticulture. (See p. 376)

CHENOPODIACEAE - Goosefoot Family Often fleshy annual or perennial herbs, shrubs (for description see p. 50). *Chenopodium* (*cheno* - goose; *podion* - little foot, refers to leaves) - Temp, ± 300 species, 22 in SA, introduced.

★ *Chenopodium ambrosioides* Sandworm Plant; Galsiektebos, Hondepisbos (A); khola-bosiu, mokhankha, poea-e-kholo, setla-bocha, setlama-se-habea (SS); unsukumbili, puniyi, umbikicane, imhlabampethu, unukani (X) (*ambrosioides* - ambrosialike)

Up to 1(1,2) m. Common weed on disturbed soil. Stems slender, drooping. Leaves long, narrow, grey-green. Flowers small, in spikes (Aug-Jun). The plant has a characteristic scent. Widely used in traditional medicine to treat a variety of ailments from coughs, stomach ache, eczema to sandworm and used as an insecticide.

Salicornia (*sal* - salt; *cornu* - horn) - Fleshy, leaves reduced (for description see p. 50).

Salicornia meyeriana Saltmarsh Plant (see p. 50)

AMARANTHACEAE - Amaranthus family Mostly herbs (for description see p. 50). *Amaranthus* (*amarantos* - immortal, refers to long lasting qualities of the flower) - Annual herbs. Common weeds worldwide, ± 25 species, ± 15 in SA.

★ *Amaranthus hybridus* Pigweed; Hanekam, Kalkoenslurp, Misbredie, Rooibossie, Sprinkaanbossie, Wilde-aartappelbos (A); theepe-ea-bokoni (SS); umfino, umtyutyu, unomdlomboyi (X); imbuya, isheke (Sw,Z); amangamane, umbhido (Z) (*hybridus* - hybrid, sharing characters of two species)

Erect, much branched, annual herb, up to 1 m. Cosmop weed (from Trop America). Stems stout, grooved. Leaves simple, alternate, tapering to narrow tips. Inflorescences long, dense, 50-150 mm (Dec-May). Leaves and young shoots used as spinach (*imifino*) with the lowest moisture content and highest protein and carbohydrate content of the *imifino* analysed in SA. Dried to store for winter use.

Olaf Wirminghaus

Viscum anceps

Van Wyk & Malan

Viscum rotundifolium

Geoff Nichols

Viscum verrucosum

Tony Abbott

Rumex sagittatus

Caroline Fox

Salicornia meyeriana

Van Wyk & Malan

★ *Rumex crispus*

Tony Abbott

★ *Chenopodium ambrosioides*

Van Wyk & Malan

★ *Amaranthus hybridus*

527

Pupalia (from eastern name *pupali*) - Herbs or undershrubs. Afr, India, Malaysia, the Philippines, 4 species, 3 in SA.

Pupalia lappacea [= *P. atropurpurea*] Forest Burr; Bosklits (A); isinama esibomvu (Z)
(*lappacea* - burrlike)

Slender shrub, 300-900 mm, scrambling up to 2,5 m. Widespread, in thicket, woodland, on forest margins. Stems and leaves finely hairy. **Leaves:** Opposite, variable, 20-140 x 15-50 mm, stalks ± 10 mm. **Flowers:** In terminal inflorescences, compact at first, then elongating, stem ± 150 mm; flowers in clusters, ± 10 mm diam, each flower surrounded by cluster of hooked spines, woolly hairs between (Oct-Jul). **Fruit:** A burr. **General:** Used in traditional medicine to cure fever. (See p. 376)

Achyranthes *(achyron* - chaff, husk; *anthos* - flower) - Shrubby herbs; leaves opposite; elongated terminal inflorescences, segments pointed, hard. In warm parts of Old World, ± 6 species, 1 in SA.

★ *Achyranthes aspera* [= *A. sicula*] Burrweed; Haak-en-steek-klitsbossie, Knapse-kêrel, Langklits (A); lemanamana, lenamo (Sw); ibundlubundlu, isinama, ulimi-lwengwe , usibambangubo (Z) (*aspera* - rough)

Scrambling shrub, up to 2 m. In grassland, thicket, throughout Tropics. Stems 4 ribbed, hairy. **Leaves:** Variable, 50-220 x 13-80 mm. **Flowers:** In terminal spikes, dense at first, elongating ± 340 mm; flowers 7 mm, white, pink, green, purple (throughout year). **Fruit:** Silvery green, bracteoles with starry spines which attach to people and animals. **General:** Fruit eaten by birds. Used traditionally to treat chest pains and stomach ache. Also, elsewhere in the world, for a wide variety of ailments.

Alternanthera *(alterno* - alternate; *anthera* - flower) - Herbs. Austr, Trop America, ± 170 species, 4 introduced in SA.

★ *Alternanthera pungens* Paper Thorns, Khaki Burrweed; Kakiedubbeltjie (A); ikhungele (Z) (*pungens* - prick or puncture)

Prostrate herb, forming mats. Widespread in disturbed areas. Tap root. Stems root at nodes. Seeds pierce skin, an unpleasant nuisance in disturbed areas, in lawns.

PHYTOLACCACEAE - Pokeweed Family Herbs, undershrubs (trees). ***Phytolacca*** - (for description see p. 52).

Phytolacca octandra Inkberry, Pokeweed; Bobbejaandruif, Inkbessie (A); ama-hashe, ayatsala (X); umnanja (X,Z); umnyandla (Z) (see p. 52)

AIZOACEAE - Brakbos Family Annual or perennial herbs or shrublets. Leaves opposite or in whorls. Petals absent or small. Fruit a capsule. Trop, subtrop, mostly S Afr, ± 128 genera, ± 1850 species, ± 23 genera in SA.

Psammotropha (*psammos* - sand; *trophos* - one who feeds) - Perennial herbs or shrublets; leaves in rosettes and whorls; flowers small, clustered. Endemic to S Afr, 10 species.

Psammotropha myriantha impepho-tshani (Z)

Dwarf herb, up to 300 mm, solitary or in multiple tufts forming **small cushions, depressed in centre**. In rocky areas, grassland, coast to 2150 m, E Cape to Tanz. Stems thick, short, erect, concealed by rosette of leaves. **Leaves:** ± 30 x 3 mm, narrow, strap-shaped, sharp tipped, with bristle, **not narrowed to base, midrib projecting beneath**, margins slightly thickened. **Flowers:** Stems slender, erect, 30-300 mm, simple or branched; flowers in whorls, small, crowded, often with small bractlike leaves (Aug-Mar), sweetly scented or strongly honey scented. **General:** Used in traditional medicine and for traditional perfumed ointments.
Similar species: *P. mucronata* Leaf tufts not depressed in centre, leaves thinner, needlelike, translucent; flowering stems very slender, less crowded.

LAURACEAE - Laurel Family Woody plants, herbaceous parasites with leaves reduced to scales. Include *Ocotea*, the Stinkwood tree genus, and the exotic Avocado, Cinnamon and Camphor trees. Trop, ± 52 genera, ± 2850 species, 5 genera in SA. ***Cassytha*** (of Semitic origin, used by the Greeks for the parasitic plant now known in English as 'dodder laurel' of the same genus. Not related to 'dodder' *Cuscuta*, Convolvulaceae) - Twining parasitic herbs; stems fine, yellowish, attaching to the host plant with disc-like suckers. Mostly Austr, ± 16 species, 3 in SA, 1 an introduced weed.

★ *Cassytha filiformis* False Dodder; Nooienshaar, Vrouehaar (A); umkhunga (Z)
(*filiformis* - shaped like threads)

Twining parasite, in profusion. Widespread weed in grassland and thicket. Stems slender, yellowish green, with short suckers. Leaves reduced to tiny scales. Flowers tiny. Fruit ± 5 mm diam, translucent pinkish red. **Similar species:** *C. pondoensis* Whole plant hairy, growing tips and inflorescences rusty. (For photograph see p. 140)

CAPPARACEAE - Caper Family. ***Maerua*** - Shrubs, trees or scramblers (for descriptions see p. 142).

Maerua juncea subsp. *crustata* Rough-skinned Bush-cherry (see p. 142)

528

★ *Achyranthes aspera*

Psammotropha mucronata

C J Ward

Lal Greene

★ *Achyranthes aspera*

Pupalia lappacea

Psammotropha mucronata

C J Ward

Geoff Nichols

Pam Cooke

★ *Alternanthera pungens*

Braam van Wyk

★ *Cassytha filiformis*

Geoff Nichols

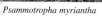

Psammotropha myriantha

Phytolacca octandra

Maerua juncea

Rosemary Williams

Martin von Fintel

Geoff Nichols

CRASSULACEAE - Crassula Family Herbs or soft shrubs, usually succulent. *Crassula* - Delicate annual or perennial herbs, softly woody to succulent shrubs, growth form variable, including aquatic (for descriptions see p. 142).

Crassula perforata (*perforatus* - perforated)

Perennial succulent, branches up to 600 mm. On rock faces, in dry scrub on cliffs, S Cape to KZN. **Leaves:** 8-20 x 3-15 mm, grey-green, margins horny, red or yellow, hairless or with fine hairs, tips pointed or blunt, narrowing abruptly to base which is more or less fused to opposite leaf. **Flowers:** In elongate inflorescences, flowers stalkless, in widely spaced clusters; flowers very small, creamy pale yellow, lobes spreading to recurved, calyx lobes fleshy, usually brown to red (Nov-Apr). **General:** Interesting plant for dry areas of garden, and also for containers.

FABACEAE (LEGUMINOSAE) - **Pea or Legume Family** Second largest flowering plant family (for description see p. 388). *Sutherlandia* (named after James Sutherland, 1639-1719, first superintendent of Edinburgh Bot Gardens) - Softly woody shrubs; leaves pinnate; flowers large, red; pods inflated. Cultivated in Europe since 1683. Endemic, 5 species in SA.

Sutherlandia frutescens Balloon Pea; Kankerbossie (A); umnwele (X, Z) (see under *S. montana* p. 58)

DICHAPETALACEAE - Poison Leaf or Gifblaar Family Trees or shrubs. Underground stems. Leaves alternate, with stipules. Flowers regular. Fruit fleshy, 1 seeded. Asia, Afr, Madag, America, 3 genera, ± 300 species, 2 genera in SA. *Dichapetalum* (*dicha* - in two; *petalon* - petal, petals may be bilobed) - Trop, especially Afr, ± 190 species, 2 in SA.

Dichapetalum cymosum Poison Leaf; Gifblaar (A) (*cymosum* - flowers in flat, round clusters)

Dwarf shrub from extensive woody rhizome, up to 450 mm, **in large colonies**. In woodland, grassland, **on sandy soils**, KZN to Nam, Zim, Moz. **Leaves:** Alternate, velvety hairy or hairless, 50-130 x 2-45 mm, pale green, hard, veins prominent beneath. **Flowers:** In small inflorescences, stem ± 30 mm; flowers 5-8 mm, pale green (Sep-Mar). **Fruit:** 40 x 25 mm, oval, yellow when ripe. **General:** Leaf very poisonous to stock. Fruit eaten by the San; seed reputed to be poisonous.

EUPHORBIACEAE - Rubber or Euphorbia Family Herbs, shrubs, trees, twiners, succulent or not, often with milky sap (for description see p. 276). *Tragia* (*tragos* - he-goat, Latinised name for 16th century German Hieronymus J Bock (*bock* - goat) - Perennial herbs; stems twining or erect, often with stinging hairs; petals absent, calyx 3 lobed, enlarging to surround fruit. In warm regions, ± 178 species, 14 species in SA.

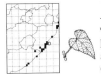

Tragia glabrata [= *T. durbanensis*] Stinging Nettle Creeper; Rankbrandnetel (A) (*glabrata* - hairless)

Twining herb, stems up to 2 m. In woodland, on forest margins. **Hairless or thinly hairy. Leaves:** ± 75 x 50 mm, tapering to tip, stinging hairs on veins, olive green above, **grey-green beneath**, margins serrated, stalks ± 30 mm. **Flowers: Tiny,** on erect stems ± 50 mm (Sep-May). **Fruit:** Bright green, streaked dark green, hairs silvery, drying out and splitting with an audible crack. **General:** Browsed by game. Attracts butterflies of the genera *Byblia* and *Eurytela*. Hairs sting fiercely!
Similar species: *T. meyeriana* imbabatane (Sw); imbabazane, ubangalala (Z) **Erect herb**, up to 400 mm; in moist thicket; hairy throughout; leaf stalks short; inflorescences ± 130 mm, calyx lobes with lobed margins, bristly, hairs stinging. Used in traditional medicine to cause sexual excitement.

Ctenomeria (*kteis, kten* - a comb; *mero* - a plant) - Twining herbs or shrublets; leaves 3-5 veined from base. In hot areas, ± 20 species, 1 in SA.

Ctenomeria capensis

Tall, twining herb, stems up to 3 m. In forest and thicket. Stems sparsely hairy, hairs face downwards. **Leaves:** Alternate, heart-shaped to lobed, ± 70 x 50 mm, **paler beneath**, margins wavy, slightly toothed, stalks ± 30 mm. **Flowers:** In spikelike inflorescences, numerous male flowers above, 1 or 2 female flowers at base (Oct-Apr). **Fruit:** Capsule bristly. **General:** Stinging hairs.

Clutia (named after Outgers Cluyt, 17th century Dutch botanist, curator of Leyden Bot Gardens) - Shrubs, herbs; leaves alternate, usually stalkless; flowers in leaf axils, male in small clusters, female solitary, on separate plants. Afr, Arabia, ± 70 species, ± 33 in SA.

Clutia katharinae (named after Katharine Saunders, 1824-1901, botanical artist and plant collector)

Spindly shrub, ± 1,2 m. In scrub and on forest margins, 1500-2400 m. Stems with long, silky white hairs. **Leaves:** 25-50 x 10 mm, blunt tipped, narrowing to base, **silky hairy. Flowers:** Male and female on separate plants, small, white (throughout year, Mar-Dec).

Sutherlandia frutescens

Crassula perforata

Dichapetalum cymosum

Tragia glabrata

Tragia meyeriana

Ctenomeria capensis

Clutia katharinae

531

Clutia cordata Grassland Clutia *(cordata* - heart-shaped)

Shrublet, up to 700 mm. In grassland. Rootstock woody. Stems usually simple, erect. **Hairless throughout. Leaves: Firm**, 18-30 x 12-30 mm, **pale bright green, roundish**, veins distinct beneath, tip pointed, **base ± heart-shaped**, stalks short. **Flowers:** Male and female on separate plants, clustered in axils, stalks 5-10 mm (Aug-Nov). **Fruit:** Capsule ± 5 mm diam, faintly warty.

Clutia monticola Branching Clutia *(monticola* - growing on mountains)

Single- or multi-stemmed shrublet, up to 600 mm. In grassland. Rootstock woody. Stems angular, leafy. Plant hairless. **Leaves:** Oval, ± 50 x 30 mm, narrowing to tips, firm, pale green turning pink with age; translucent gland dots. **Flowers:** Greenish white, male and female on stalks (Jul-Dec). **Fruit:** Capsule ± 5 mm diam.

Euphorbia (named after Euphorbus, 1st Century physician to King Juba of Mauritania) - Herbs, shrubs, trees, usually with milky sap, sometimes succulent; flowers reduced, within a cyathia or 'cup' rimmed with glands. Cosmop, ± 2000 species, ± 200 in SA.

Euphorbia bupleurifolia Melkbol (A); intsele (X); inkamamasane, insema (X, Z) (*bous* - an ox, bull; *pleuron* - a rib, the side; or ancient Greek name for umbelliferous plant, *Bupleurum*)

Spineless dwarf succulent, 40-200 mm. In grassland. **Bulblike stem, 40-70 mm diam, marked with scars of fallen leaves. Leaves:** 50-70 x 20 mm, deciduous, in terminal tuft. **Flowers:** Cyathia solitary, stem 10-50 mm, several amongst leaves; bracts ± 10 x 20 mm, green turning reddish (summer). **General:** Used in traditional medicine to treat cracked skin on feet, cancerous sores and swellings on lower limbs.

Euphorbia epicyparissias Wild Spurge; Melkbos, Pisgoedbossie (A); ikhanda lentuli (Z) (*epi* - upon; *kyparissos* - cypress, possibly refers to the growth form, resembling that of a cypress)

Perennial, spindly shrub, up to 1 m, in colonies. In grassland, on streambanks, up to 2300 m. Stem simple at base, branching above, rough with leaf scars, dark reddish bark. **Leaves: Crowded**, alternate, spreading or curved up, narrow, ± 25 mm. **Flowers:** Cyathia with 2 large bracts, yellowish green, in spreading terminal clusters, 20-75 mm diam (Aug-May).

Euphorbia ericoides ikhanda lentuli (Z) (*ericoides* - resembling *Erica* or heather)

Slender, erect, up to 500 mm. In rocky grassland. Stems woody, branches often whorled. Hairless. **Leaves: Closely packed, small**, ericalike, 4-8 x 1 mm, **pointing down**, margins rolled under. **Flowers:** Cyathia with 2 large bracts, terminal (Oct-Apr). **Fruit:** Round, ± 4 mm diam.

Euphorbia knuthii (named after Paul Knuth, German botanist, author of a classic work on flower pollination)

Spiny dwarf succulent, 50-150 mm. In dry woodland. **Main root tuberous**, contracted at the top to a slender main stem with many branches at ground level. Stems simple **or branched, darker grey-green with light green markings** narrowing to base, 6-12 mm thick, 3-4 angled, with conelike projections (tubercles). **Spines:** In pairs, 4-8 mm, brown turning grey, with or without a pair of minute prickles at their base. **Leaves:** 3-5 mm, soon dropping. **Flowers:** Cyathia solitary, stalks 4-8 mm. **Fruit:** Capsule deeply 3 lobed, ± 4 mm diam, **on recurved stalk. Similar species:** *E. schinzii* Klipmelkbossie (A); sihlohlwana (Sw) Stems plain green, no tuberous root; flowers and fruits stalkless; very variable, spreading or sometimes forming rounded cushionlike clumps.

Euphorbia natalensis inkalamasane, inkamamasane, umnhlonhlo (Z)

Perennial tufted herb, 150-600 mm, **often forming dense stands**. In grassland, coast to 2440 m. Woody rootstock. Stems simple or branched towards top, woody, yellow (pink at base), very leafy. **Leaves:** Long, whorled, ± overlapping, 8-25 x 1-7 mm, grey-green, hairless, **straight, blunt or tips pointed, upcurved**, stalkless. **Flowers:** Cyathia in terminal clusters, ± 50 mm diam, **2 large roundish bracts**, yellow-green tinged purple (Aug-Apr). **General:** The Zulu names *inkalamasane* means 'the one that cries sour milk' and *inkamamasane* means 'the one that squeezes sour milk'.

Lal Greene

Martin von Fintel

Wally Menne

Martin von Fintel

Clutia monticola

Clutia cordata ♂

Clutia cordata ♀

Euphorbia knuthii

Geoff Nichols

Tony Abbott

Euphorbia bupleurifolia

Euphorbia epicyparissias

Martin von Fintel

Euphorbia natalensis

Trevor Coleman

Martin von Fintel

Euphorbia ericoides

Euphorbia ericoides

533

Euphorbia pentagona **Noorsdoring (A)** (*penta* - five; *gona* - a corner, joint, a knee, an angle)
Compact, succulent shrub, 1,5-3 m. In dry forest, on cliffs. Main stem erect, branching freely higher up, stems often clustered in whorl-like groups, usually 5-6 angled (4-7), 10-40 mm diam, angles sharp with broadly triangular groove. **Spines:** Solitary, 6-15 mm, regularly scattered on angles, sometimes absent. **Leaves:** Tiny, dropping early. **Flowers:** Cyathia solitary or in clusters of 3-4, on tips of branches. **Fruit:** Capsule roundish, 4-6 mm diam. **General:** Cultivated at Kew Gardens since 1823.

Euphorbia pulvinata **Prickly-leaved Cushion Euphorbia; Voetangel (A); sihlohlwana (Sw); inkamamasane, isihlehle (Z)** (*pulvinata* - cushion-shaped)
Spiny dwarf succulent, 150-350 mm, forming domed cushions up to 1,5 m diam. In rocky grassland, E Cape to N Prov. Branches 25-150 x 25-33 mm, 7-10 angled, green, triangular grooves ± 4 mm deep, flattening with age. **Spines:** Solitary, 6-12 mm. **Leaves:** Deciduous, tiny in certain areas, 20-30 mm in northern populations, narrow or broad. **Flowers:** Cyathia clustered at tips of branches, yellowish green, purple, red-brown (Sep-Jan). **Fruit:** ± 4 mm diam, slightly 3 angled. **General:** Used in traditional medicine. Very variable over its wide range. Popular garden plant.

Euphorbia striata **Milkweed, Spurge; Melkgras (A); mohlatsise, mositsane (SS)** (*striata* - striped or furrowed)
Slender, **single stemmed** herb, up to 500 mm. Widespread in coarse grassland, damp areas, coast to 1980 m. Woody rootstock. **Leaves:** Clustered towards tips of stems, ± 40 x 3 mm, clasping, **erect,** tapering to **sharply pointed tip,** margins red. **Flowers:** Cyathia in loose terminal inflorescences, bracts ± 10 mm broad; flowers yellow (red) (Aug-Feb). **Fruit:** Capsule 3 angled, slightly rough, ± 3 mm diam. **General:** Used in traditional medicine for stomach disorders and to flavour sour milk.

Euphorbia trichadenia **Melkbol (A)** (*trichadenia* - hairy glanded, refers only to Angolan specimens)
Perennial herb, up to 150 mm. In grassland, woodland, SA, Angola, Zim. Large tuber ± 140 x 100 mm with underground stem, 2-5 branches above ground. **Leaves:** Long, slender, ± 40 x 10 mm, stalkless, slightly fleshy, **folded,** sometimes absent. **Flowers:** Cyathia 1-5, on short stalks ± 10 mm diam, petal-like lobes fringed, cream, yellow to pinkish (Jul-Jan). **Similar species:** *E. pseudotuberosa* Flowers smaller.

Monadenium (*mono* - one; *aden* - gland, refers to the cuplike bracts of the flowerhead;) - Dwarf perennials; stems cylindrical, succulent; flower bracts in pairs forming a bract cup with overlapping margins. Afr, ± 25 species, 1 in SA.

Monadenium lugardiae **Monadenium; umhlebe (Sw,Z); umhuwa (Z)** (named after Charlotte Lugard, 1859-1939, botanical artist who found the plant on a collecting expedition with her husband)
Succulent, up to 600 mm. In thicket, rocky areas, KZN to Bots. Stems simple or branched at base, 15-40 mm diam. Sap clear. **Leaves:** Clustered towards top of stems, 15-90 x 5-30 mm, leaving conspicuous leaf scars when dropping in winter. **Flowers:** Within cuplike bracts, ± 10 mm, hanging (Sep-Jan). **Fruit:** On recurved stalk. **General:** Used in traditional medicine as a purgative and by diviners to obtain clear vision before meetings. Decorative garden or container plant. Beware of very painful effect of sap on soft skin or eyes.

ANACARDIACEAE - Mango/Cashew Family Trees or shrubs. Male and female flowers on same or separate plants. Leaves 3 foliolate or compound. Fruit fleshy. Important economically for the Cashew, Pistachio, Mango; as resins, oils and lacquers from the Varnish and Mastic trees. Trop, subtrop, ± 70 genera, ± 875 species, 13 genera in SA. *Rhus* (*rhus* - red, refers to leaves turning red in autumn) - Leaves usually 3 foliolate; male and female flowers on separate plants; fruits small, fleshy. Trop, subtrop, ± 200 species, ± 111 in Afr, ± 80 in SA.

Rhus discolor **Grassveld Currant; Grasveldtaaibos (A); kopshane, mohlohlooane (SS); inhlangushane (Sw); inkobesehlungulu, intlokotshane, umnungamabele (X)** (*discolor* - of different colours)
Dwarf shrub, 0,5-1 m. In grassland, often in large colonies. Stems simple or branched. **Leaves:** Very variable shape and size, 3 foliolate; leaflets ± 82 x 18 mm, grey-green above, **velvety brown to white beneath, tips sharply pointed,** margins entire or toothed, stalks flattened above, ± 11 mm. **Flowers:** In much branched inflorescences, ± 140 mm, extending beyond leaves (Oct-May). **Fruit:** Shiny yellowish brown, ± 5 x 4 mm. **General:** Fruit eaten by people but said to cause constipation. Plant ritually burnt to ensure a good crop. (See p. 576)

Euphorbia pentagona

E. pentagona

Euphorbia pulvinata

Euphorbia pulvinata

Euphorbia pulvinata

Euphorbia striata

Monadenium lugardiae

Monadenium lugardiae

Euphorbia trichadenia

Rhus discolor

Rhus discolor

535

Rhus kwazuluana

Dwarf shrub, 0,6-1 m, in dense colonies. In grassland, on rocky hillsides, NE KZN. Stems branched, with small raised dots, branchlets dark brown. **Leaves:** 3 foliolate, **held erect**; terminal leaflets ± 80 x 8 mm, narrowing to **sharp tips, stalks slightly winged**, ± 20 mm. **Flowers:** In much branched inflorescences ± 90 mm (Jan-Feb). **Fruit:** Oval, shiny light brown, ± 4 x 2 mm.

Rhus pondoensis (from Pondoland)

Slender shrublet, up to 1 m. In grassland, in widely separated localities from E Cape to N Prov. Sparsely branched, **ribbed**, sometimes peeling. **Leaves: Erect, neat, almost clasping stem,** 3 foliolate; leaflets **rigid,** terminal leaflets ± 40 x 6-15 mm, margins white, **tips sharp. Flowers:** Inflorescences ± 70 mm, flowers crowded on short branches (Jan-Apr). **Fruit:** Asymmetric, shiny, reddish brown, ± 5,8 x 6,8 mm.

CELASTRACEAE - Spike-thorn Family Woody trees or shrubs. Flowers with fleshy, nectar-producing disc around ovary. Seeds often surrounded by colourful aril. Mainly trop, ± 55 genera, ± 850 species, ± 12 genera in SA. *Salacia* (after Roman goddess of the sea, wife of Neptune) - Trees, shrubs or climbers. Trop, subtrop, ± 150 species, 5 in SA.

Salacia kraussii ibhonsi, ihelehele, umgunguluzane, umnozane (Z) (see p. 64)

HIPPOCRATEACEAE Sometimes placed under Celastraceae. Shrubs, lianas or trees. Flowers regular, with nectar-secreting disc surrounding ovary. *Hippocratea* (after Hippocrates, ± 460-377 BC, father of science, pharmaceutical botanist, originator of doctors' Hippocratic Oath) - Trees, climbing shrubs, branching at right angles; fruit separates into 3 flattened carpels. Trop, subtrop, ± 100 species., ± 9 in SA.

Hippocratea delagoensis Zululand Paddle-pod; isifindwane (Z) (named after Delagoa Bay in Mozambique)

Scrambling shrub, up to 10 m. In thicket, dry forest, N KZN to Moz. Stems red-brown with raised white dots. **Leaves:** ± 70 x 35 mm, leathery, tips blunt, **margins toothed,** veins prominent on both surfaces. **Flowers:** In branched clusters, **petals dark green with pale margin** (Oct-Jan). **Fruit:** In 3 parts, each ± 50 x 28 mm, **tips pointed,** seeds winged. **General:** Vigorous garden climber. **Similar species:** *H. schlechteri* subsp. *peglerae* Leaves larger, fewer; fruit tips indented.

SAPINDACEAE - Litchi /Soapberry Family Trees, shrubs or vines with tendrils. Trop, ± 131 genera, ± 1450 species, 13 genera in SA. *Cardiospermum* (kardia - heart; sperma seed) - Climbing herbs; inflorescence branched, ending in a pair of tendrils; fruit a bladdery capsule. Attracts butterflies. Mostly Trop America, ± 20 species, 4 in SA.

★ *Cardiospermum halicacabum* Lesser Balloon Vine; Blaasklimop (A); ikhambi-leziduli, uzipho (Z)

Annual climber. Weed in damp, disturbed areas. Leaflets ± 45 x 20 mm, irregularly lobed, margins toothed. Flowers small, white, male and female usually on separate plants (throughout year). Fruit 3 lobed, wider than long, inflated. Visited by bees, wasps. Used in traditional medicine to treat diarrhoea, catarrh and body sores. **Similar species:** ★ *C. grandiflorum* Stems hairy; fruits pointed, longer than broad.

MELIANTHACEAE - Melianthus Family Trees or shrubs. *Melianthus* - Honey Flowers (for descriptions see p. 64).

Melianthus villosus Maroon Honey Flower; Kruidjie-roer-my-nie (A); ibhonya (Z)

(*villosus* - shaggy)

Shrub, up to 2 m. In moist areas, on forest margins, up to 1800 m. **Leaves:** Densely hairy, 3-7 pairs leaflets, ± 140 mm, margins deeply toothed, stipules 20-25 mm. **Flowers:** Erect inflorescences; sepals brownish purple, petals small, pink to purplish brown (Nov-Feb). **Fruit:** Inflated, 4 angled. **General:** Flower produces copious nectar. Poisonous leaves have an unpleasant scent when crushed. (See p. 578)

RHAMNACEAE - Buffalo-thorn Family Trees, shrubs or climbers, often spiny. Cosmop, ± 49 genera, ± 900 species, 9 genera in SA. *Helinus* (elinus - a twiner) - Climber, with tendrils. Afr, Madag, India, ± 5 species, 1 in SA.

Helinus integrifolius Soap Creeper; Seepbos (A); ityolo, ubulawu obude, ukum-buqwekwe (X); ubhubhubhu, uphuphuphu, uxuphukwekwe (Z) (*integrifolius* - leaves with smooth unbroken margins)

Sprawling climber. In bushveld, rocky wooded places. Tendrils unbranched. **Leaves:** ± 30 mm, **blade thin, tips blunt, rounded, with short, sharp protuberance. Flowers:** In few-flowered inflorescences; flowers small, white to green (Oct-Apr). **Fruit:** 3 lobed, ± 8 mm, tipped with remains of calyx. **General:** Fruit edible. Used in traditional medicine to treat hysteria, backache and to sooth irritation caused by sandworm. Grown from seed, attractive creeper. A butterfly larvae host plant.

Rhus kwazuluana

David Johnson

Rhus pondoensis

Tony Abbott

Hippocratea delagoensis

Wayne Matthews

Hippocratea schlechteri var. *peglerae*

Tony Abbott

Hippocratea delagoensis

Wayne Matthews

Salacia kraussii

Tony Abbott

★ *Cardiospermum halicacabum*

Geoff Nichols

Melianthus villosus

Hilliard & Burtt

Helinus integrifolius

Martin von Fintel

537

VITACEAE - Vine or Grape Family Climbers with tendrils, or shrubs, sometimes succulent (for description see p. 280).
Cissus (*kissos* - ivy) - Climbers, sometimes succulent; flowers with 4 petals; fruit a berry. 8 species in SA.

Cissus cussonioides (*cussonioides* - leaves like *Cussonia*)

Spreading, flat-topped herb, up to 450 mm. In rocky grassland. Rootstock woody, stems tough. **Leaves:** ± 140 mm, deeply lobed, stalkless. **Flowers:** In branched inflorescences (Oct-Nov). **Fruit:** ± 14 x 10 mm.

Cissus fragilis **Forest Grape Vine; umvusankunzi (Z)** (*fragilis* - fragile)

Slender, climbing, deciduous shrub. In woodland, forest. Rootstock large, tuberous. Stems cylindrical, tendrils simple. **Leaves: Slightly succulent,** ± 90 x 85 mm, dull dark green above, **shiny pale green beneath,** margins toothed, 3-5 veins from base, stalks ± 45 mm. **Flowers:** In sparsely branched clusters, stems ± 20 mm; flowers small, ± 4 mm (Dec-Jun). **Fruit:** Roundish, 15 x 10 mm, shiny dark green. **General:** Flowers visited by wasps. Birds eat fruit. Easily grown from seed, good fence plant.

Cissus quadrangularis **Cactus Vine, Succulent-stemmed Wild Grape; ijovane, isinwazi, umhlushwane, umnhlonhlwanyane (Z)** (*quadrangularis* - 4 angled or square)

Robust, succulent climber. In dry woodland, thicket, KZN to Trop Afr, India and the Philippines. Stems 10-50 mm diam, fleshy, angles winged, 2-15 mm, edged with reddish brown line, with tendrils. **Leaves:** At growing tip, ± 40 x 30 mm, 3 lobed, margins toothed, **falling early. Flowers:** In branched inflorescences, ± 100 mm wide; flowers small, yellow (Oct-Mar). **Fruit:** 8 mm diam, red. **General:** Fruit eaten by birds. Used in traditional medicine elsewhere in Africa to treat pain, burns, wounds and gastro-intestinal complaints. Good container plant, grown from stems.

Cissus rotundifolia **Bushveld Grape; umjovane (Z)** (*rotundifolia* - round leaves)

Succulent climber. In dry woodland, thicket, KZN to Trop E Afr to Arabia. Stems 4-5 angled, much branched, tendrils branched. **Leaves: Roundish to heart-shaped,** 40-80 mm, thick, fleshy, round to oval, margins bluntly toothed, stalks ± 10 mm. **Flowers:** In sparse inflorescences, ± 150 mm; flowers ± 35 mm, creamy green (Sep-Jan). **Fruit:** 15 x 13 mm, red-brown. **General:** Browsed by antelope. Succulent container plant on trellis, good cover for sunny banks. Easily grown from cuttings.

STERCULIACEAE - Cocoa/Sterculia Family Herbs, shrubs or trees. ***Hermannia*** (for descriptions see p. 66).

Hermannia cristata **Crested Hermannia** (see p. 66)

PASSIFLORACEAE - Granadilla Family Climbers with tendrils (shrubs or herbs). Stem often enlarged. Flower with corona often present. Fruit wall dry or leathery, seeds often with pulpy aril. Cultivated as ornamentals or for edible fruit. Trop and warm temp, especially Americas, ± 17 genera, ± 575 species, ± 5 genera in SA.
Basananthe (*basanos* - touchstone, black igneous rock used as test for gold, refers to black seeds) - Herbs or small climbers, with or without tendrils; leaves entire or lobed; 1-3 small flowers in axils, bisexual, petals absent or smaller than sepals, corona well developed; fruit 3-4 valved capsule, seeds black. Afr, ± 25 species, 5 in SA.

Basananthe sandersonii [= *Tryphostemma sandersonii*] **Miniature Granadilla** (named after John Sanderson, 1820-81, journalist, plant collector, honorary secretary Natal Agricultural & Horticultural Society)

Perennial herb, 200-600 mm. In grassland, on forest margins, coast to 1700 m, E Cape to S Tanz. Woody rootstock. Stems hairless. **Leaves: Slightly succulent,** 20-160 x 7-40 mm, margins finely toothed, stalks short, stipules short. **Flowers:** Small, ± 10 mm, **petals absent,** stalks ± 45 mm (Sep-Feb). **Fruit:** ± 20 mm. **General:** Frequently seen on recently burnt areas.

Passiflora (*passiflora* - passion flower) - Climbers; flower petals resemble sepals, sometimes absent, corona simple or complex. The Granadilla *P. edulis* and a number of other species are widely cultivated. Americas, SE Asia, Indo Austr, W Pacific, ± 370 species. Not indigenous to Afr, 3 species are locally established weeds.

★ *Passiflora subpeltata* **Wild Granadilla; Granadina, Wildegrenadella (A)**
(*subpeltatum* - shield-shaped, refers to leaves)

Perennial climber, up to 5 m. In woodland, bush clumps, roadsides, riverbanks. Garden escape, originally from C and S America. Stems cylindrical, with tendrils. Leaves shallowly 3 lobed, blue-grey-green beneath, stipules large, 15-40 mm. Flowers white, ± 50 mm diam, bracts and bracteoles inconspicuous (Nov-Jun). Fruit green ripening yellow, leathery, ± 50 mm. (See p. 156) **Similar species:**
★ *P. foetida* Flowers pink or lilac, bracts and bracteoles conspicuous, deeply divided, feathery, forming a whorl enveloping flower and fruit; unpleasantly scented.

538

Cissus cussonioides

Wally Menne

Cissus fragilis

Trevor Coleman

Cissus quadrangularis

Geoff Nichols

Cissus rotundifolia

Geoff Nichols

Hermannia cristata

Lal Greene

Basananthe sandersonii

Braam van Wyk

★ *Passiflora subpeltata*

Martin von Fintel

★ *Passiflora foetida*

Geoff Nichols

ACHARIACEAE - Herbaceous climbers or scrambling shrubs, with or without tendrils. Male and female flowers separate. Endemic to SA, 3 genera, 3 species. ***Ceratiosicyos*** (*keration* - pod; *sikyos* - cucumber, refers to fruit) - Herbaceous climber; fruit a ribbed capsule. 1 species.

Ceratiosicyos laevis Cucumber Pod Creeper (*laevis* - smooth)

Herbaceous climber. In forest, SE Cape to N Prov. Hairless. **Leaves:** 5-7 lobed, 30-140 x 30-120 mm, margins toothed, stalks 20-140 mm. **Flowers:** Bell-like, small, male and female separate, yellowish green (Aug-Jun). **Fruit: Elongated, ribbed capsule,** ± 80 x 8 mm, tapered to tip and base.

CACTACEAE - Cactus/Prickly Pear Family Spiny, succulent herbs or shrubs (for description see p. 290). ***Rhipsalis*** (*rhips* - wickerwork; *alis* - pertaining to, refers to slender, interlacing branches) - Fleshy shrubs, sometimes epiphytic; stems round, often jointed; leaves scalelike. America, Asia, Afr, ± 50 species, 1 in SA, the only wild cactus in SA.

Rhipsalis baccifera [= *R. cassytha*] Mistletoe Cactus, Hanging Wild Cactus; Bostou (A); ugebeleweni (Z) (*baccifera* - with berries)

Straggling, pendulous, epiphytic succulent. On trees or rocks in evergreen forests, E Cape to Trop Afr, widespread in S and C America. Stems soft, 3-6 mm diam, blue-green, irregularly branched, becoming woody at base, hairless and spineless, except in juvenile stage. **Flowers:** Solitary or in pairs, ± 4 mm diam, 6-10 petals, greenish white, with conspicuous bulbous base (throughout year). **Fruit:** Round, fleshy, 5-10 mm diam, translucent white, pink or red, juice sticky. **General:** Fruits eaten by birds. Used in traditional medicine to treat chest complaints. (See p. 158)

TRAPACEAE - Water Chestnut Family Floating annuals. Leaves with inflated stalks. Fruit 1 seeded, 2-4 horned, covered by soft flesh. Fruits edible, cultivated in China. One genus, 3 species, 1 in SA.

Trapa natans Water Chestnut; Waterkastaiing (A); inyiva, inyazangoma-amanzeni (Z) (*trapa* - kalkitrapa, a 4 spiked iron ball thrown to alarm horses in battle; *natans* - floating leaves)

Annual, floating, aquatic herb, sometimes in large 'rafts'. In lakes and pans, KZN, Afr, Europe, Asia, naturalised in N America and Austr. **Leaves:** Submerged leaves rootlike; aerial leaves simple, **floating in a rosette**, blade triangular, 15-50 x 15-80 mm, shiny dark green above, margins deeply toothed, **stalks inflated and spongy in middle. Flowers:** Solitary, 8-16 mm, white (throughout year). **Fruit:** Triangular nut with 2-4 horns (from persistent calyx lobes), very variable in size and shape of horns. **General:** Kernels of seeds tasty, collected in large quantities, dried and stored in rural areas. Also eaten by water fowl.

APIACEAE (UMBELLIFERAE) - **Carrot Family** Mostly herbs, a few small trees, usually aromatic (for description see p. 294). ***Hydrocotyle*** (*hydros* - water; *kotyle* - cup, refers to plant found in damp places, leaves cup-shaped) - Perennial herbs, usually trailing, rooting at joints; leaves long stalked. Cosmop, ± 130 species, 5 in SA.

★ *Hydrocotyle bonariensis* Perdekloutjies (A) (from Bonaria, in Buenos Aires, S America)

Perennial, low-growing herb. In moist places, often in sandy soil near brackish lagoons (from S America). Slender creeping stems, rooting at nodes. Hairless. Leaves ± 120 mm diam, margins shallowly lobed, stalks ± 300 mm, attached inside margin. Flowers small, in terminal clusters on long stems (throughout year). Fruits round, flattened. Visited by black ants.

Centella (possibly diminutive of *cento* - a patchwork covering) - Perennial herbs, usually creeping. Mostly SA, except for *C. asiatica* which is pantrop, ± 40 species.

★ *Centella asiatica* Marsh Pennywort; Varkoortjies, Waternavel (A); bolila-balinku (SS); icudwane (Z)

Creeping herb, up to 130 mm. A weed in damp places, throughout trop, subtrop. Rooting at nodes, stems sometimes purplish. Leaves solitary or clustered, 10-70 mm, smooth, shiny green, roundish, deeply heart-shaped at base, margins with thickened, rounded teeth, stalks ± 130 mm. Flowers small, greenish white to dark red, stems 15-50 mm (Sep-May). Leaves cooked as a vegetable. Used in traditional medicine to treat skin complaints and alimentary ulcers.

Centella glabrata Persiegras, Sweetkruie (A); isiwisa (Z) (*glabrata* - hairless)

Slender, low-growing herb, up to 200 mm. In grassland, E Cape to Malawi. Variable. **Many stems from woody base, purplish brown with white hairs. Leaves:** In clusters or pairs, 10-40 x 3 mm, shiny dark green, base narrowing to short indistinct stalk. **Flowers:** In short clusters, whitish green (Sep-May). **General:** Used in traditional medicine and as a charm against hail.

540

Ceratiosicyos laevis

Martin von Fintel

Trapa natans

Geoff Nichols

Trapa natans

Geoff Nichols

★ *Centella asiatica*

Trevor Coleman

Rhipsalis baccifera

Wayne Matthews

Rhipsalis baccifera

Martin von Fintel

★ *Hydrocotyle bonariensis*

Geoff Nichols

Centella glabrata

Tony Abbott

541

PERIPLOCACEAE - Periploca Family Perennial herbs, shrubs, lianas, with milky latex. Leaves opposite. Flowers sometimes with corona, 5 stamens forming a column, pollen loose (granular). Similar to Apocynaceae and Asclepiadaceae (differing only in pollination mechanism), sometimes placed there as a subfamily. Old World, 62 genera, ± 170 species, 8 genera in SA. *Tacazzea* (ancient Ethiopian name for the plant)- Reddish brown warty bark; leaves with prominent, reticulate veins, midrib glandular; flowers small, no distinct tube, corona in 2 series. Afr, ± 15 species.

Tacazzea apiculata **Crawcraw Vine; isimondane (Z)** (*apiculata* - refers to the narrowed leaf tip)
Woody climber. On forest margins, E Cape to Sudan. **Leaves:** 60-100 x 30-70 mm, tips blunt to indented, with brown short sharp point. **Flowers:** In loose inflorescences; outer corona lobes broader at base, becoming spirally twisted above, 2-3 cleft at tip, inner lobes small, fleshy (Nov-Jan). **Fruit:** Paired, 50-70 mm. **General:** Used traditionally as a tonic and, in Cameroon, to relieve itching skin or 'crawcraw'.

Petopentia (anagram of the genus *Pentopetia*) - Recently split off the genus *Tacazzea*. Afr endemic, 1 species.

Petopentia natalensis [= *Tacazzea natalensis*] **Propeller Vine**
Liana. On forest margins, in woodland. **Bark reddish brown. Leaves:** 75-130 x 25-65 mm, with pronounced parallel veins. **Flowers:** In branched clusters, 25-40 mm diam; flowers yellowish green with reddish central line, lobes spreading, **twisted in middle like an aeroplane propeller**, corona short with erect long appendage protruding from centre (Oct-Dec). **Fruit:** Paired, ± 90 x 14 mm, thick skinned to woody.

Raphionacme (*rhaphis* - needle; *akme* - point) - Perennial herbs; leaves often with veins distinct beneath; flowers in forks of branches, tube almost always distinct; staminal corona in 1 series, 5 erect, free lobes fused at their base with the anther filaments to the mouth or mouth of the corolla tube. Afr endemic, ± 30 species, 17 in SA.

Raphionacme flanaganii **Flanagan's Raphio** (named after Henry Flanagan, 1861-1919, Komga farmer and plant collector, whose garden and herbarium were bequeathed to the nation)
Twiner, stems up to 4 m. In sand forest, coast to 1000 m. Stems annual, **brown, with raised dots. Leaves:** 50-110 x 12-40 mm, **velvety. Flowers:** Lobes **reflexed**, 6-7 x 3 mm, tube 2-3 mm, velvety outside, yellowish with red triangle at base, staminal corona lobes ± square at base, in 3 parts, upper central appendage slender, white, **anther appendages large, white, spoonlike, erect** (Oct-Jan). **Fruit:** ± 50 mm.

Raphionacme galpinii [= *R. elata*] **Galpin's Raphio** (after E E Galpin, 1883-1941, amateur botanist)
Solitary stems, 50-230 mm, **erect**. In grassland, on rocky hillsides, up to 1200 m, E Cape to N Prov. **Leaves:** 25-75 x 7-20 mm. **Flowers:** Hairy outside, tube 2-4 mm deep, lobes 4-6 x 1,5 x 3 mm, staminal corona as for *R. flanaganii* but upper middle part extended into 4,5 mm narrow appendage which projects over the flower centre, maroon to brown (Sep-Dec). **General:** Browsed by animals, roots eaten by people. **Similar species: *R. procumbens* Creeping Raphio** In grassland, up to 1520 m; stem creeping; leaves ± velvety; flowers hanging, lobes ± 3 mm, corona lobes with middle appendage short, toothlike, anther appendages merged into sharp cone (Oct-Jan).

Raphionacme lucens **Coastal Raphio** (*lucens* - shining)
Branching herb, up to 300 mm. In coastal grassland, Zululand, S Moz. **Stems tall, unbranched. Leaves:** Shiny above. **Flowers:** In compact clusters near tips of stems; flowers sulphur green and maroon, tube 2-3 mm, lobes oval, 4-5 x 2-2,5 mm, corona lobes pinkish to green, similar to *R. flanaganii* but **middle appendage twisted** (Jul-Jan). **Fruit:** Solitary or paired, **long, narrow**, 110-150 x 4-5 mm.

Raphionacme palustris **Long-pod Raphio** (*palustris* - refers to marshy habitats)
Up to 500 mm. In swampy areas, wet grassland, coast to 1000 m, KZN endemic. Stems erect, branching. **Leaves:** 50-60 x 20-30 mm, **veins translucent, midvein sunken above, prominent below, side veins parallel, looping at margin. Flowers:** In clusters; tube 3-4 mm, lobes oval, 1-2 mm spreading, corona lobes converging, tips threadlike, point 2 lobed (Sep-Oct). **Fruit: Solitary, long, 180-270 x 8-10 mm.**

ASCLEPIADACEAE - Milkweed/Butterflyweed Family *Xysmalobium* (*xysma*- thread; *lobos* - lobes, refers to either the follicle or the threadlike corona lobes) - Perennial, non-climbing herbs; stem tuber or deep seated caudex; flowers bell-like, lobes bloblike, pollinia pendulous. Genus is under revision. Mostly Trop, subtrop Afr, ± 40 species, ± 20 in SA.

Xysmalobium asperum **Sandpaper Cartwheel** (*asperum* - rough, refers to rough hairs)
Reclining, 150-300 mm. Among rocks in grassland, 450-1800 m, KZN to N Prov. **Stems forking at base. Leaves:** 9-80 x 7-30 mm, **roughly hairy. Flowers:** Inflorescences ± 20 mm diam; lobes usually **reflexed, without apical convex bumps**, 3-5 x 2-3 mm (Sep-Jan). **Fruit:** ± 70 x 20 mm with longitudinal rows of small spines.

Tacazzea apiculata

Tacazzea apiculata

Petopentia natalensis

Raphionacme flanaganii

Raphionacme galpinii

Petopentia natalensis

Raphionacme lucens

Raphionacme palustris

Raphionacme procumbens

Xysmalobium asperum

543

Xysmalobium parviflorum Octopus Cartwheel *(parvus - small; florus - flower)*
Bushy herb, 120-300 mm, in colonies. On very rocky slopes in short grassland, 900-2100 m. Stems **much branched**. **Leaves:** 20-45 x 6-20 mm, leathery, margins thickened, veins brown. **Flowers:** In solitary inflorescence or 2-4 terminally; **flowers stiffly erect, small, ± 3 mm diam**, lobe tips inflexed (Oct-Apr), sickly sweet scent. **Fruit:** Solitary, 40-80 x 10-15 mm with parallel green stripes. (See p. 578)

Xysmalobium stockenstromense Mountain Uzura *(named after Stockenstrom, town in E Cape)*
Erect herb, 500-800 mm. In annually burnt grassland, **1200-2500 m. Stem solitary**, 1-2 branches from base. **Leaves:** Erect, **closely clustered**, 60-200 x 15-45 mm, **waxy, margins wavy. Flowers:** Lobes erect, tips slightly rolled under, covered in stout white hairs (Nov-Jan), musty or strong cinnamon smell. **Fruit:** Solitary, 70-100 x 20-30 mm, slightly inflated, shallowly ridged with **stout, blunt, recurved spines**.

Xysmalobium undulatum Milkwort, Uzura; Bitterhoutwortel (A); leshokhoa, pohot-shehele (SS); iyeza elimhlophe, nwachaba (X); ishongwane (fruit), ishongwe (plant) (X,Z)
(undulatum - refers to wavy leaf margin)
Robust, erect herb, 0,2-1,8 m. In grassland, coast to 2000 m, SA to Kenya. Stems 1(3), annual. **Leaves: Large, 80-270 x 10-78 mm, hairy. Flowers:** Lobes erect, tips recurved, **stout white hairs at tip** (Oct-Jan). **Fruit:** Solitary or paired, 90-100 x 35-50 mm, **inflated, covered in long, recurved soft bristles. General:** Used in traditional medicine to treat headaches, dysentery, colic and as charms to divert storms, prevent poisoning and make dogs keen hunters. Widely used medicinally in Afr and elsewhere. Sold in Europe under the name *Uzura*. Young leaves used as a pot herb. 'Parachute' hairs from seeds used to stuff pillows.

Schizoglossum *(schizo* - cut or split; *glossa* - tongue, refers to the corona lobe which is often split into 2 or more parts)* - Perennial herbs; carrotlike stem tuber; stems annual, erect, usually solitary, with milky latex; leaves ± stalkless; inflorescences 2-15 flowered, lobed to base, corona lobes scalelike, often complex, pollinia pendulous, attached at their sides to the translators. About 12 species, S Afr endemic.

Schizoglossum bidens Variable Split-tongue/Schizoglossum *(bi - two; dens - tooth)*
Erect herb, 20-900 mm. In grassland, E Cape to N Prov, coast to 2600 m. **Leaves: In whorls or irregular**, 15-70 x 1-9 mm. **Flowers:** Lobes ± erect, **2,5-6** x 1-3,5 mm, **margins turned back, corona appendages simple or forked, anther appendages hidden beneath style tip** (Sep-Apr). **Fruit:** Solitary, 45-74 mm, tip beaked, covered in soft, recurved bristles. **General:** 7 subspecies. Subsp. *pachyglossum*, usually more than 300 mm; widespread; rarely branched; leaves 1,5-9 mm wide; inflorescences stemless, flowers green. (See p. 578)

Schizoglossum cordifolium Common Split-tongue/Schizoglossum *(cordate* - heart-shaped; *folium* - leaf)*
Erect herb, 150-600 mm. In open grassland or sparsely wooded savanna, coast to 2400 m, W Cape to N Prov. Stems simple (branched). **Leaves: In well spaced, opposite pairs**, 20-40 x 2-3 mm. **Flowers:** Lobes erect, **5-7** x 3-4,5 mm, tips curving inwards, **margins strongly turned back, corona appendages 2 pronged, ± touching, anther appendages clearly visible** (Aug-May). **Fruit:** Solitary, 58-70 x 13 mm, narrowing gradually to beaked tip, stalk recurved. **General:** Roots eaten.

Aspidoglossum *(aspido* - shield; *glossa* - tongue, refers to corona lobes)* - Erect herbs; stem tubers small; inflorescences stalkless, clustered towards tops of stems, corona lobes erect, flattened, scalelike, not fleshy. Afr, ± 34 species, 22 in S Afr.

Aspidoglossum ovalifolium [= *Schizoglossum ovalifolium, S. robustum*] Variable Shield-tongue
(ovali - oval; *folium* - leaves)*
Herb, **70-330 mm.** In grassland, E Cape to Moz. Stems unbranched, **usually solitary. Leaves:** Crowded towards tip of stem, **14-35 x 0,5-12 mm. Flowers:** Lobes 4-7 x 2-4 mm, **green striped brown or dark purplish brown**, upper surface with long erect hairs, lower surface hairless or with short downy hairs (Oct-Apr), curious scent. **Fruit:** Erect, ± 40 mm, tapering to pointed tip, covered in recurved bristles.

Xysmalobium parviflorum

Ray Boardman

Xysmalobium undulatum

Lal Greene

Xysmalobium parviflorum

Martin von Fintel

Xysmalobium stockenstromense

Martin von Fintel

Xysmalobium undulatum

Trevor Coleman

Xysmalobium undulatum

Pam Cooke

Schizoglossum bidens

Martin von Fintel

Schizoglossum cordifolium

Martin von Fintel

Aspidoglossum ovalifolium

Geoff Nichols

545

Miraglossum (*mira* - astonishing or miraculous; *glossa* - tongue, refers to ornate corona lobes) - Perennial herbs; stem tuber small, carrotlike; 2-8 flowers in stalkless inflorescences, lobes reflexed, usually densely hairy, corona lobes thick, fleshy; fruit erect, covered in soft bristles or thick down, stalk recurved. SA endemic, 7 species.

Miraglossum pilosum [= *Schizoglossum pilosum*] **Hooked Miracle Tongue** (*pilosum* - hairy)
Erect herb, 120-360 mm. In annually burnt grassland, often against rocks, 900-1740 m. **Leaves:** 15-37 x 2-14 mm, ± stalkless. **Flowers:** Lobes 5-6 x 3 mm, concave, covered in long hairs beneath, **corona lobe erect, appendage tip simple, slightly hooked inwards** (Oct-Dec). **Fruit:** Solitary, smooth, no bristles.

Miraglossum pulchellum [= *Schizoglossum pulchellum*] **Horned Miracle-tongue** (*pulcher* - beautiful)
Herb, 200-550 mm. In open grassland, 600-2300 m, KZN to N Prov. **Leaves:** Erect or close to stem, opposite or irregular, 20-50 x 1-5 mm, margins rolled under, hairy. **Flowers:** Lobes oval, ± 8 x 4 mm, convex, lower surface densely covered in brown hairs, **corona erect, appendage tips reflexed away from flower centre, like a rhino horn** (Oct-Jan). **Fruit:** 35-70 mm, covered in upwardly curved bristles.

Miraglossum verticillare [= *Schizoglossum verticillare*] **Wreathed Miracle-tongue** (*verticillus* - whorl)
Erect herb, 100-350 mm. In rocky grassland, 900-1800 m. **Leaves:** Erect, never whorled below, whorled and smaller at flowering nodes, 17-45 x 1-2 mm, hairy. **Flowers:** Lobes 4,5-6,5 x 2,5-3,5 mm, outer surface with brown hairs, inner surface finely grey hairy, **corona lobe appendages curl round to the right to form a wreath over the style tip** (Oct-Feb).

Periglossum (*peri* - around; *glossum* - tongue) - Grasslike herbs; stems solitary, erect, unbranched; inflorescences compact, style tip flat, not exceeding the anthers, pollinia sausage or teardrop-shaped. S Afr endemic, 5 species.

Periglossum angustifolium **Round Head** (*angustus* - narrow; *folium* - leaves)
Herb, 300-760 mm. Usually in unburnt grassland, up to 2000 m. **Leaves:** Erect to spreading, **45-130 x 1-3 mm**, midrib prominent below. **Flowers:** Cuplike, lobes ± 7 x 3 mm, tips abruptly pointed, yellow inside, reddish brown outside, **outer corona lobes triangular, inner corona lobes slender, threadlike** (Jan-Mar).

Gomphocarpus (*gompho* - club; *carpus* - fruit) - Shrublike herbs; fibrous rootstock; stems erect, hollow; milky latex; inflorescences hanging, lobes reflexed, corona lobes sac-like; fruits usually inflated. Used in traditional medicine. Afr, Arabia, Medit, ± 18 species, ± 9 in S Afr. Introduced weed in Americas, Austr.

Gomphocarpus physocarpus [= *Asclepias physocarpa*] **Milkweed, Balloon Cottonbush, Hairy Balls; Balbossie (A); umbababa, umbemiso, umangwazane, umqumnqwewe, uphuphuma, usingalwesalukazi (Z)** (*physo* - bladdery; *carpus* - fruit)
Annual or perennial herb or shrub, 0,5-2 m. In grassland, disturbed areas, coast to 900 m, E Cape to Kenya. **Stems solitary below, branched well above base, hairless. Leaves:** 50-100 x 7-20 mm. **Flowers:** Lobes 7-9 x 4,5-6 mm, corona square, white (throughout year). **Fruit:** Solitary, inflated, **roundish**, 38-70 mm diam, covered in soft spines. **General:** A weed in places. Hardy garden plant, attracts butterflies, fruits very decorative. Stems used for fibre (*usingalwesalukazi* refers to the fibre used for sewing *isidwaba*, skirts of old women). Reportedly poisonous. Used traditionally to treat stomach ache, headache and warts. (See p. 168)

***Gomphocarpus* sp. nov.**
Perennial shrub, 0,4-1,9 m. In grassland, 800-850 m, N KZN endemic. Stems branched near base, **young parts covered in white down. Leaves:** (60)115-150 x 5-11 mm. **Flowers: Inflorescence bracts prominent**, 12-20 mm; lobes 9-12 x 5-7 mm, greenish mauve, creamy green, **corona D-shaped, purplish brown**, stems and stalks 20-35 mm (Nov-Dec). **Fruit:** Covered in soft long purplish spines.

Pachycarpus (*pachy* - thick; *carpus* - fruit, refers to the thick skinned fruits) - Perennial herbs (for description see p. 580).

Pachycarpus appendiculatus **Soccerball Pachycarpus, Soccerball Thick-fruit; ukhathimuthi (Z)** (*appendiculatus* - small appendages, refers to corona or flaplike appendages to corona)
Erect herb, 220-500 mm. In rocky grassland, up to 1200 m. Stems slender to robust. **Leaves:** 40-105 x 20-55 mm, leathery, hairless to softly hairy or rough. **Flowers:** 14-26 mm, lobes **reflexed**, 10-20 x 5-15 mm, corona lobes ± free, **lower part with 2 side flaps, side by side on upper surface, upper part erect, leaflike, narrowed basally** (Oct-Mar). **Fruit: Inflated**, winged in upper half. **General:** Very poisonous.

Miraglossum pilosum

Miraglossum pulchellum

Gomphocarpus physocarpus

Miraglossum verticillare

Periglossum angustifolium

Gomphocarpus sp. nov.

Pachycarpus appendiculatus

Pachycarpus appendiculatus

Gomphocarpus physocarpus

547

Pachycarpus asperifolius [= *P. inconstans, P. validus*] **Large Red Milkwort, Christmas-tree Pachycarpus; ishongwe elibomvu, ishongwe elincane (Z)** (*asper* - rough; *folius* - leaves)
Erect herb, 0,30-1 m. In unburnt grassland, amongst rocks, on forest margins, coast to 700 m, E Cape to N Prov. Stems usually unbranched, stout. **Leaves:** 30-130 x 10-60 mm, leathery, veins prominent, margins more or less wavy, with rough, stiff, stout hairs. **Flowers:** Inflorescences at nodes; flowers 11-28 mm, **reflexed**, divided almost to base, brownish, greeny white or yellowish green, lobes 8-25 x 7-14 mm, margins rolled under, **corona lobes almost bloblike**, produce copious sticky nectar (Oct-Mar). **Fruit:** Round, 80-100 mm, **inflated**, weakly 5 ridged. **General:** Used in traditional medicine to treat hysteria, stomach complaints, headaches and as a charm against evil. Sap from leaves rubbed in dogs' mouths to make them aggressive.

***Pachycarpus campanulatus* Fairy-bell Pachycarpus/Thick-fruit** (*campanulatus* - bell-shaped)
Slender herb, 150-600 mm. In annually burnt grassland, 500-2100 m. Stems **unbranched**, plant harshly hairy. **Leaves:** 64-165 x **2-10 mm, margins rolled under, midvein prominent below. Flowers:** 2-5 in **solitary, terminal inflorescence**; flowers large, **usually hanging**, 10-50 mm, **fused to over halfway**, lobes short, inflexed or reflexed (Nov-Feb). **Fruit: Not inflated**, spindle-shaped to narrowly oval. **General:** Subsp. *campanulatus*, south of the Tugela River; 2-5, larger flowers, 24-50 mm, corona lobes long, 9-15 mm. Subsp. *sutherlandii*, E Cape to N Prov; 2-14 smaller flowers, 10-30 mm, corona lobes short, 2-8 mm.
(See p. 170)

***Pachycarpus concolor* Astral Pachycarpus/Thick-fruit; ishongwe (Z)** (see p. 580)

***Pachycarpus coronarius* Crowned Pachycarpus/Thick-fruit** (*coronatus* - crowned)
Erect herb 500-700 mm. In grassland. Stems **unbranched**, thin to stout, hairy. **Leaves:** Spreading erect, **long and narrow**, 40-120 x 10-25 mm, margins slightly thickened, veins prominent, harshly hairy. **Flowers: In 2s**, clustered in upper nodes and terminally; flowers large, ± 36 mm, **lobes erect**, ± 30 x 25 mm, tips recurved, corona lobes free, spreading, **long, boat-shaped** (Nov-Dec).

Pachycarpus dealbatus [= *P. ligulatus*] **Tongued Pachycarpus, Tongued Thick-fruit; ishongwe, ukhatimuthi (Z)** (*dealbatus* - whitewashed, refers to the colour of some plants)
Erect herb, 150-500 mm. In grassland or in sparsely wooded thornveld, up to 1500 m, W Cape to Mpum. Stems **unbranched, stout**, ± hairy. **Leaves:** Spreading erect, shape variable, 40-110 x 10-42 mm, margins smooth, ± wavy, sticky. **Flowers:** 4-8 in ± stalkless inflorescences, terminally and at nodes; flowers 10-23 mm, corolla bell-shaped (hiding the column), **lobes erect**, 6-16 x 7-13 mm, reflexed at tips, corona lobes free, **spoon-shaped**, **without wings or flaps on upper surface**, corona distinctly dilated at tip, 3-6 mm, almost immediately erect and crowding the column (Nov-Mar). **Fruit:** Solitary, 50-100 mm, oval to spindle-shaped, tip rounded, surface with 6 toothed wings (KZN) or plain ridges (E Cape). **General:** *P. dealbatus* var. nov. Up to 600 mm, N KZN; flowers pale yellow-green with purple markings outside, ± 25mm, corolla shallow and cuplike (exposing the column), corona lobes linear from base, only slightly dilated at tip, 1-2,5 mm, spreading horizontally before becoming erect near tips (Dec-Feb).

***Pachycarpus natalensis* Natal Pachycarpus, Natal Thick-fruit; ishongwe elibomvu elikhulu (Z)**
Erect herb, 300-520 mm. In annually burnt grassland, often among rocks, 600-1200 m. Stems slender or stout, hairless to softly hairy. **Leaves:** Spreading-erect, 40-80 x 20-45 mm, margins flat with slightly thickened rim. **Flowers:** 2-5 in mostly stalkless inflorescences at nodes and terminally; flowers 14-21 mm, ± divided to base, hairless above, hairy below, lobes roundish, 11-17 x 5-11 mm, **spreading**, sometimes slightly reflexed, **with tips at least curved up** (Oct-Feb). **Fruit:** 90-100 x 25 mm, semi-inflated, surface 6 winged. **General:** Used in traditional medicine to treat stomach complaints and as an infusion sprinkled on eggs to prevent dogs eating them (it makes them violently ill).

Pachycarpus asperifolius

Tony Abbott

Pachycarpus asperifolius

Tony Abbott

Pachycarpus campanulatus

Tony Abbott

Pachycarpus concolor

Martin von Fintel

Pachycarpus coronarius

Geoff Nichols

Pachycarpus campanulatus

Martin von Fintel

Pachycarpus dealbatus

Lal Greene

Pachycarpus dealbatus var. nov.

Martin von Fintel

Pachycarpus natalensis

Martin von Fintel

Asclepias (Aesculapius, immortalised as god of medicine) - Perennial herbs with milky latex (for description see p. 416).

Asclepias brevicuspis Cusped Turret-flower (*brevi* - short; *cuspis* - with short, sharp point)
Herb, 130-430 mm. In grassland, 50-1500 m. **Stems reclining, tips erect. Leaves:** 12-100 x 0,3-5,5 mm, sparsely hairy, tips sharply pointed. **Flowers: In terminal inflorescence**; lobes 6,5-10 x 2,5-4,5 mm, pale mauve to greenish, corona long, narrow, reaching style tip, anther wing distinctly notched along its length (Aug-Feb). **Fruit:** Tip beaked, streaked darker green. **General:** Hybridises with *A. eminens*. **Similar species:** *A. navicularis* (see p. 418).

Asclepias brevipes Northern Meadow-star; Bokhorinkie (A) (*brevis* - short; *pes* - foot)
Perennial herb, 120-295 mm. In grassland, stony ground, up to 1600 m, KZN to N Prov. Stems annual, 1(3), **usually unbranched. Leaves:** 12-80 x **0,8-2 mm, margins rolled under**, covered in short, harsh hairs. **Flowers: Small, in 4s, at nodes and terminally**; flowers **starlike**, lobe tips turned up, ± 6 x 3 mm, **corona lobes slipper-shaped, small** (Sep-Dec). **Fruit:** 50-80 x 5-10 mm, tip narrowly beaked. **Similar species:** *A. stellifera* (see p. 418). Natural hybrids occur.

Asclepias cultriformis Satellite-dish; ishongwe elimpofu (Z) (*cultratus* - curved like a scimitar)
Perennial herb, 150-300 mm. In grassland, on stony slopes, up to 2100 m, KZN to N Prov. Stem solitary, annual; plant **covered in long white hairs. Leaves:** 25-50 x 6,5-16 mm. **Flowers:** Terminal inflorescence; lobes spreading, tips turned up, 12-14 x 8-11 mm, **densely hairy** on outer surface, margins fringed with long white hairs, corona large, **square and hooked on inner tip** (Nov-Jan). **General:** Roots collected in bundles, preserved in huts by smoke; pieces then burnt to ward off lightning.

Asclepias dregeana Button-heads (named after Johann Drège 1794-1881, German horticulturist, professional collector, in SA from 1826-1834)
Herb, 75-300 mm. In grassland, up to 1800 m. 1-3 erect, annual stems, **covered in short curved rusty brown hairs. Leaves:** 19-75 x 4-38 mm, margins sometimes tightly wavy. **Flowers: In nodding inflorescences; flowers green**, lobes 5,5-10 x 4-5,5 mm, corona lobes laterally compressed, ± square, appearing almost solid (Oct-Dec). **Fruit:** 75-115 x 12-20 mm, 4 serrated wings, tip bluntly beaked. **General:** 2 varieties differ in size, colour and corona lobe shape.

Asclepias eminens [= *Stenostelma eminens*] **Large Turret-flower; montsuku, motsoko (SS)**
(*eminens* - standing out, refes to the large, protruding corona)
Perennial herb, 160-370 mm. In grassland, on rocky hillsides, 600-1800 m, KZN to Zim. Annual stems, branched from base or **reclining, tips erect. Leaves:** 10-105 x 1-6 mm, sparse rough hairs or none, base eared. **Flowers: Terminal inflorescences**; lobes reflexed, 10-20 x 3-6 mm, **corona lobes very long, overtopping the style tip, anther wing with distinct notch along its length** (Nov-Jan). **Fruit:** 75-100 x 6-13 mm, narrowing to long pointed beak. **General:** Plant eaten raw, cooked as spinach, also boiled with milk, as a tonic. Flowers smaller in the north (Zim).

Asclepias praemorsa Sandstone Wire-stem (*praemorsus* - as if bitten, refers to corona lobe)
Perennial herb, 240-780 mm. In rocky grassland, on Natal Group Sandstone, coast to 450 m. **Stems annual, usually solitary, unbranched**, wiry, erect, nodes very long. **Leaves: Long, narrow**, 30-115 x 1-3 mm. **Flowers:** 4-10 in semi-hanging inflorescences; lobes 5-7 x 3-5 mm, **corona lobes sac-like, greatly overtopping the style tip, anther appendages large, straplike** (Sep-Feb).

Pentarrhinum (*penta* - 5; *rhinos* - nose, refers to corona lobes with horned appendages in *P. insipidum*) - Perennial twiner; leaves with conspicuous scars in axils; corona lobes free, with pointed hornlike tip. Afr, 2 species, 1 in SA.

Pentarrhinum insipidum African Heartvine; Donkieperske (fruit), **Hondepisbossie, Wildekomkommer (A)** (*insipidus* - tasteless)
Vine, stems 2-3 m. On forest margins, in woodland, coast to 2200 m. W Cape to Ethiopia. **Leaves: 230-650 x 200-500 mm**, weakly hairy, stalks 17-50 mm. **Flowers:** Inflorescences hanging at nodes; lobes reflexed, 4-6 x 2,5-3,5 mm, green to reddish purple (white form found in coastal KZN), corona ivory, yellow or orange, lobes erect, **fleshy, with long thin hornlike appendage** (Dec-Apr), fragrant, aromatic scent. **Fruit:** Erect, 55-85 x 15-20 mm, covered in 2-4 mm spines. **General:** Leaves, stems, fruits cooked all over Afr; flavour said to be nutty, peppery or like asparagus.

Asclepias brevicuspis

Asclepias cultriformis

Asclepias brevipes

Asclepias dregeana

Asclepias dregeana

Asclepias eminens

Asclepias praemorsa

Pentarrhinum insipidum

551

Cynanchum (*kynos* - dog; *ancho* - to strangle) - Perennial herbs, shrubs, vines. Some species poisonous to stock, some with insecticidal properties, anti-tumour activity and analgesic effects. Pantrop, ± 250 species, 12 in SA.

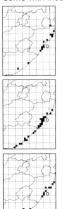

Cynanchum ellipticum [= *C. capense*] Common Dog-wort; Bobbejaantou, Klimop, Melktou (A) (*ellipticus* - elliptical, oval)

Vine, stems 2-3 m. In thicket, dune forest, coast to 1500 m, E Cape to Moz. **Leaves:** 20-40 x 10-20 mm, **soft, tips blunt, veins prominent below. Flowers:** Lobes 2-4 x 1 mm, tips slightly twisted, corona lobes fused, cuplike, gynostegial column **stalkless** (Mar-Sep), scented. **Fruit:** 45-60 x 6-8 mm. **General:** Causes livestock poisoning.

Cynanchum natalitium Natal Dog-wort; Klimop (A)

Vine. In dune forest or scrub. Stems woody at base, bark corky. **Leaves:** 20-50 x 15-35 mm, **semi-fleshy to ± leathery,** tips blunt to sharply pointed. **Flowers:** Lobes 3,5-5 x 1,5-2 mm, corona lobes fused, cuplike, margins 5 toothed, gynostegial column stalked (Mar-Jul), scented. **Fruit:** 40-45 x 5-8 mm. **General:** Reputedly a fish poison.

Cynanchum obtusifolium Poison Dog-wort; Bostou, Melk(bobbejaan)tou, Nenta (A); ishongwe-elinabawo (Z) (*obtusum* - blunt; *folium* - leaves)

Vine, stems up to 3 m. In dune forest, scrub. **Leaves:** 2-40 x 15-40 mm, **blunt,** with hairlike tips, **base rounded to heart-shaped. Flowers:** 3-4 x 1-1,5 mm, **corona lobes 5, free, toothlike, gynostegial column stalkless** (Jan-Jul), sweetly scented. **Fruit:** 40-50 x 10-12 mm, keeled and grooved, tip beaked. **General:** Used traditionally to treat illnesses caused by witchcraft and as charms against evil. Poisonous to stock.

Sarcostemma (*sarx* - fleshy; *stemma* - wreath, refers to corona) - Succulents; ± leafless; corona in 2 series, outer corona collarlike around base of 5 lobed, inflated inner corona. Trop, subtrop Afr, Asia, Austr, ± 15 species, 2 in SA.

Sarcostemma viminale Caustic Vine; Melktou, Spantou, Wolfsmelk (A); maphosa (Sw); ingotshwa (Sw,Z); umbelebele/umpelepele (X,Z) (*viminalis* - pertaining to twigs)

Vine, stems up to 7 m. In dry areas, Afr, Asia, Austr. **Stems succulent,** ± 6 mm diam, **grey-green,** older stems corky. **Leaves:** Reduced to scales. **Flowers:** Lobes 3,5-7 x 1,5-2 mm (all year, Dec-Jan), sweetly scented. **Fruit:** 64-180 x 6-8 mm, tips blunt. **General:** Young stems, fruit eaten as a relish, browsed by animals. Used in traditional medicine to treat heartburn, ulcers, septic sores, venereal disease, as a diuretic and to increase milk at lactation.

Secamone (from Arabic *squamone*, the name of *S. aegyptiaca*) - Climbers, scrambling shrubs; flowers small, corona lobes 5, small, simple, fleshy, 8 pollinia to a pollinarium; fruit paired. Trop, subtrop, Afr, Asia, Austr, ± 100 species, 5 in SA.

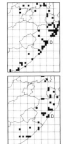

Secamone filiformis Narrow-leaved Secamone (*fili* - narrow; *formis* - form, refers to leaves)

Climber. In dry woodland, E Cape to Zim, Moz. Older stems woody. **Leaves: Narrow,** 9-35 x **2-10 mm,** hairless or with scattered reddish hairs, **silvery grey beneath,** with tiny bumps, midvein prominent. **Flowers:** Lobes 1-1,5 x 0,5-1 mm (blooms throughout year). **Fruit:** Paired, erectly spreading, slender, 40-60 x 3 mm.

Secamone gerrardii Gerrard's Secamone; ubuka (X); inhlule-lemamba, ugobandlovu, umhlonyise (Z) (named after William Gerrard, who collected the type specimen in the mid 1800s)

Woody climber. In forest, E Cape to N Prov. **Older stems woody, covered in large, winged, corky ridges. Leaves:** 20-55 x 7-20 mm, ± fleshy, **hairless. Flowers:** Lobes ± 5 x 1,5 mm, hairless, tips rounded (Sep-Jun), scented. **Fruit:** 60-80 x 10 mm. **General:** Used traditionally to treat chest pains, spinal complaints.

Sisyranthus (*sys* - pig; *anthos* - flower) - Perennial grasslike herbs; stems annual; flowers usually hairy on upper surface, corona lobes 5, ± free to base, fleshy, small appendage at tip; fruits paired, ± parallel. S Afr endemic, 14 species.

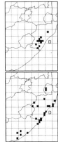

Sisyranthus trichostomus Hairy Grass-flower (*trich* - hairs; *stoma* - mouth, refers to flower tube)

Herb 350-600 mm. In grassland, 700-900 m, KZN endemic. **Leaves:** Spreading or reflexed, 50-165 x 1-2,8 mm, margins rolled under. **Flowers: In tightly clustered, roundish, terminal inflorescence;** lobes spreading, 2-4,5 x 2-3 mm, hairless, tube bell-like, 1,5-3 mm, **densely bearded in mouth,** hairs tinged yellow (Sep-Dec).

Sisyranthus virgatus Thin Grass-flower (*virgatus* - long, slender)

Herb up to 750 mm. In grassland. **Leaves:** 60-90 x 1 mm, margins minutely toothed. **Flowers: In loose inflorescences;** lobes 3 x 1,5 mm, **densely bearded, with long white hairs, forming tufts at tips,** corona lobes inflexed, overtopping the style tip (Sep-Apr). **Similar species:** *S. fanniniae* Flower lobes shorter, 2,5 mm, inner surface hairy at tips, hairless in middle, tube mouth hairy.

Cynanchum ellipticum

C J Ward

Cynanchum natalitium

Tony Abbott

Cynanchum obtusifolium

Wally Menne

Cynanchum obtusifolium

C J Ward

Sarcostemma viminale

Wayne Matthews

Secamone filiformis

C J Ward

Secamone gerrardii

Geoff Nichols

Sarcostemma viminale

Martin von Fintel

Sisyranthus trichostomus

Martin von Fintel

Sisyranthus cf. *fanniniae*

Tony Abbott

Sisyranthus cf. *virgatus*

Martin von Fintel

553

Brachystelma (*brachy* - short; *stelma* - crown, refers to the often extremely small corona) - Low-growing perennial herbs; stems usually annual, fleshy; roots or fleshy disclike stem tuber; milky latex; flower lobes fused, long or short, tube usually shorter than lobes, corona in 2 series; fruit spindlelike, solitary or paired, erect. Widely cultivated. Tubers of most species eaten by people and animals. Trop, subtrop Afr, Asia, Austr, most diverse in S Afr, over 100 species, ± 70 in SA.

Brachystelma natalense Natal Brachystelma

Herb, 250-500 mm. In grassland, on Natal Group Sandstone, KZN endemic. **Stem simple, erect** (± branched, if the main stem has been grazed). **Leaves:** 20-45 x 13-35 mm, 5 veined from base, margins entire, covered in white hairs, stalks ± 5 mm. **Flowers: Very small, nodding,** lobes spreading, 2-3 x 1,2 mm, tips pointed, green (Oct-Feb). **Fruit:** Solitary, 100-150 x 45 mm, narrowing gradually to a point. **General:** First collected in 1883. Thought to be extinct until recently rediscovered on the outskirts of Greater Durban. Threatened by development and grazing.

Brachystelma pygmaeum Pygmy Brachystelma (*pygmaeus* - pygmy, refers to dwarf habit)

Herb 40-80 mm. On rocky ridges in open grassland, up to 1000 m, E Cape to N Prov. Stems ± branched, shortly hairy. **Leaves:** 10-50 x 1,5-15 mm, margins flat, thinly hairy below, ± hairless above, **not fully developed at flowering. Flowers:** 1-3 in upper nodes; flower lobes spreading, 5-6 x 2 mm (Aug-Mar). **Fruit:** Erect, 50-60 x 4-5 mm. **General:** Subsp. *pygmaeum,* flower **lobe tips pointed, fused to form narrow cage** around tube mouth and gynostegial column. Subsp. *flavum,* flower **lobe tips free, not forming a cage.**

Ceropegia (*keros* - wax; *pege* - fountain) - Perennial, often twining, semi-succulent herbs (for description see p. 172).

Ceropegia cimiciodora Bedbug Ceropegia (*cimex* - scientific name for bedbug, refers to scent)

Succulent vine, up to 3 m. In thorn scrub, on sandy soil, KZN to N Prov. Stems sparingly branched, ropelike, twining, shiny grey speckled with green. **Leaves: Rudimentary. Flowers:** 1-2 from nodes, on short stems, ± 50 mm, mouth large, funnel-shaped, lobes free, **spreading, expanding, starlike,** ± 20 mm diam, stalks ± 8 mm (Nov), smell similar to that of bedbugs. **Fruit:** Paired, spreading-erect to reflexed, curved, long, thin, with knoblike tips.

Ceropegia pachystelma [= *C. undulata*] Bird-cage Ceropegia; Kombrua (A) (*pachy* - stout; *stelma* - crown, refers to the corona)

Soft vine, up to 3 m. Twining in bush clumps, KZN to Moz, Nam. Stems annual. **Leaves:** 50 x 30 mm, **± fleshy, margins ± wavy. Flowers:** Few to many, **opening in succession;** tube straight or curved, 15-25 mm, lobes 5-12 mm, **slender, tips joined to form a cage wider than the tube. Fruit:** Narrowly spindle-shaped, 60-140 mm. **General:** Flowers generously.

Ceropegia sandersonii Giant Ceropegia, Sanderson's Ceropegia (see p. 174)

Tenaris (*teina* - to stretch, refers to the flower lobes) - Perennial herbs (for description see p. 418).

Tenaris chlorantha (for description see under *T. rubella* p. 418)

Fockea (named after Hendrick Focke, 1802-1856, Dutch botanist from Bremen who collected in Surinam) - Perennial semi-succulent vines or shrublets; stem tuber large, fleshy, turnip-shaped, stems usually slender above, woody at base; corona and stamens inserted at mouth of tube, anther appendages inflated and pollinarium without translator arms. Some plants are apparently several centuries old, yet remain dwarf in stature. The large fleshy tubers can weigh more than 22 kg and are filled with water. The flesh can be turned into a sweet preserve. Arid areas, trop, subtrop, SA to Kenya, 11 species, 5 in SA.

Fockea tugelensis Tugela Fockea (named after the Tugela river valley in KZN where it was first collected)

Perennial herb, 150-460 mm. In dry areas, on stony hillsides on granite or lime-stone, KZN endemic. Stem tuber large, turnip-shaped, with white, soft, spongy, watery flesh. Several annual stems from base, mostly unbranched, erect or twining, sparsely covered in minute hairs. **Leaves:** ± erect, 25-50 x 4,5-9 mm, thinly hairy above and on prominent midrib below, **margins flat,** stalks 3,5-4,5 mm. **Flowers:** 2-6, in short stalked inflorescences clustered at nodes, opening successively; **flowers small,** divided 10-50% of length, **lobes short,** spreading, narrow, 2-8,5 x 1,5 mm, margin folded and twisted, **corona lobe tips 20-15 toothed,** stalks short (Nov-Apr). **Fruit:** Not yet known. **General:** This species is sometimes placed under *F. angustifolia.*

Brachystelma natalense

Geoff Nichols

Brachystelma pygmaeum

Martin Kunhardt

Ceropegia cimiciodora

Geoff Nichols

Ceropegia pachystelma

Martin von Fintel

Tenaris cf. *chlorantha*

Wally Menne

Fockea tugelensis

Trevor Coleman

Ceropegia sandersonii

Geoff Nichols

555

LAMIACEAE (LABIATAE) - Sage or Mint Family Herbs or shrublets, aromatic (for description see p. 470).
Ocimum (from the Greek and Latin *okimon* - an aromatic plant, basil) - Herbs or small shrubs; leaves gland dotted; flowers in whorls of 6, in terminal, spikelike inflorescences. Used medicinally and as a culinary herb. About 6 species, 2 indigenous to SA.

Ocimum gratissimum [= *O. urticifolium* subsp. *urticifolium*] **Wild Basil; umbijazane, umnandi, uqabukhulu (Z)** (*gratissimum* - very pleasing)
Erect perennial herb or soft shrub, up to 2 m. In woodland, SA to Trop Afr, S Asia.
Leaves: 25-120 x 12-65 mm, hairy, **margins toothed. Flowers:** In **dense**, slightly branched inflorescences, 50-150 mm, bracts persistent; flowers 4-5 mm, white, calyx **woolly** (Dec-Mar). **General:** Culinary herb, lemon or clove scented.
Similar species: *O. americanum* [= *O. canum*] Leaf margins entire; inflorescences elongate, flower clusters well spaced, calyx with straight white hairs.

RUBIACEAE - Gardenia/Coffee Family Herbs, shrubs or trees. Leaves opposite or whorled, stipules between leaf stalks. Petals united into a tube. Fruit crowned with persistent calyx. Economically important for several crops such as coffee, quinine and ornamentals such as Gardenias and Ixoras. Cosmop, ± 630 genera, ± 10200 species, 63 genera in SA.
Eriosemopsis (*eriosemopsis* - like *Eriosema*) - Erect herbs; rootstock woody; densely shaggy hairy, stipules small, joined at tip; flowers clustered in axils. Pondoland, KZN endemic, 1 species.

Eriosemopsis subanisophylla (*subanisophylla* - irregular, unequal leaves)
Up to 600 mm. In grassland, up to 800 m. Rare. **Leaves:** 40-60 x 30-40 mm, leathery to papery, hairy, strongly veined from base, veins protrude beneath. **Flowers:** In dense clusters in axils, stalks 10-30 mm, softly hairy; flowers ± 12 mm diam, calyx hairy (Oct-Feb).

Pygmaeothamnus (*pygmaios* - dwarf; *thamnos* - bush) - Perennial herbs; flowers clustered in axils. S Afr, ± 3 species.

Pygmaeothamnus chamaedendrum **Pygmy Medlar, Sand Apple; Goorappel (A); umgulutane, umkhuma (Sw)** (*chamaedendrum* - dwarf tree)
Perennial dwarf herb, up to 250 mm. In rocky places, up to 1980 m. Stems woody. **Leaves:** Clustered at top of stems, variable, **more or less hairy**, stipules scaly, with tuft of hairs. **Flowers:** In branching clusters, mostly below leaves; flowers ± 10 mm, greenish yellow, lobes curled backwards, pointed, tube short, ± 5 mm, calyx 5 lobed, hairless (Oct-Feb), scented. **Fruit:** Fleshy, ± 15 x 8 mm. **General:** Fruit edible.

Pachystigma (*pachys* - thick; *stigma* - stigma) - Dwarf shrubs or perennial herbs; leaves short stalked, stipules united; flowers clustered in axils, calyx as long as flower tube, calyx lobes leafy; fruit round, fleshy. S Afr, ± 10 species.

Pachystigma venosum [= *P. latifolium*] **Dwarf Medlar; igqulamntwana, isivithogwane (Z)** (*venosum* - poisonous)
Erect, robust shrublet, up to 650 mm. In grassland. Rootstock woody. Stems with few branches, **sparsely hairy or hairless. Leaves:** In 2s or 3s, ± 80 x 45 mm. **Flowers:** In axils of lowest leaves; flowers ± 8 mm diam, creamy green, **calyx lobes long, narrow** (Oct-Mar). **Fruit:** Round, smooth, green ripening dull brownish, crowned with persistent calyx. **General:** Fruit edible.

Anthospermum (*anthos* - flower; *sperma* - seed, the male flowers may carry a small ovary capable of producing seed) - Herbs, shrublets; leaves opposite or whorled; flowers small, 4 lobed. Afr, Madag, ± 39 species, ± 21 in SA.

Anthospermum herbaceum [=*A. lanceolatum*] (*herbaceum* - succulent stem, herblike)
Variable, straggling, trailing or erect herb, up to 1 m, or trailing stems ± 2,5 m, or a cushionlike mat. In grassland, moist thicket, on forest margins, SW Cape to Ethiopia. Thinly downy. **Leaves: In well spaced pairs, short leafy shoots in axils**, ± 55 x 25 mm. **Flowers:** Small, greyish yellow to reddish purple (throughout year), sweetly scented. **Similar species:** *A. hispidulum* Dwarf, stout shrub, up to 500 mm, covered in short, white, bristly hairs; leaves in dense whorls, lower leaves ± 10 x 3 mm, **margins rolled back.** *A. streyii* On rocky outcrops in grassland, KZN S Coast, prostrate, cushion forming; leaves needlelike, often curved, flowers larger.

Galium (*gala* - milk, used to curdle milk) - Herbs; leaves whorled, stipules leaflike. Cosmop, ± 400 species, ± 13 in SA.

Galium scabrelloides (*scabra* - rough)
Perennial shrublet, 0,5-1(1,2) m. On forest margins, in scrub. Stems climbing or trailing, mostly with white spreading hairs.Very variable. **Leaves:** In whorls, 15-20 x 1-4 mm, tips pointed, **white hairy, margins with coarse prickles, strongly rolled under. Flowers: In branching inflorescences**, flowers small, hairy outside, yellow, cream or greenish, lobes long, pointed. **Fruit:** Covered in **straight spreading hairs.**

Geoff Nichols

Ocimum gratissimum

Ocimum americanum

Geoff Nichols

Eriosemopsis subanisophylla

Tony Abbott

David Johnson

Pygmaeothamnus chamaedendrum

Tony Abbott

Anthospermum hispidulum

Tony Abbott

Anthospermum streyi

Geoff Nichols

Pachystigma venosum

Tony Abbott

Anthospermum herbaceum

Martin von Fintel

Galium scabrelloides

557

Rubia (*ruber* - red, refers to roots) - Scrambling or climbing herbs; roots woody; stems 4 angled, mostly with recurved prickles; leaves in whorls, with prominent veins; fruit fleshy. Europe, Asia, Afr, ± 60 species, ± 3 in SA.

Rubia cordifolia Sticky-leaved Rubia; Bruidskrans, Rooihoutjie, Vaskloubossie (A); mahlatsoa-meno, seharane (SS); intila-lubombo (Sw); impundisa, intwalalubombo, umalibombo (Z) (*cordifolia* - heart-shaped leaves)

Straggling herbaceous climber, stems up to 5 m. In shady places, coast to mountains, Afr to India. **Stems angled, rough with tiny prickles. Leaves: 4 whorled**, 25-55 x 5-30 mm, ± 5 veins from base, **veins and margins with prickles, stalks 15-60 mm. Flowers:** In branched inflorescences; flowers ± 5 mm diam, green (Mar-Dec). **Fruit:** Fleshy, ± 4 mm diam, purplish black. **General:** Used in traditional medicine as a mouthwash and to treat colic, sore throat, chest complaints, impotence, menstrual problems. Used by diviners to provide insight, protection. Love charm emetics.

CUCURBITACEAE - Cucumber/Pumpkin/Gourd Family Herbs, prostrate, trailing or climbing (for description see p. 308).
Gerrardanthus (named after William Gerrard, naturalist and traveller, collected in Natal in 1860, died in Madagascar in 1866) - Climbers; rootstock tuberous; fruit elongate, skin dry, papery. Afr, 2 species in SA.

Gerrardanthus macrorhizus isisema sehlathi (Z) (*macrorhizus* - long/big roots)

Woody climber, up to 8 m. In forest, up to 800 m. Tuber large, flattened, ± 1,5 m diam. Stems woody at base. **Leaves:** 3-7 lobed, 30-80 mm diam, hairless, lobes unequal. **Flowers:** Male: in clusters on short stem, flowers ±12 mm diam, brownish. Female: solitary (Feb-May). **Fruit:** 3 angled, ± 65 x 20 mm, brownish yellow, seeds winged. **General:** Used traditionally as a purgative for pregnant women.

Gerrardanthus tomentosus (*tomentosus* - densely covered in soft hairs)

Robust creeper, up to canopy. On rocky, forested slopes. Natal Group Sandstone endemic. Tuber huge, stems robust. **Leaves:** 5-7 lobed, 60-120 mm diam, shortly hairy above, densely hairy beneath. **Flowers:** Male: in clusters, stems slender ± 100 mm, bracts leafy, ± 10 mm, flowers ± 18 mm diam. Female: solitary or 3-4 in clusters (Feb-Mar). **Fruit: Narrowly bell-shaped, 10 veined, smooth**, 60-70 x 25 mm. **General:** Empty capsules look remarkably like bats. Tuber eaten by moles.

Zehneria (named after Joseph Zehner, an Austrian botanical artist) - Scrambling herbs (for description see p. 206).

Zehneria parvifolia (see p. 206)

Citrullus (*citrus* plus diminutive, refers to round fruit) - Annual or perennial herbs; leaves deeply 3-5 lobed. Afr, Asia, Medit, ± 5 species, ± 3 in SA.

Citrullus lanatus Bitter Melon, Common Wild Melon, Tsamma Melon; Bitterappel, Karkoer (A); kaate, lehapu, mokakaoane, semane tjoko (SS); litjoti (Sw); ibhece, ikhabe (Z) (*lanatus* - woolly or cottony)

Prostrate annual creeper, stems up to 10 m. In sandy grassland, indigenous in the Kalahari, naturalised worldwide. **Leaves:** 60-200 x 40-150 mm, rough, deeply lobed, margins lobed and finely toothed, stalks 40-120 mm. **Flowers:** Male and female solitary, on same plant, ± 30 mm diam greenish yellow (Nov-Apr). **Fruit:** 60-200 mm diam, shell hard, not woody, green mottled grey, flesh juicy. **General:** Fruit eaten raw or cooked, also made into a preserve, seeds ground to a meal. Used as a charm to prevent worms damaging crops.

Trochomeria (*trochos* - a wheel; *meris* - a part) - Scrambling or prostrate herbs (for description see p. 80).

Trochomeria hookeri (see p. 80)

Lagenaria (*lagena* - large flask; *aria* - fruit) - Vigorous herbaceous climbers (for description see p. 206).

Lagenaria sphaerica [=*L. mascarena*] Wild Melon; Wildekalbas (A); iselwa-makhosi, uselwa, uthangazane olukhulu (Z) (see p. 206)

ASTERACEAE (COMPOSITAE) - Daisy Family The largest family of flowering plants (for description see p. 208).
Ambrosia (*ambrosia* - food of Greek and Roman gods) - Mostly America, ± 35 species, some widespread weeds, 3 in SA.

★ *Ambrosia artemissiifolia* Ragweed (*artemissiifolia* - leaves like *Artemisia*)

Robust annual or short lived perennial herb, up to 2 m. In disturbed soils, coast to 1700 m (from America). Leaves finely dissected, softly hairy, aromatic or not. Male inflorescences in slender terminal spikes ± 100 mm. Female inflorescences clustered below male spikes (Oct-Apr). Browsed by stock.

558

Rubia cordifolia — Martin von Fintel

Gerrardanthus macrorhizus — Geoff Nichols

Gerrardanthus tomentosus — Richard Symmonds

Zehneria parvifolia — C J Ward

Gerrardanthus tomentosus — Geoff Nichols

Citrullus lanatus — Geoff Nichols

Trochomeria hookeri — C J Ward

Citrullus lanatus — Van Wyk & Malan

Lagenaria sphaerica — Jo Onderstall

★ *Ambrosia artemisiifolia* — C J Ward

MONOCOTYLEDONS - Single seed leaf, parallel veins; flower parts in threes or multiples of three.
TYPHACEAE (*typhos* - marsh; *typhe* - plant such as the Cat's Tail or Bulrush, used for stuffing beds) **- Bulrush Family**
Aquatic. Cosmop, 1 genus, ± 12 species, 2 in SA.

Typha capensis Bulrush; Papkuil (A); motsitla (SS); ingcongolo, umkhanzi (X); ibhuma (Sw,Z)

Perennial, up to 2,5 m, in large communities. Widespread along watercourses, in marshy areas. **Leaves:** Sheathing, 40-150 x 4-20 mm. **Flowers:** Upper spike: **male**, 150-300 mm, yellowish, soon shed. Lower spike: **female**, ± 180 mm, velvety dark brown (Dec-Mar). **Fruit:** Inflorescence bursts open to release tiny fluffy wind-dispersed seeds. **General:** Birds use leaves and stems to support and build nests. Root, lower stem and new shoots edible. Leaves used for thatch, mats and baskets. Fluffy seed used to stuff pillows. Widely used traditionally to treat venereal diseases, diarrhoea, urinary problems, bleeding, swelling and as an aid in expulsion of afterbirth.

CYPERACEAE - Sedge Family Grasslike herbs usually found near water or damp areas. Stems triangular or cylindrical, solid, mostly without joints (grass stems jointed, often hollow). Leaves present, in 3 ranks or reduced to tubular sheaths. Flowers small, clustered in spikelets on upright or spreading branches or in heads, forming collectively an inflorescence. Cosmop, ± 98 genera, ± 4350 species, 40 genera in SA. (See p. 502)
Cyperus (*kypeiros* - a rush or sedge) - Cosmop, ± 650 species, ± 70 in SA.

Cyperus compressus (*com* - together; *pressus* - pressed)

Annual, up to 300 mm tufted. In damp areas or weed of cultivation. Roots fibrous. **Leaves:** Basal, grasslike, grey-green, sheaths often reddish. **Flowers:** Inflorescence a single head, or with one to several rays that also carry heads of 3-6 flattened, greyish green to reddish brown, neat spikelets. **General:** Decorative container plants.

Cyperus crassipes (*crassus* - thick; *pes* - foot)

Robust perennial, up to 500 mm. Natural in seashore sands in Maputaland, trop, not found further south. Strong rhizome and elongate stolons. **Leaves:** Basal, 3-10 mm wide, bright green. **Flowers:** Inflorescence a head with short or longer branches carrying many spikelets, ± 25 mm x 3-4 mm, bracts several, ± 25 mm.

Cyperus denudatus Winged Sedge (*denudatus* - stripped of leaves or hairs)

Perennial, up to 600 mm. In permanent water of swamps and streams, sometimes in wet depressions in grassland, E Cape to Trop Afr. Rhizome thick, woody. **Leaves:** Usually leafless, reduced to stem sheaths, bright green. **Flowers:** Inflorescence branches spreading; flowerheads shiny golden brown, bracts short, stem **conspicuously 3 angled, becoming winged** (Sep-Jun). **General:** The winged stem is the main photosynthetic organ of the plant. **Similar species:** *C. sphaerospermus* (see p. 504).

Cyperus dives [= *C. immensus*] Giant Sedge; likhwane (Sw); ikhwane, insikane (Z) (*dives* - rich or plentiful)

Robust perennial, up to 2 m, in large colonies. In marshy areas, on riverbanks, E Cape to Trop Afr. **Leaves:** Basal, ± 2000 x 25 mm, bright green, **margins sharply toothed**. **Flowers:** Inflorescence ± 200 mm diam, branches smooth, spreading, **bracts rough edged**, stem stout, 3 angled, **sharp edged**; spikelets **yellowish green to golden brown** (Sep-Apr). **General:** Used to make sleeping mats. Clearing of streambank vegetation for sugar cane has encouraged the spread of this species. Host to the destructive Eldana Beetle, *Eldana saccharina*.

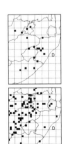

Cyperus haematocephalus (*haimatos* - blood red; *cephalus* - head)

Slender perennial, up to 800 mm. In damp places in grassland. **Leaves:** ± 400 x 5 mm. **Flowers:** Inflorescence with 4-6 rays; flowerheads round; spikelets compressed, congested, greenish brown to dark greyish brown, stems slender, 3 angled below inflorescence.

Cyperus longus Waterbiesie (A); indawo (Z) (*longus* - long)

Robust perennial, 600-800 mm. In shallow, periodically inundated depressions in grassland, usually rooted where water is deepest, SA to Medit. Stoloniferous. **Leaves:** 7-10 mm wide, 2 main veins parallel with midrib. **Flowers:** Inflorescences compound or simple; spikelets long, narrow, rich dark brown, overtopped by leaflike bracts, ± 200 mm, stem 3 angled. **General:** Used in traditional medicine to treat colds and stomach ailments in children. Sap reputed to be poisonous.

Typha capensis

Cyperus crassipes

Cyperus compressus

Cyperus dives

Cyperus haematocephalus

Cyperus dives

Cyperus denudatus

Cyperus longus

561

Cyperus prolifer Dwarf Papyrus (*prolifer* - producing offsets)

Perennial, 0,45-1 m, in colonies. Coastal, in well aerated water of streams and marshes, NE Cape, up E coast of Afr, islands off E Afr coast. Rhizome short. **Leaves:** Reduced to sheaths. **Flowers:** Inflorescence round, ± 150 mm diam, stem 3 angled or roundish, bracts short (Sep-May). **General:** Very attractive garden plant.

Cyperus rotundus Purple Nut Sedge, Nut-grass (*rotundus* - round)

Perennial, up to 250(500) mm. In moist, disturbed places; widespread weed, cosmop. Rhizome slender, tuberous. **Leaves:** Basal, often blue-green below, grasslike. **Flowers:** Inflorescence a head of one to few dark purplish black spikelets (Nov-Mar). **General:** Widely used in traditional medicine around the world. This species, with *C. esculentus,* is reputed to be one of the most formidable weeds in KZN and most of the world, spreading rapidly by means of small tubers. Very variable. A second widespread form is a coastal weed, N of Durban; more robust; inflorescence larger, spikelets brown to reddish green.

Cyperus rupestris Russet Rock Sedge (*rupestris* - rock dwelling)

Perennial 60-150 mm, in dense tufts. Widespread in shallow soil over rock or on rocky ground up to 2100 m. **Leaves:** Basal, wiry or succulent, ± 17 mm wide. **Flowers:** Inflorescence of shiny dark reddish brown spikelets, bracts ± 70 mm, stem 3 angled at top, persistent brown leaf sheaths at base (summer). **General:** A variable species in need of further study. Coastal plants (on sandstone) differ from those in midlands and uplands, with changes too from north to south.

Cyperus semitrifidus (*semi* - half; *trifidus* - cut into three parts)

Erect, tufted, sparsely leafy perennial, up to 300 mm. In shallow soil on rocky outcrops. Rhizome woody, stems bulbous woody at base. Variable. **Leaves:** Curved outwards, ± 250 x 1-4 mm. **Flowers:** Rays ± 30 mm; spikelets reddish to dark purplish black, stem 3 angled at top.

Pycreus (anagram of *Cyperus*) - Cosmop. About 120 species, ± 21 in SA.

Pycreus nitidus leya-butle, motaoa-taoane (SS); ikhwane, intsekane (Z) (*nitidus* - shining)

Robust perennial, up to 300 mm, often forming floating mats over water. On margins of swamps, streams and estuaries, E Cape to Trop Afr. Stolons long, covered in leaf sheaths. **Leaves:** Basal and along stems, bright green. **Flowers:** Inflorescence branched, at tip of bare portion of stem, spikelets shiny dark brown (summer). **General:** Rhizomes dried and threaded into necklets or placed among garments for their scent. Used in traditional medicine to treat chest colds. **Similar species:** *P. macranthus* Robust; inflorescence usually unbranched. *P. mundii* Blue-green leaves, not as robust nor as wide; flowerheads not shiny.

Pycreus polystachyos inconcodwane (Sw) (*polystachyos* - having many spikes)

Perennial (sometimes short lived), erect, 0,6-1 m, tufted. Common at coast in moist areas including slightly saline conditions, and in warm temp regions throughout the world. **Leaves:** Basal, flat, wavy, ± 300 x 3 mm. **Flowers:** Inflorescence a head of dense, greenish golden brown clusters, stem sharply angular (throughout year).

Cyperus prolifer

Cyperus semitrifidus

Cyperus rupestris

Cyperus rotundus

Pycreus nitidus

Pycreus macranthus

Pycreus polystachyos

Mariscus (old name used by Pliny for a rush) - *Mariscus* is doubtfully distinct from *Cyperus*. More or less cosmop, ± 200 species, ± 32 in SA.

Mariscus solidus (solidus - solid)
Robust perennial, up to 1,5 m, densely tufted. Along watercourses, in fringing grassland, coast and inland. Rhizome thick, woody. **Leaves:** Basal, many, ± 15 mm wide, faintly bluish green, rough. **Flowers:** Massive inflorescence, with bracts, many rays carrying heads of narrow, coarse spikelets.

Ficinia (named after Heinrich Ficinus, a German botanist) - Afr, mainly SA, predominantly S Cape, ± 60 species.

Ficinia cinnamomea (cinnamome - cinnamon coloured)
Slender and straggling or erect leafy perennials, 100-310 mm, loosely tufted. In damp grassland or on rock. Well developed stolons. **Leaves:** ± 200 mm. **Flowers:** Solitary flowerhead with 5-10 spikelets ± 8 mm, pale brown, upper sheath leafless, lower pale brown, long, bristly, bracts 2, lower 25-75 mm, suberect.

Fuirena - More or less cosmop in warmer areas, ± 40 species, 14 in SA.

Fuirena hirsuta (hirsuta - hairy)
Perennial, 400-600(1,2) m. In damp or wet conditions in coastal areas, on flood-plains. Rhizome woody, 3-8 mm diam, stems ± 20 mm apart. **Leaves:** 100-150(280) x 4-9 mm, more or less hairy. **Flowers:** In 1-3 terminal heads, 6-20 mm wide, congested, spikelets ± 8 x 4 mm. Stems round or bluntly 3 angled (Aug-Apr).

Fuirena pachyrrhiza (pachys - thick; rhiza - root)
Perennial, up to 1,5 m. In damp places along streamlets, in tall vegetaion on dune forest margins. Rhizome ± 7 mm wide, horizontal, woody, with leafy stems. **Flowers:** Inflorescence a series of branches on stems, carrying small groups of dark, spiky spikelets. **General:** In other regions plants shorter, spikelets longer, less spiky (resembling *F. pubescens*).

Scirpus (scirpus - a rush, bulrush)- Diverse genus with ± 300 species worldwide. Presently undergoing breakdown into smaller genera. Strictly no species in SA. The SA species are now under *Schoenoplectus*, *Bolboschoenus* and other genera not included here.

Scirpus ficinioides (ficinioides - resembling Ficinia)
Robust, 450-600 mm. On damp, marshy ground, up to 3000 m, fairly widespread in SA. Rhizome slightly elongate. **Leaves:** Basal, inconspicuous. **Flowers:** Head compact, sometimes branched, stem firm, rounded. **General:** Indicator of under-ground water.

Schoenoplectus (schoinos - a rush; plektos - twisted) - Transferred from *Scirpus*. About 18 species in SA.

Schoenoplectus corymbosus [= Isolepis corymbosa, Scirpus corymbosus, S. inclinatus] roro-ro-ea-mokhoabo (SS); inchoboza (Sw) (corymbosus - clusters of flowers)
Robust, perennial 1-2 m, often partially submerged. In marshy areas, on banks of rivers, streams and dams, up to 1900 m. **Leaves:** Reduced to sheaths at base. **Flowers:** Inflorescence branched, reddish brown, with short, hard, pointed bract, stem cylindrical (late summer). **General:** Used for weaving.

Schoenoplectus scirpoides [= Schoenoplectus littoralis, Scirpus littoralis] Wand Sedge; Steekbiesie (A); ingqumbe (Z) (scirpoides - rushlike)
Perennial, up to 2,8 m. Growing in large estuarine communities, usually partially submerged. Rhizome well developed. **Leaves:** None, or occasionally developing under water. **Flowers:** Inflorescence branched, golden brown (throughout year). **General:** Used to construct fish traps but lacks the fibrous nature suitable for weaving.

Mariscus solidus

Mariscus solidus

Ficinia cinnamomea

Scirpus ficinioides

Schoenoplectus corymbosus

Fuirena pachyrrhiza

Fuirena hirsuta

Schoenoplectus scirpoides

565

Isolepis (*iso* - equal; *lepis* - a scale) - About 27 species in SA.

Isolepis prolifera [= *Scirpus prolifer*] **Trailing Sedge; incapha (Z)** (*prolifera* - proliferates from the inflorescence)
Perennial, tufted, up to 450 mm. Colonises damp bare sand, grassland, E Cape to Moz. **Leaves:** Reduced to sheaths. **Flowers:** Small, compact heads. **General:** Cultivated as a garden plant in SA.

Bolboschoenus (from the Greek *bolbos* - a bulb; *schoinos* - a rush, a reed) - Cosmop, ± 15 species, 3 in SA.

Bolboschoenus glaucus **Mzinene Club Rush; Snygras (A)** (*glaucus* - blue-green, grey)
Robust perennial, up to 1,5 m. In riverine vleis in organic rich, black soil, N KZN to Trop Afr. Rhizome elongate, tuberous at stem bases. **Flowers:** Inflorescence with rays carrying clusters of spiky, cylindrical spikelets ± 50 mm, stems 3 angled, leafy. **General:** Recently separated from *B. maritimus*.
Similar species: *B. maritimus* [= *Scirpus maritimus*] **Snygras (A)** W Cape to Transkei (E Cape); inflorescence more variable, either a solitary spikelet, a compact head or branched with rays, spikelets shorter, broader, less spiky. A European species, possibly of early introduction to S Afr by migrating wetland birds and/or man. Long naturalised. Fruits used as food source by early man.

Eleocharis (from the Greek *heleos* - marsh, *charis* - delight, grace, beauty) - Cosmop, ± 250 species, 15 in SA.

Eleocharis dregeana **Finger Sedge; sechaba (SS)** (named after Johann Drège, 1794-1881, German horticulturalist, botanical collector and traveller who came to the Cape in 1826 with brother Carl and set up as collectors)
Perennial, mostly up to 300 mm. In marshes, flowing or standing water, often partly submerged, mostly midlands and uplands, up to 2450 m. Rhizome with closely packed stems forming tuft. **Leaves:** Reduced to stem sheaths. **Flowers:** Inflorescence spikelet solitary, ± 20 mm, usually less, stems slightly flattened. **General:** Very variable, inadequately known, often confused with other species of the genus, particularly *E. palustris* which is probably a species of the N Hemisp.

Eleocharis limosa (*limosa* - full of mud)
Perennial up to 1 m, tufted. In moist places, river banks, swamps. Elongated rhizome. **Flowers:** Inflorescences whitish to greyish brown, 15-36 mm, stems round, 3-5(10) mm diam, bluish green (Aug-Mar). **General:** Flower parts eaten by juvenile Long-horned grasshoppers and a small beetle. Heads often proliferate.

Fimbristylis (from the Greek *fimbria* - a fringe; *stylis* - style) - More or less cosmop in warm and temp regions, ± 200 species, ± 10 in SA.

Fimbristylis complanata (*complanata* - flattened)
Perennial up to 350 mm. Common and widespread in dense stands in moist coastal and inland grassland. Rhizome compact. Variable in robustness. **Flowers:** Inflorescence rayed, less often headlike, spikelets dark brown, 5-8(12) x 2 mm, style branches 3. Nutlets tiny, whitish when ripe. Stems closely packed, flattened, often twisted, dark green, **ligule a fringe of short hairs**.

Fimbristylis obtusifolia (*obtusus* - blunt; *folia* - leaves)
Perennial, sparsely tufted, 50-700 mm. Coastal dunes, in estuarine and low-lying grassland, usually where there is input of fresh water, widespread worldwide. **Leaves:** In basal rosette, short, stiff, slightly succulent, pale green, blunt tipped, brown sheathed at base. **Flowers:** Inflorescence with each ray bearing a compact, dark brown head of small spikelets (Oct-May).

Isolepis prolifera

Bolboschoenus glaucus

Bolboschoenus maritimus

Eleocharis limosa

Eleocharis limosa

Eleocharis dregeana

Fimbristylis complanata

Fimbristylis obtusifolia

567

Bulbostylis (*bolbos* - a bulb; *stylos* - a style, refers to bulbous base of styles) - Fairly cosmop in warm to temp regions, ± 120 species, ± 15 in SA.

Bulbostylis hispidula [= *Fimbristylis hispidula*] (*hispidus* - shaggy or rough)

Annual, 20-400 mm. Frequent in moist sand as a pioneer, often a weed of cultivation. Extremely variable in size, robustness, hairiness. **Flowers:** Inflorescence with 1-6(20) spikelets, angled by triangular nuts at maturity (Jul-Apr).

Cladium (*cladium* - branch or sprout) - Stems and leaves used to make paper in Danube delta. Small genus of 2-3 species, Canada, N America, Afr, Europe.

Cladium mariscus (*mariscus* - a type of rush)

Robust perennial up to 2,5 m. In stands, on margins of swamps, near streams. Rhizome ± 10 m diam, with stolons. **Flowers:** Inflorescence a series of heavy clusters of small spikelets; stems with many, wide, rough leaves.

Rhynchospora (*rhyncho* - beaked; *spora* - seed) - Cosmop, mainly American, ± 225 species, ± 8 in SA.

Rhynchospora corymbosa Saw Grass (*corymbosa* - flowers in flat topped clusters)

Robust perennial up to 2 m. Coastal, lowland marshy areas, up to 1000 m. **Leaves:** Basal and on flowering stem, broad, bright green, keeled. **Flowers:** Inflorescence branched, spiky golden brown flower clusters (throughout year). **Similar species:** *Carpha glomerata* Inflorescence less spiky.

Scleria (*scleros* - hard*)* - More or less cosmop, mostly in trop and subtrop regions, ± 200 species, 20 in SA.

Scleria angusta Swamp Forest Scleria (*angusta* - narrow)

Robust perennial, 1,3-2,5 m, in clumps. In water, in shade of relic patches of coastal swamp forest. Rhizome elongated. **Leaves:** On stems, **pleated**, ± 16 mm wide, **tip appears to be bitten or chewed off. Flowers:** Inflorescence branched, spikelets compact, 35-60 mm. **Fruit:** Smooth, white with purple markings. **General:** Decorative ornamental.

Scleria natalensis

Perennial, 500-850 mm. In seasonally damp, open or semi-shaded places. Rhizome reddish brown. **Leaves:** 4-11 mm wide, sheath with tongue 2-5 mm. **Flowers:** Inflorescence with terminal cluster 25-65 x 15-20 mm and smaller side clusters; 2-4 per node at 2-3 nodes, exserted 30-230 mm from sheaths, bracts leafy.

Scleria poiformis

Stout perennial, 1,3-1,8 m. In open shallow lakes and pans on coastal plain, N KZN to Moz, Madag, India, Malaysia, Philippines, N Austr. Rhizome elongate, 5-17 mm thick. **Leaves:** Mostly crowded towards base, 20-40 mm wide, ± 5 mm thick at base, sheaths usually split almost to base. **Flowers:** Inflorescence a solitary, terminal cluster, 100-200 x 50-120 mm, spikelets reddish brown.

Carex (*caric* - sedge) - A genus that has provided evidence for the great evolutionary age of the sedges, producing fruits that hardly differ from remains identified from Tertiary strata 70-30 million years before the present time. Cosmop in moist temp climates, also Arctic and Antarctic regions. Mostly N Hemisp, ± 1700 species, ± 19 in SA.

Carex cognata Nodding Sedge; Knikkende Rietgras (A) (*cognatus* - related)

Perennial, 0,5-1 m, tufted. Widespread in open marshy areas, on river banks, up to 2500 m, E Cape to Tanz. **Leaves:** Basal, ± 600 x 10 mm. **Flowers:** Inflorescence 50-70 mm, with 5-7 pale golden brown spikes, each drooping on slender stalk. Occasionally stalks are short so that spikes are upward pointing (Nov-Feb).

Carex zuluensis

Robust perennial, up to 1 m. Frequent amongst shrubs in rough grassland on forest margins, often on steep east and south facing slopes, in shade of forest and plantations. **Leaves:** Margins and keel rough. **Flowers:** In dense spikes, 50-150 mm. **Similar species:** *C. spicato-paniculata* Difficult to separate without dissection.

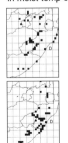

Bulbostylis hispidula   C J Ward

Cladium mariscus   C J Ward

Cladium mariscus   C J Ward

Rhynchospora corymbosa   Nolly Zaloumis

Scleria natalensis   C J Ward

Scleria poiformis   C J Ward

Scleria angusta   Nolly Zaloumis

Scleria angusta   Nolly Zaloumis

Scleria poiformis   Nolly Zaloumis

Carex cognata   Nolly Zaloumis

Carex zuluensis   Tony Abbott

ARACEAE - Arum Lily Family 'Petal' is a modified leaf called a spathe (for description see p. 340).
Gonatopus (*gonion* - angle or knee; *pous* - a foot, refers to the kneelike swelling on the leaf stalk) **- Leaves solitary, pinnately to 4 pinnately lobed. Trop and subtrop Afr, ± 5 species, 2 in SA.**

Gonatopus angustus [= *G. rhizomatosus*] **Celery Arum** (*angustus* - narrow, small)

Up to 600 mm. In dune forest, bushveld, KZN to Moz, Malawi. **Horizontal rhizome** ± 200 x 30 mm or longer. **Leaves: Solitary, 2-4 pinnate,** blade ± 200 mm; leaflets ± 80mm, **forming wing on to rachis. Flowers:** Usually 1 spathe, ± 70 mm, green to creamy pink with black streaks, soon drying up; spadix ± 50 mm, white, stem ± 250 mm, mottled grey-green (Nov-Feb). **General:** Not often seen in flower.

Gonatopus boivinii **Sandforest Arum** (named after Louis Boivin, French botanical collector)

Robust, up to 1,2 m. In sand forest, forest amongst rocks, N KZN to Trop Afr. Tuber ± 120 mm diam, **round. Leaves: Solitary, 3 pinnate,** lowest 300-450 mm; leaflets ± 75 mm, stalk sturdy, bent at middle, finely speckled, with green-brown horizontal bands. **Flowers:** 1-5, spathe ± 220 x 40 mm, dull greenish yellow on outer surface, white streaked grey-brown within, spadix creamy yellow, ± 150 mm, stem ± 350 mm (Nov-Dec). **General:** Interesting shade plant for subtrop conditions.

RESTIONACEAE - Cape Reed Family Resembles some sedges but rhizomes creeping, stems solid. Leaves seldom present, split leaf sheath rolled around stem at each node. Unisexual flowers hidden by bracts, male and female often on separate plants. S Hemisp, ± 41 genera, ± 420 species, mostly SW Cape in SA, ± 28 genera, ± 320 species. ***Restio*** (*restis* - a rope or cord, refers to early use of restios) - Austr, SA, ± 150 species, ± 80 in SA.

Restio zuluensis **Zulu Restio**

Up to 400 mm. In seasonally waterlogged swamps, marshy areas. Creeping rhizomes ± 3 mm diam. **Leaves:** Solid, round stems, branching, ± 9,5 mm diam; sheaths 7-12 mm, pale brown with fine red speckling, upper margin translucent. **Flowers:** (Dec). **General:** This is the only *Restio* species found in a subtrop area.

Calopsis (*kalos* - beautiful; *opsis* - sight) - Rushlike plants; stems branching. Mostly SW Cape, 24 species in SA.

Calopsis paniculata (*panicula* - a tuft)

Along streams in marshy areas, Cape to S KZN, probably restricted to sandstone, rare above 600 m. Stems olive green. **Leaves:** Sterile stems leafy, sheaths 25 mm. **Flowers:** Inflorescence much branched, 150-200 mm; floral bracts overlapping, internodes not elongated.

JUNCACEAE - Rush Family Petals dry and scaly. Stems solid or hollow. Leaves grasslike, soft and flat or hard and cylindrical, often reduced to an open or tubular sheath. Cosmop, 8 genera with ± 315 species, 3 genera in SA.
Prionium (*prion* - saw) - Plant with fibrous stem, leaves in spiral rosette. Genus with 1 species endemic to SA.

Prionium serratum **Palmiet; intsikane (X)** (*serratus* - serrated)

Robust, semi-aquatic, up to 2 m, in large stands. In marshy coastal areas, E Cape to C Afr. **Main stem:** 50-100 mm diam, with **fibrous black leaf bases. Leaves:** Arranged spirally, ± 1000 x 80 mm, thick, leathery, grey-green, margins and keel sharply serrated. **Flowers:** In much branched inflorescence, ± 500 mm; flowers small, brown (Sep-Dec). **General:** Decorative. Used for stabilising streambanks. Fibrous black leaf sheaths often washed up on beaches.

Juncus (*juncus* - rush) - Leaves closely resemble grasses and sedges. Cosmop, ± 250 species, ± 22 in SA.

Juncus kraussii **Matting Rush; incema (Sw,Z)** (after Christian Krauss, 1812-1890, collector)

Perennial, up to 1,5 m, in large colonies. In brackish marshes, S Afr, Austr, S America. **Leaves:** Tough, round, spine tipped; **sheath shiny black. Flowers:** Purplish brown, topped by spine tipped bract (Oct-Feb). **General:** Decorative garden plant. Important commercially, leaves and stems used to weave sleeping mats and beer strainers. Bundles of stems and/or mats are traditional gifts at Zulu weddings.

Juncus lomatophyllus **Leafy Juncus** (*lomatos* - fringe; *phyllon* - leaves)

Robust perennial, up to 1 m, in colonies. Near streams, in marshes, coast to uplands, widespread, SW Cape to Zim. Stolons spreading, leafy. **Leaves:** In basal rosette, ± 200 x 15 mm, smooth pale green, flat, soft, base reddish. **Flowers:** In much branched inflorescence; flowers dark brown (summer, throughout year in NE KZN). **General:** Very attractive. Grazed by hippopotamus.

Wally Menne

Geoff Nichols

Gonatopus angustus

Geoff Nichols

Gonatopus angustus

Wayne Matthews

Gonatopus boivinii

Wally Menne

Restio zuluensis

Tony Abbott

Calopsis paniculata

Rick Taylor

Juncus kraussii

René Glen NBI

Juncus lomatophyllus

Tony Abbott

Prionium serratum

571

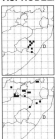

ASPHODELACEAE - (for description see p. 224). **Kniphofia** - **Red-hot Pokers** (for description see p. 226) .

Kniphofia brachystachya Poker (brachystachya - bearing short spikes)
Slender, up to 650 mm, solitary or in small groups. In moist mountain grassland up to 2400 m. **Leaves:** Erect, rigid, ± **280 x 12 mm,** shallowly keeled. **Flowers: In dense inflorescence,** ± 90 x 15 mm, bracts oval, brown to purplish brown; buds erect, brownish, **flowers ± 5 mm,** dull yellow to purplish brown (Nov-Jan).

Kniphofia typhoides Bulrush Poker (typha - bulrush, inflorescence resembles this plant)
Up to 750 mm, solitary or in small groups. In marshy areas, 1300-1800 m. **Leaves: Arranged in a fan, 350-650** x 8-25 mm, **blue-green, erect,** bending near tip, slightly keeled, slightly twisted. **Flowers: In dense inflorescence, 150-300 x 15-25 mm,** tip rounded, **bracts rounded**; buds erect, flowers small, 4-6 mm, brown to purplish brown, erect or spreading (Feb-Mar), faintly scented.

SMILACACEAE - Tough, spiny scramblers with tendrils. Rhizome woody. Leaves with flat blade and a stalk. Male and female flowers on separate plants. Fruit a berry. Trop, subtrop, 3 genera, ± 320 species, 1 genus in SA. **Smilax** (smilax ancient Greek name of obscure meaning) Description same as for family. One species in SA.

Smilax anceps [= S. kraussiana] **Thorny Rope, Leg-ripper; Doringtou, Wag-'n-bietjie-klimop, Wyfieklimop (A); inchachabutane (Sw); iyala, iyali, ingungwa, ingqaqa-bulani, inkunkwa, ulimi-lwenyathi (Z)** (anceps - 2 edged, flattened, compressed)
Scrambling climber. In grassland, thicket, forest, E Cape to E Afr. Thorns sharp, hooked; tendrils paired. **Leaves:** 60-100 x 30-60 mm, coppery when young. **Flowers:** Clusters ± 30 mm diam; flowers ± 10 mm, creamy green (throughout year). **Fruit:** ± 5 mm diam, red to purplish black. **General:** Widely used elsewhere in Afr to treat numerous ailments. (See p. 514)

IRIDACEAE - **Iris Family** Corms or rhizomes (for description see p. 236). **Gladiolus** (for description see p. 238).

Gladiolus dalenii African Gladiolus, Natal Lily (see p. 44, 516)

Gladiolus ecklonii Sheathed Gladiolus; kxahla, litsoantsoang, makhabebe (SS); sidvwana (Sw) (named after Christian Ecklon, 1795-1868, apothecary, traveller and plant collector)
0,35-1 m. In grassland, coast to 2250 m, E Cape to Bots. Corms **15-50 mm** diam, fibrous tunic brown, ± 60 mm up stem. **Leaves:** In stiff spreading fan, ± 240 x 30 mm, margins red or yellow, or ± 700 x 15 mm, no conspicuous margins, **midrib curved at base. Flowers:** 6-14, **bracts large, 35-110 mm, keeled**; tepal lobes ± 60 mm, silvery white, **densely speckled** red-brown, grey or mauve, with green or yellow blotch on lower lobes (Dec-Apr), sweetly scented. **Fruit:** Capsule ± 30 mm. **General:** Corms eaten raw or cooked. Used traditionally to treat rheumatic pain.

Gladiolus woodii sidvwana (Sw) (named after John Medley Wood, 1827-1915, botanist)
Up to 600 mm. In grassland, on rocky hillsides, 800-2000 m. Corm ± 30 mm diam, fibrous tunics extend up neck ± 70 mm. **Leaf: Solitary, basal,** ± 600 x 8 mm, hairy, margins, midrib prominent, **produced after flowers**; stem leaves ± 260 mm. **Flowers:** ± 25 mm, yellowish, pale blue, dark maroon or red-brown, lower tepal lobes yellowish, bracts ± 20 mm (Sep-Dec). **Fruit:** Capsule ± 10 mm. (See p. 112, 240)

ORCHIDACEAE - **Orchid Family** (for description see p. 240). **Satyrium** - Terrestrial herbs (for description see p. 362).

Satyrium parviflorum Devil Orchid; ilabatheka elikhulu elibomvu, impimpi enkulu (Z) (parviflorum - small flowers)
Slender to robust, 0,15-1,3 m. In grassland, coast to 2300 m, S Cape to Trop Afr. **Leaves:** Basal, ± 300 x 100 mm, from separate shoot or at base of flowering stem, often withered at flowering. **Flowers:** Inflorescence ± 300 mm; flowers **yellowish green** tinged dark maroon, **drying brown soon after opening,** spurs ± 15 mm (Sep-Mar), sweetly scented. **General:** Used as protective and love charms (See p. 520).

Monadenia (monos - single; adenos - a gland, refers to the single gland of the pollinia) - Afr, ± 16 species in SA.

Monadenia brevicornis (brevicornis - with short horns)
200-600 mm. Widespread in grassland, up to 2500 m, E Cape to Malawi, Madag. **Leaves:** Clasping at base, narrow, ± 80 mm. **Flowers:** In long, narrow, crowded inflorescence; flowers greenish or yellowish, dull red on back of hood and base of lip, **spur ± 11 mm, club-shaped, pointed** (Sep-Apr).

Lal Greene

Lal Greene

Martin von Fintel

Kniphofia brachystachya　　　　　　　*Kniphofia brachystachya*　*Kniphofia typhoides*

C J Ward

Lal Greene

Lal Greene

Smilax anceps　　　　　　　*Gladiolus ecklonii*　　　　　　　*Monadenia brevicornis*

Lal Greene

Martin von Fintel

Martin von Fintel

Gladiolus dalenii　　　　　*Gladiolus woodii*　　　　　*Satyrium parviflorum*

Disa (possibly from *dis* - rich or opulent) - Undergound tubers (for description see p. 240).

Disa hircicornis (*hircus* - goat; *cornis* - horn)
Slender to robust, up to 600 mm. In swampy areas, up to 1500 m, KZN to Trop Afr. **Leaves:** Leafy, mottled and barred red at base. **Flowers:** In dense inflorescence; **flowers overlapping,** pale pink to purplish red, lip whitish, side sepals ± 6 mm, **hood with spur ± 13 mm, pointing upwards at base, hooked** (Oct-Mar).

Pterygodium (*pterygoeides* - winglike, refers to side petals) - Terrestrial herbs; flowers with median sepal and petal joined to form a very shallow hood, lip with short or tall appendage, no spur. Mainly SW Cape, ± 17 species.

Pterygodium magnum [= *Corycium magnum*] (*magnum* - large, strong)
Robust, up to 1,5 m. In marshy grassland, on floodplains, 900-1800 m. **Leaves:** ± 250 x 60 mm. **Flowers:** In crowded inflorescence; flowers greenish yellow, spotted or streaked red-purple, **petals 8-10 mm, fringed,** lip ± 6 mm, white mottled purple, fringed (Jan-May). **General:** Often grows amongst *Leucosidea sericea*.

Corycium (*korys* - helmet; *ium* - resembling, refers to shape of hood) - Terrestrial herb; dorsal sepal and petals joined to form a deep hood, side sepals often fused at base, lip with appendage. Endemic, ± 15 species in SA.

Corycium nigrescens Black-faced Orchid; Moederkappie (A); umabelembuca (Z)
Slender to robust, up to 500 mm. In grassland, 1000-2000 m, S Cape to Mpum. **Leaves:** Erect, overlapping, ± 200 mm. **Flowers:** In dense inflorescence, bracts with long, slender points; flowers small, rounded, brown to black, **lateral sepals joined for most of length,** lip appendage ± 4 mm (Dec- May). **General:** Infusion from roots used traditionally to ward off evil. **Similar species:** *C. dracomontanum* Side sepals only joined for half their length; difficult to distinguish from *C. nigrescens.*

Acrolophia (*akros* - summit; *lophos* - crest, refers to crest on lip) - Terrestrial herb; leaves leathery, in 2 ranks; flowering stem branched, flowers similar to those of *Eulophia* but smaller. Endemic to SA, 7 species.

Acrolophia cochlearis impimpi (Z) (*cochlearis* - shell-like)
Robust, up to 900 mm. Usually in damp areas, on sandy soils, in coastal scrub and grassland, coast to 700 m, S Cape to KZN. **Leaves:** 4-9, **thick, in 2 ranks. Flowers:** In widely branched inflorescence; **flowers small**, less than 10 mm wide, greenish brown, white, tinged purple (Aug-Jan). **General:** Infusion from roots traditionally used by young men when courting.

Eulophia (*eu* - good, well, true, nice; *lophos* - crest)- Terrestrial herbs (for description see p. 370).

Eulophia tenella intongazimbovana (Z) (*tenella* - very soft, tender)
Very slender, 150-600 mm. In grassland, SA to E Zim. **Leaves:** 100-420 x 2-6 mm. **Flowers:** Small, sepals ± 9 mm, green to brownish purple, petals creamy yellow, lip midlobe bright yellow, spur 2-3 mm, stout (Nov-Jan). **General:** Easily overlooked in long grass. Used in traditional medicine as protective and love charms and to treat infertility.

Bulbophyllum (*bolbos* - bulb; *phyllum* - leaf, pseudobulbs bear 1-2 leaves at tip) - Epiphyte or lithophyte; rhizomes stout, creeping, pseudobulbs 3-4 angled; inflorescence often swollen or flattened in upper portion, arising from base of pseudobulb, flowers small, lip hinged very delicately to foot of column. Trop, subtrop, ± 1000 species, 3 in SA.

Bulbophyllum sandersonii (named after John Sanderson, 1820-1881, plant collector)
Up to 100 mm. In masses, on rocks and trees in forest, E Cape to Trop Afr. Pseudobulbs angled, 30-50 x 30-40 mm, green or yellow. **Leaves:** Thin, 40-120 x 15-20 mm, tip bilobed. **Flowers:** 6-16 in **short spike**, 25-100 mm, like a flattened knife blade in the upper half, margin wavy; flowers small, maroon or yellowish, open fully, median sepal upright, side sepals narrowing to point, inner surface velvety (Oct-Mar). **General:** Easily cultivated.

Bulbophyllum scaberulum (*scaberulum* - rough, perhaps refers to flower spike)
Up to 220 mm. In large masses on rocks and trees, in moist forest in light shade, E Cape to Trop Afr. Pseudobulbs 20-40 x 16-20 mm, widely spaced. **Leaves:** Fleshy, 60-100 x 15-20 mm, tip shortly bilobed. **Flowers: 24-40, in a longer spike** than *B. sandersonii,* gradually elongating, ± 220 x 18 mm; flowers ± 9 mm wide, **not opening fully,** mottled, yellowish green, purplish brown, median sepal curving forwards, side sepals oval (Oct-Dec). **General:** Easily cultivated.

Disa hircicornis

Dez Weeks

Pterygodium magnum

Lal Greene

Pterygodium magnum

Olaf Wirminghaus

Acrolophia cochlearis

David Johnson

Corycium nigrescens

Godfrey Symons

Corycium nigrescens

Lal Greene

Bulbophyllum scaberulum

Emile Plumstead

Bulbophyllum scaberulum

Geoff Nichols

Bulbophyllum sandersonii

Darrel Plowes

Eulophia tenella

Anne Rennie

575

DICOTYLEDONS - Two seed leaves, net veins; flower parts in fours, fives or multiples of these.
BALANOPHORACEAE - Parasitic on roots of trees and shrubs. Trop, subtrop, ± 18 genera, ± 44 species, 2 genera in SA.
Sarcophyte (*sarx* - flesh; *phyton* - plant) - Leaves reduced to scales; male and female flowers on separate plants; inflorescence much branched; smells of rotting flesh. 2 species in Afr, 1 in SA.

Sarcophyte sanguinea Wolwekos (A); ihlule, umavumbuka (Z) *(sanguinea* - blood red)

Male plant up to 300 mm, female plant shorter. Parasitic on roots of *Acacia* species. **Leaves:** Reduced to scales. **Flowers:** Inflorescence much branched. Male: taller and narrower, anthers white. Female: shorter, rounder, fleshy (Sep-Jan). **General:** Foul smell attracts masses of insects. Resembles fungi rather than flowering plants. Used in traditional medicine to treat dysentery, swollen glands and irregular menstruation. The Zulu name *umavumbuka* means 'the one that pops up'.

HYDNORACEAE - **Jackal's Food Family** Parasitic on roots. Flowers solitary, large, 'funguslike'. Two genera, 1 in S America, 1 in Afr, 3 species SA. *Hydnora* ((h)nduon - truffle) - Leafless; fleshy, warted rhizome; unpleasant smell.

Hydnora africana Warty Jackal Food; Bobbejaankos, Jakkalskos (A); idolo-lenkonyane, ubuklunga (X); umavumbuka (Z)

Up to 150 mm. Parasitic on *Euphorbia* roots. **Flowers:** Fleshy, rough brown outside, smooth orange within, opening into 3 segments, white spongy cushion on inner lobes (Nov-Dec), foul smelling when old. **Fruit:** Roundish, ± 80 mm diam, taking up to 2 years to mature, filled with jellylike pulp. **General:** Smell attracts insects which are held inside by hairs, only escaping when the hairs wither. Plant becomes woody with age. Fruit pulp tastes like potato and is eaten by people, birds, jackals, small mammals, porcupines, baboons. Used for tanning leather and in traditional medicine to treat diarrhoea. The Zulu name *umavumbuka* means 'the one that pops up'.

MYROTHAMNACEAE - **Resurrection Plant Family** Small shrub, resinous. Leaves opposite, folded fanwise, stalk-sheathing at base, forming a joint with blade. Male and female flowers on separate plants, no petals or calyx. *Myrothamnus* (*myron* - balsamic juice; *thamnus* - bush) Single genus, 1 species in Afr, 1 in Madag.

Myrothamnus flabellifolius Resurrection Plant; Opstandingsplant, Sinkings-bos (A); uvukakwabafile (Z) *(flabellifolius* - in the shape of a small fan)

Shrublet, 0,2-1,2(3) m, in colonies. In shallow soil on exposed rock, 600-1900 m, Cape to Kenya, Zaïre. Stems rigid, much branched, aromatic. **Leaves:** In opposite pairs, ± 14 x 8 mm, tips broad, wavy, folding fanwise. **Flowers:** In spikes, red-brown (Sep-Nov). **General:** In dry weather the whole plant withers and appears to die, leaves folding. Revives within hours after rain. Widely used in traditional medicine.

FABACEAE (LEGUMINOSAE) - **Pea/Legume Family** (for description see p. 388). *Rafnia* - Shrubs (for description see p. 258).

Rafnia elliptica (see p. 258)

Pseudarthria (*pseudo* - false; *arthron* - joint) - Herbs or shrubs, softly woolly (for description see p. 396).

Pseudarthria hookeri Velvet Bean, Bug-catcher; Fluweelboontjie (A); uphandosi, uqhonqho, uqwashu (Z) (see p. 396)

Mucuna (name of a Brazilian plant) - Herbs or climbing shrubs (for description see p. 60).

Mucuna coriacea Hellfire Bean; Brandboon (A); umkhokha (Sw) (for description see p. 60)

Canavalia (from 'Kanaval' - Malabar name for these herbs)- Climbers or creepers (for description see p. 396).

Canavalia rosea [= *C. maritima*] Beach-bean Canavalia; Strandboontjie (A) (see p. 396)

EUPHORBIACEAE - **Rubber/Euphorbia Family** (for description see p. 276). *Euphorbia* (for description see p. 278).

Euphorbia grandicornis Rhino Thorn; isihlehle, isiphapha (Z) (see p. 278)

ANACARDIACEAE - **Mango/Cashew Family** Trees, shrubs. *Rhus* - Leaves usually 3 foliolate (for descriptions see p. 534).

Rhus discolor Grassveld Currant; Grasveldtaaibos (A); inhlangushane (Sw); inkobesehlungulu, intlokotshane, umnungamabele (X) (see p. 534)

Rhus harveyi (named after William Harvey, 1811-66, botanist who published on SA flora)

Shrublet, up to 1 m. In rocky grassland, NW KZN. Rare. Branches tawny. **Leaves:** 3 foliolate, stalks 20-75 mm; leaflets stalkless, leathery, dark green above, pale below, hairless or with rough short hairs, margins slightly thickened, veins tawny, terminal leaflets, ± 55 x 27 mm. **Flowers:** In much branched inflorescences, ± 140 mm (Jan). **Fruits:** ± 6 mm diam, shiny yellowish brown.

Hydnora africana

Darrel Plowes

Myrothamnus flabellifolius

Trevor Wolf

Rafnia elliptica

Tony Abbott

Pseudarthria hookeri

Darrel Plowes

Sarcophyte sanguinea

Paul Dutton

Mucuna coriacea

Jo Onderstall

Rhus discolor

Wally Menne

Canavalia rosea

Trevor Coleman

Rhus harveyi

Rodney Moffett

Euphorbia grandicornis

Lorraine van Hoeff

577

MELIANTHACEAE - Trees or shrubs. *Melianthus* - **Honey Flowers** (for descriptions see p. 64).

Melianthus villosus Maroon Honey Flower; Kruidjie-roer-my-nie (A); ibhonya (Z) (see p. 536)

GUNNERACEAE - **Gunnera Family** (named after Johan Gunner, 1711-1777, Norwegian bishop of Trondheim who wrote a flora of Norway) Herbs of moist places. Leaves in basal rosette, large, round, with long stalks. Inflorescence a tall spike. C and S America, Madag, Malaysia, Tasmania, New Zealand, Hawaiian Is,1 genus, ± 50 species, 1 in SA.

Gunnera perpensa Wild Rhubarb; Wilderabarber (A); qobo (SS); uqobho (Sw); iphuzi lomlambo (X); imfeyesele, ugobho, uklenya (Z); uxobo (X,Z) (*perpensa* - hanging on) Robust, perennial herb, up to 1 m. In damp marshy areas, coast to 2400 m, Cape to Ethiopia. Covered in short hairs. Rhizome ± 30 mm diam, flesh yellow. **Leaves:** Tufted, **large**, 40-250 x 60-380 mm, margins lobed, with small rough edged teeth, stalks 250-450 mm. **Flowers:** In spikes 200-900 mm; flowers tiny, pinkish reddish brown, male flowers above, female below (Sep-Feb). **Fruit:** Small, fleshy. **General:** Stems and roots peeled and eaten raw, also used to make beer. Used in traditional medicine to ease childbirth, assist in expulsion of the placenta in cattle and women and, with other plants, to treat kidney and bladder complaints. Attractive foliage plant in damp parts of the garden.

ASCLEPIADACEAE - **Milkweed/Butterflyweed Family** Herbs, shrubs, vines, epiphytes or succulents, with milky latex. Leaves usually opposite, sometimes whorled or absent. Flowers bisexual, petal lobes 5, free or fused, sometimes with a corona, stamens forming a column with simple to complex fleshy basal corona in 1-2(3) whorls, pollen in waxy masses (pollinia), attached in pairs. Fruit solitary or paired follicles. Sometimes placed with Apocynaceae which it resembles vegetatively and florally (not sexually). Also similar to Periplocaceae, differing in pollination mechanism. Cosmop, ± 253 genera, ± 2000 species, 63 genera in SA. *Xysmalobium* (*xysma* - threads; *lobos* - lobes) - Perennial, non-climbing herbs (for description see p. 542).

Xysmalobium orbiculare False Thick-fruit (*orbiculare* - probably refers to the round leaves or corona lobes) **Stout, erect herb**, 1-1,5 m. Among rocks in grassy valleys and on Natal Group Sandstone, coast to 1500 m. **1(3) stems. Leaves:** 40-110 x 10-60 mm, leathery, margins entire. **Flowers:** 10-25(50), in erect, round inflorescences, **stem 8-30 mm**; flower lobes reflexed, white with green veins, margins purplish brown, hairless (Oct-May).

Xysmalobium parviflorum Octopus Cartwheel (see p. 544)

Schizoglossum (*schizo* - cut or split; *glossa* - tongue) - Perennial herbs (for description see p. 544).

Schizoglossum atropurpureum Red Milkwort; Basoetoraap, Melkwortel (A); sehoete-moro (SS); ishongwe (elincane elibomvu) (Z) (*atro* - blackish or very dark; *purpureum* - purple) Erect herb, 0,16-1,3 m. In tall grass or scrub on forest margins, coast to 2000 m. Stems simple. **Leaves:** 20-50 x 6-30 mm. **Flowers:** Lobes erect, oblong, **concave**, 4,5-7 x 1-4 mm (Jan-Mar), caramel scented. **Fruit:** Solitary, spindle-shaped, 45-55 mm, with bluntish bristles. **General:** Roots bundled and preserved by smoke, used to ward off lightning. Root eaten raw, sweet tasting. Subsp. *atropurpureum*, in tall grass in unburnt areas, 1200-2040 m; **stems long**, 0,6-1,3 m; **inflorescences sometimes branched**, 8-15 flowers, **petals almost black**, stalks 8-12 mm. Subsp. *virens*, **shorter**, up to 600 mm; on margins of coastal bush, in grassland, coast to 900 m; **flowers yellowish green**, stalks 10-15 mm. Subsp. *tridentatum*, less than 600 mm; flowers dark purplish black, stalks 5-10 mm.

Schizoglossum bidens Variable Split-tongue/Schizoglossum (see p. 544)

Schizoglossum hamatum Hooked Split-tongue/Schizoglossum (*hamatum* - hooked, possibly refers to petals) Erect herb, 250-600 mm. In grassland, on dry slopes or among rocks in areas that are seldom burnt, 540-2100 m. **Leaves:** 22-44 x 8-25 mm, base blunt to heart-shaped. **Flowers:** Lobes **large, 8-11 x 4-7 mm**, concave, hairless, **corona lobe appendages 2-3 mm, deeply divided, greatly overtopping the style tip** (Jan-Mar). **Fruit:** Solitary, ± 60 mm, spindle-shaped. **Similar species:** *S. rubiginosum* In tall, coarse grassland near Harding; leaves narrower, 2-3 mm; flowers reddish.

Schizoglossum stenoglossum Simple Split-tongue/Schizoglossum (see p. 300,)

Melianthus villosus

David Johnson

Schizoglossum stenoglossum

Martin von Fintel

Gunnera perpensa

Lal Greene

Schizoglossum atropurpureum

Lal Greene

Xysmalobium orbiculare

Martin von Fintel

Xysmalobium parviflorum

Tony Abbott

Schizoglossum bidens

Martin von Fintel

Schizoglossum hamatum

Tony Abbott

Schizoglossum hamatum

Martin von Fintel

Aspidoglossum (*aspido* - shield; *glossa* - tongue, refers to corona lobes) - Erect herbs, often grasslike; stem tubers; milky latex; inflorescences clustered towards tops of stems, corona flattened, lobes not fleshy. Afr, ± 34 species, 22 in SA.

Aspidoglossum glanduliferum Sticky Shield-tongue (*glanduliferum* - bears glands)
Erect, **260-500 mm**. In grassland. Stems usually unbranched. **Leaves:** Erect, opposite, **25-35 x 1-2 mm**, margins thickened, rolled under, stalkless. **Flowers:** Lobes spreading, 12,5-4 x 1,5-2,5 mm, with **longitudinal stripes**, upper surface hairless, sparsely to densely softly hairy beneath, often glandular, corona lime green (Sep-Jan).

Miraglossum (*mira* - astonishing; *glossa* - tongue) - Perennial herbs (for description see p. 546).

Miraglossum superbum Crucifix Miracle-tongue (*superans* - rise above, refers to magnificent corona lobes which not only rise above the style tip but are superb)
Erect herb, 250-500 mm. In grasslands, usually on black peaty soils, 1500-2100 m, KZN endemic. **Leaves:** Erect, crowded or irregular, 15-40 x 0,5-2 mm, margins rolled under, ± hairy or not. **Flowers:** Lobes oval, 6-9 x 4 mm, convex, hairless, **corona lobe erect, appendage tip large, crosslike**, dark maroon (Jan-Feb).

Pachycarpus (*pachy* - thick; *carpus* - fruit, refers to the thick skinned fruits) - Perennial herbs; very deep seated fleshy caudex; stems simple or branched, with latex; leaves usually leathery; flowers often very large, lobes fused for over two thirds their length, corona lobes flattened, ± with ornamental wings and appendages; fruit solitary, often inflated, thick skinned, hairless. Afr endemic, ± 40 species, 24 in SA.

Pachycarpus concolor Astral Pachycarpus/Thick-fruit; ishongwe (Z) (*concolor* - same colour)
Herb 200-650(900) mm. In open grassland, from dry stony hill slopes to flat sandy coastal flats, coast to 1200 m, E Cape to Zim. Stems stiff, ± erect, **usually unbranched. Leaves:** Shape variable, 40-125 x 5-40 mm, margins flat to wavy, harshly hairy. **Flowers: In 2s**, 1-2 per node, **stems short, 0-20 mm**; flowers large, 11-25 mm, lobes oval, **spreading-erect**, purplish brown, green, yellowish or with spots (Oct-Apr). **Fruit:** Oval, 60-100 x 28-33 mm, **semi-inflated**, ± 5 fleshy ridges. **General:** A bitter vegetable. Plants in E Cape smaller, stems ± reclining, leaf margins smooth or slightly wavy. North of KZN plants are large, robust, erect, leaves lance-shaped, margins strongly wavy. Zululand plants are similar, with long narrow leaves. (See p. 548) **Similar species:** *P. transvaalensis* Perennial herb, up to 730 mm; in grasslands, N KZN, Mpum, Swaz; inflorescences 2-4(5) flowered, stems 10-55 mm (Oct-Dec). (See p. 170) *P. decorus* (see p. 170).

Pachycarpus grandiflorus Grand Pachycarpus/Thick-fruit (*grandis* - big; *florus* - flower)
Robust, 200-500 mm. In open grassland, 150-2000 m. Stems branched from base or unbranched, with soft or harsh hairs. **Leaves:** 25-112 x 8-30 mm, **leathery**, margins ± wavy. **Flowers:** 2-6(9) in inflorescences; flowers large, 30-45 mm, **inflated, round,** hairy or not outside, lobes 10-28 mm, greeny yellow with purplish spots or pure yellow (Nov-Apr). **Fruit:** Oval, 90-120 mm, **semi-inflated**, surface 6-7 winged or heavily ridged. **General:** Subsp. *grandiflorus*, stems, leaves roughly or sparsely hairy. Subsp. *tomentosus*, at about 2000 m; stems and leaves densely hairy or with dense, long wavy hairs. (See p. 300)

Pachycarpus macrochilus Large-lipped Pachycarpus, Large-lipped Thick-fruit
(*macro* - large; *chilus* - lips, refers to the corona lobe structure)
Erect herb, 140-330 mm. In short, often rocky, mountain grassland, **at high altitudes ± 2300 m**. Stems slightly hairy. **Leaves:** 30-150 x 17-43 mm, margins ± wavy, harshly hairy, stalks 5-15 mm. **Flowers:** 2-6, in inflorescences; flowers 16-28 mm, spreading, **cup-shaped**, lobes 13-25 x 9-17 mm, **erect, tips slightly reflexed** (Oct-Jan). **Fruit:** Not yet known. **General:** Eaten by goats.

Asclepias (after Aesculapius, immortalised as god of medicine) - Perennial herbs (for description see p. 416).

Asclepias macropus Tailed Cartwheels (*macro* - large; *-pous* - foot, refers to large corona lobes)
Stems reclining, 150-400 mm. In grassland, often sourveld, 900-2000 m, KZN to N Prov. 4-5 annual stems, **forking from near base. Leaves:** Spreading, 25-65 x 22-35 mm, leathery, veins prominent below, harshly hairy, stalks 4-11 mm. **Flowers:** 12-30 in erect, **dense, solitary, roundish inflorescences**, 44-64 mm diam, stems 75-150 mm; flower lobes extremely reflexed with tips turned up, ± 8 x 4,5 mm, **corona lobes square, compressed sideways, upper outside end extended into a very long, pointed, tail-like appendage** (Jan- Feb). **Fruit:** Not yet known.

Aspidoglossum glanduliferum

Miraglossum superbum

Pachycarpus concolor

Pachycarpus grandiflorus

Pachycarpus grandiflorus

Pachycarpus macrochilus

Pachycarpus cf. *transvaalensis*

Asclepias macropus

Asclepias macropus

581

Anisotoma (*aniso* - unequal; *tomos* - slice or piece, possibly refers to the petals which appear to be asymmetrical) - Perennial herbs; many stems prostrate, trailing; roots clustered, thick, fleshy; milky latex; leaves opposite ± heart-shaped; corona lobes 5, fixed only at base, free above, tip entire to forked. SA endemic, 2 species.

Anisotoma pedunculata Common Spiderweb (*pedunculatus* - peduncle, flower stalk)

Perennial herb, stems 150-600 mm. In grassland (annually burned), up to 2100 m, E Cape to N Prov, mainly Drakensberg. Several stems, latex clear. **Leaves:** Spreading, lying flat on ground, 8,5-38 x 6-35 mm, stalks 4-19 mm. **Flowers:** 2-10 in erect inflorescences, **stem long, erect, 12-50 mm**; flower lobe tips reflexed, ± 4,5 x 1,5 mm, **margins rolled back**, corona lobes ± oblong, entire or toothlike with a hairy pointed or forked appendage (Oct-Jan). **Fruit:** Not yet known.

Brachystelma (*brachy* - short; *stelma* - crown, refers to the often extremely small corona) - Perennial herbs; stems usually annual, erect to prostrate; roots fleshy, clustered or disc-like stem tuber; milky latex; flower lobes fused, long or short, tube usually shorter than lobes, corona in 2 series; fruit spindlelike, erect. Widely cultivated. Tubers of most species eaten by people and animals. Afr, Asia, Austr, most diverse in S Afr, over 100 species, ± 70 in SA.

Brachystelma sp. nov.

45-120 mm. On steep, very rocky slopes, between boulders, E Cape endemic. **Stems prostrate**, much branched at base. **Leaves:** Small, **4-11 x 3-9 mm**, stalks 1,5-7 mm. **Flowers:** Solitary, stalkless at lower nodes, 18-23 mm, star-shaped, lobes spreading, long and tapering to a point, **9-11,5 x 2 mm** (at base), sparsely hairy on upper surface, brownish with yellowish green bands towards base, **stalks 45-80 mm** (Nov). **Fruit:** Purplish brown, broad at base, tapering to slender tips.
Similar species: *Brachystelma australe* In humus, on Natal Group Sandstone ledges, Pondoland endemic; stems erect at first, reclining later; outer corona V-shaped. Also similar, *B. pulchellum* (see p. 584).

Brachystelma barberae Barber's Brachystelma; Platvoetaasblom (A) (named after Mary Barber née Bowker 1818-1899, who collected insects and plants)

Perennial herb, 60-100 mm. In grassland, 750-1000 m, E Cape to Zim. Stems 1-3, erect. **Leaves:** 25-100 x 8-25 mm, margins flat, thinly, coarsely hairy, stalks short, produced after flowers. **Flowers:** ± 25 in **round inflorescences, paired, opposite**, stemless; **flowers large, 75-100 mm diam, cagelike**, lobes erect, narrow, 20-45 x 5-7 mm, tips united (Sep-Dec). **General:** Flowers all open at once. Stem tuber eaten.

Brachystelma circinatum Bird-cage Brachystelma; Wilde-aartappel (A) (*circinnatus* - coiled inwards from tip, refers to curved tips of flower lobes)

Perennial herb, 50-300 mm. In grassland. E Cape to Bots. Stems 1-3, branching in upper part, erect. **Leaves:** 5-15 x 1-7 mm, flat or folded upwards, margins ± wavy, hairy or hairless, stalks short. **Flowers: In 2s** at nodes; **flowers cagelike**, lobes erect, narrow, 4-25 x 1-1,5 mm, tips united, tube short 3 mm, **inner corona lobes not elongated above the style tips** (Oct). **Fruit:** 60-90 x 3-4 mm, tapering to pointed tip. **General:** Stem tuber eaten. (See p. 172)

Brachystelma foetidum [= B. rehmannii] Foetid Brachystelma; Hottentotsbrood (A); seru (Sw) (*foetidus* - evil smelling, refers to the unpleasant odour of mature flowers)

Perennial herb, 70-150 mm. In grassland, KZN to N Prov, Bots. Stems branching in upper parts. **Leaves:** 5-30 x 3-10 mm, folded upwards, margins wavy, ± hairy. **Flowers:** 2-6 in stalkless inflorescences, at nodes; flower lobes 12-25 mm, reflexed at narrow tips, margins rolled under towards tips, tube 6-10 mm deep, **inner corona lobes not longer than style tips** (Oct-Feb), foul smelling. **Fruit:** 1-2, 60-100 x 6 mm, with short hairs. **General:** Peeled tubers eaten. Used as a remedy for colds.

Brachystelma gerrardii [= Brachystelma nigrum, Brachystelmaria gerrardii] Gerrard's Brachystelma (named after William Gerrard, naturalist and explorer who came to Natal in 1861)

Perennial herb, 220-350 mm. In grassland, KZN, Swaz, a gap, then the Waterberg, N Prov. Rare. **Solitary stem** usually unbranched, erect, woolly. **Leaves:** 19-45 x -38 mm, margins flat or ± wavy, short hairs above, **woolly beneath**. **Flowers:** Solitary, in upper nodes; **flowers propellerlike, lobes erect in lower third, then constricted, upper parts spreading reflexed**, 9-20 x 4-6 mm, margins slightly reflexed, upper surface with small protruberances, lower smooth, margins with red-purple club-shaped hairs (Nov-Feb). **Fruit:** Paired, slender, ± 100 mm. **General:** Roots eaten. Flowers metallic blue-green in the south, dark green in the north.

Anisotoma pedunculata

Brachystelma australe

Brachystelma barberae

Brachystelma circinatum

Brachystelma sp. nov.

Brachystelma foetidum

Brachystelma sp. nov.

Brachystelma gerrardii

Brachystelma gerrardii

Brachystelma pulchellum **Beautiful Brachystelma** (*pulchellus* - beautiful, diminutive)
Stems 75-250 mm. In grassland, on Natal Group Sandstone, KZN endemic. **Stems prostrate, branched near base.** Leaves: 15-20 x 16 mm on older stems, margins flat. **Flowers:** 1-2 at upper nodes; flowers maroon, lobes spreading, **± 4 x 1,5 mm**, tips pointed, margins rolled under, **calyx lobes not completely hidden by petal lobes** (Nov-Feb). **Fruit:** Erect, 30-50 mm. **Similar species:** *B. australe* (see p. 582).

Brachystelma tenue **Canary Cage Brachystelma** (*tenuis* - thin or fine)
Perennial herb, 50-100 mm. In grassland, Maputaland endemic. **Stems sparsely branched above, spreading or erect,** densely hairy. **Leaves:** 5-20 x 4-6 mm, sometimes folded, margins flat, mostly hairless. **Flowers:** 1-2 in axils at upper nodes, 15-20 mm diam, lobes erect, slender, 14-18 mm, united at tips, **cagelike**, inner corona lobes not elongated above the style tip (Jan).

Ceropegia (*keros* - wax; *pege* - fountain) - Perennial, often twining, semi-succulent herbs (for description see p. 172).

Ceropegia africana **African Ceropegia**
Perennial vine, 0,1-1 m. In scrub, often on shale, W Cape to Mpum. Stems slender to robust. **Leaves:** Spreading, 8-25 x 3-13 mm, ± **fleshy,** margins flat or wavy, tips pointed. **Flowers:** 2-3 at nodes, 16-25 mm, tube more or less straight, cagelike above, lobes erect, 6-12 mm, narrow throughout, tips fused, margins rolled under, fringed, keel with few purple hairs (Dec-Mar).

Ceropegia woodii [= *C. linearis* subsp. *woodii*] **Wood's Ceropegia, Necklace Vine, String of Hearts; isidakwa, uvemvane samatshe (Z)** (after John Medley Wood, 1827-1915, curator, Natal Herbarium, credited with the establishment of Uba cane, the most successful variety for sugar production in KZN)
Vine, 0,25-1 m. On rocky ledges, up to 1000 m, E Cape to N Prov. Stems **trailing, prostrate or climbing. Leaves:** 6-18 mm diam, sometimes whitish along the veins. **Flowers:** 18-25 mm, lobes **6-8 x 3-4,5 mm, spoon-shaped,** fused at tips to form cagelike structure, margins with purplish hairs inside (Jan-Apr). **Fruit:** 50-70 x 3 mm. **General:** Stems eaten raw for water. Used traditionally to treat chest complaints thought to be brought on by poisoning. **Similar species:** *C. linearis* (see p. 174).

Duvalia (named after French botanist H A Duval) - Succulent herbs; stems short, 4-6 angled, often forming dense mats; flowers deeply divided, lobes spreading, corona elevated, covered by, or in contact with the disc-like outer staminal corona. Widely grown, many horticultural hybrids. Afr, Arabia, 17 species, 13 in S Afr.

Duvalia polita [= *D. parviflora*] **Polished Star** (*politus* - polished, refers to the flower)
20-100 mm. In dry places, 1000-1600 m, KZN to Angola, Malawi. Stems 7-15 mm diam, **bluntly 6 angled,** angles with short, fat tubercles tipped with narrow pointed tooth. **Flowers:** 3-4 in cluster; 20-38 mm diam, **very smooth, shiny on basal two thirds,** lobes 10-15 x 7-11 mm, **wide at base,** smooth in upper half, **long, club-shaped purple hairs on basal half,** stalks 15-25(30) mm (Feb-Mar). **Fruit:** Paired, mottled dark and lighter green. **General:** Stems eaten raw. Widely cultivated.

Stapelia (after Johan van Stapel, Dutch botanist, died 1636) - Perennial succulent herbs (for description see p. 302).

Stapelia leenendertziae **Leendertz's Carrion Flower; Aaskelk, Aasklok, Rooi-aasblom (A)** (named after Reino Leendertz (Mrs Pott), 1869-1965, botanist at Transvaal Museum)
Succulent herb, 75-150 mm. In dry thicket, KZN to N Prov. Stems branched at base, 9-13 mm diam, 4 angled, sides concave, angles with small teeth tipped with rudimentary leaves, velvety. **Flowers:** 1-2, **tubular to bell-shaped, fused for most of length,** 60-75 mm, lobes 55-64 x 38 mm at base, inner surface smooth, hairless, outer surface shortly hairy (Mar-May, Oct-Nov), very disagreeable foetid smell. **Fruit:** Paired, ± parallel, stout, 115-140 x 17 mm, green mottled lighter green.

Orbea (*orbis* - orb, refers to the disc-like corolline corona) - Succulent herbs; stems 4 angled, tubercles sharp tipped, spreading, pair of spines below; staminal corona complex, inner series 5 lobed, spreading horizontally, fused, outer series 5 lobed, erect, fleshy, hornlike, fused at base to inner series. Many cultivated hybrids. Afr, ± 20 species, 18 in SA.

Orbea longidens [= *Stapelia longidens*] **Long-tooth Orbea** (*long* - long; *dens* - tooth)
Succulent tufted herb, 60-150 mm. In dry woodland, thicket, N KZN to Moz. Stems branched near base, ± reclining, then erect, 9-11 mm wide, **tubercles or teeth 12-25 mm. Flowers:** 1-3, flat on soil, 30-50 mm diam, upper surface with slender spoon-shaped hairs, hairless beneath, lobes spreading (Apr-May). **Fruit:** Erect, slightly apart, ± 180 x 13 mm, green striped paler green.

Brachystelma tenue

Brachystelma pulchellum

Ceropegia africana

Ceropegia woodii

Duvalia polita

Stapelia leendertziae

Orbea longidens

585

Orbea macloughlinii [= *Stapelia macloughlinii*] **Macloughlin's Orbea** (named after Alfred McLoughlin, 1886-1960, who contributed significantly to the study of orchids and succulents)
Succulent tufted herb, up to 100 mm. In dry areas, Pondoland endemic. Tubercles tipped with sharp tooth, green or with purple margins. **Flowers:** Near base of stems, 40-50 mm diam, upper surface faintly wrinkled, **lobes spreading,** ± 16 x 11 mm, margins strongly recurved, **vibrating hairs,** centre of flower stalked (Feb-Mar).

Orbea paradoxa [= *Stultitia paradoxa*] **Paradoxical Orbea; umanhlangwane (Z)** (*para* - side by side; *doxa* - glory, refers to the fact that it is unusual but of equal glory in the genus)
Succulent herb, 70-100 mm. Near seasonal vleis and in dry stony areas, N KZN to S Moz. Stems ± 10 mm diam, tubercles 10-20 mm. **Multiplication of small tubercles towards tips of stems. Flowers:** Small, 20-24 mm diam, hairy, especially in **angles of lobes where there is a short, pointed secondary lobe** (Dec-May).

Orbea woodii [= *Stapelia woodii*] **Wood's Orbea** (named after John Medley Wood, 1827-1915, botanist, collector, first curator of Natal Herbarium, who published widely on flora of KZN)
Succulent herb, 40-75 mm. In dry woodland. Stems 6-11 mm wide, tubercles ± 15 mm, tipped with sharp tooth. **Flowers:** At base of young stems, 30-45 mm diam, lobes spreading, **convex,** upper surface wrinkled, **vibrating dark purple hairs on margins, cushionlike corona at mouth** (Nov-Apr). Smells like human faeces.

Pachycymbium (*pachy* - thick; *cymbe* - boat, refers to flowers) - Differs from *Orbea* with flowers short stalked, small, rigidly thick and fleshy, bell-shaped, inflorescences produced along upper stem nodes, corona totally enclosed in the flower tube, inner corona lobes not overtopping the style tip. Afr, Arabia, 32 species, 8 in SA.

Pachycymbium keithii [= *Caralluma keithii*] **Keith's Thick-boat** (named after D R Keith who first collected the plant in Swaziland)
Dwarf succulent herb, up to 90 mm. In dry areas, KZN to Zim. Stems 30-45 mm wide, tubercles 10-15 mm. **Flowers:** Small, 12,5 mm, purplish red with some white spots, **minutely warty** with **5 angled, purple cushion ring,** outer corona cuplike, inner corona slender, inflexed over the column (Feb-Apr).

Pachycymbium ubomboense [= *Caralluma ubomboensis*] **Ubombo Thick-boat** (named after the Lebombo mountains, KZN where it was first discovered in 1930)
Succulent herb, 40-80 mm. In dry areas, 300-1350 m, KZN to Zim. Stems fleshy, angles pronounced, tubercles sharply pointed, tipped with rudimentary leaves. **Flowers: In erect clusters,** ± 9 mm diam, lobes spreading, 3-4 x 2 mm, outer corona 5 lobed, flattened sideways, fused at base, inner corona 5 lobed, erect, tonguelike.

Huernia (named after Dutch missionary Justus Huernius, 1587-1652, an early plant collector in the Cape) - Succulent herbs; stems 2-6 angled; flowers with intermediate corolla lobes. Widely cultivated. Afr, Arabia, 30-68 species, ± 41 in SA.

Huernia hystrix **Porcupine Huernia, Toad Plant; usilelo, umanhlangwane (Z)** (*hystrix* - porcupine, refers to the long, banded, little bumps that cover the upper surface)
Succulent herb, 30-70 mm. In dry thicket, E Cape S Zim. Stems 9-13 mm wide, 5 angled, swollen tubercles tipped with hard tooth. **Flowers:** 25-50 mm diam, lobes spreading, 12-17 x 12-17 mm, upper surface covered in fleshy pointed bumps, inner corona overtopping and touching the style tip (throughout year). **General:** Subsp. *hystrix,* flowers large, ± 50 mm diam. Subsp. *parvula,* flowers small, ± 35 mm diam.

Huernia pendula **Bootlace Huernia; bellabella (X)** (*pendulus* - pendulous, drooping, hanging)
Succulent herb, 450-900(1500) mm. On rocky ledges, E Cape. **Stems hanging, appearing jointed, roundish with shallow angles, small bumplike tubercles. Flowers:** ± 15 mm diam, upper surface wrinkled, densely covered with tiny bumps, lobes **horizontally spreading,** 4 x 6-7 mm, **tips pointed and slightly reflexed,** inner corona not reaching style tip. **Fruit:** Suberect, 25-45 x 5-7 mm.

Huernia zebrina **Zebra Huernia; umanhlangwane (Z)** (*zebrinus* - regularly striped)
Succulent herb, 50-75 mm. In dry woodland, KZN to Bots, Nam. Stems 9-11 mm wide, 5 angled, **angles compressed, tubercles sharply pointed, tipped with hard tooth. Flowers:** 38-45 mm diam, lobes 11 x 6 mm, fused at base into a disc around the tube mouth, **prominent very shiny cushion corona,** inner corona rising high above the style tip (Dec-Mar). **Fruit:** Erect, fiddle-shaped, tip very pointed.

Orbea macloughlinii

Orbea paradoxa

Orbea woodii

Pachycymbium ubomboense

Pachycymbium keithii

Huernia hystrix

Huernia hystrix

Huernia pendula

Huernia zebrina

587

Tylophora (*tylos* - lump or swelling; *phoreo* - carrying, refers to the corona lobes) - Perennial climbers; rootstock fibrous; flowers small, staminal corona lobes bloblike; fruit erect, sometimes winged. Said to be poisonous, sometimes causing blisters. Widely used medicinally, some species testing positive for combating nasobronchial allergies and having anaphylactic, anti-tumour and anti-inflammatory activity. Afr, Madag, Asia, Austr, ± 50 species, 10 in S Afr.

Tylophora flanaganii Flanagan's Teardrop; inhlanhla, umusa (Z) (after Henry Flanagan, 1861- 1919, Komga farmer, plant collector whose private garden and herbarium were bequeathed to the nation)

Climber, stems up to ± 4 m. In forest, woodland, up to 1400 m. Stems woody at base. **Leaves:** 30-90 x 20-64 mm, abruptly tapering to drip tip. **Flowers:** In clusters at tips of **forking stems, 50-120 mm, at nodes**; ± 10 mm diam, deep reddish purple, lobes spreading, **corona lobes simple, fleshy, toothlike** (Nov-Apr). **Fruit:** ± 37 mm, tip a pointed beak. **General:** Used in traditional medicine to treat stomach ailments.

Dregea (after collecter Johann Drège, 1794-1881) - Perennial woody climbers (for description see p. 176).

Dregea floribunda Mousy Bat-fruit (see p. 176)

SOLANACEAE - Tomato/Potato/Tobacco Family (for description see p. 478). *Datura* - Herbs, shrubs, trees (see p. 188).

★ *Datura stramonium* Common Thorn Apple; Bloustinkblaar, Gewone Stinkblaar (A); lijowe (Sw); umhlavuthwa, umvumbangwe (X); ijoli, ijoye, iloyi (Z) (see p. 188)

SCROPHULARIACEAE - Snapdragon Family Annual or perennial herbs, shrubs, climbers (for description see p. 480). *Jamesbrittenia* (named after British botanist James Britten, 1846-1924) - Stamens hidden (for description see p. 480).

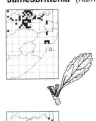

Jamesbrittenia burkeana [= *Sutera burkeana*] Dark-centred Sutera; Bruinblommetjie, Geelblommetjie (A) (named after Joseph Burke, 1812-73, who collected with Carl Zeyher in 1840-42)

Much branched shrublet, 0,3-1,5 m. In rocky grassland, open woodland or scrub, 750-1800 m. Stems slender, hairy, glandular hairy. **Leaves:** In tufts, 4-12 x 2-6 mm, **blade folded, sickle-shaped**, gland dotted above, glandular hairy beneath, glands glistening, margins deeply toothed or lobed. **Flowers:** In terminal inflorescences; flowers ± 22 mm, mauve with dark maroon centre, outlined in orange, lobes often recurved (blooms throughout year). **General:** Hardy, suitable for hot dry gardens.

Jamesbrittenia huillana [= *Sutera huillana*, *S. brunnea*] Geelblommetjie (A)

Shrublet, 0,15-1,2 m. On rocky ground, KZN to Zim, Nam. Stout woody base, stems slender, with downy, glistening glands. **Leaves:** Opposite, 10-30 x 2-10 mm, **margins toothed towards tip**, slightly lobed. **Flowers:** Clustered towards end of stems; flowers ± 27 mm, brown, orange to yellow, bulging slightly at throat, lobes narrow, calyx divided almost to base (Oct-Apr). **Similar species:** *J. atropurpurea* Leaves smaller, margins mostly entire; flowers scattered irregularly along branches.

PLANTAGINACEAE - Plantain/Plantago Family Herbs. Leaves parallel veined. Flowers in dense inflorescences. Cosmop, 3 genera, ± 275 species, 1 genus in SA, mostly introduced weeds. *Plantago* (Latin name for Plantain).

★ *Plantago lanceolata* Narrow-leaved Ribwort; Oorpynhoutjie, Smalblaar-plantago, Smalweegblaar (A); bolila-nyana, setla-bocha (SS); indlebe-kathekwane encane (Z) (*lanceolata* - lancelike)

Perennial herb, up to 600 mm. On disturbed ground, weed (from Europe). Leaves ± 300 x 25 mm, dark green, veins parallel, margins entire or slightly toothed, winged stalk ± 200 mm. Flowers in compact inflorescences 20-30 mm (Jul-Jan). Seeds used like sago in other regions. Pollen causes hayfever. Used traditionally to treat earache.

★ *Plantago major* Broadleaved Ribwort; Platvoet (A); bolila (SS); indlebe-kathekwane enkulu (Z) (*major* - larger than the type)

Perennial herb, up to 800 mm. Weed in moist areas (from Europe). Leaves ± 350 x 40 mm, light green, margins scalloped. Flowers in slender inflorescences, ± 450 mm (Nov-Apr). Leaves and roots eaten, seeds used like sago. Used in traditional medicine to ensure easy childbirth, treat mouth and ear ailments, diarrhoea.

LOBELIACEAE - Lobelia Family (description see p. 208). *Monopsis* - Annual or perennial herbs (for description see p. 496).

Monopsis unidentata Wild Brown Violet (*unidentata* - one tooth)

Perennial herb, prostrate or erect, robust or slender, up to 750 mm. In moist grassland, damp and disturbed places, SW Cape to KZN. **Leaves:** 5-20 x 0,5-9 mm, margins entire or 1-2 toothed, lower leaves more strongly toothed. **Flowers:** 7-14 mm, brownish cream or purple, stalks 35-100 mm (Oct-May). **Fruit:** Capsule erect, oval, ± 7 x 6 mm.

Tylophora flanaganii

Dregea floribunda

Jamesbrittenia huillana

Jamesbrittenia burkeana

★ *Plantago lanceolata*

★ *Plantago major*

★ *Datura stramonium*

Monopsis unidentata

589

GLOSSARY PLATE 1

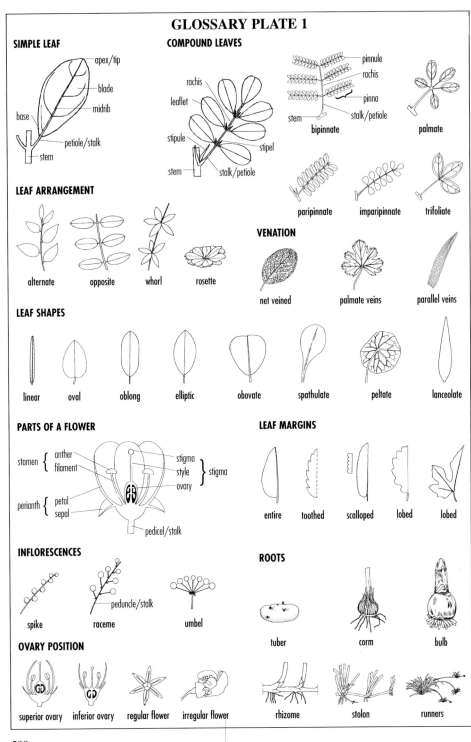

SIMPLE LEAF
apex/tip
blade
midrib
base
petiole/stalk
stem

COMPOUND LEAVES
rachis
leaflet
stipule
stem
stalk/petiole
stipel

pinnule
rachis
pinna
stem
stalk/petiole
bipinnate

palmate

paripinnate   imparipinnate   trifoliate

LEAF ARRANGEMENT
alternate   opposite   whorl   rosette

VENATION
net veined   palmate veins   parallel veins

LEAF SHAPES
linear   oval   oblong   elliptic   obovate   spathulate   peltate   lanceolate

PARTS OF A FLOWER
stamen { anther / filament
stigma
style
ovary
} stigma
perianth { petal / sepal
pedicel/stalk

LEAF MARGINS
entire   toothed   scalloped   lobed   lobed

INFLORESCENCES
peduncle/stalk
spike   raceme   umbel

ROOTS
tuber   corm   bulb

OVARY POSITION
superior ovary   inferior ovary   regular flower   irregular flower

rhizome   stolon   runners

590

GLOSSARY PLATE 2

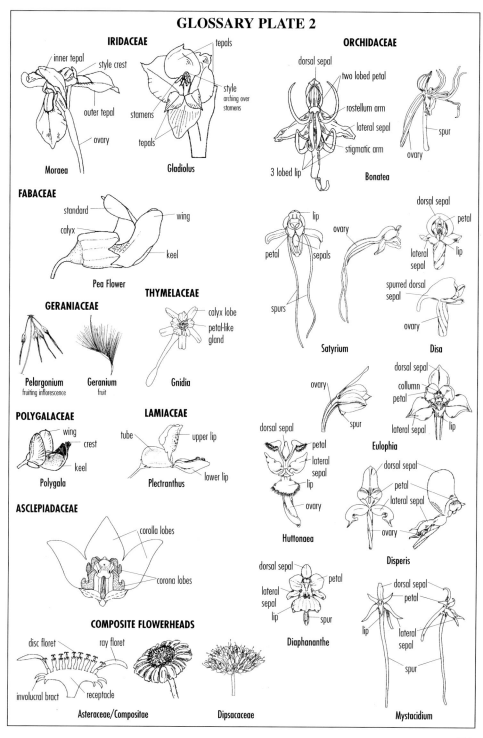

IRIDACEAE

inner tepal
style crest
outer tepal
ovary

Moraea

tepals
style
arching over
stamens
stamens
tepals

Gladiolus

ORCHIDACEAE

dorsal sepal
two lobed petal
rostellum arm
lateral sepal
stigmatic arm
3 lobed lip
ovary

Bonatea

spur

FABACEAE

standard
calyx
wing
keel

Pea Flower

lip
ovary
petal
sepals
spurs

Satyrium

dorsal sepal
petal
lateral
sepal
lip

spurred dorsal
sepal
ovary

Disa

THYMELACEAE

calyx lobe
petal-like
gland

GERANIACEAE

Pelargonium
fruiting inflorescence

Geranium
fruit

Gnidia

POLYGALACEAE

wing
crest
keel

Polygala

LAMIACEAE

tube
upper lip
lower lip

Plectranthus

ASCLEPIADACEAE

corolla lobes
corona lobes

dorsal sepal
petal
lateral
sepal
lip
ovary

Huttonaea

ovary
spur

dorsal sepal
collumn
petal
lateral sepal
lip

Eulophia

dorsal sepal
petal
lateral sepal
ovary

Disperis

dorsal sepal
petal
lateral
sepal
lip
spur

Diaphananthe

dorsal sepal
petal
lip
lateral
sepal
spur

Mystacidium

COMPOSITE FLOWERHEADS

disc floret
ray floret
involucral bract
receptacle

Asteraceae/Compositae

Dipsacaceae

GLOSSARY

achene	a small, dry, non-splitting, one seeded fruit
annual	a plant which germinates from seed, flowers, sets seed and dies in the same year
appendage	a secondary part attached to a main structure
aquatic	growing in water
aril	fleshy outer covering of a seed

achene

berry	fleshy, pulpy fruit without a stone
bilateral	2-sided
brachyblasts	a short branch of limited growth, bearing leaves and sometimes flowers and fruit; a spur
bract	a reduced leaf or leaflike structure at base of flower or inflorescence
bulbils	a small bulb arising from the base of a larger bulb

appendage

capsule	a dry, splitting fruit
carrion	dead, rotten flesh
cataphylls	membranous scale leaves
caudex	the persistent swollen stem base of certain herbaceous perennials
chevron	bent bar of inverted V shape
cladodes	a flattened stem with the form and function of a leaf
composite flowerhead	an apparently simple flower made up of many small flowers
corymb	short, broad, more or less flat-topped inflorescence, outer flowers opening first
cyathia/cyathium	the flowering head in genus *Euphorbia*, cuplike with a single pistil and male flowers with a single stamen
deciduous	not evergreen, leaves falling at the end of one season of growth

aril

cladodes

drupe	a fleshy, one seeded fruit, the seed enclosed in a stony endocarp eg peach

composite flowerhead

endemic	naturally found only in a particular and usually restricted geographic area or region
epicalyx	a whorl of bracts below a flower which resembles an outer calyx
epiphyte	a plant growing on another which does not draw food or water from it
ericoid	having narrow, needlelike, rolled leaves like *Erica* or heather
estuary	tidal mouth of a river
estuarine	growing in, inhabiting or found in an estuary

cyathia/cythium

fibrous	containing or resembling fibres
flaccid	limp, floppy

gynophore	an elongated stalk bearing the pistil in some flowers
gynostegium	a structure formed from the fusion of the anthers with the stigmatic region of the gynoecium (as in Asclepiadaceae)

epicalyx

herb	a plant without an above ground woody stem, the stems dying back to the ground at the end of the growing season
herbaceous	not woody, soft branches before they become woody
hybrid	offspring produced from genetically different parents

gynophore

592

hypanthium	a cuplike extension formed by the fused basal parts of the calyx, corolla and androecium usually enclosing the pistils
inflorescence	a flowering shoot bearing more than one flower; the arrangement of flowers on the flowering shoot
involucre	one or more whorls of bracts close beneath a flower or flower cluster

hypanthium

latex	milky sap
legume	a dry fruit splitting on both sides like a pea pod
lenticel	a small raised pore developing in woody stems when epidermis is replaced by cork
lignotuber	woody stem tuber
linear	long and narrow with ± parallel sides
lithophyte	plant that grows on stone or rock
lorate	strap-shaped

latex

monocarpic	flowering and bearing fruit only once and then dying

node

nectary	an organ which produces nectar, often appears as a scale, pit or protuberance
node	position on the stem where leaves or branches originate

papillae	minute pimplelike bumps or protuberances
pappus	modified (much reduced) calyx of Compositae/Asteraceae made up of scales or bristles at the tip of the achene

papus

parasite	plant or animal living in or on another, drawing food and water at least partly from it
perennial	a plant that lives 3 or more years
perianth	collective term for corolla (petals) and calyx (sepals)
petiolode	an organ which resembles a petal (usually a stamen)
pod	a dry, splitting fruit
pollinia/pollinium	a mass of waxy pollen grains (sticking together) transported as a unit during pollination

pollinia/pollinum

prickle	a small, woody, pointed outgrowth from the bark or epidermis of a plant
pseudobulb	swollen segment of stem of one or more internodes

radial	spreading from a common centre
ranks (leaves)	a row, especially a vertical row
ray	a branch of an umbel inflorescence
rosette	a dense, radiating cluster of leaves (or other organisms) at or near ground level
rostellum	a small beak; an extension from the upper edge of the stigma in orchids

ranks

ray

saccate	bag-shaped, pouchy
scale	any thin, flat, dry, membranous body, usually a degenerate leaf
sessile	without a stalk, attached directly
sheath/sheathing	any long, ± tubular portion of an organ which surrounds at least part of another organ
simple	undivided ie leaf not divided into leaflets; inflorescence not branched

saccate

sinus	space or recess between 2 lobes or divisions of an organ, ie leaf or petal	
spadix	a thick fleshy spike or column with tiny flowers crowded on it	
spathe	a large bract or modified leaf surrounding a flower cluster or spadix, sometimes coloured and petal-like eg *Zantedeschia*	
spike	an unbranched elongated inflorescence with stalkless flowers	spadix/spathe
spikelet	a small spike or secondary spike; the ultimate flower cluster of grasses and sedges consisting or 1-many flowers subtended by two bracts	
spur	a hollow, tubelike extension of a petal or sepal	
stipels	a small stipulelike structure at the base of a leaflet	
succulent	juicy and fleshy eg leaves and stems of *Aloe*	spur
tendril	a modified leaf, leaflet, branch or inflorescence of a climbing plant that coils around suitable objects and helps support and elevate the plant	
tepal	a segment of a perianth which is not differentiated into a calyx and corolla (sepals and petals)	tendril
tubercle	a nodule or small tuber, as on roots of some legumes	
tuberous	resembling a tuber, producing tubers	
umbel	usually a flat-topped inflorescence with the stalks arising more or less from a common point like an umbrella	
utricle	a small bladder-shaped appendage/structure or a small, thin walled, one seeded, bladdery inflated fruit	tepal
vestigial	imperfectly developed	
wing	a thin, flat margin bordering a structure	
whorls/whorled	arrangement of similar parts in a circle at the same level	tubercle

ABBREVIATIONS

A	Afrikaans	Madag	Madagascar	SS	South Sotho
Afr	Africa(n)	Mar	March	S	south(ern)
Apr	April	May	May	Sep	September
Aug	August	Medit	Metiterranean	sp	species
Austr	Australia	Moz	Mozambique	spp	species (pl)
Bot	Botanic(al)	Mpum	Mpumalanga	subtrop	subtropical
cosmop	cosmopolitan	N	north(ern)	subcosmop	subcosmopolitan
Dec	December	Nam	Namibia	Sw	Swaziland
diam	diameter	Nov	November	Tanz	Tanzania
E	east(ern)	Oct	October	temp	temperate
Feb	February	Old World	Europe, Asia,	Th	Thonga
Hemisp	Hemisphere		Africa	Trop/trop	tropic(al)
ined	unpublished	p	page	USA	United States
Is	island(s)	paleotrop	paleotropic(al)		(of America)
Jan	January	pantrop	pantropical	W	west(ern)
Jul	July	pp	pages	X	Xhosa
Jun	June	prof	professor	Z	Zulu
KZN	KwaZulu-Natal	Prov	Province	Zam	Zambia
Les	Lesotho	S Afr	Southern Africa	Zim	Zimbabwe

SELECTED BIBLIOGRAPHY

A great number of scientific journals and books have been referred to when researching this Field Guide. Some of those that are accessible to the general public are listed.

Arnold, T H & B C de Wet (1993) Plants of southern Africa: names and distribution. Mem Bot Survey of SA No: 62. National Botanical Institute
Batten, A, & H Bokelmann (1966) Wild flowers of the eastern Cape Province. Books of Africa
Batten, A. (1988) Flowers of Southern Africa. Southern Book Publishers
Berglund, A (1976) Zulu Thought Patterns & Symbols. Hirst in assoc. with David Phillip
Botha, Charles & Julia (1995) Bring Nature Back to your Garden. Wildlife Society (Natal Branch)
Bromilow, Clive (1995) Problem Plants of SA. Briza Publications
Bruton M N and K H Cooper (1980) Studies on the Ecology of Maputaland. Rhodes University/Wildlife Society
Codd, L E (1968) The South African species of *Kniphofia*. Bothalia 9
Compton, R H (1976) The Flora of Swaziland. JSAB, Suppl Vol no: 11
Dlamini, Ben (1981) Swaziland Flora, their local names and uses. Ministry of Agriculture, Swaziland
Fabian, A, and G Germishuizen (1997) Wild Flowers of Northern South Africa. Fernwood Press
Fox, F W and M E Norwood Young (1982) Food from the Veld. Delta Books
Gibson, Janet (1975) Wild Flowers of Natal (coastal region) Wildlife Society (Natal Branch)
Gibson, Janet (1978) Wild Flowers of Natal (inland region) Wildlife Society (Natal Branch)
Giddy, Cynthia (1974) Cycads of South Africa. Purnell
Goldblatt, Peter (1986) The Moraeas of Southern Africa. Annals Kirstenbosch National Botanic Gardens 14
Goldblatt, Peter (1989) The Genus *Watsonia*. Annals Kirstenbosch National Botanic Gardens 18
Goldblatt, Peter (1996) *Gladiolus* in Tropical Africa. Timber Press, Portland, Oregon
Goode, Douglas (1993) Cycads of Africa. Struik
Gordon-Gray, K D (1995) Cyperaceae in Natal. Strelitzia 2, National Botanical Institute
Jacot-Guillarmod, Amy (1971) Flora of Lesotho (Basutoland). Lehre. Cramer
Harrison, E R (1972) Epiphytic Orchids of Southern Africa. Natal Branch, Wildlife Society
Henderson, Lesley (1995) Plant Invaders of Southern Africa. Plant Protection Research Institute
Heywood, V H, S D Davis (1994) Centres of Plant Diversity. Vol 1: Europe, Africa, South West Asia and the Middle East. World Wide Fund for Nature
Hilliard, O M (1977) Compositae in Natal. University of Natal Press
Hilliard, O M (1987) Grasses, Sedges, Restiads & Rushes of the Natal Drakensberg. Ukhahlamba Series, No. 2 University of Natal Press
Hilliard, O M (1990) Flowers of the Natal Drakensberg - The lily, iris and orchid families and their allies. Ukhahlamba Series No. 4, University of Natal Press
Hilliard, O M, and B L Burtt (1971) Streptocarpus. An African plant study. University of Natal Press
Hilliard, O M, and B L Burtt (1987) The Botany of the Southern Natal Drakensberg. National Bot Gardens
Hilliard, O M, and B L Burtt (1991) *Dierama*, The Hairbells of Africa. Acorn Books
Hilton-Taylor, Craig (1996) Red Data List of Southern African Plants. Strelitzia 4, National Botanical Institute
Hutchings, Anne et al (1996) Zulu Medicinal Plants. University of Natal Press
Irwin, Dave and Pat (1992) A Field Guide to the Natal Drakensberg (2nd Edition). Rhodes University
Jeppe, Barbara (1974) South African Aloes. Purnell
Joffe, Pitta (1993) The Gardeners Guide to SA Plants. Tafelberg Publishers Limited
Killick, Donald (1990) A Field Guide - The Flora of the Natal Drakensberg. Jonathan Ball & Ad Donker
Lewis, G J, Obermeyer A A & T T Barnard (1972) *Gladiolus*: revision of the SA species. Purnell
Onderstall, Jo (1984) SA Wild Flower Guide: Transvaal Lowveld and Escarpment. Botanical Society of SA
Onderstall, Jo (1996) Wild Flower Guide: Mpumalanga & Northern Province. Dynamic Ad.
Pooley, E S (1993) Trees of Natal, Zululand & Transkei. Natal Flora Publications Trust
Pooley, A C, and Ian Player (1995) KwaZulu-Natal Wildlife Destinations. Southern Book Publishers
Rebelo, Tony (1995) Proteas, A field guide to the Proteas of Southern Africa. Fernwood Press
Roberts, Margaret (1990) Indigenous Healing Plants. Southern Book Publishers
Ross, J H (1972) Flora of Natal. Bot Survey Memoir No. 39
Rourke, J P (1982) The Proteas of Southern Africa. Centaur
Stewart, Joyce, H P Linder, E A Schelpe, A V Hall (1982) Wild Orchids of Southern Africa. MacMillan
Van der Walt, J J A, P J Vorster (1977-1988) Pelargoniums of Southern Africa. Vols 1-3. National Bot Gardens
Van Jaarsveld, E J (1994) Gasterias of South Africa. Fernwood Press
Van Jaarsveld, E J The *Plectranthus* Handbook. National Botanic Gardens
Van Wyk, Ben-Erik, Gideon Smith (1996) Guide to the Aloes of South Africa. Briza Publications
Van Wyk, Ben-Erik, Bosch van Oudtshoorn & Nigel Gericke (1997) Medicinal Plants of SA. Briza Publications
Van Wyk, Braam & Sasa Malan (1997) Field Guide to the Wild Flowers of the Highveld (2nd edition) Struik
Walker, Joan (1996) Wild Flowers of KwaZulu-Natal. W R Walker Family Trust

CONTACT ADDRESSES

CONSERVATION AUTHORITIES AND BOTANIC GARDENS
KwaZulu-Natal Conservation Services, PO Box 662, Pietermaritzburg 3200
Natal National Botanical Gardens, PO Box 21667, Mayor's Walk, Pietermaritzburg 3208
Regional Director, Water Affairs & Forestry, Private Bag X9029, Pietermaritzburg 3200
Dept of Economic Affairs, Environment & Tourism, Private Bag X3513, Kokstadt 4700
Durban Parks Department, Botanical Gardens, Durban 4001
Lowveld National Botanic Garden, PO Box 1024, Nelspruit 1200
Pretoria National Botanic Garden, NBI, Private Bag X101, Pretoria 0001
Witwatersrand National Botanic Garden, PO Box 2194, Wilropark 1731
Free State National Botanic Garden, PO Box 29036, Bloemfontein 9300

SOCIETIES AND OTHER ORGANISATIONS:
Botanical Society (KZN Branch)
       Pietermaritzburg: PO Box 21667, Mayor's Walk 3208
       Durban & Coast: PO Box 35197, Northway 4065
Clivia Club (Natal Branch), PO Box 126, Eston 3740
Cycad Society of South Africa, RAU, PO Box 524, Auckland Park 2006
Dendrological Society, PO Box 104, Pretoria 0001
       Celtis Branch: PO Box 101227, Scottsville 3209
       Zululand Branch: PO Box 35, Kwambonambi 3915
Herb Association of Southern Africa, PO Box 1831, Estcourt 3310
PlantLife, PO Box 111, Port Edward 4295
Succulent Society, Private Bag X10, Brooklyn 0011
TIMBERWATCH, PO Box 22028, Mayor's Walk 3208
Tree Society, PO Box 4116, Johannesburg 2000
Wildlife & Environment Society (KwaZulu-Natal Branch), 100 Brand Road, Durban 4001

HERBARIA:
KwaZulu-Natal
Bews Herbarium, University of Natal, PO Box 375, Pietermaritzburg 3200
Donald Killick Herbarium, KZN Conservation Services, PO Box 662 Pietermaritzburg 3200
Natal Herbarium, National Botanical Institute, Botanic Gardens Road, Durban 4001
Skyline Herbarium, PO Box 419, Uvongo 4270
Umtamvuna Herbarium, Umtamvuna Nature Reserve, PO Box 25, Port Edward 4295
University of Zululand Herbarium, Department of Botany, Private Bag 1001, KwaDlangezwa 3886
Ward Herbarium, University of Durban-Westville, PO Box 57001, Durban 4001

Eastern Cape
Herbarium, Dept of Botany, University of Transkei, Private Bag X1 UNITRA, Umtata
Selmar Schonland Herbarium, PO Box 101, Grahamstown

Free State
Geo Potts Herbarium, Dept of Botany and Genetics, University of the Orange Free State,
       PO Box 339, Bloemfontein 9300
Herbarium of the National Museum, PO Box 266, Bloemfontein 9300

Lesotho
Biology Dept, National University of Lesotho, PO Roma 180, Lesotho

Gauteng
C E Moss Herbarium, University of Witwatersrand, PO Wits 2050
National Herbarium, NBI, Private Bag X101, Pretoria 0001
HGWJ Schweickerdt Herbarium, Dept of Botany, University of Pretoria 0002

Mpumalanga
Mpumalanga Herbarium, PO Box 1990, Nelspruit

Swaziland
National Herbarium, Malkerns Research Station, PO Box 4, Malkerns, Swaziland

Mozambique
LMA Herbarium, National Institute of Agronomic Research, PO Box 3658, Maputo, Mozambique

KZN SPECIALIST INDIGENOUS PLANT NURSERIES, NURSERIES STOCKING SOME INDIGENOUS PLANTS AND KZN INDIGENOUS LANDSCAPING CONTRACTORS AND CONSULTANTS

A list of names and addresses of the above categories of nurseries, landscaping contractors and consultants can be obtained free of charge from the Natal Herbarium, Wildlife and Environment Society, Botanical Society and Natal National Botanic Garden.

NOTE

A permit is required from the local Nature Conservation authority
or the landowner to collect plants in the wild.

A QUICK GUIDE TO IDENTIFICATION

Don't pick the plant. 'Take the book to the plant, not the plant to the book'.

Make careful observations on the following:

- Height and shape of plant
- Shape of leaves, arrangement on stem, length of stalk
- Shape and colour of flowers, number of petals, stamens and styles
- Arrangement of flowers
- Shape and colour of fruits
- Hairiness
- Habitat and abundance

(with acknowledgement to 'The Wild Flowers of Britain and Northern Europe'
by Richard Fitter & Alastair Fitter, Collins 1974)

INDEX

Current scientific names printed in **bold** type, synonyms in *italic*.
★ Indicates alien invasive plants.
Page numbers in **bold** refer to where the species description occurs.

612

626